Transforming Learning. Transforming Lives.

CENTERING ON
Value

CENTERING ON
Choice

CENTERING ON
Engagement

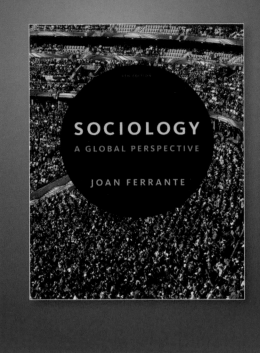

EIGHTH EDITION

SOCIOLOGY

A Global Perspective

Joan Ferrante

Northern Kentucky University

WADSWORTH
CENGAGE Learning™

Australia • Brazil • Japan • Korea • Mexico • Singapore • Spain • United Kingdom • United States

***Sociology: A Global Perspective,*
Eighth Edition**
Joan Ferrante

Sponsoring Editor: Erin Mitchell
Developmental Editor: Rebecca Dashiell
Assistant Editor: Linda Stewart
Editorial Assistant: Mallory Ortberg
Media Editor: Melanie Cregger
Marketing Manager: Andrew Keay
Marketing Communications Manager: Laura Localio
Content Project Manager: Cheri Palmer
Design Director: Rob Hugel
Art Director: Caryl Gorska
Print Buyer: Karen Hunt
Rights Acquisitions Specialist: Roberta Broyer
Production Service: Jill Traut, MPS Limited, a Macmillan Company
Text Designer: Ellen Pettengell
Photo Researcher: Bill Smith Group
Text Researcher: Sue Howard
Copy Editor: Heather McElwain
Illustrator: MPS Limited, a Macmillan Company
Cover Designer: Caryl Gorska
Cover Image: © SOCCER/Balan Madhavan/ Alamy
Compositor: MPS Limited, a Macmillan Company

Library of Congress Control Number: 2011928896

Student Edition:

ISBN-13: 978-1-111-83390-9

ISBN-10: 1-111-83390-7

Loose-leaf Edition:

ISBN-13: 978-1-111-83527-9

ISBN-10: 1-111-83527-6

Wadsworth
20 Davis Drive
Belmont, CA 94002-3098
USA

Cengage Learning is a leading provider of customized learning solutions with office locations around the globe, including Singapore, the United Kingdom, Australia, Mexico, Brazil, and Japan. Locate your local office at **www.cengage.com/global.**

Cengage Learning products are represented in Canada by Nelson Education, Ltd.

To learn more about Wadsworth, visit **www.cengage.com/wadsworth.**

Purchase any of our products at your local college store or at our preferred online store **www.cengagebrain.com.**

Printed in the United States of America
1 2 3 4 5 6 7 15 14 13 12 11

To my mother, Annalee Taylor Ferrante and in memory of my father, Phillip S. Ferrante (March 1, 1926–July 8, 1984)

BRIEF CONTENTS

CONTENTS

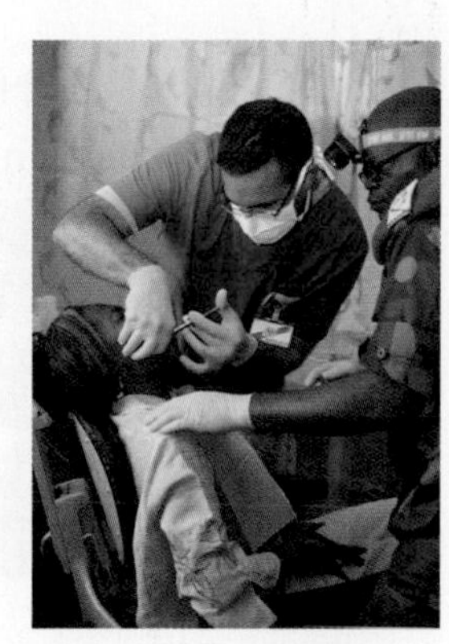

8 SOCIAL STRATIFICATION 180
With Emphasis on the World's Richest and Poorest

9 RACE AND ETHNICITY 212
With Emphasis on Brazil

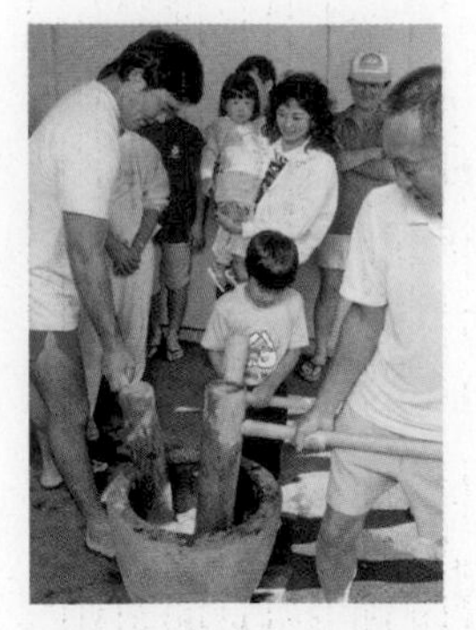

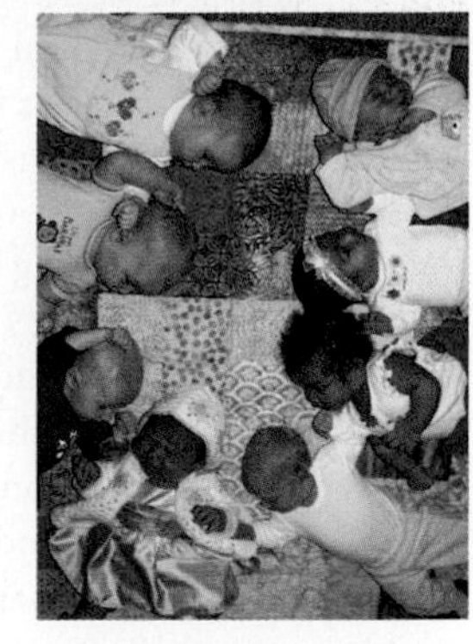

BOXES

The Sociological Imagination

The Global Comparisons

No Borders, No Boundaries

Working For Change

PREFACE

This eighth edition of *Sociology: A Global Perspective* retains its distinctive integrative approach. Each chapter pairs a sociological topic with a country or global-scale issue that becomes the focus of sociological analysis. The chosen pairings give the concepts and theories presented in each chapter a purpose. That purpose is to:

1. showcase sociology as offering the conceptual tools for understanding global-scale issues and changes and their impact on daily lives; and
2. strengthen the way sociology is presented so that readers, inundated by information explosion, will come away with a sense of satisfaction in taking the time to read, of all things, a textbook.

Major Changes to This Edition

These goals are especially evident in the descriptions of changes to the five most heavily revised chapters that follow:

- The first chapter—The Sociological Imagination—now features the mobile phone as the object of sociological analysis. The chapter opens with this question: Have you ever tried to imagine going one day without your phone? How would your life change? The sociological perspective takes readers beyond their personal dependency on mobile phones to think about how that innovation has revolutionized relationships. As one measure of the mobile phone's importance, consider that at this time there are an estimated 5.3 billion mobile phones in a world of 7 billion people. I imagine what six classic theorists—Comte, Marx, Weber, Durkheim, DuBois, and Addams—would say about the mobile phone if each were alive today. My hope is that opening the book with a focus on something deeply personal will build readers' confidence in sociology as a discipline that is worth their time to learn.
- Chapter 6, Formal Organizations with emphasis on McDonald's, now places that well-known global corporation in the context of the industrial food system. Keep in mind that McDonald's does not produce or even cook the food it sells to customers. Like other fast food corporations, it relies on suppliers from around the United States and the world to process menu items. The rise of the industrial food system has spawned a variety of slow food movements and organizations, each aiming to address some related issue, ranging from animal rights/welfare to school lunch reform.
- In the previous edition, Chapter 9—Race and Ethnicity—emphasized the global story behind the peopling of the United States. This edition shifts that emphasis to Brazil because that country's ideas of race and ethnicity offer an interesting contrast to the United States. Brazilian racial identity is built around the idea that everyone is multiracial and no racial group is distinct from another. This is in sharp contrast to the United States, where the races are still viewed as distinct categories. We use sociological concepts and theories to think about how ideas of race are constructed and the effects race has on life chances, race relations, and identity. With regard to ethnicity, the United States government recognizes only two ethnic groups: Hispanic and non-Hispanic. In contrast, the Brazilian government only recognizes the ethnic identities of the indigenous peoples.
- Chapter 11—Economics and Politics—has shifted its emphasis from Iraq to India. India is one of two rising powers (the other is China) expected to challenge the global power and influence of the United States. India is best known in the United States as an outsourcing destination, most notably of customer service and IT jobs. For all its publicity, however, only about 2.5 million of its 450 million-strong labor force works in high-tech and service industries. We apply the sociological concepts to compare and contrast the Indian and American economic and political systems and, in the process, gain insights about the major forces shaping employment opportunities in the two countries.
- Chapter 15 changes title from "Population and Urbanization with Emphasis on India:" to "Birth, Death, and Migration with Emphasis on Extreme Cases." The title change more accurately reflects the three key human experiences that determine population size, growth and other dynamics. In this chapter, we compare extreme cases or those countries that experience the highest and the lowest birth rates, including the teen birth rate; death rates including infant and maternal, and in- and out-migration rates.

We emphasize extreme cases because doing so allows us to frame the end points on the continuum of human experience. For example, if we know the teen birth rate in

Niger is 199 per 1,000 teens, we know that there are 199 births for every 1,000 teen females each year. To put it another way, each year, 20 percent or one in five teens have a baby. If we know that the teen birth rate in South Korea is 1 per 1,000, we know that there is 1 birth for every 1,000 teen females each year. What do these rates suggest about the lives of females who are teenagers in each country? If you were a teenage girl, how would you see your future if you lived in Niger versus South Korea? The point is that rates help us to think about these experiences and allow us to think more deeply about our own and others' lives.

Other Changes

Before elaborating on the changes specific to the other chapters, I will point out less obvious changes common to all chapters. First, I worked hard to further strengthen the rationale underlying the connection between chosen country/global issue and the chapter topic with which it is paired. This book's purpose, which is to showcase sociology's power to help people think about the most compelling issues of our time, is realized when that connection is crystal clear. Second, I now open and close each chapter with online poll questions asking readers to think about something going on in their lives, a decision they have made or some behavior in which they have engaged. The questions help to link seemingly personal concerns to larger sociological processes described in that chapter. Students can go online to see how their answers compare to those of other students using this textbook. Third, I reviewed and updated all statistics including text, tables, and charts, making sure that each statistic enhanced student understanding of the sociological material covered. Fourth, I critically reviewed photographs, dropping those that were outdated and adding photos that effectively represented the sociological processes described.

My revision plan also involved changes to the four types of chapter boxes. The **Sociological Imagination boxes** have been revised with the aim of further clarifying the intersection between seemingly personal experiences and remote and impersonal social forces. **Global Comparison boxes** are written with greater emphasis on how life chances are shaped in part by the country in which one happens to live. **No Borders, No Boundaries boxes** are especially important for illustrating the ever-increasing flow of goods, services, money, people, information, and culture across national borders. Finally, almost all the **Working for Change boxes** from the previous edition have been replaced. This box focuses on solutions—specifically, on people who are doing or have done something to change the system or who have persuaded others to change their behavior in ways that benefit society. Most of the Working for Change boxes were written by sociology majors at Northern Kentucky enrolled in a Senior Seminar course I taught in Fall 2010. Those students and their contributions are listed in the acknowledgement section of this preface.

There are also a number of chapter-specific changes. For these chapters, the country/global issue of emphasis has not changed but new sections have been added or existing sections have been updated:

Chapter 2 (Theoretical Perspectives and Methods of Social Research: With Emphasis on Mexico) focuses on the 700 miles of constructed fences, walls, and other barriers along the U.S.–Mexico border. The conflict and symbolic-interactionist perspective sections have been heavily revised to reflect the most recent sociological literature on the meanings and effects of these barriers. The section formerly titled "Relationships between Independent and Dependent Variables" has changed to "Proving Cause." The corresponding shift in emphasis makes this complex idea more accessible to students.

Chapter 3 (Culture: With Emphasis on North and South Korea) includes a number of important changes that help to illustrate cultural diffusion and other processes, including the debut of Korean pop artists on the global stage (cultural diffusion); the new U.S. military policy of allowing its servicemen and women to live among the Korean population instead of on military bases; and the recent reunions of North and South Korean relatives who have not seen or otherwise communicated with one another since 1953.

Chapter 4 (Socialization: With Emphasis on Israel and the Palestinian Territories) now reflects changes related to the Israeli blockade of Gaza and the long-standing efforts to reach an agreement between Palestinians and Israelis.

Chapter 5 (Social Interaction: With Emphasis on the Democratic Republic of the Congo) still considers how HIV/AIDS is an ongoing global story that cannot be understood apart from European colonization of the DRC and other African countries. Although HIV/AIDS seems like an old story now, today's students are connected to that story when they are warned of HIV/AIDS in abstinence and sex education classes. In this edition, I tried to emphasize this student connection and also to show how HIV/AIDS can be related to "conflict minerals," most notably the minerals needed to manufacture electronic products upon which the world has come to depend (for example, wireless phones and computers). I have added a section on social structure and institutions and used these concepts to illustrate how the exploitation of DRC labor and resources has been institutionalized.

As in the previous edition of Chapter 7 (Deviance, Conformity, and Social Control: With Emphasis on the People's Republic of China), a key sociological assumption about deviance—what is considered deviant varies across time and place—is illustrated by contrasting conceptions of deviance during and after the Cultural Revolution. This

chapter has been updated to reflect the dramatic changes in the Chinese economy. A late 1980s study on preschools in China and the United States is replaced with a study conducted in 2008. I have also added a new section on Foucault's disciplinary society.

Chapter 8 (Social Stratification: With Emphasis on the World's Richest and Poorest) now includes a key table that contrasts selected types of consumption (auto, wireless phones, bottled water) in the wealthiest and poorest countries. A revised discussion of social class presents a creative study in which researchers ask respondents to assess a series of hypothetical wealth distributions without telling them the distribution that applies to the United States. Ninety percent of respondents indicated that they would not want to live in a country where the wealthiest 20 percent control 80 percent of the wealth. The United States, of course, has such a distribution.

The focus of Chapter 10 (Gender) remains American Samoa. This chapter now includes a section on sexuality. It also includes a new section on documenting and explaining the global subordination of women. Finally, a section on the concept of intersectionality has been added.

Chapter 12 (Family: With Emphasis on Japan) updates data and information on Japan's response to two demographic trends having a profound effect on family life in that country. Those trends are the low fertility rate and the aging of its population. The chapter also includes a new section on caregiving. This phenomenon is relevant to families, because they are assuming greater caregiving responsibilities as populations age.

Chapter 13 (Education: With Emphasis on the European Union) now includes two new sections featuring Randall Collins's credential society and Pierre Bourdieu's theory of economic and cultural capital.

Ancillary Materials

Sociology: A Global Perspective is accompanied by a wide array of supplements prepared to create the best learning environment inside and outside the classroom for both the instructor and the student.

Student Resources

Study Guide. This student learning tool, written by Joan Ferrante and Kristie Vise (Northern Kentucky University), includes 15 to 25 study questions for each chapter to guide reading, 5 concept application scenarios, practice tests containing 20 to 25 multiple-choice and 5 to 10 true–false questions, suggested Internet resources to enhance chapter material, applied research activities, and additional background information on the focus country, territory, or theme for each chapter.

Practice Tests. Written by Margaret Weinberger of Bowling Green State University, the practice tests booklet contains 50 unique questions per chapter, including multiple-choice, true–false, and fill-in-the-blank questions, giving students a greater opportunity to study for quizzes and exams.

Instructor Resources

Test Bank. Written by Joan Ferrante and Kristie Vise, this enhanced and updated test bank consists of 90 to 100 multiple-choice questions and 30 to 35 true–false questions per chapter, all with answers, page references, question type (knowledge, comprehension, or applied), and sources (indications of whether the questions are new or also appear in the study guide). The test bank also includes 5 concept application questions, 25 to 40 short-answer questions, and 3 to 5 essay questions per chapter.

PowerLecture™ with ExamView®. PowerLecture instructor resources are a collection of book-specific lecture and class tools on either CD or DVD. The fastest and easiest way to build powerful, customized, media-rich lectures, PowerLecture assets include chapter-specific PowerPoint® presentations, images, animations and video, instructor manuals, test banks, useful web links, and more. PowerLecture media-teaching tools are an effective way to enhance the educational experience.

Instructor's Resource Manual. The instructor's manual offers the instructor detailed chapter outlines, Teaching Tips that correspond with specific sections of the book, online polling questions, and background notes on each chapter's country of emphasis. Written by Joan Ferrante and Kristie Vise the fully updated and revised manual will help you teach the global perspective with confidence.

WebTutor™ with eBook. Jumpstart your course with customizable, rich, text-specific content within your Course Management System:

- *Jumpstart*—Simply load a WebTutor cartridge into your Course Management System
- *Customizable*—Easily blend, add, edit, reorganize, or delete content
- *Content*—Rich, text-specific content, media assets, ebook, quizzing, weblinks, discussion topics, interactive games and exercises, and more

CengageNOW. CengageNOW™ is an online teaching and learning resource that gives you more control in less time and delivers better outcomes—NOW.

Sociology CourseMate. *Sociology: A Global Perspective*, Eighth Edition, includes Sociology CourseMate, which helps you make the grade.Sociology CourseMate includes:

- an interactive eBook, with highlighting, note taking, and search capabilities
- interactive learning tools including:
  - Quizzes
  - Flash cards
  - Videos
  - Games
  - and more!

Login to CengageBrain.com to access these resources related to your text in Sociology CourseMate.

CourseReader. Easy-to-use and affordable access to primary and secondary sources, readings, and audio and video selections for your courses with this customized online reader. CourseReader for Sociology helps you to stay organized and facilitates convenient access to course material, no matter where you are.

Acknowledgments

The eighth edition update builds on the efforts of those who helped me with this and previous editions. Four people stand out as particularly influential: Sheryl Fullerton (the editor who signed this book in 1988), Serina Beauparlant (the editor who saw the first and second editions through to completion), and Chris Caldeira (the editor who developed the revision plan and guided me through the writing of the seventh edition). Chris is now enrolled in the PhD sociology program at the University of California–Davis. A glance at photo credits reveals that Chris took many of the photos (49 to be exact) for this edition. Chris was also a consultant on this edition. In this regard, we had many important conversations that set the goals guiding this revision. I also benefited from numerous discussions with her about how to present sociology in ways that both engage instructors and those new to the discipline. I am fortunate to have Erin Mitchell as my current editor. I most appreciate Erin's generosity, enthusiasm, and belief in my approach to sociology. I am also grateful to her for coming up with a revision plan for this edition that gave me great flexibility in selecting photographs. Erin understands my vision and this book's purpose. In short, she is a key and valued advocate.

Of course, any revision plan depends on thoughtful, constructive, and thorough reviewer critiques. In this regard, I wish to extend my deepest appreciation to those who have reviewed this edition and/or its update:

Brian Aldrich, *Winona State University*

Shaheen A. Chowdhury, *College of Dupage*

Kay Coder, *Richland College*

Janine DeWitt, *Marymount University*

Monique Diderich, *Shawnee State University*

Sara J. Fisch, *Scottsdale Community College*

Mary Grigsby, *University of Missouri*

Liza Kuecker, *Western New Mexico University*

Joyce Mumah, *Utah State University*

Cristina Stephens, *Kennesaw State University*

Greg Walker, *Lock Haven University of Pennsylvania*

When only one name—the author's—graces the cover of this textbook, it is difficult to convey just how many people were involved with its production. Their names appear in the most unassuming manner on the copyright page, belying the significant role they played in shaping the book. Perhaps the least recognized of those named on the copyright pages are production editors. For this edition, I was fortunate to work with Cheri Palmer and Jill Traut who take care of an overwhelming number of details associated with the book, including coordinating the work of the copyeditor, photo researcher, designer, proofreader, author, and others into a textbook ready to go to press. Both handled this pressure in ways that seemed effortless. But then such a style is a sign of true professionals—making something very few people can do seem effortless.

Apart from the support I received from Wadsworth/Cengage Learning on this updated and past editions, I also received ongoing support and interest from many sociology faculty at my university who have either read or used my textbook on occasion; Prince Brown, Jr. (emeritus professor), Kris Hehn, Boni Li, J. Robert Lilly (who was my undergraduate professor), Jamie McCauley, and Kristie Vise. Kristie is now the co-author on the test bank, student study guide and instructor's resource manual. I am grateful that she has accepted this role. I would also like to thank NKU professor of Visual Arts, Barbara Houghton and her husband Rick Farley for contributing photographs for the India and other chapters.

For the past three editions, I have had the privilege of working with Missy Gish, who has a bachelor's degree in sociology and a master's in liberal studies. Missy worked behind the scenes taking photos for the book, assisting with photo research, updating tables and charts, checking references, and preparing chapters for production. On the surface, Missy's job description may seem simple, but I must emphasize that these tasks require an alertness, attention to detail, and ability to handle the stress associated with meeting deadlines that very few people possess.

I would like to thank the following NKU sociology majors who contributed boxes for this edition: They are

- Keram J. Christensen, Doing Good by Being Bad
- Devon Cowherd, The Cell Phone as a Revolutionary Tool
- Jessica Ezell, Care to Learn
- Brooke Goerman, Transgender Day of Remembrance

- Victoria Michel, Measuring Happiness
- Margaret Muench, A South Korean Helps Bring a University to China and North Korea
- Ashley Novogroski, Positive Deviants
- Ashley Novogroski, The Buy Local Movement
- Dayna Schambach, Building Green, Affordable, High-Quality Design Homes
- Gennifer Toland, Becoming Athletes—Expanding Conceptions of Self
- Staci Wood, Putting Down the Cell Phone to Learn Firsthand

I wish to express my deepest appreciation to my mother, Annalee Taylor Ferrante—who keeps my files, alerts me to news and other media reports that inform my thinking, and helps me in updating the text. My mother, who is 81 years old, cooks full-course dinners for my husband and me several times a week. The care with which she prepares food and the exquisite results has no parallel. This is no easy feat in a world dominated by heavily processed and prepackaged foods and ingredients.

As always, I also express my love for and gratitude to my husband, colleague, and friend Robert K. Wallace who is without a doubt my greatest supporter. In closing, I acknowledge, as I have done in all editions of this and other books, the tremendous influence of Horatio C Wood IV, MD, on my academic career and philosophy of education. Dr. Wood died on May 28, 2009. His death only served to intensify the warmth and gratitude I continue to feel for him. In reflecting on the important mentoring role Dr. Wood has played in my life, I cannot help but wonder why there seem to be few, if any, explicit acknowledgments of the deep emotions felt for those who have the greatest influence on our work. The emotions I felt for Dr. Wood were an important component of what was, by any measure, a constructive relationship. These emotions allowed me to gauge his specialness and they gave purpose, excitement, and direction to my learning, writing, and teaching.

1 THE SOCIOLOGICAL IMAGINATION

With Emphasis on the MOBILE PHONE

Have you ever tried to imagine going one day without your phone? How would your life change? If you have a mobile phone, you own one of 5.3 billion mobile phones in the world (U.S. Central Intelligence Agency 2011). It is likely that the vast majority of owners have come to need and depend on them just as you do. Sociologists see mobile phones as a social force that shapes human interaction and activity. In studying this phone, they consider how that invention shapes the way people see the world and interact with others. They also consider how people use, adapt to, and respond to this invention. Finally, sociologists study how mobile phones affect the way people relate to groups, organizations, and institutions.

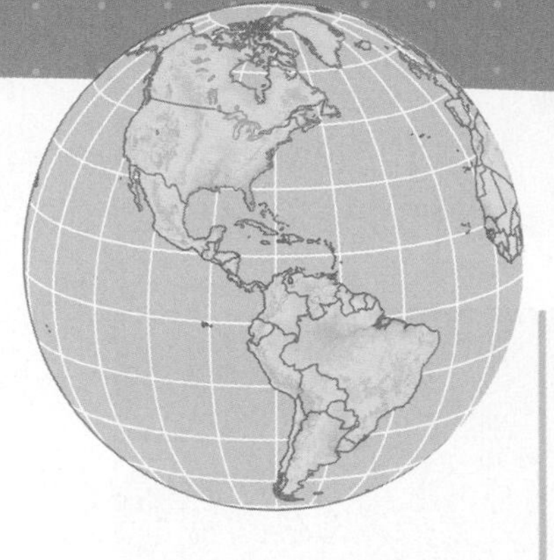

Why Focus On MOBILE PHONES?

CORE CONCEPT 1 ***Sociology*** **is the scientific study of human activity in society. More specifically, it is the study of the social forces that affect the things people do with and to one another.**

The activities sociologists study are too many to list but, as you will learn from reading this textbook, sociologists study human activities as they relate to immigration, racial classification, religion, education, and much more. Specifically, sociologists are interested in social forces like the mobile phone that shape and change any human activity, including the ways people think about themselves and others and the things they do to and with one another. **Social forces** are anything humans create that influence or pressure people to interact, behave, respond, or think in certain ways. This textbook is about those many social forces that shape our lives.

The mobile phone is a perfect vehicle for illustrating the sociological perspective. For one, it is a human-created technology that has transformed or will transform every aspect of life. The revolutionary feature of the mobile phone is that it frees people from being in a specific physical space when they communicate with others. While the landline phone allowed us to communicate with others in faraway places, all parties had to arrange to be in a fixed location—an office, at home, in a telephone booth. In addition, people waited until they got home to some fixed location to tell someone what had happened in their day. Now people can share what is happening as it happens

With mobile phones, people are no longer confined to a fixed location. They can communicate while driving or walking to class. It doesn't matter if they are skydiving, on a mountaintop, at a party, or at church. In addition the technology is such that the mobile phone can function as a miniature laptop with Internet access and as a multimedia device allowing people to exchange photographs, text messages, music, videos, and anything that can be digitalized. Mobile phones also allow people to choose from millions of applications that facilitate social and business transactions and that meet needs for just about any kind of information or entertainment.

Online Poll

At what age did you get your first cell phone?

- ○ Before I was 10 years old
- ○ 10 to 11 years old
- ○ 12 to 13 years old
- ○ 14 to 15 years old
- ○ 16 to 17 years old
- ○ 18 or older
- ○ Don't own a mobile phone

To see how other students responded to these questions, go to **www.cengagebrain.com.**

The Sociological Imagination

CORE CONCEPT 2 The sociological imagination is a quality of mind that allows people to see how remote and impersonal social forces shape their life story or biography.

A **biography** consists of all the day-to-day activities from birth to death that make up a person's life. Social forces are considered remote and impersonal because, for the most part, people have no hand in creating them, nor do they know those who did. Think about how old you were (or if

Teaching Tip: Ask students if they can tell about a time when their cell phone saved the day or a time when it ruined the day. For example, the cell phone may have come in handy to report an accident or it may have rung at a bad time. One student told me that a family member's cell phone rang as her grandmother was living her last moments of life.

you were even alive) when the mobile phone first appeared on the market in 1984. How old were you when it first became popular in 1995? What was your age in 2005, the year the number of mobile phones exceeded the number of landlines (Hanson 2007)? It is likely that you had no direct involvement in the invention and development of the mobile phone but you become involved any time you decide to use a mobile phone. You become involved any time you check for messages upon waking up in the morning and before going to bed or anytime you text while driving (or refrain from doing so). Likewise, you become involved when you decide to turn off your mobile phone to give someone your complete attention or you choose to ask a stranger for directions rather than rely on the GPS function on your phone. The point is that when people respond to social forces in their lives, they become part of that force. People can embrace social forces, be swept along, be bypassed by them, and most importantly, challenge them.

Why is it important to develop the **sociological imagination**—a point of view that allows us to identify seemingly remote and impersonal social forces and connect them to our biographies? The payoff for those who acquire the sociological imagination is that they can better understand their own biography, recognize that choices exist, and that their choices have larger consequences for others. The concept *social facts* is useful for conceptualizing social forces that impact our lives.

Missy Gish

Missy Gish

The sociological imagination allows you to consider how larger social forces—the time in history, the place one lives, the technologies at hand—affect the individual biography. How might the mobile phone and land line phone shape a child's view of the world and sense of self in relation to others? For one thing, the child who uses a mobile may not learn to associate a person they are talking to with a specific place.

The Study of Social Facts

What happens when you leave the house without your phone and you get to your destination realizing that you left it behind? Does your mind race with thoughts like "what will my mother, partner, friend, or boss think if they call or text and I don't reply within, say 15 minutes? How will I let people know where I am and why they haven't heard from me?" French sociologist Émile Durkheim defined **social facts** as ideas, feelings, and ways of behaving "that possess the remarkable property of existing outside the consciousness of the individual" (Durkheim 1982, p. 51). That is, for the most part, social facts do not originate with the people experiencing them. From the time we are born, the people around us seek to impose upon us ways of thinking, feeling, and acting that we had no hand in creating. The words and gestures people use to express thoughts; the monetary and credit system used to pay debts; the rules governing mobile phone use and

sociology The scientific study of human activity in society.

social forces Anything humans create or take notice of that influence or pressure people to interact, behave, respond, or think in certain ways.

biography All the day-to-day activities from birth to death that make up a person's life.

sociological imagination A point of view that allows us to identify seemingly remote and impersonal social forces and connect them to our biographies.

social facts Ideas, feelings, and ways of behaving "that possess the remarkable property of existing outside the consciousness of the individual."

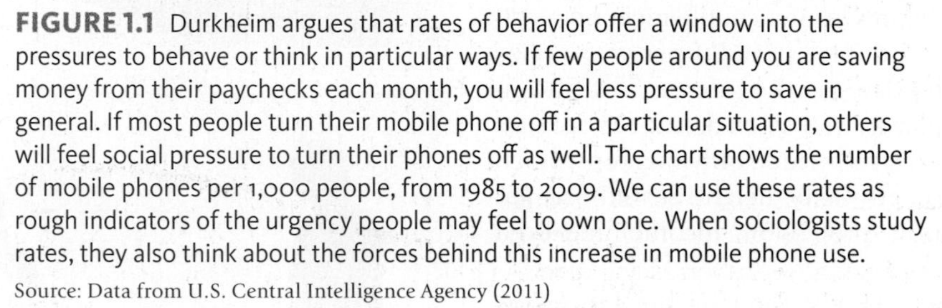

FIGURE 1.1 Durkheim argues that rates of behavior offer a window into the pressures to behave or think in particular ways. If few people around you are saving money from their paychecks each month, you will feel less pressure to save in general. If most people turn their mobile phone off in a particular situation, others will feel social pressure to turn their phones off as well. The chart shows the number of mobile phones per 1,000 people, from 1985 to 2009. We can use these rates as rough indicators of the urgency people may feel to own one. When sociologists study rates, they also think about the forces behind this increase in mobile phone use.

Source: Data from U.S. Central Intelligence Agency (2011)

etiquette; the beliefs and rituals of the religions people follow—all were created seemingly without their input. Thus social facts have a life that extends beyond the individuals who carry them out.

Not only do social facts exist outside individuals, but they also have coercive power. When people freely and unthinkingly conform to social facts, that power "is not felt or felt hardly at all" (Durkheim 1982, p. 55). Only when people resist do they come to know and experience the power of social facts. Durkheim wrote that he was not forced to speak French or to use the legal currency, but it was impossible for him to do otherwise. "If I tried to escape the necessity, my attempt would fail miserably. . . . Even when in fact I can struggle free from these rules and successfully break them, it is never without being forced to fight against them" (Durkheim 1982, p. 51). In other words, even when people challenge them, social facts make their power known by the difficulty people experience trying to do things and think in different ways. Still, it is impressive that most of us can probably think of at least one example in which we resisted following social facts. People who decide to not use a mobile phone face the inconvenience, the questioning, and even anger from others that comes with that decision (for example, "How am I supposed to get a hold of you if I need you?" "Are you serious?" "You'll lose your connection to the world!").

For Durkheim, social facts also included what he called **currents of opinion**, the state of affairs with regard to some way of being. The intensity of these currents is broadly reflected in rates summarizing various behaviors—for example, marriage, suicide, or birth rates. Durkheim believed the rates at which people around us marry, take their own life, or give birth to children both influence and reflect others' thinking and behavior on these matters. The intensity of that current of opinion shapes the behavior of people who live in the society.

The Sociological Consciousness

Sociologist Peter L. Berger offers one of the best descriptions of the sociological imagination or what he calls sociological consciousness. Berger (1963) equates sociologists with curious observers walking the neighborhood streets of a large city, fascinated with what they cannot see taking place behind the building walls. The buildings themselves offer few clues beyond hinting at the architectural tastes of the people who built the structures and who may no longer live there. According to Berger, the wish to look inside and learn more is analogous to the sociological perspective.

Berger offers the following example to illustrate his point. In the United States, we assume that people marry because they are in love. Popular belief states that love is a violent, irresistible emotion that strikes at random. Upon investigating the characteristics of people who marry,

currents of opinion The state of affairs with regard to some way of being.

Technology Tip: To illustrate the power of social facts, use a news segment highlighting the case of a man who decided to take his wife's maiden name as his last name and the "resistance" he encountered. The YouTube title is "Baby Has No Birth Certificate Following Dad's Name Change" and the link is www.youtube.com/watch?v=qZkAE68XD1c.

however, we find that Cupid's arrow actually seems to be guided by considerations of age, sex, height, income, education, race, and so on. Thus, it is not solely the emotion of love that causes us to marry; rather, when certain conditions are met (for example, when a person is the "right" height in relation to ours), we allow ourselves to "fall in love."

Sociologists investigating patterns of courtship and marriage in the United States soon discover a complex web of motives related to "class, career, economic ambition, aspirations of power and prestige" (Berger 1963, pp. 35–36). For example, people meet potential spouses and partners in the social circles they move in (work, school, church, neighborhoods, and so on). Considerations of class and education are obviously present if a couple meet on a college campus where the tuition is $1,600 per year versus $40,000. For those who date via the Internet, social considerations come into play as well when dating service subscribers narrow the search to include only men or women of a particular age, race, ethnicity, height, sexual orientation, geographic location, profession, income, and even eye color.

Photo courtesy of Conceptual Photo Illustration/Released

Chris Caldeira

Although sociologists do not dismiss the role of love in shaping a couple's decision to form a marriage or partnership, they do focus on the social considerations (such as age, sex, height, income, sexual orientation, education, and race) that must be present before people allow themselves to fall in love. In the case of the two couples pictured, what social considerations appear to be at work?

Once people decide to marry, the next steps to follow have already been laid out for them, and "though there is some leeway for improvisations, too much ad-libbing is likely to risk the success of the whole operation" (Berger 1963, p. 87). Note that neither the future bride nor the future groom "invented" these steps. Friends, family, clergy, jewelers, florists, caterers, musicians, wedding planners, and others serve as the guardians of tradition and help ensure that the steps are followed. These guardians do not have to exert much pressure on the couple, because these expectations "have long been built into their own projections of the future—they want precisely what society expects of them" (p. 87). As Berger notes, the "miracle of love now begins to look somewhat synthetic" (p. 36). This statement does not mean that sociologists dismiss the emotion of love as wholly irrelevant. Rather, they look beyond the popular meanings and publicly approved interpretations of why people say they marry.

The discipline of sociology offers us theories, concepts, and methods needed to look beyond popular meanings and explanations of what is going on around us. Berger (1963) points out that sociologists, by the very logic of their discipline, are driven to debunk the social systems they study. One should not mistake this drive as being located in a sociologist's temperament or personal inclination. Apart from their field of study, sociologists may be "disinclined to disturb the comfortable assumptions" about what is going on around us (p. 29). Nevertheless, the sociological perspective compels sociologists to explore levels of reality that dig below the surface. The logic of the discipline presupposes a "measure of suspicion about the way in which human events are officially interpreted by the authorities, be they political, juridical or religious in character" (p. 29). In their effort to explore levels of reality that dig below the surface, sociologists also make distinctions between troubles and issues.

Troubles and Issues

CORE CONCEPT 3 Sociologists distinguish between troubles, which can be resolved by changing the individual, and issues, which can be resolved only by addressing the social forces that created them.

C. Wright Mills (1959) defines **troubles** as personal needs, problems, or difficulties that can be explained as individual shortcomings related to motivation, attitude, ability, character, or judgment. The resolution of a trouble, if it

Teaching Tip: Ask students to write a "personal" ad for their ideal partner. What social characteristics (e.g., characteristics that are socially valued) are most important to them?

can indeed be resolved, lies in changing the individual in some way. Mills states that when only one man or woman is unemployed in a city of 100,000, that situation is his or her personal trouble. For its relief, we properly look to that person's character, skills, and immediate opportunities (that is, we think, "She is lazy," "He has a bad attitude," "He didn't try very hard in school," or "She had the opportunity but didn't take it").

By comparison, an **issue** is a matter that can be explained only by factors outside an individual's control and immediate environment. When 24 million men and women are unemployed or underemployed in a nation with a workforce of 156 million, that situation is an issue. Clearly, we cannot hope to solve this kind of employment crisis by focusing on the character flaws of 24 million individuals. According to Mills, an accurate description of the problem and of the possible solutions to it requires us to think beyond individual shortcomings and to consider the underlying social forces that create them.

Mills argues that many people cannot see the intricate connection between their personal situations or troubles and the larger social forces. Mills also argues that most people cannot (or do not want to) see how their gains and successes connect to others' so-called losses and failures in life (see Sociological Imagination). For example, it is hard to recognize that a person's success at connecting 24/7 with peers is often achieved at the loss of meaningful contact with parents and others. Mills believes that most people lack this awareness because they do not possess a quality of mind that enables them to grasp the interplay between self and world and between biography and the large social forces pressuring them to think and behave as they do.

In *The Sociological Imagination*, Mills (1959) asks, "Is it any wonder that ordinary people feel they cannot cope with the larger worlds with which they are so suddenly confronted?" (pp. 4–5). Is it any wonder that people often feel trapped by the social forces that affect them? As Mills pointed out, we live in a world in which information dominates our attention and overwhelms our capacity to make sense of all we hear, see, and read every day. Consequently, we may be exhausted by the struggle to learn from that information about the forces that shape our daily lives. According to Mills, people need "a quality of mind that will help them to use information" to think about "what is going on in the world and what may be happening within themselves" (p. 5). Mills calls this quality of mind the *sociological imagination*. The payoff for those who possess a sociological imagination is that they can better understand their own experiences and fate by locating them in a larger historical, cultural, and social context; they can recognize the responses available to them by becoming aware of the many individuals who share their situations.

The sociological imagination is evident in the work of the earliest and most influential sociologists. In fact, one can make the case that the discipline of sociology emerged as part of an effort to understand how a social force known as the Industrial Revolution changed people's lives in countless ways.

The Industrial Revolution

CORE CONCEPT 4 Sociology emerged in part as a reaction to the Industrial Revolution, an ongoing and evolving social force that transformed society, human behavior, and interaction in incalculable ways.

The Industrial Revolution is the name given to the changes in the way goods were produced, food was grown, people got from one place to another, extracted resources from the earth, and communicated and interacted with one another. In short, the Industrial Revolution transformed virtually every aspect of society. The defining feature of the Industrial Revolution was **mechanization**, the process of replacing human and animal muscle as a source of power with external sources derived from burning wood, coal, oil, and natural gas. Before mechanization, goods were produced and distributed at a human pace. New sources of power eventually replaced hand tools with power tools, sailboats with freighters, and horse-drawn carriages with trains. Mechanization changed how goods were produced and how people worked. It turned workshops into factories, skilled workers into machine operators, and handmade goods into machine-made goods. With industrialization, products previously crafted by a few skilled people were now standardized and assembled by many relatively unskilled workers, each involved in part of the overall production process. Now no one person could say, "I made this; this is a unique product of my labor." The factory owners gained power over the artisans as machines rendered them obsolete. Now people with little or no skill could do the artisan's work—and at a faster pace (Thrall 2007).

Industrialization did more than change the nature of work; it changed notions of time and space. A social order that had existed for centuries vanished, and a new order—familiar in its outline to us today—appeared (Lengermann 1974). A series of developments—the

troubles Personal needs, problems, or difficulties that can be explained as individual shortcomings related to motivation, attitude, ability, character, or judgment.

issue A matter that can be explained only by factors outside an individual's control and immediate environment.

mechanization The process of replacing human and animal muscle as a source of power with external sources derived from burning wood, coal, oil, and natural gas.

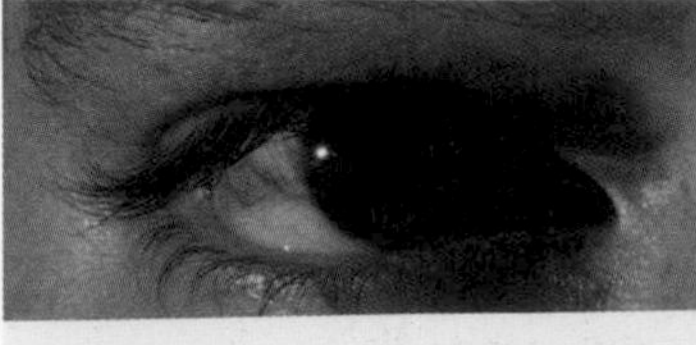

The Sociological Imagination Making Connections between Troubles and Issues

We know that there is a connection between troubles and issues when we can demonstrate that a seemingly personal problem would not exist if the person lived at another time in history or another place in the world. You should not interpret this fact to mean that people have no control over what happens to them or that they have no choices. Rather it is important to see that better choices can be made if people understand the larger context. We show four examples of seemingly personal troubles that would likely not exist if the people affected lived elsewhere in the world or at a different time.

Missy Gish

Megan and Michael met while in college and married soon after they graduated. They brought student loans to the relationship –a combined total of $80,605.70. They pay $525.58 per month, which represents 8.5 percent of their income. But Megan and Michael are not alone. In the United States, 66 percent of graduates leave college with an average loan to repay valued at $23,200, a loan that may take 20 to 30 years to pay off (Bernard 2009). The size of the debt burden American students assume is not one that students in the European Union (EU) face. This is because a greater share of the cost of higher education in Europe is taxpayer subsidized, often to the level that it is free. But even in those EU countries where a college education is not free, the cost is much lower than in the United States.

Missy Gish

A parent feels like she knows little to nothing about her son's friends or her son's life for that matter. She routinely checks her son's mobile phone to see who he calls or texts. Her son does not like this. The problem she faces can be traced in part to the fact that wireless phones are viewed as a personal item not to be shared with others, even family members. Because of this, callers do not have to speak to a third party before reaching the person of interest. There is no need to make "small talk" to a third party answering the phone. On the one hand, mobile phones expand individuality and privacy. On the other hand, parents talk to their children directly and in effect miss opportunities to connect with those, who in the past might have answered a landline phone. Is it any wonder some parents can feel left out?

railroad, the steamship, the cotton gin, the spinning jenny, running water, central heating, electricity, the telegraph, and mass-circulation newspapers—transformed how people lived their daily lives and with whom they interacted. Coal-powered trains, for example, turned a monthlong trip by stagecoach into a daylong one. These trains permitted people and goods to travel day and night; in rain, snow, or sleet; and across smooth and rough terrain. Railroads increased the human and freight traffic to and from previously remote and unconnected areas. The railroad caused people to believe they had annihilated time and space (Gordon 1989). In addition, railroads facilitated an unprecedented degree of economic interdependence, competition, and upheaval. Now people in one area could be priced out of a livelihood if people in another area could provide goods and materials at a lower price (Gordon 1989).

The Industrial Revolution drew people from even the most remote parts of the globe into a process that produced unprecedented quantities of material goods. The historical period known as the Age of Imperialism (1880–1914) involved the most rapid industrial and colonial expansion in history. During this time, rival European powers (such as Britain, France, Germany, Belgium, Portugal, the Netherlands, and Italy) competed to secure colonies and, by extension, exploit the labor and natural resources within those colonies. By 1914, for example, all of Africa had been divided into European colonies. By that year, 84 percent of the world's land area had been affected by colonization,

Missy Gish

June is a college student who spends about $250 per month on gasoline. She cannot understand why gas is so high. She earns $8 per hour after taxes, which means that she works 31 hours each month just to pay for gas. June's trouble with money cannot be separated from the larger reasons gas prices are so high. The United States consumes 18.8 million barrels of oil each day or 6.9 billion barrels per year. It represents 4.6 percent of the world's population and consumes 19 percent of all oil produced in the world. The United States is able to supply 50 percent of its oil needs domestically, and imports oil from foreign countries for the remaining 50 percent. The dependence on foreign oil is expected to climb as the United States has only about 21 billion barrels of proven oil reserves. That amount represents about three years of oil consumption (U.S. Energy Information Administration 2011).

Sgt. Mark Fayloga

Although he is the son of a white mother and a black father, President Barack Obama (2008) is referred to as the first black president of the United States. During his campaign, he spoke about some of the problems he encountered: "At various stages in the campaign, some commentators have deemed me either 'too black' or 'not black enough.' . . . The press has scoured every exit poll for the latest evidence of racial polarization. . . ." Obama's experiences are not simply personal. Sociologists see race as a socially created way of categorizing people. As such, it is a social force of immense significance. As we will learn, early on in U.S. history, its lawmakers decided that a parent and his or her biological offspring can be classified as different races. Any discernible evidence of African ancestry made someone black. Obama's experience would be very different if he lived in Brazil, where he would likely be assumed multiracial and classified as brown and perhaps even white.

and an estimated 500 million people were living as members of European colonies (*Random House Encyclopedia* 1990).

The Industrial Revolution changed everything—the ways in which goods were produced, the ways in which people negotiated time and space, the relationships between what were once geographically separated peoples, the ways in which people made their livings, the density of human populations (for example, urbanization), the relative importance and influence of the home in people's lives, access to formal education (the rise of compulsory and mass education), and the emergence of a consumption-oriented economy and culture. The accumulation of wealth became a valued and necessary pursuit. In *The Wealth of Nations*, Adam Smith argued that the invisible hand of the free market (capitalism) embodied in private ownership and self-interested competition held the key to a nation's advancement and prosperity. The unprecedented changes caught the attention of the early sociologists who wrote in the nineteenth and early twentieth centuries. In fact, sociology emerged out of their efforts to document and explain the effects of the Industrial Revolution on society.

CORE CONCEPT 5 Early sociologists were witnesses to the transforming effects of the Industrial Revolution. They offered lasting conceptual frameworks for analyzing the ongoing social upheavals.

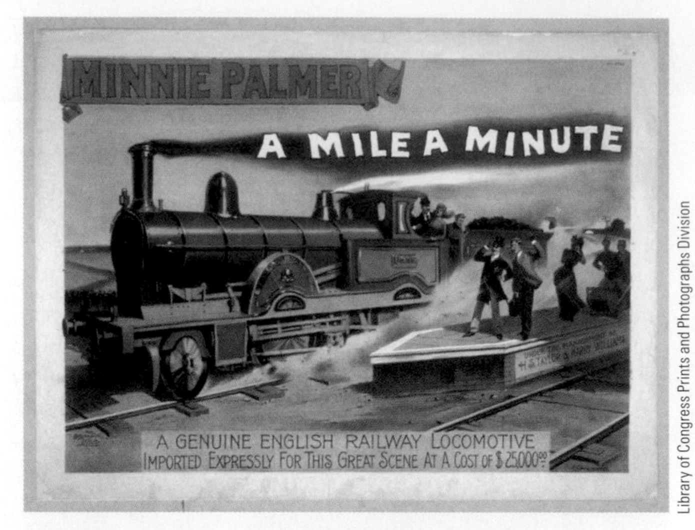

Coal-powered locomotives celebrated in this 1891 poster permitted people to travel day and night; in rain, snow, or sleet; across smooth and rough terrain—turning monthlong trips into daylong ones. Railroads increased opportunities for personal mobility and boosted the freight and passenger traffic to and from previously remote areas.

Sociology emerged as an effort to understand the dramatic and almost immeasurable effects of the Industrial Revolution on human life across the globe. Although the early sociologists wrote in the nineteenth and early twentieth centuries, their observations remain relevant. Because most of us living today know only an industrialized life, we lack the insights that came from living through the transformation. To grasp the significance of these observations, consider the following anecdote. In a recent interview, a scientist maintained that we are close to understanding the mechanisms governing aging, and that people might soon live to be 150 years old. If aging mechanisms are in fact controlled, the first people to witness the change will have to make the greatest adjustment. In contrast, people born after this discovery will know only a life in which they can expect to live 150 years. If these post-discovery humans are curious, they may wish to understand how living to age 150 shapes their lives. To fully understand this subject, they will have to look to those who recorded life before the change and who made sense of their adjustments to the so-called advancement. So it is with industrialization: To understand how it shaped and continues to shape human life (and how it has shaped sociology), we can look to six of the early sociologists.

Three of the six sociologists covered are nicknamed the "big three." Those three are Karl Marx, Émile Durkheim, and Max Weber. Sociologists universally agree that these three are the giants in the field and that their writings form the heart of the discipline. It is safe to say that all sociologists who have come after Marx, Durkheim, and Weber have been deeply influenced by their ideas even as they expand, refine, and challenge them (Appellrouth and Edles 2007).

We also include three other central figures: Auguste Comte, because he gave sociology its name, and Jane Addams and W.E.B. DuBois. DuBois focused attention on the color line, and Jane Addams championed sympathetic knowledge or knowledge gained from living and working among those being studied. The color line and sympathetic knowledge are certainly core ideas within sociology.

Upon discussing the work of each of these six sociologists, we consider how each would write about the transformative nature of the mobile phones on thinking, interaction, and human activity. Keep in mind that the early sociologists witnessed the introduction of many inventions that annihilated space and time including the telegraph (1838) and cablegram, which allowed messages to be sent to countries on opposite sides of the Atlantic (1866) and the Pacific Oceans (1902). These inventions freed communication from having to travel with humans or animals across space (for example, via pony express or trains). The early sociologists were the first to witness this great leap in communication, and their view of the world was surely informed by this newfound ability. The first message ("Glory to God in the highest; on earth, peace and good will toward men") send across the Atlantic in 1858 took over 17 hours to transmit; by 1866 cable, the cable could transmit eight words a minute; and by 1900, the speed reached 120 words per minute (SchoolNet 2011). Now fiber-optic cables lie below the ocean instead of copper cables, and they can transmit more than 84 billion words per second (Geere 2011).

The early sociologists witnessed the ability to physically separate the message from a messenger. What separates their time in history from today is that we live in a time when people do not have to be in a fixed space/place to receive or send a message. Still, the early sociologists give us a language and perspective that helps us to frame and think about revolutions in communication.

Auguste Comte (1798–1857)

The French philosopher Auguste Comte, known as the father of positivism, gave sociology its name in 1839. **Positivism** holds that valid knowledge about the world can be derived only from *sense experience* or knowing the world through the senses of sight, touch, taste, smell, and hearing and from making empirical associations (for example, evidence of cause and effect must be observed). Comte advanced the "law of three stages," which maintains that societies develop according to three stages: (1) the theocratic, (2) the metaphysical, and (3) the

positivism A theory stating that valid knowledge about the world can be derived only from *sense experience* or knowing the world through the senses of sight, touch, taste, smell, and hearing, and from empirical associations.

Technology Tip: For some images of the Industrial Revolution, visit the Library of Congress Prints and Photographs division (www.loc.gov/pictures). Use keywords "oil," coal," or "industrialization."

Library of Congress Prints and Photographs

Lisa Southwick

The illustration celebrates the first message sent via underwater cable on August 17, 1858, between Newfoundland (Canada) and Valentia Bay (Ireland). The two men grasp hands as the distance between them is shortened. One might imagine that those who sent cablegram messages felt they had conquered time and space, much as we feel today when we bridge distance using e-mail, texting and social networking platforms. (Chiles 1987).

positive. In the theocratic stage, people explain the events going on in the world as the work of personified deities—those deities may be objects such as the sun or trees, a variety of gods, or a supreme deity. Deities possess supernatural qualities that allow them to exert their will over humans and nature. In the metaphysical stage, people draw upon abstract and broad concepts to define features of reality that cannot be observed through the senses or direct experience. Metaphysics deals with big philosophical questions such as the nature of the human mind, the meaning of life, and good versus evil. In the positive stage (stage 3)—the conceptually superior stage according to Comte—people use scientific explanations grounded in observation and experimental designs to understand the world. Comte placed sociology in this third stage of thinking; he maintained that sociologists were scientists who studied the results of the human intellect (DeGrange 1939). What did he mean by this?

First, sociology is a science and only those sociologists who follow the scientific method can presume to have a voice in describing and guiding human affairs. The scientific method rejects personal opinions and political agendas in favor of disciplined and objective strategies in thinking about and addressing social issues and making effective policies. Second, sociologists study the things humans have created: an idea, an invention, or a way of behaving and the effects those creations have on society.

Comte recommended that sociologists study **social statics**, the forces that hold societies together such that they endure over time, and **social dynamics**, the forces that cause societies to change. Comte's preoccupation with forces of order and change is not surprising given that he was writing at a time when the Industrial Revolution was transforming society in unprecedented ways.

Comte on the Mobile Phone If Auguste Comte were alive today, he would emphasize the dramatic and far-reaching changes associated with the mobile phone. At the same time, he would also consider that, in spite of thousands of changes to the ways in which people relate to one another, specific relationships do not break down into something beyond recognition. Some news headlines illustrate this point:

- "Local Drivers Pulled Over during Cell Phone Sweep: Cell Phone Crackdown Last November Netted 1,000" (*San Diego News* 2011).
- "Man Used Roommate's Cell Phone to Lure Robbery Victim with a Text Message Asking Him to Come Over" (WAFB.com 2011).
- "Starbucks Releases New Payment System for Mobile Phones" (Ferri 2011).
- "4th Annual Cell Phone Film Festival" (India PRWire 2011).

All four headlines describe a way the mobile phone has changed the way people relate—a change in reasons police pull over drivers, in the way a robber might lure a potential victim, in the way customers pay for a product, and in how people watch a film. Although these four changes are quite dramatic, there is still a timeless element to each event—police have always engaged in traffic sweeps, criminals

social statics The forces that hold societies together such that they endure over time.

social dynamics The forces that cause societies to change.

always look for ways to lure unsuspecting victims, people have always had to pay for products and services, and films have been around for some time. The mobile phone did not break down, beyond recognition, relationships between police and drivers, robbers and victims, consumers and coffee venders, and moviegoers and filmmakers.

Karl Marx (1818–1883)

The political philosopher Karl Marx was born in Germany but spent much of his professional life in London, working and writing in collaboration with Friedrich Engels. One of Marx and Engels's most influential writings is *The Communist Manifesto*, a 23-page pamphlet issued in 1848, and translated into more than 30 languages (Marcus 1998). Upon reading it today, more than 150 years later, one is "struck by the eerie way in which its 1848 description of capitalism resembles the restless, anxious and competitive world of today's global economy" (Lewis 1998, p. A17).

The *Manifesto* includes these famous lines: "The workers have nothing to lose but their chains; they have a whole world to gain. Workers of all countries, unite." In an essay marking the 150th anniversary of *The Communist Manifesto*, John Cassidy (1997) wrote that "in many ways, Marx's legacy has been obscured by the failure of Communism, which wasn't his primary interest. In fact, . . . Marx was a student of capitalism, and that is how he should be judged" (p. 248).

Marx sought to analyze and explain how **conflict** drives social change. The character of conflict is shaped directly and profoundly by the means of production, the resources (land, tools, equipment, factories, transportation, and labor) essential to the production and distribution of goods and services. Marx viewed every historical period as characterized by a system of production that gave rise to specific types of confrontation between an exploiting class and an exploited class. For Marx, class conflict was the vehicle that propelled people from one historical epoch to another.

From Marx's perspective, the system of production accompanying the Industrial Revolution gave rise to two distinct classes: the **bourgeoisie**, the profit-driven owners of the means of production, and the **proletariat**, those individuals who must sell their labor to the bourgeoisie. Marx devoted his life to documenting and understanding the causes and consequences of this fundamental and unequal divide. Marx expressed profound moral outrage over the plight of the proletariat, who, at the time of his writings, were unable to afford the products of their labor and suffered from deplorable living conditions.

Karl Marx believed that the bourgeoisie's pursuit of profit was behind the explosion of technological innovation and the never-before-seen increase in the amount of goods and services produced during the Industrial Revolution. In a capitalist system, profit is the most important measure of success. Marx described class conflict as an antagonism that grows out of the opposing interests held by these two parties. The bourgeoisie's interest lies with making a profit and the proletariat's with increasing wages. To maximize profit, the bourgeoisie work to cut labor costs by investing in labor-saving technologies, employing the lowest-cost workers, and finding the cheapest materials to make products.

The capitalist system is a vehicle of change in that it requires technology and products to be revolutionized constantly. Marx believed that capitalism was the first economic system capable of maximizing the immense productive potential of human labor and ingenuity. He also felt, however, that capitalism ignored too many human needs and that too many people could not afford to buy the products of their labor. Marx believed that if this economic system were in the right hands—the hands of the workers or the proletariat—public wealth would be more than abundant and would be distributed according to need. Instead, according to Marx (1887), capitalism survived and flourished by sucking the blood of living labor. The drive is a "boundless thirst—a werewolf-like hunger—that takes no account of the health and the length of life of the worker unless society forces it to do so" (p. 142). That thirst for profit "chases the bourgeoisie over the whole surface of the globe" in search of the lowest-cost labor and resources to make products (Marx 1881, p. 531).

Marx also named a third class, the finance aristocracy, who lived in obvious luxury among masses of starving, low-paid, and unemployed workers (Bologna 2008, Proudhon 1847). The finance aristocracy includes bankers and stockholders seemingly detached from the world of "work." Marx (1856) described this source of income as "created from nothing—without labor and without creating a product or service to sell in exchange for wealth." The finance aristocracy speculates or employs financial advisors to speculate for them. Although some speculation has a power of inventiveness, "it is at the same time also a gamble and a search for the 'easy life'; as such it is the art of getting rich without work . . . without giving anything equivalent in exchange; it is the cancer of production, the plague of society and of states" (Bologna 2008, Proudhon 1847).

Marx on Mobile Phones If Karl Marx were alive today, he would certainly focus his attention on means of production as it relates to wireless phones. He would be particularly interested in the fact that more than 5 billion

conflict The major force that drives social change.

bourgeoisie The profit-driven owners of the means of production.

proletariat Those individuals who must sell their labor to the bourgeoisie.

Technology Tip: Although Karl Marx died in 1883 he is very much in the news. Ask students to go to Google News and use search term "Karl Marx." Have students read 4–5 articles and summarize how Marx/Marxist ideas are portrayed (e.g., are his ideas treated with respect or is he mocked?).

wireless phones are in use around the world and that billions of phones have been discarded since they became popular in 1995. Marx would ask who manufactured these billions of phones? To answer this, Marx would draw upon the research of social scientist Pun Ngai (2005), who worked in a Chinese electronics factory with a dormitory for workers.

In *Made in China: Women Factory Workers in a Global Workplace,* Ngai writes of female workers who labor 12 or more hours per day on five to six hours of sleep in a closed factory environment (windows sealed and covered with plastic) so that employees do not lose concentration by looking outside. The work was repetitive, mindless, and never ending. Watched by an electronic eye, the workers earned about 45 cents per hour. Although the workers did not know where the cameras were placed, they were nevertheless aware of their relentless gaze. As one woman described it, "I don't need to use my mind anymore. I have been doing the same thing for two years. Things come and go, repeating every second and minute. I can do it with my mind closed" (p. 83).

Ngai found that almost every task on the assembly line involved working with or exposure to highly toxic chemicals. Coupled with a stressful work environment and lack of sleep, not surprisingly, chronic pain was pervasive among the factory workers. Among the most common symptoms reported were headaches, backaches, eye strain, sore throats, nausea, and menstrual pain.

Marx, who wrote more than 110 years ago about the exploitation of labor, could not have anticipated the complex supply chain through which a product such as the mobile phone passes, beginning with extraction of raw materials to eventually reaching the consumers' hands. In spite of its small size, a mobile phone can contain from 600 to 1,000 parts, depending on brand. Marx would still argue that factory labor and the labor of those who extract and process raw materials for the wireless phones are the backbone of the industry. Handset makers such as RIM, Nokia, Samsung, Apple, and Sony, and carriers such as AT&T and Verizon could not exist without this labor.

If Karl Marx were alive today, he would most certainly focus on those who assemble and test wireless phones, their low earnings, the long hours worked per week, and adverse working conditions.

Because firms "guard information about pricing deals they have negotiated and often compel the silence of their suppliers and contractors through nondisclosure agreements," it is virtually impossible to secure financial records documenting income, revenue, and profits of all the parties involved in the production and distribution of wireless phones (Dedrick, Kraemer, and Linden 2010, p. 7). There is some financial data on some of the major mobile phone companies as it relates to gross profits and manufacturing costs, including the cost of assembly and testing. Table 1.1 shows that the assembly and test costs are very low relative to the revenue earned per phone.

TABLE 1.1 Selected Financial Indicators for Four Major Headset Suppliers of Smart Phones

Financial Indicator	Motorola Razr	Palm Treo 650	RIM Curve	Nokia
Total Amount Received From Consumer Including Subsidy from Servicer Provider	$349.00	$418.00	$426.00	N/A
Cost of 600 to 1,000 Parts, Components	$137.92	$178.99	$100.30	$182.44
Assembly and Testing	$5.81	$11.58	$7.95	$7.51
Gross Profit*	$206.00	$228.00	$238.00	N/A
Return on Assets**	13%***	7%	No estimate	N/A

Gross profit is the difference between revenue from product and the cost of making it before things like overhead, payroll, and taxes are deducted.

***Return on assets* is calculated by dividing a corporation's annual earnings by its total assets to estimate a return on investment.

***For the year researchers estimated this number, the actual percentage was 23%; the company had received a substantial tax break. Without this tax break, the return would have been 13%.

N/A = Not applicable.

Source: Data from Dedrick, Kraemer, and Linden 2010.

Émile Durkheim (1858–1917)

To describe the Industrial Revolution and its effects, Frenchman Émile Durkheim focused on the division of labor and solidarity. The division of labor is the way a society divides and assigns day-to-day tasks. Durkheim was interested in how the division of labor affected **solidarity**, the system of social ties that connects people to one another and to the wider society. This system of social ties acts as cement binding people to each other and to the society. Durkheim observed that industrialization changed the division of labor from relatively simple to complex and, by extension, changed the nature of solidarity. Durkheim believed that the sociologist's task is to analyze and explain the solidarity. As you will see later in this textbook, Durkheim's preoccupation with the ties that bind is evident in his writings on education, deviance, the division of labor, and suicide. By way of introduction to Durkheim's emphasis on the ties that bind, we turn to his writings on suicide.

In *Suicide*, Durkheim argued that it is futile to study the immediate circumstances that lead people to kill themselves, because an infinite number of such circumstances exist. For example, one person may kill herself in the midst of newly acquired wealth, whereas another kills herself in the lap of poverty. One may kill himself because he is unhappy in his marriage and feels trapped, whereas another kills himself because his unhappy marriage has just ended in divorce. In one case, a person kills himself after losing a business; in another case, a lottery winner kills herself because she cannot tolerate her family and friends fighting one another to share in her newfound fortune. Because almost any personal circumstance can serve as a pretext for suicide, Durkheim concluded that there is no situation that could not serve as an occasion for someone's suicide.

Durkheim also reasoned that no central emotional quality was common to all suicides. We can point to cases in which people live on through horrible misfortune whereas others kill themselves over seemingly minor troubles. Moreover, we can cite examples in which people renounce life at times when it is most comfortable or at times of great achievement. Given these conceptual difficulties, Durkheim offered a definition of suicide that goes beyond its popular meaning (the act of intentionally killing oneself). This definition takes the spotlight off the victim and points it outward toward the ties that bind (or fail to bind) people to others in the society. In short, Durkheim viewed suicide as a severing of relationships. To make his case, he argued that every group has a greater or lesser propensity for suicide. The suicide rates for various age, sex, and race groups in the United States, for example, show that suicide is more prevalent for some categories of people—the elderly, males, 15- to 19-year-olds—than for other categories. From a sociological point of view, these differences in suicide rates cannot be explained by pointing to each victim's immediate circumstances.

Instead, Durkheim examined the social ties that bind or fail to bind social categories to others. For example, all people who suddenly find themselves in the unemployed category must adjust to life without a job. That adjustment may entail finding a way to live on a reduced budget, trying to stay cheerful while hunting for a job, or feeling uncomfortable around friends who have a job. According to Durkheim, it is inevitable that a certain number of those in the unemployed category will succumb to social pressures and choose to sever the relationships from which such pressures emanate.

Durkheim identified four types of social ties, each of which describes a different kind of relationship to the group: egoistic, altruistic, anomic, and fatalistic. **Egoistic** describes a state in which the ties attaching the individual to others in the society are weak. When individuals are detached from others, they encounter less resistance to suicide. The lives of the chronically ill, for example, are often characterized by excessive individuation if friends, family, and other acquaintances avoid interacting with the ill person out of fear of upsetting the patient or themselves.

Altruistic describes a state in which the ties attaching the individual to the group are such that the person has no life beyond the group. In these situations, a person's sense of self cannot be separated from the group. When such people commit suicide, it is on behalf of the group they love more than themselves. The classic example is members of a military unit: The first quality of soldiers is a sense of selflessness. Soldiers must be trained to place little value on the self and to sacrifice themselves for the unit and its larger purpose.

Anomic describes a state in which the ties attaching the individual to the group are disrupted due to dramatic changes in social circumstances. Durkheim gave particular emphasis to economic circumstances such as a recession, a depression, or an economic boom. In all cases, a reclassification occurs that suddenly casts individuals into a lower or higher status than before. When people are cast into a lower status, they must reduce their requirements, restrain their needs, and practice self-control. When individuals are cast into a higher status, they must adjust to increased prosperity, which unleashes aspirations and

solidarity The system of social ties that connects people to one another and to the wider society. This system of social ties acts as "cement" binding people to each other and to the society.

egoistic A state in which the ties attaching the individual to others in the society are weak.

altruistic A state in which the ties attaching the individual to the group are such that he or she has no life beyond the group.

anomic A state in which the ties attaching the individual to the group are disrupted due to dramatic changes in economic circumstances.

Technology Tip: Émile Durkheim is still in the news even though he died in 1918. Go to Google News and use search term "Emile Durkheim." Have students review headlines and read 4–5 articles in which Durkheim is mentioned. Is there a pattern?

expands desires to an unlimited extent. A thirst to acquire goods and services arises that cannot be satisfied.

Fatalistic describes a state in which the ties attaching the individual to the group involve discipline so oppressive it offers no chance of release. Under such conditions, individuals see their futures as permanently blocked. Durkheim asked, "Do not the suicides of slaves, said to be frequent under certain conditions, belong to this type?" (1951, p. 276).

Durkheim on the Mobile Phone If Durkheim were alive today, he would focus on the ways mobile phones affect solidarity or the ties that bind people to each other and society. He would seek to understand how mobile phones affect the nature of the social bonds people form. Broadly speaking, the mobile phone (unlike the landline phone) allows people to communicate with others regardless of location—that is, people with mobile phones do not need to be in a fixed location, such as in their home at an agreed-upon time, to communicate with others. And as mobile phones increasingly allow Internet access, the potential to connect with others will increase dramatically. Callers or texters may now intrude into just about any situation (a football game, a public bathroom, a classroom, a doctor's office). In addition, people can take advantage of applications (apps) and/or browse the Internet looking for immediate answers to questions (for example, directions, places to eat) and track friends and family through social networking sites. Durkheim would ask how this technological breakthrough might strengthen, weaken, or facilitate current and new social ties. He would find that, depending on how people use them, the mobile phone has the potential to:

- *strengthen and cultivate ties.* The ability to contact someone 24/7 regardless of location can work to "strengthen the formation and maintenance of deep bonds." People communicate, not to conduct business, but for the purpose of expressing affection, offering support, giving advice, and otherwise validating the centrality of the relationship even when physically separated (Geser 2004). In this sense, mobile phones facilitate nomadic intimacy, an ability to remain connected to those who make up the core of someone's personal network even at a distance and while on the move (Fortunati 2000). Depending on the frequency of calls and intensity of the social bond, the mobile phone reduces the probability that people are receptive to information outside personal networks because they are increasingly absorbed and distracted with communicating with those in core networks (Geser 2004).
- *increase the chances that behavior can be monitored.* Unless a mobile phone is turned off, it is possible to determine geographic location of the person in possession of it. It is also possible to obtain records of texts, calls, and Internet use and to even watch what is going on in a distance location through surveillance apps. Parents, partners, police, and others can check up on children, partners, friends, or potential criminals. Likewise, the extremely dependent can "stalk" another with an onslaught of texts and calls demanding an immediate response.
- *weaken ties with those sharing a physical space.* When people use their mobile phone to text, call, or browse the Internet in public spaces, it signals to other parties in that physical space that the mobile phone user is preoccupied. This preoccupation substantially reduces the chances that a person on the phone will notice or interact with those sharing the physical space (for example, a park, a classroom, a waiting room, an airport). The activities and people are relegated to the background. When a mobile phone rings or signals a message while someone is engaged in a face-to-face conversation, it can send the message to conversation partners that they are not significant or important enough to deserve exclusive attention (Geser 2004). When the person answers the phone, conversation partners must assume the role of "hanging bystander" or engage in a "waiting strategy," left to think about whether or not to continue with the interaction (Ling 1997). Finally when everyone in a family or other primary group owns a personal phone, "knowledge about each other's communication networks declines. Specifically, we may find that each family member has many acquaintances and ongoing interactions unknown to the other family members" (Geser 2004).

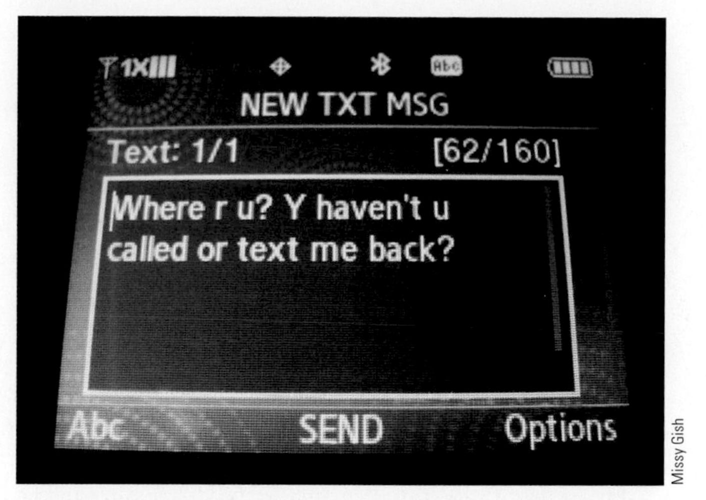

Missy Gish

If Durkheim were alive today, he would focus on the ways mobile phones shape relationships between people in new ways. What does this text message say about the relationship between sender and receiver?

fatalistic A state in which the ties attaching the individual to the group involve discipline so oppressive it offers no chance of release.

- *organize like-minded people to protest, demonstrate, celebrate, or otherwise participate in some public event.* The mobile phone can function as a community-organizing tool allowing leaders and participants to send out text messages in mass, or to post and check messages on Facebook. Participants can repost posts and forward messages to others they know. Finally, interested parties can check news coverage and reports as it happens.

Max Weber (1864–1920)

The German scholar Max Weber made it his task to analyze and explain how the Industrial Revolution affected **social actions**—actions people take in response to others—with emphasis on the forces that motivate people to act. In this regard, Weber suggested that sociologists focus on the broad reasons that people pursue goals, whatever those goals may be. He believed that social action is oriented toward one of four ideal types—ideal, not in the sense of being the most desirable, but as a gauge against which actual behavior can be compared. In the case of social action, an ideal type is a deliberate simplification or caricature of what motivates people to act, in that it exaggerates and emphasizes the distinguishing characteristics that make one type of action distinct from another. In reality, social action is not so clear-cut but involves some mixture of the four types:

1. *Traditional*—a goal is pursued because it was pursued in the past (that is, "that is the way it has always been").
2. *Affectional*—a goal is pursued in response to an emotion such as revenge, love, or loyalty (soldiers throw themselves on a grenade out of love and sense of duty for those in their unit).
3. *Value-rational*—a valued goal is pursued with a deep and abiding awareness of the symbolic significance of the actions taken to pursue the goal, meaning that "there can be no compromises or cost-accounting, no rational weighing of one end against another" (Weintraub and Soares 2005). Instead, action is guided by codes of conduct that prohibit certain kinds of behavior and permit others. With value-rational action, the way in which people go about achieving a goal is valued as much as the goal itself—perhaps even more so as, in an effort to stay true to a code of conduct, the goal may not be realized (Weintraub and Soares 2005).
4. *Instrumental-rational*—a valued goal is pursued by the most efficient means, often without considering the appropriateness or consequences of those means. It is result-oriented action. In the context of the Industrial Revolution, the valued goal is profit and the most efficient means are the cost-effective ones taken without regard for their consequences to workers or the environment. In contrast to value-rational action, this type of action does not require or prohibit the manner by which people go about achieving goals—any way of achieving the desired end is allowed as long as the end is achieved. One might equate this type of action with an addiction in the sense that the person will work to acquire a drug or other desired state at any cost to self or to others. There is an inevitable self-destructive quality to this form of action (Henri 2000). In the short run, the instrumental-rational action (with no constraints on behavior) will defeat the value-rationally motivated actors. However, in the long run, the "anything goes" approach will eventually collapse on itself.

Weber maintained that in the presence of industrialization, behavior was less likely to be motivated by tradition or emotion and was more likely to be instrumental-rational. Weber was particularly concerned about instrumental-rational action because he believed that it could lead to disenchantment, a great spiritual void accompanied by a crisis of meaning.

Weber on Mobile Phones Weber believed that sociologists should focus on the broad reasons that people pursue goals, whatever those goals may be. If Weber were alive today, he would consider how people reject or embrace mobile phones as a way of achieving a variety of goals. Specifically, under what conditions do people turn to the mobile phone as a means to preserve a tradition? As means to expressing emotion? As a vehicle for maintaining a valued standard or code of conduct? As a vehicle for achieving a goal, regardless of adverse consequences to self and others?

Tradition-Driven Social Action People can embrace the mobile phone as a tool for preserving some valued tradition. One specific example involves Pope Benedict and the Vatican staff who use mobile phone technology to convey the Catholic message to youth seeking a connection to that religion. On World Youth Day, the Pope texted daily messages to attendees, and organizers erected digital prayer walls even as the Vatican warned that obsessions with such technologies are affecting time needed to engage in spiritual pursuits (Beaumont 2008). The Vatican has also posted religious manuscripts and ancient texts online.

Emotion-Driven Social Action People can choose the mobile phone as a tool that allows them to quickly access social networking sites such as Facebook, Twitter, and dating sites to fulfill the emotional need for social contact with others. People may also choose the mobile phone as a way to connect with and mobilize those who share causes to which they are deeply committed.

Value-Rational Action Here people choose mobile phones as a means for meeting responsibilities or as a way of maintaining contact from a distance. That responsibility may

social actions Actions people take in response to others.

Technology Tip: Like Marx and Durkheim, Weber is also in the news. Ask students to go to Google News and use search terms "Max Weber." Have students review headlines and read 4–5 articles in which Weber is mentioned. Identify any themes or key ideas.

Department of Defense

This mobile phone, rigged as a detonator for an improvised explosive device, represents an example of instrumental rational action in that the mobile phone is used as a tool to achieve a goal by any means necessary.

involve parenting children from a distance, acting as a caregiver to parents or grandparents, monitoring criminal behavior so as catch and record "wrongdoings" of violations of codes, and so on.

Instrumental-Rational Action The mobile phone can be part of a "by any means necessary mentality" for achieving a desired goal. In this situation, the phone is part of an arsenal of tools to achieve a goal. The phone might become a tool thieves use to pinpoint potential victims, as when a criminal watches for bank customers withdrawing large sums of cash and then texts an accomplice to follow and rob that person at the right moment. The phone could be used to detonate a roadside or other homemade bomb from a safe distance.

W.E.B. DuBois (1868–1963)

W.E.B. DuBois wrote about the "strange meaning of being black" and about the color line. In *The Souls of Black Folk* (1903)—a book that has been republished in 119 editions (Gates 2003)—DuBois announced his preoccupation with the "strange meaning of being black here in the dawning of the Twentieth Century." The strange meaning of being black in America includes a **double consciousness** that DuBois defined as "this sense of always looking at one's self through the eyes of others, of measuring one's soul by the tape of a world that looks on in amused contempt and pity." The double consciousness includes a sense of two-ness: "an American, a Negro; two souls, two thoughts, two unreconciled strivings; two warring ideals in one dark body, whose dogged strength alone keeps it from being torn asunder." DuBois's preoccupation with the strange meaning of being black was no doubt affected by the facts that his father was a Haitian of French and African descent and his mother was an American of Dutch and African descent (Lewis 1993). Historically in the United States, a person has been considered "black" even when his or her parents are of different or blended "races." To accept this idea, we must act as if whites and blacks do not marry each other or produce offspring together and as if one parent, the "black" one, contributes a disproportionate amount of genetic material—so large that it negates the genetic contribution of the other parent.

In addition to writing about the "strange meaning of being black" and about racial mixing, DuBois also wrote about the **color line**, a barrier supported by customs and laws separating nonwhites from whites, especially with regard to their place in the division of labor. The color line originated with the colonial expansion that accompanied the Industrial Revolution. That expansion involved rival European powers (Britain, France, Germany, Belgium, Portugal, the Netherlands, and Italy) competing to secure colonies, and by extension, the labor and natural resources within those colonies. The colonies' resources and labor fueled European and American industrialization. DuBois (1919) traced the color line's origin to the scramble for Africa's resources, beginning with the slave trade upon which the British Empire and American republic were built, costing black Africa "no less than 100,000,000 souls" (p. 246). DuBois maintained that the world was able "to endure this horrible tragedy by deliberately stopping its ears and changing the subject in conversation" (p. 246). He further maintained that an honest review of Africa's history could only bring us to conclude that Western governments and corporations coveted Africa for its natural resources and for the cheap labor needed to extract them.

DuBois on the Mobile Phone If W.E.B. DuBois were alive today, he would think about the mobile phone, using the color line as a lens. He would focus on the "scramble" for the resources needed to produce mobile phones and other electronic products. The raw materials needed to produce wireless phones come from all over the world. The resources needed to make circuit boards, LCD screens, and batteries include gold, lead, nickel, zinc, tantalum, oil, limestone, mercury, copper, cadmium, and lithium (U.S. EPA 2010). The phrase *scramble* is an apt one because it suggests that all parties involved in the hunt to secure and control these resources are part of a frantic competition. The history of all previously named resources and many others involved a scramble to exploit labor and resources of non-European

double consciousness According to DuBois, "this sense of always looking at one's self through the eyes of others, of measuring one's soul by the tape of a world that looks on in amused contempt and pity." The double consciousness includes a sense of two-ness: "an American, a Negro; two souls, two thoughts, two unreconciled strivings; two warring ideals in one dark body, whose dogged strength alone keeps it from being torn asunder."

color line A barrier supported by customs and laws separating nonwhites from whites, especially with regard to their place in the division of labor.

Technology Tip: W.E.B. DuBois is also a sociological theorist in the news. Ask students to go to Google News using "W.E.B. DuBois" as a search term. Read 4–5 articles to gain clues on how this theorist's ideas inform journalists today.

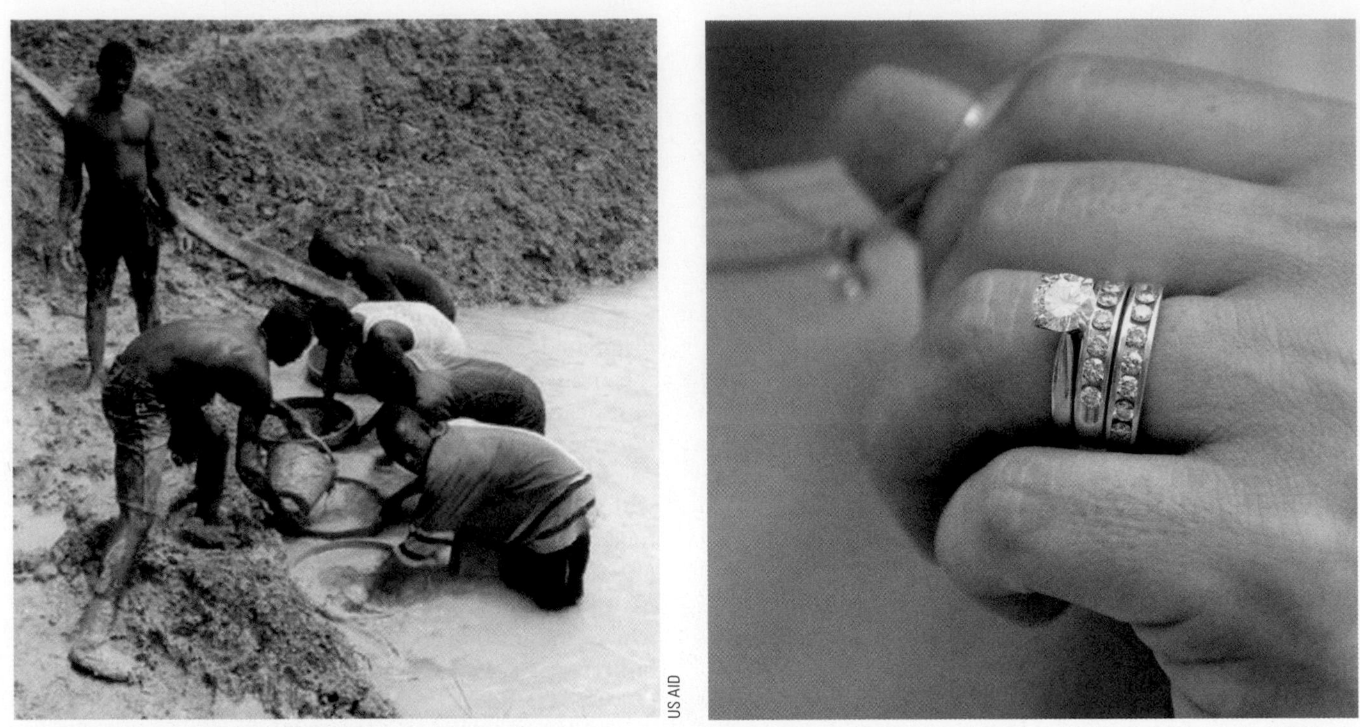

As a result of the demand for diamonds, miners working for very low wages in the war-torn Democratic Republic of the Congo (DRC) and elsewhere produce some 800 million gem- and industrial-quality diamonds per year. U.S. consumers—about 4.6 percent of the world's population—buy almost 50 percent of these stones (Cockburn 2002). The ongoing wars in the DRC are fueled in large part by factions seeking control over diamond mines and other resources.

peoples. DuBois would be particularly interested in the scramble for tantalum. Tantalum is an ore needed to help regulate voltage and store energy in wireless phones and other electronic products. DuBois would point to the connection between wireless phones and the ongoing war and conflicts raging in a seemingly faraway place: the DRC.

The largest exporter of tantalum is Australia. Other major exporters include Canada, China, Ethiopia, Brazil, and Mozambique. Additional countries believed to have significant quantities of tantalum are Saudi Arabia, Egypt, and Greenland. According to geological reports, the Democratic Republic of the Congo has at times accounted for about 10 percent of the world's tantalum production (USGS 2011). The United Nations and others have pointed to the scramble for tantalum in eastern DRC country as the cause of armed conflict, human rights abuses, and destruction of wildlife. In 2001, the United Nations Security Council issued a report citing "massive looting of resources"—specifically tantalum, gold, diamonds, and timber—as a key reason for the war raging in the DRC. At that time, the war involved seven African countries and was referred to as Africa's First World War. In 2003, another United Nations report again cited the "scramble" for tantalum as fueling the war that was responsible for an estimated 5.4 million deaths since 1998. Although the war ended in 2003, armed militias have continued to exploit tantalum and other resources from eastern Congo. While there have been some attempts to stop the purchase of "conflict minerals," those efforts have been thwarted by DRC troops who sell them on the black market (United Nations 2010). Of course, black market activity is not part of official trade data. One report by the Commerce Resources Corporation (an exploration company) estimated that the "output in the DRC last year accounted for about 90 percent of global production at around 2 million pounds" (Taylor 2010).

Jane Addams (1860–1935)

In 1889, Jane Addams (with Ellen Gates Starr) cofounded one of the first settlement houses in the United States, the Chicago Hull House. Settlement houses, which originated in London, were community centers that provided services to the poor and other marginalized populations. These centers were supported by the wealthy donors from the surrounding community and by university faculty and college students who lived with, served, and learned from these populations. Hull House, considered one of the largest and most influential settlements in the United States, offered educational, cultural, and social services to immigrants and other diverse populations of Chicago. At the time of Hull House's founding, immigrants constituted almost 50 percent of Chicago's population, which was second in size only to New York's immigrant population. Hull House was established at a time when Chicago was industrializing and in the midst of unprecedented growth that started in 1860, when the city's population was 10,000; over the course of the next 50 years, it grew to 2 million. The dramatic increase was accompanied by a variety of social problems, including homelessness, substandard housing, unemployment, and exploitive and unsafe working conditions.

Hull House's facilities included a night school for adults, morning kindergarten classes, clubs for girls and boys, a public kitchen, an art gallery, a coffeehouse, recreation facilities (including a swimming pool), a music school, a drama group, and a library. The Hull House had strong ties with the University of Chicago School of Sociology; through her community-based work, Jane Addams influenced sociological thought and work in an area of the discipline now known as "public sociology." Not only did she establish a variety of programs and services to address the needs of Chicago's urban population, but Addams also worked to give those populations a voice and to change the way society operated with regard to child labor, juvenile justice, industrial safety, working hours, women's and minority rights, and a variety of other areas (Deegan 1978, Hamington 2007).

The Chicago sociologists considered her work "social work" and an appropriate specialization for women. For that reason, female students tended to intern and live at Hull House. Addams, however, did not consider her work social work. She maintained that the settlements were equivalent to an applied university where knowledge about how to change the situation of people could be applied and tested. Addams advocated for **sympathetic knowledge**, firsthand knowledge gained by living and working among those being studied because "knowing one another better reinforces the common connection of people such that the potential for caring and empathetic moral actions increase" (Addams 1912, p. 7; see Sociological Imagination: Acquiring Firsthand Knowledge).

Addams made a point of never addressing a "Chicago audience on the subject of the Settlement and its vicinity without inviting a neighbor to go with me, that I might curb my hasty generalization by the consciousness that I had an auditor who knew the conditions more intimately than I could hope to do" (Addams 1910, p. 80).

As one measure of Addams's influence and popularity in American society, consider that in the results of one newspaper poll asking, "Who among our contemporaries are of the most value to the community?" Addams was voted second, after Thomas Edison (U.S. Library of Congress 2008). However, when Addams publicly opposed U.S. involvement in World War I (1914–1918), she was branded a traitor and unpatriotic and was expelled from the Daughters of the American Revolution. Many years later, in 1931, Jane Addams was awarded the Nobel Peace Prize for her work to promote peace, which included her opposition to the war and her humanitarian efforts assisting President Herbert Hoover in providing food aid and other relief to those living in enemy nations (Abrams 1997). Jane Addams's influence on the discipline of sociology is apparent, as she helped to found the American Sociological Association.

How do the economically disadvantaged who cannot afford mobile phones (or any phone for that matter) make important calls or stay in touch with family and friends when pay phones, which used to be located in and outside of public places, have disappeared? That question would be of great concern to sociologist Jane Addams.

Addams on the Mobile Phone If Jane Addams were alive today, she would emphasize the mobile phone as an empowering tool to address problems faced by the disadvantaged and underserved in the United States and around the world (see Working for Change: Mobile Phone Banking in India). She would be particularly interested in profiling those without access to mobile phones or a landline phone, especially as public pay phones become more difficult to find. The latest survey suggests that 82 percent of Americans over 18 years of age own mobile phones, and 75 percent of 12- to 17-year-olds own such a phone. She would applaud programs that help to provide mobile phone services to people who cannot afford them. One

sympathetic knowledge Firsthand knowledge gained by living and working among those being studied.

Technology Tip: Jane Addams and the Hull House, which she founded, are still in the news today. Ask students to go to Google News and use "Jane Addams" as a search term to find articles on her ideas and accomplishments.

The Sociological Imagination Unplugged

During my junior year of college, I quickly realized that for my resume to stand out I needed to become actively involved on campus. While searching for a group, I came across the student organization Kiksuya, which is dedicated to promoting Native American awareness and raising funds for the reservation of Pine Ridge, South Dakota.

While my knowledge of Native American culture was rather limited in that I knew that in general Native Americans face hardships, I wanted to help—I just didn't know how. So I joined and the following semester, I, along with other Kiksuya members, organized a volunteer trip to Pine Ridge Reservation with the help from our faculty advisor, Dr. Nicole Grant, who provided us with the information and cultural sensitivity needed to make the trip successful. As we prepared for the trip we discussed technology. Since we were traveling to a poverty-stricken area, we all agreed to unplug—to leave our technological devices at home or at least in the van. We knew that those who lived in Pine Ridge couldn't afford such luxuries and so we determined that it really wasn't necessary to take our iPods or mobile phones along.

For the first time since being in my possession, my purple Verizon flip phone stayed at home. That mobile phone usually inhabits my right pocket, nothing else. I need to have a connection with the outside world. What if someone needs me? What if something happens? What if I receive a text message, or heaven forbid, someone actually calls me? No matter the time of day or my location, I am on duty. Always. My phone startles me awake in the morning with shrill beeps. My phone is the first thing I look at upon waking and the last thing I touch before reaching sleep. The mobile phone is my god. Yet on this volunteer trip, my pocket remained empty. I actually didn't bring any electronic devices, even though the others did. I wanted to push away anything that had to do with my culture so I could learn and focus all my energy on the experiences at hand. My mind wanders enough without me texting someone every four seconds to find out what is going on in the "world." I know too well the temptations of technology.

At our fingertips we have a tool that allows us to do just about anything all within our own personal bubbles. For many, no matter if in class or driving, the task at hand never takes priority over checking the mobile phone. Text messages must be read and answered immediately. There were moments where I wished that I had taken my phone on the trip. Or a book. Something. Staring out the window of the van, all I could see was relentless land. Dusty hills sweeping across the plains. The beauty is unsurpassable yet it still seemed as if the drive might never end. As we neared our destination, I did not see mobile phone towers placed awkwardly amidst the hills. Few, if any, electrical lines stretched strangely across plateaus.

While on the reservation, however, one asinine inconvenience stood out: the lack of technology. And not only a lack, but it was nonexistent. Not once did I see a mobile phone or an iPod except in the hands of a volunteer. Not once did I see someone on Pine Ridge updating their status on Facebook or even posing for a photograph. Technology on the reservation seemed to only exist in the minds, and literally in the hands, of the volunteers. Is technology a necessity, something one cannot exist without? Is technology required to live and to thrive as a people? To be a part of a culture that breathes peace and humility is technology a true necessity?

Unhooked and unplugged, I'm glad I left my phone at home. Instead of carrying on meaningless chatter with those who will survive perfectly fine while I am away, I was able to learn so much more. Technology is an amazing convenience, but it can also is a major inconvenience. If I had been texting, I would have missed the young child who asked if she could show me her family's sweat lodge. I would have missed the boy climbing onto his new bunk bed we constructed; the joy on his face for this was his first bed. I would have missed the sweet scents drifting with the wind. I would not have noticed the People. We tend to forget not only the people, but also that those people are not merely faces in faraway places. They are our brothers, our sisters, our friends . . . Mitakuye Oyasin. We are all related. We are all in this fight together. If only we could look past the insignificant, trivial issues that the media promotes, stop bowing down to the Cell Phone God, and remove the blinders that technology can create, then perhaps we might pay attention to issues of social justice.

On that volunteer trip, I was handed an opportunity to try to bridge the ravine that plummets between us and the

such program is SafeLink Wireless; it provides wireless phones free of charge to those who cannot afford them and offers free minutes—typically 68 minutes a month—which are paid for by the Universal Service Fund tax added to all phone bills. The SafeLink Program has over 2 million customers in 32 states. This service allows those who are low-income and homebound, for example, to make calls in an emergency (SafeLink Wireless 2011; Richtel 2009).

The Importance of a Global Perspective

CORE CONCEPT 6 A global perspective assumes that social interactions do not stop at political borders and that the most pressing social problems are part of a larger, global situation.

Native American People. To work directly alongside the Lakota I learned about their customs and to see life from a different perspective—the perspective of the lost and forgotten, the perspective of the unwanted, the bruised and the hurt. To witness firsthand the poverty on Pine Ridge Reservation kindled a fire deep inside volunteers, and deep within myself. The generosity of the Lakota people and the love they carry for each other and their land, brings tears in all eyes. What I tried to give to the reservation by volunteering manual labor is absolutely minute in comparison with the values and new ideas with which I returned. I received a new outlook on life, an appreciation for everything previously taken for granted, and for all the luxuries we don't even consider as luxuries like the ability to walk in the next room and flip on the light switch. Or the air conditioning. Or the heat. I wouldn't have acquired that new outlook if I had been wrapped up in my cell phone, or in an iPod or a laptop. I would have instead heard, "And she said that he said. . . ." Wasted time. I'm glad I was able to smell the clean, unpolluted air, and walk through mountainous terrain, listening to songs of the wind. My pocket's not so lonely now; it can survive some time alone, just as I can unhook myself from mainstream culture, and think about the actual necessities in life.

There is a peaceful, ignorant belief that there is no such thing as poverty in America, and if there is, the individual must be the problem. Never society. Oh, the luxury of complete obliviousness. Before this trip, the Native American seemed to be something in a childhood story, a myth—cowboys and Indians, feathers and headdresses, scalping, warriors on a raid riding to kidnap a young blue-eyed child, the noble savage, primitive and scantily clad. I viewed the Native Americans as something in the past, as a lost culture, a lost group of people.

Now Disney representations no longer pollute my mind. I no longer imagine the painted warrior, or the young Indian princess, or the thriving casino; instead I think of third-world countries. I think of no electricity, no garbage facilities for disposal, little to no running water, limited access to vaccinations against disease, extreme depression, alcoholism, the mother who does without so her child might survive. I think of daunting weather conditions, of tired hands and sore feet, and of men who cannot be breadwinners for there are virtually no jobs on the reservation. But above all, I remember to think that in spite of the harsh life poverty has brought, hope persists—a stubborn streak, clinging to life and praying for change. Amidst the debris the wind carries across the land, a family lives. A people struggle to just see the dawn of a new day. With the average annual income less than $4,000 a year, how can one survive? Sacrifice.

Ken Banks, kiwanja.net

The NKU students who traveled to Pine Ridge helped with a variety of construction projects such as the one pictured.

I have come to learn that amidst broken promises and disregarded treaties, the Lakota culture still flourishes. Core values of honesty, humility, sacrifice, love, peace, and respect still define the People. Technology is not the necessary force needed to usher in the dawn of a new day or to whisper the first words to a newborn. Technology is not necessary in a culture that gives highest priority, not to the individual, but to the entire community. These priorities are the values with which the People live and the values by which the People die. Maybe, if we put down our phone and stopped texting trivial information, we'd realize that to create change and equality, we first must change within ourselves.

Source: Written by Staci Wood, Northern Kentucky University, Class of 2011.

Global interdependence is a situation in which human interactions and relationships transcend national borders and in which social problems within any one country—such as unemployment, drug addiction, water shortages, natural disasters, or the search for national security—are shaped by social forces and events taking place outside the country, indeed in various parts of the globe. Global interdependence is part of a dynamic process known as **globalization**—the

global interdependence A situation in which social activity transcends national borders and in which one country's problems—such as unemployment, drug abuse, water shortages, natural disasters, and the search for national security in the face of terrorism—are part of a larger global situation.

globalization The ever-increasing flow of goods, services, money, people, information, and culture across political borders.

Technology Tip: For some photographic images of Pine Ridge Indian Reservation, check out photographs by Aaron Huey at http://www.aaronhuey.com/#/photo-galleries-1/undefined

Working for Change Mobile Phone Banking in India

In West Delhi, India, a 21-year-old repairman named Sonu Kumar sits in his repair shop tinkering with the innards of what appears to be an unsalvageable electronic device. He pulls out a screwdriver and with just a few turns the device springs to life. The customer hands Kumar some cash that he puts in his pocket. In the past, that money would have stayed there because, like many who reside in India, Kumar did not have a bank account.

Historically, people in India and other countries where a large proportion of the population lives in poverty just kept their money on their person or an insecure place in their home. But now a mobile phone–based banking system has gone into effect, making it easier for people to secure accounts, conduct transactions, and save money. This new banking system also makes it easier for the migrant workers in India to send money home to their families. The founders of this banking system, Abhishek Sinha and his brother Abhinav, were once migrant workers in Delhi who had no secure way to send money they earned home to their families in Bihar. So the brothers started this program to meet the needs of the poor in India who simply don't have the time or means to travel to a bank, wait in line, and deal with deposit minimums.

This banking system is known as Eko India Financial Services, and it opened in 2010. The service relies on local marketplaces and drugstores acting as "banks." Those who wish to deposit money hand a participating store owner the cash and their mobile phone. Then the clerk or store owner takes the money, types in a code, and the transaction is made. The mobile phone number serves as the client's bank account number, and the codes that store owners type in register the transaction with the State Bank of India.

Eko's mission is to give everyone a bank account. The organization's overarching goal is to build a low-cost, secure, and convenient electronic infrastructure that expands the reach of financial institutions to include those without banking in urban and rural areas and, in the process, to democratize financial services.

Source: Written by Devon Cowherd, Northern Kentucky University, Class of 2011.

ever-increasing flow of goods, services, money, people, technology, information, and other cultural items across political borders (Held et al. 1999). This flow has become more dense and quick moving as space- and time-related constraints separating people in various locations seemingly dissolve. As a result of globalization, no longer are people, goods, services, technologies, money, and images fixed to specific geographic locations (see No Borders, No Boundaries).

The classic sociologists were wide ranging and comparative in their outlooks. They did not limit their observations to a single academic discipline, a single period in history, or a single society. They were particularly interested in the transformative powers of history, and they located the issues they studied according to time and place. All lived at a time when Europe was colonizing much of Asia and Africa; when Europeans were migrating to the United States, Canada, South Africa, Australia, New Zealand, and South America; and when enslaved people and/or indentured servants were moving to new areas to fill demands for cheap labor. Sociologist Patricia M. Lengermann (1974) describes the significance of European expansion and movement of peoples on the discipline of sociology:

> Explorers, traders, missionaries, administrators, and anthropologists recorded and reported more or less accurately the details of life in the multitudes of new social groupings which they encountered. . . . Never had man more evidence of the variety of answers which his species could produce in response to the problems of living. This knowledge was built into the foundations of sociology—indeed, one impulse behind the emergence of the field must surely have been Western man's need to interpret this evidence of cultural variation. (1974, p. 37)

This textbook continues this tradition by incorporating a global perspective throughout. It applies sociological concepts and theories to a wide range of critical issues, international relationships, and events affecting the United States that cannot be separated from a larger global context (Held et al. 1999). A global perspective is guided by the following assumptions:

- Globalization is not new, although the scale of global interdependence changed dramatically with the Industrial Revolution, which created a production process that draws labor and raw materials from even the remotest corners of the world to produce unprecedented quantities of material goods and services, which are distributed unevenly.
- Globalization has been further intensified by the mobile phones, the Internet, and related digital technologies, which allow people around the world to communicate instantaneously. In addition, it has increased global competition for jobs that involve processing, managing, and analyzing information.
- Globally established social arrangements that we never see deliver to us products and services, including apple

No Borders No Boundaries Globalization

Globalization involves economic, political, and cultural transformations. There are at least four positions on the nature of these transformations (Appelrouth and Edles 2007):

Position 1: Globalization is producing a homogeneous world characterized by (1) a belief that freedom of expression and appreciation of, and respect for, human and cultural differences should be universally valued, and (2) a fusion of distinct cultural practices into a new world culture. This respect and fusion is embodied in trends such as world beat, world cuisine, and world cinema. Globalization includes the emergence of global citizens, who think of the world as one community and feel a responsibility to the planet. This global culture can be shared and experienced via wireless phones.

Position 2: Globalization is producing a homogeneous world by destroying variety and the local cultures that get in the way of progress or simply cannot compete against large corporations. The engines of cultural destruction—sometimes referred to as McWorld and Coca-colonization—are consumerism and corporate capitalism. How is globalization destroying local cultures? As one example, when people eat a Big Mac or drink a Coke, they are consuming more than a burger or a drink; they are also consuming American/Western images and their associated values. Those values relate to importance placed on food (the time to prepare and eat it), the nature of the relationship between the cook and the person eating (personal versus anonymous), and the place of the individual in relationship to the group (that is, I can eat whatever I want whenever I want versus I eat what others are eating at standard times of the day).

Position 3: Globalization actually brings value to and appreciation for local products and ways of doing things. Consumption of goods and services is not a one-way exchange in which the buying culture simply accepts a foreign product as it is known and used in the exporting culture(s). Although the products of corporate capitalism penetrate local markets, they do not eliminate demand for local ingredients and products. Moreover, local tastes are incorporated into corporate offerings. Coca-Cola, for example, offers 450 different brands in 200 countries, many brands that we may not have heard about, such as Inca Ko, a sparkling beverage available in South America; Samurai, an energy drink available in Asia; and Vita, an African juice drink. Just because a Big Mac or a Coke can be found anywhere in the world does not mean that locally, regionally, or nationally inspired products vanish. Likewise, in recent years, the wireless phone has become widespread throughout the continent of Africa as evidenced by the large number of subscribers—400 million. Facebook, Twitter, and other social networking sites are also very popular. As a result, Facebook has launched several African-language versions including Swahili, Hausa, and Zulu. Many African celebrities such as soccer stars are gaining a global audience (Essoungou 2010).

Position 4: Globalization and its interconnections intensify cultural differences by actually "sparking religious, ethnic, and cultural conflicts as people fight to preserve their identity and particular way of life," by resisting Western influences that have dominated globalization to date, by asserting an identity that "clashes" with Western ideals (that is, individualism, freedom of expression, democracy), or by protecting and enforcing boundaries even as they are opened and erased (Appelrouth and Edles 2007, p. 568). Gatekeepers such as airport security and border patrol officers seek to process travelers and cargo from around the world as quickly as possible and, at the same time, close access to real and imagined threats. As a case in point, there are an estimated 300 million annual border crossings from Mexico into the United States (one indicator of global interdependence). In hopes of preventing this massive exchange of people, the United States has constructed 700 miles of strategically placed fences along that border, including reinforced fencing, physical barriers, lighting, cameras, and sensors to stop illegal crossings (Dinan 2007).

juice containing concentrate from Austria, China, Turkey, and other countries (Lemert 1995; Zaniello 2007).

- The global exchange of goods, services, and influences is uneven, with some countries—most notably, the United States and People's Republic of China—as dominant trading partners.
- Multinational and global corporations are key players in structuring and facilitating social relationships that transcend national boundaries.
- Efforts to open and erase national boundaries are accompanied by simultaneous efforts to protect and enforce boundaries. Gatekeepers such as airport security and border patrol officers seek to process travelers and cargo from around the world as quickly as possible and yet close access to high-risk threats.
- As part of the pursuit of profit, multinational corporations are increasingly gaining and solidifying control over scarce and valued basic life-sustaining resources, such as water, seeds, human organs and tissue, and DNA (Zaniello 2007).

Depending on where you live and who you are, globalization plays out differently. On the one hand, it connects the economically, politically, and educationally advantaged

Teaching Tip: The "No Borders No Boundaries" box describes four positions on how globalization affects cultures and communities. Ask students to read the box and indicate which of the four positions relates to what they have observed about globalization.

to one another while pushing to the sidelines those who are not so advantaged. On the other hand, it connects those working at the grassroots level to protect, restore, and nurture the environment and to enhance access to the basic resources disadvantaged people need to live a dignified existence (Calhoun 2002; Brecher, Childs, and Cutler 1993).

Why Study Sociology?

As we have learned, sociologists study any topic that relates to human interaction and activity. For this reason, it is impossible to actually list all the topics sociologists study. Keep in mind that it is not the topic of study that distinguishes sociology from other disciplines; it's the framework sociologists apply to analyze any topic. The following lists some of the courses sociologists teach. The list is by no means exhaustive, but it does offer a glimpse of the wide range of human activities that sociologists study.

Sociology of Corrections
Police and Society
Marriage and the Family
Sociology of Environment
Sociology of Law
Race and Ethnic Relations
Popular Culture
Juvenile Delinquency
Sociology of Aging
Sociology of Work and Occupations
Population
Urban Society
Current Social Issues
Women and Crime
Sociology of Firearms
Technology and Society
Deviance and Social Control
Community Corrections
Sociology of Medicine
Death and Dying
Sport and Play in Society
Sociology of Music
Ads, Fads, and Consumer Culture
Small Groups

CORE CONCEPT 7 The sociological perspective offers a useful framework that can be used to address work-related issues and tasks. Studying sociology also includes learning important career-oriented skills.

People who majored in sociology work in corrections, banking, social services, community work, business, health services, customer service, publishing/journalism/public relations, marketing, survey research, government, and teaching. In addition, sociology majors go on to graduate school in a number of disciplines and professions, including sociology, law, business, and education. Because sociology cannot be connected with a specific occupation (such as an accountant or a psychologist), sociology students must be able to explain to their parents, relatives, and employers the usefulness of the courses and degree. When employers, parents, friends, and other outsiders to the discipline of sociology ask, "Why did you major in sociology?" or "Why take sociology classes?" the reply must be convincing. Responses such as "I like people" or "sociology is about people, and I want to work with people" are too vague and will lead to puzzled looks and responses such as "So what can you do with that kind of degree?" Replies should point to the distinctive aspects of the sociological perspective. Sociology is a discipline that looks beyond individuals to the social forces that shape social interaction and activities.

The sociological perspective, with its focus on human activities and relationships and the forces that shape them, informs decision making. This perspective is valuable because most work-related tasks and issues revolve around successfully coordinating interactions among employees, clients, consumers, suppliers, and other interested parties. In particular, a degree, minor, concentration, or strong interest in sociology will give you the following distinct analytical skills:

- To anticipate the intended and unintended consequences of corporate, government, or other policies, practices, and technologies.
- To identify and project population trends, including those of birth, death, migration, marriage, divorce, and family size.
- To appreciate and consider viewpoints other than your own.
- To use the methods of social research to recognize and provide useful information.
- To collect information via interviews, questionnaires, observation, case studies, secondary data analysis, and content analysis, and to analyze the results.
- To avoid using superficial knowledge or personal bias as a basis for making decisions and recommendations that affect others.

Online Poll

Estimate the number of mobile phones you have owned to date.

○ Only one
○ Three or less
○ Four to six
○ Seven to ten
○ More than ten

To see how other students responded to these questions, go to **www.cengagebrain.com.**

Teaching Tip: Share with students the courses the sociology department/program offers at the college/university they attend.

Ken Banks, kiwanja.net

Summary of CORE CONCEPTS

The chapter introduces the sociological perspective and it uses the mobile phone as a vehicle for illustrating how sociological concepts and theories help us to understand the social forces that shape social interaction and human activity. In studying the mobile phone, sociologists consider how this invention shapes the way people see the world and the interactions they have with others. They consider how people use, and adapt and respond to this invention. Sociologists also study how the mobile phone affects the way people relate to groups, organizations, and institutions.

CORE CONCEPT 1 Sociology is the scientific study of human activity in society. More specifically, it is the study of the social forces that affect the things people do with and to one another.

Sociologists are interested in understanding differences and change. Specifically they are interested in the social forces that trigger change and help to create differences in the way people think and do things. The mobile phone is a perfect vehicle for illustrating the sociological perspective because it is a human-created technology that has transformed or will transform every aspect of life. The revolutionary feature of the mobile phone is that it frees people from being in a physical space when they communicate with others.

CORE CONCEPT 2 The sociological imagination is a quality of mind that allows people to see how remote and impersonal social forces shape their life story or biography.

Social forces are considered remote and impersonal because, for the most part, people have no hand in creating them, nor do they know those who did. People can embrace social forces, be swept along, be bypassed by them, and most importantly challenge them. No matter the response, social forces shape a person's behavior and ways of thinking. Durkheim offers the concept of social facts to help us think about larger social forces. Peter Berger equates sociologists with curious observers walking the neighborhood streets of a large city, fascinated with what they cannot see taking place behind the building walls. The wish to look inside and learn more is analogous to the sociological perspective.

CORE CONCEPT 3 Sociologists distinguish between troubles, which can be resolved by changing the individual, and issues, which can be resolved only by addressing the social forces that created them.

Troubles are personal needs, problems, or difficulties that can be explained in terms of individual shortcomings in motivation, attitude, ability, character, or judgment. The resolution of a trouble, if it can indeed be resolved, lies in changing the individual in some way. By comparison, an issue is a matter that can be explained only by factors outside an individual's control and immediate environment. Issues can only be resolved by implementing solutions that change or offset the influence of underlying social forces. The sociological imagination is a quality of mind that allows people to make connections between biography and seemingly remote and impersonal social forces and historical events.

CORE CONCEPT 4 Sociology emerged in part as a reaction to the Industrial Revolution, an ongoing and evolving social force that transformed society, human behavior, and interaction in incalculable ways.

The Industrial Revolution is the name given to the changes in manufacturing, agriculture, transportation, and mining that transformed virtually every aspect of society. The defining feature of the Industrial Revolution was mechanization. The Industrial Revolution changed everything—the way in which goods were produced, the ways in which people negotiated time and space, the relationships between what were once geographically separated peoples, the ways in which people made their livings, the density of human populations (that is, urbanization), the relative importance and influence of the home in people's lives, access to formal education (the rise of compulsory and mass education), and the emergence of a consumption-oriented economy and culture. The accumulation of wealth became a valued and necessary pursuit.

CORE CONCEPT 5 Early sociologists were witnesses to the transforming effects of the Industrial Revolution. They offered lasting conceptual frameworks for analyzing the ongoing social upheavals.

Auguste Comte invented the name "sociology" during the most dramatic period of the Industrial Revolution. Karl Marx sought to analyze and explain conflict, which he saw as being shaped by the means of production. Émile Durkheim wrote about solidarity—the ties that bind people to one another—and about how the Industrial Revolution profoundly changed those ties. Max Weber set out to analyze and explain the course and consequences of social actions. Weber maintained that in the presence of industrialization, behavior was less likely to be guided by tradition or emotion and more likely to be instrumental-rational. W.E.B. DuBois wrote about the origins of the color line and about the "strange meaning of being black" in America. Jane Addams advocated for sympathetic knowledge—firsthand knowledge gained by living and working among those being studied. Each of the six theorists has left us with concepts and theories that apply to the world in which we live today.

CORE CONCEPT 6 A global perspective assumes that social interactions do not stop at political borders and that the most pressing social problems are part of a larger, global situation.

This textbook incorporates a global perspective throughout. It applies sociological concepts and theories to a wide range of critical issues, international relationships, and events affecting the United States that cannot be separated from a global context.

CORE CONCEPT 7 The sociological perspective offers a useful framework that can be used to address work-related issues and tasks. Studying sociology also includes learning important career-oriented skills

Sociology offers a useful perspective for thinking about what is going on in the world and what may be happening within ourselves. This perspective allows us to locate personal successes, failures, and fate in a broader social context and become aware of the many individuals who share (or do not share) our situation. The discipline offers a framework for recognizing, analyzing, and addressing critical social issues. In addition to the personal and social benefits of studying and applying sociology, a major or minor in sociology or even a series of sociology courses can open up a variety of career opportunities.

Resources on the Internet

Login to CengageBrain.com to access the resources your instructor requires. For this book, you can access:

Sociology CourseMate

Access an integrated eBook, chapter-specific interactive learning tools, including flash cards, quizzes, videos, and more in your Sociology CourseMate.

CENGAGENOW™

Take a pretest for this chapter and receive a personalized study plan based on your results that will identify the topics you need to review and direct you to online resources to help you master those topics. Then take a post-test to help you determine the concepts you have mastered and what you will need to work on.

CourseReader

CourseReader for Sociology is an online reader providing access to readings, and audio and video selections to accompany your course materials.

Visit **www.cengagebrain.com** to access your account and purchase materials.

Key Terms

altruistic 14
anomic 14
biography 4
bourgeoisie 12
color line 17
conflict 12
currents of opinion 5
double consciousness 17
egoistic 14
fatalistic 15
global interdependence 21
globalization 21
issue 7
mechanization 7
positivism 10
proletariat 12
social action 16
social dynamics 11
social facts 4
social forces 4
social statics 11
sociological imagination 4
sociology 4
solidarity 14
sympathetic knowledge 19
troubles 7

THEORETICAL PERSPECTIVES AND METHODS OF SOCIAL RESEARCH

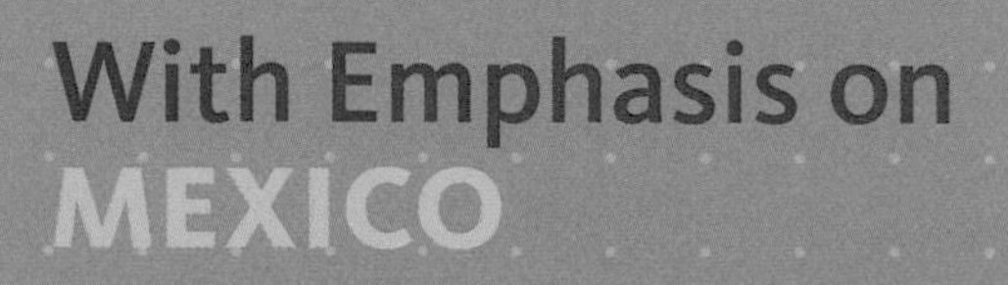

2

Sociologists view theory and research as interdependent because both are needed to analyze any issue. Theories are frameworks that help us to think about and describe what we see going on in the world around us, and research involves strategies for making objective observations about those issues. In this chapter, we draw upon sociological theories and methods of research to analyze the 700 miles of newly constructed fence that separate the United States from Mexico. This photo shows one stretch of the fence that runs on the Nogales, Arizona side of the border.

Why Focus On MEXICO?

The United States and Mexico share a 2,000-mile border that hundreds of millions of people on both sides cross each week to work, shop, socialize, and vacation. The border includes 700 miles of walls, border fences, and other barriers to prevent undocumented immigrants from crossing into the United States. About 80 miles of these barriers, referred to as the Wall of Shame in Mexico, were built in the mid-1990s. In 2006, Congress passed the Secure Fence Act, authorizing the construction of at least 630 miles of strategically placed barriers, including "two layers of reinforced fencing, the installation of additional physical barriers, roads, lighting, cameras and sensors" between Tecate, California, and Brownsville, Texas (see Figure 2.1). Today about 40 percent of this 2,000-mile border is fortified. The border has also become militarized. In addition to the 20,000-plus border guards and thousands of army reservists, high-tech surveillance devices, drones, and military equipment are also dedicated to preventing undocumented immigrants and illicit drugs from entering the United States. One description of the border barriers follows: "It stops and starts, without rhyme or reason, along the Rio Grande River's levees, leaving miles of gaps. It highlights the city's economic divide: It's the first thing folks in the poorer barrios see when they look out their windows, while richer folks enjoy unaltered views of palm trees and manicured fairways when they tee off on private golf courses. It zigs and zags through residents' backyards, through citrus orchards—an ugly red scar on a green, subtropical landscape" (Del Bosque 2010).

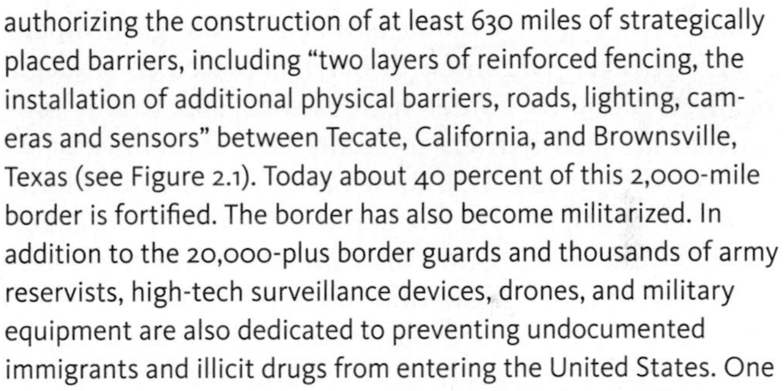

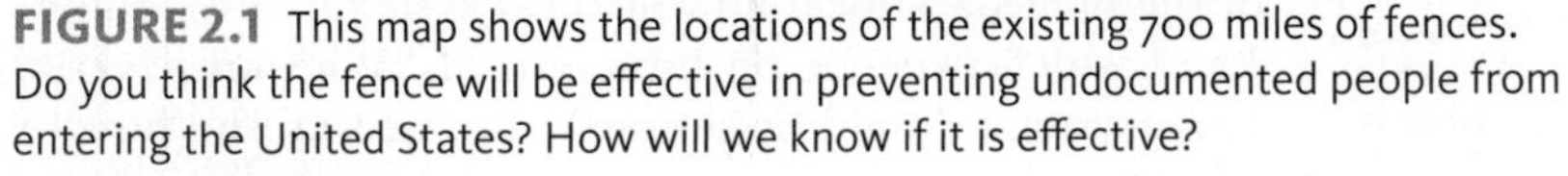

FIGURE 2.1 This map shows the locations of the existing 700 miles of fences. Do you think the fence will be effective in preventing undocumented people from entering the United States? How will we know if it is effective?

We draw upon the three major sociological perspectives and methods of social research to assess the border barriers. The three perspectives help us to describe and think about the fences and their purposes. The methods of research offer guidelines for collecting and analyzing data related to the barriers' impact on undocumented immigrants, surrounding communities, and other affected parties. Although we are focusing on understanding the border barriers, we can apply the perspectives and methods of research to any issue or situation.

Technology Tip: For different views of the border fence, go to Google images and plug in the key words "U.S.-Mexico border fence."

Online Poll

Before reading this introduction, did you know that the U.S. Congress had passed a law requiring the construction of border barriers along the U.S.–Mexican border?

- ○ Yes
- ○ No

Do you support the construction of 700 miles of walls, fences, and other barriers?

- ○ Yes
- ○ No
- ○ Don't know

To see how other students responded to these questions, go to **www.cengagebrain.com**.

What do we make of the facts that the U.S. government has constructed 700 miles of barriers placed in strategic locations along its border with Mexico, but that it constructed no such barriers to secure U.S. shorelines or its border with Canada? Will these barriers, and focus on the Mexican border, be effective at preventing undocumented workers from crossing into the United States? For answers to these questions, we can draw upon the three theoretical perspectives and the methods of social research.

Theoretical perspectives are frameworks for thinking about what is going on in the world around us. In sociology, there are three broad theoretical perspectives: functionalist, conflict, and symbolic interaction. Each perspective has a distinct focus and is organized around fundamental assumptions about how societies operate and how the people in them relate to one another and their surroundings. Each offers a central question to direct thinking about any issue or situation. Finally, each perspective offers a vocabulary to help answer these questions. We begin an overview of the functionalist perspective and then apply it to the border barriers.

Functionalist Perspective

CORE CONCEPT 1 **Functionalists focus on how the "parts" of society contribute in expected and unexpected ways to maintaining and disrupting an existing social order.**

Functionalists focus on the existing order and how it is maintained. They define society as a system of interrelated, interdependent parts. To illustrate this vision, functionalists use the human body as an analogy for society. The human body is composed of parts such as bones, cartilage, ligaments, muscles, a brain, a spinal cord, nerves, hormones, blood, blood vessels, a heart, a spleen, kidneys, and lungs. All of these body parts work together in impressive harmony. Each functions in a unique way to maintain the entire body, but it cannot be separated from other body parts that it affects and that in turn help it function.

Society, like the human body, is made up of parts, such as schools, automobiles, sports teams, funeral rites, ways of greeting people, religious rituals, laws, languages, household appliances, and border barriers. Like the various body parts, each of society's parts is interdependent and *functions* to maintain a larger system. Functionalists define a **function** as the contribution a part makes to order and stability within the society.

Consider sports teams—whether they be Little League, grade school, high school, college, city, Olympic, or professional teams. Sports teams function to draw audiences whose members are often extremely different from one another economically, culturally, linguistically, politically, religiously, and in other ways. Loyalty to a sports team transcends individual differences and fosters a sense of belonging to the school, company, city, or country associated with it.

In the most controversial form of this perspective, functionalists argue that all parts of society—even those that do not seem to serve a constructive purpose, such as poverty, crime, undocumented immigration, and drug addiction—contribute in some way to maintaining an existing order. In fact, functionalists argue that a part would cease to exist if it did not serve some function. Thus they strive to identify how parts—even seemingly problematic ones—contribute to the stability of the social order. Consider one function of poverty: Poor people often "volunteer" for over-the-counter and prescription drug tests. Most new drugs, from AIDS vaccines to allergy medicines, must eventually be tried on healthy human subjects to determine their potential side effects (for example, rashes, headaches, vomiting, constipation, and drowsiness) and appropriate dosages. The chance to earn money motivates subjects to volunteer for these clinical trials. Because payment is relatively low, however, the tests attract a disproportionate share of low-income, unemployed, or underemployed people as subjects (Morrow 1996).

This function of poverty shows why a part of the society that everyone agrees is problematic and should be eliminated remains intact: It contributes to the stability of the pharmaceutical and medical systems, the credibility of which depends on human trials. Without poverty, these systems would be seriously strained to find human subjects to test out procedures and new products. As you might imagine, this line of reasoning can lead to charges that functionalists defend the status quo. To address some

theoretical perspectives Frameworks for thinking about what is going on in the world around us.

function The contribution a part of a society makes to the existing social order.

U.S. Air Force photo by Tech. Sgt. Charity Barrett/Released

From a functionalist perspective, sport teams and celebrities function to transcend differences among fans and foster a sense of belonging to the school, city, or country the team or celebrity represents.

of this criticism, sociologist Robert K. Merton (1967) introduced the concepts of *manifest* and *latent functions*, as well as *dysfunctions*. These concepts help us to think, not just about a part's contribution to order and stability, but its other effects, especially unanticipated effects.

Manifest and Latent Functions and Dysfunctions

Merton distinguished between two types of functions that contribute to maintaining an existing social order: manifest functions and latent functions. **Manifest functions** are a part's anticipated or intended effects on that order. **Latent functions** are the unanticipated or unintended disruptive effects to the social order. To illustrate this distinction, consider the manifest and latent functions associated with annual community-wide celebrations, such as fireworks displays on the Fourth of July and concerts in the park. Corporate sponsors often join with city government to mount such events. Three manifest functions readily come to mind: The community celebration functions (1) as a marketing and public relations event for the city and for corporate sponsors, (2) as an occasion to plan activities with family and friends, and (3) as an experience that draws the community together for celebration.

At the same time, several unanticipated, or latent, functions are associated with community celebrations. First, such celebrations put the spotlight on public transportation systems as people take buses or ride trains to avoid traffic jams. Second, such events function to break down barriers across neighborhoods. People who do drive may find that they must park some distance from the event, often in neighborhoods that they would not otherwise visit. Consequently, after they park, people have the opportunity to walk through such neighborhoods and observe life up close instead of at a distance.

Merton also points out that parts can have **dysfunctions**; that is, they can have disruptive consequences to the social order or to some segment of society. Like functions, dysfunctions can be either manifest or latent. **Manifest dysfunctions** are a part's anticipated disruptions to order. Anticipated disruptions that seem to go hand in hand with community-wide celebrations include traffic jams, closed streets, piles of garbage, and a shortage of clean public toilets.

In contrast, **latent dysfunctions** are unanticipated or unintended disruptions to the social order. For instance,

manifest functions Intended or anticipated effects that a part has on the existing social order.

latent functions Unintended or unanticipated effects that a part has on the existing order.

dysfunctions Disruptive consequences of a part to the existing social order.

manifest dysfunctions A part's anticipated disruptions to an existing social order.

latent dysfunctions Unintended, unanticipated disruptions to an existing social order.

Teaching Tip: Go to the instructor's resource manual for a chart showing manifest functions, latent functions, and dysfunctions of community-wide celebrations.

community-wide celebrations often have some unanticipated disruptive consequences. Sometimes people celebrate so vigorously that the celebration has the unintended consequence of lowering worker productivity, as people miss class or work the day of the event or the day after.

The Functionalist Perspective on Border Barriers

To see how the functionalist theory can be applied to a specific issue, we will consider how functionalists analyze the U.S.–Mexico border barriers. Functionalists ask, "What are the anticipated and unintended consequences of the border barriers?" Functionalists apply the concepts of manifest and latent functions and dysfunctions to answer this question. The purpose of the analysis that follows is not to generate an exhaustive list of functions and dysfunctions associated with the border barriers, but to demonstrate how functionalists frame any issues.

Manifest Functions

To identify the manifest functions (*anticipated* effects on social order and stability) of the border barriers, we need to understand why the United States constructed them in the first place. In the mid-1990s, three major border cities constructed 80 miles of barriers: San Diego (Operation Gatekeeper), El Paso (Operation Hold the Line), and Nogales (Operation Safeguard). The three operations were a response to the real or imagined belief that the United States was being overrun by undocumented immigrants. In addition, the overall reported crime rate along the border was 30 percent higher than the national average. Newspaper accounts at that time "described large groups of immigrants, serviced by Mexican food and drink vendors in a carnival atmosphere," waiting on the Mexican side of the border for after-dark surges into the United States, overwhelming the border agents (U.S. Department of Justice 2007). In response, the U.S. government shifted its emphasis from apprehension after entry to prevention, erecting barriers, and increasing the number of border agents in areas believed to have the highest numbers of undocumented entries.

In 2006, Congress passed the Secure Fence Act, authorizing construction of more strategically placed border barriers. This act was a response to reports that millions of undocumented immigrants were living in the United States and to post-9/11 priorities of achieving operational control "over the entire international land and maritime borders of the United States." The act gave highest priority to the southwest border, calling for 700 miles of fencing and security improvements between the Pacific Ocean and the Gulf of Mexico (Secure Fence Act 2006). See Figure 2.1.

Eugenio del Bosque

The construction of 700 miles of fence has redirected flows of undocumented immigrants in the direction of the 1,300 miles of unfenced border areas.

The manifest functions associated with constructing the border barriers have included the following:

1. A reported decrease in the number of undocumented immigrants apprehended crossing the newly secured areas of the border
2. Success in forcing undocumented entries away from secured urban areas to less populated unsecured areas and through rough terrain and climates (such as steep mountains, deep canyons, thick brush, the extreme cold of winter, and the searing heat of summer) to give Border Patrol agents a strategic advantage
3. An overall drop in the reported crime rate on the U.S. side of the border from 30 percent higher than the national average to 12 percent

Latent Functions

The construction of barriers along the border has had the following latent functions (*unanticipated* effects on social order and stability):

1. Cooperation between Mexican and U.S. officials in launching the Border Safety Initiative Program to prevent injuries and fatalities of those trekking through the desert and other rough terrain to enter the United States
2. The creation of the Border Patrol Search, Trauma, and Rescue team, which responds to *all* incidents involving people in distress, not just incidents involving undocumented immigrants (The team has rescued tens of thousands of people.)
3. A border barrier that doubles as a volleyball net, allowing U.S. and Mexican volleyball players on each side of the border to face off as part of goodwill festivals and other cross-border celebrations

Manifest Dysfunctions

The construction of the barriers has been associated with several manifest dysfunctions (anticipated disruptions of the existing order), including the following:

1. Increased apprehensions of undocumented immigrants in border counties not secured by barriers
2. A reported crime rate that was higher than the national average in some thinly populated counties with unsecured barriers
3. Increased fatalities as undocumented immigrants now risk their lives to enter the United States through the desert and other inhospitable terrain
4. Increased numbers of undocumented immigrants paying smugglers, or coyotes, to guide them into the United States. Before the barrier construction, human smuggling was a "mom-and-pop" operation with a typical fee of $500. Now human smuggling is highly organized, and the typical fee has increased to more than $2,000. Organized drug cartels are also now in the business of smuggling the undocumented across the border (*The Economist* 2008).
5. An increase in illicit businesses that facilitate undocumented immigrants' entry into the United States (for example, businesses that issue fraudulent documents)

Courtesy of Tomas Castelazo

The border fences have forced undocumented immigrants to enter the United States through desert and other inhospitable terrains, resulting in a manifest dysfunction of increasing the number of fatalities among illegal immigrants. The monument is to those who died crossing the border since 1994, the year the first fence was built dividing Tijuana from San Diego.

Latent Dysfunctions

Several latent dysfunctions (unanticipated disruptions to the social order) have followed the construction of the barriers:

1. Dramatic disruptions to the grazing, hunting, watering, and migration patterns of wildlife ("If it doesn't fly, it's not getting across." [Pomfret 2006])
2. Some barrier construction sites were not subjected to environmental impact review (Archibold 2009)
3. Decrease in the number of undocumented workers returning home to Mexico after completing seasonal work in the United States for fear that they may be unable to cross back into the United States to work
4. Redirected flows of undocumented immigrants to areas of the United States unaccustomed to this movement, fueling the perception that the United States is being "invaded" by undocumented migrants (Massey 2006)
5. Disruptions to economically and socially interdependent border communities now separated by barriers. About 75 percent of those who legally cross from Mexico into the United States do so to shop. Towns like Nogales, Arizona, with 20,000 inhabitants, depend on Mexican shoppers from Nogales, Sonora (population 190,000). As the number of border patrol officers increased and took more time to check documents and to search vehicles, the time waiting to cross increased. From a business perspective, Mexicans are now spending more time waiting and less time shopping. Because of the longer lines and wait, fewer Mexicans drive into the United States, but instead come in as pedestrians. And pedestrians cannot carry as many purchases as they can with a car (*The Economist* 2008).

Department of Defense

A border fence now separates Nogales, Arizona, from Sonora, Mexico. How do you think the construction of the border fence affected interactions among people in the two cities?

Conflict Perspective

CORE CONCEPT 2 The conflict perspective focuses on conflict over scarce and valued resources and the strategies dominant groups use to create and protect the social arrangements and practices that give them an advantage in accessing and controlling those resources.

Teaching Tip: When reviewing manifest and latent functions and dysfunctions of the border fence, remind students that decisions about what is a latent or manifest function/dysfunction depends on point of view. For some students a function and dysfunction listed as unanticipated in this text may be something they anticipated. The concepts are valuable because they make us think harder about the consequences of the fence.

National Archives and Records Administration

Library of Congress Prints and Photographs Division

For at least 100 years or more, the United States has both invited and deterred workers from the Mexican side of the border. One photo, taken in 1926, shows Border Patrol officers in Laredo, Texas, forming a "wall" with cars and guns to prevent illegal immigrants from crossing. The other photo shows Mexican workers recruited by U.S. Farm Security Program in 1943, traveling by train to Arkansas, Colorado, Nebraska, and Minnesota to harvest beets.

In contrast to functionalists, who focus on social order, conflict theorists focus on conflict as an inevitable fact of social life and as the most important agent for social change. Conflict can take many forms, including physical confrontations, exploitation, disagreement, tension, hostility, and direct competition. In any society, advantaged and disadvantaged groups compete for scarce and valued resources (access to material wealth, education, health care, well-paying jobs, and so on). Those who gain control and access to these resources strive to protect their own interests against the competing interests of others.

Conflict theorists ask this basic question: Who benefits from a particular social arrangement, and at whose expense? In answering this question, they seek to identify the dominant and subordinate groups as well as to describe the social arrangements that the dominant groups have established, consciously or unconsciously, to promote and protect their interests. Exposing these practices helps explain the unequal access to valued and scarce resources. Not surprisingly, the advantaged seek to protect their position, whereas the relatively disadvantaged seek to change their position.

Dominant groups explain their advantages using a **facade of legitimacy**—an explanation that members of dominant groups give to justify the social arrangements that benefit them over others. On close analysis, however, this explanation turns out to be based on "misleading arguments, incomplete analyses, unsupported assertions, and implausible premises" (Carver 1987, pp. 89–90). To illustrate, consider that employers who exploit workers justify such exploitation by pointing out that workers who are dissatisfied with their working conditions, wages, or benefits are free to quit. On close analysis, we see that this justification does not hold if only because the employee "has but wages to live upon, and must therefore take work when, where, and at what terms he can get it. The workman . . . is fearfully handicapped by hunger" (Engels 1886). Another common justification employers give for exploiting labor is to suggest that the exploited really benefit (for example, that a $2.00-per-hour job—or even a $0.48-per-hour job—is better than no job). Consider the following interview with an American woman who employs an undocumented immigrant to care for her children. In particular, pay attention to how this woman justifies the demands she makes on this woman:

> *MR. BEARDEN (reporter):* There are some that believe that people who hire undocumented aliens gain an unfair power over them; it gives them influence over them because they're, in a sense, collaborating in something that's against the law. Do you agree with that, or have any thoughts about that?
>
> *DENVER WOMAN:* I guess I would disagree with that. The one thing that you get in undocumented child care or the biggest thing that you probably get, my woman from Mexico was available to me 24 hours a day. I mean, her cost of living in Mexico and quality of life in Mexico compared to what she got in my household were two extremes. When we hired her, she said, "I'll be available all hours of the day, I'll clean the house, I'll cook." They do everything. And if you hire someone from here in the States, all they're going to do is take care of your children. So not only do you have a differentiation in price, you have a differentiation in services in your household. I have to admit that was, at that point, with a newborn infant, wonderful to have someone who was so available. . . .
>
> *MR. BEARDEN:* And it's not like indentured servitude?

facade of legitimacy An explanation that members of dominant groups give to justify the social arrangements that benefit them over others.

Video Tip: The U.S. Customs and Border Patrol posts a number of short on-line videos with titles like "This is CBP - A Fast-Paced Video Glimpse of Border Security" and "America's Frontline Against Terrorism." They provide insights about the amount of resources the United States is expending to secure this part of the border (versus the Canada–U.S. border). They can be accessed at www.cbp.gov/xp/cgov/newsroom/multimedia/video/border_security_videos.

Working for Change Remittance Income from Migrants

International remittances are monies earned by people living or working in one country and sent to someone (usually family and friends) in a home country. An estimated 200 million migrants worldwide send home more than $440 billion to help 500 million people pay for food, medicine, clothing, housing, education, and land. Because senders do not always use official channels (such as banks or Western Union) to send this money, it is likely that the actual amount remitted exceeds the $440 billion estimate by at least another $33 billion (World Bank 2010; Robinson 2003). As one measure of how widespread this practice is, consider that an estimated 20 million people born in Latin American countries live in a foreign country (*Stalker's Guide to International Migration* 2003). Half of these 20 million people send home an estimated $23 billion per year (Van Doorn 2003). An Inter-American Development Bank poll found that almost one in five adult Mexican residents receives money from relatives working in the United States. One in every four Guatemalan and El Salvadoran adults receives such money (Suro 2003b; Thompson 2003).

The sum of $414 billion in remittance represents the "monetary expression of a profound human bond" between migrants and the families they left behind (Suro 2003a, p. 2). Taken together, remittances represent an important source of income for developing countries. For many small island economies, remittances—along with foreign aid and tourism—represent one of the only sources of income. Many critics of foreign aid policies and programs believe that remittance "aid" represents an ideal altruistic self-help model (Kapur 2003, p. 10).

Although remittance aid clearly has many positive effects, it would be naive to think that remittances alone could eliminate poverty, drive economic development, and reduce budget deficits (Lowell, De la Garza, and Hogg 2000). Some of the potential positive effects are reduced by the cost to send money home, a cost that can exceed 23 percent of a remittance when check-cashing fees, money transfer fees, currency conversion fees, and fees on the receiving end are considered. Some critics estimate that reducing these fees by just 5 percent could generate another $16 billion in remittance aid. Banks and other financial institutions have taken notice of this money flow and are competing with Western Union and MoneyGram to offer transfer services. Such competition may work to reduce transfer fees. Nevertheless, many migrants cannot use banks' services because of the migrants' undocumented status and because of high checking account and electronic transfer fees.

Top Five Countries Receiving Annual Remittances (in billions)

India	$55
China	$51
Mexico	$22.6
Philippines	$21.3
France	$15.9

Source: Data from World Bank 2010.

DENVER WOMAN: That crossed my mind, and after she had been here for six months or so, we went to a schedule where she finished at 6 or 7 o'clock at night. And I don't think I ever really took advantage of her. Once a week I'd have her get up with the baby, so I didn't. . . . She was available to me, but I don't feel like I really took advantage of her, other than the fact that I paid her less and she was certainly more available. But she got paid more here than she would have gotten paid if she'd stayed where she was. (Bearden 1993, p. 8)

Conflict theorists take issue with the logic that this Denver woman employs to justify the low pay and high demand she makes. An honest assessment would suggest that this Denver woman is protecting and promoting her interests (having someone available at all hours of the day to cook, clean, and provide child care) at the expense of the undocumented worker's freedom to have a life apart from work.

The Conflict Perspective on the Border Barriers

In analyzing the construction of 700 miles of border barriers along the U.S.–Mexican border, conflict theorists ask "Who benefits from the barriers and at whose expense?" In answering this question, they would point out an obvious fact: The barriers secure a border that separates a high-wage and low-wage economy. In this regard, (1) the barriers are just one of many measures that the United States has put in place over time to control the flow of low-wage undocumented labor from Mexico, but not eliminate it; and (2) the barriers serve as a potent political symbol used to convey the illusion that United States is in control of its borders during a time of almost intolerable economic uncertainty.

Controlling the Flow of Undocumented Labor The barriers can be viewed as part of a long series of efforts by U.S. government to strategically draw from a very large low-wage labor pool in Mexico while also protecting the country from an "invasion" of Mexico's poor who have historically been viewed as unfair competitors taking jobs away from Americans because employers play them less (Zolberg 1999). Although it is certainly true that many undocumented immigrants risk life and limb to escape an economy where they are paid about $4.50 per day to enter one that pays $60 to $80 per day, we must remember that they are enticed by employers offering them jobs, albeit jobs with wages and conditions (for example, seasonal, long hours) that are unacceptable to many Americans. Since 1880, it has been the employers (those who purchase labor) on the U.S. side who have ultimately determined the size and destination of migration flows to the United States from Mexico. In fact, the U.S. economy has always depended on documented and undocumented Mexican workers to fill low-status, physically demanding, entry-level, seasonal, and cyclical jobs—jobs like dishwashers, farm workers, meat packers, maids, day laborers, roofers, and caretakers of children and elderly—whether or not the American public or politicians liked it (Massey, Durand, and Malone 2002, Cornelius 1981, Judis 2006).

In light of this longstanding and mutual dependence, the barriers are simply one part of the "odd bundle of legal measures and administrative practices that have accumulated over the decades" to control the sea of low-wage laborers "willing" to come to the United States to work (Zolberg 1999, p. 76).

The Barriers as a Political Symbol From a conflict point of view, the construction of barriers and the accompanying militarization of the border is less about deterring undocumented border crossings from Mexico and more about crafting an image that gives the appearance of control and security during a time of economic and national insecurity (Andreas 2009). In essence, constructing barriers and militarizing the southwestern border focuses everyone's attention on the border as *the* source of the United States' problems. In the meantime, the real forces threatening economic and national security—which are global in scale and difficult to control—are left largely unchallenged and unaddressed.

One irony of the 2006 Secure Fence Act relates to its stated aim of gaining control over all borders. Yet the act called for 700 miles of strategically placed fencing and security improvements along the 2,000 miles of U.S.–Mexico border. Also left largely unsecured were the 3,987 miles with Canada, the 1,538-mile Alaska–Canada border, and the coastlines of the United States (Beaver 2006). A 2010 Homeland Security report estimated that only about 900 miles of all U.S. borders can be classified as secure (U.S. Customs and Border Patrol 2010).

Another irony of the Secure Fence Act aimed at securing borders as a response to 9/11 was the fact that the 16 hijackers who flew and successfully crashed three of four planes into the World Trade Center towers and the Pentagon entered the United States legally (with documents or visas). Still, the Secure Fence Act gave highest priority to securing its southwest border. In addition, the most credible research studies estimate that 40 to 50 percent of 11.6 million undocumented immigrants living in the United States entered legally and overstayed their visas (Andreas 2009). In evaluating these statistics, simply consider that, in 2009, 162.3 million nonimmigrant visas were issued to foreign nationals who legally came to the United States to work, vacation, and study.

In addition, when we consider the fact that more than 15 million jobs have been outsourced from the United States to India, China, and elsewhere since 2000, and that the Internet allows workers around the world to compete for information-based jobs, we can see that undocumented labor from Mexico is one small player in what is a global competition for jobs. In the midst of economic insecurity, politicians can point to the Mexican border as evidence that concrete steps are being taken to addres the situation—for example, building barriers, militarizing the border by sending the National Guard and increasing the number of Border Patrol agents, and issuing lucrative contracts to such corporations as Boeing, Lockheed Martin Raytheon, and Northrop Grumman to construct barriers and provide equipment needed to secure the border. For example, Boeing was awarded a multibillion-dollar contract to supply small unmanned aerial surveillance vehicles that can be launched from Border Patrol truck beds, and equip as many as 1,800 watchtowers with cameras, heat and motion detectors, and other sensors (Witte 2006).

In light of this information, conflict theorists have no trouble answering the question, "Who benefits from the construction of the 700 miles of barriers, and at whose expense?" The answer is clear: American politicians, employers, and defense contractors are among the clear beneficiaries.

Symbolic-Interactionist Perspective

CORE CONCEPT 3 Symbolic interactionists focus on social interaction and related concepts of self-awareness/reflexive thinking, symbols, and negotiated order.

Sociologist Herbert Blumer coined the term *symbolic interaction* and outlined its essential principles. Symbolic interactionists focus on **social interaction**, everyday encounters in which people communicate, interpret, and respond to one another's words and actions. These theorists ask, when involved in interaction, how do people involved in interaction "take account of what each other is doing or is about to do" and then direct their own conduct accordingly

social interaction Everyday encounters in which people communicate, interpret, and respond to each other's words and actions.

(Blumer 1969)? The process depends on (1) self-awareness, (2) shared symbols, and (3) negotiated order.

Self-Awareness

Self-awareness occurs when a person is able to observe and evaluate the self from another's viewpoint. People are self-aware when they imagine how others are viewing, evaluating, and interpreting their words and actions. Through this imaginative process, people become objects to themselves; they come to recognize that others see them, for instance, "as being a man, young in age, a student, in debt, trying to become a doctor, coming from an undistinguished family and so forth" (Blumer 1969, p. 172). In imagining others' reactions, people respond and make adjustments (apologize, change facial expressions, lash out, and so on).

Shared Symbols

A **symbol** is any kind of object to which people assign a name, meaning, or value (Blumer 1969). Objects can be classified as physical (cell phones, cars, a color, the facial expression), social (a friend, a parent, a celebrity, a bus driver), or as abstract (freedom, greed, justice, empathy). In the context of driving, for example, the color green has come to symbolize "go or proceed." Objects can take on different meanings depending on audience and context: A tree can have different meanings to an urban dweller, a farmer, a poet, a home builder, an environmentalist, or a lumberjack (Blumer 1969). People learn meanings that their culture attaches to objects from observing others. By observing, people learn such things as that a wave of the hand means good-bye or that one should not send text messages during a funeral service.

To illustrate the difference in symbolic meanings that Americans and Mexicans attach to a map of the United States, consider that when most Americans view a map of their country, they do not think that one-third of the territory once belonged to Mexico. In contrast, when people in Mexico view the map of the United States, they likely think the Southwest portion was once part of their country.

Negotiated Order

When we enter into interaction with others, we take for granted that a system of expected behaviors and shared meanings is already in place to guide the interaction. Although expectations are in place, symbolic interactionists emphasize that established meanings and ways of behaving can be reinforced and affirmed during interaction, but that they can also be ignored, challenged, or changed (Blumer 1969). In most interactions, room for negotiation exists; that is, the parties involved have the option of negotiating other expectations and meanings. The **negotiated order**, then, is the sum of existing expectations and newly negotiated ones (Strauss 1978).

To illustrate, college students know, for example, that when they enter a classroom on the first day of class, they should not walk to the front of the room and give instructions to the class. Likewise, professors know that on the first day of class, students expect them to give an overview of the course and lay out expectations such as no texting during class. Already established expectations are in place, guiding interaction. Usually, however, some room for negotiation exists; that is, the parties involved have the option of negotiating a social order. So on the first day of class, a professor may negotiate with students, indicating it is okay to check text messages when the professor is passing out assignments but not during lecture or class discussions. However, professors know that they cannot "negotiate" a social order in which students pay money to receive a desired grade.

The Symbolic-Interactionist Perspective on United States–Mexico Barriers

As we have learned, symbolic interactionists study people as they engage in social interaction. Thus, with regard to the border barrier, the following would be of great interest to symbolic interactionists who would seek to immerse themselves in the border world:

- interactions between border control agents and those crossing legally and illegally;
- the way Border Patrol agents are recruited and trained;

symbol Any kind of physical phenomenon to which people assign a name, meaning, or value.

negotiated order The sum of existing expectations and newly negotiated ones.

Video Tip: The U.S. Customs and Border Patrol posts videos that highlight day-to-day experiences of border patrol agents. Of particular relevance is "Protecting U.S. Borders." It can be found at www.cbp.gov/xp/cgov/newsroom/multimedia/video/border_security_videos/bp_videos/.

No Borders No Boundaries Interaction That Straddles the U.S.–Mexican Border

The border between Mexico and the United States stretches for almost 2,000 miles. The border region extends 60 miles south into Mexico and 60 miles north into the United States and includes 12 million people (Brown 2004). "From the perspective of the border, borderlines are not lines of sharp demarcation, but broad scenes of intense interactions in which people from both sides work out everyday accommodations based on face-to-face relationships. Each crosser seeks something that exists on the other side of the border. Each needs to make herself or himself understood on the other side of the border, to get food or gas or a job" (Thelen 1992, p. 437).

This map shows the tremendous amount of two-way traffic across the border, as well as attempts by the United States to control that traffic.

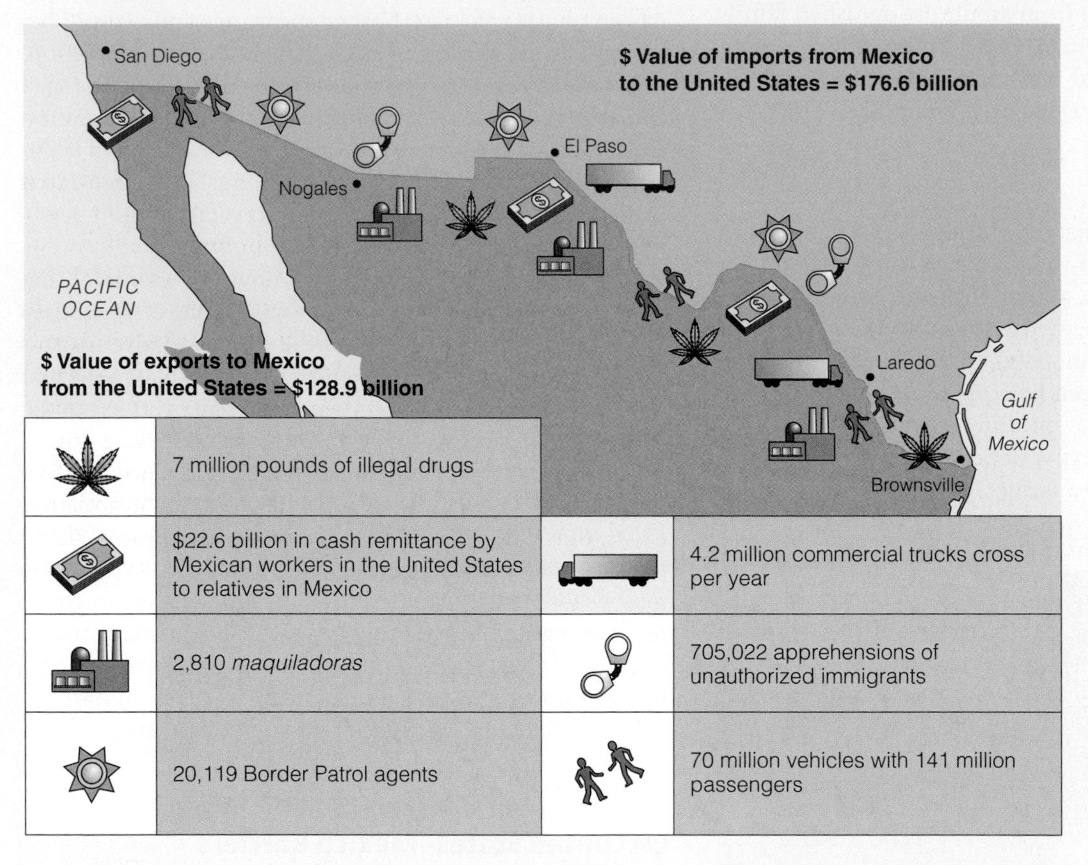

FIGURE 2.2
Selected Inventory of Border Activity Per Year

Sources: Data from U.S. Department of Homeland Security (2009, 2010), Migration Immigration Source (2006), U.S. Department of Transportation (2010), Ellingwood (2009), Haddal (2010)

- the interactions between undocumented immigrants and contacts already living in the United States;
- the way employers knowingly or unknowingly hire undocumented immigrants;
- the strategies undocumented immigrants use to blend into American society upon entry; and
- the strategies undocumented immigrants use to escape detection when passing though official border crossings.

As one example of the symbolic-interactionist emphasis on the close-up and personal, consider the following description of border agents inspecting cars and their passengers entering one of the world's busiest border crossings in California. This description helps us understand how many unauthorized immigrants manage to blend in with the crowds passing through official ports of entry (see No Borders, No Boundaries: "Interaction That Straddles the U.S.–Mexican Border"):

> Primary inspectors had to dispose of entering vehicles at an average of one per 45 seconds. In this time, the officer had to enter the license plate number into the Customs computer system, read the results (to see if there was any previous record of smuggling or illegal entry, or indeed any "lookout" rumors in the system), verbally ask about nationality and, if occupants had brought anything back from Mexico, inspect any immigration documents provided and examine the occupants of the car for their comportment (to see, for example, if they were nervous or sitting rigidly). Using this set of clues, some clear and others quite vague, the officer either cleared the car into

Teaching Tip: Notice that there are more than 20,000 border patrol agents assigned to the U.S.–Mexico border. Point out that there are about 1,400 agents assigned to the Canada–U.S. border, which is twice as long.

> the U.S. without further inspection, or sent the vehicle to the side for an appropriate secondary inspection. If an admitted car was later stopped and found to have some narcotics or undocumented immigrants, the computer records would reveal who allowed the vehicle to enter. On the other hand, if the inspector took too long making decisions, it would back up traffic, with consequences including exacerbating air pollution and slowing down the interchange of people and goods on the Tijuana–San Diego corridor, the most important passage in the Mexico–U.S. free trade system. (Heyman 1999, p. 626)

Based on this description of border-crossing activity, it is easy to apply the core concepts that drive the symbolic-interactionist analysis of interactions: self-awareness/reflexive thinking, symbols, and negotiated order. In such situations, both drivers/passengers and agents are imagining how the other party is viewing their actions, evaluating their appearance, attaching meaning to their motives, and interpreting their words. Both parties are aware of the existing expectations, rules, and policies for crossing the border, but do on-the-spot "negotiations" to speed up inspection.

Critique of Three Sociological Theories

To this point, we have seen how each of the three sociological perspectives guide analysis of the border barriers through central questions and key concepts. Keep in mind that, taken alone, no single perspective can offer a complete picture of a situation. But we can acquire a more complete picture by applying all three. Of course, each theory has its strengths and weaknesses.

Concerning the border barriers, one strength of the functionalist theory is that it gives a balanced overview of the barriers' intended and unintended consequences to the existing social order. One weakness of that perspective is that it leaves us wondering about the border barriers' *overall* effects. That is, do the manifest and latent functions of the border barriers outweigh the manifest and latent dysfunctions?

One strength of the conflict theory is that it forces us to look beyond popular justifications for border barriers—to control undocumented migration—and to explore questions about whose interests are being protected and promoted and at whose expense. A weakness of the conflict theory is that it presents a simplistic view of the relationship between advantaged and disadvantaged groups: Dominant groups are portrayed as all-powerful and capable of imposing their will without resistance from subordinate groups, who are portrayed as exploited victims.

One strength of the symbolic-interactionist theory is that it encourages firsthand, extensive knowledge about how the border barriers shape interactions between Border Patrol agents and legal and undocumented immigrants. If the border barriers stop unauthorized movement into the United States, how do undocumented immigrants manage to evade the Border Patrol? One weakness of the approach is that we cannot be sure if the observations are unique to those being observed or apply to all interactions between Border Patrol agents and legal and undocumented immigrants.

We have reviewed the three major theoretical perspectives (see Figure 2.3). Now we turn to the various ways of data gathering and analysis that sociologists (no matter what their perspective) use to formulate and answer meaningful research questions.

	Functionalist Perspective	**Conflict Perspective**	**Symbolic Interactionist Perspective**
Focus:	Order and stability	Conflict over scarce and valued resources	Social interaction
Key Terms:	Function, dysfunction, manifest, latent	Conflict facade of legitimacy	Self-awareness, shared symbols, negotiated order
Vision of Society:	System of interrelated parts	Dominant and subordinate groups in conflicts over scarce and valued resources	Web of social interactions
Central Question(s):	Why does a part exist? What are the anticipated and unintended consequences of a part?	Who benefits from a particular pattern or arrangement, and at whose expense?	How do involved parties experience, interpret, influence, and respond to what they and others are doing in the course of interacting?
Strength:	Balanced analysis of positive and negative effects	Encourages analysis beyond popular explanations	Encourages direct, firsthand, and extensive analysis
Weakness:	Defends existing social arrangements Difficult to determine overall effect	Presents simplistic view of dominant-subordinate groups or relationships	Generalizability of observation is difficult to determine

FIGURE 2.3 Overview of the Three Theoretical Perspectives

Critique of the Sociological Perspectives: Ask students to write an anonymous paragraph indicating which one of the three perspectives most helps them to think about the 700-miles of fence and other barriers along the U.S. Mexico border. Collect papers and redistribute randomly. Ask for volunteers to read the paragraph they were handed.

Methods of Social Research

CORE CONCEPT 4 Sociologists adhere to the scientific method; that is, they acquire data through observation and leave it open to verification by others.

Research is a data-gathering and data-explaining enterprise governed by strict rules (Hagan 1989). **Research methods** are the various techniques that sociologists and other investigators use to formulate or answer meaningful research questions and to collect, analyze, and interpret data in ways that allow other researchers to check the results.

Theory and research are interdependent, because (1) theories inspire research, whose results can be used to support, disprove, or modify those theories; (2) the results of social research can inspire theories; and (3) theories are used to interpret facts generated through research. All sociologists are guided by the scientific method when they investigate human activities. The **scientific method** is an approach to data collection that relies on two assumptions: (1) knowledge about the world is acquired through observation, and (2) the truth of that knowledge is confirmed by verification—that is, by others making the same observations.

Researchers collect data that they and others can see, hear, taste, touch, and smell; that is, they focus on what they observe through the senses. They report the process they used to make their observations so that interested parties can duplicate, or at least critique, that process. If observations cannot be duplicated, or if repeating the study yields results that differ substantially from those of the original study, we consider the study suspect. Findings endure as long as they can withstand continued reexamination and duplication by the scientific community. "Duplication is the heart of good research" (Dye 1995, p. D5). No finding can be taken seriously unless other researchers can repeat the process and obtain the same results.

When researchers know that others are critiquing and checking their work, the process serves to reinforce careful, thoughtful, honest, and conscientious behavior. Moreover, this "checking" encourages researchers to maintain **objectivity**; that is, it encourages them not to let their personal, or subjective, views about the topic influence their observations or the outcome of the research.

This description of the scientific method is an ideal one, because it outlines how researchers and reviewers should behave. Ideally, researchers should be guided by the core values of honesty, skepticism, fairness, collegiality, and openness (National Academy of Sciences 1995). In practice, though, some research is dismissed as unimportant and unworthy of examination simply because the topic or the researcher is controversial or because the findings depart from mainstream thinking. Moreover, some researchers fabricate data to support a personal, an economic, or a political agenda. The extent to which researchers actually adhere to core values remains unknown.

Research should be carefully planned; the enterprise of gathering and explaining facts involves a number of interdependent steps (Rossi 1988):

1. Choosing the topic for investigation or deciding on the research question
2. Reviewing the literature
3. Identifying core concepts
4. Choosing a research design, forming hypotheses, and collecting data
5. Analyzing the data
6. Drawing conclusions

Researchers do not always follow these six steps in sequence, however. They may not define the topic (step 1) until they have familiarized themselves with the literature (step 2). Sometimes an opportunity arises to gather information (step 4), and a project is defined to fit that opportunity (step 1).

Although the six steps need not be followed exactly in sequence, all must be completed at some point to ensure the quality of the project. In the sections that follow, we will examine each stage. Along the way, we will refer to sociological and other research that focuses on unauthorized immigration and the border barriers' effect on deterring entry. Where appropriate, we will emphasize two sociological studies: *Patrolling Chaos: The U.S. Border Patrol in Deep South Texas* by Robert Lee Maril (2004) and "The Social Process of Undocumented Border Crossing among Mexican Migrants" by Audrey Singer and Douglas S. Massey (1998). Singer and Massey's research is part of a larger project known as the Mexican Migration Project, a multidisciplinary effort involving researchers in the United States and Mexico (Mexican Migration Project 2007).

Step 1: Choosing the Topic for Investigation

The first step of a research project involves choosing a topic or deciding on a research question. It would be impossible to compile a comprehensive list of the topics that

research A data-gathering and data-explaining enterprise governed by strict rules.

research methods Techniques that sociologists and other investigators use to formulate or answer meaningful research questions and to collect, analyze, and interpret data in ways that allow other researchers to verify the results.

scientific method An approach to data collection in which knowledge is gained through observation and its truth is confirmed through verification.

objectivity A stance in which researchers' personal, or subjective, views do not influence their observations or the outcomes of their research.

sociologists study, because almost any subject involving humans represents a potential target for investigation. Sociology is distinguished from other disciplines not by the topics sociologists investigate, but by the perspectives needed to study topics. Researchers choose their topics for a number of reasons. Personal interest is a common and often understated motive. It is perhaps the most significant reason that someone picks a specific topic to study, especially if we consider how researchers eventually choose one topic from a virtually infinite set of possibilities.

Good researchers explain to their readers why their topic or research question is significant. This explanation is vital because it clarifies the purpose and importance of the project and the researcher's motivation for doing the work. Sociologists Audrey Singer and Douglas S. Massey (1998) studied "the social process of undocumented border crossings among Mexican migrants" (p. 561). The two researchers chose this topic for several reasons: (1) It is a politically divisive topic in the United States; (2) little is known about how migrants evade borders guarded by agents, maneuver around or bypass border barriers (some triple-deep), and escape detection by surveillance equipment; and (3) knowing the extent of undocumented entries helps us judge whether border barriers or other barriers are effective deterrents.

In this step, researchers often announce the perspective guiding their investigation. Sometimes they announce it directly by indicating that they are writing from one or more theoretical traditions or perspectives. Sometimes they announce their guiding perspective(s) indirectly; that is, readers surmise the perspective from the way researchers frame the question or analysis. That Singer and Massey (1998) focused on undocumented immigrants' social ties to others who have crossed the border successfully without authorization suggests that the two researchers are drawing upon the symbolic interaction perspective to frame their analysis. One also notices that Singer and Massey take a conflict perspective when they suggest that constructing border barriers and implementing other border control strategies "sit well with the public," because the U.S. government "appears to be defending the United States against alien invaders while not antagonizing U.S. business interests" (pp. 563–564).

Step 2: Reviewing the Literature

All good researchers consider existing research. They read what knowledgeable authorities have written on the chosen topic, if only to avoid repeating earlier work. More importantly, reading the relevant literature can generate insights that researchers may not have considered. Even if researchers believe that they have a revolutionary idea, they must still consider the works of other thinkers and show how their new research verifies, advances, and corrects past research.

At the end of most research papers, authors cite the literature that has influenced that work. This list can include dozens to hundreds of citations. For their research on undocumented border crossings, Singer and Massey (1998) cited 44 references. They used the existing literature to identify factors that help them predict how many times an undocumented migrant will be apprehended trying to evade detection. Those factors: (1) the nature and intensity of U.S. enforcement efforts, (2) characteristics of the migrant that enhance the chance of success (such as previous success at crossing borders), and (3) ties to other undocumented migrants (such as a parent, other relative, or friend) who succeeded in unauthorized entry.

Step 3: Identifying and Defining Core Concepts

After deciding on a topic and reading the relevant literature (albeit not necessarily in that order), researchers typically state their core concepts. **Concepts** are powerful thinking and communication tools that enable researchers to give and receive complex information efficiently. The mention of a concept triggers in the minds of people who know its meaning a definition and a range of important associations that help frame and focus observations. One core concept for sociologists studying undocumented immigration is the *unauthorized immigrant* (also referred to as an undocumented or illegal immigrant or migrant), defined as a noncitizen residing in the United States whom the American government has not admitted for permanent residence or for specific authorized temporary work or stays. Another core concept is *interpersonal ties*, or the network of connections that include parents, siblings, or other relatives or friends and acquaintances who guide or otherwise help (or fail to help) migrants enter the United States undetected.

Step 4: Choosing a Research Design and Data-Gathering Strategies

Once researchers have clarified core concepts, they decide on a **research design**, a plan for gathering data on the topic they have chosen. A research design specifies the population to be studied and the **methods of data collection**, or the procedures used to gather relevant data. One research design is not inherently better than another; researchers

concepts Thinking and communication tools used to give and receive complex information efficiently and to frame and focus observations.

research design A plan for gathering data that specifies who or what will be studied and the methods of data collection.

methods of data collection The procedures a researcher follows to gather relevant data.

Technology Tip: Ask students to use Google News or some other news service search engine. Search using the term "sociologist" to find news stories in which sociologists are quoted or featured. This exercise will help students to see the variety of topics sociologists study.

choose the design that best enables them to address the research question at hand (Smith 1991).

Researchers must decide whom or what they are going to study. The most common "thing" sociologists study is individuals, but they may also decide to study traces, documents, territories, households, small groups, or individuals (Rossi 1988):

- **Traces** are materials or other evidence that yield information about human activity, such as the items that people throw away, the number of lights turned on in a house, or changes in water pressure. Researchers who study undocumented border crossings might learn about paths undocumented immigrants take into the United States by observing the litter they leave behind, including "one-gallon plastic bottles, jeans, T-shirts, candy wrappers, socks, underwear, discarded purses, and inexpensive tennis shoes" (Maril 2004, p. 166).
- **Documents** are written or printed materials, such as magazines, advertisements, graffiti, birth certificates, death certificates, prescription forms, and traffic tickets. Researchers interested in the process by which Homeland Security chose and secured land for the 700 miles of barriers might look at U.S. Army Corp of Engineers' letters proclaiming the land was needed to build barriers and specifying the process by and condition under which land would be relinquished (Del Bosque 2010).
- **Territories** are places that have known boundaries or that are set aside for particular activities. They include countries, states, counties, cities, neighborhoods, streets, buildings, and classrooms. Sociologists who study territories focus on activity within the territory they select. Sociologists may choose to study communities divided by the barriers.
- **Households** include all related and unrelated people who share the same dwelling. When studying a household, researchers collect information about the household itself. They might want to determine the number of people living in the household and the household income (that is, the combined income of all people living in the same dwelling). For their research on undocumented border crossings, Singer and Massey (1998) drew upon interviews of households in 34 Mexican communities. Among other kinds of information, the researchers collected data on household size and on the number of household members who have made successful unauthorized entries into the United States.
- **Small groups** are defined as 2 to about 20 people who interact with one another in meaningful ways (Shotola 1992). Examples include father–child pairs, doctor–patient pairs, families, sports teams, circles of friends, and committees. Concerning a doctor–patient interaction, a sociologist might study the length of time the doctor spends with each patient. Keep in mind that the focus is on the doctor–patient *relationship*, rather than on the doctor or the patient *per se*. For his book *Patrolling Chaos,* Robert Maril studied a small group. Specifically, he accompanied 12 Border Patrol agents on 60 ten-hour shifts along the border.

Eugenio del Bosque

Researchers who study unauthorized border crossings may look for artifacts left behind, dropped, or discarded as a way to document paths migrants take as they trek toward the United States. Here we see a pair of pants left behind in a remote area on the Mexican side of the border.

National Archives

Sociologists who study activity along a border station such as that pictured here have chosen to study territories. They may choose to determine the average time it takes a vehicle, once it pulls into a line, to cross from the Mexican side to the U.S. side.

traces Materials or other forms of physical evidence that yield information about human activity.

documents Written or printed materials used in research.

territories Settings that have borders or that are set aside for particular activities.

households All related and unrelated people who share the same dwelling.

small groups Groups of two to about 20 people who interact with one another in meaningful ways.

Because of time constraints, researchers cannot study entire **populations**—the total number of individuals, traces, documents, territories, households, or groups that exist. Instead, they study **samples,** or portions of the cases from a larger population.

Sampling Ideally, sociologists should study a **random sample**, in which every case in the population has an equal chance of being selected. The classic, if inefficient, way of selecting a random sample is to assign a number to every case, place cards on which the numbers are written into a container, thoroughly mix the cards, and pull out one card at a time until the desired sample size is achieved. Rather than employ this tedious system to generate their samples, most of today's researchers use computer programs. If every case has an equal chance of becoming part of a sample, then theoretically the sample should be a **representative sample**—that is, one with the same distribution of characteristics (such as age, sex, and ethnic composition) as the population from which it is selected. For example, if 56.4 percent of the population from which a sample is drawn is at least 30 years old, then approximately 56.4 percent of a representative sample should be that age. In theory, if the sample is representative, then whatever holds true for the sample should also hold true for the larger population.

Obtaining a random sample is not as easy as it might appear. For one thing, researchers must begin with a **sampling frame**—a complete list of every case in the population—and each member of the population must have an equal chance of being selected. Securing such a complete list can be difficult. Campus and city telephone directories are easy to acquire, but lists of, say, U.S. citizens, adopted children in the United States, or American-owned companies with operations in Mexico are more difficult to obtain. Almost all lists omit some people (such as individuals with unlisted telephone numbers, members too new to be listed, or between-semester transfer students) and include some people who no longer belong (such as individuals who have moved, died, or dropped out). What is important is that researchers consider the extent to which the list is incomplete and update it before drawing a sample. Even if the list is complete, researchers must also think of the cost and time required to take random samples and consider the problems of inducing all sampled people to participate.

Researchers sometimes select nonrandom samples to study people who they know are not representative of the larger population but who are easily accessible such as high school and college students. Researchers may choose unrepresentative samples for other important reasons: (1) little is known about members of the sample, (2) they have some special quality or characteristic, or (3) their experiences clarify important social issues.

Singer and Massey (1998) used data collected from a random sample of 6,341 households in 34 communities in Mexico. This data was supplemented by a nonrandom sample of 484 U.S. households in which undocumented immigrants from each of the 34 communities in Mexico were now living. For his study *Patrolling Chaos*, Maril chose a nonrandom sample that consisted of one Border Patrol station among nine in the McAllen, Texas, sector of the southwest border. The border station, which he observed for two years, employed 300 men and women to guard a 45-mile stretch of the Rio Grande, which marks the Texas–Mexico border. In particular, Maril observed 12 agents as they worked ten-hour patrol shifts.

Methods of Data Collection

Besides identifying whom or what to study, the design must include a plan for collecting information. Researchers can choose from a variety of data-gathering methods, including self-administered questionnaires, interviews, observation, and secondary sources.

Self-Administered Questionnaire A **self-administered questionnaire** is a set of questions given to respondents, who read the instructions and fill in the answers themselves. The questions may require respondents to write out answers (open ended) or to select one that best reflects their answer from a list of responses (forced choice). Self-administered questionnaires are one of the most common methods of data collection. The questionnaires found in magazines or books, displayed on tables or racks in service-oriented establishments (such as hospitals, garages, restaurants, grocery stores, and physicians' offices), and mailed to households are all self-administered questionnaires.

This method of data collection offers a number of advantages. No interviewers are needed to ask respondents questions, and the questionnaires can be given to large numbers of people at one time. Also, an interviewer's facial expressions or body language cannot influence respondents, so the respondents feel freer than they otherwise might to give unpopular or controversial responses.

populations The total number of individuals, traces, documents, territories, households, or groups that could be studied.

samples Portions of the cases from a larger population.

random sample A type of sample in which every case in the population has an equal chance of being selected.

representative sample A type of sample in which those selected for study have the same distribution of characteristics as the population from which it is selected.

sampling frame A complete list of every case in a population.

self-administered questionnaire A set of questions given to respondents who read the instructions and fill in the answers themselves.

Teaching Tip: Point out that the ability to construct a survey is a valuable skill. For more on survey construction, recommend the guide posted on www.statpac.com/survey-design-guidelines.htm.

Self-administered questionnaires pose some problems, too. Respondents can misunderstand or skip over questions. When questionnaires are mailed, set out on a table, or published in a magazine or newspaper, researchers must wonder whether the people who choose to fill them out have opinions that differ from those of people who ignore the questionnaires. The results of a questionnaire depend not only on respondents' decisions to fill it out, answer questions conscientiously and honestly, and return it, but also on the quality of the questions and on a host of other considerations.

Interviews Compared with self-administered questionnaires, **interviews** are more personal. In these face-to-face or telephone conversations between an interviewer and a respondent, the interviewer asks questions and records the respondent's answers. As respondents give answers, interviewers must avoid pauses, expressions of surprise, or body language that reflects value judgments. Refraining from such conduct helps respondents feel comfortable and encourages them to give honest answers.

Interviews can be structured or unstructured, or some combination of the two. In a **structured interview**, the wording and sequence of questions are set in advance and cannot be altered during the interview. In one kind of structured interview, respondents choose answers from a response list that the interviewer reads to them. In another kind of structured interview, respondents are free to answer the questions as they see fit, although the interviewer may ask them to clarify answers or explain them in more detail. For their study on undocumented border crossings, Singer and Massey (1998) relied on data collected from structured interviews with heads of households in Mexico and the United States. Among other questions, interviewers asked the following: How many people have ever lived in the household, including those who no longer live there? How many people from the household have experience in migrating to the United States? For each person who has such experience, how many trips have they made to the United States, including the year of the first and last trip? How long did they stay in the United States? What occupation did they hold, and what did it pay? How many of those trips were made without documentation? How many trips resulted in deportation? What was the place of crossing and with whom was the crossing made? Did they use a coyote, and if yes, how much was the coyote paid? Interviewers also asked about each immigrant's ability to speak and understand English.

United States Census Bureau

Interviews are face-to-face sessions where the interviewer asks questions and records the respondent's answers. The interview can be structured or unstructured.

In contrast to the structured interview, an **unstructured interview** is flexible and open ended. The question-and-answer sequence is spontaneous and resembles a normal conversation in that the questions are not worded in advance and are not asked in a set order. The interviewer allows respondents to take the conversation in directions they define as crucial. The interviewer's role is to give focus to the interview, ask for further explanation or clarification, and probe and follow up on interesting ideas expressed by respondents. The interviewer appraises the meaning of respondents' answers and uses the information learned to ask follow-up questions. Talk show hosts, for instance, often use an unstructured format to interview their guests. Sociologists, however, have goals much different from those of talk show hosts. For one thing, sociologists do not formulate questions with the goal of entertaining an audience. In addition, they strive to ask questions in a neutral way, and no audience reaction influences how respondents answer. Robert Maril (2004) used unstructured interviews as he rode with border agents during their ten-hour shifts and at other times. As he describes it, "under the scorching sun and in the dead of night along the banks of the Rio Grande, I asked these men and women what they knew, what they had seen, and what they thought. In no uncertain terms and with direct, sometimes alarming honesty, they told me" (p. 16).

Observation As the term implies, **observation** involves watching, listening to, and recording behavior and

interviews Face-to-face or telephone conversations between an interviewer and a respondent, in which the interviewer asks questions and records the respondent's answers.

structured interview An interview in which the wording and sequence of questions are set in advance and cannot be changed during the interview.

unstructured interview An interview in which the question-and-answer sequence is spontaneous, open-ended, and flexible.

observation A research technique in which the researcher watches, listens to, and records behavior and conversations as they happen.

The Sociological Imagination The Life of a Citus Picker

For his book *Coyotes: A Journey through the Secret World of America's Illegal Aliens,* Ted Conover (1987) used a participant observation research design to capture the intersection of biography and society as it related to undocumented workers. Conover decided that, to learn truly meaningful information about undocumented immigrants, he had to go beyond formal interviews, government statistics, and news reports. He had to live with his research subjects. Conover's book includes a chapter on the art of citrus fruit picking. The following excerpt stresses that, by participating in and not just observing the life of a fruit picker, Conover learned that picking oranges is not something just anyone can do; certain skills are needed if one is to work all day at a fast enough pace to keep from getting fired:

> It required a vast store of special knowledge and dexterity. Not only did you need to know the optimum position of the ladder against a given tree, for example, you also had to be able to get it there fast and deftly. Men half my size could manipulate the twenty-foot ladders as though they were balsa wood, but in my hands the ladder was a heavy, deadly weapon. I had bruised a friend's arm with my ladder one day and had nearly broken my own when, with sixty pounds of oranges in the bag around my neck, I had slipped from its fifth rung and been grazed as it followed me to the muddy ground. . . . Handling the fruit itself was a further challenge. To be successful, you had to pick with both hands simultaneously. This meant your balance had to be good—you couldn't hold on to a branch or the ladder for support. And you had to twist the fruit off: pull hard on a Valencia without twisting and you're likely to get the whole branch in your hand. Planning was also important: Ideally, you would start with your sack empty at the top of the tree and work your way down. Oranges would just be peeking out the top of the sack when your feet touched the soil, if you did it right; you topped off the bag by grabbing low-hanging fruit on your way to the tractor. (pp. 42–43)

Source: *Coyotes: A Journey through the Secret World of America's Illegal Aliens,* Ted Conover (1987), pp. 42–43.

conversations as they happen. This research technique may sound easy, but it entails more than just watching and listening. The challenge of observation lies in knowing what to look for while remaining open to other considerations; success results from identifying what is worth observing. "It is a crucial choice, often determining the success or failure of months of work, often differentiating the brilliant observer from the . . . plodder" (Gregg 1989, p. 53). Good observation techniques must be developed through practice; observers must learn to recognize what is worth observing, be alert to unusual features, take detailed notes, and make associations between observed behaviors.

If observers come from a culture different from the one under study, they must be careful not to misinterpret or misrepresent what is happening. Imagine for a moment how an uninformed, naive observer might describe a sumo wrestling match: "One big, fat guy tries to ground another big, fat guy or force him out of the ring in a match that can last as little as three seconds" (Schonberg 1981, p. B9). Actually, for those who understand it, sumo wrestling is "a sport rich with tradition, pageantry, and elegance and filled with action, excitement, and heroes dedicated to an almost impossible standard of excellence down to the last detail" (Thayer 1983, p. 271).

Observational techniques are especially useful for three purposes: (1) studying behavior as it occurs, (2) learning information that cannot be surveyed easily, and (3) acquiring the viewpoint of the people under observation. Observation can take two forms: participant and nonparticipant. **Nonparticipant observation** consists of detached watching and listening; researchers merely observe but do not interact with the study subjects or become involved in their daily life. In contrast, researchers engage in **participant observation** when they join a group and assume the role of a group member, interact directly with individuals whom they are studying, assume a position critical to the outcome of the study, or live in a community under study (see Sociological Imagination: "The Life of a Citrus Picker"). Maril's research qualifies as participant observation, because, for all practical purposes, he became involved in the daily life of the people he studied, even "actively participated in some of the policing techniques and procedures [he] was observing" (p. 18).

In both participant and nonparticipant observation, researchers must decide whether to hide their identity and purpose or to announce them. One major reason for choosing concealment is to avoid the **Hawthorne effect,**

nonparticipant observation A research technique in which the researcher observes study participants without interacting with them.

participant observation A research technique in which the researcher observes study participants while directly interacting with them.

Hawthorne effect A phenomenon in which research subjects alter their behavior when they learn they are being observed.

Teaching Tip: In "The Life of a Citrus Picker," Ted Conover uses participant observation to learn about this kind of work. Ask students to read the box and then describe the job they do or to observe someone doing a job (e.g. a teacher, custodian, coach, sales clerk) following the style of Conover.

a phenomenon in which research subjects alter their behavior when they learn they are being observed. The term *Hawthorne effect* originated from a series of worker productivity studies involving female employees of the Hawthorne, Illinois, plant of Western Electric, conducted in the 1920s and 1930s. Researchers found that no matter how they varied working conditions—bright versus dim lighting, long versus short breaks, frequent versus no breaks, piecework pay versus fixed salary—workers' productivity increased. One explanation for this finding was that workers were responding positively to having been singled out for study (Roethlisberger and Dickson 1939).

If researchers choose to announce their identity and purpose, they must give participants adequate time to adjust to their presence. Usually, if researchers are present for a long enough time, their subjects will eventually display natural, uninhibited behaviors. Maril (2004) chose to announce his identity, and agents often referred to him as the "professor from the university." He noted that the majority of agents who worked at the station seemed to pay little attention to him after a couple of months. Maril believed that the agents were, with a few exceptions, "open and honest with me not just because they came to trust me, but because few, if any, had ever been asked about their work as agents. . . . They were anxious to talk and show me what they knew" (p. 16).

Secondary Sources (Archival Data) Another data-gathering strategy relies on **secondary sources (archival data)**—that is, data that have been collected by other researchers for some other purpose. Government researchers, for example, collect and publish data on many areas of life, including births, deaths, marriages, divorces, crime, education, travel, and trade. Any researcher who takes some existing data set and then applies it to address a different research question is using a secondary source (Horan 1995).

Another kind of secondary data source consists of materials that people have written, recorded, or created for reasons other than research (Singleton, Straits, and Straits 1993). Examples include television commercials and other advertisements, letters, diaries, home videos, poems, photographs, artwork, graffiti, movies, and song lyrics.

Identifying Variables and Specifying Hypotheses

As researchers acquire a conceptual focus, identify a population, and determine a method of data collection, they also identify the variables they want to study. A **variable** is any characteristic that consists of more than one category. The variable "sex," for example, is generally divided into two categories: male and female. The variable "mode of crossing the border" can be divided into three categories: alone, with family or friends, and with coyote.

Sometimes researchers strive to find associations between variables to explain or predict behavior. The behavior to be explained or predicted is the **dependent variable**. The variable that explains or predicts the dependent variable is the **independent variable**. The relationship between independent and dependent variables is described in a **hypothesis**, or trial explanation put forward as the focus of research, which predicts the relationship between independent and dependent variables. Specifically, it predicts how a change in an independent variable brings about a change in a dependent variable. Hypotheses that could be tested using Singer and Massey's data include the following:

- **Hypothesis 1.** The more proficient undocumented immigrants are in English, the less likely they are to be apprehended by Border Patrol.
- **Hypothesis 2.** The more times an undocumented immigrant crosses the border into the United States without being apprehended, the more likely the immigrant will be to cross alone.

In hypothesis 1, the independent variable is English-language proficiency and the dependent variable is

Eugenio del Bosque

Sociologists Singer and Massey worked to identify the variables that help us predict the probability that undocumented immigrants will be apprehended.

secondary sources (archival data) Data that have been collected by other researchers for some other purpose.

variable Any trait or characteristic that can change under different conditions or that consists of more than one category.

dependent variable The variable to be explained or predicted.

independent variable The variable that explains or predicts the dependent variable.

hypothesis A trial explanation put forward as the focus of research; it predicts how independent and dependent variables are related and how a dependent variable will change when an independent variable changes.

Technology Tip: Ask students to go to Google News and use the search term "hypothesis." Select an article that features a hypothesis. Choose one that has a clear independent and dependent variable. Bring the hypothesis to class.

likelihood of apprehension. In hypothesis 2, the independent variable is number of successful border crossings and the dependent variable is likelihood of crossing alone.

CORE CONCEPT 5 If findings are to matter, researchers must create meaningful operational definitions.

A major reason that researchers collect data is to test and propose hypotheses. If their findings are to matter, other researchers must be able to replicate their study. So, researchers need to give clear, precise definitions and instructions about how to observe and/or measure the variables under study. In the language of research, such definitions and accompanying instructions are called **operational definitions**.

An analogy can be drawn between an operational definition and a recipe. Just as people with basic cooking skills should be able to follow a recipe to achieve a desired end, people with basic research skills should be able to replicate a researcher's observations if they know the operational definitions (Katzer, Cook, and Crouch 1991). Operational definitions include clear, precise definitions and instructions about how to observe or measure variables. They help researchers determine whether a behavior of interest has occurred.

Suppose a researcher is interested in the question of who washes hands after using a public toilet. An operational definition of hand washing would include an account of what must take place for a researcher to count someone as a hand washer. If people simply run water over their fingertips or rinse their hands quickly without using soap, should the behavior count as hand washing? What if people use soap but wash only their fingertips? Should a behavior count as hand washing only if it satisfies the guidelines issued by the American Society for Microbiology? Those guidelines specify using warm or hot running water and soap while washing for 10 to 15 seconds "all surfaces thoroughly, including wrists, palms, back of hands, fingers and under fingernails" (American Society for Microbiology 1996). Researchers must address these kinds of questions in creating operational definitions.

Consider the operational definition of English-language proficiency used in the Singer and Massey study:

Do you speak and understand English?
___ Does not speak or understand.
___ Does not speak but understands a little.
___ Does not speak but understands well.
___ Both speaks and understands a little.
___ Both speaks and understands well.

Other questions related to English-language proficiency include asking the immigrants in which settings they speak English when living in the United States. The settings of interest include at home, at work, with friends, and while shopping; the frequency of using English in each setting is recorded as never, sometimes, often, or always.

Operational definitions do not have to take the form of questions. They may be precise accounts or descriptions of what a researcher observed and what the context of the observations was. If operational definitions are not clear or do not indicate accurately the behaviors they were designed to represent, they have questionable value. Good operational definitions are both reliable and valid. **Reliability** is the extent to which an operational definition gives consistent results. For example, Singer and Massey's operational definition of English-language proficiency many not yield reliable answers when the person answering questions has weak English-language proficiency. Thus, if you asked a respondent the question at two different times, he or she might give two different answers. One way to increase the reliability of this question could be to have a Spanish- and English-proficient interviewer rate the person's level of proficiency.

Validity is the degree to which an operational definition measures what it claims to measure. Professors, for example, give tests to measure students' knowledge of a particular subject as covered in class lectures, discussions, reading assignments, and other activities. Students may question the validity of this measure if the questions on a test reflect only the material covered in lectures. They may argue that the test does not measure knowledge of all the material covered or assigned. Remember, when assessing validity, always ask, *Is the operational definition really measuring what it claims to measure?* For example, is the question *Do you speak and understand English?* likely to yield valid responses about English-language proficiency? One problem with this operational definition is disagreement as to what constitutes speaking *a little* English and speaking English *well.* What if a person's proficiency falls somewhere between *a little* and *well*? All people who answer this question probably have their own understanding of what speaking *a little* or *well* means.

Likewise, is the number of apprehensions a valid measure of the effectiveness of a border control initiative such as barrier construction? Should effectiveness be measured by increased apprehensions or decreased apprehensions? Increased apprehensions could mean barriers are effective in forcing undocumented immigrants into territories where the Border Patrol has a strategic advantage; they could also mean that the barriers are ineffective, because for every one undocumented immigrant caught, four manage to cross (see Figure 2.4).

operational definitions Clear, precise definitions and instructions about how to observe and/or measure the variables under study.

reliability The extent to which an operational definition gives consistent results.

validity The degree to which an operational definition measures what it claims to measure.

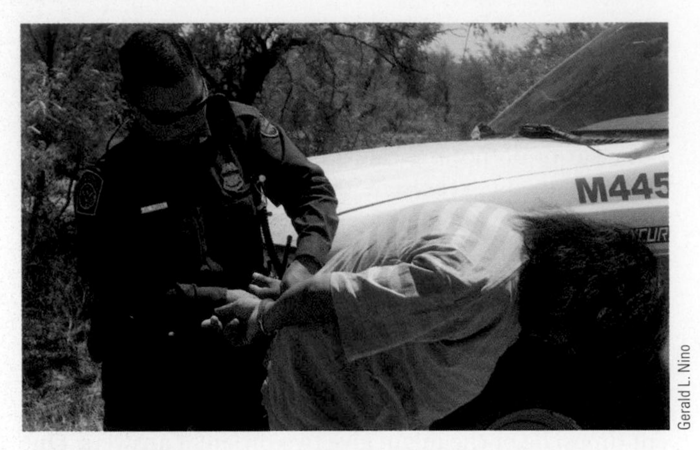

Gerald L. Nino

Is number of apprehensions the best way to measure the effectiveness of border fences? Increased apprehensions could mean one of two things: the fence is effective in forcing undocumented immigrants into territories where border patrol have a strategic advantage, or the fence is ineffective because, for every one undocumented immigrant caught, four manage to cross.

Steps 5 and 6: Analyzing the Data and Drawing Conclusions

When researchers reach the stage of analyzing collected data, they search for common themes, meaningful patterns, and links. Researchers must "pick and choose among the available numbers [and observations] and then fashion a format" (Hacker 1997, p. 478). In presenting their findings, researchers may use graphs, frequency tables, photos, statistical data, and so on. The choice of presentation depends on which results are significant and how they might be best shown (see Table 2.1).

Generalizability Besides choosing a format in which to present data, sociologists comment on the **generalizability** of findings, the extent to which the findings can be applied to the larger population from which the sample was drawn. Both the sample used and the response rate are important in determining generalizability. If a sample is

TABLE 2.1 Basic Statistics Researchers Use to Convey Findings

The following table shows the number of unauthorized immigrants apprehended each year from 1992 through 2010. One can see that the number of apprehensions has dropped with construction of the border barriers. But are apprehensions the best measure of effectiveness? Could it be that the undocumented are simply staying in the United States rather than returning home after seasonal employment ends? Could it be that the undocumented have found new ways to enter undetected? Massey thinks that this might be the case.

Year	Undocumented Immigrants Apprehended on U.S-Mexico Border (in millions)
2010	.45
2009	.69
2008	.73
2007	.88
2006	1.11
2005	1.17
2004	1.14
2003	.91
2002	.93
2001	1.24
2000	1.64
1999	1.54
1998	1.52
1997	1.37
1996	1.51
1995	1.27
1994	.98
1993	1.20
1992	1.18

Source: **Data from Homeland Security, Office of Immigration Statistics (2010)**

n: number of cases (19 years of data)

Mean: The sum of all apprehensions from 1992 through 2010, divided by the total number of years considered (19). Over the 18-year period, the average number of apprehensions was 1.13 million.

Standard deviation (s.d.): A measure that shows how far the data are spread from the mean. About two-thirds of data falls one standard deviation from the mean. Most of data (at least 95 percent) falls within two standard deviations of the mean, and almost all of data (99.7 percent) will fall within three standard deviations of the mean. For the 19-year period specified in the table, the standard deviation is .32 million or 320,000. We will not present the formula here but the standard deviation can be easily calculated in Microsoft Excel or some other spreadsheet. To calculate the spread of data around the mean, add *and* subtract the standard deviation from the mean once, twice, or three times. To calculate the range of apprehensions that are one standard deviation from the mean, simply add .32 to the mean (1.13 million) and subtract .32 from the mean. The results tell you that 66 percent of the data falls between .81 and 1.45 million. To calculate the range of apprehensions over the past 19 years that are two standard deviations, add and subtract the standard deviation multiplied by two from the mean.

Minimum: The lowest number of apprehensions (450,000 apprehensions in 2010).

Maximum: The highest number of apprehensions (1.64 million apprehensions in 2005).

Range: The difference between the highest value and the lowest value. In this case, the range of apprehensions falls between .45 million in 2010 and to 1.64 million in 2005, a difference of 1.19 million.

Mode: The value that occurs most often. In this case, there is no mode as the 19 values are all different.

n: A symbol that stands for the number of respondents or cases. In this case, n is 19.

Median: The number that 50 percent of the cases fall above and 50 percent fall below. For the 19 years of apprehension data, half of the years listed had fewer than 1.17 million apprehensions, and half had more than 1.17 million.

Teaching Tip: Students may need some help interpreting the numbers in Table 2.1. Point out that the numbers are in millions, which means that the reader will move the decimal place six places. So .45 is equivalent to 450,000 and 1.18 is equivalent to 1,180,000.

Singer and Massey (1998) calculated the probability that an undocumented migrant would be caught for the years 1964 through 1994. In 1964 the probability of getting caught was about 33 percent. In 1994 that probability dropped to about 15 percent. This drop in probability suggests that a decline in the number of apprehensions is only one measure of success at deterring undocumented migrants. As we will see in the next section, the more crucial measure involves knowing the number that attempted to enter and the percentage who were eventually caught.

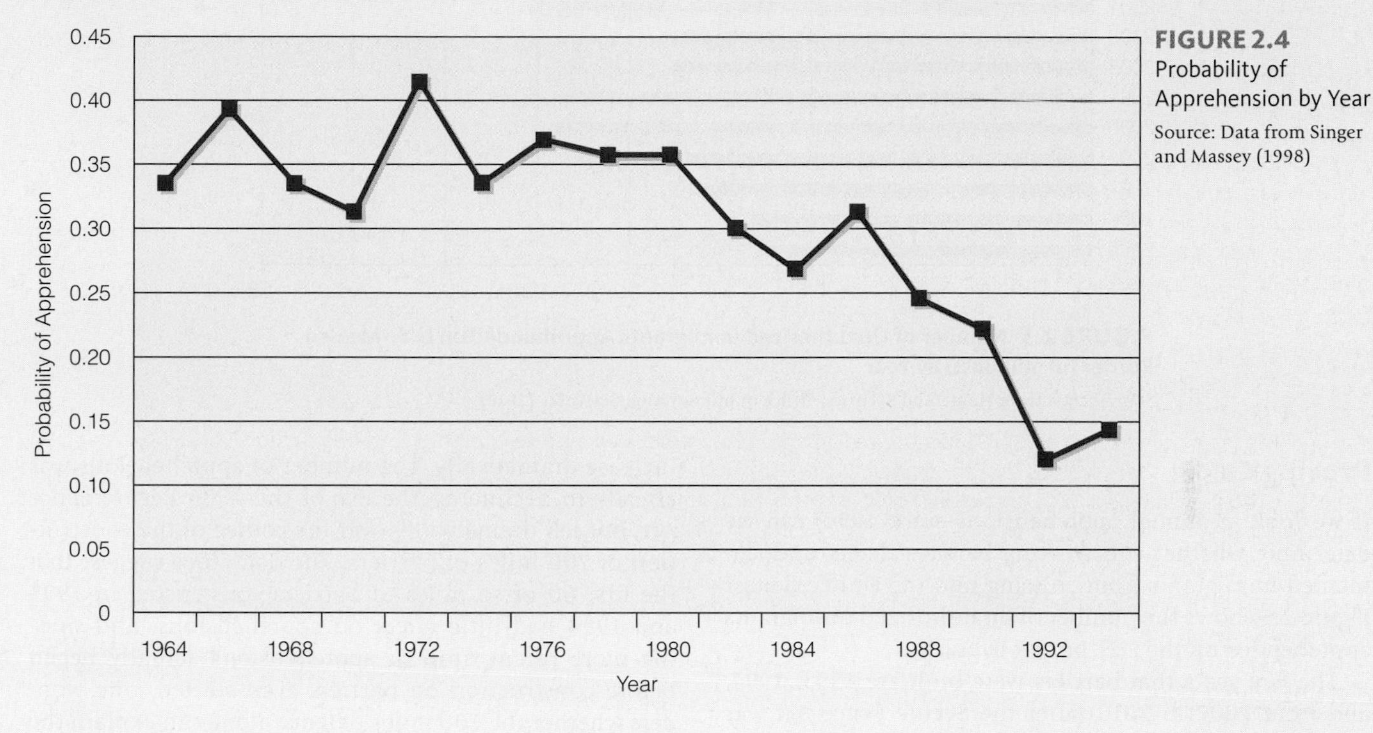

FIGURE 2.4 Probability of Apprehension by Year

Source: Data from Singer and Massey (1998)

randomly selected, if almost all subjects agree to participate, and if the response rate for every question is high, we can say that the sample is representative of the population and that the findings are theoretically generalizable to that population. Recall that Singer and Massey (1998) used data derived from structured interviews with a sample of 6,341 randomly selected households in 34 Mexican communities. The response rate varied by community (from a 100 percent response rate in two rural communities to an 84 percent response rate in a large urban community); the average response rate was 94 percent. Such a high response rate suggests that Singer and Massey's findings are generalizable to the undocumented population. In particular, Singer and Massey found that, despite the apparent buildup of enforcement resources and the implementation of Operations Hold the Line and Gatekeeper, the probability of apprehensions fell in the late 1980s through early to mid-1990s. Singer and Massey's conclusions can be extended to analyzing the success of the border barriers. Although the border barriers may indeed be successful, their success cannot be determined from by simply showing a decline in apprehensions. To really determine success, we must also know how many undocumented attempted to enter, what percentage were caught, and how many have just stayed put in the United States.

Also keep in mind that even when samples are random, the generalizations that follow can never be presented as statements of certainty that apply to everyone. In the case of Maril's (2006) research, the findings probably cannot be generalized to *all* Border Patrol stations. Still his research on the border from the perspective of the Border Patrol agents does lend support to Singer and Massey's findings. Specifically, Maril agued that highly visible border control strategies—border barriers, increases in the number of agents, and increased surveillance—are "a grand pretense" because the majority of undocumented immigration and opportunities to enter illegally exist "far from the public eye" (p. 287).

generalizability The extent to which findings can be applied to the larger population from which a sample is drawn.

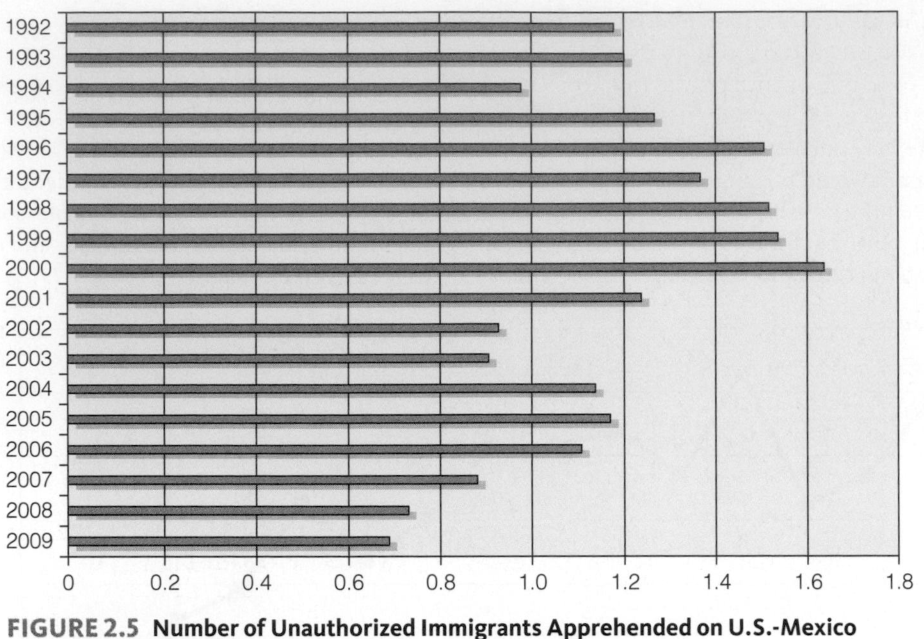

FIGURE 2.5 Number of Unauthorized Immigrants Apprehended on U.S.-Mexico Border (in millions), by Year

Source: Data from Homeland Security, Office of Immigration Statistics (2010)

Proving Cause

If we look at annual apprehensions since 1990, can we determine whether constructing barriers deters undocumented immigrants from crossing into the United States? Figure 2.5 shows the number of unauthorized immigrants apprehended on the U.S. border over time.

The key years that barriers were built are 1993, 1994, and from 2007 to 2010 (after the Secure Fence Act was passed in 2006). Figure 2.5 shows a decline in apprehensions around 1993 and 1994, but then apprehensions rise again to pre-barrier levels. The year before the barriers were constructed apprehensions began to decline. Should we consider the barriers a success? That is, are decreases in apprehensions the result of the barriers? To "prove" this, we must demonstrate three things: First, that barrier construction occurred before apprehensions began their decline. Figure 2.5 shows that apprehensions increased in the years following construction in 1993 and 1994. The bar chart also shows that the decline in apprehensions begin in 2006, the year the Secure Fence Act was passed and before construction of an additional 700 miles of fence began.

Second, there must be a clear association between barrier construction and drop in apprehensions as barriers were put in place. Note that apprehensions decline between 1993 and 1994 but then in subsequent years increase dramatically. The number of apprehensions was already in decline on the eve of the 2006 Secure Fence Act, but fell dramatically over the course of the construction of 700 miles of barriers. The data does suggest that the first 80 or so miles of barriers constructed in 1993 and 1994 had little effect on apprehensions, and since the more recent drop in apprehensions actually began before construction on barriers even started, one wonders whether the 700 miles of fence alone can explain the sharp decline.

Third, to further prove that the border barriers are responsible for the decline must eliminate the possibility of a **spurious correlation**. That means we must show that the association between barrier construction and the decline in apprehensions is not the result of coincidence. In other words, the barrier construction may not actually be the "cause" of the decline. Instead some third factor makes it appear as if the barriers "caused" the decline. In this regard, sociologists consider other reasons that might explain the decline. One possibility is that the ongoing economic recession starting in 2007 and 2008, accompanied by high unemployment, was the real reason apprehensions declined as job opportunities in the United State were less plentiful. Consider that many undocumented migrants work in construction. Might the decline in apprehensions really be explained by the collapse of the housing market? Why immigrate to the United States when there is no work? Second, undocumented workers might have changed the way they enter the United States and the length of time they stay after arriving, giving the appearance that the flow of undocumented workers has subsided. That is, undocumented workers return home

spurious correlation A correlation that is coincidental or accidental because the independent and dependent variables are not actually related; rather, some third variable related to both of them makes it seem as though they are.

less often for fear of getting apprehended; they hire coyotes; they travel alone instead of with a group; and so on. By one estimate, four out of five undocumented immigrants have come to rely on coyotes to help them evade the border patrol or to guide them through unsecured areas or remote desert and mountainous areas (Cornelius 2008).

Third, there is a possibility that border control agencies manipulate data on apprehensions so that it appears they are meeting performance goals. A Government Accountability Office (2009) study showed many instances where Border Patrol reported achieving performance goals but did not have documentation to back up their proclamations. In fact, the study reported "a lack of management oversight, and unclear checkpoint data collection guidance resulted in the overstatement of checkpoint performance results in fiscal year 2007 and 2008 agency performance reports, as well as inconsistent data collection practices at checkpoints" (p. i).

Online Poll

Do you think the United States should build a wall across the entire 2,000-mile border with Mexico?

- ○ Yes
- ○ No
- ○ Don't know

Do you think the dramatic decline in border apprehensions is a good measure of the border barriers' effectiveness at reducing the flow of undocumented workers into the United States?

- ○ Yes
- ○ No, some other factor such as economic recession must be considered.

To see how other students responded to these questions, go to **www.cengagebrain.com**.

Summary of CORE CONCEPTS

In this chapter, we learned that sociological perspectives offer a set of guiding questions and key concepts to explain social issues. Three major perspectives inform the discipline of sociology: functionalist, conflict, and symbolic-interactionist. We used these perspectives to analyze the barriers, walls, and fences along the U.S.–Mexico border. We also used the methods of sociological research to assess whether the border barriers deter undocumented immigration.

CORE CONCEPT 1 Functionalists focus on how the "parts" of society contribute in expected and unexpected ways to maintaining and disrupting an existing social order.

We used the functionalist perspective to understand the border barriers as a "part" of society and to ask what are its anticipated (manifest) and unintended (latent) consequences to the existing social order? The barriers manifest functions include deterring and controlling the flow of undocumented immigration; the barriers' latent functions include providing a volleyball "net" for residents on either side to use during community gatherings. The barriers also have disruptive functions that are manifest and latent. One manifest dysfunction is that the increased border security pushes undocumented immigrants to seek help crossing from coyotes. A latent dysfunction is that many communities have been severed by a barrier.

CORE CONCEPT 2 The conflict perspective focuses on conflict over scarce and valued resources and the strategies dominant groups use to create and protect the social arrangements and practices that give them an advantage in accessing and controlling those resources.

Technology Tip: Visit the National Public Radio website (npr.org) and enter the keywords "Immigration: Do Border Fences Work?" to hear a segment that examines the "effectiveness of barriers, borders and walls in other nations."

Conflict theorists ask this basic question: Who benefits from a particular social pattern or arrangement? In the case of the barriers, conflict theorists argue that an honest analysis would suggest that American politicians, employers, and military contractors benefit the most at the expense of undocumented immigrants from Mexico. The focus on the Mexican border draws attention away from a global trend to outsource jobs to the lowest-wage markets and makes it appear that something is being done to protect U.S. workers.

CORE CONCEPT 3 Symbolic interactionists focus on social interaction and related concepts of self-awareness/reflexive thinking, symbols, and negotiated order.

Symbolic interactionists focus on social interaction and ask, How do involved parties experience, interpret, influence, and respond to what they and others are doing while interacting? They draw upon the following concepts: (1) reflexive thinking, (2) symbol, and (3) negotiated order to think about any social situation. This perspective encourages researchers to personally immerse themselves in the situation they are studying. Symbolic interactionists observe interactions between border guards and those crossing with an eye toward understanding how undocumented immigrants cross through checkpoints into the United States.

CORE CONCEPT 4 Sociologists adhere to the scientific method; that is, they acquire data through observation and leave it open to verification by others.

When doing research, sociologists explain why their research topic is important, tie their research in with existing research, and specify the core concepts guiding analysis. Sociologists decide on a plan for gathering data, identifying whom or what they will study and how they will select (sample) subjects for study. Sociologists use a variety of data-collection methods, including self-administered questionnaires, interviews, observation, and secondary sources. In addition, they propose and test hypotheses that specify the relationship between independent and dependent variables. In their study of undocumented migration into the United States, Audrey Singer and Douglas Massey followed the scientific method. In his study of the border patrol, so did Robert Lee Maril.

CORE CONCEPT 5 If findings are to matter, researchers must create meaningful operational definitions.

Operational definitions are clear, precise definitions and instructions about how to observe and/or measure the variables under study. They must be both reliable and valid. The operational definition must yield consistent measures and it must measure what it claims to measure. The Department of Homeland Security, for example, is using the number of border apprehensions as one important operational definition of the barriers' effectiveness, but we have learned this measure may not be the best indicator of effectiveness because undocumented immigrants may be simply changing the way they enter the United States. Also keep in mind that applying this measure to the southwest border barriers may take our eye off other legal and undocumented ways of entering the country. Recall that as many as half of the estimated 11.6 million undocumented immigrants in the United States may simply have overstayed their visas, of which 162 million are issued each year.

Resources on the Internet

Login to CengageBrain.com to access the resources your instructor requires. For this book, you can access:

Sociology CourseMate

Access an integrated eBook, chapter-specific interactive learning tools, including flash cards, quizzes, videos, and more in your Sociology CourseMate.

Take a pretest for this chapter and receive a personalized study plan based on your results that will identify the topics you need to review and direct you to online resources to help you master those topics. Then take a posttest to help you determine the concepts you have mastered and what you will need to work on.

CourseReader

CourseReader for Sociology is an online reader providing access to readings, and audio and video selections to accompany your course materials.

Visit **www.cengagebrain.com** to access your account and purchase materials.

Key Terms

concepts 41
dependent variable 46
documents 42
dysfunctions 31
facade of legitimacy 34
function 30
generalizability 48
Hawthorne effect 45
households 42
hypothesis 46
independent variable 46
interviews 44
latent dysfunctions 31
latent functions 31
manifest dysfunctions 31
manifest functions 31
methods of data collection 41
negotiated order 37
nonparticipant observation 45
objectivity 40
observation 44
operational definitions 47
participant observation 45
populations 43
random sample 43
reliability 47
representative sample 43
research 40
research design 41
research methods 40
samples 43
sampling frame 43
scientific method 40
secondary sources (archival data) 46
self-administered questionnaire 43
small groups 42
social interaction 36
spurious correlations 50
structured interview 44
symbol 37
territories 42
traces 42
theoretical perspectives 30
unstructured interview 44
validity 47
variable 46

CULTURE

3 With Emphasis on NORTH AND SOUTH KOREA

Sociologists see people as shaped by their cultural experiences. In the broadest sense of the word, *culture* is the human-created strategies for adapting and responding to one's surroundings. In this chapter, we will consider how the 1953 construction of a strict border zone separating North from South Korea has shaped and still shapes the lives of the Koreans on both sides. This photo offers some insights about how the Korean people's lives have been affected. Here, North Koreans are shown waving good-bye to their South Korean relatives who crossed the border to visit them at the Diamond Mountain Resort in North Korea. That visit marked the first time, since 1953, that they have seen or otherwise communicated with one another. In that year, the Korean War ended and the peninsula was divided into North and South Korea. The moment the division took effect, an estimated five million Koreans were working, living, visiting, and shopping on the "wrong" side and found themselves stuck, never to return home or see relatives stuck on the other side.

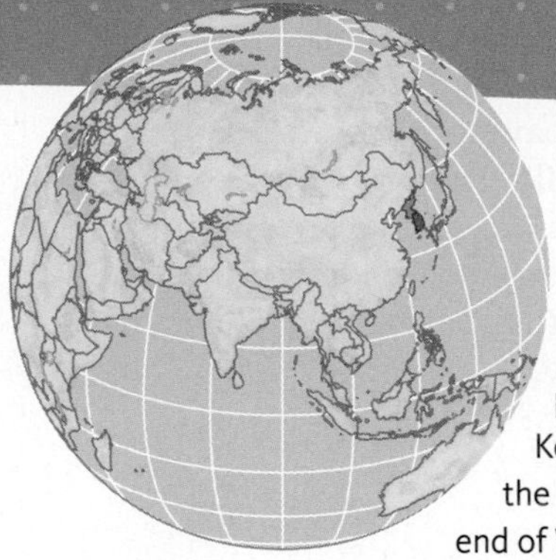

Why Focus On NORTH AND SOUTH KOREA?

Today, about 27,000 U.S. military personnel are stationed in South Korea. U.S. military involvement on the Korean Peninsula dates back to the end of World War II, when Premier Joseph Stalin of the Soviet Union, Prime Minister Winston Churchill of Great Britain, and President Franklin Roosevelt of the United States met in 1945 and, "without consulting even one Korean," agreed to chop Korea in half (Kang 1995, p. 75). The Korean War began in 1950, after the North Korean government invaded South Korea. Both sides endured heavy casualties as they fought to control the peninsula. In 1953, the war ended in a stalemate, with the 1945-drawn boundary still in place. A 2.5-mile-wide border of barbed wire and land mines known as the demilitarized zone (DMZ) separates North from South Korea. To the north of the border are 1.2 million North Korean soldiers. To the south are 740,000 South Korean troops, in addition to the U.S. troops.

Over the course of the past 60 years, more than 7.5 million U.S. servicemen and women have fought, died, and otherwise served to maintain the division between the two countries. Today, North Korea possesses a communist-style government and has one of the most isolated and centrally planned economies in the world. South Korea, on the other hand, is a republic, and its economy ranks among the top 15 in the world (U.S. Central Intelligence Agency 2011).

In this chapter, we consider how sociologists think about and describe any culture. We apply the sociological framework to North and South Korea. More specifically, we use this framework to think about the profound effects the Korean War and the subsequent division of the Korean Peninsula into north and south has had on Korean culture, on the meaning of being Korean, and on the relationship between the United States and the two Koreas. This division has affected the life of every North and South Korean resident who lived through the event and who has been born since. It has also affected the lives of millions of U.S. servicemen and servicewomen, their families, and significant others.

FIGURE 3.1

Online Poll

Do you have a connection with South Korea? (Check all that apply.)

- ○ No
- ○ Yes, served in military, or a family member served
- ○ Yes, I am/my immediate family is from Korea
- ○ Yes, I claim Korean ancestry
- ○ Yes, I know someone who adopted a Korean baby
- ○ Yes, a person of Korean ancestry married into our family
- ○ Yes, a friend who is Korean
- ○ Yes, other

To see how other students responded to these questions, go to **www.cengagebrain.com.**

The Challenge of Defining Culture

CORE CONCEPT 1 **In the most general sense, culture is the way of life of a people.**

More specifically, sociologists define **culture** as the human-created strategies for adjusting to their surroundings and to those creatures (including humans) that are part of those surroundings. As we will learn, the list of

Video Tip: Show the author video introduction to Chapter 3, which can be found on the Power Lecture CD. A transcript of the video is included in the Instructor's Resource Manual.

Discussion Tip: Ask if anyone has served in South Korea or if they have a relative who has served in Korea since 1945?

human-created strategies is endless. These strategies include the automobile as a strategy for transporting people (and their possessions) from one point to another; language as a strategy for communicating with others; and the online community Facebook.com as a strategy for presenting the self to others, learning about others, and building social networks. Culture cannot exist without a **society**, a group of interacting people who share, perpetuate, and create culture.

We use the word *culture* in ways that emphasize differences: "The cultures of X and Y are very different"; "There is a culture gap between X and Y"; "It is culture shock to come from X and live in Y." Our use of the word suggests that we think of culture as having clear boundaries, as an explanation for differences, and as a source of misunderstandings. In light of the seemingly clear way in which we use the word, we may be surprised to learn that sociologists face several conceptual challenges in thinking about culture:

- How do you describe a culture? To put it another way, is it possible to find words to define something so vast as the way of life of a people? What exactly is American or Korean culture?
- How do we know who belongs to a culture? Does a person who appears Korean and who has lived in the United States most of his or her life belong to Korean or American culture? Is everyone who lives in South Korea or North Korea, Korean?
- What are the distinguishing characteristics that set one culture apart from others? Is eating rice for breakfast a behavior that makes someone Korean? Is an ability to speak Korean a characteristic that makes someone Korean? Are Koreans who live in Mexico and speak Spanish Korean?

This chapter offers a framework for thinking about culture that considers both its elusiveness and its importance in shaping human life. A few words of caution are in order before delving into this subject. Although this chapter considers the cultures of South Korea, North Korea, and the United States, we can apply the concepts discussed here to understand any culture and frame other cross-cultural comparisons. As you read about culture, remember that North and South Korea are broadly referred to as countries possessing an Eastern (or Asian) culture and that the United States is regarded as a country possessing a Western culture. Therefore, many of the patterns described here are not necessarily unique to the Koreas or the United States; rather, they are shared with other Eastern or Western societies. At the same time, do not overstate the similarities among countries that share a broad cultural tradition.

Do not assume, for example, that South and North Korea share the same culture. Although they undoubtedly have many similarities, the two nations have very different economic and political systems. "North Korea is a place that is shrouded in mystery and conjecture; . . . for so long it has chosen to close itself off from the rest of the world that little information flows in or out of the place" (Sharp 2005a). Likewise, do not assume that South Korea is just like Japan, for example. As we will see, much of South Korean identity is intricately linked with the idea of being "not Japanese" (Fallows 1988). To assume that South Korea is like Japan is equivalent to assuming that the United States is just like a Western European country, such as Germany. As we know, however, the United States is a country that celebrates its independence from European influence.

Courtesy of Prince Brown, Jr.

Spc. Jason C. Adolphson

Since 1945, millions of American soldiers of all races and ethnic groups, including Korean Americans, have served in South Korea. The top photo shows soldiers serving in South Korea in the 1960s, the bottom photo shows soldiers serving in South Korea today.

culture The way of life of a people; more specifically, the human-created strategies for adjusting to their surroundings and to those creatures (including humans) that are part of those surroundings.

society A group of interacting people who share, perpetuate, and create culture.

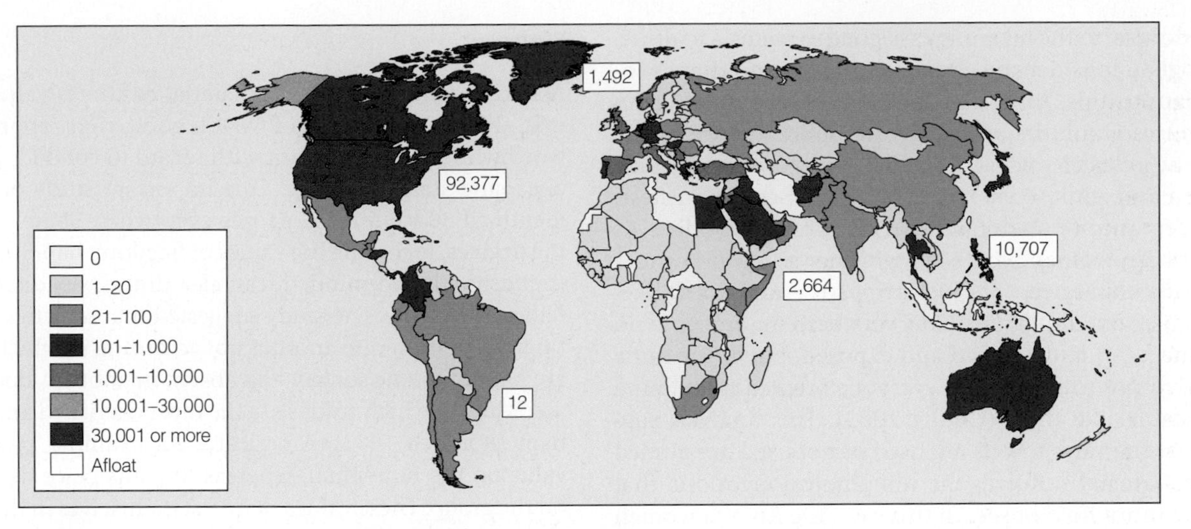

FIGURE 3.2 Number of U.S. Military Personnel by Country
The U.S. military presence in South Korea has shaped the cultures of North and South Korea. The Korean Peninsula is not the only place where the United States has such a presence. Figure 3.2 shows U.S. military personnel are stationed in 140 countries. How might the presence of the U.S. military affect a country's culture?
Source: Data from Department of Defense (2009)

Material and Nonmaterial Components

Culture consists of material and nonmaterial components. **Material culture** consists of all the natural and human-created objects to which people have attached meaning. Material culture includes plants, trees, minerals or ores, dogs, cars, trucks, microwave ovens, computers, video cameras, and iPods. When sociologists think about material culture, they consider the uses to which an item is put and the meanings assigned by the people who use it (Rohner 1984).

Learning the meanings that people assign to material culture helps sociologists grasp the significance of those objects in people's lives. Faucets, showers, tubs, soap, and towels are examples of material culture that people use to cleanse their bodies. Most Americans associate these items with bathrooms, relatively small rooms that offer a private space for washing the body. Although private bathrooms exist in Korea, most Koreans also associate these items with public bathhouses. An American woman visiting Korea described her experience with a bathhouse:

> Looking around, I noticed that all the women were completely naked—at a Korean bath, you check your modesty at the door, and the towel is for scrubbing, not drying or draping. After stripping down, I tentatively stepped through steamy glass doors, into the world of the baths—a large, noisy, cheerful area where about 100 women of all ages and small children of both sexes were scrubbing, chatting, and soaking. To one side were rows of washing stations, with faucets, hand showers, and mirrors set low to the ground. (Koreans, like Japanese, sit while washing.) (McClane 2000)

Two European women visiting South Korea offer similar observations: "The most amazing thing is the range of ages here, from grandmother to babies, all enjoying the same place. . . . It takes a few trips here to get used to walking around naked. . . . And you never see your own grandmother naked in [Great Britain]" (ABC News/Travel 2010).

Department of Defense

The Korean War Memorial in Washington, D.C. is an example of material culture. It includes 19 statues, approximately 7 feet, 3 inches tall: 14 Army members, three Marines, one Navy member, and one Air Force member. The statues represent an ethnic cross section of the men who fought in the Korean War: 12 Caucasians, three African Americans, two Hispanic Americans, one Asian American, and one Native American.

material culture All the natural and human-created objects to which people have attached meaning.

Discussion Tip: Ask if anyone has served in the U.S. military abroad. To what extent did they interact with the resident population? What did they learn about the culture?

In addition to the meanings assigned to material culture, sociologists consider the ways material culture shapes social relationships. American sociologists studying Korean bathhouses would be struck by the public nature of the bath, the relaxed and casual relationships among nude children and adult women, the lack of self-consciousness, and acceptance of one's own body and others' bodies. As one Western woman who went with her sister-in-law to a bathhouse explained, "She just stripped . . . and doing likewise to her son, didn't notice my very hesitant moves to do the same. . . . I felt so weird and exposed, but at the same time tried not to show it, as everyone seemed to be quite comfortable like that" (Chung 2003). This analysis suggests that the ways towels are used or not used are guided by **nonmaterial culture**, the nonphysical creations that people cannot hold or see. In this case, the Korean women do not define a towel (material culture) as something used to cover themselves because they are influenced by the nonmaterial component of Korean culture, which encompasses beliefs, values, norms, symbols, and language.

Beliefs

Beliefs are conceptions that people accept as true, concerning how the world operates and where the individual fits in relationship to others. Beliefs can be rooted in blind faith, experience, tradition, or in science. Whatever their accuracy or origins, beliefs can exert powerful influences on actions as they are used to justify behavior, ranging from the most generous to the most violent. Some beliefs follow:

- Anyone who wants to can grow up to become president of the United States.
- Ongoing conversation, rather than silence, validates a relationship.
- Athletic talent is something you are born with.
- Anyone can develop athletic talent if they work hard, practice, and persist.
- It is fine for young children of both sexes to bathe with their mothers, grandmothers, and other women in a public bathhouse.

nonmaterial culture Intangible human creations, which we cannot identify directly through the senses.

beliefs Conceptions that people accept as true, concerning how the world operates and where the individual fits in relationship to others.

values General, shared conceptions of what is good, right, appropriate, worthwhile, and important with regard to conduct, appearance, and states of being.

norms Written and unwritten rules that specify behaviors appropriate and inappropriate to a particular social situation.

folkways Norms that apply to the mundane aspects or details of daily life.

Values

A second component of nonmaterial culture is **values**: general, shared conceptions of what is good, right, appropriate, worthwhile, and important with regard to conduct, appearance, and states of being. One important study on values identified 36 values that people everywhere share to differing degrees, including the values of freedom, happiness, true friendship, broad-mindedness, cleanliness, obedience, and national security. The study suggested that societies are distinguished from one another not according to which values are present in one society and absent in another, but rather, according to which values are the most cherished and dominant (Rokeach 1973). Americans, for example, place high value on the individual, whereas Koreans place high value on the group. These values manifest themselves in the American preference to bathe alone and the Korean preference to share the experience with others in public bathhouses.

Sports offer some insights about a culture's values. The national sport of South Korea is tae kwon do. That sport values physical power when it is used in self-defense and only in an amount necessary to gain control over an aggressor. Tae kwon do athletes also value freedom, justice, and using power to build a better world. By contrast, football—arguably the national sport of the United States—places a high value on aggression. Hard hits to opponents are highly valued and replayed as game highlights. The object of the American football game is to advance the ball into "enemy" territory and score by invading an opponent's end zone.

Norms

A third component of nonmaterial culture is **norms**, written and unwritten rules that specify behaviors appropriate and inappropriate to a particular social situation. Examples of written norms are rules that appear in college student handbooks, on signs in restaurants (No Smoking Section), and on garage doors of automobile repair centers (Honk Horn to Open). Unwritten norms exist for virtually every kind of situation: wash your hands before preparing food; do not hold hands with a friend of the same sex in public; leave at least a 20 percent tip for waiters; remove your shoes before entering the house. Some norms are considered more important than others, and so the penalties for their violation are more severe. Depending on the importance of a norm, punishment can range from a frown to death. In this regard, we can distinguish between folkways and morés.

Folkways are norms that apply to the mundane aspects or details of daily life: when and what to eat, how to greet someone, how long the workday should be, how many times caregivers should change babies' diapers each day. As sociologist William Graham Sumner (1907) noted, "Folkways give us discipline and support of routine and habit"; if we were forced constantly to make decisions

Discussion Tip: Ask students if they were presented with an opportunity to use a public bath house in Korea as described above, would they agree? If yes, would they still agree if a small child of either sex accompanied them?

We can gain insights about what values dominate in a society when we examine its most popular, celebrated sports. The photo from a U.S. Naval Academy football game suggests aggressive and hard-hitting play is valued. The photo of South Korean marines demonstrating tae kwon do skills suggests an appreciation for skills that can be used to defend oneself from an aggressor.

about these details, "the burden would be unbearable" (p. 92). Generally, we go about everyday life without asking why until something reminds us or forces us to see that other ways are possible.

Consider the folkways that govern how a meal is typically eaten at Korean and American dinner tables. In Korea, diners do not pass items to one another, except to small children. Instead, they reach and stretch across one another and use their chopsticks to lift small portions from serving bowls to individual rice bowls or directly to their mouths. The Korean norms of table etiquette—reaching across instead of passing, having no clear place settings, and using the same utensils to eat and serve oneself food from platters and bowls—deemphasize the individual and reinforce the greater importance of the group.

Americans follow different dining folkways. They have individual place settings, marked clearly by place mats or blocked off by eating utensils. It is considered impolite to reach across another person's space and to use personal utensils to take food from the communal serving bowls. Instead, diners pass items around the table and use special serving utensils. That Americans have clearly marked eating spaces, do not typically trespass into other diners' spaces, and use separate utensils to take food reinforces values about the importance of the individual.

Often, travel guides and cultural guides list folkways that foreign travelers should follow when visiting a particular country. The U.S. military introduced a new housing policy in February 2010 that allows military families to live off base in housing complexes with Korean neighbors. In preparation, the military created culturally oriented videos to educate Americans about Korean folkways, pointing out that "we are guests" in Korea and not to expect Koreans to make concessions to American ways of doing things. The videos titled "Being a Good Neighbor" describe a number of Korean folkways:

- Dogs in Korea are likely tiny things that you can carry in your pocket so big dogs are a new phenomenon, especially for children. Keep your dogs on a leash.
- Barbeques are a no-no. Koreans see them as fire hazards, and the smoke is a nuisance.
- Recycling is very important in Korea. It is a way of life enforced by law, and citizens pay for those items that cannot be recycled. (2nd Infantry Division 2010, CNN 2010)

Morés are norms that people define as essential to the well-being of a group. People who violate morés are usually punished severely: They may be ostracized, institutionalized in prisons or mental hospitals, sentenced to physical punishment, or condemned to die. In contrast to folkways, morés are regarded as "the only way" or "the truth" and as thus are unchangeable. Most Americans, for example, have strong morés against public nudity, especially when adults

morés Norms that people define as critical to the well-being of a group. Violation of morés can result in severe forms of punishment.

are in the presence of children. They believe that children should be shielded from seeing adults without clothes and that children are more vulnerable when naked in the presence of adults who are also nude. Koreans, on the other hand, do not view public nakedness in the right context to be morally wrong or as a danger to children. Instead, they view the body as something to be accepted for what it is. Americans who visit Korean bathhouses report, to their surprise, that they adjust quickly to social nudity and come to see being naked among others as unremarkable.

Symbols

We learned in Chapter 2 that symbols are any kind of physical or conceptual phenomenon—a word, an object, a sound, a feeling, an odor, a gesture or bodily movement, or a concept of time—to which people assign a name and a meaning. The meaning assigned is not evident from the physical phenomenon or idea alone. For example, what do the numbers 2-0-1-5 and 1-0-0, taken on their own, mean? Many societies, Christian and non-Christian, locate themselves in time by referencing the birth of Jesus Christ. Thus, "AD 2015" symbolizes 2,015 years since the traditionally recognized birth of Christ. AD is the abbreviation for *anno Domini* (Latin for "in the year of the Lord"). In North Korea, people locate themselves in time by referencing the year Kim Il Sung, the country's founding and "eternal" president, was born. At the time of this writing, the numbers 1-0-0 symbolize 100 years since his birth in 1912, with 1912 being year 1.

Language

In the broadest sense of the word, **language** is a symbol system involving the use of sounds, gestures (signing), and/or characters (such as letters or pictures) to convey meaning. When people learn language, they learn a symbol system. Those learning spoken languages must learn the agreed-upon sounds that convey words, and they must learn the rules that specify relationships among the chosen words. That is, we cannot convey ideas by vocalizing the relevant words in any order we choose. As the author of this textbook, I often ask my students, "Are you reading the book?" I cannot expect students to understand this question if I say the words in some random order like "Are book reading you?" English-language speakers follow a subject-verb-object order (We are reading the book). Koreans, on the other hand, follow a subject-object-verb format (We book are reading). As another example, rules governing word order apply to stating first and last names. Consider that Koreans tend to identify themselves by stating their family name

language A symbol system involving the use of sounds, gestures (signing), and/or characters (such as letters or pictures) to convey meaning.

C. Todd Lopez

The Korean table has no clear place settings. In addition, Korean diners use the same utensils for serving and eating. Most people living in the United States prefer individual place settings marked clearly by place mats or blocked off by eating utensils.

first and then their given name. In effect, the family name is given precedence over the individual's first name.

Learning a language and its rules is the key to human development and interaction. The level and complexity of human language sets people apart from the other animals. In addition, language is among the most important social institutions humans have created. That is, language is a predictable social arrangement among people that has emerged over time to facilitate human interaction and communication.

The Role of Geographic and Historical Forces

CORE CONCEPT 2 Geographic and historical forces shape culture.

Sociologists operate under the assumption that culture acts as a mediator between people and their surroundings (Herskovits 1948). Thus, material and nonmaterial culture represent responses to historical and geographic challenges. Note that cultural responses are not always constructive and may have unintended consequences. The 1953 division of the Korean Peninsula into North and South Korea was a response to a historical event that affected the personal lives and culture of Koreans on both sides of the DMZ. It was a geographic event in that the division confined some Koreans to the north of the line and others to the south. For the most part, people in the two Koreas have not communicated or interacted with each other since 1953, effectively evolving into two separate cultures. To date about 20,000 North and South Koreans have reunited briefly, and an estimated 80,000 Koreans, now in their mid-80s, are on waiting lists to see relatives. Some South Koreans travel to newly opened resorts in North Korea that are isolated from that county's population

Discussion Tip: Ask students how many have studied a foreign language or know a second language. Then ask is there is some feature of the language that offers insights about the broader culture.

This map on a highway memorial sign in South Dakota shows the Korean Peninsula and the boundary known as the DMZ (demilitarized zone) that has separated the two societies since 1953. It is considered the most militarized border in the world.

(Korean Overseas Information Service 2006). About 100 South Korean firms, part of a special industrial zone, employ tens of thousands of North Koreans workers (CNBC 2010).

Although the division of the Korean peninsula was one key event that shaped North and South Korean cultures, one important historical event that has shaped American culture—especially the way Americans think about and use energy—was the Spindletop, a Texas oil gusher of 1901. That discovery made the United States the largest producer of oil at the time and the most powerful nation in the world. "Oil was the new currency of the industrialized world, and America was rich. . . . Few Americans realized that their country was different or particularly fortunate. . . . They soon began to take their subterranean wealth for granted. . . . People in other industrialized nations were more aware of America's blessing. Being less sure of their sources of energy, they were warier about its dispensation. America quickly turned its industrial plant and its electrical grids over to oil" (Halberstam 1986, p. 87).

In contrast to the United States, North and South Korea produce no oil and consequently must import all their oil. Until the mid-1970s, the United States produced all the oil it consumed. It still produces 50 percent of the oil it consumes (about 9 million barrels a day). This history of abundance shaped the way Americans use appliances. For example, South Koreans, North Koreans, and Americans use appliances such as refrigerators differently. Consider that South Koreans try to minimize the amount of electricity the refrigerator uses to keep food cold by opening the refrigerator

North Korea

Size of military. 1.17 million (active); 9.7 million (reserves)

Total Annual military expenditures. $5.5 billion

Per capita military spending. $230.9

Military expenditures (percentage of GDP). 33.9%

South Korea

Size of military. 1.1 million (active); 8.2 million (reserves)

Total Annual military expenditures. $27.1 billion

Per capita military spending. $557

Military expenditures (percentage of GDP). 2.8%

United States

Size of forces stationed in South Korea. 26,339

Total Annual military expenditures for Korean operation (est.). $3 + billion

FIGURE 3.3 The most heavily armed border in the world is the demilitarized zone that divides North and South Korea. Consider as one indicator of the costs of maintaining this division is that North Korea spends about 33.9 percent of its gross domestic product (GDP) on its military, whereas South Korea spends $27.1 billion, representing 2.8 percent of GDP. The United States spends about $3 billion each year to station 26,339 troops in South Korea.

Sources: Data from U.S. Central Intelligence Agency (2010), Global Issues (2010), Department of Defense (2008)

TABLE 3.1 Oil Reserves and Consumption in United States, South Korea, and North Korea

	United States	South Korea	North Korea
Proven Oil Reserves (in barrels)	19.12 billion	0.0	0.0
Barrels of Oil Consumed per Day	18.7 million	2.2 million	16,000
Population Size	310.2 million	48.6 million	22.8 million
Per-Person Consumption of Oil per Year (in barrels)	22.0	16.4	2.55

Note: A barrel of crude oil provides about 44 gallons of petroleum products.
Source: Data from U.S. Central Intelligence Agency (2011)

door only as wide as necessary to remove an item, blocking the opening with their bodies to minimize the amount of cold air that escapes. Americans tend to open the refrigerator door wide and leave it open until they decide what they want or until after they move the desired item to a stove or countertop. Most North Koreans do not have refrigerators, and they follow a folkway of shopping for food daily or preserving foods using salt (Yoo Gwan Hee 2009).

Because Koreans depend entirely on foreign sources for oil and other resources, they are especially vulnerable to any event that might disrupt the flow of resources into their country. This vulnerability reinforces the need to use resources sparingly and not to take them for granted. The relative lack of natural resources may ultimately explain Koreans' conservation-oriented behavior (see Table 3.1). It also helps to explain why South Korean government is making plans to become one of the world's top three producers of wind power (Chosun Ilbo 2009).

In summary, conservation- and consumption-oriented values and behaviors are rooted in circumstances of shortage and abundance. To understand this connection, recall a time when your electricity or water was turned off. Think about the inconvenience you experienced after a few minutes and how it increased after a few hours. The idea that one must conserve available resources takes root. People take care to minimize the number of times they open the refrigerator door. Now imagine how a permanent resource shortage or almost total dependence on other countries for resources can affect people's lives. In contrast, you can imagine how a greater abundance of resources breaks down conservation-oriented behaviors.

The Transmission of Culture

For the most part, people do not question the origin of the objects around them, the beliefs they hold, the values they follow, the norms to which they conform, the symbols they use, or the words they use to communicate and think about the world "any more than a baby analyzes the atmosphere before it begins to breathe it" (Sumner 1907, p. 76). Nor are people usually aware of other ways of thinking and behaving, because much of their culture was in place before they were born. Thus, people think and behave as they do simply because they know no other way. And, because these behaviors and thoughts seem natural, we lose sight of the fact that culture is learned.

CORE CONCEPT 3 Culture is learned.

Parents transmit to their offspring via their genes a biological heritage that is common to all humans yet uniquely individual. The genetic heritage common to humans gives us a capacity to learn and speak a language, to stand upright, and to use our fingers and thumbs to grasp objects, and many other capabilities. If these traits seem overly obvious, consider that they allow humans to speak innumerable languages, perform countless movements, and devise and use many inventions and objects (Benedict 1976).

Regardless of their physical appearance (for example, eye shape and color, hair texture and color, skin color), babies are destined to learn the ways of the culture into which they are raised. That is, our genes endow us with our human physical characteristics, but not our cultural

Gregory Caldeira

This child, born in South Korea, was adopted by parents living in the United States. Thus he is destined to learn the culture of the parents who raise him.

Discussion Tip: In light of the material on consumption and conservation-oriented behavior, ask students to describe areas of their lives in which they overconsume resources (e.g. long showers, use too many paper towels, leave lights on). Also ask if there are areas of their lives in which they make a concerted effort to conserve.

Working for Change Kim Chin-Kyung's Dream Comes True to Build Universities in China and North Korea

Kim Chin-Kyung is a remarkable 75-year-old, South Korean man who has helped fund and build two universities, one located in China and a second just opened in North Korea. During the 1950s, Kim was a soldier in the South Korean army that fought alongside the U.S. military against North Korean and Chinese armies. He was 15 years old at the time. He was one of 17 men in his unit consisting of 800 who survived a massacre. When Kim thought he was about to die, he made a promise that if he survived he would send love back to his enemies. He survived and stood by his promise. Kim gave and raised money to build a college in the countries that were once his enemies.

After the war, Kim owned and managed a taxi company in South Korea. After making a trip to visit his cousin, who was attending college in Pensacola, Florida, Kim found that he liked the area so much he decided to immigrate to the United States. He became wealthy running a small chain of fashion shops in South Korea and Florida between 1960 and 1990.

In 1989, Kim approached the Chinese government with the proposal for building a small vocational school in Yanji, but he raised suspicion about his motives. Eventually the Chinese government accepted his offer but rejected his proposal that the school motto be "Truth, Love, Peace." By 1992, he had funded and built the Yanbian University of Science and Technology (YUST) in China. Kim and his wife moved into YUST to live among the students where he formed bonds with the students and encouraged them to give back to their communities. As a result of his influence, the university requires students to volunteer at local nursing homes and orphanages. Today, YUST is considered one of China's top universities and, as a gesture of appreciation, the Chinese government agreed that the school motto should be that which Kim originally proposed: "Truth, Love, Peace."

According to the YUST website, the university's educational goals are:

- To realize a righteous society and develop well-rounded education based on truth, love, peace.
- To educate by providing practical opportunities for creativity, cooperation, and volunteer service.
- To provide students with up-to-date knowledge by employing internationally distinguished scholars and professors.
- To encourage the creative intelligence of individuals and urge them to contribute to the development of society.
- To educate students with an eye toward globalization, in accordance with China's policy of openness and innovation.

The second university Kim helped to fund and build is in North Korea. He originally made the proposal to the North Korean government in 1998, when he traveled to Pyongyang with food aid from China. Kim was arrested in his hotel room and accused of being an agent for the U.S. Central Intelligence Agency (CIA). He was interrogated for six weeks, and Kim was almost broken by the relentless questioning. The situation became so bad that Kim even began writing out his will and bequeathed his organs for transplants and medical study in Pyongyang. He eventually succeeded in convincing the North Korean officials that he was actually trying to help the country, and was released from prison.

Some time later (in 2000), Kim was back in China working in his office when he was approached by the same North Korean man who had arrested him. The man asked Kim if he still wanted to build a university. The North Korean government wanted Kim to duplicate YUST in Pyongyang. Ten years later, in April 2010, classes began at Pyongyang University of Science and Technology (PUST). The programs offered at the university include information technology, industry and management, and life sciences. The university opened with 160 undergraduates and masters-level graduate students chosen by the North Korean government from its top colleges and from the political and military elite. Students receive free tuition, room, board, and books, which are financed by foreign donors and individual sponsors. Kim hopes to eventually attract a student body of 2,600 graduate and undergraduate students, and a faculty of 250. Officials say that, in late 2010 or early 2011, the university will also open two more programs—architecture and engineering and public health.

PUST is supported and operated by people and organizations in the United States, South Korea, China, and other parts of the world. PUST is an experimental university that was established to train generations of North Korean students and offer an education, fortified with international influences, the technical skills, and the knowledge required to make positive contributions to a global community undergoing rapid and constant change. PUST will also encourage students to become aware of the cultural influences that create differences in thinking, and to become world citizens for a better future. Kim believes that it is our duty as good world citizens to employ peaceful means to resolve conflicts that keep people from different cultures, ideals, and beliefs apart. PUST cultivates an atmosphere that supports the free exchange of ideas with individuals from other cultures in a spirit of brotherhood. The university hopes that it will be able to make significant contributions in bringing about a truly lasting peace and prosperity on the Korean Peninsula, through building mutual trust and by sharing new ways for looking at the world.

Source: Written by Maggie Muench, Northern Kentucky University (class of 2011).

characteristics. We cannot assume that someone is part of a particular culture simply because he or she looks like someone we expect to come from that culture. This fact becomes obvious to Korean American youth who travel to South Korea as part of cultural immersion programs. "Many say they have never felt so American as when they are slurping noodles in Korea. Even their slurps have an American accent" (Kristof 1995, p. 47).

The Role of Language

Human genetic endowment gives us a brain that is flexible enough to allow us to learn the languages that we hear spoken or see signed by the people around us. As children learn words and the meanings of words, they learn about their culture and what is important to it. They also acquire a tool that enables them to think about the world, interpret their experiences, establish and maintain relationships, and convey information.

For example, in Korean society, it is nearly impossible to carry on a conversation, even among siblings, without considering age. This is because age is an exceedingly important measure of status: The older a person is, the more status or recognition he or she has in the society. Korean language acknowledges the importance of age by its use of special age-based hierarchical titles for everyone. In fact, words used to address a brother or sister acknowledge his or her age in relation to the speaker. This is true even if the sibling is a twin, because one twin was born first. Furthermore, Korean forms of address do not allow the speaker to refer to elder brothers or sisters by their first names. A boy addresses his elder brother as *hyung* and his elder sister as *muna*; a girl addresses her elder brother as *oppa* and her elder sister as *unni*. Regardless of gender, however, people always address their younger siblings by their first names (Kim and Kirby 1996).

Consider another example of how language channels thinking. Americans use the word *my* to express "ownership" of people or things over which they do not have exclusive rights: my mother, my school, my country. The use of *my* reflects the American preoccupation with the needs of the individual over those of the group. In contrast, Koreans express possession as shared: our mother, our school, our country. The use of the plural possessive *our* reflects the Korean preoccupation with the group's needs over the individual's interests.

linguistic relativity hypothesis The idea that "no two languages are ever sufficiently similar to be considered as representing the same social reality. The worlds in which different societies live are distinct worlds, not merely the same world with different labels attached."

The language differences previously described suggest that people see the world through the language(s) they have learned. The mind—or more precisely, the linguistic systems in our minds—gives order to a kaleidoscope of images, sounds, and impressions bombarding us. The words we have at our disposal allow us to organize the world, to notice some things and not others, and to ascribe significance to what we do notice. Keep in mind that when we learn a language, we become parties to an agreement to communicate and organize our thoughts in a particular way—to "an agreement that holds throughout our speech community and is codified in the patterns of our language" (Whorf 1956, pp. 212–214).

Linguists Edward Sapir and Benjamin Whorf advanced the **linguistic relativity hypothesis**, which states that "No two languages are ever sufficiently similar to be considered as representing the same social reality. The worlds in which different societies live are distinct worlds, not merely the same world with different labels attached" (Sapir 1949, p. 162). Sapir and Whorf (1956) argue that unless people's linguistic backgrounds are similar, the same physical evidence does not lead to the same picture of the universe. So, for example, the sound coming from a bird leads a speaker of English to think that the bird is *singing*, whereas it leads a speaker of Korean to think that the bird is *weeping*. Although the Korean and English languages channel thinking in different ways, do not assume that communication between the two speakers is impossible. It may take some work, but it is possible to translate one language into the other.

The Importance of Individual Experiences

The information presented thus far may suggest that culture is simply a blueprint that guides, and even determines, thought and behavior. If that were true, then everyone would be cultural replicas of one another. Of course, they are not. Although culture is a blueprint of sorts, it also functions as a "tool kit" that allows people to select from and add to a menu of cultural options (Schudson 1989, p. 155).

How does this selection process work? A baby enters the world and becomes part of an already established set of human relationships. Virtually every event that the child experiences—being born, being fed, being cleaned, being talked to, toilet training, talking, playing, and so on—involves people. Those in the child's life may include a father, mother, grandparents, brothers, sisters, playmates, other adult relatives, neighbors, babysitters, and others (Wallace 1952). All these people consciously or unconsciously expose and pass on to that child their own "versions" of culture, with emphasis on aspects they believe children should know. The child, especially as he or she ages, may accept, reject, or modify those versions, and even seek new cultural experiences. Consider the case of Kim Il

Sung, the founding president of North Korea. Kim Il Sung's father raised him as Christian. As a youth, Kim attended church regularly, even playing the organ. However, when he took power in 1948, he abolished Christianity in the country, "keeping a couple of churches for show but staffing them with actors and actresses to impress foreign visitors with his tolerance" (Kristof 2005, p. 25). The case of Kim Il Sung suggests that individuals cannot be viewed as passive agents who simply absorb the culture around them.

Culture as a Tool for the Problems of Living

CORE CONCEPT 4 Culture provides a variety of formulas that enable individuals to adjust to the challenges of being human.

For example, all people feel emotions and experience hunger, thirst, and sexual desire; all people age and eventually die. In turn, all cultures have developed "formulas" to address these biological inevitabilities. Formulas exist for eliminating human waste; caring for children; satisfying the need for food, drink, and sex; channeling and displaying emotions; and eventually dying. In this section, we focus on the cultural responses for relieving hunger and expressing social emotions.

Cultural Formulas for Relieving Hunger

All people become hungry, but the formulas for stimulating and satisfying appetite vary considerably across cultures. One indicator of a culture's influence is how people define only a portion of the potential food available to them as edible. For example, insects such as grasshoppers, locusts, and ants are edible and are an excellent source of protein, but not everyone chooses to eat them. Dogs and snakes are among the foods defined by many Koreans and other Asian peoples as edible. On the other hand, most Americans find it appalling that someone would eat dog meat, but they have no trouble eating deer, lamb, beef, or pork. Cultural formulas for relieving hunger not only help people to "decide" what is edible, but to "decide" who should prepare the food, how the food should be served and eaten, how many meals should be consumed in a day, at what times meals should be eaten, and with whom one should eat.

South Korean formulas for satisfying hunger center also around kimchi, a spicy cabbage dish that is served with every meal. Rice is also a staple of the South Korean diet. North Korean diet depends on rice and corn. In the case of North Korea, the country relies on foreign aid to feed an estimated 16 million people (of 23 million). Corn, not rice, is one of the most donated food items. Even South Korea sent 400,000 tons of corn to North Korea in 2010 (*Asia News* 2005, *Bangkok Post* 2010). Furthermore, the average North Korean cannot afford rice, as 2.2 pounds cost the equivalent of 30 percent of the average monthly salary (BBC News 2005).

Missy Gish

Kimchi is the most popular side dish for Korean meals. Although there are hundreds of varieties, the main ingredient is fermented napa cabbage, radish, green onion, or cucumber.

Much of the American diet is affected by corn, although few Americans fully recognize its pervasiveness. Corn (in one form or another) appears in soft drinks, canned foods, candy, condensed milk, baby food, jams, instant coffee, instant potatoes, and soup, among other things (Vissar 1986). Like corn, rice and the by-products of rice plants have many uses: to feed livestock; to make soap, margarine, beer, wine, cosmetics, paper, and laundry starch; to warm houses; to provide inexpensive fuel for steam engines; to make bricks, plaster, hats, sandals, and raincoats; and to use as packing material to prevent items from breaking in shipping.

Cultural Formulas for Social Emotions

Culture also provides formulas for expressing **social emotions**, internal bodily sensations that we experience in relationships with other people. Empathy, grief, love, guilt, jealousy, and embarrassment are a few examples of social emotions. Grief, for instance, is felt at the loss of a relationship; love reflects the strong attachment that one person feels for another person; jealousy can arise from fear of losing the affection of another (Gordon 1981). People do not simply express social emotions directly,

social emotions Internal bodily sensations that we experience in relationships with other people.

Teaching Tip: For more examples of corn-based products, go to the Ontario Corn website where a list of products is posted. The Ontario Corn website claims that about 1/5 of all items in a typical grocery store are made from corn.

however. Rather, they interpret, evaluate, and modify their internal bodily sensations upon considering "feeling rules" (Hochschild 1976, 1979).

Feeling rules are norms that specify appropriate ways to express the internal sensations. They also define sensations that one should feel toward another person. In the dominant culture of the United States, for example, same-sex friends are supposed to like one another but not feel anything resembling romantic love. It is also generally unacceptable for same-sex people to hold one another or to "celebrate" their friendship by holding hands in public. In this regard, the U.S. Army publishes a list of "must-know items" about South Korea for American soldiers stationed there. It informs them that their feeling rules do not apply in South Korea. One item says, "Don't be surprised to see two Korean women or men walking arm in arm. They are just good friends and there is nothing sexual implied" (U.S. Army 1998).

The process by which we come to learn feeling rules is complex; it evolves through observing others' actions and in interactions with others. In her novel *Rubyfruit Jungle*, Rita Mae Brown (1988) describes a situation in which feeling rules shape the way the central character, Molly, evaluates an encounter between her father, Carl, and his friend, Ep. Ep's wife has just died and Carl is comforting his friend. In this passage, Molly reflects on the feeling rules that apply to men:

> I was planning to hotfoot it out on the porch and watch the stars but I never made it because Ep and Carl were in the living room and Carl was holding Ep. He had both arms around him and every now and then he'd smooth down Ep's hair or put his cheek next to his head. Ep was crying just like Leroy. I couldn't make out what they were saying to each other. A couple of times I could hear Carl telling Ep he had to hang on, that's all anybody can do is hang on. I was afraid they were going to get up and see me so I hurried back to my room. I'd never seen men hold each other. I thought the only things they were allowed to do was shake hands or fight. But if Carl was holding Ep maybe it wasn't against the rules. Since I wasn't sure, I thought I'd keep it to myself and never tell. (p. 28)

This example shows that people learn norms that specify how, when, where, and to whom to display emotions. Somehow Molly learned that men do not hold one another—perhaps because she had never encountered such images. That is, her culture provided her with no images of men comforting one another in the way that Carl was comforting Ep.

Feeling rules can also apply to the social emotions people feel and display toward political leaders. In the case of North Korea, it is difficult for Americans and South Koreans to imagine how much Kim Il Sung, the country's founding and "eternal" president, and his son Kim Jong Il dominate North Korea's emotional life, culture, and landscape (McGeown 2003; Winzig 1999). Even defectors and outside observers maintain that most North Koreans feel genuine emotion for their leaders, especially for Kim Il Sung (Demick 2010). One defector recalled the emotions he felt when he took ideology classes in college: "I cried often. I was so touched by the consideration Kim Il Sung showed for his people" (Kristof 2005). Why do North Koreans feel such emotion for leaders who, by many accounts, have mismanaged the country? Programs and activities in North Korea offer some answers:

- In North Korea, students from nursery school through college take hundreds of hours of coursework that focuses on the lives and accomplishments of the two Kims, but especially of the father.
- People, places, and objects connected to Kim Il Sung are treated as sacred. "His parents, grandparents, wife, and oldest son are still worshipped as an extension of Kim. Objects that he touched on his visits to collective farms or universities are covered with glass or draped with a veil" (Hunter 1999).
- Images of Kim Il Sung and Kim Jong Il are everywhere. Their portraits hang on the walls in all public buildings and households. All adults wear small badges showing Kim Il Sung's photo on their lapels or shirts (Sharp 2005b).

REUTERS/Truth Leem

Two South Korean protesters hold signs with images of Kim Il Sung (top), former and now deceased president of North Korea (1948–1994), his son, Kim Jong Il who is the current president (1994–present), and his grandson Kim Jong-un, who is being groomed to succeed the current president. The protestors are rallying against the North Korean's alleged sinking of a South Korean navel vessel in 2010, killing 46 sailors on board.

feeling rules Norms that specify appropriate ways to express internal sensations.

Video Tip: ABC News produced a series of videos about life in North Korea. Each is about two minutes in length. Use the search terms on abc.com "ABC News Sacred Ground Kim Jong Il's Birthplace" for a profile of the leader and his policies. For a second video on North Korean films, use the search terms "ABC News North Korea's Tinseltown."

- An estimated 80 percent of the titles in a given bookshop are about the Kims or are written by one or both Kims. There are no dissident authors in North Korea who challenge the Kims' writings (Sharp 2005b; Winzig 1999).
- Major buildings and institutions are named after the Kims, and there are more than 40,000 Kim Il Sung Revolutionary Thought Study Rooms in the country (Koreascope 1998; Winzig 1999).

Cultural Diffusion

CORE CONCEPT 5 People borrow material and nonmaterial culture from other societies.

Most people tend to think that the material and nonmaterial culture that surrounds them is "homegrown"—that it originated in their society. Journalist Nicholas D. Kristof (1998) offers an example:

> I once asked my 5-year-old son, who has grown up largely in Tokyo, about his favorite Japanese foods. Gregory thought for a moment and decided on rice balls and McDonald's. It makes perfect sense to think of Big Macs as Japanese food, since McDonald's is a much more important part of his life in Japan than it is when we are on vacation in America. In particular, given the cramped homes in which most Japanese live, when his Japanese friends have birthdays the most common place to hold parties is McDonald's. (p. 18)

The point is that most people tend to underestimate, ignore, or distort the extent to which familiar ideas, materials, products, and other inventions are connected in some way to outside sources or are borrowed outright from those sources (Liu 1994). The process by which an idea, an invention, or some other cultural item is borrowed from a foreign source is called **diffusion**. The word *borrow* is used in the broadest sense: It can mean to steal, imitate, plagiarize, learn, purchase, or copy. The opportunity to borrow occurs whenever people from different cultures make contact, whether face-to-face, by phone or fax, through televised broadcasts, or via the Internet (see No Borders, No Boundaries).

Basketball, a U.S. invention, has been borrowed by people in 213 countries, including those in South Korea, where 23 clubs are registered with the Federation of International Basketball (2010). Baseball, another U.S. invention, has been borrowed by people in more than 90 countries, including South Korea, which lost to Japan in the finals of the 2009 World Baseball Classic (World Baseball Classic 2010). Likewise, an estimated 86,000 South Koreans have "borrowed" religion of the Jehovah's Witnesses, not just in name but in acting as proselytizing members (Adherents.com 2010). Jehovah's Witnesses trace their beginning to a small group of Bible students who

Lance Cpl. Frederick J. Coleman

Tae kwon do is a Korean form of martial arts. Cultural diffusion takes place when this Grand Master leads a class of American children in the fundamentals of kicking, blocking, and board breaking.

met near Pittsburgh, Pennsylvania, and eventually published the *Watchtower* magazine in 1879. Jehovah's Witness missionaries first came to Korea in 1914 (Hankyoreh 2007). Today, the magazine is published in more than 470 languages, and the religion counts 5.8 million practicing members in 240 lands (Watchtower Bible and Tract Society of Pennsylvania 2004).

Instances of opportunities for cultural diffusion are endless and can easily be found by skimming the newspaper headlines. Consider the following examples:

- "Chinese Tourists Prefer Korea" (Kim Tae-gyu 2010)
- "GM Korea Brings Special Edition of Cadillac Escalade to South Korea" (Malaysian News Agency 2010)
- "Kansas University Forges Korean Ties" (Bae Hyung-jung 2010)
- "[Korean] Universities Lure Foreign Students" (*Korea Joong Ang Daily* 2010)
- "Far East Movement Hits No. 1 on U.S. Billboard Charts" (Korea.net 2010a)
- "Polish TV Introduces Korean Food" (Korea.net 2010b)

People of one society do not borrow ideas, materials, or inventions indiscriminately. Instead, borrowing is almost always selective. That is, they are choosy about which features of the item they adopt. Even the simplest invention is really a complex of elements, including various associations and ideas of how it should be used. Not surprisingly, people borrow the most concrete and most tangible elements and then develop new associations and shape the item to serve new ends (Linton 1936). One might be surprised to

diffusion The process by which an idea, an invention, or some other cultural item is borrowed from a foreign source.

Courtesy of Installation Management Command

Thomas the Train, the creation of a British clergyman for his son, first appeared in a 1946 book, *Thomas the Tank Engine.* In 1979, a British writer and producer turned the book into a successful TV series, *Thomas and Friends*, that eventually became a worldwide hit (Just Thomas 2011). This Thomas the Train pictured is part of the Lotus Lantern Festival in South Korea. Notice that the Koreans borrowed Thomas and turned him into a lantern. They also added a child conductor holding a lotus flower. The festival celebrates the birth of Buddha.

learn that male circumcision in South Korea can be traced to contact with the U.S. military during the Korean War. Koreans, however, depart from the American practice of circumcising male babies at birth. In fact, only one percent of South Korean babies are believed to be circumcised at birth; most circumcisions occur during the elementary and middle school years (Ku et al. 2003).

In contrast to South Korea, the North Korean government limits cultural diffusion opportunities by restricting access to information from the outside world. With rare exceptions, the 22.5 million people of North Korea cannot receive mail or telephone calls from outside the country. Nor can they travel beyond their country's borders (Brooke 2003a). One North Korean defector claims that "all the tape recorders and radios have to be registered. At registration, they cut off and solder the tuning dial to make sure you don't have a 'free' radio" (Brooke 2003b, p. A8). In addition, North Korean officials confiscate mobile phones from visitors while they are in the country, assign official escorts, and inspect and delete some photographs from cameras upon departure (Branigan 2010). Although the North Korean government restricts cultural diffusion, North Korean people, especially those living along the border with China, find ways to acquire illicit radios, mobile phones, CD players, stereos, and televisions, which offer access to a world beyond North Korea (Mac-Kinnon 2005; Caryl and Lee 2006). In the past five years, North Korea has issued visas to U.S. and other foreign peoples to attend important festivals and celebrations (BBC News 2005). Foreign reporters covering these events learned, to their surprise, that the *Da Vinci Code* was a hit and Celine Dion songs are popular (Branigan 2010).

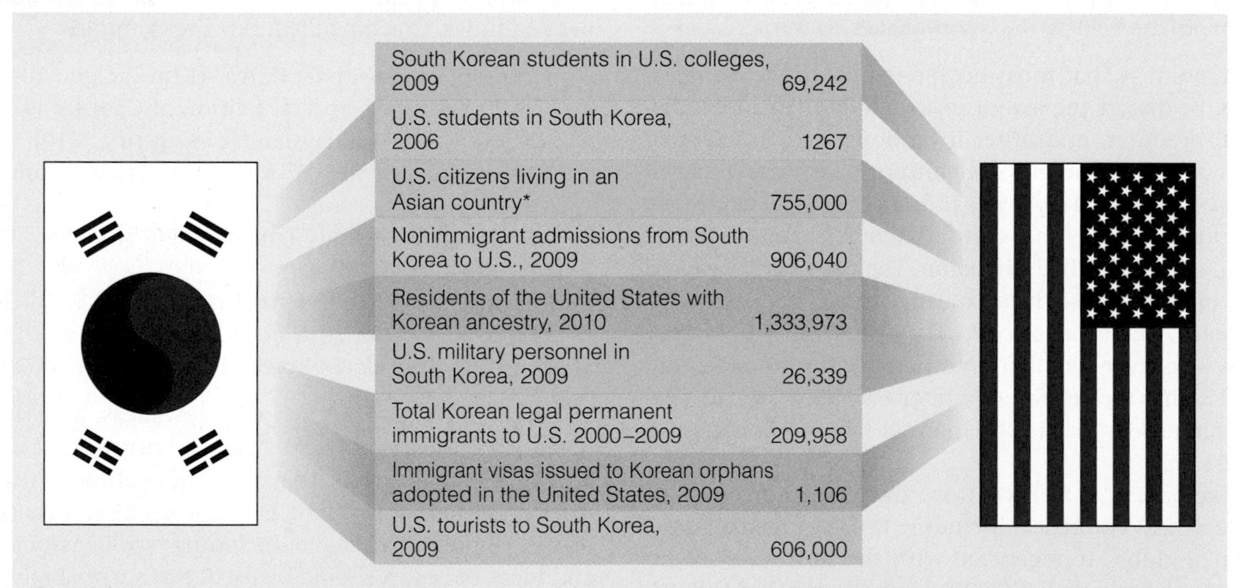

South Korean students in U.S. colleges, 2009 69,242
U.S. students in South Korea, 2006 1267
U.S. citizens living in an Asian country* 755,000
Nonimmigrant admissions from South Korea to U.S., 2009 906,040
Residents of the United States with Korean ancestry, 2010 1,333,973
U.S. military personnel in South Korea, 2009 26,339
Total Korean legal permanent immigrants to U.S. 2000–2009 209,958
Immigrant visas issued to Korean orphans adopted in the United States, 2009 1,106
U.S. tourists to South Korea, 2009 606,000
*Data not available for South Korea.

FIGURE 3.4 Opportunities for cultural diffusion between the United States and South Korea
There are many opportunities for Americans in Korea to learn and borrow Korean ways as evidence by the presence of U.S. troops in South Korea, international trade, and the departure and return of many Koreans who have attended colleges and universities in the United States. Notice, for example, that almost 70,000 South Koreans are enrolled in U.S. colleges and universities.

Source: Data from U.S. Bureau of the Census (2010), U.S. Central Intelligence Agency (2011); U.S. Department of Commerce (2010); U.S. Department of Defense (2008); U.S. Department of Homeland Security (2010); Association of American Residents Overseas (2011)

Discussion Tip: Ask students for examples of cultural diffusion. To get discussion going, ask if anyone knows the country in which the Pokémon video game, card game, and fictional world originated. The answer is Japan. The company that manufactured the product is Nintendo. One interesting point to make is that the inspiration for the fictional world can be traced to the Japanese inventor's fascination with insect collecting, a popular hobby in Japan. Pokémon includes 494 fictional species, which critics claimed were too many for children, especially American children, to remember. Of course we know children proved the critics wrong.

No Borders No Boundaries K-Pop/Korean Pop Music

Sociologists define *popular culture* as any aspect of culture that is embraced by the masses within and outside of that society from which it is believed to originate. Examples include a sandwich (such as the Big Mac), a doll (such as Barbie), a television show (such as *Desperate Housewives*), a book (*Seven Habits of Highly Effective People*), a movie (such as *Harry Potter and the Deathly Hallows*), an item of clothing (such as blue jeans), and a phrase (such as "She's so fly"). Any analysis of popular culture must consider the industries that sell and market it, including the ways by which it reaches the masses: whether it be via commercials, television programs, radio, You-Tube or newspapers—to name a few. K-pop or Korean pop music is making a sustained debut on the global market. At the time of this writing, some of the best -known South Korean groups were Big Bang, TVXQ, 2PM, and Girls' Generation; a Korean American group Far East Movement (for example, "Like a G6") was also popular. In response to the growing popularity of Korean pop music, two Korean Americans—Johnny Noh and Paul Han—launched a celebrity news website Allkpop.com in 2007, to "help spread this now global phenomenon." Their website reportedly attracts 2 million visitors each month. About 40 percent of the visits are from K-pop fans based in the United States, with 10 percent from fans based in Canada and 10 percent from Singapore. Noh and Han believe that "Korea has the idol formula down pat; they are very polished in their mannerisms on stage and in society. Fans are able to fall in love not only with artists' music, but their personalities as well" (Garcia 2010).

Girls' Generation, a nine-member female pop group, can introduce themselves in four languages—Korean, English, Japanese, and Chinese. The group believes that learning foreign languages is the key to reaching audiences outside of South Korea (Wall Street Journal 2010). "We've been really focusing on the language these days, especially since we want to be able to connect with our foreign fans. It takes time, patience, and a lot of practice but we really wanna be able to express ourselves to our foreign fans." These nine females seek to circumvent the U.S. and European music markets, by unifying the Asian market and building it into "the biggest market in the world" (Allkpop 2010).

Kyodo/Newscom

The Home Culture as the Standard

> **CORE CONCEPT 6 The home culture is usually the standard that people use to make judgments about another culture.**

Most people come to learn and accept the ways of their culture as natural. When they encounter foreign cultures, therefore, they can experience mental and physical strain that comes with reorienting to new ways of thinking and behaving. Sociologists use the term **culture shock** to describe that strain. In particular, they must adjust to a new language and to the idea that the behaviors and responses they learned in their home culture, and have come to take for granted, do not apply in the foreign setting. The intensity of culture shock depends on several factors: (1) the extent to which the home and foreign cultures differ, (2) the level of preparation for or knowledge about the new culture, and (3) the circumstances (such as vacation, job transfer, or war) surrounding the encounter. Some cases of culture shock are so intense and unsettling that people become ill. Among the symptoms are "obsessive concern with cleanliness, depression, compulsive eating and drinking, excessive sleeping, irritability, lack of self-confidence, fits of weeping, nausea" (Lamb 1987, p. 270).

Minor league outfielder for the Charlotte Stone Crabs, Kyeong Kang experienced culture shock when he moved with his family from South Korea to Norcross, Georgia, when he was 14 years old. His family moved to the United States so he could play baseball in high school. Kang experienced culture shock because when he first came to the

culture shock The strain that people from one culture experience when they must reorient themselves to the ways of a new culture.

United Sates he "didn't know any English at all." Other culture adjustments Kang remembers include not having to wear uniforms in school, the lack of respect for elders, and McDonald's with no shrimp burgers on the menu (Gantt 2010).

Do not assume that culture shock is limited to experiences with foreign cultures. People can also experience **reentry shock**, or culture shock in reverse, upon returning home after living in another culture (Koehler 1986). In fact, some researchers have discovered that many people find it surprisingly difficult to readjust to the return home after spending a significant amount of time elsewhere. As in the experience of culture shock, they face a situation in which differences jump to the forefront.

The intensity of reentry shock depends on an array of factors, including (1) the reason for being in the host culture, (2) the length of time lived in the host culture, and (3) the extent of the returnee's immersion in the everyday lives of people in the host culture. Symptoms of reentry shock are essentially the mirror image of those associated with culture shock. They include panic attacks ("I thought I was going crazy"), glorification of the host culture, nostalgia for the foreign ways, panic, a sense of isolation or estrangement, and a feeling of being misunderstood by people in the home culture. This comment by one American returning from abroad illustrates:

> America was a smorgasbord. But within two weeks, I had indigestion. Then things began to make me angry. Why did Americans have such big gas-guzzling cars? Why were all the commercials telling me I had to buy this product in order to be liked? Material possessions and dressing for success were not top priorities in the highlands. And American TV? I missed the BBC. (Sobie 1986, p. 96)

U.S. soldiers returning from their tour of duty in Iraq experience reentry shock as well. One staff sergeant interviewed by the *New York Times* indicated that he was now "less tolerant of stupid people, . . . stupid people doing stupid things." He was particularly irritated by the questions, "Did you kill anyone?" and "How did it feel?" (Myers 2003, p. A1).

Although many people expect to have problems adjusting to a stay in a foreign culture and even prepare for such difficulties, most do not expect to have trouble adjusting upon return to their home culture. Because reentry shock is unexpected, many people become anxious and confused and feel guilty about having problems with readjustment ("How could I possibly think the American way was anything but the biggest and the best?"). In addition, they may worry about how family, friends, and other acquaintances will react to their critical views of the home culture; they may be afraid that others will view them as unpatriotic.

The experience of reentry shock points to the transforming effect of an encounter with another culture (Sobie 1986). That the returnees go through reentry shock means that they have experienced up close another way of life and that they have come to accept the host culture's norms, values, and beliefs. Consequently, when they come home, they see things in a new light.

One reason people experience culture and reentry shock is that they hold the viewpoint of **ethnocentrism**. That is, they use one culture as the standard for judging the worth of foreign ways. From this viewpoint, one way is the center of everything, and all other ways are "scaled and rated with reference to it" (Sumner 1907, p. 13). Thus, other cultures are seen as "strange," or worse, as "inferior" (see The Sociological Imagination: "Opposing Viewpoints on Same-Sex Adults Holding Hands").

Ethnocentrism

Several levels of ethnocentrism exist. Arguably the more harmless type of ethnocentrism is simply defining foreign ways as peculiar, as did some Americans who attended the 1988 Summer Olympic Games in Seoul, South Korea. Upon learning that some Koreans eat dog meat, some visitors made jokes about it. People speculated about the consequences of asking for a doggy bag, and they made puns about dog-oriented dishes: Great Danish, fettuccine Alfido, and Greyhound as the favorite fast food (Henry 1988). Keep in mind that Koreans don't eat their pet dogs; rather, they eat a "special breed of large tan-colored dogs raised especially for canine cuisine" (Kang 1995, p. 267). In fact, Koreans who eat dogs would argue that Americans who eat pigs, cows, chickens, and lambs are in no position to judge them (Kang 1995).

The most extreme and destructive form of ethnocentrism is **cultural genocide,** in which the people of one society define the culture of another society not as merely offensive, but as so intolerable that they attempt to destroy it. There is overwhelming evidence, for example, that Japanese tried to exterminate Korean culture between 1910 and 1945. After Japan annexed Korea in 1910, Japanese became the official language, Koreans were given Japanese names, Korean children were taught by Japanese teachers, Korean literature and history were abandoned, ancient temples—important symbols of Korean heritage—were razed, the Korean national anthem was banned, and the Korean flag could not be flown. Even Korean flowers

reentry Shock Culture shock in reverse; it is experienced upon returning home home after living in another culture.

ethnocentrism A viewpoint that uses one culture, usually the home culture, as the standard for judging the worth of foreign ways.

cultural genocide An extreme form of ethnocentrism in which the people of one society define the culture of another society not as merely offensive, but as so intolerable that they attempt to destroy it.

Student Activity: Ask students to browse the Internet for a handbook issued by international students attending college in the United States. Typically these handbooks include a section that prepares international students for living in the United States. What about American culture is emphasized as something that might take some adjustment on the part of the student? (One example of a typical handbook can be found at http://uwf.edu/internationaloffice/pdf/ISO_Handbook.pdf.

The Sociological Imagination Opposing Viewpoints on Same-Sex Adults Holding Hands

The two very different reactions—an American in Ghana and a Moroccan in the United States—to hand holding between same-sex adults illustrate the process by which people use their home culture as a standard for judging behavior. The reactions also remind us of the many subtle ways our relationships with others are shaped by cultural forces we had no hand in creating.

> In the United States it is typically unacceptable for two men to hold hands; immediately the men would be labeled homosexual. I spent some time in Ghana, Africa, several years ago and one of the first cultural differences I noticed was that men, including the men I was with, hold hands. This cultural difference definitely hit home when one day one of the men I was with took my hand as we walked. In order not to offend him, I followed through with this until an appropriate opportunity allowed me to disengage our hands. Even though I was in a country where this was perfectly acceptable, I still felt extremely uneasy with this tradition. (An American in Ghana)
>
> In Morocco, it is common to see two men who are good friends walk down the street hand-in-hand, or even kissing each other on the cheek. In the U.S., it is seen as abnormal for people to act this way. The two friends are either seen as odd, or homosexuals. It took me a while to understand the American frame of mind, and to not act the way I would in Morocco. (A Moroccan in the United States)

were banned, as Japanese officials forced Koreans to dig up their national flowers and plant cherry trees (Kang 1995). Japanese brutally suppressed all resistance on the part of Korean people. When Koreans tried to declare their right to self-determination in March 1919, thousands of people were injured or killed in clashes with the Japanese military.

Sociologist Everett Hughes (1984) identifies yet another type of ethnocentrism:

> One can think so exclusively in terms of his own social world that he simply has no set of concepts for comparing one social world with another. He can believe so deeply in the ways and the ideas of his own world that he has no point of reference for discussing those of other peoples, times, and places. Or he can be so engrossed in his own world that he lacks curiosity about any other; others simply do not concern him. (p. 474)

Another type of ethnocentrism is **reverse ethnocentrism**, in which the home culture is regarded as inferior to a foreign culture. People who engage in this kind of thinking often idealize other cultures as utopias. For example, they might label Japanese culture as a model of harmony, the United States as the model of self-actualization, and Native American culture as a model of environmental sustainability (Hannerz 1992).

People who engage in reverse ethnocentrism not only idealize other cultures, but also reject any information that contradicts their view. Journalist K. Connie Kang (1995) offers an excellent example of reverse ethnocentrism among the Korean students she taught while a visiting professor between 1967 and 1970, at Hankuk University of Foreign Studies:

> Going to the United States was a preoccupation with Koreans. America was akin to paradise, Koreans thought, and the image of America they carried in their heads was exaggerated. They really believed everyone was rich and lived in big houses with winding staircases. I tried to dispel their notions of what America was by saying that most people worked in uninteresting jobs to pay their bills and put their kids through school, but I do not think I succeeded. People want to hear only what they want to hear; it was hard to compete with the images of American life created by Hollywood. (p. 205)

Cultural Relativism

Cultural relativism is an antidote to ethnocentrism. **Cultural relativism** means two things: (1) that a foreign culture should not be judged by the standards of a home culture, and (2) that a behavior or way of thinking must be examined in its cultural context—that is, in terms of that culture's values, norms, beliefs, environmental challenges, and history. Critics of cultural relativism maintain that this perspective encourages an anything-goes point of view, discourages critical assessment, and portrays all cultures as equal in value, regardless of obviously cruel practices (Geertz 1984, p. 265).

In response to this criticism, there is no question that notions of rightness and wrongness vary across cultures, and if we look hard enough, we can probably find a "culture in which just about any idea or behavior exists and can be made to seem right" (Redfield 1962, p. 451). But that is not the purpose of cultural relativism. Ideally, cultural relativism is a perspective that aims to understand a

reverse ethnocentrism A type of ethnocentrism in which the home culture is regarded as inferior to a foreign culture.

cultural relativism The perspective that a foreign culture should not be judged by the standards of a home culture and that a behavior or way of thinking must be examined in its cultural context.

Student Activity: To learn more about South Korean culture, ask students to visit the English language online version of the *Korean Herald* (a newspaper). Are there stories/headlines that offer insights about cultural differences? What about cultural similarities with the United States?

culture on its own terms; that is, the primary aim is not to condone or discredit it. More than anything, cultural relativism is a point of view that acts as a check against an uncritical and overvalued acceptance of the home culture's ways, narrow thinking, and unsympathetic portrayals (Geertz 1984).

For example, whereas most Americans cannot understand why some Koreans eat dog meat, most Koreans are equally appalled that many Americans have such large dogs as pets and often let dogs lick their faces, and spend so much money on them when the U.S. population includes many poor and homeless people. When we consider the historical and environmental challenges that led to the Korean practice of eating dog meat, this practice might not seem so unreasonable. Whereas the United States has an abundance of fertile, flat land for grazing cattle, many Asian countries with limited space, such as North and South Korea, employ available land to grow crops, not to graze cattle. Similarly, in light of American feeling rules that limit touch and physical displays of affection between same-sex adults, Koreans might not express shock at the close relationships many Americans have with their pets, perhaps as a way of compensating. The results of an American Animal Hospital Association survey showed that almost 62 percent of respondents said that they celebrate their pet's birthday, and 31 percent said they believed that, after their spouse, their pet understood them the best (Dale 2004).

Chris Caldeira

This coin-operated laundry in Koreatown, California, reflects the changing composition of that town. Look closely and you can see three signs, each written in a different language—Korean, English, and Spanish.

Subcultures

> **CORE CONCEPT 7 In every society, some groups possess distinctive traits that set them apart from the main culture.**

When thinking about cultural variety, the concepts of subcultures and countercultures are especially useful. In every society, there are groups that share in certain parts of the mainstream culture but have distinctive values, norms, beliefs, symbols, language, and/or material culture that set them apart in some way. These groups are called **subcultures**. South Korean society has many subcultures within it. The haenyeo (women of the sea) is but one example. The haenyeo are 5,000 females who live with their families on Mara Island and are legendary for their free diving skills. These women, 85 percent of whom are 50 years and older, have been groomed since childhood to dive for shellfish in the East China Sea. They have been taught to "conserve oxygen to extend their dives and stress the importance of working in groups, like a herd of watchful seals, vigilant against shark attacks, rip current, and marauding motorboats that buzz the surface" (Glionna 2010).

Often we think we can identify subcultures simply based on physical traits, ethnicity, religious affiliation, neighborhood, age, gender, dress, or some distinctive behavior. Determining who belongs to a particular subculture, however, is actually a complex task that must go beyond simply including anyone who possesses a single social attribute or who lives in a certain place. For example, one might be tempted to think that those who live in Koreatown, which is west of downtown Los Angeles, are all of Korean ethnicity. Surprisingly, the largest ethnic group living now there are Hispanics or Latinos who make up 54 percent of the population.

Sociologists determine whether a group of people constitutes a subculture by learning the extent to which they interact with one another, share a language, share physical or virtual space, and hold certain values. One characteristic central to all subcultures is that their members are separated or cut off in varying degrees from those thought to be part of the mainstream culture. That separation may be total isolation or limited to selected aspects of life, such as work, school, recreation and leisure, marriage, friendships, religion, or housing. In addition, that separation may be voluntary, the result of geographic location, or imposed.

Sociologists use the term **countercultures** in reference to subcultures that challenge, contradict, or outright reject the dominant or mainstream culture. Sociologist Milton Yinger (1977) maintains that members of countercultures

subcultures Groups that share in some parts of the dominant culture but have their own distinctive values, norms, beliefs, symbols, language, or material culture.

countercultures Subcultures in which the norms, values, beliefs, symbols, and language the members share emphasize conflict or opposition to the larger culture. In fact, rejection of the dominant culture's values, norms, symbols, and beliefs is central to understanding a counterculture.

feel strongly that the society as structured cannot bring them satisfaction; some believe that "they have been caught in very bad bargains, others that they are being exploited," and still others think the system is broken (p. 834). Because countercultures emerge in response to an existing order, Yinger argues that "every society gets the countercultures it deserves." Countercultures express themselves by deploring society's contradictions, "caricaturing its weaknesses, and drawing on its neglected and underground traditions" (p. 850). In response, some countercultures "attack, strongly or weakly, violently or symbolically, the frustrating social order" (p. 834).

Yinger presents three broad, and at times overlapping, categories of countercultures:

- Communitarian utopians withdraw into a separate community where they can live with minimum interference from the larger society, which they view as evil, materialistic, wasteful, or self-centered. In the United States, the Old Order Amish (one of at least four Amish subcultures) constitutes a communitarian counterculture in that its members remain largely separate from the rest of the world, organizing their life so that they do not even draw power from electrical grids.
- Mystics search for "truth and for themselves" and turn inward in the process. "They do not so much attack society as disregard it, insofar as they can, and float above it in search of enlightenment" (p. 838). Buddhist monks constitute a counterculture known as *mystics* because they make a point of rejecting the material trappings of capitalistic society.
- Radical activists preach, create, or demand a new order with new obligations to others. They stay engaged, hoping to change society and its values. Strategies to bring about change can include violent and nonviolent protest. Organizers of the Gay Games constitute radical activists in that they have rejected mainstream cultural norms that limit participation in Olympic and other athletic competitions to the most skilled. Anyone, regardless of ability and sexual orientation, can qualify for the Gay Games (Federation of Gay Games 2007). Organizers of the Gay Games reject the idea that in certain sports, such as paired figure skating, the competitors must be male–female pairs.

Chris Caldeira

Buddhist monks constitute a counterculture known as *mystics* because they make a point of rejecting the material trappings of capitalistic societies. As monks, they are committed to simple living, modest dress, and vegetarian diet—ways of living that run counter to the values of capitalist-driven societies.

Online Poll

As one measure of the diffusion of Korean pop culture into the United States, please indicate whether you have heard of and listened to music by the following Korean groups. Check all that apply.

	No	I have heard of this group	Listened to music	Purchased music
Big Bang	○	○	○	○
TVXQ	○	○	○	○
2PM	○	○	○	○
Girls' Generation	○	○	○	○
Far East Movement	○	○	○	○

To see how other students responded to these questions, go **www.cengagebrain.com.**

Jack Loudermilk

Summary of CORE CONCEPTS

This photo shows a physician assistant in the U.S. Army talking to a South Korean child as she eats an "American" meal. In this chapter, we used the concepts related to culture to think about North and South Korea. More specifically, we used the concepts to think about the profound effects the Korean War and the subsequent division of the Korean Peninsula into north and south has had on Korean culture, on the meaning of being Korean, and on the relationship between the United States and the two Koreas.

CORE CONCEPT 1 In the most general sense, culture is the way of life of a people.

Sociologists define culture as the way of life of a people, specifically the human-created strategies for adjusting to the environment and to humans and other creatures that are part of the environment. Material culture is the physical creations (natural and man-made) to which people attach meaning. Nonmaterial culture includes the nonphysical creations. Sociologists are interested in meanings people assign to material culture, the ways in which material and nonmaterial culture shapes social relationships, and the ways material culture shapes and is shaped by values, norms, beliefs, symbols, and language.

CORE CONCEPT 2 Geographic and historical forces shape culture.

Sociologists operate under the assumption that culture acts as a buffer between people and their surroundings. Thus, material and nonmaterial aspects of culture represent responses to historical events and geographic challenges. The division of the Korean Peninsula into North and South Korea was a key geographic and historical event affecting the personal lives and culture of all Koreans. Where people live—north or south of the DMZ—affects whether they will learn English as a second language, eat primarily corn or rice, have access to more than one radio station, or be free to travel outside their country.

CORE CONCEPT 3 Culture is learned.

Regardless of their physical appearance, people are destined to learn the ways of the culture into which they are raised. A Korean-born boy, adopted by an American family, will be American in culture. Regardless of the culture to which we are exposed, all those who belong to that culture are replicas of one another, if only because each person experiences and learns different slices of the same culture.

CORE CONCEPT 4 Culture provides a variety of formulas that enable individuals to adjust to the challenges of being human.

Being human presents us with a number of inevitable challenges. Cultures have developed formulas to help their members respond to these challenges. Formulas exist for eliminating human waste; caring for children; satisfying the need for food, drink, and sex; channeling and displaying emotions; and eventually dying.

CORE CONCEPT 5 People borrow material and nonmaterial culture from other societies.

Cultural diffusion is the process by which an idea, an invention, or some other cultural item is borrowed from a foreign source. The borrowing may include imitating, stealing, purchasing, copying, or learning about something. The opportunity to borrow occurs whenever two people from different cultures make contact.

CORE CONCEPT 6 The home culture is usually the standard that people use to make judgments about another culture.

When people encounter a foreign culture, they can experience mental and physical strain known as culture shock. One reason people experience culture shock is that they hold the viewpoint of ethnocentrism. That is, they use their home culture as the standard for judging the worth of foreign ways. Sociologists take a position of cultural relativity when they evaluate a foreign culture. That is, they seek to hold ethnocentrism in check and work to understand a culture in all its complexity.

CORE CONCEPT 7 In every society, some groups possess distinctive traits that set them apart from the main culture.

Groups that share in certain parts of the dominant culture but have their own distinctive values, norms, beliefs, symbols, language, or material culture are called subcultures. One characteristic central to all subcultures is that their members are separated or cut off in some way from other people in the larger culture. Some subcultures are known as countercultures. That is, they challenge, contradict, or outright reject the dominant or mainstream culture. There are three broad, and at times overlapping, categories of countercultures: communitarian utopians, mystics, and radical activists.

Resources on the Internet

Login to CengageBrain.com to access the resources your instructor requires. For this book, you can access:

 Sociology CourseMate

Access an integrated eBook, chapter-specific interactive learning tools, including flash cards, quizzes, videos, and more in your Sociology CourseMate.

CENGAGENOW™

Take a pretest for this chapter and receive a personalized study plan based on your results that will identify the topics you need to review and direct you to online resources to help you master those topics. Then take a posttest to help you determine the concepts you have mastered and what you will need to work on.

CourseReader

CourseReader for Sociology is an online reader providing access to readings, and audio and video selections to accompany your course materials.

Visit **www.cengagebrain.com** to access your account and purchase materials.

Key Terms

SOCIALIZATION

4 With Emphasis on ISRAEL AND THE PALESTINIAN TERRITORIES

Socialization is a learning process that begins immediately after birth and continues throughout life. Through this process, people learn about and come to terms with the culture and behavior patterns of the society in which they live. In this chapter, we look at the ongoing Israeli–Palestinian conflict, which is at least 100 years long, to understand the role socialization plays in perpetuating that conflict. To last 100 years, the conflict must have been passed down from one generation to the next. How do new generations come to learn about the conflict? These Palestinian children learn something about it by simply gazing through a hole in a bullet-ridden fence damaged by Israel Defense Forces when who retaliated against the Palestinian town from which rockets were launched into Israel.

Why Focus On ISRAEL AND THE PALESTINIAN TERRITORIES?

Our emphasis in this chapter is on the fierce century-long conflict between Jews and Palestinians over land that both groups call home. The conflict has been going on since Jews began their return "home" around 1900, in response to widespread persecution throughout Europe. The land to which they were returning was now home to 1.2 million Palestinians. The Holocaust increased the flow of Jews to what was then Palestine. With the support of UN and United States Israel was established in 1948. Palestinians have used guns, knives, stones, strikes, boycotts, rockets, and suicide attacks to resist the Israeli government's control of Palestinian land. Israelis have used bombings, deportations, imprisonment, curfews, school closures, blockades, land seizures, targeted assassinations, and bulldozers to maintain their "right to return."

Over the years, the United States has acted as peace broker in this region, bringing Palestinian and Israeli leaders together in an effort to persuade them to work through their differences. Many Middle East analysts believe that the United States is the only country in a position to push the peace process forward.

In this chapter, we use sociological concepts and theories to help us understand how the conflict has been passed down through the generations and sustained. Keep in mind that the process by which people come to learn the culture and behavior patterns of the society in which they live, is just one factor that helps us understand why the Israeli–Palestinian conflict has lasted so long. Although we concentrate on the role socialization plays in perpetuating this conflict, the concepts and theories presented allow us to apply them to any learning process.

Online Poll

Often people talk about an event, such as the Great Depression or 9/11, that has shaped a generation. Is there such an event that has shaped the generation to which you belong?

○ Yes. Please name that event: ____________

○ Cannot think of any event

To see how other students responded to these questions, go to **www.cengagebrain.com.**

Socialization

By the time children are 2 years old, most are biologically ready to show concern for the "rules of life." They are bothered when things do not match with learned expectations: paint peeling from a table, broken toys, small holes in clothing, and people in distress all raise troubling questions. From a young child's point of view, someone somewhere has done something very wrong (Kagan 1988, 1989).

To show this kind of concern with standards, 2-year-olds must first be exposed to information that leads them to expect behavior, people, and objects to be a certain way (Kagan 1989). They develop these expectations as they interact with others in their world. For example, children go to adults with their questions and needs. Adults respond in different ways—perhaps by offering explanations, expressing concern, trying to help, showing no concern, or paying no attention. These kinds of exchanges constitute socialization.

CORE CONCEPT 1 In the broadest sense of the word, *socialization* is the process by which people develop a sense of self and learn the ways of the society in which they live.

Video Tip: Show the author's video introduction to Chapter 4, which can be found on the Power Lecture CD. A transcript of the video can be found in the Instructor's Resource Manual.

More specifically, it is the process by which humans (1) acquire a sense of self or social identity, (2) learn about the social groups to which they belong and do not belong, (3) develop their human capacities, and (4) learn to negotiate the social and physical environment they have inherited. Socialization is a lifelong process, beginning at birth and ending at death. It takes hold through **internalization,** the process in which people take as their own and accept as binding the norms, values, beliefs, and language that their socializers are attempting to pass on.

No discussion of socialization can ignore the importance of two factors: nature and nurture. **Nature** comprises one's human genetic makeup or biological inheritance. **Nurture** refers to social experiences that make up every individual's life. Some scientists debate the relative importance of genes and the social experiences, arguing that one is ultimately more important than the other. Such a debate is futile, because it is impossible to separate the influence of the two factors or to say that one is more forceful. Both nature and nurture are essential to socialization (Ornstein and Thompson 1984).

The relationship between the cerebral cortex and spoken language illustrates rather dramatically the inseparable qualities of nature and nurture. As part of our human genetic makeup (nature), we possess a cerebral cortex, which allows us to organize, remember, communicate, understand, and create. Scientists believe that humans inherit a cerebral cortex "setup" to learn any of the more than 6,000 known human languages. In the first months of life, all babies are biologically capable of babbling the essential sounds needed to speak any language. As children grow, this enormous potential is reduced, however, by their social experiences (nurture) with language. Most obviously, babies eventually learn the language (or languages) they hear spoken. For the most part, Palestinian babies hear standard Arabic spoken at home and learn Hebrew in school. Israeli babies, for the most part, hear modern Hebrew spoken at home. Because Israel is a land of immigrants, many Jewish children are exposed to Russian, Yiddish, Ladino, or Romanian as babies, but they all must eventually learn Hebrew. Most Israeli Jews do not learn Arabic.

Although humans have a biological makeup that allows them to speak a language, the language itself is learned through interactions with others. If babies are not exposed to language, they will not acquire that communication tool. Though social interaction is essential to language development, it is also essential to human development in general. If babies are deprived of social contact with others, they cannot become normally functioning human beings.

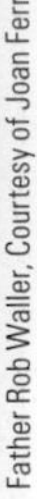

Father Rob Waller, Courtesy of Joan Ferrante

Cherie A. Thurlby

Millions of social experiences culminate to create a sense of self. These Israeli children's sense of self develops through interaction experiences that may include celebrations of Jewish cultural tradition. Social experiences can also include military training that leads one to self-identify as an Israeli soldier.

socialization The process by which people develop a sense of self and learn the ways of the society in which they live.

internalization The process in which people take as their own and accept as binding the norms, values, beliefs, and language that their socializers are attempting to pass on.

nature Human genetic makeup or biological inheritance.

nurture The social environment, or the interaction experiences that make up every individual's life.

The Importance of Social Contact

CORE CONCEPT 2 Socialization depends on meaningful interaction experiences with others.

Cases of children raised in extreme isolation or in restrictive and sterile environments show the importance of social contact (nurture) to normal development. Some of the earliest and most systematic work in this area was done by sociologist Kingsley Davis. His work on the consequences of extreme isolation demonstrates how neglect and lack of social contact influence emotional, mental, and even physical development.

Davis (1940, 1947) documented and compared the separate yet similar lives of two girls: Anna and Isabelle. During the first six years of their lives, the girls received only the minimum of human care. Both children, living in the United States in the 1940s, were classified as illegitimate. Because of that status, both were rejected and forced into seclusion; each was living in a dark, attic-like room. Anna was shut off from her family and their daily activities. Isabelle was shut off in a dark room with her deaf-mute mother. Both girls were 6 years old when authorities intervened. At that time, they exhibited behavior comparable to that of 6-month-old children.

Anna "had no glimmering of speech, absolutely no ability to walk, no sense of gesture, not the least capacity to feed herself even when food was put in front of her, and no comprehension of cleanliness. She was so apathetic that it was hard to tell whether or not she could hear" (Davis 1947, p. 434). Anna was placed in a private home for mentally disabled children until she died four years later. At the time of her death, she behaved and thought at the level of a 2-year-old child.

Like Anna, Isabelle had not developed speech, but she did use gestures and croaks to communicate. Because of a lack of sunshine and a poor diet, she had developed rickets: "Her legs in particular were affected; they 'were so bowed that as she stood erect the soles of her shoes came nearly flat together, and she got about with a skittering gait'" (Davis 1947, p. 436). She also exhibited extreme fear of and hostility toward strangers. Isabelle entered into an intensive and systematic program designed to help her master speech, reading, and other important skills. After two years in the program, she had achieved a level of thought and behavior normal for someone her age. Isabelle's success may be partly attributed to her establishing an important bond with her deaf-mute mother, who taught her how to communicate through gestures and croaks. Although the bond was less than ideal, it still gave her an advantage over Anna.

Cases of Less Extreme Isolation

Other evidence of the importance of social contact comes from less extreme cases of neglect. Psychiatrist Rene Spitz (1951) studied 91 infants who were raised by their parents during their first three to four months of life but who were later placed in orphanages. When they were admitted to the orphanages, the infants were physically and emotionally normal. Orphanage staff provided adequate care for their bodily needs—good food, clothing, diaper changes, clean

Shannon K. Cassidy

A person's overall well-being depends on meaningful interaction experiences with others. Social interaction is essential to developing and maintaining a sense of self.

nurseries—but gave the children little personal attention. Because only one nurse was available for every 8 to 12 children, the children were starved emotionally. The emotional starvation caused by the lack of social contact resulted in such rapid physical and developmental deterioration that a significant number of the children died. Others became completely passive, lying on their backs in their cots. Many were unable to stand, walk, or talk (Spitz 1951).

Children of the Holocaust

Anna Freud and Sophie Dann (1958) studied six German Jewish children whose parents had been killed in the gas chambers of Nazi Germany. The children were shuttled from one foster home to another for a year before being sent to the ward for motherless children at the Terezin concentration camp. The ward was staffed by malnourished and overworked nurses, who were themselves concentration camp inmates. After the war, the six children were housed in three different institution-like environments. Eventually they were sent to a country cottage, where they received intensive social and emotional care.

During their short lives, these six children had been deprived of stable emotional ties and relationships with caring adults. Freud and Dann found that the children were ignorant of the meaning of family and grew excessively upset when they were separated from one another, even for a few seconds. In addition, they "behaved in a wild, restless, and uncontrollably noisy manner":

> During the first days after their arrival, they destroyed all the toys and damaged much of the furniture. Toward the staff they behaved either with cold indifference or with active hostility, making no exception for the young assistant Maureen who had accompanied them from Windermere and was their only link with the immediate past. At times, they

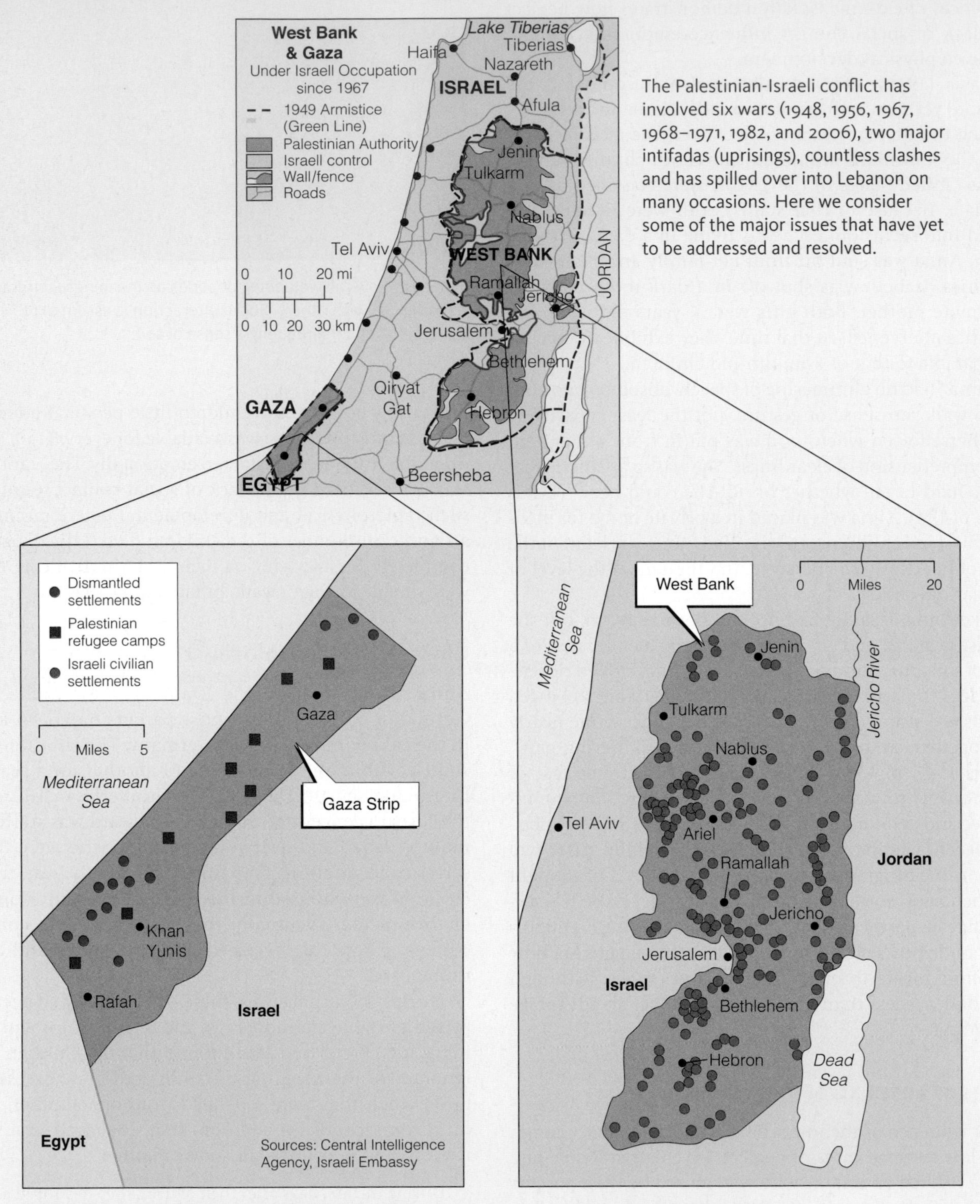

The Palestinian-Israeli conflict has involved six wars (1948, 1956, 1967, 1968–1971, 1982, and 2006), two major intifadas (uprisings), countless clashes and has spilled over into Lebanon on many occasions. Here we consider some of the major issues that have yet to be addressed and resolved.

FIGURE 4.1 Maps of Israel, West Bank and Gaza
The top map show the state of Israel and the location of the Gaza Strip and West Bank. The lower maps show where Israeli settlements are located in the West Bank and the settlements that have been dismantled in the Gaza Strip.
Sources: Central Intelligence Agency, Israeli Embassy

Video Tip: Two years into the construction of the West Bank Barrier, PBS Newshour correspondent Elizabeth Farnsworth talked to Israelis and Palestinians to learn their views. To access the video, go to the Newshour website (www.pbs.org/newshour) and enter search terms "Two Views of the West Bank Barrier."

The United States and other parties involved in the peace process have proposed a two-state solution to end the conflict. A two-state solution means that Israel remains a Jewish state and a second for Palestinians would be established and recognized. Specifically, the Palestinian territories of the West Bank and Gaza—two geographically disconnected lands—would become the new Palestinian state. The Palestinians living in Israel could opt to remain in Israel as citizens or become citizens of Palestine.

Before the two-state solution can be implemented, a number of critical issues must be resolved:

1. Israeli settlements in the Palestinian territories. Settlements are Jewish-populated communities in what are now the Palestinian Territories. These settlements are diverse in structure, ranging from outposts composed of trailers, campers, and tents to self-contained towns and cities with populations of 10,000 or more. An estimated 325 such settlements house 500,000 Jewish residents (Financial Times 2010). In 2005, the Israeli government evacuated settlers from 21 settlements in the Gaza Strip and from four West Bank settlements. Notwithstanding the recent evacuation, critics argue that the settlements are attempts to establish a significant Jewish presence on Palestinian land so that a permanent solution that gives Palestinian control over this land can never be achieved.
2. Safe passage between Gaza and the West Bank. If Gaza and the West Bank are eventually to be regarded as one state, the pressing question becomes who can control the access roads from one territory to the other? Palestinians? Israelis? A joint force? Currently, Israelis control every access route for moving goods and people into and out of the Palestinian territories.
3. Right of return. The creation of the state of Israel and the subsequent 1948 and 1967 Arab–Israeli wars resulted in Palestinian diasporas, forced scatterings of an ethnic population to various locations around the world. Several million Palestinians immigrated to surrounding countries and now live with their descendants in refugee camps in Jordan (estimated at 1.98 million); the Persian Gulf countries of Kuwait, Saudi Arabia, United Arab Emirates, Qatar (3,711,000), and Iraq (est. 450,000); Lebanon (est. 350,000); Syria (est. 340,000); and elsewhere. Approximately 1.4 million of 4.8 million Palestinians are registered with the UN as refugees. Refugees seek the right to return to the land within Israel from which they fled or were evicted (U.S. Central Intelligence Agency 2010; Bennet 2003b). From the Israeli point of view, if refugees were allowed to return, they would be overwhelmed by the numbers and cease to exist.
4. Status of Jerusalem. Both Palestinians and Israeli Jews claim Jerusalem, which is divided into East and West Jerusalem, as their capital. Under a peace agreement, the Israeli government is to be awarded West Jerusalem and the Palestinians East Jerusalem. But the Israeli government insists that the entire city is its capital. An estimated 200,000 Israelis live in settlements located in East Jerusalem.
5. The Wall. In June 2002, the Israeli government, with the support of 83 percent of Israelis, began construction on the West Bank barrier—a 350-kilometer-long obstacle comprising electrified fencing, razor wire, trenches, concrete walls, and guard towers that wind through the West Bank. The wall puts 14 percent of the West Bank on the Israeli side; at one point, the wall extends some 13 miles into the West Bank (Farnsworth 2004). The wall separates the West Bank from Israel and channels Palestinian movement from the West Bank into Israel through checkpoints. Israel claims that the wall is not a political border but rather a security border designed to keep suicide bombers and other would-be attackers out of Israel and Jewish settlements. The UN estimates that the barrier has disrupted 600,000 Palestinian lives. For example, the wall is constructed so that it completely surrounds 12 Palestinian communities, allowing residents to leave only through Israeli-controlled checkpoints (Myre 2003).
6. The Fatah-Hamas divide. The political party Fatah, founded in 1958, renounced terrorism against Israel in 1988, and acknowledged Israel's right to exist in 1993. Hamas, founded in 1987, is labeled a terrorist organization by Israel, the United States, and the European Union. In 2006, Hamas won 74 of 132 elected seats in democratically held elections, giving it the majority in Palestinian Legislative Council. Hamas (backed by Syria and Iran) took control of the Gaza Strip after five days of civil war. Fatah (backed by the United States and Jordan) remains in control of the West Bank. Israelis refused to recognize Hamas as the legitimate leader of the Palestinian people. After a series of military exchanges between Palestinian hard-liners in Gaza and Israeli forces, Israel sealed off its border with Gaza and prohibited all but the most basic necessities from entering. Egypt also sealed off its border with Gaza, leaving the residents of Gaza imprisoned within. This Fatah-Hamas division has jeopardized the two-state solution and further restricted Palestinian movement between the West Bank and Gaza.

Note, as we read about the Israeli–Palestinian conflict, we will refer to Palestinians who live in Israel as Israeli Palestinians, Jews who live in Israel as Israeli Jews, and Israelis who live in West Bank and East Jerusalem as Israeli settlers.

Technology Tip: For some compelling photographs of the West Bank Wall and Israeli settlements, go to Google images and enter those terms.

> ignored the adults so completely that they would not look up when one of them entered the room. They would turn to an adult when in some immediate need, but treat the same person as nonexistent once more when the need was fulfilled. In anger, they would hit the adults, bite or spit. (Freud and Dann 1958, p. 130)

Taken together, these cases—child orphaned during the Holocaust, the 91 orphans studied by Spitz, and the cases of Anna and Isabelle—teach us that children need close contact with and stimulation from others if they are to develop normally. Among other things, adequate stimulation means the existence of strong ties with a caring adult. These ties must be characterized by a bond of mutual expectation between caregiver and baby. In other words, there must be at least one person who knows the baby well enough to understand his or her needs and feelings and who will act to satisfy them. Under such conditions, children learn the kinds of actions that generate predictable responses: Getting excited may cause the child's father to become equally excited; crying may prompt the mother to soothe the child. When researchers set up experimental situations in which parents failed to respond to their infants in expected ways (even for a few moments), they found that the babies suffered considerable tension and distress (*Nova* 1986).

Meaningful social contact with and stimulation from others are important at any age. Indeed, strong social ties with caring people are linked to overall social, psychological, and physical well-being. On a more fundamental level, social interaction is essential to developing and maintaining a sense of self.

Sgt. Robert Holliway

During the Holocaust, many Jewish children were separated from their parents and confined to concentration camps.

Individual and Collective Memory

CORE CONCEPT 3 Socialization is impossible without memory; memories passed on from one generation to the next preserve and sustain culture.

Memory, the capacity to retain and recall past experiences, is easily overlooked in exploring socialization. On an individual level, memory allows people to know others and remember interacting with them. On a societal level, memory preserves the cultural past. Without memory, whole societies would be cut off from the past and left reinventing the wheel.

Yet, if the biological mechanisms (nature) involved in learning and then recalling names, faces, and the meaning of words and significant symbols were not present, people could not interact with one another in meaningful ways: "You have to begin to lose your memory, if only in bits and pieces, to realize that memory is what makes our lives. Life without memory is no life at all. . . . Our memory is our coherence, our reason, our feeling, even our action. Without it we are nothing" (Buñuel 1985, p. 22).

The latest neurological evidence on memory suggests that some physical trace remains in the brain after new learning takes place, stored in an anatomical entity called an engram. Engrams, or memory traces, are formed by chemicals produced in the brain. They store in physical form the recollections of experiences—a mass of information, impressions, and images unique to each person:

> It may have been a time of listening to music, a time of looking in at the door of a dance hall, a time of imagining the action of robbers from a comic strip, a time of waking from a vivid dream, a time of laughing conversation with friends, a time of listening to a little son to make sure he was safe, a time of watching illuminated signs, a time of lying in the delivery room at childbirth, a time of being frightened by a menacing man, a time of watching people enter the room with snow on their clothes. (Penfield and Perot 1963, p. 687)

Scientists do not believe that engrams store actual records of past events. More likely, engrams store edited or consolidated versions of experiences and events, which are edited further each time they are recalled.

From a sociological point of view, memory goes beyond its neurological and individual qualities to include social qualities. To participate in society, one must be able to recall such things as names, faces, places, words, symbols, and norms. In addition, they must learn and remember the language, norms, values, and beliefs of the surrounding culture. Indeed, we take it for granted that people have such information stored in memory. Memory allows us to participate in society in another way. People born at approximately the same time and place have likely lived through many of the same events. These

Teaching Tip: When discussing collective memory, consider showing students the website for the U.S. Holocaust Memorial Museum. Museums represent one way that memories are passed on from one generation to the next.

experiences—each uniquely personal and yet similar to one another—are remembered long after the event has passed. Sociologists use the term **collective memory** to describe the experiences shared and recalled by significant numbers of people (Coser 1992; Halbwachs 1980). Such memories are revived, preserved, shared, passed on, and recast in many forms, such as stories, holidays, rituals, and monuments. Virtually every Israeli Jew has memories of war and persecution. These memories may involve hiding in a shelter, saying good-bye to someone called up for military service, waiting for a loved one to return from war, or fleeing places where Jews were deemed unfit to exist.

Writer David Grossman (1998) explains that Israel is alive with memories and reminders of the past:

> There are nine hundred memorials to the war dead in this small country. . . . There is no week on the Israeli calendar in which there is not a memorial day of some sort for a traumatic event.
>
> A person walking through downtown Tel Aviv can, in the space of five minutes, set out from Dizengoff Street (where a suicide bomber murdered thirteen people two years ago), glance apprehensively at the No. 5 bus (on which another suicide bomber killed twenty-two civilians four years ago), and try to regain his composure at the Apropos Cafe (where a year ago yet another suicide bomber killed three women; none of us can forget the images of a blood-spattered, newly orphaned baby).
>
> When my daughter took her first field trip with her kindergarten classmates, they went to Yitzhak Rabin's grave and to the adjacent military cemetery. (p. 56)

Although Palestinians were part of many of the same historical events as Jews, the memories of the two groups differ because they witnessed these events from different vantage points. Displaced Palestinians retain memories of their homeland, and like the Jews, pass these memories down to their descendants, who did not experience the displacements firsthand. One way Palestinians pass on the memory is by naming their children after the cities and towns in which they lived before the 1948 war (Al-Batrawi and Rabbani 1991). Most tell their children about the places where they used to live; they teach their offspring to call those places home. They show their children keys and deeds to the houses in which they once lived (Kifner 2000). When author David Grossman (1988) asked a group of Palestinian children in a West Bank refugee camp to tell him their birthplace, each replied with the name of a formerly Arab town:

> Everyone I spoke to in the camp is trained—almost from birth—to live this double life; they sit here, very much here . . . but they are also there. . . . I ask a five-year-old boy where he is from, and he immediately answers, "Jaffa," which is today part of Tel Aviv.
>
> "Have you ever seen Jaffa?" "No, but my grandfather saw it." His father, apparently, was born here, but his grandfather came from Jaffa.
>
> "And is it beautiful, Jaffa?" "Yes. It has orchards and vineyards and the sea." And farther down . . . I meet a young girl sitting on a cement wall, reading an illustrated magazine. . . . She is from Lod, not far from Ben-Gurion International Airport, forty years ago an Arab town. She is sixteen.
>
> She tells me, giggling, of the beauty of Lod. Of its houses, which were big as palaces. "And in every room a hand-painted carpet. And the land was wonderful, and the sky was always blue. . . .
>
> "And the tomatoes there were red and big, and everything came to us from the earth, and the earth gave us and gave us more." "Have you visited there, Lod?" "Of course not." "Aren't you curious to see it now?" "Only when we return." (Grossman 1988, pp. 6–7)

Courtesy of Zachi Evenor, Israel

All societies support rituals that teach people about the past and encourage them to remember it. The charred remains of an Israeli bus, from what is known as the Coastal Road Massacre, calls out to Israelis, born 40 or more years after that date, to remember.

Development of the Social Self

Sociologists maintain that a sense of self arises when children are able to see the self as an object. The self becomes an object when children can

1. take the role of the other (role-take), and
2. name, classify, and categorize the self.

collective memory The experiences shared and recalled by significant numbers of people. Such memories are revived, preserved, shared, passed on, and recast in many forms, such as stories, holidays, rituals, and monuments.

Student Activity: Ask students to share a historical event that their parents, grandparents, or even great grand parents recall and have passed on to them. In what form were the memories shared—in the form of stories, photographs, home movies, newspaper clippings, and so on?

The Sociological Imagination The Past in the Present

In the late 19th century, a growing climate of anti-Semitism arose throughout Europe and Russia. Theodor Herzl, the founder of the modern Zionist movement, believed the only way to combat European anti-Semitism was for Jews to return to their homeland and establish the state of Israel. The Nazi Holocaust, which claimed an estimated 6 million lives, including one-third of the European Jewish population, gave the Jewish return movement a desperate urgency. The top left photo shows the faces of Jews, released from Buchenwald concentration camp on their way to what was then called Palestine in the 1940s. The hope then was to establish their own state—a state with its own armed forces to protect them from future aggression. But the land to which the Jews returned was now home to approximately 1.2 million Palestinians. The United Nations (UN) voted to partition Palestine into two independent states—one Jewish, the other Palestinian. The Palestinians could not tolerate this arrangement, arguing that they should not have to pay for European transgressions. The top right photo shows Palestinians fleeing to neighboring countries in 1948, the year Jewish leaders declared Israel an independent state and defeated Arab armies from Egypt, Syria, Jordan, Lebanon, and Iraq.

The bottom photos show the past's influence today. The bottom right photo shows Israeli children practicing for how to respond if Palestinians launch a rocket attack into their communities. The bottom left photo shows a Palestinian child sobbing after losing family members killed by Israeli shells. In fact, 50 percent of Palestinian children ages 11 to 14 report that they have seen other Palestinians arguing or upset because Israelis had killed someone they knew. The researchers also found that 25 percent of Israelis have observed someone crying or upset because Palestinians had killed someone they knew. Fifty percent of the Palestinian children report that they have seen a person killed or injured by Israelis. Ten percent of Israelis had observed a death or injury at the hands of Palestinians. The more violence a child observed, the more likely he or she was to experience frequent nightmares and to behave in aggressive ways toward others (for example, by slapping, hitting, choking, punching, or threatening others) (Science Daily 2010). Israeli author David Grossman (2010) argues that, "If you live all your life in a violent conflict, if you are born to it and your children are born to it and if you develop in yourself all those expertise that are necessary to survive in this catastrophe zone of the conflict, inevitably you lose things, inevitably you shrink in front of this harsh reality, and as long as there is no solution to the situation you become more hopeless, and then passive and apathetic and just forget that there is another alternative."

Role-Taking

CORE CONCEPT 4 People acquire a sense of self when they can role-take.

How do people learn to take the role of the other? Sociologist George Herbert Mead (1934) maintains that the key to role-taking is self-awareness. According to Mead, people possess self-awareness when they can comprehend their place in social activities going on around them. Mead maintained that we learn to do this through a three-stage interactive process that involves imaginative **role-taking**, or stepping into another person's shoes by which to imaginatively view and assess our (and others) behavior, appearance, and thoughts. Those stages are (1) preparatory, (2) play, and (3) games. Each stage involves a progressively more sophisticated level of imaginative role-taking.

role-taking The process of stepping into another person's shoes by which to imaginatively view and assess our (and others) behavior, appearance, and thoughts.

Preparatory Stage (age 2 and under) In the preparatory stage, children have not yet developed the cognitive ability to role-take. They mimic or imitate people around them but often do not know the meaning of what they are imitating. In this stage, children mimic what others around them are doing or repeat things they hear. In the process, young children learn to function symbolically; that is, they learn to name things when they repeat words that they hear others speaking, and they learn that particular actions and words have meanings that arouse predictable responses from others. For example, Israeli children may be taught early on that undivided Jerusalem is the capital of Israel. Similarly, Palestinian children may be taught that their "real" home is in a former Palestinian city that is now considered an Israeli city, even before the children learn notions of geography and can understand the historical circumstances of their living arrangements.

Naccarata
©AP Photo
Mohammed Omer
AP Photo/Oded Balilty

Both Palestinian and Israeli children, like children in nearly every culture, learn to sing patriotic songs and say prayers before they can understand the words. Observers to the West Bank and Gaza are struck by the fact that as soon as some 2-year-old Palestinian children "saw the cameras come out, they were up and alert, hands outstretched as taut fingers made in unison the victory sign for our photos. No [Palestinian] child we met anywhere wanted to be photographed without that sign" (Bourne 1990, p. 70).

Play Stage (ages 2 to 6) Mead saw children's play as the mechanism by which they practice role-taking. Mead defined **play** as a voluntary, spontaneous activity with few or no formal rules. Play is not subject to constraints of time (for example, 20-minute halves) or place (for example, a regulation-size field). Children, in particular, play whenever and wherever the urge strikes. In play, children make rules as they go; they are not imposed by rulebooks or referees. Children undertake play for entertainment or pleasure. These characteristics make play less socially complicated than organized games, such as baseball.

In the play stage, children pretend to be **significant others**—people or characters such as cartoon characters, a parent, or the family pet—who are important in a child's life, in that they greatly influence the child's self-evaluation and way of behaving. When a little girl plays with a doll and pretends to be the doll's mother, she talks and acts toward the doll the same way her mother talks and acts toward her. By pretending to be a mother, the child gains a sense of the mother's expectations and perspective and learns to see herself as an object (through the doll) from her mother's point of view.

play A voluntary and often spontaneous activity with few or no formal rules that is not subject to constraints of time or place.

significant others People or characters who are important in an individual's life, in that they greatly influence that person's self-evaluation or motivate him or her to behave in a particular manner.

Courtesy of Chris Brown

Palestinian children flashing the V sign, an important symbolic gesture representing victory over Israel. To the uninformed observer, this symbolic gesture might represent peace.

Rafah Today

These Palestinian children are playing at being an Israeli soldier and captured Palestinians. The child with the toy gun pretends to be an Israeli soldier making the children, who pretend to be Palestinian resistance fighters, kneel with hands behind their heads.

In the play stage, children's role-taking comes from what they see and hear going on around them. Most Palestinian children in the West Bank and Gaza have never seen an adult male Israeli without a gun. Palestinian children's play reflects their experiences: The children pretend to be Israeli soldiers arresting and beating other Palestinian children, who are pretending to be stone throwers. They use sticks and cola cans as if they were guns and teargas canisters (Usher 1991). One evening, ABC News featured a segment on Palestinian children who engaged in this type of play. When a reporter asked whether they preferred to be soldiers or stone throwers, the children replied, "Soldiers, because they have more power and can kill." For their part, Israeli children have had little experience with Palestinians except, perhaps, as manual laborers or "terrorists." Thus, it is hardly surprising that some Israeli kindergartners pretend that Israelis are Smurfs (the good guys in a TV program) and Palestinians portray Gargamel (the enemy of the Smurfs in the program). Israeli children pretend to be soldiers because both men and women must serve in the Israeli military, beginning at age 18.

Game Stage (age 7 and older) In Mead's theory, the play stage is followed by the game stage. **Games** are structured, organized activities that involve more than one person. They are characterized by a number of constraints, such as established roles and rules and a purpose toward which everyone's mental energy and activity is directed. When people gather to play a game of baseball, for example, they do not have to decide the rules of the game. The rules are already in place. To be a successful pitcher, for example, one must understand not only how to play that position but how the position of pitcher relates to the other positions.

When children first take part in organized games, their efforts seem chaotic. This chaos exists because children have not yet developed the cognitive capacity to see how each role fits with others. As they learn to play games, children also learn to (1) follow established rules, (2) take simultaneously the roles of all participants, and (3) see how their role fits in relation to an established system of expectations. In particular, children learn that what is happening with other positions affects how they play the position they occupy. They learn that under some circumstances such as when a ball is hit in their direction, their position takes on added importance and that at other times their position assumes lesser significance.

Through games, children learn to organize their behavior around the **generalized other**—a system of expected behaviors and meanings that transcend the people participating. An understanding of the generalized other is achieved by simultaneously and imaginatively relating the self to many others playing the game. Through this imaginative process, the generalized other becomes incorporated into a person's sense of self (Cuzzort and King 2002). So when children play games such as baseball, they practice fitting their behavior into an already established system of expectations. This ability is the key to living in society because most of the time, whether it is at school, work, or home, we are expected to learn and then fit into an already established system of roles and expectations.

games Structured, organized activities that usually involve more than one person and a number of constraints, such as established roles, rules, time, place, and outcome.

generalized other A system of expected behaviors, meanings, and viewpoints that transcend those of the people participating.

Discussion Tip: Ask students to share their memories of a favorite toy and to describe how they remember playing with that toy. Did it involve role-taking?

Lisa Southwick

During the game stage, children practice fitting their behavior into an already established system of rules by taking on a position with defined relationships to other positions. It appears that these children do not yet understand the role they should play relative to their teammates and opponents, as all energy is focused on getting to the soccer ball.

© Reuters/CORBIS

These Israeli Jewish and Palestinian children are participating in a program based in the United States known as Friends Forever, a grassroots organization that promotes peace between groups whose communities are engaged in intense conflicts. Among other things, the youth participate in games that build trust among those whose lives have been divided and separated by conflict.

Not surprisingly, "get to know you" games are the tools used in programs designed to break down barriers between Palestinian and Israeli Jewish children and adolescents (Friends Forever 2010). "The games can involve activities like throwing an orange into the air, calling a person's name to catch it, throwing it again with another's name, and again and again as the whoops of laughter fill the room. Then they all crowd together, take each other's hands, and turn around until they are enmeshed in a tangle of arms. Intertwined with each other, they try to unravel themselves without letting go. They talk to each other, giving advice, crouching so another can step over an arm, stooping so others can swing arms over heads, spinning around, trying to turn the snarled mess of . . . bodies into a clean circle" (Shipler 1986, p. 537).

Although these games seem merely fun, sociologists contend that participants are learning to see things from another's perspective and to play their parts successfully in a shared activity. The participants cannot be effective unless they understand their own roles in relation to everyone else's. Although the children trying to untangle themselves may not be fully aware of it, they are learning that a Palestinian (or an Israeli) can be in a position like their own. To untangle the knot, participants must be able to understand everyone else's situation.

The Importance of Symbols to Role Taking

CORE CONCEPT 5 Meaningful social interaction depends on the involved parties sharing significant symbols.

To role-take, children must not only learn to step outside the self to see and evaluate it from another's point of view, they must also learn the meaning of **significant symbols,** gestures that convey the same meaning to the people transmitting and receiving them. Mead (1934) defined **gesture** as any action that requires people to interpret its meaning before responding. Language is a particularly important gesture because people interpret the meaning of words before they react. In addition to words, gestures also include nonverbal cues, such as tone of voice, facial expression, posture, and other body movements or positions that convey meaning. Through gestures, others convey how they are evaluating our appearance and behavior.

A sense of self emerges the moment children learn the symbols or self-referent terms to distinguish the self (including I, me, mine, first name, and last name) and to specify the statuses one holds in society (athlete, doctor, child, Palestinian of Gaza or West Bank, Jewish settler in the West Bank, Israeli Arab, and so on). Mead maintains that the self is always recognized in relationship to others. That is, one can be a student only in relationship to teachers and fellow students. Similarly, one can be an athlete

significant symbol Gestures that convey the same meaning to the persons transmitting them and receiving them.

gesture Any action that requires people to interpret its meaning before responding.

Discussion Tip: Ask students to describe a game they played as a child. Make sure they think of a game that corresponds with sociologists' conception of games. Assess the game in light of Mead's theory.

only in relationship to other athletes, an audience, a referee, and so on. And one can only be a Jewish settler in relationship to the Palestinians living in the West Bank and East Jerusalem (see Working for Change).

Mead described the self as having two parts—the me and the I. The **me** is the social self—the part of the self that is the product of interaction with others and that has internalized the rules and expectations. More specifically, the me is the sense of self that emerges out of role-taking experiences. The **I** is the active and creative aspect of the self. It is the part of the self that questions the expectations and rules for behavior. The I is capable of acting in unconventional, inappropriate, or unexpected ways. The I takes chances that can pay off if others label the person breaking rules and defying expectations as unique or one of a kind. At other times, such risk taking backfires as when the risk taker is defined as an unstable or dangerous person. The existence of the me and the I suggests that the self is dynamic and complex.

The Looking-Glass Self

A self depends on an ability to imaginatively view one self from the point of view from another. Cooley coined the term **looking-glass self** to describe the way in which a sense of self develops: People act as mirrors for one another. We see ourselves reflected in others' real or imagined reactions to our appearance and behaviors. We acquire a sense of self by being sensitive to the appraisals of ourselves that we perceive others to have: "Each to each a looking glass, / Reflects the other that [does] pass" (Cooley 1961, p. 824).

As we interact, we visualize how we appear to others, we imagine a judgment of that appearance, and we develop a feeling somewhere between pride and shame: "The thing that moves us to pride or shame is not the mere mechanical reflection of ourselves but . . . the imagined effect of this reflection upon another's mind" (Cooley 1961, p. 824). Cooley went so far as to argue that "the solid facts of social life are the facts of the imagination." Because Cooley defined the imagining or interpreting of others' reactions as critical to self-awareness, he believed that people are affected deeply even when what they imagine is exaggerated or distorted. The individual responds to the perceived rather than to a person's actual assessment.

In the case of Palestinians and Israelis, each group aims a number of powerful images at the other. For example, many Palestinians call Israeli Jews "nazis" and equate the Israeli military presence and the walls confining Palestinian movement in the West Bank and Gaza—and the accompanying system of identification cards, checks, and imprisonments—with the concentration camps of World War II. These labels are quite painful to Jews, who see little similarity between the Holocaust and the Palestinian situation. One Israeli soldier assigned to a Palestinian refugee camp imagined how he appeared to Palestinian youth: "The Palestinian boys would look at you with hatred, such hatred that it reminded me of how the Jews in concentration camps in the Holocaust looked at [the guards]. You are the most evil thing on earth right now, like it was during the Holocaust. You are the persecutor" (Nelsen 2006, p. 56).

Many Israeli Jews retaliate by calling Palestinians "Arabs"—in effect a way of telling Palestinians that the "Palestinian" people do not exist. By using the label "Arabs," Jews are declaring that "Arabs" do not need a state; they can simply live in one of the surrounding Arab countries. Some Jews also treat Palestinians as culturally primitive and incapable of managing their own affairs. They remind the Palestinians that Jews are responsible for turning the "worthless" desert land occupied previously by a "backward" Palestinian people into a modern, high-technology state.

Both Mead's and Cooley's theories suggest that self-awareness and self-identity derive from social relationships and from an ability to step outside the self and imagine it from another's perspective. Although Cooley and Mead described the mechanisms (imitation, play, games, looking-glass self) by which people learn to role-take, neither theorist addressed how a person acquires this level of cognitive sophistication. To answer this question, we turn to the work of Swiss psychologist Jean Piaget, whose work reaches across many disciplines, including sociology, biology, and education.

Cognitive Development

Piaget was the author of many influential and provocative books about how children think, reason, and learn. His ideas about how children develop increasingly sophisticated levels of reasoning stemmed from his study of water snails, which spend their early life in stagnant waters. When transferred to tidal water, these snails engage in motor activity that develops the size and shape of the shell to help them remain on the rocks and avoid being swept

me The social self—the part of the self that is the product of interaction with others and that has internalized the rules and expectations.

I The active and creative aspect of the self that questions the expectations and rules for behavior.

looking-glass self A process in which a sense of self develops, enabling one to see oneself reflected in others' real or imagined reactions to one's appearance and behaviors.

Working for Change Becoming Athletes—Expanding Conceptions of Self

More than fifty years ago, individuals with intellectual disabilities were placed in institutions that were dark and often brutal, or they lived in back rooms of family homes and were objects of sympathy, curiosity, and fear. Intellectual disability is difficult to define but it is said to exist when people score significantly below-average on a test of mental ability and when people are limited in their ability to function in key areas of daily life, including communicating with others, self-care, and getting along in social situations. Intellectual disability is sometimes referred to as a cognitive disability or mental retardation (Centers for Disease Control 2011).

In the 1960s, Dr. Frank Hayden, a Toronto sports scientist was studying the effects of regular exercise on intellectually disabled students. His research was considered groundbreaking because it showed that people with intellectual disabilities could train to become physically fit and to acquire the necessary skills to participate in sports. He found the lack of opportunity to participate, not the condition itself, was responsible for the low levels of fitness observed among the intellectually disabled. His research caught the attention of Eunice Kennedy Shriver and became the intellectual foundation for an organization that was to be called the Special Olympics (Schutten 2008).

The Special Olympics began as a day camp in the backyard of Eunice Kennedy Shriver in Potomac, Maryland. Spurred by two phone calls from parents who could not get their children into summer camps because they had intellectual disabilities and were not welcome, Shriver held the first camp in 1962 for 75 children. Through the camp, she hoped to promote involvement in physical activity and competitive opportunities for children with intellectual disabilities. She was inspired further by her sister Rosemary Kennedy who had undergone a lobotomy to calm her severe mood swings that left her with severe permanent intellectual disability. Shriver was also inspired by her travels across the United States, visiting institutions that housed people with intellectual disabilities and seeing firsthand their terrible living conditions and the lack of opportunities for physical activities. The Special Olympics has grown from a backyard event to an international one that draws thousands of participants from more than 180 countries.

The first International Special Olympics Games were held in Soldier Field in Chicago between July 19 and 20, 1968. One thousand athletes from Canada and 26 states competed in track and field, aquatics, and floor hockey events. Like the Olympic Games, the Special Olympics followed the four-year cycle of summer and winter games. The first winter Special Olympics was held in Steamboat Springs, Colorado, February 5 to 11, 1977 (Special Olympics 2011).

Since 1968, the Special Olympics has been held in many different countries. Today more than three million athletes ages 8 and older participate in Special Olympics sports training and competition.

The purpose of this program is to show that people with intellectual disabilities can be productive citizens, with the help of special education and rehabilitation. Shriver (1962) believed that 75 to 85 percent of those labeled "retarded" or "feeble-minded" can be educated and hold jobs. Another 10 percent can learn and make small contributions, such as washing dishes and other household duties. Shriver also believed that the public needed to understand and accept the disabled because the lack of support from the broader community is one reason this population is not provided opportunities to compete. The Special Olympics has given individuals with disabilities that opportunity to be athletes and refer to themselves as athletes.

"Let me win. But if I cannot win, let me be brave in the attempt."

Official motto of the Special Olympics

Source: Written by Jennifer Toland, Class of 2011, Northern Kentucky University.

away (Satterly 1987). Building on this observation, Piaget arrived at the concept of active adaptation, a biologically based tendency to adjust to and resolve environmental challenges.

Piaget believed that learning and reasoning are important adaptive tools that help people meet and resolve environmental challenges. Logical thought emerges according to a gradually unfolding genetic timetable. This unfolding must be accompanied by direct experiences with people and objects; otherwise, a child will not realize his or her potential ability.

Piaget's model of cognitive development includes four broad stages: sensorimotor, preoperational, concrete operational, and formal operational. Children cannot proceed from one stage to another until they master the reasoning challenges of earlier stages. Piaget maintained that reasoning abilities cannot be hurried; a more sophisticated level of understanding will not show itself until the brain is ready. Children construct and reconstruct their conceptions of the world as they experience the realities of living.

In the sensorimotor stage (from birth to about age 2), children explore the world with their senses (taste, touch, sight, hearing, and smell). The cognitive accomplishments of this stage include an understanding of the self as separate from other people and the realization that objects and people exist even when they are out of sight. Before this notion takes hold (at about 7 months of age), children act as if an object does not exist when they can no longer see it.

Children in the preoperational stage (ages 2 to 7) think anthropomorphically; that is, they assign human feelings to inanimate objects. They believe that objects such as the sun, the moon, nails, marbles, trees, and clouds have motives, feelings, and intentions (for example, dark clouds are angry; a nail that sinks to the bottom of a glass filled with water is tired). Children in the preoperational stage cannot appreciate that matter can change form but still remain the same in quantity (for example, they believe a 12-ounce cup that is tall and narrow holds more than a 12-ounce cup that is short and wide; height is the variable by which they judge the amount, failing to consider diameter). In addition, children in this second stage cannot conceive how the world looks from another's point of view. Thus, if a child facing a roomful of people (all of whom are looking in his or her direction) is asked to draw a picture of how someone in the back of the room sees the audience, the child will draw the picture as he or she sees the people (showing their faces rather than the backs of their heads). Finally, children in the preoperational stage tend to center their attention on one detail and fail to process information that challenges that detail.

Missy Gish

Around the age of 2, babies acquire the cognitive ability to imaginatively step outside the self and see it from another's perspective. One indicator that a baby can do this is when he recognizes himself in a mirror.

By the time children reach the concrete operational stage (from about ages 7 to 12), they have mastered the conceptual challenges of the second stage, but they have difficulty in thinking hypothetically or abstractly without reference to a concrete event or image. For example, children in this stage have difficulty envisioning life without them in it. One 12-year-old struggling to grasp this idea said to me, "I am the beginning and the end; the world begins with and ends with me."

Black-and-white thinking does not just apply to children. Israeli author David Grossman (2010) describes how black-and-white thinking cannot possibly capture the complexities of the Palestinian–Israeli conflict. He notes that some Israeli leftists never allow themselves to think about the danger that Israel faces because they unconditionally trust Palestinians and their good will. Some rightists never allow themselves to feel even the slightest twinge of guilt or moral responsibility for the evil Israelis have inflicted on the Palestinians. Grossman argues that neither party is in contact with reality of the situation.

In the formal operational stage (from the onset of adolescence onward), people can think abstractly. For example, people can conceptualize their existence as a part of a much larger historical continuum and a larger context. They no longer see the world in black-and-white terms; rather, they see it in shades of gray. Apparently, this progression by stages toward increasingly sophisticated levels of reasoning is universal, although the content of people's thinking varies across cultures. For example, all children in the preoperational stage (stage 2) focus their attention on a single detail to the exclusion of information that might challenge it. But the details they learn to focus on vary by culture. Israeli children are taught to be suspicious not only of unattended packages and bags in airports but also of empty cups, bottles,

Student Activity: Test Piaget's theory that children in preoperational stage cannot appreciate that matter can change form but still remain the same in quantity (for example, they believe a 12-ounce cup that is tall and narrow holds more than a 12-ounce cup that is short and wide). You can test the idea by presenting a child between the ages of 2 and 7 with two 12-oz glasses of different shapes filled with their favorite drink. Make sure that you pour the drink into each glass in front of the child to show that the same amount goes in each glass. Then ask the child which glass holds more of their favorite drink. Try the experiment on a child older than seven.

and cans anywhere. In *Arab and Jew*, David Shipler (1986) describes his frustrations in explaining to his young children that they did not have to follow this rule now that they were in the United States. When he set some bags of newspapers on the curb to be picked up, his children reported suspicious packages outside; and when he asked his 7-year-old son to pick up a plastic cup in the street and throw it away, "He adamantly refused to go near it, and he remained solidly unmoved by my extravagant assurances that we didn't have to worry about bombs on a quiet, tree-lined suburban street in America" (Shipler 1986, p. 83).

Agents of Socialization

> CORE CONCEPT 6 **Agents of socialization—significant others, primary groups, in-groups, and institutions—shape our sense of self; they also teach us about and how to respond to the social and physical environment.**

It is impossible to list all the agents of socialization. Specific examples include the family, peers, military units, teachers, religious leaders and mass media. In the sections that follow we pay special attention to groups and mass media (a social institution).

Groups as Agents of Socialization

In the most general sense, a **group** is two or more people who do the following:

1. Share a distinct identity (the ability to speak a specific language, biological descent from a specific couple, membership in a team or a military unit)
2. Feel a sense of belonging
3. Interact directly or indirectly with one another

Groups vary according to a host of characteristics, including size, cohesion, purpose, and duration. Sociologists identify primary groups and in-groups and out-groups as particularly important agents of socialization.

Primary Groups

A **primary group**—such as a family, military unit, or peer group—is a social group that has face-to-face contact and strong emotional ties among its members. Primary groups are not always united by harmony and love; for example, they can be united by hatred for another group. In either case, the ties are emotional. The members of a primary group strive to achieve "some desired place in the thoughts of [the] others" and feel allegiance to the other members (Cooley 1909, p. 24). Although a person may never achieve the desired place, he or she may remain preoccupied with that goal. In this sense, primary groups are "fundamental in forming the social nature and ideals of the individual" (Cooley 1909, p. 23).

The family is an important agent of socialization because it gives individuals their deepest and earliest experiences with relationships and their first exposure to the rules of life. In addition, the family teaches its members about the social and physical environment and ways to respond to that environment. When that environment is stressful, the family can buffer its members against the effects of that stress; alternatively, it can exacerbate the effects. Sociologists Amith Ben-David and Yoav Lavee (1992) offer a specific example of this buffering function. The two sociologists interviewed 64 Israelis to learn how their families responded to the 1990 SCUD missile attacks Iraq launched on Israel during the Persian Gulf War. During these attacks, families gathered in sealed rooms and put on gas masks. The researchers found that families varied in their responses to this life-threatening situation.

Some respondents reported the interaction during that time as positive and supportive: "We laughed and we took pictures of each other with the gas masks on" or "We talked about different things, about the war, we told jokes, we heard the announcements on the radio" (p. 39). Other respondents reported that little interaction among family members occurred but a feeling of togetherness prevailed: "I was quiet, immersed in my thoughts. We were all around the radio. . . . Nobody talked much. We all sat there and we were trying to listen to what was happening outside" (p. 40). Some respondents reported that interaction was tense: "We fought with the kids about putting on their masks, and also between us about whether the kids should put on their masks. There was much shouting and noise" (p. 39). Ben-David and Lavee's findings are supported by a 2008 study of 29 middle school–age students in the Israeli city of Sderot who experienced seven years of ongoing rocket attacks launched by Palestinians in the Gaza Strip. The study found that strong support systems involving family, friends, and school cushioned the effects of

agents of socialization Significant others, primary groups, in-groups and out-groups, and institutions that (1) shape our sense of self or social identity, (2) teach us about the groups to which we do and do not belong, (3) help us to realize our human capacities, and (4) help us negotiate the social and physical environment we have inherited.

group Two or more people who share a distinct identity, feel a sense of belonging, and interact directly or indirectly with one another.

primary group A social group that has face-to-face contact and strong emotional ties among its members.

Discussion Tip: Ask students to review the Amith Ben-David and Yoav Lavee study above. In which of the three ways do they think their family would respond in a similar crisis?

Department of Defense

When exposed to difficult situations, the family can buffer or exacerbate the impact on family members. This family's home has been destroyed by floods. A parent's calm and determined response can offset the potential traumatic effects.

SSG Dan Yarnall

A military unit is a primary group. During military training, soldiers become so close that they fight for one another, rather than for the victory per se, in the heat of the battle.

depression induced by long-term exposure to attacks (Science Daily 2008).

As these cases illustrate, even under extremely stressful circumstances, such as war, the family can teach responses that increase or decrease that stress. Clearly, children in families that emphasize constructive responses to stressful events have an advantage over children whose parents respond in destructive ways.

Like the family, a military unit is a primary group. A unit's success in battle depends on the existence of strong ties among its members. Soldiers in this primary group become so close that they fight for one another, rather than for victory per se, in the heat of battle (Dyer 1985). In Israel, the military represents a place where immigrants from almost 100 national and cultural backgrounds become Israelis, bonding with one another and with native Israelis (Rowley 1998). Military units train their recruits always to think of the group before themselves. In fact, the paramount goal of military training is to make individuals feel inseparable from their unit. Some common strategies employed to achieve this goal include ordering recruits to wear uniforms, to shave their heads, to march in unison, to sleep and eat together, to live in isolation from the larger society, and to perform tasks that require the successful participation of all unit members. If one member fails, the entire unit fails. Another key strategy is to focus the unit's attention on fighting together against a common enemy. An external enemy gives a group a singular direction, thereby increasing its internal cohesiveness.

The Israeli military is an important agent of socialization. Almost every Israeli can claim membership in this type of primary group because virtually every Israeli citizen—male and female—serves in the military (three years for men and about two years for women). Men must serve on active duty for at least one month every year until they are 51 years old (U.S. Central Intelligence Agency 2011).

Similarly, military training is an important experience for many Palestinians. Palestinian youth—especially those living in Syrian, Lebanese, Egyptian, and Jordanian refugee camps (which are outside Israeli control)—join youth clubs and train to protect the camps from attack. The focus on defeating a common enemy helps establish and maintain the boundaries of the military unit. All types of primary groups have boundaries—a sense of who is in the group and who is outside it. The concepts of in-group and out-group help us understand these dynamics.

In-groups and Out-groups

A group distinguishes itself by the symbolic and physical boundaries its members establish to set it apart from nonmembers. Examples of physical boundaries may be gated communities, walls to separate one neighborhood or country from another, special buildings such as prisons or churches, or other distinct geographic settings. Symbolic boundaries include membership cards, colors, or dress codes such as a uniform. A group also distinguishes itself by establishing criteria for membership including a certain ancestry, a particular physical trait, or some accomplishment (for example, a specified level of education, passing a test, qualifying for a team, paying dues, or buying certain attire). The boundaries and membership criteria are ways groups distinguish "us" from "them."

Discussion Tip: Ask if any students have served in the military. If so, invite those students to describe how military training socialized them to think of the group over the individual.

Sociologists use the terms in-group and out-group in reference to intergroup dynamics. An **in-group** is the group to which a person belongs, identifies, admires, and/or feels loyalty. An **out-group** is any group to which a person does not belong. Obviously, one person's in-group is another person's out-group. In-group formation is built on establishing boundaries and membership criteria. In-group members think of themselves as "us" in relation to some specific or even amorphous "them" (Brewer 1999). Examples of specific in-group/out-group pairings include rival gangs such as the Bloods and the Crips or the teams formed for a reality television show such as *Survivor*. More amorphous in-group/out-group pairings include Christians and Muslims, Jews and Palestinians, Fatah and Hamas, Steelers versus Bengals fans, and the far left and far right. Amorphous means that members are very different. In-group and out-group dynamics are such that very different people are bound together because they share something very important to their identity such as a political agenda or religious affiliation.

When sociologists study in-group and out-group dynamics, they ask, "Under what circumstances does the presence of an out-group unify an in-group and create an 'us' versus 'them' dynamic?" Three circumstances are described.

1. An in-group assumes a position of moral superiority over an out-group. Moral superiority is the belief that an in-group's standards represent the only way. In fact, there is no room for negotiation and no tolerance for other ways (Brewer 1999). Moral superiority can express itself in a variety of ways, including refusing to interact with or show interest in anyone in an out-group, establishing laws segregating an in-group from an out-group, or engaging in violence toward an out-group.
2. An in-group perceives an out-group as a threat. In this situation, in-group members believe (rightly or wrongly) that an out-group threatens its way of life. The in-group holds real or imagined fear that the out-group is seeking
    - political power,
    - control of scarce and valued resources,
    - a larger share of the "pie,"
    - retribution for past wrongs, or
    - return of lost power.
3. In-group/out-group tensions may be evoked for political gain. Those with political ambitions may deliberately evoke in-group/out-group tensions as a strategy for mobilizing support for some political purpose (Brewer 1999). Thus, a candidate running for elected office may declare an out-group such as union-busting conservatives, undocumented workers, or gays a threat to the American way of life as a strategy for rallying support.

One can argue that the presence of Palestinians functions to unify Israeli Jews, who are culturally, linguistically, religiously, and politically diverse. Since Israel's founding, Jews from 102 different countries, speaking 80 different languages, have settled there (Peres 1998). Twenty-two percent were born in Europe or the United States. Almost 10 percent were born in an African or Asian country (U.S. Central Intelligence Agency 2011). These diverse Israeli Jews share a common language (Hebrew), the desire for a homeland free of persecution, and an ongoing conflict with the following: Palestinians in the West Bank and Gaza, Palestinians in Israel, and Arabs in surrounding states. "Israeli Arab" is the label the Israeli government applies to the Palestinians who did not leave in 1948 or 1967 and to their descendants. These Palestinians number about 1.3 million people—about 24 percent of Israel's population. They live in 116 "Arab-only" communities and seven so-called "mixed" cities, in which Palestinians live in separate communities adjacent to Jewish communities (Nathan 2006). The Palestinians who live in Israel prefer the label "Israeli Palestinians."

Similarly, the presence of Jews acts to unite an equally diverse Palestinian society, which includes West Bank Palestinians, Gaza Palestinians, and Israeli Palestinians, who also come from different ethnic and religious groups, clans, and political orientations.

Because little interaction occurs between in-group and out-group members, they know little about one another. This lack of firsthand experience deepens and reinforces misrepresentations, mistrust, and misunderstandings between members of the two groups. Thus, members of one group tend to view members of the other in the most stereotypical of terms. Yoram Bilu at Hebrew University of Jerusalem designed and conducted a particularly creative study to examine the consequences of in-group/out-group relations in the West Bank. Bilu and two of his students asked youths aged 11 to 13 from Palestinian refugee camps and Israeli settlements in the West Bank to keep journals of their dreams over a specified period. Seventeen percent of Israeli youths wrote that they dreamed about encounters with Arabs, whereas 30 percent of the Palestinian youths dreamed about meeting Jews. Among the 32 dreams of meetings between Jews and Arabs, not one character was identified by name. Not a single figure was defined by a personal, individual appearance. All the descriptions were completely stereotyped—the characters defined only by their ethnic identification (such as "Jew," "Arab," or "Zionist") or by value-laden terms with negative connotations (such

---

in-group A group to which a person belongs, identifies, admires, and/or feels loyalty.

out-group Any group to which a person does not belong.

as "the terrorists" or "the oppressors"). The majority of the interactions in the dreams indicate a hard and threatening reality, a fragile world with no defense:

> An Arab child dreams: "The Zionist Army surrounds our house and breaks in. My big brother is taken to prison and is tortured there. The soldiers continue to search the house. They throw everything around, but do not find the person they want. . . . They leave the house, but return, helped by a treacherous neighbor. This time they find me, and my relatives, after we have all hidden in the closet in fright."
>
> A Jewish child dreams: ". . . suddenly someone grabs me, and I see that it is happening in my house, but my family went away, and Arab children are walking through our rooms, and their father holds me, he has a keffiyeh and his face is cruel, and I am not surprised that it is happening, that these Arabs now live in my house." (Grossman 1988, pp. 30, 32–33)

There are at least 12 youth camps in the United States and Canada designed to bring Palestinians and Israeli Jews together with the hope of bridging the in-group/out-group divide with specially designed activities such as the following:

> The Israeli and Palestinian youth probably have never physically touched each other. They may arrive with images of the other as inhuman, even aliens or monsters. In one program, they are asked to find someone they don't know well in the group, someone they consider "other." It may be someone they were afraid of, or still are afraid of.
>
> They are told to look at one another. And then, they are told to ask permission, and then find the pulse on one another's wrist. Then they do the same with the arteries in their necks. Then they place their hands on the others' breastbone to feel their hearts, while they continue to look at each other. "This can be very powerful, because they've never touched their enemy, and they realize that 'she feels like me,'" says the program director. (Fetzer Institute 2005)

Often an in-group and an out-group clash over symbols—objects or gestures that are clearly associated with and valued by one group. Members of the out-group can define these objects as so threatening that they seek to eliminate the objects: destroying the symbol becomes a way of destroying the group. The wall the Israeli government built to divide the West Bank from Israel is a significant symbol for both Palestinians and Israeli Jews. Jews see it as a protection against suicide attacks. Palestinians see it as a severe restriction of their movement to and from and within the West Bank, impeding their ability to cross into Israel to work and shifting the boundaries between Israel and a future Palestinian state.

It is important to know that in-groups and out-groups also exist within Palestinian and Israeli society. Palestinians are divided according to which political party they support: the relatively secular Fatah or Islamic Hamas; in addition, about 10 percent of Palestinians are Christian. Among Israelis, clear divisions exist between Sephardic Jews, with North African and Middle Eastern roots, and Ashkenazi Jews, with European roots. An estimated 50 percent of Israelis do not actively practice a religion, 30 percent consider themselves practicing Jews, and 18 percent are ultraorthodox. The ultraorthodox are exempt from military service, a policy that creates resentment among Jews who must serve in the military and then the reserves until they are 51 years old (BBC News 1998b).

Nancy Hemminger (Courtesy of Joan Ferrante)

Palestinian graffiti artists draw a scene that speaks to what the wall dividing Israel and the West Bank is not: a comfortable, home-like environment with a great view. To get a sense of the wall's size, notice the people standing in front of the arm chair.

Our discussion of in-groups and out-groups shows that one's self-identity revolves around group membership. In the section that follows, we examine how the self-identity of Palestinian suicide bombers/martyrs is tied to the in-group to which they belong, and by extension, to the out-group to which they do not belong.

Suicide: The Severing of Relationships We learned in Chapter 1 that Durkheim defined suicide as "the severing of relationships." Recall that Durkheim identified four types of problematic social relationships: (1) egoistic (weak ties to the group), (2) altruistic (strong ties to the group), (3) anomic (dramatic change in which the individual is cast out of the group into a higher or lower status), and (4) fatalistic (a state in which individuals see their future as hopelessly blocked).

According to the Israeli security service, known as Shin Bet, between June 2002 and June 2004, the years leading up to the construction of the wall, there were 145 suicide bombers/martyrs who carried out, or tried but failed to carry out, an attack (Harel 2004a). This represents 0.5 percent of the 29,000 attacks (ranging from stone throwing to planting bombs) that Palestinians carried out against Israelis. Here are some things we know about suicide bombers/martyrs that suggest altruistic motives:

- Palestinians who put their lives on the line are typically motivated by "revenge for acts committed by

Israelis." One suicide bomber/martyr explained his motives with these words: "I want to avenge the blood of the Palestinians, especially the blood of the women, of the elderly, and of the children, and in particular the blood of the baby girl Iman Hejjo, whose death shook me to the core" (Margalit 2003). Another suicide bomber/martyr's mother noted that her daughter was filled with pain after five Israeli soldiers killed her brother, Fadi. "She was full of pain about that. Some nights she woke screaming, saying she had nightmares about Fadi" (Burns 2003).

- Approximately 75 percent of Palestinians support suicide attacks (Lahoud 2001). Suicide attackers/martyrs are treated as celebrities in the sense that they are instantly "propelled from being no one to being someone who is glorified, and lionized with poems and [they] live on in this historical chain of heroic martyrs, being remembered and saluted for longer than if [they] had not undertaken this kind of operation" (Natta 2003). Even small children know the names of suicide bombers (Margalit 2003).

Several other characteristics distinguish suicide bombers/martyrs as well. Although Durkheim would classify the conditions that support the individual Palestinian's decision to commit a suicide attack as altruistic, he would find it noteworthy that two-thirds of all suicide attackers were between the ages of 17 and 23 (and most were younger than 30) and that 86 percent were single. These characteristics suggest that, although suicide bombers/martyrs may be acting in the name of the larger Palestinian society and in the name of someone wronged by Israelis, they are also relatively detached from others (such as a spouse and children), and because of that detachment, they will encounter less resistance to carrying through on the suicide than those attached to others through marriage or parenthood.

Mass and Social Media

Mass media are forms of communication designed to reach large audiences without face-to-face contact between those conveying and those receiving the messages. Examples of mass media include magazines, newspapers, commercials, books, television programs, websites, radio broadcasts, video games, and music CDs. The tools of mass media—such as television, radio, the Internet, and smart phones—introduce their audiences to a variety of people, including sports figures, news makers, cartoon characters, politicians, actors, disc jockeys, and musicians. Some audience segments become so emotionally attached to these figures that they count themselves as fans following celebrities' lives, desiring the products celebrities endorse, and otherwise seeking to emulate them or live vicariously through them.

For the first time in human history, average people have digital tools at their fingertips to reach mass audiences. At the time of this writing, two websites that potentially allow users to present the self to millions of people—YouTube.com and Facebook.com—ranked second and third on the Global 500 of websites (Alexa 2010). These two ranked among the ten most popular websites accessed in Israel, and the United States, and the Palestinian territories (Alexa 2010). YouTube contains thousands of videos chronicling various viewpoints on the Palestinian–Jewish conflict. Simply using the search word *Palestinian* yields hits titled "Palestinian Rap," "Palestinian Heroes," and "Palestinian Child Prisoner."

An influential medium of mass communication in the United States is television; 98.2 percent of American households have an average of 2.7 televisions, and 72.4 percent have a cable connection or satellite dish antenna (U.S. Census Bureau 2009). Each day, the average American watches about 5.1 hours of TV. That translates into 35.7 hours per week (Nielsenwire 2009). It would be impossible to make definitive statements about the mass media's effect on people's sense of self and on their relationships with others. Studies have been done on virtually every type of mass media, showing both positive and negative consequences. For example, studies show that television can function as an important educational tool but it can also impede development of critical academic skills, such as reading.

One example of the power of television to reach mass audiences is *Sesame Street*. The most watched children's television show in history, it airs in at least 120 countries. It first aired in the United States in 1969, with a groundbreaking multiracial cast. *Sesame Street*'s mission is to level the educational playing field for all preschool children. Joan Ganz Cooney, the originator of *Sesame Street*, maintains that "our producers are like old-fashioned missionaries. . . . It's not religion they're spreading, but it's learning

Courtesy of Chris Brown

Suicide bombers/martyrs pose before their death for pictures that will be shown on posters that honor or celebrate their death.

mass media Forms of communication designed to reach large audiences without face-to-face contact between those conveying and those receiving the messages.

Discussion Tip: Ask students to stand up if they have a Facebook account and to remain standing until you call a number out that exceeds their number of friends. Start with 200 friends and gradually increase by 50. Then ask students for unusual stories about how they connected with someone through Facebook or another social media.

No Borders No Boundaries Cell Phone and Internet

The chart shows the number of landline versus mobile phones per 1,000 people in the Palestinian territories, Israel, and the United States. Notice that people in West Bank and Gaza have 88 landline phones per 1,000 people compared to 424 per 1,000 in Israel and 484 per 1,000 in the United States. People living in the Palestinian territories have 585 mobile phones per 1,000 people compared to 1,301 per 1,000 people in Israel and 871 per 1,000 in United States. One reason that Israel's rate is so high is that 20 to 33 percent of Palestinian mobile phone users subscribe through Israeli networks (Mobile Active 2008). The fact that the number of landlines per 1,000 people is so much smaller in the Palestinian territories suggests that, until recently, Gaza and the West Bank did not have an infrastructure to support easy and instant communication with others. The mobile phone and Internet have changed that. Mobile phones are used to record and report news as it occurs. And in times of violent conflict, blood banks, for example, send texts to potential donors alerting them that the need is critical. Those on both sides of the conflict use Twitter to share opinions and broadcast news (Mobile Active 2008). During times of intense conflict, incoming international calls can increase by 30 percent over the normal volume (Public Radio International 2009). We do not have reliable figures about how many people have access to the Internet but we can predict that, along with the cell phone, the Internet has dramatically increased both sides' ability to tell others about the conflict and how it is experienced as it happens.

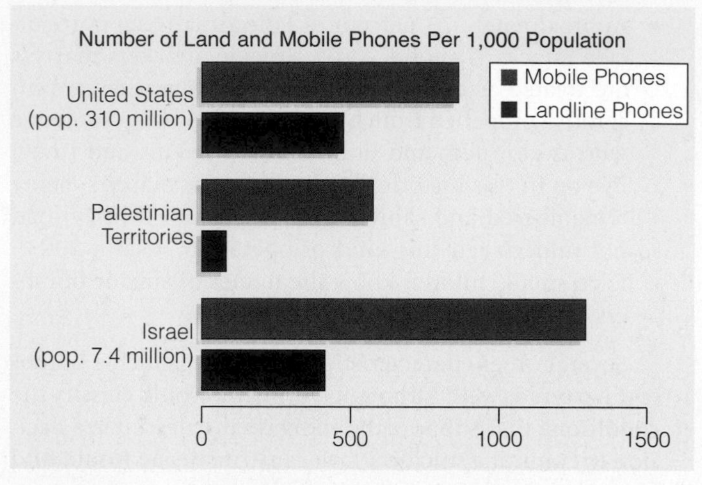

FIGURE 4.2

Source: Data from U.S. Central Intelligence Agency (2011)

and tolerance and love and mutual respect" (Independent Lens 2006).

In Israel and the Palestinian territories, *Sesame Street* airs as *Sesame Stories*, because the idea that a neutral street exists where Palestinians and Jews might gather together is not a believable scenario in that part of the world. *Sesame Stories* concentrates on (1) teaching young viewers respect and understanding for their own and other cultures, (2) promoting a peaceful resolution to the hundred-year conflict between Palestinians and Jews, and (3) presenting positive images of Palestinian and Jewish children. In one episode, Israeli and Arab friends stage a peaceful protest to stop one of the Muppets from banging his drum too loudly. In another episode, a Palestinian girl living in a refugee camp finds a water bottle on the street and takes it upon herself to plant something in it. She gets no encouragement from those around her, who claim that nothing can grow in a refugee camp. The producers place great emphasis on the girl's finding a clear container rather than, say, a tin can, as Jewish children are taught not to pick up items if they cannot see what is in them (Salamon 2002). These producers believe that shows emphasizing themes of hope, integration, and friendship will have lasting effects on Palestinian and Jewish viewers (Deutsche Welle 2003). A pretest and posttest study of the impact of *Sesame Stories* programming suggests an increase in Jewish and Palestinian viewers' use of prosocial strategies to resolve conflicts and positive attributes to describe each other (Cole et al. 2003).

Socialization across the Life Cycle

It is important to realize that socialization takes place throughout the human life cycle. There are at least eight major stages of the lifecycle. Sociologists who study the life cycle stages emphasize the interaction and social challenges peculiar to each. Because we have devoted considerable attention to early childhood socialization, we quickly review stages 1 through 3 and give special focus to stages 4 through 8.

Stages 1 through 3 (Infancy, Toddler, Preschool)

During stage 1 (infancy), it is important that caretakers give consistent, predictable care. Inadequate, unpredictable care leaves infants uncertain of their ability to elicit care and makes them feel that the world is not reliable (Erikson 1950). In stage 2 (toddler), the child's nervous and muscular systems mature, and abilities in one area are frustrated by inabilities in another. Toddlers possess enough motor

Teaching Tip: To illustrate the reach and influence of Sesame Street, go to Google News and enter "Sesame Street" as search terms. The search will likely yield hundreds of news stories. Just reading titles of news stories will offer insights.

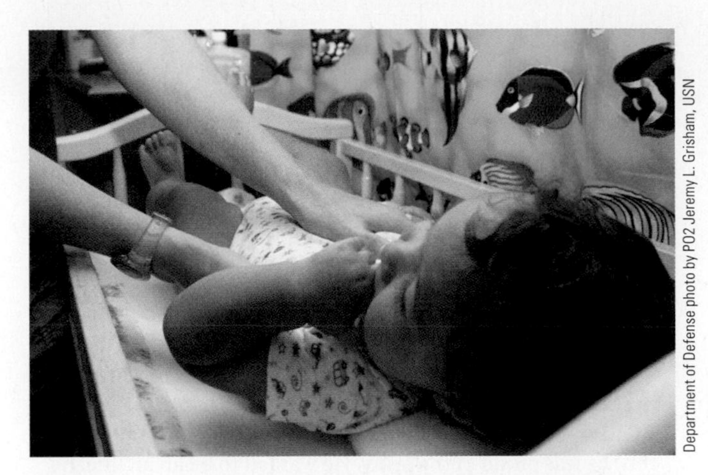
Department of Defense photo by PO2 Jeremy L. Grisham, USN

During stage 1, it is essential that children receive predictable and consistent care from caregivers so that they come to see the world as reliable.

skills to move around and explore but are not yet aware of the consequences of their actions. Growing abilities clash with inabilities, and this stage becomes a battle for autonomy. Caregivers must protect children from danger, be tolerant yet firm, and support children in their efforts to be independent. If caregivers are critical, overprotective, or discouraging of children's attempts to master the environment, the children may feel shame and doubt, especially if parents resent their children's inabilities for interfering with the parents' independence (Erikson 1950).

Stage 3 (preschool) corresponds with Mead's play stage, in that children play at being the kind of person they hope to grow up to be. They "hitch their wagons" to the people they admire most in their immediate lives; they identify with these figures and imagine being them. If the gap between an admired person and the child's skills is too large, children become frustrated and think, "I am no good compared with X." Adults must show approval and encouragement and let children know they are equal in worth, if not yet ability. Without such reassurance, "the danger is that they will feel guilt over the goals contemplated and the acts initiated" (Erikson 1950, p. 84).

Stage 4 (Ages 6 to 12)

Systematic instruction is central to this stage. Recognition is won by doing things. If their teachers are secure and respected, children develop a positive identification with those who know how to do things. If assignments are meaningful, children learn the pleasure that comes with steady attention and perseverance. In this setting, they come to enjoy performing tasks and take pride in doing things well. Industry involves doing things beside and with others (Erikson 1950).

The danger at this stage is developing a sense of inadequacy and inferiority—the feeling that one will never contribute anything or be any good. Palestinian children face the industry-inferiority tension when Israeli authorities close their schools for extended periods. The loss of meaningful, systematic instruction stimulates children to search for their own meaningful activity. Many Palestinian schoolchildren have chosen to participate by throwing stones, an action defined as a meaningful contribution toward securing a homeland.

Stage 5 (Adolescence)

This stage is characterized by rapid body growth and genital maturation. At this time, adolescents also develop ideas about what they will do with their lives. In other words, they begin to search for an identity. As they search, they are often preoccupied with how they appear in the eyes of others. They struggle with being a part of a group and being themselves. As they work to establish an identity, adolescents may overidentify with unrealistic cultural or group heroes and exclude people they deem "different."

Stage 6 (Young Adulthood)

During this stage, young adults form close and intimate bonds with others. A mark of a healthy personality is the ability to love and to work. People with this ability can work productively without losing the capacity to be sexual and loving. The opposite of intimacy is self-absorption, which involves "the readiness to isolate, if necessary, to destroy those forces and people whose essence seems dangerous to one's own" (Erikson 1950, p. 264).

The work lives and personal lives of most Israelis are interrupted repeatedly by military obligations. Israeli men must leave their jobs and families at least once a year to serve in the army. Palestinians frequently sacrifice work and family when they protest the occupation with strikes, work stoppages, and business closings. Israeli officials also disrupt Palestinian work and family life when they close access roads and Palestinian businesses. Each group holds the other responsible for the state of affairs, and each seeks to control or resist the other (see Sociological Imagination: "Israeli Jews as Aggressors and Victims").

Stage 7 (Middle Age)

Ideally, those in middle age make an effort to guide and help establish the next generation and to pass on what they have contributed to life. This stage is characterized by a strengthened commitment to the care of cherished people and objects. Its counterpart is stagnation and interpersonal impoverishment (Erikson 1988, p. 16).

Someone who chose a path of commitment to future generations is Israeli prime minister Yitzhak Rabin, who was assassinated by a Jewish right-wing extremist for seeking a peaceful solution to the Israeli–Palestinian conflict.

The Sociological Imagination Israeli Jews as Aggressors and Victims

The biographies of Israeli soldiers cannot be separated from the historical force that pushed Israelis and Palestinians together on land both claim as rightfully their home. In *The Other Side of Israel,* Susan Nathan interviews an Israeli soldier who imagines how he would feel if Palestinians were in power and conducting home searches the way his Israeli unit had conducted them:

> I try to imagine the reverse situation: if they had entered my home, not a police force with a warrant but a unit of solders, if they had burst into my home and shoved my mother and little sister into my bedroom and forced my father and my younger brother and me into the living room, pointing their guns at us, laughing, smiling, and we didn't always understand what the soldiers were saying while they emptied drawers and searched through things. Oops, it fell, broken—all kinds of photos of my grandmother and grandfather, all kinds of sentimental things that you wouldn't want anyone else to see. There is no justification for this. If there is a suspicion that a terrorist has entered a house, so be it. But just to enter a home, any home: here I've chosen one, look, what fun. We go in, we check it out, we cause a bit of injustice, we have asserted our military presence and then we move on. (Nathan 2006, pp. 213–214)

In *Occupied Minds,* Arthur Nelsen profiles Roni Hirschenson, a 62-year-old Jew whose sons Amir and Elad were Israeli soldiers. Hirschenson is a member of the group Families Forum, an organization of bereaved Palestinians and Israeli Jews working toward reconciliation. An excerpt from the profile follows:

> Amir volunteered for the paratroops, three months after he joined the army. He was a good, generous person, very close to his brother. He also believed in two states for two peoples but he was proud of the army. He wanted to be an architect. I was at my workshop when I heard about the attack that killed him. . . . It was on the news that a suicide bomber blew himself up among a group of soldiers at Beit Lid junction. I knew Amir was staying at another base so I thought he was safe. I didn't know that he'd been sent to the junction to guard against terrorists. He wasn't hurt by the first explosion but when he went to help his friends, another suicide bomber blew himself up, and he found his death. . . . Elad [who subsequently committed suicide] was also a soldier. The last words he wrote were that he couldn't stand the pain of the loss of his brother and that life was useless when you have lost your closest one like this. (Nelsen 2006, pp. 194–195)

Rabin "took the road of peace with the Palestinians, not because he possessed great affection for them or their leaders. . . . Rabin decided to act, because he discerned very wisely that Israeli society would not be able to sustain itself endlessly in a state of an unresolved conflict. He realized long before many others that life in a climate of violence, occupation, terror, anxiety and hopelessness, extracts a price Israel cannot afford" (Grossman 2006). In contrast to Rabin's response are the responses of Palestinians and Israeli Jews who see no end to the hundred-year conflict, "having been born into war and raised in it, and in a certain sense indoctrinated by it." They see this madness as "the only life," with "no option or even the right to aspire [to] a different life" (Grossman 2006).

Stage 8 (Old Age)

In old age, "one faces the totality of life. Old people see their lives as a whole. At last, life hangs together," and one comes to accept the life one has lived and to acknowledge the people significant to it (Erikson 1982, p. 102). Old age involves the realization that one's biography is the "accidental coincidence of but one life cycle in but one segment of history." With this realization comes a sense of comradeship with all human beings. If acceptance is not achieved, one feels despair about oneself and the world and believes that the remaining time is too short to try again or change things. Despair is often expressed as disgust or displeasure with institutions and people. On

The Raging Grannies is a grassroots organization dedicated to making a significant impact on issues that affect their communities and the planet. Here, the Raging Grannies are protesting Chevron's use of deceptive advertising to sway voters to vote "no" on Proposition 26, a California ballot initiative that passes on the costs of cleaning up corporate pollution to taxpayers.

TABLE 4.1 Selected Demographic Characteristics of Gaza, the West Bank, and Israel

The table shows the population characteristics of Israel, the Gaza Strip, and West Bank. Which area has the highest percentage of the population age 14 or younger? Which area has the highest fertility rate? Based on unemployment and poverty rates, which area seems in greatest distress? How might social distress and a disproportionately young population shape developmental challenges outlined by Erikson? How might these factors fuel the ongoing conflict?

	Gaza	West Bank	Israel
Birth rate (per 1,000 people)	36.2	24.9	19.5
Number of children born to average woman (fertility rate)	4.9	3.12	2.7
Infant mortality (per 1,000 live births)	17.71	15.4	4.17
Percent of population 14 or younger	44	37.3	27.9
Percent of population 65 or older	2.6	3.7	9.9
Percent of population living in poverty	70.0	46.0	23.6
Percent of unemployment	40	19	7.6

Source: Data from U.S. Central Intelligence Agency (2011).

the other hand, if all goes well, wisdom is the fruit of the struggle to accept the life one has lived in the face of physical disintegration (see Table 4.1).

Resocialization

CORE CONCEPT 7 Over a lifetime, people make social transitions that entail acquiring new roles, shedding old roles, and integrating new roles with current roles. In making these transitions, people undergo resocialization.

Resocialization is a process that involves breaking with behaviors and ways of thinking that are unsuited to existing or changing circumstances, and replacing them with new, more appropriate ways of behaving and thinking. Much resocialization happens naturally and involves no formal training; people simply learn as they go. For example, people who marry, have children, and graduate from college must learn ways to live their lives as they transition from single to married, from childlessness to parenthood, and from college student to a career. On the other hand, some circumstances require that people undergo formal training and demonstrate that they have internalized appropriate knowledge, suitable values, and correct codes of conduct. Medical doctors attend seminars to keep up with changes in their specialty, and people seek debt counseling at the request of creditors. Those who have lost loved ones in conflict or wars must go through a process of resocialization, in which they relearn how to live life without them.

In general, it is easier to resocialize people when they want to be resocialized than when they are forced to give up old values and behaviors. In addition, resocialization programs are likely to be successful when participants gain rather than lose status.

Voluntary versus Imposed Resocialization

Resocialization can be voluntary or imposed. Voluntary resocialization occurs when people choose to participate in a process or program designed to remake them. Examples of voluntary resocialization are wide ranging: the unemployed youth who enlists in the army to acquire a technical skill, the prescription drug addict who seeks treatment, the alcoholic who decides to join Alcoholics Anonymous.

Imposed resocialization occurs when people are forced into a program designed to train them, rehabilitate them, or correct some supposed deficiency in their earlier socialization. People drafted into the military, sentenced to prisons, court-ordered to attend parenting classes, or committed to

resocialization The process that involves breaking with behaviors and ways of thinking that are unsuited to existing or changing circumstances, and replacing them with new, more appropriate ways of behaving and thinking.

Global Comparisons Estimated Number of Jews Living in Each of the World's Countries

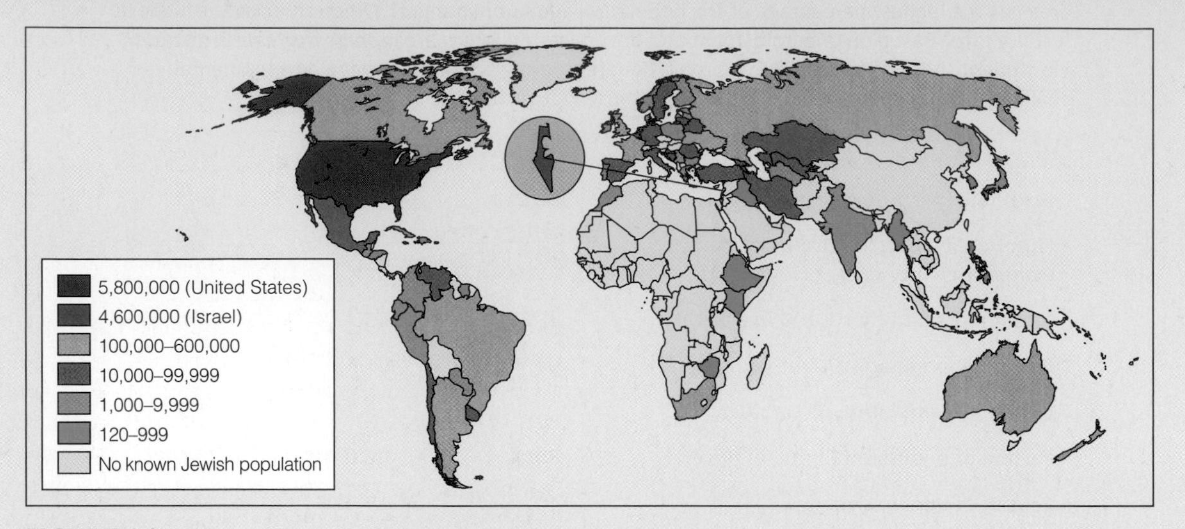

FIGURE 4.3

Source: Data from *Jewish Communities of the World*, Institute of World Jewish Congress (2006, 2010)

The map shows the estimated number of Jews living in each country of the world. Keep in mind that the European pogroms (government-instigated massacres and persecution) and severe economic crises between 1880 and 1914 pushed Jews out of Europe, not just to Israel, but to many countries around the world, especially the United States. In addition, the Holocaust increased the flow of Jewish refugees out of Europe to other countries, but especially to Israel. Wherever they immigrated, the Jewish immigrants had to adjust to their new homes through the resocialization process. According to the World Jewish Congress, an estimated 13 million Jews now live in 120 countries. The largest number of Jews lives in the United States (5.8 million), followed by Israel (4.6 million).

The eight cities with the largest Jewish populations are New York (1.9 million), Los Angeles (585,000), Miami (535,000), Paris (350,000), Philadelphia (315,000), Chicago (250,000), Boston (228,000), and San Francisco (210,000).

mental institutions represent examples of those who undergo resocialization that is forced upon them.

In *Asylums*, sociologist Erving Goffman (1961) wrote about a particular type of setting called **total institutions** in which people are isolated from the rest of society to undergo systematic resocialization. Total institutions include homes for the blind, the elderly, the orphaned, and the indigent; mental hospitals; prisons; concentration camps; army barracks; boarding schools; and monasteries and convents. In total institutions, people surrender control of their lives, voluntarily or involuntarily.

total institutions Institutions in which people surrender control of their lives, voluntarily or involuntarily, to an administrative staff and carry out daily activities with others required to do the same thing.

As "inmates," they then carry out daily activities (eating, sleeping, recreation) in the "immediate company of a large batch of others, all of whom are [theoretically] treated alike and required to do the same thing together" (Goffman 1961, p. 6). Their total character is symbolized by barriers to social interaction, "such as locked doors, high walls, barbed wire, cliffs, water, forests, or moors" (p. 4).

Goffman (1961) identified common procedures for staff at any total institution to follow to resocialize inmates. When the inmates arrive, the staff strips them of their possessions and their usual appearances (and the accessories and services by which their appearances are maintained). In addition, the staff sharply limits interactions with those outside the institution, as a way of establishing a "deep initial break with past roles" (p. 14). The staff typically follows "admission procedures," such as taking a life history, photographing, weighing, fingerprinting, assigning numbers, searching, listing personal possessions for storage,

Courtesy of Robert K. Wallace

Total institutions are settings in which people voluntarily or involuntarily surrender control of their lives to an administrative staff that supervises their behavior. One could argue that the Gaza Strip and West Bank meet the criteria of a total institution as the Israelis have sealed off the territories and control the movement and life of people who live there.

undressing, bathing, disinfecting, haircutting, issuing institutional clothing, instructing as to rules, and assigning to quarters. New arrivals allow themselves to be shaped and coded into objects that can be fed into the administrative machinery of the establishment (p. 16).

Goffman maintained that the admission procedures function to prepare inmates to shed past roles and to assume new ones. Inmates participate in enforced activities that are designed to meet institutional goals. Those goals may be to care for the incapable, to keep inmates out of the community, or to teach people new roles (for example, to be a soldier, priest, or nun).

In general, it is easier to resocialize people when they want to be resocialized than when they are being forced to abandon old values and behaviors. Furthermore, resocialization occurs more readily when acquiring new values and behaviors that require competence rather than subservience (Rose, Glazer, and Glazer 1979). Herein lies the dilemma in finding a resolution to the Palestinian–Israeli conflict. Factions on both sides attempt to forcibly resocialize the other side to change its position about land rights. Israelis build walls, control movement, deport, imprison, impose curfews, close schools, level houses, and kill. Palestinians throw stones, strike, boycott Israeli products, launch missiles, and employ suicide bombers/martyrs to kill. A significant percentage of Palestinians and Israelis seem to believe that if they make life miserable enough for the other group, their group will gain a homeland. The problem is that if one side wins through intimidation and force, the other side by definition assumes a subservient position and, in the long run, is likely to challenge the legitimacy of the other's victory (Elbedour, Bastien, and Center 1997).

Robert K. Wallace

Summary of CORE CONCEPTS

The Israeli–West Bank barrier symbolizes the present state of affairs and the depth of the divide between the Palestinians and Israeli Jews. Although the Israeli Jews have the power to physically separate themselves from the Palestinians and control their movement, they do not have the power to end the conflict. The Palestinian message shown in this photo acknowledges that both sides have spilled blood, but, as in all conflicts, the blood of the weaker party in a conflict is often dismissed as deserved and inevitable. This chapter used the concepts and theories related to socialization to explore the social mechanisms by which this conflict has been perpetuated over the course of at least 100 years.

CORE CONCEPT 1 In the broadest sense of the word, *socialization* is the process by which people develop a sense of self and learn the ways of the society in which they live.

It is also the process by which humans learn about the social groups to which they primarily belong and to which they do not belong, realize their human capacities, and learn to negotiate the social and physical environment they have inherited. No discussion of socialization can ignore the importance of nature and nurture. Nature comprises one's human genetic makeup or biological inheritance. Nurture refers to the social experiences that make up every person's life. The chapter considers some of the millions of social experiences that have created Palestinian and Israeli Jew identities.

CORE CONCEPT 2 Socialization depends on meaningful interaction experiences with others.

Meaningful social contact with and stimulation from others are important at any age. Indeed, strong social ties with caring people are linked to overall social, psychological, and physical well-being. More fundamentally, social interaction is essential to developing and maintaining a sense of self.

CORE CONCEPT 3 Socialization is impossible without memory; memories passed on from one generation to the next preserve and sustain culture.

No one can participate in society without the ability to remember such things as names, faces, places, words, symbols, and norms. We take it for granted that people have language, norms, values, and beliefs of the surrounding culture stored in memory. People born at approximately the same time and place have likely lived through many of the same events. These experiences are remembered long after an event has passed. Both Palestinians and Israeli Jews have different collective memories that each group revives, preserves, shares, passes on, and recasts in many forms, such as stories, holidays, rituals, and monuments.

CORE CONCEPT 4 People acquire a sense of self when they can role-take.

Role taking involves stepping outside the self and imagining how others view its appearance and behavior from an outsider's perspective. Children learn to role-take through a three-stage process involving imitation, play, and games. We considered how this three-stage process applies to the ongoing conflict. The looking-glass self concept is useful for understanding the process by which people visualize how they appear to others, imagine a judgment of that appearance, and develop a feeling somewhere between pride and shame. The imagining is critical to self-awareness.

Piaget's model of cognitive development addresses how people come to acquire this level of cognitive sophistication to step outside the self and view it from another's point of view. It includes four stages: sensorimotor, preoperational, concrete operational, and formal operational. Piaget maintained that reasoning abilities cannot be hurried; a more sophisticated level of understanding will not show itself until the brain is ready.

CORE CONCEPT 5 Meaningful social interaction depends on the involved parties sharing significant symbols.

A significant symbol is a word, gesture, or other learned sign that conveys "the same meaning for the person transmitting it as for the person receiving it" (Theodorson and Theodorson 1979, p. 430). Language is a particularly important significant symbol, because the shared meanings attached to words allow us to communicate and convey meanings. Significant symbols also include symbolic gestures or signs such as the Palestinian and Israeli flags, the V sign, and the walls that physically separate the two parties.

CORE CONCEPT 6 Agents of socialization—significant others, primary groups, in-groups and out-groups, and institutions (such as mass media)—shape our sense of self, and teach us about the groups to which we do and do not belong.

Agents of socialization (1) shape our sense of self or social identity, (2) teach us about the social groups to which we do and do not belong, (3) help us to realize our human capacities, and (4) help us negotiate the social and physical environment we have inherited.

CORE CONCEPT 7 Over a lifetime, people make social transitions that entail acquiring new roles, shedding old roles, and integrating new roles with current roles. In making these transitions, people undergo resocialization.

Resocialization is a process that involves breaking with behaviors and ways of thinking that are unsuited to existing or changing circumstances, and replacing them with new, more appropriate ways of behaving and thinking. In making these transitions, people undergo voluntary and involuntary resocialization. Erikson's life stage model consists of eight stages, each of which is marked by a crisis, a struggle with the challenges or the developmental tasks that a particular life stage presents. The struggle accompanied by resocialization shape one's thinking about the self and others. Sociologist Erving Goffman wrote about a particular type of setting called total institutions in which people are isolated from the rest of society to undergo systematic resocialization. In total institutions, people surrender control of their lives, voluntarily or involuntarily.

Resources on the Internet

Login to CengageBrain.com to access the resources your instructor requires. For this book, you can access:

Sociology CourseMate

Access an integrated eBook, chapter-specific interactive learning tools, including flash cards, quizzes, videos, and more in your Sociology CourseMate.

Take a pretest for this chapter and receive a personalized study plan based on your results that will identify the topics you need to review and direct you to online resources to help you master those topics. Then take a posttest to help you determine the concepts you have mastered and what you will need to work on.

CourseReader

CourseReader for Sociology is an online reader providing access to readings, and audio and video selections to accompany your course materials.

Visit **www.cengagebrain.com** to access your account and purchase materials.

Key Terms

SOCIAL INTERACTION

5

With Emphasis on THE DEMOCRATIC REPUBLIC OF THE CONGO

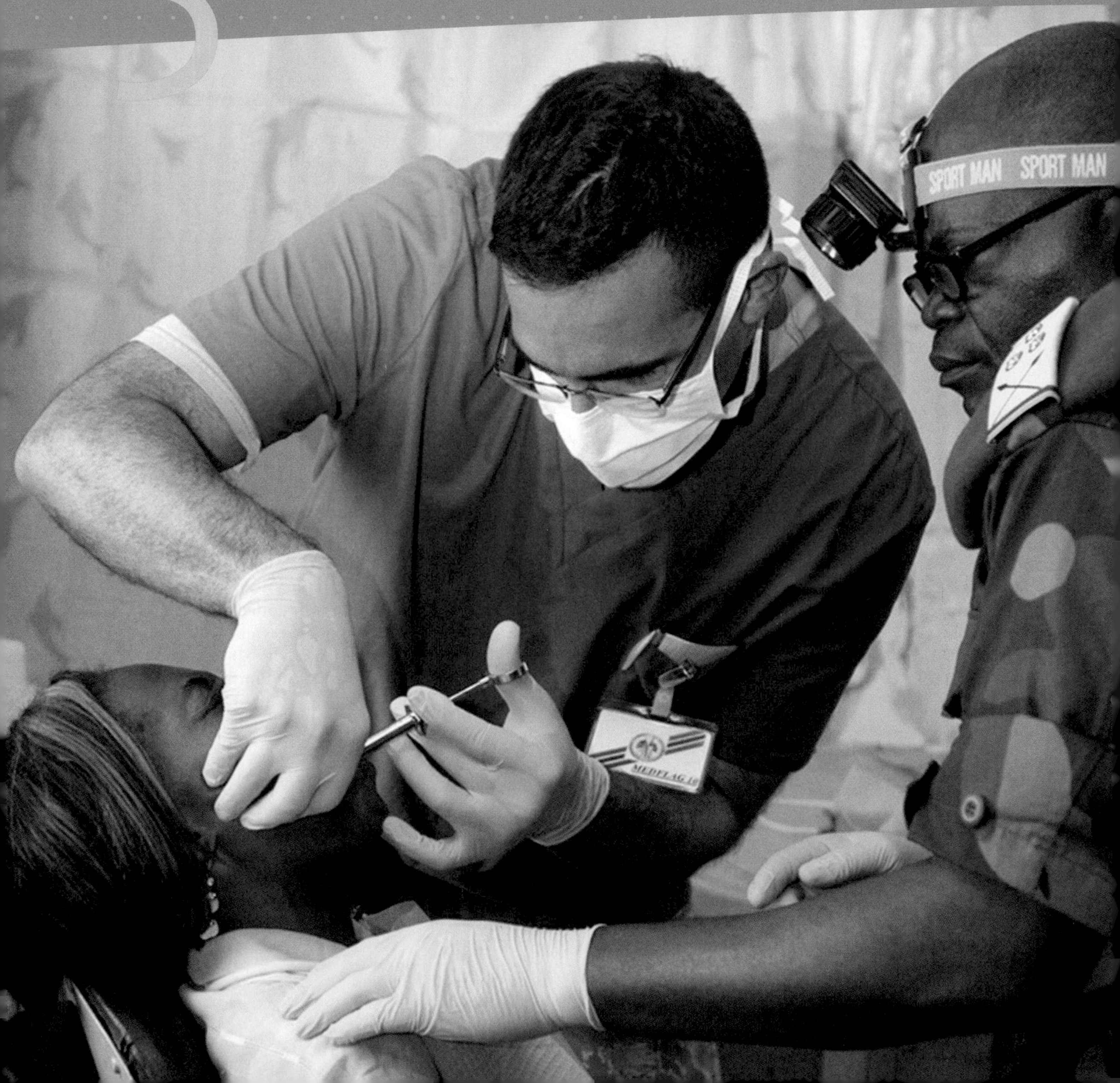

This photo shows a U.S. Air Force captain from Sacramento, California, and a dentist from the Armed Forces of the Democratic Republic of the Congo (DRC) preparing a DRC patient for dental treatment. The Air Force captain is part of a joint training exercise with the U.S. and DRC militaries focusing on humanitarian and civil assistance. This chapter is about social interaction, and the larger social forces that bring people together. And once people come together, sociologists seek to identify the factors that shape the content and direction of interaction. What social forces brought these three together in interaction? The social forces can be traced back to those that brought Europeans and Africans together under colonization in 1884. Colonization and its aftermath set the stage for the millions of interactions that would eventually lead to the emergence of HIV and AIDS. It also helps explain the need for humanitarian assistance in DRC today.

Why Focus On THE DEMOCRATIC REPUBLIC OF THE CONGO?

For many students born after 1981, HIV and AIDS has always been a fact of life, covered in sex education classes along with other sexually transmitted diseases. The condition known as AIDS was first given that name in 1981—30 years ago. AIDS stands for acquired immune deficiency syndrome. HIV stands for human immunodeficiency virus. When I ask my students where and how HIV and AIDS originated, most say that they know it has something to do with Africa and monkeys. And when I press them further, they think it has something to do with Africans who ate monkeys or engaged in sexual acts with them. Many of my students also connect the origins of AIDS and HIV with gay individuals, but they are quick to point out that anyone who exchanges bodily fluids (for example, blood, semen, breast milk) with an already infected person puts themselves at risk.

The story of HIV/AIDS does involve Africa, monkeys, and gays but the role each plays is more complex than you might ever imagine. To unravel this story, we focus on the Democratic Republic of the Congo (DRC). The DRC was once a Belgian colony. It was first known as Congo Free State (1884–1908) and then the Belgian Congo (1908–1960), until it gained independence in 1960, at which point the country's name changed to Zaire (1960–1997). We focus on the DRC because, in 1980, AIDS researchers identified the first known sample of HIV-infected blood in a Congolese blood bank. The frozen, stored blood sample was taken in 1959, from a volunteer participating in a medical study. That does not mean that African people started the global epidemic, however. Rather, focusing on the country in which this sample was stored forces us to consider how one case of HIV infection grew to the 33.4 million cases worldwide that exist today. Of course, millions of intimate interactions between those with and without HIV infection explains, in part, how HIV/AIDS became a global epidemic. But that is only part of the story. It is also important to know the circumstances that drew people from Belgium and from other countries across the globe to the DRC, and the larger social forces that shaped the interactions among them.

AIDS researchers believe that the story of this global epidemic started in southeastern Cameroon around 1930, when the virus "jumped" from a chimpanzee to a human host. For the virus to survive and lead to an epidemic, it had to jump from human to human and make its way to a big city, where human hosts were many; the closest such city was Léopoldville (later renamed Kinshasa), in what was then the Belgian Congo but is today known as the DRC (Abraham 2006). Obviously, the story of HIV/AIDS involves the study of interaction at the face-to-face intimate interpersonal level but, as we will see, it also involved millions of indirect interactions involving contaminated needles. As we will see, the origin and spread of HIV/AIDS cannot be understood apart from the European colonial practices that put millions of Africans at risk of contracting HIV/AIDS (Moore 2004).

Online Poll

Before reading this introduction, in what part of the world did you believe HIV/AIDS originated?

○ San Francisco
○ South America
○ Europe
○ Africa
○ Don't know

Before reading this introduction, what had you heard about the origins of HIV/AIDS, specifically about how it came into being?

○ Something to do with monkeys in Africa
○ Something to do with gays
○ Something to do with blood
○ Some other source

To see how other students responded to these questions, go to **www.cengagebrain.com.**

Sgt. James D. Sims

Video Tip: Show the author's video introduction to Chapter 5, which can be found on the Power Lecture CD. A transcript of the video is included in the Instructor's Resource Manual.

Social Interaction

> **CORE CONCEPT 1 When sociologists study interactions, they seek to understand the larger social forces that bring people together in interaction and that shape the content and direction of that interaction.**

Sociologists define **social interaction** as a situation in which at least two people communicate and respond through language, gestures, and other symbols to affect one another's behavior and thinking. In the process, the parties involved define, interpret, and attach meaning to all that goes on during an encounter. Social interaction includes situations ranging from chance encounters (two strangers standing in line making small talk about the weather) to highly regulated encounters in which the parties are compelled to interact in specified ways (a drill sergeant training soldiers).

With regard to HIV/AIDS, sociologists ask a variety of questions including: What kinds of interactions led to the emergence of HIV/AIDS? What forces increase the likelihood that HIV-infected and noninfected people interact? To answer these questions, we begin by exploring an important social force—industrialization and an expanding division of labor—that drew people from all over the world to the DRC and to Africa. These social forces set the stage for the social interactions involved with the transmission of HIV/AIDS.

Division of Labor

> **CORE CONCEPT 2 The division of labor is an important social force that draws people into interaction with one another and shapes their relationships.**

Émile Durkheim was one of the first sociologists to write about the social forces that contributed to the rise of a "global village." In *The Division of Labor in Society*, Durkheim (1933) provides a general framework for understanding the forces underlying global-scale interactions. According to Durkheim, an increase in population size and density increases the demand for resources (such as food, clothing, and shelter). This demand, in turn, stimulates people to find more efficient methods for producing goods and services, thus advancing society "steadily towards powerful machines, towards great concentrations of [labor] forces and capital, and consequently to the extreme division of labor" (Durkheim 1933, p. 39). As Durkheim describes it, **division of labor** refers to work that is broken down into specialized tasks, each performed by a different set of workers specifically trained to do that task. The workers do not have to live near one another; they often live in different parts of a country or different parts of the world. Not only are the tasks geographically dispersed, but the parts and materials needed to manufacture products also come from many locations around the world.

In their search for natural resources and for low-cost (even free) labor, European governments vigorously colonized much of Asia, Africa, and the Pacific in the late nineteenth and early twentieth centuries. In 1883, King Leopold II of Belgium claimed as his private property one million square miles of land that encompassed 15 million people. Leaders of 13 European countries and the United States who were attending the Berlin West Africa Conference formally legitimized Leopold's personal hold over the land in 1885 (see Figure 5.1). The purpose

Meeting the Rear Column at Banalya, from "In Darkest Africa" by H.M. Stanley, published 1890.

As early as 1871, the British-born journalist and explorer Henry Morton Stanley led expeditions along the Congo River, documenting the commercial possibilities of the land and making "deals" to acquire land for King Leopold. In his diary he wrote, "Every cordial-faced aborigine whom I meet . . . I look upon . . . as a future recruit to the ranks of soldier-laborer" (Hochschild 1998, p. 68).

social interaction An everyday event in which at least two people communicate and respond through language and symbolic gestures to affect one another's behavior and thinking.

division of labor Work that is broken down into specialized tasks, each performed by a different set of people trained to do that task. The people doing each task often live in different parts of the world. Not only are the tasks specialized, but the parts and materials needed to manufacture products also come from many different regions of the world.

Discussion Tip: Since HIV/AIDS came to public attention in the early 1980s, this means that the disease has always existed for those 30 years of age and younger. Ask students when they first remember learning about HIV/AIDS and to describe those memories of how they learned such a disease existed.

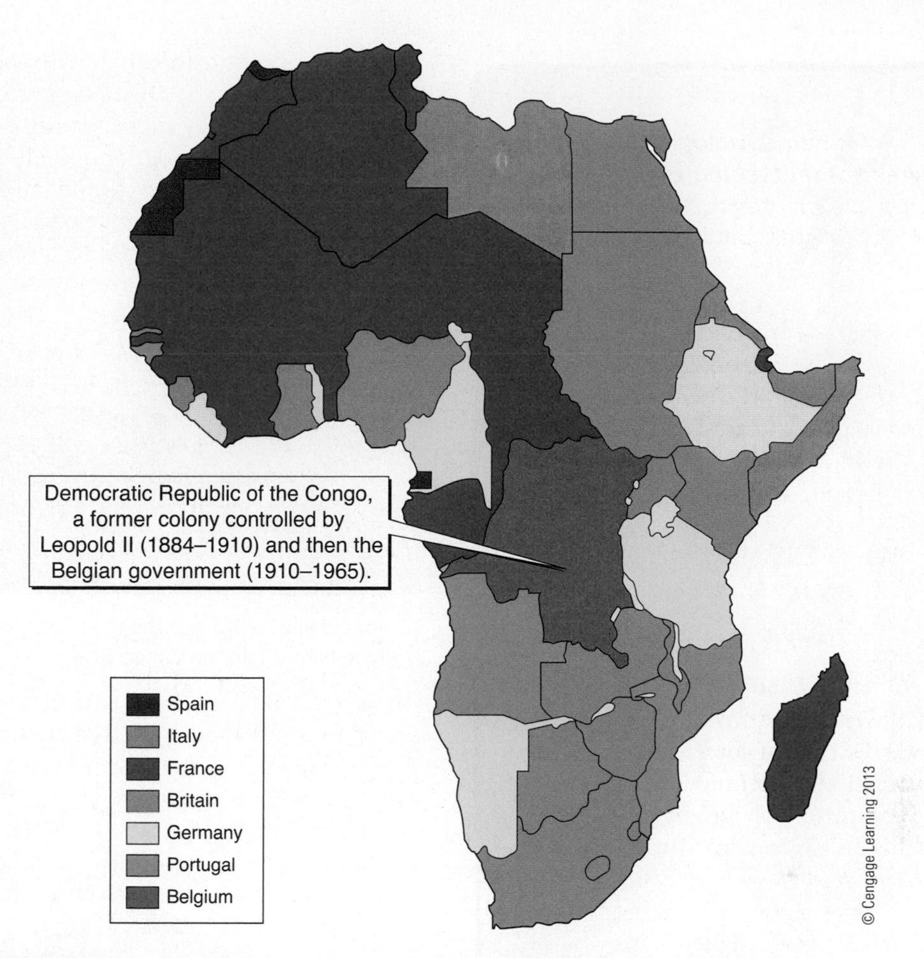
Democratic Republic of the Congo,
a former colony controlled by
Leopold II (1884–1910) and then the
Belgian government (1910–1965).
Spain
Italy
France
Britain
Germany
Portugal
Belgium
© Cengage Learning 2013

FIGURE 5.1 By 1913, almost all of Africa had been divided into European colonies. Which countries controlled the largest share of the African continent? How does a foreign power manage to take control of people and their resources?

of that conference was to carve Africa into colonies and divide the continent's natural resources among competing colonial powers (Witte 1992). The vast amount of land awarded to Leopold contained as many as 450 ethnic groups, ranging "from citizens of large, organizationally sophisticated kingdoms to the Pygmies of the Ituri Rain Forest, who lived in small bands with no chiefs and no formal structure or government" (Hochschild 1998, p. 72).

For 23 years, Leopold capitalized on the world's demand for rubber, ivory (to be used in making piano keys, billiard balls, snuff boxes), palm oil (a machine-oil lubricant and an ingredient in soaps such as Palmolive floating soap), coffee, cocoa, lumber, and diamonds. His reign over the Congo was the "vilest scramble for loot that ever disfigured the history of human conscience and geographical location" (Conrad 1971, p. 118). The methods he used to extract rubber for his own personal gain involved atrocities so ghastly that, in 1908, international outrage forced the Belgian government to assume administration of the country. Both Leopold and the Belgian government forced the indigenous Africans to leave their villages to work the mines, cultivate and harvest crops, and build and maintain roads and train tracks. Keep in mind that the "roads were not built for Africans. Their purpose was to provide the Europeans with easy access into the interior in order to maintain order, increase trade, and get raw materials out" (Mark 1995, p. 220).

The Belgian Congo's capital city, Léopoldville (now Kinshasa), became the major inland port connecting all of Central Africa to the West and beyond. The capital—located on the Congo River (the "river that swallows all rivers" running through what is now the DRC, Zambia, Angola, Tanzania, Cameroon, and Gabon)—attracted Europeans and Africans. All trade originating within 8,000 miles of waterways "fanning out, like the veins of a leaf" from Léopoldville passed through that city (Forbath 1977, p. 12). Figure 5.2 shows the location of the former capital in relation to the many surrounding rivers.

As industrialization proceeded in Europe and the United States, the demand for various raw materials grew. The world came to depend on the Congo as a source of copper, cobalt (needed to manufacture jet engines), industrial diamonds, zinc, silver, gold, manganese (needed

Video Tip: Show some or all of the documentary, *Congo: White King, Red Rubber, Black Death*. It is available online at http://topdocumentaryfilms.com/congo-white-king-red-rubber-black-death/.

King Leopold's Soliloquy: A Defense of His Congo Rule, By Mark Twain, Boston: The P. R. Warren Co., 1905, Second Edition.

In 1885, Leopold II, king of Belgium, calculated that his "yearly income from the Congo is millions." The Congo Free State, from which Leopold acquired wealth, is now named the Democratic Republic of Congo. Leopold's wealth was derived from forcing African people to extract rubber, diamonds, and ivory. The methods Leopold employed to exploit labor and acquire resources offer important clues to the origin of HIV and AIDS.

Urbain Ureel, Courtesy of Joan Ferrante

A Leopoldville shipyard in the 1930s. Shipyard workers are pushing barges into the Congo River.

Brian Smithson

In a 24-hours-a-day, seven-days-a-week operation, European and Asian logging companies remove an estimated 10 million cubic meters of wood each year from forests in Central African countries, including the DRC (Peterson and Ammann 2003).

to make steel and aluminum dry cell batteries), coltan (a heat-resistant mineral used in cell phones, laptops, and PlayStations), and uranium (needed to generate atomic energy and fuel the atomic bomb) (Oliver 2006). This relentless demand continues to fuel the ongoing conflict in the DRC, even after the independence from Belgium in 1965, when Mobutu Sese Seko assumed power of the country (called Zaire when it gained independence) with the help of the United States. Mobutu and those he appointed exploited the country's resources for their own personal gain. In 1997, Mobutu was forced out of office by Laurent Kabila, who was backed by the governments of Rwanda and Uganda that sent troops into the DRC. From 1997 to 2002, the DRC was the site of what some have called Africa's World War. Armies from Rwanda, Uganda, Burundi, Zimbabwe, Chad, Angola, and Namibia fought with and against Congolese government forces and rebel groups in an effort to control the DRC's resources, especially resources in the northeast and eastern part of the country (French 2009). Today various military forces and rebel groups still fight to control the country's resources (Turner 2009).

Teaching Tip: The image of King Leopold (above) is from a pamphlet published by Mark Twain in 1905 entitled *King Leopold's Soliloquy.* Show some of the illustrations, captions, and quotes from this pamphlet so students can see how Twain made his case.

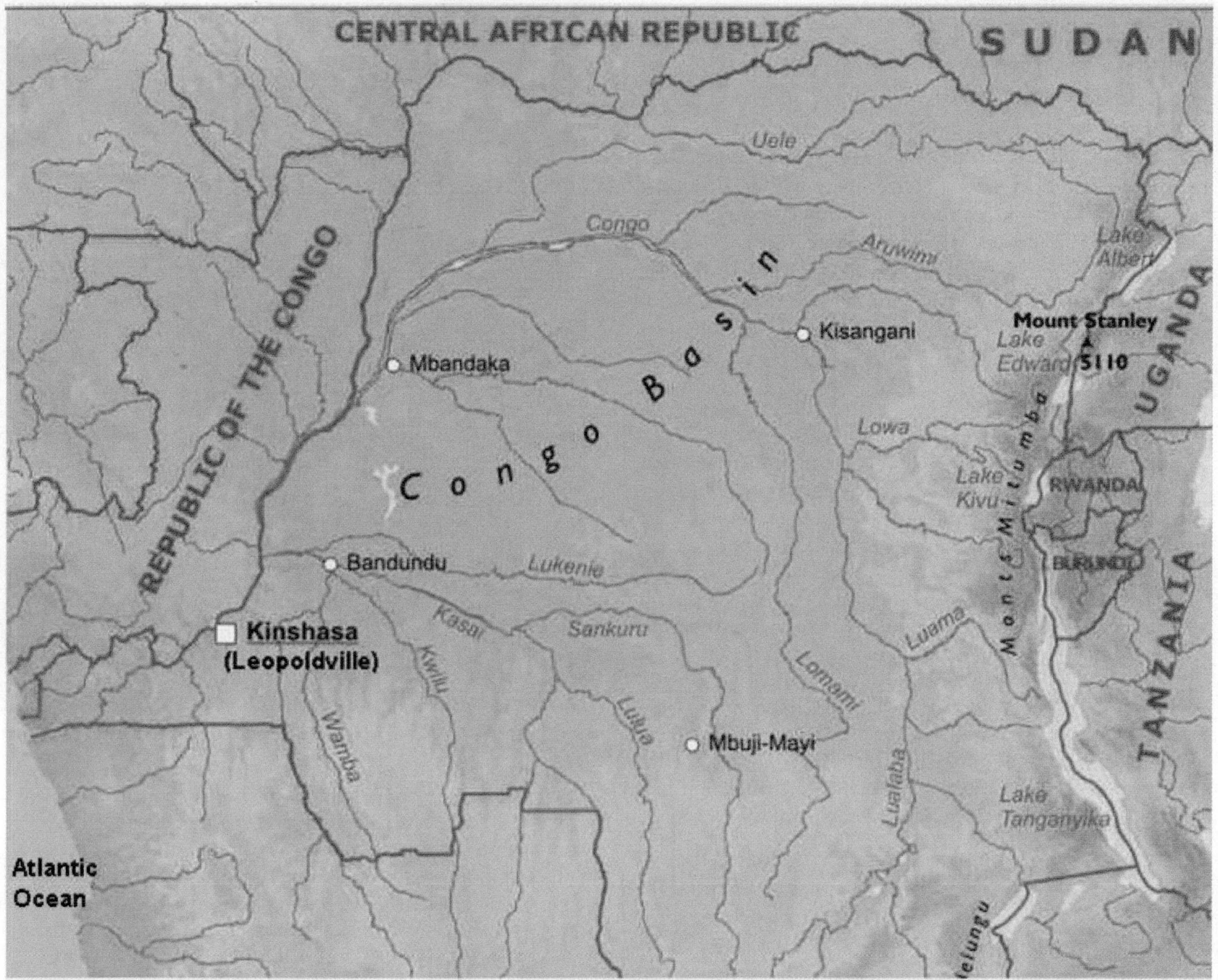

FIGURE 5.2 The map shows Leopoldville, the capital of the Belgian Congo. It was located on the Congo River—the "river that swallows all rivers" running through what is now the DRC, Zambia, Angola, Tanzania, Cameroon, and Gabon. The capital city attracted Europeans and Africans, who traded along the 8,000 miles of waterways that passed through the city and then out to sea.

Solidarity: The Ties That Bind

To this point, we have used the DRC as an example of how industrialization and colonization were inextricably interconnected and as an illustration of how the division of labor expanded to encompass workers and resources from around the world. Durkheim noted that, as the division of labor becomes more specialized and as the sources of materials to make products become more geographically diverse, a new kind of solidarity emerges. He used the term **solidarity** to describe the system of social ties that acts as a glue or cement connecting people to one another and the wider society. Durkheim observed that *mechanical* solidarity is characteristic of preindustrial societies and that a new kind of solidarity, *organic,* is characteristic of industrial societies.

Mechanical Solidarity

Mechanical solidarity characterizes a social order based on common ways of thinking, behaving, and seeing the world. In this situation, a person's "first duty is to resemble everybody else"—that is, "not to have anything personal about one's [core] beliefs and actions" (Durkheim 1933, p. 396). Durkheim believed that this similarity derived from the simple division of labor. In other words, a simple

solidarity The system of social ties that acts as a glue or cement connecting people to one another and the wider society.

mechanical solidarity Social order and cohesion based on a common conscience, or uniform thinking and behavior.

Teaching Tip: Take time in class to study the map of the Congo River above, which flows out into the Atlantic Ocean. Note that it is the "river that swallows all rivers" running out of Zambia, Angola, Tanzania, Cameroon, and Gabon. The capital city of Leopoldville drew people from across Africa and from Belgium and other European countries.

division of labor causes people to be more alike than different, because they do the same kind of tasks to maintain their livelihood. This similarity gives rise to common experiences, skills, core beliefs, attitudes, and thoughts. In societies characterized by mechanical solidarity, the ties that bind individuals to one another are based primarily on kinship, religion, and a shared way of life. To understand how society is organized around a shared way of life, consider the lifestyle of the Mbuti pygmies, a hunting-and-gathering people who, before colonization, lived in the Ituri Forest (an equatorial rain forest) in what is now the northeastern DRC. Their society represents one of the many ways of life that colonization forced people to abandon. Keep in mind that the Mbuti represent but one culture disrupted by colonization.

> The Mbuti share a forest-oriented value system. Their common conscience derived from the fact that the forest gives them food, firewood, and materials for shelter. It is not surprising that the Mbuti recognize their dependence upon the forest and refer to it as "Father" or "Mother" because as they say it gives them food, warmth, shelter, and clothing just like their parents. Mbuti say that the forest also, like their parents, gives them affection. . . . The forest is more than mere environment to the Mbuti. It is a living, conscious thing, both natural and supernatural, something that has to be depended upon, respected, trusted, obeyed, and loved. The love demanded of the Mbuti is no romanticism, and perhaps it might be better included under "respect." It is their world, and in return for their affection and trust it supplies them with all their needs. (1965, p. 19)

Mbuti are aware of the ongoing destruction of the rain forest by companies that push them farther into the forest's interior. The pygmies agree that if they leave the forest and become part of the modern world, their way of life will die: "The forest is our home; when we leave the forest, or when the forest dies, we shall die. We are the people of the forest" (Turnball 1961, p. 260).

Tom Stoddart/Getty Images

In societies characterized by organic solidarity, people's lives depend on those in distant places. Cell phones, laptops, and other electrical equipment upon which we depend to stay connected to others cannot work without minerals such as coltan. Most of us fail to realize that thousands in the Congo mine coltan and minerals with their bare hands and shovels. In addition, not only are their lives at risk from ongoing conflict over resources but miners also are exposed to toxic and radioactive substances (UNEP/GRID—Arendal 2010).

Organic Solidarity

A society with a complex division of labor is characterized by **organic solidarity**—a social order or system of social ties based on interdependence and cooperation among people performing a wide range of diverse and specialized tasks. Specialized means that the tasks needed to make a product or to deliver a service performed by workers, often in different locations, who have been trained to do a specified task or tasks in the overall production process. The final product depends on contributions or many occupational categories. Relationships in the larger society reflect this specialization in that people relate to one another in terms of their specialized roles in the division of labor. Thus we buy tires from a dealer; we interact with a customer service representative by telephone or computer; we travel in an airplane flown by pilots and are served by flight attendants; we pay a supermarket cashier for coffee; and we deal with a lab technician when we give or sell blood. We do not need to know these people personally to interact with them. Likewise, we do not need to know the people behind the scenes: the rubber gatherer, the ivory hunter, the coffee grower, or the logger working in the DRC who contributed to making the products we purchase. In sum, most day-to-day interactions are fleeting, limited, impersonal, and instrumental (that is, we interact with people for a specific reason, not to get to know them).

When the division of labor is complex and when the materials for products are geographically scattered, few individuals possess the knowledge, skills, and materials to be self-sufficient. Consequently, people find that they must depend on others for the goods they buy and services they need. A complex division of labor increases differences

organic solidarity Social order or system of social ties based on specialization, interdependence, and cooperation among people performing a wide range of diverse and specialized tasks.

among people, in turn leading to a decrease in common ways of thinking and behaving. Nevertheless, Durkheim argued, the ties that bind people to one another, based on specialization and interdependence, can be very strong, because people need one another to survive.

Disruptions to the Division of Labor

Durkheim hypothesized that societies become more vulnerable as the division of labor becomes more complex and jobs more specialized. He was particularly concerned with the kinds of events that break down individuals' ability to meaningfully connect with society and others through their work. Such events include (1) industrial and commercial crises caused by plant closings, massive layoffs, epidemics, technological revolutions, or war; (2) workers' strikes; (3) job specialization, insofar as workers are so isolated that few people grasp the workings and consequences of the overall enterprise; (4) forced labor, such that people have no choice in the work they do; and (5) inefficient management and development of workers' talents and abilities, so that work for them is nonexistent, irregular, intermittent, or subject to high turnover.

To illustrate how disruptions to the division of labor break the social ties that bind, consider the case of a factory worker, Joel Goddard, after he was laid off by Ford Motor Company. Goddard was married with two children. After he lost his job, his daily interactions shifted from colleagues at work to contacts with people at the unemployment office. Moreover, he lost the structure in his life that came with the routine of his job. Instead of working, he watched TV, fished, or read want ads. His ties were further disrupted when friends from work moved out of state to find employment. Goddard eventually took a job selling insurance and found himself selling to his acquaintances. He later quit, and then his wife decided to go to work. However, her success at work strained their marriage because it reminded Goddard of his failures.

Since at least 1884, the DRC has experienced these disruptions to the division of labor. In that year, King Leopold II took control of the Congo Free State, and for decades after, the people in that region were subjected to forced labor. Armies of black conscripts under the command of white officers would march into villages and take women—mothers, daughters, sisters, wives—hostage and force men—sons, husbands, fathers, brothers—to go into the rain forest to harvest rubber or to mine resources (Hochschild 2009). As we will see, under this brutal system of forced labor, the conditions that facilitated the emergence of HIV/AIDS arose.

Recall that scientists believe that around 1930 the HIV virus "jumped" form a chimp to a human host. But how did the host come in contact with a chimpanzee? We know that working conditions were so harsh that Congolese people were left vulnerable to disease. "Forced labor camps of thousands had poor sanitation, poor diet, and exhausting labor demands. It is hard to imagine better conditions for the establishment of an immune-deficiency disease" (Moore 2004, p. 545). Biological anthropologist Jim Moore (2004) describes a scenario under which that jump probably occurred:

> [The] fisherman flees his small village to escape a colonial patrol demanding its rubber quota [which he cannot meet]; as he runs, he grabs one of the unfamiliar shotguns that recently arrived in the area. While hiding for several days, he shoots a chimpanzee [for food] and, unfamiliar with the process of butchering it, is infected with simian immunodeficiency virus (SIV), a retrovirus that is found in primates. On return to the village he finds his family massacred and the village disbanded. He wanders for miles, dodging patrols, until arriving at a distant village. The next day he is seized by a railroad press gang and marched for days to the labor site, where he (along with several hundred others) receives several injections for reasons he does not understand. During his months working on the railroad, he has little to eat and is continually stressed, susceptible to any infection. He finds some solace in one of the camp prostitutes (themselves imported by those in charge), but eventually dies of an undiagnosed wasting—the fate of hundreds in that camp alone.

To escape the kind of brutality Moore described, tens of thousands of Congolese fled into the unfamiliar jungle and forests in search of food and safety. There many were bitten by infected tsetse flies and contracted sleeping sickness, an infectious disease with symptoms that include severe headache, fever, weakness, and uncontrollable sleepiness. To care for this condition, "well-meaning, but undersupplied doctors" treated it with serial injections of medicines. Workers were also routinely inoculated to prevent small pox and dysentery. "The problem was that multiple injections given to arriving gangs of tens or hundreds were administered with only a handful of syringes. The importance of sterile technique was known but not regularly practiced. Transfer of pathogens would have been inevitable. And to appease the laborers, in some of the camps sex workers were officially encouraged" (Moore 2006, p. 545).

In the context of HIV/AIDS, it is highly significant that millions of laborers were also tested for sleeping sickness with spinal taps, a medical procedure also involving needles that, at that time in history, were not disposable or subjected to sterilization. A combination of factors set the stage for origin and the eventual transmission of AIDS and HIV across a global stage:

- An exhausted labor force vulnerable to diseases, most notably sleeping sickness and HIV/AIDS;
- Medical testing and treatment that involved unsterilized needles; and
- People from all over the world extracting resources and doing business.

Teaching Tip: Unemployment and underemployment result from disruptions to the division of labor. Review current unemployment data in light of Durkheim's analysis. That data can be found at the U.S. Bureau of Labor Statistics website.

Global Comparisons Percentage of Adult Population with HIV/AIDS by Country

The map shows the prevalence of HIV/AIDS by country. Which areas of the world have the highest prevalence of HIV/AIDS? Notice on the map, which gives country-by-country breakdowns, that between 5 and 15 percent of the population in the DRC has HIV or AIDS. At a minimum, that represents 1 in every 20 people. How does the history of colonization inform your understanding of the AIDS prevalence in Africa?

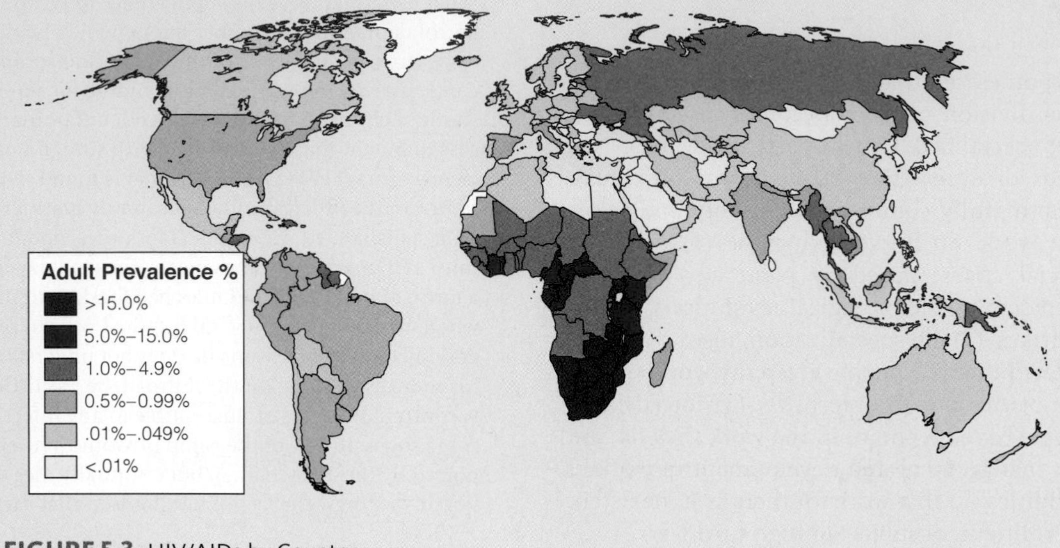

FIGURE 5.3 HIV/AIDs by Country
Source: U.S. Central Intelligence Agency (2007)

Industrialization and colonization drew people from the most remote regions of the world into a process that produced unprecedented quantities of material goods, primarily for the benefit of the colonizing powers. The demand for the raw materials to fuel industrialization pulled people from not just Belgium, but from all over the world into the Congo region and throughout Africa. This was accompanied by concerted efforts to increase the volume of goods and services produced, the reach of markets, and the speed at which goods, services, and labor were delivered. Railroads, freighters, and airplanes (by 1920, there was a Belgium–Congo flight) became part of an infrastructure that increased opportunities for more and more people to enter and leave the DRC and to interact (including sexually) with people they would otherwise never have met (Wrong 2002). In this context, HIV/AIDS cannot be viewed simply as a disease, but as a disease that grew out of millions of social interactions (see Figure 5.4).

SPC Preston E. Cheeks, USA

As one indicator of the massive movement of humans in general, consider that approximately 703 million people take international trips each year (World Tourism Organization 2007). Approximately 42 million foreign visitors enter the United States (excluding day-trippers), and 25.2 million U.S. residents travel to foreign countries (U.S. International Trade Administration 2007).

To this point, we have considered the context under which HIV/AIDS emerged. In the second half of this chapter, we focus on face-to-face interaction, by which interacting parties communicate and respond through language and symbolic gestures to affect another's behavior and thinking. While interacting, the parties define, interpret, and attach meaning to all that goes on around them and between them. That interaction is embedded in a social structure.

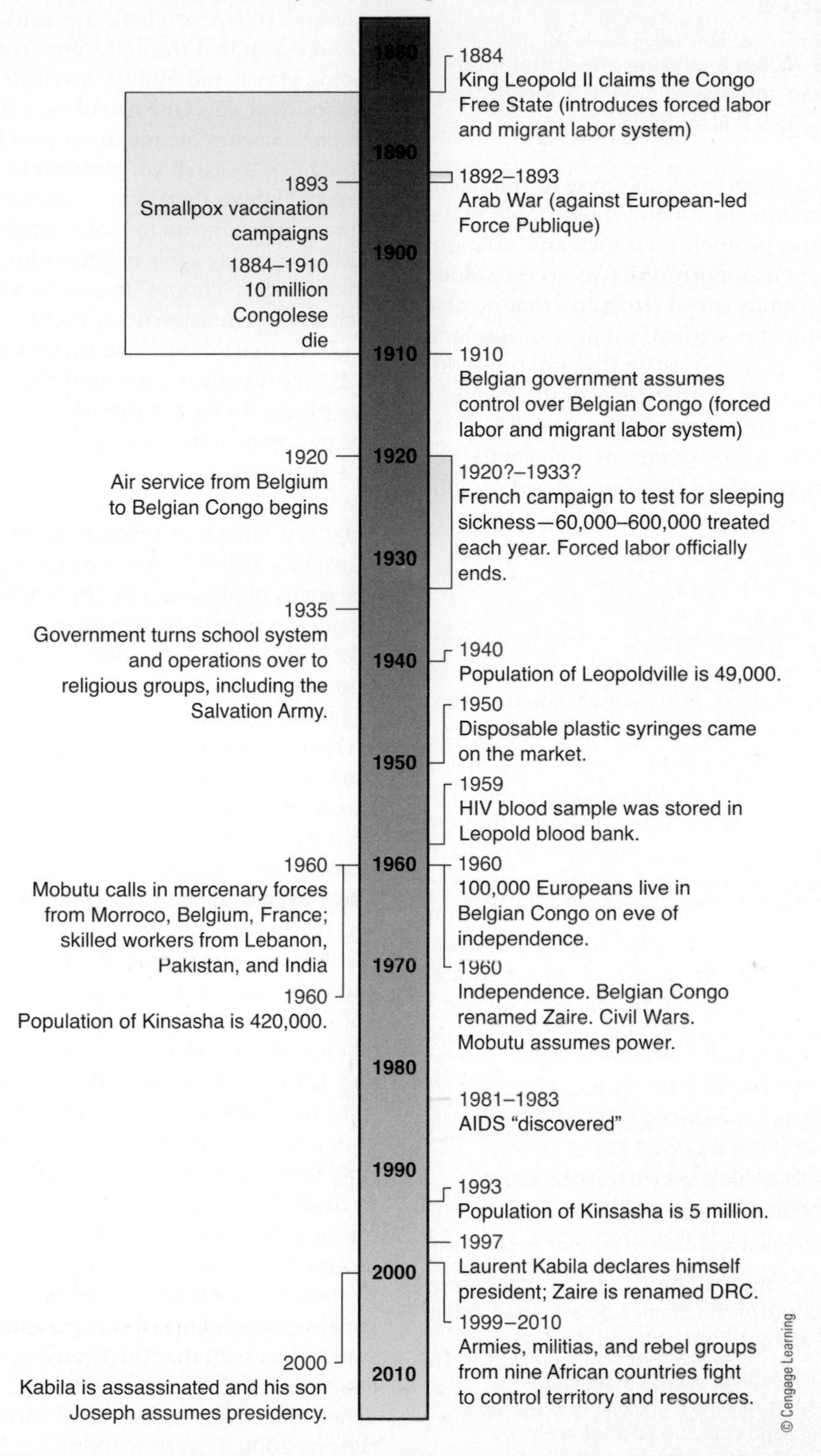
Democratic Republic of Congo Timeline 1880–2010
1880
1890
1900
1910
1920
1930
1940
1950
1960
1970
1980
1990
2000
2010
1884
King Leopold II claims the Congo Free State (introduces forced labor and migrant labor system)
1892–1893
Arab War (against European-led Force Publique)
1893
Smallpox vaccination campaigns
1884–1910
10 million Congolese die
1910
Belgian government assumes control over Belgian Congo (forced labor and migrant labor system)
1920
Air service from Belgium to Belgian Congo begins
1920?–1933?
French campaign to test for sleeping sickness—60,000–600,000 treated each year. Forced labor officially ends.
1935
Government turns school system and operations over to religious groups, including the Salvation Army.
1940
Population of Leopoldville is 49,000.
1950
Disposable plastic syringes came on the market.
1959
HIV blood sample was stored in Leopold blood bank.
1960
Mobutu calls in mercenary forces from Morroco, Belgium, France; skilled workers from Lebanon, Pakistan, and India
1960
Population of Kinsasha is 420,000.
1960
100,000 Europeans live in Belgian Congo on eve of independence.
1960
Independence. Belgian Congo renamed Zaire. Civil Wars. Mobutu assumes power.
1981–1983
AIDS “discovered”
1993
Population of Kinsasha is 5 million.
1997
Laurent Kabila declares himself president; Zaire is renamed DRC.
1999–2010
Armies, militias, and rebel groups from nine African countries fight to control territory and resources.
2000
Kabila is assassinated and his son Joseph assumes presidency.
© Cengage Learning

FIGURE 5.4 Time Line of Major Events in the DRC. This time line begins when King Leopold II claims the Congo Free State as his personal property. With the help of an army, he forces locals to extract rubber, diamonds, ivory, and other resources that fuel industrialization in the West. The time line ends with the current state of affairs in which armies, militia, and rebel groups from as many as nine surrounding countries and from within the Congo fighting to gain control of DRC resources. Ironically, even today armed groups regularly force villagers (as did King Leopold and the Belgium government) to carry supplies, ammunition, and water. One survey found that 50 percent of people living in eastern Congo had been forced to do such work (Hochschild 2009).

Social Structure

> **CORE CONCEPT 3 When analyzing any social interaction, or any human activity, sociologists locate the social structure in which it is embedded.**

A **social structure** is a largely invisible system that coordinates human interaction in broadly predictable ways. Social structures shape people's identities and relationships to others and their opportunities to access valued resources. Sociologists study social structures that involve as few as two people (doctor–patient, shopper–store clerk, parent–child), that are global in scale (the pharmaceutical industry), national in scale (the Democratic Republic of the Congo), and that are of just about any size (a local bar, an extended family, a work camp or a hospital). Social structures encompass at least four interrelated components: statuses, roles, groups, and institutions.

Status

Sociologists use the term *social status* in a very broad way. **Social status** is a human-created and defined position in society. Examples are endless but include female, teenager, doctor, patient, sister, homosexual, heterosexual, employer, employee, soldier, and unemployed. A social status has meaning only in relation to other social statuses. For instance, the status of a physician takes on quite different meanings depending on whether the physician is interacting with another physician, a patient, or a nurse. Thus, a physician's behavior varies depending on the social status of the person with whom he or she is interacting. Note that some statuses, such as sister, are ascribed. **Ascribed statuses** are the result of chance in that people exert no effort to obtain them. Birth order, race, biological sex, and age qualify as ascribed statuses. Other statuses, such as nurse's aide and college student, are **achieved statuses**; that is, they are acquired through some combination of personal choice, effort, and ability. Ascribed and achieved statuses are not clear-cut. One can always think of cases in which people take extreme measures to achieve a status typically thought of as ascribed; they undergo sex transformation surgery, lighten their skin to appear to be another race, or hire a plastic surgeon to look younger. In addition, ascribed statuses can play a role in determining achieved statuses, as when females "choose" to enter a female-dominated career such as elementary-school teacher, or when men "choose" to enter a male-dominated career such as car repairman.

People usually occupy more than one social status. Sociologists use the term **status set** to capture all the statuses any one person assumes (see Figure 5.5). Sometimes one status in a status set overshadows the others such that it shapes every aspect of life and dominates social interactions. Such a status is known as a **master status**. Unemployed, retired, ex-convict, and HIV-infected can qualify as master statuses. The status of physician can be a master status as well, if everyone, no matter the setting (party, church, fitness center), asks health-related questions or seeks health-related advice from the person occupying that status.

In the DRC between 1884 and 1960, European and African nationalities were master statuses. During this time, white European males (predominantly Belgian) occupied the following kinds of positions: commissioned military officers, steamboat captains, district commissioners, and station chiefs. Belgian men and women also traveled to the Congo as physicians and missionaries. The black Congolese and other Africans who lived in the Belgian colony could only find work as porters, canoe paddlers, miners, rubber gatherers, soldiers and low- to mid-level administrative and technical staff. Congolese women worked as maids, house servants, and prostitutes, and because there were always labor shortages, women were also pressed to work on roads and plantations (Lyons 2002). Most Congolese were forced to take these physically demanding positions out of desperation or the threat of death from the Force Publique, a white-led repressive military force comprising African males from many ethnic groups both inside and outside of the Congo. Until independence in 1960, the Congo maintained a rigid system of racial segregation in all areas of life. The segregated school system was such that the Congolese were denied access to education beyond primary school. At the time of independence, only 17 Congolese had earned a university degree (Wrong 2000, Edgerton 2002).

Role

Sociologists use the term **role** to describe the behavior expected of a status in relation to another status—for example, the role of physician in relation to a patient.

social structure A largely invisible system that coordinates human interaction in broadly predictable ways.

social status A human-created and defined position in society.

ascribed statuses Social statuses that are the result of chance in that people exert no effort to obtain them. A person's birth order, race, biological sex, and age qualify as ascribed characteristics.

achieved statuses Social statuses acquired through some combination of personal choice, effort, and ability. A person's marital status, occupation, and educational attainment are considered examples of achieved statuses.

status set All the statuses an individual assumes.

master status One status in a status set that overshadows the others such that it shapes every aspect of life and dominates social interactions.

role The behavior expected of a status in relation to another status.

(Photos: Jillian Daugherty)

FIGURE 5.5 Status Set and Master Status

Jillian occupies many statuses including sister, weight lifter, and assistant to a college basketball coach. Her master status, however, is that of a person with Down syndrome. Having Down syndrome is considered a master status because that status overshadows her other statuses. In other words, it is often hard for people to see beyond Jillian's master status and think of her as having a full and active life. Other statuses are, at best treated as secondary to her master status. That is, Jillian is not just seen as a weight lifter; she is a weight lifter with Down syndrome.

Patients can expect doctors to establish a diagnosis, to not overtreat, to prescribe a treatment plan, and to not make sexual advances (Hippocratic Oath 1943). Physicians expect their patients to answer questions honestly and to cooperate with a treatment plan. The distinction between role and status is this: People occupy statuses and enact their statuses through roles.

Any given social status is associated with an array of roles, called a **role set**, (Merton 1957). The social status of school principal is associated with a role set that is composed of relationships with students, parents, teachers, and other school staff. Quite often **role performances**, the actual behaviors of the person occupying a role, do not meet expectations—as when some physicians knowingly perform unnecessary surgery or when some patients fail to comply with treatment plans. The concept of role performance reminds us that, in their actual behavior, people carry out their roles in unique ways. Still, there is a predictability to role performances because when role performances deviate too far from expectations,

role set The array of roles associated with a given social status.

role performance The actual behavior of the person occupying a role.

Discussion Tip: Ask students to give an example of someone (including themselves) whose master status overshadows other statuses that person holds.

FROM PHOTOGRAPHS, CONGO STATE
"The pictures get sneaked around everywhere."— Page 40.

King Leopold's Soliliquy: A Defense of His Congo Rule, By Mark Twain, Boston: The P. R. Warren Co., 1905, Second Edition.

One of the most grisly policies of Leopold's rule was to sever a hand (often right) of Congolese who refused to gather rubber. Soldiers were under orders to turn in a hand for every bullet they fired, as proof that they were using bullets to kill people (and not animals or for target practice). Often soldiers would sever the hands of people to cover for other uses of bullets.

penalties—ranging in severity from a frown to imprisonment and even death—are, more often than not, applied (Merton 1957). A professor who misses class too many times will eventually be reported to a department chair or dean. An extreme example relates to the serious punishment meted out in the Congo when rubber gatherers and other forced laborers failed to perform roles as expected, no matter how absurd those expectations. To ensure that rubber gatherers met "expectations," family members were held hostage. Failing to gather enough rubber could mean death for a spouse, parents, or children. If a village refused to participate in forced labor, company troops shot everyone in sight so that nearby villagers were clear about expectations (Hochschild 1998, p. 165).

If we consider that people hold multiple statuses and that each status is enacted through its corresponding role set, we can identify at least two potential sources of stress and strain: role conflict and role strain.

Role Conflict **Role conflict** is a predicament in which the roles associated with two or more distinct statuses that a person holds conflict in some way. For example, people who occupy the statuses of college student and full-time employee often experience role conflict when professors expect students to attend class and keep up with coursework *and* employers expect employees to be available to work hours that leave little time for schoolwork. The student-employee must find ways to address this conflict between the two statuses, such as working fewer hours, quitting the job, skipping class, or studying less.

Role Strain **Role strain** is a predicament in which there are contradictory or conflicting role expectations associated with a single status. For example, doctors have an obligation to do no harm to their patients. At the same time, doctors have an obligation to pay office staff. Some physicians may feel pressured to recommend expensive and unnecessary medical treatments to generate sufficient revenue to stay in business.

Cultural Variations in Role Expectations

Role expectations associated with statuses vary across cultures. In the United States, patients expect those who occupy the status of doctor to use available technology such as X-rays, CAT scans, and MRIs to diagnose medical conditions; to prescribe drugs; and to recommend surgery. These expectations are shaped by a core cultural belief in the ability of science to solve problems. Western medicine uses all available tools of science to establish the cause of a disease, combat it for as long as possible, and ideally return the body to a healthy state. In view of this cultural orientation, it is not surprising that U.S. physicians rely heavily on technology to diagnose and cure disease. This reliance is reflected in the fact that the United States, with less than 5 percent of the world's population, consumes an estimated 52 percent of the world's pharmaceutical supply (World Health Organization 2004). This is equivalent to 3.7 billion prescriptions filled per year, or 12 prescriptions for every man, woman, and child (Kaiser Family Foundation 2009).

We can contrast the American expectations with those Congolese hold for the traditional African healer. The

role conflict A predicament in which the roles associated with two or more distinct statuses that a person holds conflict in some way.

role strain A predicament in which there are contradictory or conflicting role expectations associated with a single status.

social relationship between the African healer and patient is very different from that between the U.S. physician and patient. Like American physicians, traditional healers recognize and treat the organic and physical aspects of disease. But they also attach considerable importance to other factors: supernatural causes, social relationships (hostilities, stress, family strain), and psychological distress. This holistic perspective allows for a more personal relationship between healer and patient. Sociologist Ruth Kornfield observed Western-trained physicians working in the Congo's urban hospitals and found that success in treating patients was linked to the physicians' ability to tolerate and respect other models of illness and include them in a treatment plan. Among some ethnic groups in the Congo, when a person becomes ill, the patient's kin form a therapy management group and make decisions about treatment. Because many people in the Congo believe that illnesses result from disturbances in social relationships, the cure must involve a "reorganization of the social relations of the sick person that [is] satisfactory for those involved" (Kornfield 1986, p. 369; also see Kaptchuk and Croucher 1986, pp. 106–108).

Given these culturally rooted beliefs regarding the cause and treatment of disease, it is not surprising to learn that Europeans and Africans clashed over how to handle a sleeping sickness epidemic in the late 1920s and early 1930s. Recall that sleeping sickness is contacted when humans are bitten by infected tsetse flies. The most notable symptom is uncontrollable sleeping such that a person may fall asleep in the midst of activity, including work. As you might imagine, Europeans were concerned about this disease because the African workforce was affected.

Europeans assumed that sleeping sickness and other African diseases could be controlled, even eliminated, through testing, technology, and medicines. With regard to sleeping sickness, those techniques and technologies involved spinal taps to screen for the condition and the drug tryparsamide to treat it. About 80 percent of patients were "cured," but side effects included partial or complete loss of vision (Rockefeller University Hospital 2011). Most Congolese were suspicious of the European campaign against sleeping sickness. They believed that Europeans were responsible for the dramatic increase in cases of sleeping sickness and other diseases. Specifically, the Congolese believed that the forced labor was exhausting them, making them vulnerable to disease. Moreover, it was the dramatic disruptions to their way of life that put them in environments where they came in contact with the tsetse flies. In sum, they believed that this sleeping sickness was man-made. For the Congolese, diagnosis required careful investigation to identify the ultimate cause behind physical symptoms, and treatment focused on reintegrating the sick person into the social fabric (Lyons 2002). In *The Colonial Disease*, Maryinez Lyons (2002) argues that it "is vital to understand the profound importance and depth of this Congolese belief regarding cause and treatment" (p. 183). This is something the U.S. military doctors working in the DRC realize as they are paired with Congolese counterparts (see Sociological Imagination).

Urbain Ureel, Courtesy of Joan Ferrante

Europeans' approach to diagnosing sleeping sickness involved taking a blood sample through a finger prick or taking spinal fluid, shown here, through a lumbar puncture (spinal tap). In Africa, sleeping sickness was considered the AIDS of the early twentieth century.

Urbain Ureel, Courtesy of Joan Ferrante

People line up for sleeping sickness screening. In light of the labor needs at the time, the Belgian government and other Western players in Congo ventures considered diseased and dead Africans as economic losses. Thus, sleeping sickness posed a grave threat in need of control. Sleeping sickness campaigns were institutionalized through a network of rural clinics, screenings and injection centers, and hospitals. Between 1923 and 1938, an estimated 26 million exams were performed in the Belgian Congo (Lyons 2002).

Groups

Like statuses and roles, groups are an important component of social structure. A **group** consists of two or more people interacting in largely predictable ways and who share

group Two or more people interacting in largely predictable ways and who share expectations about their purpose for being.

Discussion Tip: The World Health Organization has a fact sheet on sleeping sickness, also known as African Trypanosomiasis. To locate use Google and enter search terms "Fact Sheet WHO Sleeping Sickness." Note that sleeping sickness was considered the "AIDS" of the 20th century in Africa. The Animal Planet website posts a short video describing how sleeping sickness takes hold. To locate use Google and enter search terms "Animal Planet sleeping sickness."

The Sociological Imagination Healing as a Cultural Collaboration

Sgt. James D. Sims

KINSHASA, Democratic Republic of Congo, September 9, 2010—Crowds gathered, some with pre-registered tickets in hand, others with just a hope of being seen by a healthcare professional in Kinshasa.

"I saw a crowd of people and asked what was going on," said Ousmane Kalotho Mutuala, a Kinshasa resident. "When they told me it was for medical care, I immediately went and got my friend who can barely see because his eyes are so bad and came back to try and get in."

The lines started forming hours before the humanitarian civic action site opened its doors for medical and dental care to the residents of Kinshasa. Residents that had tickets were registered in advance, ensuring they would be seen on a certain date. Even though some residents, like Mutuala, did not have tickets, medical providers saw them.

"Unfortunately there is a much bigger demand then what we have assets for," said Major Curt Kroh of Washburn, N.D., a physician assistant with the North Dakota National Guard's 814th Army Support Medical Company, which is based in Bismarck. "However, we stayed until we ran out of time and material."

Kroh is taking part in MEDFLAG 10, a joint medical exercise that allows U.S. military medical personnel and their Armed Forces of the Democratic Republic of the Congo (FARDC) counterparts to work side by side while providing humanitarian assistance to Kinshasa residents.

Approximately 25 FARDC and U.S. medical and dental personnel, and an additional 50 support staff, provided services. Over a four-day period, FARDC and U.S. medical personnel provided assistance to approximately 2,000 Congolese.

Patients were treated for various illnesses ranging from high blood pressure to malaria. The most common problem encountered was residents with eye problems, because they have never been examined, said Kroh. In addition to medical attention, dentists provided care ranging from basic oral hygiene to tooth extraction.

"The bulk of the medical care that was provided in the exam rooms was by FARDC doctors," said Kroh. "The FARDC doctors are very well involved in the treatment of the local population."

While all residents could not be seen and all problems could not be treated, residents were entered into the medical system and given referral letters for follow-up care.

Source: Staff Sergeant Kassidy Snyder (2010)

expectations about their purpose for being. Group members hold statuses and enact roles that relate to the group's purpose. Groups can be classified as primary or secondary. Primary groups are characterized by face-to-face contact and by strong emotional ties among members who feel an allegiance to one another. Examples of primary groups include the family, military units, cliques, and peer groups.

Secondary groups consist of two or more people who interact for a specific purpose. Thus, by definition, secondary group relationships are confined to a particular setting and specific tasks. Members relate to each other in terms of specific roles. People join secondary groups as a means to achieve some agreed-upon end, whether it be to cheer for a sports team, to achieve a status (college graduate), or to accomplish specific goals such as changing entrenched norms and fundamental assumptions. Secondary groups

secondary groups Two or more people who interact for a specific purpose. Secondary group relationships are confined to a particular setting and specific tasks.

can range from small to extremely large in size. They include a work unit, college classroom, parent–teacher associations, and churches. Larger secondary groups include fans gathering in a stadium, colleges, Wal-Mart employees, and activist organizations (see Working for Change: "Doing Good by Being Bad").

Within the DRC, large numbers of people are part of secondary groups, including the United Nations Peacekeeping Force believed to number 18,000, nongovernmental organizations such as Oxfam, World Vision, and Hope In Action seeking to address social problems resulting from the ongoing conflict. There are also corporations around the world whose products depend on minerals extracted from the Congo. A UN report listed a sample of 85 corporations who import DRC minerals through Rwanda alone. (Note that primary groups can form or be embedded within these secondary groups.)

Staff Sgt. Kassidy Snyder

Sgt. James D. Sims

The U.S. military's reach extends to the DRC. Here Congolese citizens sit under a tent waiting to see U.S. and Congolese medical staff as part of a humanitarian and civic assistance outreach program. The second photo shows the commander of U.S. Army Africa, being greeted by the Armed Forces of the Democratic Republic of the Congo (FARDC) military police and music battalion.

Institutions

A fourth component of social structure is **institutions**, relatively stable and predictable social arrangements created and sustained by people that have emerged over time with the purpose of coordinating human activities to meet some need, such as food, shelter, or clothing. Institutions consist of statuses, roles, and groups. Examples of institutions include government, education, medicine, and sports (Martin 2004). Institutions have a number of important characteristics:

1. Institutions have a history. Institutions have standardized ways of doing things that have come to be viewed as custom and tradition. That is, most people accept these ways without question. In the United States, the military is an institution with a global reach. The United States has a military presence in more than 100 countries, including the DRC. The military is stationed in places where the United States has strategic and national security interests. In the DRC, the government as an institution has operated "as a system of organized theft," beginning with the government of Leopold II to Kabila, the present leader's government. All in power have used their office to exploit the country's natural resources and people for personal gain (Hochschild 2009). Likewise, outside governments and militarized group powers have always sought to control the DRC resources. In other words, exploitation of the DRC has been institutionalized.
2. Institutions continuously change. Over time, ways of doing things become outdated and are replaced by new ways. Change can be planned, orderly, forced, and chaotic. Change can come from within or from outside the institution. We know, for example, that the institution of medicine is always changing to accommodate new technologies, new research, evolving demographics, and so on. Likewise, the DRC has changed over time, but those changes have been largely fueled by consumer, corporate, and military interests in the country's resources. King Leopold exploited rubber and ivory when he controlled the Congo Free States. Today the country is exploited for those items and much more including coltan, copper, cobalt, diamonds, gold, and cassiterite; forests and wildlife, timber, coffee, ivory; livestock, tobacco, tea, palm oil, and land.
3. Institutions allocate scarce and valued resources in unequal ways. They also allocate privileged and disadvantaged status. These inequalities can be reflected in individuals' salaries, benefits, degree of autonomy, and

institutions Relatively stable and predictable social arrangements created and sustained by people that have emerged over time with the purpose of coordinating human activities to meet some need, such as food, shelter, or clothing. Institutions consist of statuses, roles, and groups.

Teaching Tip: Point out that King Leopold II exploited what was to become the DRC for its diamonds. Today that exploitation continues, not only in the DRC but other African countries. PBS has created an excellent PowerPoint presentation that explains the process by which diamonds have become something desired and valuable. Simply search for "PBS From Military Engagement to Engagement Rings."

Working for Change Doing Good by Being Bad

Social change occurs only through perseverance and collaboration among committed parties. Changing entrenched norms and fundamental assumptions can oftentimes be a daunting task. The women's rights movement, civil rights movement, and the gay rights movement are examples of the kind of sustained collective action necessary to achieve change. In the 1980s and 1990s, ACT UP (AIDS Coalition to Unleash Power) was one highly visible activist gay rights group. Since its inception, ACT UP has progressed from civil action tactics (letters and phone calls to legislators) to public demonstrations and protests (rallies, picketing, tossing ashes of AIDS victims over the fence surrounding the White House).

Arguably, the gay rights movement started with the Stonewall riots in 1969, in New York City when police raided yet another gay bar—this time the Stonewall Inn (Columbia 2004). Having enough of the oppression, gays and lesbians took to the streets with pride. The HIV and the AIDS epidemic (the Centers for Disease Control labeled it an "epidemic" within the first year) became public in 1981, when a *New York Times* article highlighted the emergence of a new disease, first noted, among San Francisco gays and originally labeled GRID, for gay-related immune deficiency (Malone 2000). As the disease spread, gays and lesbians banded together at the local level to establish social service centers to help care for the ill and to lobby legislators for policy changes. ACT UP grew from local chapters to a national activist organization in 1986. One event, in particular, spurred the emergence of a national organization—Bowers v. Hardwick, stemming from an August 3, 1982, arrest of Michael Hardwick for breaking Georgia's antisodomy laws. Hardwick sued the state to repeal the law, which eventually ended with the 1986 Supreme Court decision denying the repeal (Gould 2009, p. 122). After that decision, gay and lesbian groups realized routine tactics were no longer effective, so they banded together and took to the streets. Activists demonstrated holding banners and signs proclaiming "Silence = Death" and "The government has blood on its hands: One AIDS death every half hour" and "Healthcare is a right" (Gould 2009, p. 240). ACT UP declared its mission as follows: to meet "the challenge of the AIDS epidemic and its crisis of conscience with vigilant acts of political and cultural provocation—thereby giving voice to the essential creative will of our humanity" (ACTUPNY 2010).

What drove this political movement and associated activism? There is one quality that all activist groups share: emotion. Emotion is one key factor that motivates individuals to take action, if not for themselves, then for a larger cause in which they deeply believe (Gould 2009). ACT UP organized a multitude of civil disobedience events to raise awareness and publicity about the impact of HIV/AIDS, the treatment of gays, as well as about the slow movement of the Reagan administration to take action (Lowenstein, Lechner, & Bruun 2007, p. 154). ACT UP called attention to and stood up against pharmaceutical companies' profit-driven drug development; fought for early access to drugs during testing phases and prior to FDA approval; and argued for more public education on the disease and preventative measures. In each instance, they won (Gage, Richards, & Wilmot 2002). The newspaper headlines suggest some of the strategies used to draw attention to their cause and demands; the key strategy was disrupting the existing order.

March 1987: ACT UP sat in the street at Broadway in New York City, stopping traffic.

amount of prestige. When the institution is a country, the inequalities are reflected in measures that capture the well-being of its residents. In that vein, the DRC is home to a vast amount of mineral wealth, but that wealth is distributed in a way that leaves the 66 million people who live there among the world's poorest.

4. Institutions promote ideologies that legitimate their existence. These legitimating ideologies are largely created and advanced by those occupying the most advantaged statuses or by those who benefit from institutionalized ways of doing things. The masses often accept these ideologies and resist change. Those who have exploited the DRC over the past 100 or more years have justified that exploitation by pointing to a "primitive" people in need of a civilizing forces (for example, colonization), or by dismissing the DRC as a failed state and its situation as hopeless. Such ideologies camouflage the role this exploitation has played in creating the long-standing chaos, poverty, and despair in that country.

The Dramaturgical Model of Social Interaction

CORE CONCEPT 4 Social interaction can be viewed as if it were a theater, people as if they were actors, and roles as if they were performances before an audience.

Sociologist Erving Goffman's (1959) writings revolve around the assumption that "life is a dramatically acted

Teaching Tip: The ACT UP organization challenges institutionalized structures or ways of responding and behaving. On its webpage (www.actupny.org) ACT UP posts a guide to civil disobedience. In that guide organizational leaders explain "Getting Arrested: Why do we do it?"

March 1987: ACT UP rallied outside FDA on Wall Street. Drug approval process was shortened by two years, allowing AIDS patients access to medications sooner. Seventeen people were arrested.

October 1988: ACT UP protests outside FDA in Washington DC. The FDA office closes in response. Over 1,000 protest, and nearly 180 are arrested. Drug testing is expedited.

April 1989: ACT UP members use rivets and steel plates to barricade themselves into drug company offices, demanding lowered prices on AZT, an AIDS medication costing over $8,000 annually.

September 1989: AZT manufacturer reduces price by 20 percent, to $6,400 annually. Seven ACT UP members also invade the New York Stock Exchange and halt trading, hanging banners and chaining themselves to the VIP balcony, yelling chants.

October 1992: Over 8,000 ACT UP members storm across the White House fence security line to toss the ashes of friends and family lost to AIDS over the fence onto White House lawn (ACTUPNY, 2006).

ACT UP's campaigns and successes continued into the 1990s. Today, ACT UP still exists but its visibility has declined. This has been due, in part, to the death of many key leaders from AIDS. Moreover, with hundreds to thousands of deaths each year and greater numbers becoming infected, emotion and despair overwhelmed many activists to the point of exhaustion. Conflict between ACT UP chapter leaders also led to the decline in ACT UP initiatives. Furthermore, as the younger generations of gays and lesbians come of age, the AIDS fight is thought of as something long ago and unknown; activism was not a major priority (Gould 2009). ACT UP's decline can also be attributed to a lack of collaboration with non-gay organizations that might have helped to sustain emotional energy and political support (GLBTQ 2004). Finally, ACT UP achieved many of its goals, which lessened intensity of purpose.

ACT UP, despite declining visibility, demonstrates the power of people when they come together for a purpose. Members of the gay and lesbian community banded together to change viewpoints, increase awareness, demand medical intervention, and demand government involvement. Today ACT UP still advocates for public awareness and for access to pharmaceuticals, for not only the homosexual community, but also for Africa and other AIDS-stricken populations. In 2007, ACT UP was rejuvenated when Larry Kramer led demonstrations in Times Square, New York, against the "Don't Ask, Don't Tell" policy (Wockner 2007). In 2010, this policy was repealed, ending discrimination against gays and lesbians in the U.S. military.

Perhaps Vito Russo, a founding member of New York City ACT UP, who died of AIDS complications in 1990 at the age of 44, best anticipated ACT UP's legacy when he stated, "Someday the AIDS crisis will be over, remember that. And when that day comes . . . people will hear the story that once there was a terrible disease in this country and all over the world, and that a brave group of people stood up and fought and, in some cases gave their lives, so that other people might live and be free" (Lowenstein, Lechner, & Bruun, p. 156). ACT UP, like many other organizations that effect real change, followed this strategy: doing good by being bad.

Source: Written by Keram J. Christensen, Northern Kentucky University, Class of 2011.

thing" (p. 72). He offered the **dramaturgical model** for analyzing social encounters. Dramaturgical sociology focuses on the ways in which those involved in social interactions work to create, maintain, dismantle, and present a shared understanding of reality (Kivisto and Pittman 2007).

Managing Impressions

When managing impressions, some people behave in completely calculating ways with the goal of evoking a particular response (Goffman 1959). An example of such calculation involves someone posting a photograph taken ten years earlier as an up-to-date likeness on a social networking website. Likewise, thieves posing as utility workers, who knock on doors and request permission to enter under false pretenses, are thoroughly calculating in their attempt to gain entrance so they can rob the occupants.

Impression management is not always self-serving; sometimes people have to talk or behave in a particular

dramaturgical model A model in which social interaction is viewed as if it were a theater, people as if they were actors, and roles as if they were performances before an audience in a particular setting.

impression management The process by which people in social situations manage the setting, their dress, their words, and their gestures to correspond to the impression they are trying to make or the image they are trying to project.

way, because the status they occupy requires them to do so. Coaches work to hide any doubts about whether they think their team can win an upcoming game. They engage in impression management because that is what coaches are expected to do. At other times, people are unaware that they are engaged in impression management because they are simply behaving in ways they regard as natural. Women engage in impression management when they put on makeup, dye their hair, or shave their legs, even if they never question the reason for doing so, which is to present themselves as something they are not. Men engage in impression management when they hide their emotions in stressful situations so that no one questions their masculinity.

Goffman (1959) judges the success of impression management by whether an audience "plays along with the performance." If the audience plays along, the actor has successfully projected a desired definition of the situation or has at least cultivated an understanding among the audience that they will pretend to play along. According to Goffman, there are times that an audience pretends to play along simply because that actor is "a representative of something" considered important to the society; that is, the audience gives deference, not "because of what they personally think of that actor but in spite of it" (p. 210). Most students, for example, manage to stay awake in class or at least give the appearance that they are paying attention, even when they think the teacher is not very good. They do so, not out of respect for the teacher they view as incompetent, but out of respect for the position that the teacher occupies.

Goffman (1959) recognized that there is a dark side to impression management that occurs when people manipulate their audience in deliberately deceitful and hurtful ways. Such was the case when King Leopold presented his interests in the Congo as purely philanthropic. He established the International African Association as a front for his profit making and exploitative ventures. Leopold's stated aim was to bring a humanizing influence to the Congo—an effort that included establishing a chain of medic posts and scientific centers across the region and abolishing Afro-Arab slave trade. In reality, Leopold pushed out Arab slave traders so he could control the labor and resources. Through Henry Morton Stanley, Leopold signed treaties with 450 African chiefs, who were unfamiliar with the written word and the concept of treaties that read like the following: "In return for one piece of cloth per month, give up . . . all their territories . . . such that all roads and waterways running through this country, the right of collecting tolls on the same, and all mining, fishing, and forest rights are to be the absolute right of the said Association" (Hochschild 1998, p. 72).

While impression management has a dark side, it can also be constructive. If people said whatever they wanted and behaved entirely as they pleased, social order would break down. Goffman argues that social order depends on people at least conveying the impression that they are living up to the societal expectations, standards, and agreements. According to Goffman, people in most social interactions weigh the costs of losing their audience against the costs of losing their integrity. If keeping the audience seems more important, impression management is deemed necessary. If being completely honest and upfront seems more important, we may take the risk of losing our audience.

The tension between revealing and concealing information comes into play when people test positive for HIV. If they disclose the test results, they risk discrimination, including loss of their jobs, insurance coverage, friends, and family (Markel 2003). This risk explains why many HIV-infected people fail to disclose their HIV status, even to sexual partners or when giving blood. In a study of 203 HIV-infected patients treated at two East Coast hospitals, Michael Stein (1998) and his colleagues found that more than half the group claimed to be sexually active. Of these 129 patients, 40 percent had not disclosed their HIV-positive status to partners with whom they had had sex in the past six months. In addition, only 42 percent reported that they always used a condom. In another study, almost one-third of a group of 304 HIV-positive blood donors indicated that they had donated blood because their colleagues had pressured them to do so.

Front and Back Stage

Goffman used a variety of concepts to elaborate on the process by which impressions are managed—including the idea of front and back stage. Just as the theater has a front stage and a back stage, so too does everyday life. The **front stage** is the area visible to the audience, where people feel compelled to present themselves in expected ways. Thus, when people step into an established social role such as a teacher in relation to students or a doctor in relation to patients, they step onto a front stage such as a classroom or an examining room (Goffman 1959). The **back stage** is the area out of the audience's sight, where individuals let their guard down and do things that would be inappropriate or unexpected in a front-stage setting. Because back-stage behavior frequently contradicts front-stage behavior, we take great care to conceal it from the audience. In the back stage, a "person can relax, drop his front, forgo his speaking lines, and step out of character" (Goffman 1959, p. 112).

The division between front stage and back stage can be found in nearly every social setting. Often that division

front stage The area visible to the audience, where people feel compelled to present themselves in expected ways.

back stage The area out of the audience's sight, where individuals let their guard down and do things that would be inappropriate or unexpected in a front-stage setting.

is separated by a door or sign signaling that only certain people such as employees can enter the back stage without permission or knocking. Goffman uses a restaurant as an example of a social setting that has clear boundaries between the back stage and front stage. Restaurant employees do things in the kitchen, pantry, and break room (back stage) that they would never do in the dining areas (front stage), such as eating from customers' plates, dropping food on the floor and putting it back on a plate, and yelling at one another. Once they enter the dining area, however, such behavior stops. Of course, a restaurant is only one example of the many settings in which the concepts of front stage and back stage apply.

In relation to the AIDS crisis, we can identify many settings that have a front stage and a back stage, including hospitals, doctors' offices, and blood banks. A U.S. government General Accountability Office (GAO 1997) study revealed that front stage–back stage dynamics affected the way blood donors answered screening questions. The study found that 20 percent of blood donors claimed they would have answered those questions differently if they had been in a more private setting. In other words, one in five donors did not give honest answers to screening questions because they were on the "front stage"—that is, others were within hearing distance and the donors feared disclosing answers that might be judged harshly. Such questions included the following: "Are you in good general health?" "Are you a male who has had sex with another male even once since 1977?" "Have you ever taken street drugs by needle, even once?" "Since 1977, have you ever exchanged sex for drugs or money?" "Have you had sexual contact with anyone who was born in or lived in Cameroon, Central African Republic, Chad, Democratic Republic of the Congo, Equatorial Guinea, Gabon, Niger, or Nigeria since 1977?"

Photographer's Mate 3rd Class Lamel J. Hinton

Alex Peck, Medical Antiques

Today when we draw blood and give injections, we use single, disposable syringes and needles. But disposable syringes did not become the norm until the mid-1970s. The case pictured shows hypodermic needles and syringes from the early twentieth century. Recall that tens of millions of African people were tested and treated for sleeping sickness, making it is highly unlikely that adequate sterilization of syringes and needles occurred between each use.

Attribution Theory

CORE CONCEPT 5 People assign causes to their own and others' behaviors. That is, they propose explanations for their own and other's behaviors, successes, and failures and then they respond accordingly.

Social life is complex. People need a great deal of historical, cultural, and biographical information if they are to truly understand the causes of even the most routine behaviors. Unfortunately, it is nearly impossible for people to have this information at hand every time they seek to explain a behavior. Yet, despite this limitation, most people attempt to determine a cause, even if they rarely stop to examine critically the accuracy of their explanations. As most of us know very well, ill-defined, incorrect, and inaccurate perceptions of cause do not keep people from forming opinions and taking action.

Attribution theory relies on the assumption that people make sense of their own and others' behavior by assigning a cause. In doing so, they often focus on one of two potential causes: dispositional (internal) or situational (external). **Dispositional causes** are forces over which individuals are supposed to have control—including personal qualities or traits, such as motivation level, mood, and effort. **Situational causes** are forces outside an individual's control—such as the weather, bad luck, and

dispositional causes Forces over which individuals are supposed to have control—including personal qualities or traits, such as motivation level, mood, and effort.

situational causes Forces outside an individual's immediate control—such as weather, chance, and others' incompetence.

Discussion Tip: To get at the variety of social interactions that put one at risk of contracting HIV/AIDS (from the medical community's point of view), review some of the questions from a "blood donor history questionnaire." Simply use "blood donor history questionnaire" as a search term and several questionnaires will come up.

What is HIV/AIDS?

According to the Centers for Disease Control (CDC, 2011), HIV (human immunodeficiency virus) is the virus that causes AIDS. This virus is passed from one person to another through exchanging infected blood or other body fluids, including semen, vaginal fluid, breast milk, cerebrospinal fluid surrounding the brain and spinal cord, synovial fluid surrounding bone joints, and amniotic fluid surrounding a fetus.

AIDS stands for acquired immunodeficiency syndrome.

Acquired means that the disease is not hereditary but develops after birth from contact with a disease-causing agent (in this case, HIV).

Immunodeficiency means that the disease is characterized by a weakening of the immune system.

Syndrome refers to a group of symptoms that collectively indicate or characterize a disease. In the case of AIDS, symptoms can include the development of certain infections or cancers, as well as a decrease in the number of certain cells in a person's immune system.

A physician makes a diagnosis of AIDS by using specific clinical or laboratory standards. The symptoms of AIDS are not unique to that condition. An HIV-infected person receives a diagnosis of AIDS after developing one of the 25 CDC-defined AIDS indicator illnesses. These illnesses include invasive cervical cancer, recurrent pneumonia, Kaposi's sarcoma, toxoplasmosis of the brain, and wasting syndrome due to HIV. An HIV-positive person who has not experienced one of the 25 indicator illnesses can receive an AIDS diagnosis based on tests showing that the number of CD4+ T cells per cubic millimeter of blood has dropped below 200.

Keep in mind that a diagnosis of AIDS depends on how the medical community defines the condition. Before 1993, many indicator illnesses were unique to the gay population with AIDS. Under the revised definition, HIV-positive women with cervical cancer are officially diagnosed as having AIDS. In 1993, the official definition of AIDS was revised to include HIV-related gynecological disorders, such as cervical cancer and HIV-related pulmonary tuberculosis or recurrent pneumonia as conditions that indicated AIDS. Before this definition change, physicians did not advise women with cervical cancer to be tested for HIV and did not treat HIV-positive women with this condition as if they had AIDS (Barr 1990; Stolberg 1996). The revised definition added 40,000 people to the total number diagnosed with AIDS.

others' incompetence. Usually people stress situational factors to explain their own failures and dispositional factors to explain their own successes (for example, "I failed the exam because the teacher can't explain the subject" versus "I passed the exam because I studied hard"). With regard to other people's failures or shortcomings, people tend to stress dispositional factors ("She doesn't care about school"; "He didn't try"). With regard to others' successes, people tend to emphasize situational factors ("She passed the test because it was easy"). Right or wrong, the attributions people make affect how they respond.

Many people stress dispositional traits to explain the cause of HIV/AIDS, arguing that certain groups of people behaved in careless, irresponsible, bizarre, or immoral ways. When I ask my students—most of whom were born after 1981 (the year AIDS was recognized as a disease)—about the origin of AIDS, they repeat these popular beliefs. With regard to Africa, students point to the evidence that the virus jumped from chimpanzees to humans—specifically from chimps to African hunters who were bitten or scratched by chimps. With regard to homosexuals, students point to high-risk and promiscuous behavior.

When evaluating the chimp-hunter and homosexual hypotheses, consider that chimps had been hunted for thousands of years. Why did the leap from monkey to human occur in 1930? We must consider situational factors that facilitated this leap. Think about the thousands of people fled into the forests and came in contact with chimps, the testing and inoculation campaigns with unsterilized needles, and a population that was weak and sick from forced labor. The point is that it took these factors to eventually push the virus onto the global scene 50 years later in 1981, the year it was first noticed (Moore 2004).

With regard to homosexual origins, we must ask the following: Are the categories male homosexual/bisexual and heterosexual mutually exclusive? If yes, that would mean that heterosexual sex is always penis-vaginal? One of the most comprehensive studies on sexual behavior in the United States found that between 13.2 and 37.5 percent of heterosexual respondents said they had engaged in anal sex with another sex partner at some time. Between 55.6 and 83.6 percent of the hetereosexuals surveyed indicated that they had had oral sex with another sex partner in the past year (Michael et al. 1994). An Urban Institute study financed by the U.S. government surveyed a representative sample of 1,297 males between the ages of 15 and 19 and found that two-thirds had had experience "with noncoital behaviors like oral sex, anal intercourse, or masturbation by a female" (Lewin 2000, p. 18A). The point is that we could probably learn more about how HIV spreads if we classified HIV cases by type of sex act (oral, anal, vaginal)

Discussion Tip: In 1980–1981, AIDS was known as the "GRIDS" or "Gay-Related Immune Deficiency Syndrome." Have students look for news stories printed in the early 1980s about GRIDS. One headline from the *New York Times* reads "New Homosexual Disorder Worries Health Officials."

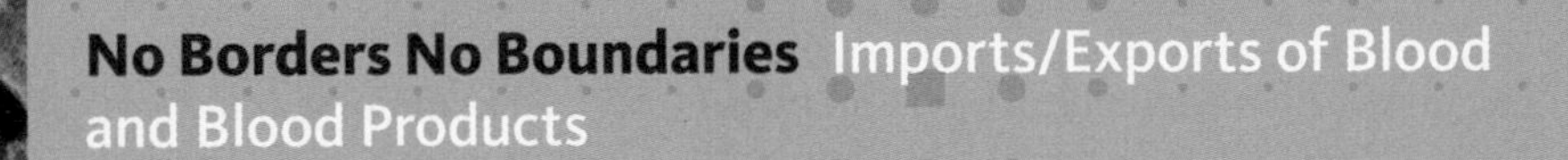

No Borders No Boundaries Imports/Exports of Blood and Blood Products

U.S. corporations supply about 60 percent of the world's plasma and blood products. For at least four years after HIV/AIDS was identified, U.S. blood bank officials continued to publicly affirm their faith in the safety of the country's blood supply, insisting that screening donors was unnecessary. Yet, these officials never revealed to the public the many shortcomings in production methods that could jeopardize the safety of blood. (By *shortcomings*, we mean deficiencies in medical knowledge and the level of technology rather than simply negligence.) Blood bank officials later argued that they practiced this concealment to prevent a worldwide panic. (In Goffman's terminology, blood bank officials did not want to "lose their audience.") Such a panic would have brought chaos to the medical system, which depends on blood products. This delay in implementing screening ultimately exposed many people to infection, especially hemophiliacs. Hemophiliacs were at higher risk of contracting HIV because their plasma lacks Factor VIII, a blood product that aids in clotting, or because their plasma contains an excess of anticlotting material (U.S. Centers for Disease Control 2010). In fact, we now know that 50 percent of hemophiliacs became infected with HIV from contaminated Factor VIII treatments before the first case of AIDS appeared in this group (*Frontline* 1993).

To truly understand the global AIDS epidemic, we need to consider the role of exported blood products in transmitting HIV. The amount of blood products exported from the United States to other selected countries as a percentage of the receiving country's total need is graphed below. These rates apply to today but also to 1981, the year that HIV was "discovered" and scientists first learned that it was in the blood supply. Notice that Japan imports 98 percent of its blood products from the United States—about 46 million units of concentrated blood products and 3.14 million liters of blood plasma (Yasuda 1994).

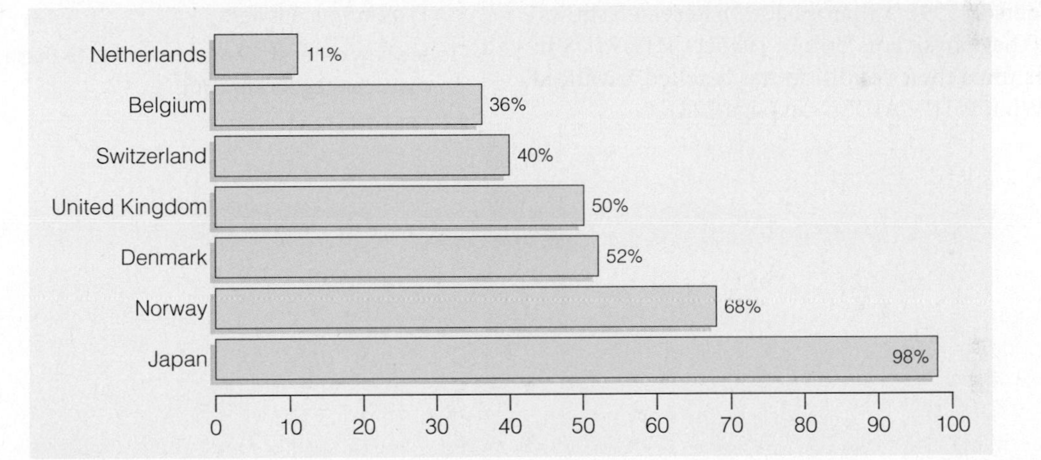

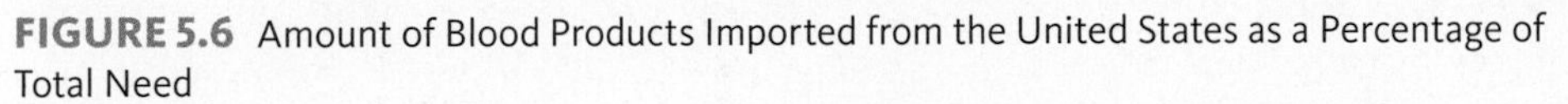

FIGURE 5.6 Amount of Blood Products Imported from the United States as a Percentage of Total Need

Sources: U.S. International Trade Administration (2010); International Federation of Pharmaceutical Manufacturers Associations (1981).

rather than identifying the categories of people having sex (homosexual/bisexual or heterosexual).

Attributing cause to dispositional factors—personal sexual practices, preferences, and appetite—works to reduce uncertainty about the source and spread of the disease. The rules are clear: If we can isolate "those people" who deserve or earned the disease, we are safe (Grover 1987; Sontag 1989). Such logic supports the naming of a scapegoat. A **scapegoat** is a person or group blamed for conditions that (a) cannot be controlled, (b) threaten a community's sense of well-being, or (c) shake the foundations of an important institution. Often the scapegoat belongs to a group that is vulnerable, hated, powerless, or viewed as different. The public identification of scapegoats gives the appearance that something is being done to protect the so-called general public; at the same time, it diverts public attention from those who have the power to assign labels. In the United States, the early identification

scapegoat A person or group blamed for conditions that (a) cannot be controlled, (b) threaten a community's sense of well-being, or (c) shake the foundations of an important institution.

of AIDS as the "gay plague" diverted attention from blood banks and the risks associated with medical treatments involving blood and blood products. Blood bank officials could maintain that the supply was safe as long as homosexuals abstained from giving blood.

From a sociological perspective, dispositional explanations that blame a group are simplistic and potentially destructive, not only to the group but also to the search for solutions. When a specific group and its behaviors emerge as targets, the solution is framed in terms of controlling that group. In the meantime, the problem can spread to members of other groups who believe that they are not at risk because they do not share the "problematic" attribute. This kind of misguided thinking about risk applies even to physicians and medical researchers. Attributions about who "should" have AIDS affect the way in which AIDS is defined and diagnosed. The definition and diagnosis, in turn, influence the statistics about who has AIDS. Such attributions also affect the content of the physician–patient interaction. In other words, if physicians do not believe a patient could be HIV-positive because he or she does not possess well-publicized attributes associated with the risk (homosexual, young, African), they will not recommend testing (Henderson 1998; Villarosa 2003). Research shows, for example, that physicians do not suspect HIV/AIDS in older patients until their condition has reached advanced stages (see "What Is HIV/AIDS?" on page 124).

In evaluating arguments about the origins of HIV/AIDS, we must recognize that we simply do not know how many people are infected with HIV in the United States or worldwide. To obtain information on who is actually infected, every country in the world would have to administer blood tests to a random sample of its population. Unfortunately (but perhaps not surprisingly), people resist being tested. A planned random sampling of the U.S. population sponsored by the CDC was abandoned after 31 percent of the people in the pilot study refused to participate, despite assurances of confidentiality (Johnson and Murray 1988).

Online Poll

I have changed the way I think about the emergence of HIV/AIDS since reading this account:

- Strongly Agree
- Agree
- No change
- Disagree
- Strong Disagree
- Explain your answer:

To see how other students responded to these questions, go to **www.cengagebrain.com.**

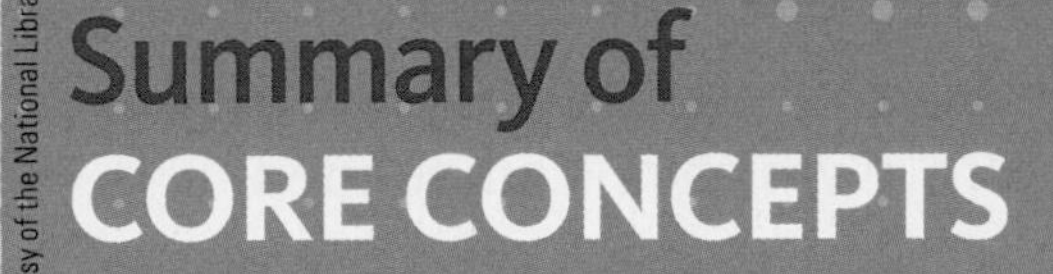

Courtesy of the National Library of Medicine

Summary of CORE CONCEPTS

When sociologists study interaction, they seek to understand the social forces that bring people together. And once people come together, sociologists seek to identify the factors that shape the interactions. This chapter applies sociological concepts and theories on social interaction to think about how a particular disease spreads through social interaction. That disease is HIV/AIDS. We consider how the disease emerged in Africa in 1930, to eventually affect people worldwide.

CORE CONCEPT 1 When sociologists study interactions, they seek to understand the larger social forces that bring people together in interaction and that shape the content and direction of that interaction.

Social interaction occurs when two or more people communicate and respond through language, gestures, and other symbols to affect one another's behavior and thinking. In the process, the parties involved define, interpret, and attach meaning to the encounter. When sociologists study social interaction, they seek to understand and explain the larger social forces that (1) bring people together in interaction, and (2) shape the content and course of interaction. With regard to HIV/AIDS, sociologists ask questions like: What forces increase the likelihood that HIV-infected and noninfected people will interact? What forces increase the likelihood that HIV-infected and noninfected people interact?

CORE CONCEPT 2 The division of labor is an important social force that draws people into interaction with one another and shapes their relationships.

Division of labor refers to work that is broken down into specialized tasks, each performed by a different set of workers specifically trained to do that task. The workers do not have to live near one another; they often live in different parts of a country or different parts of the world. Not only are the tasks geographically dispersed, but the parts and materials needed to manufacture products also come from many locations around the world. Division of labor is significant to understanding the forces that "pushed" African and European people together.

As the division of labor becomes more complex, solidarity or the social ties that bind people to one another shifts from mechanical to organic. Mechanical solidarity characterizes a social order based on a common conscience, or uniform thinking and behavior. Organic solidarity is a term applied to a social order based on interdependence and cooperation among people performing a wide range of diverse and specialized tasks. Durkheim maintained that societies and people become more vulnerable as the division of labor becomes more complex and more specialized. He was particularly concerned with the kinds of events that break down individuals' ability to connect with others in meaningful ways through their labor. Durkheim's theory is useful for placing HIV/AIDS in a broader context. For one, the European need for resources to support industrialization explains how Europeans and Africans became interdependent. Second, the forced division of labor and the means by which it was achieved are key to understanding how African people were made vulnerable to contracting the disease.

CORE CONCEPT 3 When analyzing any social interaction, or any human activity, sociologists locate the social structure in which it is embedded.

Social structures encompass at least four interrelated components: statuses, roles, groups, and institutions. The components help us to see how a social structure of exploitation emerged in the DRC and has been sustained over time. Taken together, we see that the exploitation of the DRC's people and resources by those inside and outside of the country has become institutionalized. That exploitation is, of course, key to understanding why HIV/AIDS rates are so high in the DRC.

CORE CONCEPT 4 Social interaction can be viewed as if it were a theater, people as if they were actors, and roles as if they were performances before an audience.

Social roles can be equated with the dramatic roles played by actors. In social situations, as on a stage, people engage in impression management, that is the management of the setting, their dress, their words, and their gestures to correspond to the impression they are trying to make or to an image they are trying to project. People alter their behavior depending on whether they are on the front stage (area visible to the audience, where people take care to create and maintain expected images and behavior) or back stage (area out of the audience's sight, where individuals let their guard down and do things that would be inappropriate or unexpected on the front stage). The concepts of impression management, front stage, and back stage help us to understand how Leopold engaged in impression management to disguise his exploitation of the then Congo Free State. These concepts also inform our understanding of why people give false answers to screening questions about sexual activities.

CORE CONCEPT 5 People assign causes to their own and others' behaviors. That is, they propose explanations for their own and other's behaviors, successes, and failures and then they respond accordingly.

In doing so, they often focus on dispositional (personal) or situational (external) causes. Dispositional causes are forces over which individuals are supposed to have control—including personal qualities or traits, such as motivation level, mood, and effort. Situational causes are forces outside an individual's control, such as the weather, bad luck, and others' incompetence. With regard to HIV/AIDS, it is clear that we have a better understanding of the disease origins and spread if we focus on situational factors that made African people vulnerable to the disease rather than searching for so-called personal decisions and behaviors as explanations. Also, the attributions we make about who has AIDS/HIV affects how we screen for and treat the condition.

Resources on the Internet

Login to CengageBrain.com to access the resources your instructor requires. For this book, you can access:

Sociology CourseMate

Access an integrated eBook, chapter-specific interactive learning tools, including flash cards, quizzes, videos, and more in your Sociology CourseMate.

CENGAGENOW™

Take a pretest for this chapter and receive a personalized study plan based on your results that will identify the topics you need to review and direct you to online resources to help you master those topics. Then take a posttest to help you determine the concepts you have mastered and what you will need to work on.

CourseReader

CourseReader for Sociology is an online reader providing access to readings, and audio and video selections to accompany your course materials.

Visit **www.cengagebrain.com** to access your account and purchase materials.

Key Terms

achieved statuses 114
ascribed statuses 114
back stage 122
dispositional causes 123
division of labor 106
dramaturgical model 121
front stage 122
group 117
impression management 121
institutions 119
master status 114
mechanical solidarity 109
organic solidarity 110
role 114
role conflict 116
role performance 115
role set 115
role strain 116
scapegoat 125
secondary groups 118
situational causes 123
social interaction 106
social status 114
social structure 114
solidarity 109
status set 114

6 FORMAL ORGANIZATIONS

With Emphasis on MCDONALD'S

Do you recognize this sandwich and from which fast food organization it was purchased? If you guessed McDonald's, you are correct. McDonald's represents just one organization that sells fast and processed foods. It is but one player in an efficient and complex organizational food chain. Sociologists view organizations like McDonald's as having a life that extends beyond the people who created it and make it run. This idea is supported by the fact that most organizations continue to exist even after members die, quit, retire, or get fired. The idea is also supported by the fact that the products and services organizations provide have consequences to society and human relationships that go far beyond their immediate consumption.

Why Focus On MCDONALD'S?

This chapter focuses on McDonald's, a fast food service corporation headquartered in the United States that is global in scale. Our emphasis on the McDonald's organization does not mean that McDonald's is better or worse than any other organization. Focusing on this well-known corporation allows us to apply the concepts that sociologists use to analyze any organization—in particular, to understand and appreciate their power and influence, the way they function, their internal dynamics, and their impact on society (Perrow 2000).

At this writing, McDonald's has 32,000 units in 117 countries. On any given day, approximately 60 million people eat at a McDonald's restaurant, and the fast food chain estimates that it handles 22 billion customer orders per year (McDonald's Corporation 2011a). Arguably, the golden arches is the world's most recognizable symbol for food that is *fast*, as in served quickly; easy to pick up, to eat on the run, and cheap. Of course, tens of thousands of food choices qualify as fast, easy, and cheap. We simply present McDonald's as one player among hundreds of thousands that are part of an **industrial food system**, one that produces high calorie, nutrient-low, processed food that is more available, affordable and aggressively marketed than nutritious food (Prevention Institute 2011). It is a food system in which the goal is to maximize profit achieved by speeding up the production process, increasing the amount produced, cutting labor costs, and finding the lowest-cost ingredients (see Figure 6.1). In addition to being profit-driven, industrial food depends heavily on pharmaceuticals (most notably antibiotics), chemicals (most notably fertilizers), and fossil fuel to manufacture and transport food products). Keep in mind that McDonald's does not produce or even "cook" the food it sells to customers. It relies on suppliers from around the country and the world.

As we will learn, food that is fast, easy, and cheap comes at a high price to human health, the environment, and overall quality of life. The rise of industrial food and the problems it has spawned have fueled a variety of food movements, with each aiming to address some issue ranging from animal rights/welfare to school lunch reform.

Online Poll

As a child, do you recall pestering a parent or other caregivers to take you to McDonald's?

- ○ Yes
- ○ No
- ○ Don't remember

To see how other students responded to these questions, go to **www.cengagebrain.com**.

industrial food system One that produces high-calorie, nutrient-low, processed food that is more available, affordable, and aggressively marketed than nutritious food. It is a food system in which the goal is to maximize profit, achieved by speeding up the production process, increasing the amount produced, cutting labor costs, and finding the lowest-cost ingredients. Industrial food depends heavily on pharmaceuticals, chemicals, and fossil fuels to produce, manufacture, and transport food products.

Chris Caldeira

Teaching Tip: As one way to illustrate the power of the McDonald's-related images to enrage or gratify, simply go to Google images and enter search term "McDonald's." You will find a variety of images from overweight Asian children to a billboard ad announcing the opening of a McDonald's in India.

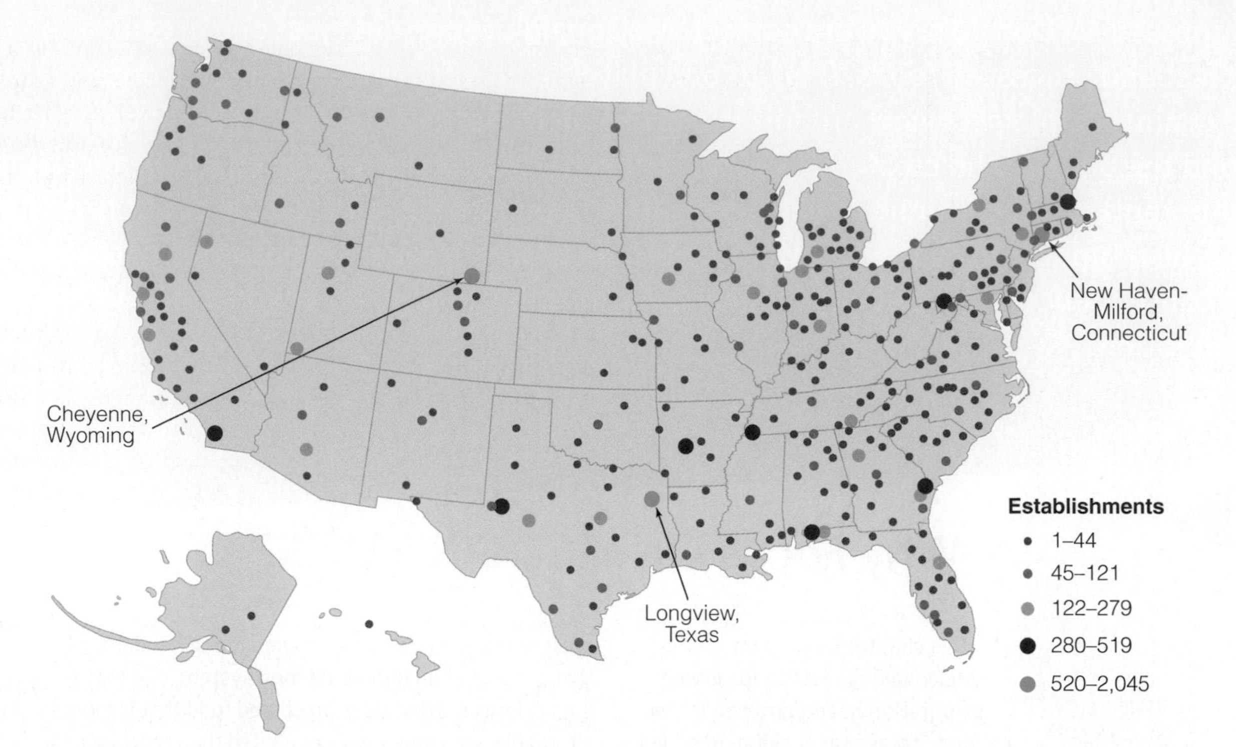

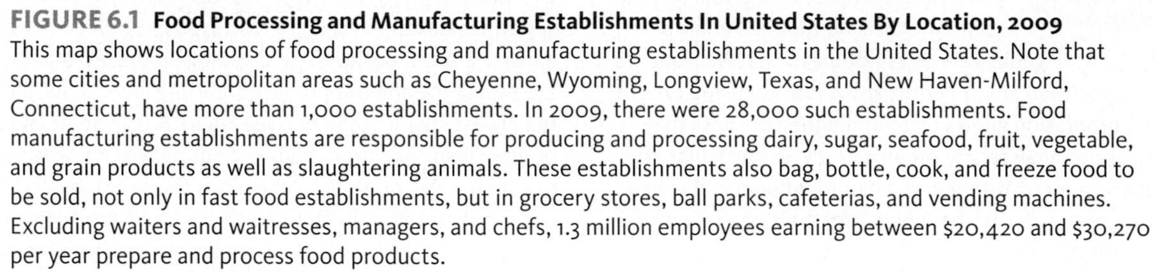

FIGURE 6.1 Food Processing and Manufacturing Establishments In United States By Location, 2009
This map shows locations of food processing and manufacturing establishments in the United States. Note that some cities and metropolitan areas such as Cheyenne, Wyoming, Longview, Texas, and New Haven-Milford, Connecticut, have more than 1,000 establishments. In 2009, there were 28,000 such establishments. Food manufacturing establishments are responsible for producing and processing dairy, sugar, seafood, fruit, vegetable, and grain products as well as slaughtering animals. These establishments also bag, bottle, cook, and freeze food to be sold, not only in fast food establishments, but in grocery stores, ball parks, cafeterias, and vending machines. Excluding waiters and waitresses, managers, and chefs, 1.3 million employees earning between $20,420 and $30,270 per year prepare and process food products.

Source: U.S.Bureau of Labor Statistics (2010).

Formal Organizations

CORE CONCEPT 1 The formal organization is a coordinating mechanism that brings together people, resources, and technology, and then channels human activity toward achieving a specific outcome or goal (Aldrich and Marsden 1988).

That outcome may be to maintain order in a community (as does a police department); to challenge an established order (as does the slow food movement and PETA—People for the Ethical Treatment of Animals); to keep track of people (as does a census bureau); to grow, harvest, or process food (as does PepsiCo); to sell goods (as does Wal-Mart); to produce oil (as does Exxon Mobil); or to provide a service (as does a hospital).

Sociologists classify formal organizations as secondary groups, thereby distinguishing them from primary groups. Primary groups fuse members into a common whole and are fundamental in shaping the "social nature and ideals of the individual" (Cooley 1909, p. 23). Primary groups are characterized by strong, emotional ties among members, who feel considerable allegiance to one another and strive to achieve "some desired place in the thoughts of [the] others" (Cooley 1909, p. 24). Examples of primary groups are the family, military units, and peer groups. It is the family that introduces us to food, and that introduction shapes our related tastes and expectations.

Secondary groups are impersonal associations among people who interact with a specific purpose. Thus, by definition, secondary-group relationships are narrow in scope (confined to a particular setting and specific tasks) and are seen as a means to achieve some agreed-upon end. Members relate to each other in terms of specific roles.

formal organization Coordinating mechanisms that bring together people, resources, and technology, and then channel human activity toward achieving a specific outcome.

secondary groups Impersonal associations among people who interact for a specific purpose.

Teaching Tip: For a complete list of cities in the United States and the number of food processing establishments in each go to http://www.bls.gov/spotlight/2010/food/data.htm#qcew.

High Stack Sandwiches
Served with choice of: Fresh-cut French Fries, Cole Slaw or Mixed Green Salad
Onion rings add $2.00
Spicy Desert Fries add $1.00
Bacon, Lettuce and Tomato $8.25
With avocado $9.25
Triple Decker Turkey Club $10.25
With bacon, cheese, avocado & tomato
Carolina Pulled BBQ Pork Sandwich $10.25
With cole slaw, pickles & tomatoes on a hamburger bun or French roll
Pork "Carnitas" Sandwich $10.50
With salsa, guacamole, cheese, & sour cream on a hamburger bun or French roll
Buffalo Chicken Sandwich

Chris Caldeira

Chris Caldeira

Look at the two menus. Which menu comes closest to the type of food you typically ordered as a child when you ate out? Which menu best represents the type of food you most often order when you eat out?

Employees of McDonald's constitute a secondary group; students at a university and fans of a football team also constitute a secondary group. One key to distinguishing primary and secondary groups is to examine the breadth of the relationships among members. If relationships are limited to a specific activity and setting such as work, a football game, or graduation ceremony, and if members only know others by what they do and not by who they are outside that setting, the group would certainly be considered secondary.

Secondary groups can range in size from small to extremely large. Examples of small secondary groups include a work unit, college students assigned to work together on a class project, and a parent–teacher association. Formal organizations, many of which are large, also qualify as secondary groups. Specific examples include McDonald's, the United States Naval Academy, and the Peace Corps. Keep in mind that members of secondary groups can form primary groups if they expand their relationships beyond the task at hand. Formal organizations are a taken-for-granted aspect of life. Simply consider that we are "born in a hospital, educated in a school system, licensed to drive by a state agency, loaned money by a financial institution, employed by a corporation, cared for by a hospital or nursing home, and at death served by as many as five organizations—a law firm, a probate court, a religious organization, a mortician, and a florist" (Aldrich and Marsden 1988, p. 362). Formal organizations can be voluntary, coercive, or utilitarian, depending on the reason that people participate (Etzioni 1975).

Voluntary organizations (also known as voluntary associations) draw in people who give time, talent, or treasure to support mutual interests, meet important human needs, or achieve a not-for-profit goal. Voluntary organizations include community service centers, politically oriented groups, religious organizations (such as ministries, churches, mosques, and synagogues), historical societies, and sports associations.

A large number of voluntary organizations have emerged to address societal problems associated with the industrial food system. One such organization is Slow Food (2011), founded in 1986 to protest the opening of McDonald's in Rome, Italy. Today this voluntary organization claims 100,000+ members in 1,300 local communities in 152 countries. Its members seek to counter (1) the rise of fast and processed foods, (2) the disappearance of food traditions, (3) the dwindling interest in knowing about the food we eat, and (4) the lack of awareness about how food choices affect the environment and others in the world.

Coercive organizations draw in people who have no choice but to participate. Organizations dedicated to compulsory socialization, such as elementary schools and the military (when there is a draft), qualify as coercive organizations. Other such organizations include rehabilitation or treatment facilities that work with individuals labeled as deviant because they are (or are seen as) not moving along normal pathways or not adequately performing their social roles (Spreitzer 1971).

Utilitarian organizations draw people seeking material gain in the form of pay, health benefits, or a new status (as conferred through a college degree, certification,

voluntary organizations Formal organizations that draw together people who give time, talent, or treasure to support mutual interests, meet important human needs, or achieve a not-for-profit goal.

coercive organizations Formal organizations that draw in people who have no choice but to participate; such organizations include those dedicated to compulsory socialization or to resocialization or treatment of individuals labeled as deviant.

utilitarian organizations Formal organizations that draw together people seeking material gain in the form of pay, health benefits, or a new status.

Chris Caldeira

There are a variety of slow food organizations, all of which exist to counter the rise and influence of fast and processed food. Some organizations encourage consumers to become locavores, a play on carnivore (that is, meat eaters), to mean consumers of food harvested and produced locally, or at least harvested within the region. In 2007, *New Oxford American Dictionary* selected *locavore* as its word of the year (Sustainable Table 2011).

or voluntarily undergoing some treatment). McDonald's qualifies as a utilitarian organization as does any organization that employs people.

From a sociological perspective, formal organizations can be studied apart from the people who designed and created them. Indeed, even as their members or employees die, quit, retire, or get fired, formal organizations have a life that extends beyond the people who constitute them (unless a catastrophe hits and the organization is completely destroyed).

The Concept of Bureaucracy

Most formal organizations can be classified as bureaucracies, organizational structures that strive to use the most efficient means to achieve a valued goal.

McDonald's Corporation coordinates the activities of 1.7 million employees in more than 32,000 restaurants located in 117 countries to fill 60 million food orders each day (McDonald's Corporation 2011a). The concept of bureaucracy can help us appreciate the organizational structure behind this monumental feat.

Sociologist Max Weber defined a **bureaucracy**, in theory, as a completely rational organization—one that uses the most efficient means to achieve a valued goal, whether that goal is feeding people, making money, recruiting soldiers, counting people, or collecting taxes. A bureaucracy has at least seven major characteristics that allow it to coordinate human activity toward achieving organizational goals. The following are those characteristics:

1. A clear-cut division of labor exists: Each office or position is assigned a specific task geared toward accomplishing the organizational goals. (One of the McDonald's Corporation's organizational goals is to deliver a meal within 90 seconds of ordering. When a customer places an order for, say, a Happy Meal, an order taker keys it into a computer; the order appears on a video screen in the kitchen where employees assemble the order, send it to the order taker, who in turn hands it to the customer.)
2. Authority is hierarchical: Each lower office or position is under the control and supervision of a higher one. (Individual McDonald's franchises are under the control of the corporate office; employees at each franchise are under the control of managers and assistant managers.)
3. Written rules specify the exact nature of relationships among personnel and describe the way tasks should be carried out. (McDonald's issues a 600-page *Operations and Training Manual* that specifies everything from how hamburgers should be placed on the grill to how to greet customers and to suggest menu items to increase the size of the order [Schlosser 2002].)
4. Positions are filled based on objective criteria (such as academic degree, seniority, merit points, or test results) and not based on emotional considerations, such as family ties or friendship. (Each year, McDonald's Corporation receives 36,000 franchise applications, of which 360 will result in new franchises. One criterion for buying a McDonald's franchise is that an applicant must have $500,000 of unborrowed cash on hand [McDonald's Corporation 2011a].)
5. Administrative decisions, rules, procedures, and activities are recorded in a standardized format and preserved in permanent files (such as McDonald's *Operations and Training Manual*).
6. Authority belongs to the position, not to the particular person who fills that position. This characteristic implies that a superior holds authority over subordinates only when they are on the clock/job and that authority does not extend beyond work hours. (Because managers at a McDonald's have authority over other employees only when they are on the time clock, managers cannot demand that employees wash their car or babysit their children.)
7. Organizational personnel treat clients as "cases" and "without hatred or passion, and hence without affection or enthusiasm" (Weber 1947, p. 340). To put it

bureaucracy An organization that strives to use the most efficient means to achieve a valued goal.

Technology Tip: Use the McDonald's restaurant locator on the Internet to find the number of McDonald's in or near a specific zip code. You might plug in the zip code of the college or university where you are teaching.

another way, no one receives special treatment. This approach is believed necessary because feeling emotion and making exceptions for special circumstances can interfere with the efficient delivery of goods and services. (According to standard operating procedures, every customer should be greeted with the words "Welcome to McDonald's. May I take your order?")

Taken together, these seven characteristics describe a bureaucracy as an **ideal type**—"ideal" not in the sense of being desirable, but as a standard against which real cases can be compared. An ideal type of a bureaucracy is a deliberate simplification or caricature, in that it exaggerates the defining characteristics of a bureaucracy (Sadri 1996). Anyone involved with an organization realizes that actual behavior departs from this ideal.

Formal and Informal Dimensions

Ideally, organizations such as McDonald's have well-defined and predictable job descriptions, rules governing relationships among personnel, and procedures for carrying out work-related tasks. The actual workings of organizations are not always clear and predictable, however, because the people in organizations vary in their ability or willingness to follow through—as when managers hire family and friends or when employees do not always treat customers the same.

Sociologists distinguish between formal and informal dimensions of organizations. The **formal dimension** is the on-paper or official aspect of the organization; it consists of job descriptions and written rules, guidelines, and procedures established to achieve valued goals. The **informal dimension** includes behaviors that depart from the formal dimension, such as employee-generated norms that evade, bypass, or ignore official policies and regulations (Sekulic 1978). For example, a manager may expect employees to work off the clock to meet goals related to labor costs; employees may give their friends free food and soft drinks when the manager is not looking; and servers may spit in a rude customer's drinks. NBC Dateline (2010) hired a survey company to review local health department inspection reports for 100 fast service restaurants the past 1.5 years to identify critical violations or situations in which employees violated operating procedures putting food at risk of contamination. Critical violations include handling ready-to-eat food with bare hands, not washing hands after using the bathroom, sick employees preparing food, and so on. Sixty-three percent of 100 restaurants sampled had at least one violation. In all, there were 1,755 critical violations (see Figure 6.2).

Although it is obvious that violating formal operating procedures (the ideal) can cause problems, it is less obvious that following rules and procedures too closely can also cause problems. The concept of rationalization helps us to understand why this is the case.

Lisa Southwick

This sign reminds food service workers to wash their hands. Many food service workers fail to follow this formal policy before handling food. This failure explains, in part, why each year 76 million Americans get sick, 300,000 are hospitalized, and 5,000 die from food-borne illnesses (Centers for Disease Control and Prevention, 2010).

Rationalization

CORE CONCEPT 2 The concept of rationalization—a process in which thought and action rooted in custom, emotion, or respect for mysterious forces is replaced by instrumental-rational thought and action—helps us understand how striving to achieve valued goals can have undesirable, even disastrous, consequences.

Formal organizations such as McDonald's strive to find the most efficient (time-saving and other cost-cutting) means to achieve its most valued goal, which is turning a profit. Although the search for these means can result in amazing feats, such as filling 60 million food orders per

ideal type A deliberate simplification or caricature that exaggerates defining characteristics, thus establishing a standard against which real cases can be compared.

formal dimension The official aspect of an organization, including job descriptions and written rules, guidelines, and procedures established to achieve valued goals.

informal dimension The unofficial aspect of an organization, including behaviors that depart from the formal dimension, such as employee-generated norms that evade, bypass, or ignore official rules, guidelines, and procedures.

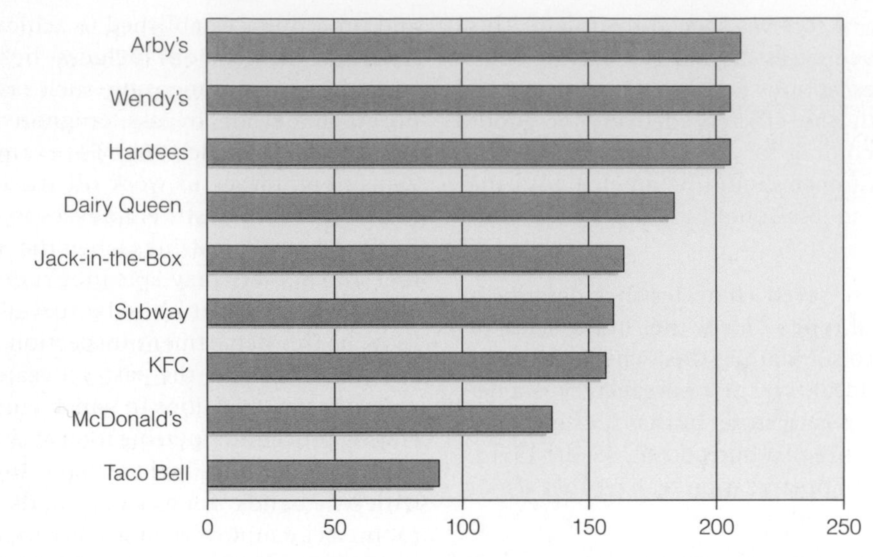

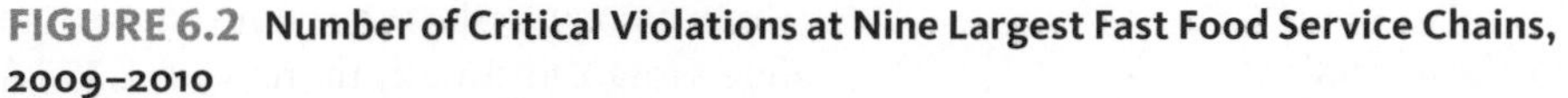

FIGURE 6.2 Number of Critical Violations at Nine Largest Fast Food Service Chains, 2009–2010

Source: Data from NBC Dateline (2010)

day, it can also have unintended, destructive consequences for workers, the public, and the environment. Rationalization applies to the dynamics underlying the never-ending quest to achieve a profit.

The growth and dominance of formal organizations goes hand in hand with a process known as rationalization. Weber defined **rationalization** as a process in which thought and action rooted in emotion (for example, love, hatred, revenge, or joy), superstition, respect for mysterious forces, or tradition is replaced by instrumental-rational thought and action. Through instrumental-rational thought and action, people strive to find the most efficient way to achieve a valued goal (Freund 1968).

One way to show how thought and action guided by emotion, tradition, superstition, or respect for mysterious forces differ from instrumental-rational thought and action is to compare two assumptions about farm animals. One assumption, portrayed by Matthew Scully (2003), presents animals (all animals, for that matter) as possessing complex emotions, including love and sorrow. Scully argues that humans have a moral obligation to treat animals with kindness and empathy. Cruelty toward animals is wrong, and when that cruelty "expands and mutates to the point where we no longer recognize the animals in a factory farm as living creatures capable of feeling pain and fear, . . . we debase ourselves" (Angier 2002, p. 9). Clearly, Scully believes that treatment of animals should be driven by emotion—kindness and empathy.

A second and contrasting assumption about farm animals and their purpose corresponds to the concept of instrumental-rational action. Here, how animals are treated cannot be separated from the desired goal of turning a profit. So factory farms, also known as concentrated animal feeding operations (CAFOs), raise thousands of cows and ten of thousands of chicken in tight quarters where they are fattened up for slaughter as quickly as possible. The living space is so tight that animals may not have room to lie down or turn around (Walsh 2009). Obviously, the more chickens, pigs, or cows a factory farm can house and the faster it can raise them, the more meat, eggs, and milk it can produce and sell. Egg and chicken suppliers raise chickens in crowded conditions that give each chicken an average of 49 square inches or 7 by 7 inches of space. Because chickens live in such close quarters, factory farm workers clip the wings and trim the beaks to prevent hens from injuring one another. Egg suppliers regularly practice "forced mating" by depriving hens of food and water for as long as two weeks (*Food Institute Report* 2000; Yablen 2000). Apparently this practice increases egg production.

Weber made several important qualifications regarding instrumental-rational thought and action. First, he used the term *rationalization* to refer to the way daily life is organized socially to accommodate large numbers of people, but not necessarily to the way individuals actually think (Freund 1968). So for example, most individuals believe that home-cooked meals are more nutritious than fast

rationalization A process in which thought and action rooted in custom, emotion, or respect for mysterious forces is replaced by instrumental-rational thought and action.

Technology Tip: Listen to an NPR interview with Matthew Scully, author of *Dominion: The Power of Man, the Suffering of Animals, and the Call to Mercy*. Go to the NPR website (www.npr.org) and enter the search terms "Animal Welfare in Matthew Scully's Dominion."

food, but they can't find the time to prepare food at home, nor can they resist the efficiency of fast food service:

> In a highly mobile society in which people are rushing, usually by car, from one spot to another, the efficiency of a fast food meal, perhaps without leaving one's car while passing by the drive-through window, often proves impossible to resist. The fast food model offers us, or at least appears to offer us, an efficient method for satisfying many of our needs. (Ritzer 1993, p. 9)

Second, rationalization does not assume better understanding or greater knowledge. In fact, Weber argues that the so-called primitive peoples can negotiate the environment in which they live without help from strangers and know how to acquire the food they consume (Freund 1968). People who live in an instrumental-rational environment typically know little about their surroundings (nature, technology, the economy). Consumers buy any number of products in the grocery store without knowing how they were made or what they consist of. People are not troubled by such ignorance; rather, they are content to let corporations set food choices.

Finally, when people identify a desired goal and decide on the means (actions) to achieve it, they seldom consider or dismiss less profitable or slower ways to achieve it. The problem may be as seemingly simple as growing potatoes that can be processed into French fries or potato chips that look and taste the same. In creating such a potato, people fail to consider that the demand for uniformity limits the varietal range of potatoes to those that are high-yielding, high in dry matter, low in sugar content, long and oval in shape, and uniform in color and flavor. With the help of science, such potatoes can be produced, but they require heavy doses of chemicals and threaten the longer-term viability of domestic potato production to meet commercial processing requirements (International Potato Center 1998).

The McDonaldization of Society

> **CORE CONCEPT 3 One organizational trend guided by instrumental-rational action is the McDonaldization of society, a process in which the principles governing fast food restaurants come to dominate other sectors of society.**

Of course, McDonald's and other fast food service organizations are not the only formal organizations that strive to deliver a product or service by the most efficient means possible. Sociologist George Ritzer (1993) describes a larger organizational trend guided by instrumental-rational action: the "McDonaldization" of society.

Ritzer sees the **McDonaldization of society** as "the process by which the principles of the fast food restaurant are coming to dominate more and more sectors of American society as well as the rest of the world" (p. 1). Those principles are (1) efficiency, (2) quantification and calculation, (3) predictability, and (4) control. **Efficiency** is an organization's claim to offer the "best" products and services, which allow consumers to move quickly from one state of being to another (for example, from hungry to full, from fat to thin, from uneducated to educated, or from sleeplessness to sleep). **Quantification and calculation** are numerical indicators that enable customers to evaluate a product or service easily (for example, get delivery within 30 minutes, lose ten pounds in 10 days, earn a college degree in 24 months, limit menstrual periods to four times a year, or obtain eyeglasses in an hour). **Predictability** is the expectation that a service or product will be the same no matter where or when it is purchased. With regard to food products, this kind of predictability requires that they be genetically and chemically modified. If consumers expect cheese, for example, to have melted and to taste the same each time they eat it, it cannot be a naturally made cheese (Barrionuevo 2007). **Control** involves guiding, monitoring, and regulating the production and delivery of a service or product (for example, by assigning a limited task to each worker, by filling soft drinks from dispensers that shut off automatically, or having customers stand in roped off lines). Control is often achieved by replacing employees with technological innovations such as robots or computer-activated voices.

Ritzer's model allows for amazing organizational feats: each year, McDonald's handles 22 billion customer visits worldwide. Keep in mind that McDonald's does not produce any of the food items it sells—it thaws, assembles, fries, and warms food processed by other organizations. For example, Simplot, Lamb Weston, and McCain Food control 80 percent of the frozen French fry market in the United States. Simplot supplies McDonald's (ProPotato 2011, Schlosser 2002).

McDonaldization of society "The process by which the principles of the fast food restaurant are coming to dominate more and more sectors of American society as well as the rest of the world" (Ritzer 1993, p. 1).

efficiency An organization's claim of offering the "best" products and services, which allow consumers to move quickly from one state of being to another (for example, from hungry to full, from fat to thin, or from uneducated to educated).

quantification and calculation Numerical indicators that enable customers to evaluate a product or service easily.

predictability The expectation that a service or product will be the same no matter where or when it is purchased.

control The guiding or regulating, by planning out in detail, the production or delivery of a service or product.

The McDonaldization model also has drawbacks. Max Weber used the phrase **iron cage of rationality** to describe the set of irrationalities generated by supposedly rational systems. For example, it may seem rational to divide up production so that anyone, even the least skilled and educated, could do the job. At the same time, a work setting that requires so little skill generates high employee turnover. In the fast food industry, the annual turnover rate can be between 150 and 200 percent (Sterrett, 2007). Likewise, it may seem rational to develop, produce, and modify potatoes that allow fries to be made uniform, but the overuse of pesticides and other chemicals the practice requires is irrational.

Expanding Market Share

One way to understand how organizations grow from local operations (McDonald's began as one restaurant in Illinois in 1955) to global giants is to consider the actions they have taken to increase profits. Organizations employ five major strategies to reach the valued goal of turning a profit: (1) lower production costs, (2) create new products that consumers "need" to buy, (3) improve existing products to make previous versions obsolete, (4) find ways for people to purchase more products ahead of their earnings, and (5) create new markets. See Figure 6.3.

Lower Production Costs Hiring employees who will work for lower wages, introducing labor-saving technologies, reducing the number of employees, and moving production facilities out of high-wage zones are major ways corporations reduce production costs.

Create New Products Obviously, new menu items represent "new products." Some new McDonald's menu items include real fruit smoothies and frappes (first introduced in 2010), McCafé coffees including lattes, cappuccinos, and mochas (introduced in 2009), the Snack Wrap (introduced in 2006), and premium salads (introduced in 2003). McDonald's and other fast food chains have been particularly successful at marketing their products to children. Happy Meals, first introduced in 1979, come with toys such as Transformers and Hello Kitty wristbands that many children (and some adults) "need" to have.

Improve Existing Products to Make Previous Versions Obsolete This strategy includes making existing food items bigger and better. Fast food companies compete, for example, to make better (hotter or crispier) French fries than their competitors do.

Headquarters Oak Brook, Illinois
First restaurant Des Plaines, Illinois, 1955
First foreign franchise Canada, 1967
First foreign franchise outside North America Costa Rica
Latest foreign franchise Warsaw, Poland
Number of U.S. restaurants 13,980
Number of foreign-located restaurants 18,498
Percentage of corporation profits derived from foreign sales 64%
Total revenue $22.7 billion
Total number of employees worldwide 1.2 million
Most well-known charitable activity Ronald McDonald House (since 1994)
U.S. *Fortune* 500 rank 108
Global *Fortune* 500 rank 378

FIGURE 6.3 Facts About McDonald's

Sources: Data from *Fortune* (2010a, 2010b); McDonald's (2011a)

Identify Ways for People to Purchase More Products Obviously, one way for a fast food company to increase profits is to persuade existing customers to eat more (Langley 2003). In fact, one might argue, at least from a purely profit-oriented perspective, that the "fattening of America" and other places in the world "may well have been a necessity" (Critser 2003). Suggestive selling is one way to increase the amount of food customers order. Order takers ask customers if they would like to add fries or purchase a larger size. Market researchers have found that when consumers use credit cards to defer payments until a later date, they are likely to spend more, and thus buy more, at the time of purchase. At one time fast food restaurants did not accept credit card payments, but that has changed. Another strategy to get people to consume more food is to expand operating hours until 1:00 or 2:00 a.m. or to even stay open 24 hours. Taco Bell invites customers in for a fourth meal—a meal between dinner and breakfast.

Create New Markets McDonald's began its expansion outside the United States in 1967, when it opened a unit in Canada. It now operates units in more than 100 foreign countries. In 2009 alone, the corporation opened about 824 new restaurants worldwide (McDonald's Corporation 2009). In an annual report to stockholders, McDonald's distinguishes between established, well-penetrated markets (such as Australia, Brazil, Japan, and the United States) and emerging markets (such as Argentina, China, Italy, and Spain), which have had franchises for more than five years but have room to add franchises. The company has also identified more than three dozen countries (such as Bolivia, Egypt, India, and the Ukraine) where it is working to introduce the fast food concept. In their drive to create new

iron cage of rationality The set of irrationalities that rational systems generate.

Student Activity: Ask students to create a Figure 6.3 for a fast food corporation other than McDonald's. Possibilities include, but are not limited to Burger King, Subway, Pizza Hut, Wendy's, Taco Bell, and Dairy Queen. How does the profile compare with McDonald's?

Missy Gish

Staying open 24 hours has helped create the concept of a fourth meal—a meal between dinner and breakfast. This is one strategy that restaurants and other businesses use to sell more products.

Missy Gish

As a strategy for creating new markets, McDonald's opened its first drive-through window in 1975. Now drive-through windows are a standard feature at most fast food restaurants.

markets, McDonald's and other fast food corporations had located restaurants in Wal-Mart and Home Depot stores, gas stations, malls, airports, and hospitals, as well as on college campuses and military bases (see No Borders, No Boundaries: "Countries without a McDonald's").

Multinational and Global Corporations

Multinational corporations (or just "multinationals") are enterprises that own, control, or license production or service facilities in countries other than where the corporations are headquartered. It is difficult to estimate the number of multinationals in the world, because Internet technologies allow as few as two people in different locations to form a corporation. The last estimate made by the United Nations put the number at 65,000 multinationals, with 820,000 foreign affiliates (Chanda 2003). Multinationals are headquartered disproportionately in the United States, Japan, and western Europe (see Global Comparisons: "The Size of the Top Ten Global Corporations Relative to National Economies"). A multinational corporation can range in size from fewer than 10 employees to millions. In fact, most multinationals employ 250 people or fewer (Gabel and Bruner 2003). Regardless of their size, multinationals compete, plan, produce, sell, recruit, extract resources, acquire capital, and borrow technology on a multicountry basis.

Multinationals establish operations in foreign countries for many reasons, including to expand markets; to obtain raw materials (such as oil and diamonds); to avoid paying taxes; to employ an inexpensive labor force; to provide low-cost services, such as call centers and help desks; and to manufacture goods, provide services, or sell products to consumers in a host country (as does Toyota, North America, Inc.). The world's largest multinational corporations are often referred to as global corporations. Theoretically, a truly global corporation should have established some kind of economic relationship in every country in the world. Probably no corporation is yet global in that sense. Still, because of their size and reach, many corporations are classified as global—most notably, those on the *Fortune* Global 500 list.

Critics of multinational corporations maintain that they are engines of destruction. That is, they exploit people and natural resources to manufacture products inexpensively. They take advantage of desperately poor labor forces, lenient environmental regulations, and sometimes nonexistent worker safety standards. Supporters of multinational corporations, by contrast, maintain that these companies are agents of progress. They praise the multinationals' ability to raise standards of living, increase employment opportunities, transcend political hostilities, transfer technology, and promote cultural understanding. In this regard, the president of McDonald's international operations notes that his corporation does not "force"

multinational corporations Enterprises that own, control, or license production or service facilities in countries other than the one where the corporations are headquartered.

The first McDonald's restaurant opened in 1955, in Des Plaines, Illinois. Since then, operations have spread to more than 100 other countries. Franchise holders are McDonald's employees and independent businesses. That is, they operate their own restaurants but must adhere to strict operating guidelines (Waters 1998). One way the corporation builds its global identity across units is by requiring all franchise holders to attend a two-week course offered in 22 languages on quality control and management at one of its four Hamburger Universities or other 22 regional training centers (McDonald's Corporation 2011a).

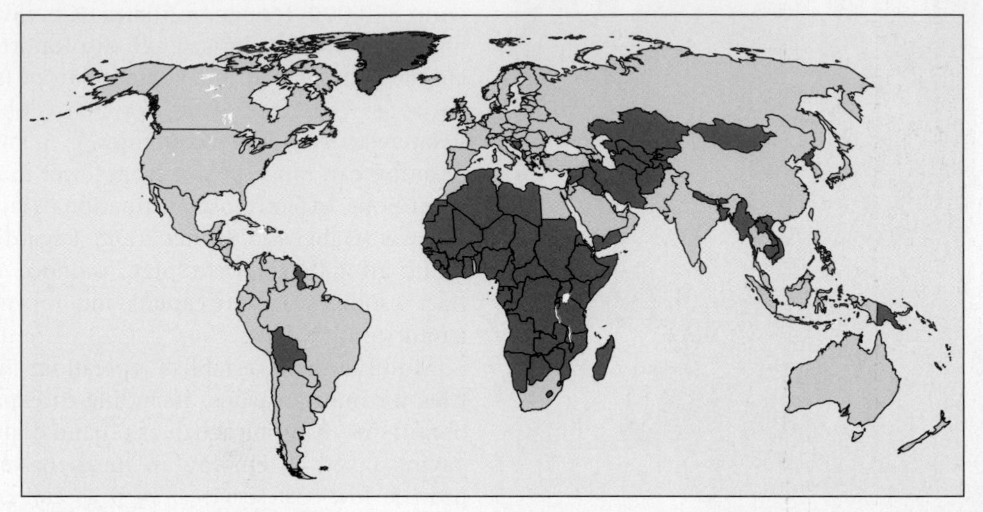

FIGURE 6.4 Countries in the World Without a McDonald's Franchise
The countries shaded in blue are countries that do not have a McDonald's franchise. What do you think that says about the country?
Source: Wikipedia (2009)

itself on foreign countries. Rather, he argues, governments around the world actively recruit the company.

In reality, we cannot make a simple evaluation that would apply to all multinationals. Obviously, on some level, multinational corporations "do spread goods, capital, and technology around the globe. They do contribute to a rise in overall economic activity. They do employ hundreds of thousands of workers around the world, often paying more than the prevailing wage" (Barnet and Müller 1974, p. 151). Critics, however, argue that, if anything, multinationals aggravate these problems, because the pursuit of profits creates social inequalities and ecological imbalances.

One can also argue that multinationals are not responsible for inequality or for other problems such as obesity. As one U.S. federal court judge stated: "a person knows or should know that eating copious orders of supersized McDonald's products is unhealthy, or may result in weight gain, it is not the place of the law to protect them from their own excesses. . . . Nobody forced them to eat at McDonald's" (Weiser 2003). McDonald's former CEO Jack Greenburg (2001) elaborated on the issue of healthy foods by arguing that "we're selling meat and potatoes and bread and milk and Coca-Cola and lettuce and everything else you can buy in a grocery store. What you choose to eat is a personal issue. Every nutritionist I've talked to says a

As measured by revenue, Wal-Mart is the world's largest global corporation, at $408 billion. This amount makes Wal-Mart the world's 28th largest economy in the world, as only 27 countries have a GNP larger than $408 billion (U.S. Central Intelligence Agency 2011).

Discussion Tip: Ask students if anyone has eaten at a McDonald's outside the United States. For those who have, ask why they chose to do so rather than eat the food of the country they were visiting? What was similar and different about the McDonald's at which they ate?

Global Comparisons The Size of the Top Ten Global Corporations Relative to National Economies

One reason that the largest multinational organizations have great influence on the societies in which they operate is related to their size. Taken together, the combined annual revenue of the ten largest global corporations is about $2.34 trillion. Only five countries in the world—the United States, China, Japan, India, and Germany—possess a gross national product that exceeds that amount. The annual revenue of the world's largest corporation, Wal-Mart, exceeds $408 billion. Only 27 countries have a gross national product that exceeds that amount: the United States, China, Japan, India, Germany, the United Kingdom, Russia, France, Brazil, Italy, Mexico, South Korea, Spain, Canada, Indonesia, Turkey, Australia, Iran, Taiwan, Poland, the Netherlands, Saudi Arabia, Argentina, Thailand, South Africa, Egypt, and Pakistan.

The World's Largest Global Corporations, 2010

Corporation	Revenues (in $ millions)	Profits (in $ millions)	Headquarters
Wal-Mart Stores	408,214	14,335	Arkansas
Royal Dutch Shell	285,129	12,518	Netherlands
Exxon Mobil	284,650	19,280	Irving, Texas
BP	246,138	16,578	London, United Kingdom
Toyota Motor	204,106	2,256	Aichi, Japan
Japan Post Holdings	202,196	4,849	Tokyo, Japan
Sinopec	187,518	5,756	Beijing, China
State Grid	184,496	−343	Beijing, China
AXA	175,257	5,012	Paris, France
China National Petroleum	165,496	10,272	Beijing, China

Source: Data from *Fortune* 2010b.

balanced diet is the key to health. You can get a balanced diet at McDonald's. It's a question of how you use McDonald's. Nobody's mad at the grocery store because you can buy potato chips and pastries there. Nobody wants a full diet of that either."

McDonald's menu includes such items as real fruit maple oatmeal, 1% low-fat milk, Fruit 'N Yogurt Parfait, apples, and a variety of salads. Still, its most popular items remain fries, Big Mac, Quarter Pounder, Chicken McNuggets, and Egg McMuffins.

To complicate matters, corporations claim that they merely respond to consumer tastes. For example, virtually all of the major fast food companies have introduced low-fat foods on their menus, and most have proven unpopular with consumers.

Nevertheless, many people question whether corporations should have the right to ignore the larger long-term effects of their products and business practices on people and the environment, even as they respond to consumer demand. The most profitable product for a corporation may prove costly for a society due to **externality costs**—hidden costs of using, making, or disposing of a product that are not figured into the price of the product or paid for by the producer. Yet, someone must eventually pay these costs (Lepkowski 1985). Such costs include those for cleaning up the environment and for medical treatment of injured workers, consumers, or other groups (see "The Obesity Epidemic in the United States" and Table 6.1).

externality costs Hidden costs of using, making, or disposing of a product that are not figured into the price of the product or paid for by the producer.

Student Activity: Ask students to go to *World Factbook* (https://www.cia.gov/library/publications/the-world-factbook/) to find out where the revenues of each of the top 10 global corporations are located relative to the national economies of the world. Once at the website, chose "Guide to Country Comparisons." Then chose "GDP (purchasing power parity)." This will yield a rank-ordered list of the world's countries and associated GDP. Locate each global corporation's revenue relative to rank-ordered list of GDP by country.

The Obesity Epidemic in the United States

An estimated one-third of U.S. adults—more than 72 million people—and 17 percent of U.S. children are obese. From 1980 through 2008, obesity rates for adults have doubled and rates for children have tripled. During the past several decades, obesity rates for all groups in society regardless of age, sex, race, ethnicity, socioeconomic status, education level, or geographic region have increased markedly.

Recent reports show that health disparities related to obesity still exist. According to the 2009 Behavioral Risk Factor Surveillance System report, from 2006 through 2008, blacks were 51 percent more likely and Hispanics were 21 percent more likely than non-Hispanic whites to be obese. During this time, the prevalence of obesity among all adults was higher for those living in the Midwest or South. In addition, the 2009 Pediatric Nutrition Surveillance System report shows that 14.6 percent of children aged 2 to 4 years from low-income households are obese.

Obesity has physical, psychological, and social consequences for adults and children. Children and adolescents are now developing obesity-related diseases, such as type 2 diabetes, that in the past were seen only in adults. One study of 5- to 17-year-olds found that 70 percent of obese children had at least one risk factor for cardiovascular disease, and 39 percent had at least two risk factors. Other associated health consequences include coronary heart disease, cancers (especially endometrial, breast, and colon), high blood pressure (hypertension), stroke, liver and gallbladder disease, sleep apnea and respiratory problems, osteoarthritis, and reproductive health complications. In 2008, obesity-related medical care costs were estimated to be as high as $147 billion.

The causes of obesity in the United States are complex and numerous, and they occur at social, economic, environmental, and individual levels. American society has become characterized by environments that promote physical inactivity and increased consumption of unhealthful food. To address this problem, approaches to public health that affect large numbers of people in multiple settings, such as communities, schools, work sites, and health care facilities, are needed. Policy and environmental approaches that make healthy choices available, affordable, and easy could be most effective in fighting obesity.

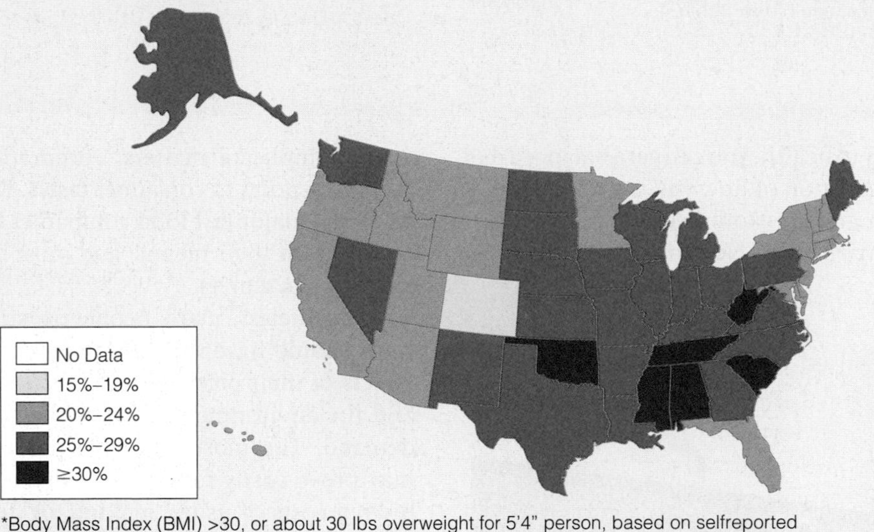

*Body Mass Index (BMI) >30, or about 30 lbs overweight for 5'4" person, based on selfreported weight and height.

FIGURE 6.5 Percentage of Adults Who are Obese, by State*

Adapted from: CDC, Behavioral Risk Factor Surveillance System, www.cdc.gov/chronicdisease/resources/publications/aag/obesity.htm.

Although multinational organizations are very powerful, consumers and watchdog groups have demonstrated that they can hold corporations in check. In many cases, informed consumers have gathered enough support to change organizational behavior and structure. Some examples follow:

- Santa Clara County, California, banned toys handed out at McDonald's and other fast food restaurants if they promote high-calorie meals (Chase 2010).
- PETA protests against McDonald's resulted in the corporation requiring its producers to give chickens more space (from 7 by 7 inches to 9 by 9 inches), to not clip

TABLE 6.1 Benefits and Drawbacks of Multinational Corporations to Host Country

Benefits
Provide new products
Introduce new technologies and develop skills
Introduce new managerial and organizational techniques
Offer employment opportunities
Provide greater access to international markets
Provide a source of foreign exchange
Support development of new ancillary or spin-off industries
Assume investment risks
Mobilize capital
Drawbacks
Products and services create new tastes and demands that undermine cultural identity and traditions
Possess a competitive advantage over local industries
Create inflationary pressures
Exploit host country's resources and labor
Dominate direction of the host country's economy
Show insufficient understanding and concern for the local economy, labor conditions, and national security interests
Restrict access to modern technology by centralizing research and development facilities in the home country and by employing home country nationals in key management positions

Source: Adapted from U.S. General Accountability Office (1978).

beaks, and to cease the practice of withholding food and water to increase egg production (Mawhorr 2000).

- A 1997 court verdict in Britain brought to public attention the way in which McDonald's producers rear and slaughter animals and advertise to children (The Verdict 1997). The visibility of the court case likely stimulated actions to improve conditions under which animals are raised, including California Proposition 2 passed in 2008, which prohibits the practice of not giving farm animals enough space to turn around, lie down, stand up, or stretch (Ballotpedia 2008).
- PETA has purchased stock in at least 80 companies including McDonald's, Kraft Foods, Safeway, Burger King, and Ruby Tuesday so that it can influence company policies related to animal welfare (CBS News 2010).

In sum, when corporate executives feel enough pressure from consumers and stockholders, they will act. However, if no consumers or only a small number of consumers speak out, their claims are often dismissed. Consider the comments from McDonald's CEO after four days of protest in Seattle against the World Trade Organization, where as many as 2,000 protesters trashed McDonald's restaurants and other businesses. The CEO noted that although 2,000 people protested, tens of millions visited a McDonald's restaurant to eat (Greenberg 2001). The point is that there is no need to be concerned about the voices of 2,000 activists when millions are voting with their feet, or mouths.

Consequences of Instrumental-Rational Action

To this point, we have focused on instrumental-rational action and its connection to the McDonaldization of society, the iron cage of rationality, the rise of multinational and global corporations, and externality costs. In the pages to come, we will consider how "by any means to an end" thinking can result in trained incapacity, tunnel vision, oligarchy, and alienation.

Trained Incapacity

> CORE CONCEPT 4 **To be efficient, organizations sometimes train employees to respond mechanically or mindlessly to the dictates of the job, leaving them unable to respond creatively to new or changing circumstances.**

Formal organizations such as McDonald's train workers to perform their jobs a certain way and reward them for good performance. When workers are trained to respond mechanically or mindlessly to the dictates of the job, however, they risk developing what economist and social critic Thorstein Veblen (1933) called **trained incapacity**—the inability to respond to new or unusual circumstances or to recognize when official rules or procedures do not apply or may be doing harm. In other words, workers are trained to do their jobs an efficient way to meet organizational goals while ignoring other important matters related to their health, the community, and the environment. Here efficient means quickly and without thought. At the root of trained incapacity is a job with little variety and repetitive tasks. Veblen argues that as variety in work decreases, the amount of thought and time needed to perform a job also decreases. The less thought involved, the less attuned workers are to the unintended consequences of their actions. In other words, efficiency supports tunnel vision and blindness to broader concerns (Wais 2005).

---

trained incapacity The inability, because of specialized training, to respond to new or unusual circumstances or to recognize when official rules or procedures are outmoded or no longer applicable.

The efficiency of the slaughterhouse assembly line is illustrative. "The old meat packing plants in Chicago slaughtered about 50 cattle an hour. Twenty years ago, new plants in High Plains slaughtered about 175 cattle an hour. Today some plants slaughter up to 400 cattle an hour—about half a dozen animals every minute, sent down a single production line, carved by workers desperate not to fall behind" (Schlosser 2002, p. 173). The company that houses such an assembly line cannot possibly care about matters such as workers' health because their profit margins may be just pennies on the pound. Speed takes precedence over worker health. The speed by which the employees must work does not allow them time to even sharpen their knives, and dull knifes add considerable stress on muscles. The "efficiency" of the operation helps to explain the high injury rate. According to the most recent data, that rate is 921.6 per 10,000 employees (U.S. Bureau of Labor Statistics 1999). Schlosser (2002) makes the case that this rate is likely higher, as many such injuries go unreported.

Social psychologist Shoshana Zuboff distinguishes between work environments that promote trained incapacity and those that promote empowering behavior. In her research, Zuboff (1988) found that management can choose to use computers in one of two ways: as automating or as informating tools. To *automate* means to use computers to increase workers' speed and consistency or to monitor performance. Computer programs that monitor the number of keystrokes per minute or the time workers spend on a task, or that push workers to do certain tasks quickly represent the use of computers as automating tools. Using computers in this way can promote trained incapacity.

Alternatively, management can use computers as informating tools. To *informate* means to empower workers with decision-making tools, such as employee-scheduling software, which ensures that enough employees are scheduled for the busiest times and shifts. Other decision-making tools include software to keep track of payroll, sales, inventory, and purchasing. On the surface, it may seem as if the software is doing the work for managers. Keep in mind, however, that managers must interpret the results and use this information to make decisions. Workers who use computers as informating tools experience work very differently from those whose work is monitored by computers.

Keith Weller—K7974-18

When we imagine what the life of a pig and her babies must be like, we envision the mother pig having enough space to lie down and be with her babies.

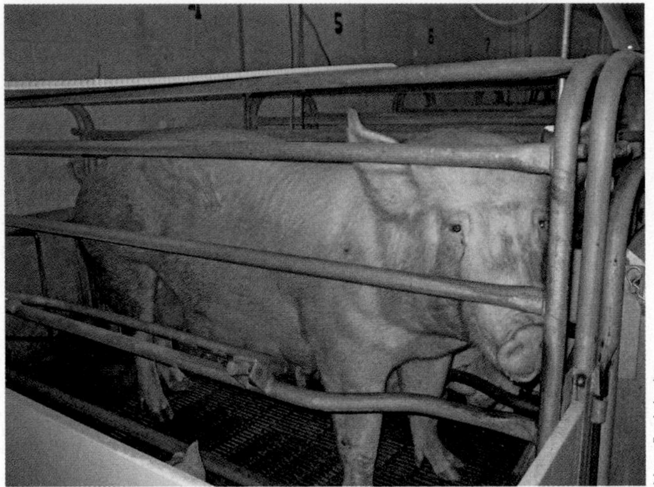

Mercy For Animals

We do not imagine a pig's life to be such that she has no room to turn around or lay down comfortably.

Statistical Records of Performance

McDonald's performance evaluators posing as customers conduct more than 500,000 unannounced visits each year to the company's 31,000 restaurants. The company also uses a checklist of 500 performance measures or questions to evaluate each of its restaurants. Items include: (1) Are restrooms clean, in good repair, and fully stocked with paper towels, soap, and toilet paper? and (2) Are current promotional materials properly displayed? (McDonald's Corporation 2003). These criteria exemplify **statistical measures of performance**, quantitative (and sometimes qualitative) measures of how well an organization and its members or employees are performing.

In an industry such as fast food service, where profits depend on being cost-conscious about every item used, statistical measures of performance exist for everything,

> whether it be the amount of milk-shakes sold per gallon of shake mix used, or the amount of cola drinks per liter of cola syrup, the amount of burgers sold per box of burgers used, the number or portions of chips per kilo used, the monetary amount of cleaning materials used as a percentage of the taking, even small things like the amount of sauces used per portion of Chicken McNuggets sold, or the amount of ketchup used per burger sold, and so on. (Gibney 1993)

statistical measures of performance Quantitative (and sometimes qualitative) measures of how well an organization and its members or employees are performing.

Executives and other managers often compile statistics on profits, losses, market share, customer satisfaction, total sales, production quotas, and employee turnover as a way to measure individual, departmental, and overall organizational performance. Such measures can be convenient and useful management tools for two reasons: They are considered to be objective and precise, and they permit comparison across individuals, time, or departments.

Based on these measures, management can reward good performance or act to correct poor performance. But statistical measures of performance also have their drawbacks. One problem is that a chosen measure may not be a valid indicator of the performance it is intended to measure. For example, a corporation's occupational safety record is often gauged by counting the number of accidents that occur on the job. But sometimes workers are exposed to toxic substances, for example, that may take years to show their effects.

A second problem with statistical measures of performance is that they can encourage employees to concentrate on achieving good scores and to ignore problems generated by their drive to score well. In other words, people tend to pay attention only to the areas of performance being measured and to overlook the areas not being measured. For example, sales increases are a common statistical measure of performance. Employees are asked to meet hourly, weekly, monthly, or annual sales goals. In addition, sales goals often increase from one evaluation period to the next. Even after achieving record sales, employees are expected to achieve higher levels in the future. (See The Sociological Imagination: "Statistical Measures of Performance.")

If sales increases and profits are the main criteria by which employees (and especially managers) are evaluated, then problems are inevitable. Managers, under pressure to make and increase profits, may force employees to work unpaid overtime. As one example, in 2010, two employees sued Taco Bell, claiming that the company did not pay them for overtime hours and for falsifying time records. The two employees sought back pay for themselves as well as for similarly situated employees (Bloomberg Business Week 2010).

USDA

Chris Caldeira

McDonald's claims to employ more than 2,000 distinct statistical measures of performance to monitor food as it moves from the farm to the restaurant. For instance, pork used to make the McRib sandwich is inspected for joint enlargement, which can be a sign of infectious arthritis, the cause of 14 percent of condemned carcasses (Goetzinger 2006). How might a meat suppliers' goal of making a profit affect willingness to notice this and other unhealthy conditions?

Oligarchy

> **CORE CONCEPT 5 Large formal organizations inevitably tend to become oligarchical: That is, power becomes concentrated in the hands of a few people, who hold the top positions.**

Oligarchy is rule by the few, or the concentration of decision-making power in the hands of a few people, who hold the top positions in a hierarchy. In fact, "One of the most bizarre features of any advanced industrial society in our time is that the cardinal choices have to be made by a handful of men . . . who cannot have firsthand knowledge of what those choices depend upon or what their results may be. . ." (Snow 1961, p. 1).

Political analyst Robert Michels (1962) believed that large formal organizations inevitably tend to become oligarchical, for the following reasons: First, democratic participation is virtually impossible in large organizations. Size alone makes it "impossible for the collectivity

oligarchy Rule by the few, or the concentration of decision-making power in the hands of a few people, who hold the top positions in a hierarchy.

The Sociological Imagination Statistical Measures of Performance

Statistical measures of performance are a part of daily life. Three examples from students in my introductory sociology classes describe how such measures are used to evaluate and motivate employees:

- "At my place of work, sales staff are rewarded according to a point system. When a customer applies for and is accepted for a store credit card, the salesperson receives 1,000 points. Employees are also awarded points according to the number of items per sale, the dollar amount per sale, and total hourly sales. When a salesperson accumulates a certain number of points, he or she can redeem them for prizes such as CD players, TVs, and gift certificates."
- "At my workplace, to earn a raise, employees must be in uniform every day. That is, employees' shoes must be the right color and they must wear the hat, pants, and shirt issued by the store. In addition, they must have the proper nametag on and shirts tucked in. Employees must rarely call in sick (a maximum of two or three times per quarter), and they cannot be late. It also helps to rarely request days off. The employees who meet these standards earn a 25-cent raise every quarter."
- "I work at a nursing home where employee absenteeism and tardiness for work were such big problems that management began to give bimonthly bonuses to correct the problem. If over the course of a two-month period an employee was never late for work and did not miss a day of work, he or she earned a $100 bonus. If the employee was late only one time and did not miss a day of work, he or she received $75. If an employee missed one day of work but had a medical excuse, he or she earned $50. Attendance improved dramatically under this system."

to undertake the direct settlement of all the controversies that may arise" (p. 66). For example, McDonald's employs about 1.2 million people and has franchises located in more than 100 countries. Obviously, "such a gigantic number of persons . . . cannot do any practical work upon a system of direct discussion" (Michels 1962, p. 65). Second, as corporations increase in size and reach, many organizational features become incomprehensible to workers. As a result, many employees work toward achieving organizational goals they did not define, cannot control, may not share, or may not understand. This situation prevents workers from participating in or evaluating decisions made by executives.

A danger of oligarchy is that key decision makers may become so preoccupied with preserving their own leadership that they do not consider the greater good. In addition, they may not have the background information necessary to understand the full implications of their choices. In such situations, they draw upon experts to provide the information.

Expert Knowledge and Responsibility

In his writings about bureaucracy, Max Weber emphasized that power lies not in the person but rather in the position that person occupies. A superior gives orders to subordinates, who are required to carry out those orders. The superior's power is supported by the threat of sanctions, such as demotions, layoffs, or firings. Sociologists Peter Blau and Richard Schoenherr (1973) recognize the importance of this form of direct power but identify a second, more ambiguous type—expert power—that they believe is "more dangerous than seems evident . . . and . . . is not readily identifiable as power" (p. 19).

According to Blau and Schoenherr (1973), expert power is connected to the fact that organizations are becoming increasingly professionalized. **Professionalization** is a trend in which organizations hire experts (such as chemists, physicists, accountants, lawyers, engineers, psychologists, or sociologists) as consultants or full-time employees. Experts have formal training in a particular area—training not from the organization, but from colleges and universities. Experts use the framework of their profession to analyze situations, solve problems, or invent new technologies. Theoretically, experts do not have, nor do they seek, control over how corporations use the information, service, or invention they provide. They may, however, feel pressure to deliver a product or to present a position that executives "need" or want to hear. For example, on its website, McDonald's states that it cares about humane treatment of animals and that it works with experts to continuously improve its standards and practices among its 484 meat suppliers (McDonald's Corporation 2011b). Realistically, experts who advise McDonald's on animal welfare issues must know on some level that they cannot offer advice that would cut into McDonald's profits. So, for example, the Scientific Advisory Committee on Animal Welfare for United Egg Producers recommends that hens need a minimum of

professionalization A trend in which organizations hire experts with formal training in a particular subject or activity—training needed to achieve organizational goals.

Discussion Tip: Ask students to read the box "Statistical Measures of Performance" and then to describe a performance measure by which they are evaluated at work.

72 square inches of space. Is seven inches by seven inches of space or even nine by nine inches enough to be considered humane conditions?

The committee (consisting of members without pay, and headed by the Dean of Agriculture and Natural Resources at Michigan State) reviewed all the existing literature, and visited egg farms, breeder companies, and equipment manufacturers. Although the committee reviewed cage and noncage egg production systems, it developed voluntary welfare guidelines for conventional cage systems because 95 percent of U.S. egg production employs that method (United Egg Producers 2011). A glance at the recommended guidelines shows that they essentially support existing practices. For example, the guidelines weigh the pros and cons of beak trimming. "Advantages of beak trimming/treatment may include reduced pecking, reduced feather pulling, reduced cannibalism, better feather condition, less fearfulness, less nervousness, less chronic stress, and decreased mortality. Welfare disadvantages may include reduced ability to feed following beak trimming/treatment, short-term pain, perhaps chronic pain, and acute stress." The guidelines recommend that breeders breed a more docile bird, minimizing the need to trim or to use one of two acceptable beak-trimming practices—trimming beaks when birds are one day old or when they are 10 days old or younger. The point is that McDonald's and other organizations can evoke the support of experts when they say the company is complying with existing practices.

Blau and Schoenherr (1973) regard this arrangement between experts and organizations as problematic because it complicates attempts to identify the ultimate decision maker. In the case of animal production, just who will take responsibility for the animals' welfare? Experts claim that they provided only the patent, information, or recommendations and thus are not in control of its application. Executives, on the other hand, claim that they followed the advice of experts who know best.

Alienation

CORE CONCEPT 6 The growth of bureaucracies to coordinate the efforts of humans as well as machines and other technology is accompanied by alienation, a state of being in which human life is dominated by the forces of its inventions.

Human control over nature increased with advances in technology and with the growth of bureaucracies to coordinate the efforts of both people and machines. Machines and bureaucratic organizations, in turn, combined to extract raw materials from the earth more quickly and more efficiently and to increase the speed with which necessities such as food, clothing, and shelter could be produced and distributed. Karl Marx believed that this increased control over nature is accompanied by **alienation**, a state of

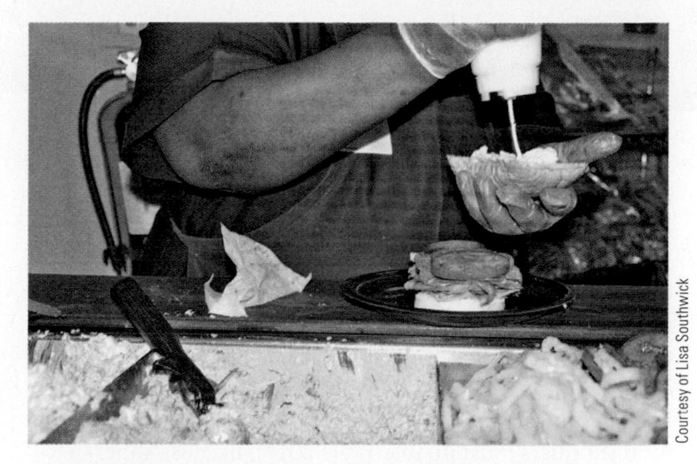

Courtesy of Lisa Southwick

According to the U.S. Bureau of Labor Statistics, the median income of fast food workers is approximately $8.00 per hour. That hourly wage does not allow workers to buy essential necessities.

being in which human life is dominated by the forces of its inventions.

Chemical substances represent one such invention; they have reduced the physical demands and risk of failure involved in growing food. Synthetic fertilizers, herbicides, pesticides, and chemically treated seeds give people control over nature, because they eliminate the need to fight weeds with hoes, prevent pests from destroying crops, and help people produce unprecedented amounts fruits and vegetables that are uniform in appearance.

These gains also have a dark side, however. In the long run, people are dominated by this invention. For example, heavy reliance on chemical technologies can cause the soil to erode and become less productive; it can also prompt insects and disease-causing agents to develop resistance to the chemicals. In addition, chemical technologies have altered the ways farmers plant crops. Planting patterns have changed from many crop varieties to a single standard cash crop, planted in rows. Consequently, some farmers have lost knowledge of how to control insects and diseases without chemicals, by interplanting a variety of flowers, herbs, and vegetables. Today, many farmers are economically dependent on a single crop and the chemical industry.

Although Marx discussed alienation in general, he wrote more specifically about alienation in the workplace. Marx maintained that workers are alienated on four levels: (1) from the process of production, (2) from the product, (3) from the family and the community of fellow workers, and (4) from the self. Workers are alienated from the *process* when they produce not for themselves or for known consumers but rather for an abstract, impersonal market

alienation A state of being in which human life is dominated by the forces of its inventions.

Teaching Tip: The U.S. Bureau of Labor Statistics offers a profile of the food manufacturing industry, including a profile of working conditions and employee earnings in various sectors. Go to http://www.bls.gov/oco/cg/cgs011.htm.

Working for Change Why Buy Local?

As an antidote to the problems of globalization, advocates of localism seek to turn consumers on to the benefits of buying from local farmers and businesses (Allen 2010). Localism applies to all economic sectors, but the majority of initiatives center around food (Allen and Wilson 2008). U.S. consumers spend more than $600 billion a year on food. However, the supermarket chains, factory farms, and food processing corporations account for 93 percent of spent "food money," leaving only about 7 percent for regional, local farmers and food suppliers (Sustainable Table 2011). Because supermarket chains stock their shelves with products obtained from all over the United States and the world, a significant share of revenue taken in leaves the community in which the stores are located. Most of the revenue earned by local farmers, however, stays in the community. In fact, if an additional one percent of the U.S. purchasing power was spent on local produce, it is estimated that farmers' incomes could increase by 5 percent (Sustainable Table 2011).

Globalization of the food chain is also known to have a negative impact on the environment, as many food and agricultural products are exported to the United States from different countries through complex, fossil fuel–dependent systems. Food in flown by airplane, shipped on freighters, and trucked across the country every day, often enduring long journeys. *Food miles* is a term used to describe the distance a particular item has traveled—from where it was grown/raised, to the stores that sell it, and then home to American refrigerators. It is estimated that the produce found in typical U.S. supermarket has traveled 1,500 miles (Sustainable Table 2011). The mileage and energy used to prevent spoilage leaves behind a sizeable carbon footprint. The fossil fuels burned release carbon dioxide (CO_2) and sulfur dioxide, which both contribute to climate change, sea/air pollution, smog, and acid rain (Sustainable Table 2011).

By the time food is consumed, it has been handled by multiple people and exposed to various environments. In addition to affecting the food's taste and quality, the risk of food-borne illness, bacterial contamination, and allergic

Chris Caldeira

reactions increases in proportion to the amount of handling and processing food undergoes. Buying locally provides fresher products, better taste, and fewer health risks. In addition, consumers and producers can get to know one another (Allen 2010). Not only can consumers ask farmers questions at the market, but they can visit the farm where food is grown. Finally, localizing the food system has the potential to address inequalities. Globalization is criticized as a process that involves exploiting workers—especially offshore workers—who earn low wages, work long hours, and are given few if any benefits (Brown 2009). Localism limits exploitation as the United States has laws in place regulating minimum wage, overtime, and workplace conditions and safety (Allen and Wilson 2008). Furthermore, agricultural workers in the United States who have suffered unemployment and wage reduction may find more job opportunities if buying local catches on. Today, the average farmer's income is equivalent to the income in 1969, even as world food production has doubled. Making local an important component of the food chain is the ultimate goal of the "buy local" movement.

Source: Written by Ashley Novogroski, Northern Kentucky University, Class of 2010.

and when they do not own the tools of production. Workers are alienated from the product when their roles are rote and limited. For the most part, those who work in the processed and fast food industries perform highly specialized and repetitive tasks. These workers are treated as easily replaceable parts in the industrial food production chain.

Workers are alienated from the *family and the community of fellow workers* when households and work environments are treated as separate. Workers can lose touch with their families when they work long shifts, late at night, early in the morning, or weekends. Such hours keep them from participating in family life and activities. Workers are alienated from the community of fellow workers when they compete for jobs, advancement, and awards. As they compete, they fail to consider how they might unite as a force and control their working conditions. In addition, workers produce for consumers outside the communities in which they live; thus workers do not know those consumers and those consumers have no personal connection to them (see Working For Change: "Why Buy Local?")

Discussion Tip: Ask students if anyone in class is involved with the local food movement as described in the box above. They may be involved as a consumer or a local farmer trying to selling a product. Does anyone in class live in a household that grows some kind of produce and/or that raises animals that yield eggs, milk, or meat?

Finally, workers are alienated from the self because "one's genius, one's skills, one's talent is used or disused at the convenience of management in the quest of private profit" (Young 1975, p. 28). When Karl Marx developed his ideas about alienation in the late 1800s, he was describing "alienation from self" as it relates to industrial society. More recently, sociologist Robin Leidner (1993) has described the alienation from self that can occur in service industries when management standardizes or routinizes virtually every aspect of the service provider–customer relationship, so that neither party feels authentic, autonomous, or sincere:

> Employers may try to specify exactly how workers look, exactly what they say, their demeanors, their gestures, even their thoughts. The means available for standardizing interactions include scripting; uniforms or detailed dress codes; rules and guidelines for dealing with service-recipients and sometimes with co-workers. . . . Surveillance and a range of incentives and disincentives can be used to encourage or enforce compliance. (pp. 8–9)

Online Poll

Do you buy locally produced food?

- ○ No, not that I am aware.
- ○ Yes, on a regular basis.
- ○ Yes, occasionally.
- ○ Yes, rarely.

To see how other students responded to these questions, go to **www.cengagebrain.com**.

Courtesy of Chris Caldeira

Summary of CORE CONCEPTS

In this chapter, we focused on McDonald's, a corporation with operations in 117 countries. As we learned, McDonald's is just one player in an efficient and complex industrial food chain. We used sociological concepts associated with formal organization to think about the forces driving the industry and its larger effects on people and the environment.

CORE CONCEPT 1 The formal organization is a coordinating mechanism that brings together people, resources, and technology, and then channels human activity toward achieving a specific outcome or goal (Aldrich and Marsden 1988).

Formal organizations can be voluntary, coercive, or utilitarian. Sociologists classify formal organizations as secondary groups, because relationships are confined to a particular setting and specific tasks and are seen as a means to achieve some agreed-upon end. Members relate to one another in terms of specific roles. Most formal organizations can be classified as bureaucracies, perfectly rational organizational structures that strive to use the most efficient means to achieve a valued goal. In the case of McDonald's, the valued goal is to make a profit. It does this by filling sixty million orders each day.

Organizations include both formal and informal dimensions: The formal dimension is the official side of the organization governed by written guidelines, rules, and policies; the informal dimension includes employee-generated norms that depart from or otherwise bypass the formal dimension. Most formal organizations can be classified as bureaucracies, organizational structures that strive to use the most efficient means to achieve a valued goal.

In theory, a bureaucracy is a completely rational organization—one that uses the most efficient means to achieve a valued goal. A bureaucracy has at least seven major characteristics that allow it to coordinate human activity toward achieving organizational goals. Two of those characteristics include an authority structure that is hierarchical and a system that treats clients as cases and not individuals per se.

CORE CONCEPT 2 The concept of rationalization—a process in which thought and action rooted in custom, emotion, or respect for mysterious forces is replaced by instrumental-rational thought and action—helps us understand how striving to achieve valued goals can have undesirable, even disastrous, consequences.

The growth and dominance of formal organizations goes hand in hand with rationalization. Instrumental-rational thought and action mean that people use any means necessary to achieve a valued goal. Instrumental-rational thought and action, for example, treat animals as profit-generating creatures: The more animals owners can raise in the space available and the faster they can raise them to maturity, the greater the profit.

CORE CONCEPT 3 One organizational trend guided by instrumental-rational action is the McDonaldization of society, a process in which the principles governing fast food restaurants come to dominate other sectors of society.

The McDonaldization of society is a process by which the organizing principles driving the fast food industry come to dominate other sectors of society. Those principles are (1) efficiency, which allows consumers to move quickly from one state of being to another (for example, from hungry to full); (2) quantification and calculation, which are numerical indicators that allow customers to evaluate a product or service easily; (3) predictability, which allows customers to expect the same product or service no matter where or when it is purchased; and (4) control, which allows the organization to manage in detail the way a product or service is produced and delivered. Weber used the phrase "iron cage of rationality" to describe the set of irrationalities generated by so-called rational systems, the drawbacks to the McDonaldization model.

One way to understand how organizations grow from local operations (McDonald's began as one restaurant in Illinois in 1955) to global giants is to consider the actions they have taken to increase profits. Organizations such as McDonald's employ five major profit-generating strategies: (1) lower production costs, (2) create new products that consumers "need" to buy, (3) improve existing products to make previous versions obsolete, (4) identify ways for people to purchase more products, and (5) create new markets.

CORE CONCEPT 4 To be efficient, organizations sometimes train employees to respond mechanically or mindlessly to the dictates of the job, leaving them unable to respond creatively to new or changing circumstances. Two mechanisms by which this occurs are trained incapacity and statistical measures of performance.

Formal organizations such as McDonald's train workers to perform their jobs a certain way and reward them for good performance. When workers are trained to respond mechanically or mindlessly to the dictates of the job, however, they risk developing trained incapacity—the inability to respond to new or unusual circumstances or to recognize when official rules or procedures are outmoded or no longer applicable.

Statistical measures of performance are used to measure how well an organization and its members or employees are performing. Such measures can be convenient and useful management tools, but they can also encourage employees to concentrate on achieving good scores and to ignore problems generated by their drive to score well. Considering that statistical measures of performance govern meat inspection, we must ask how meat suppliers' goal of turning a profit might affect willingness to condemn carcasses.

CORE CONCEPT 5 Large formal organizations inevitably tend to become oligarchical: That is, power becomes concentrated in the hands of a few people, who hold the top positions.

A danger of oligarchy is that key decision makers may become so preoccupied with preserving their own leadership that they do not consider the greater good. In addition, these decision makers may not have the necessary background knowledge to understand the full implications of their choices. Instead, they draw upon experts to provide background information. The experts may feel pressure to deliver a product or to present a position that executives "need" or want to hear. If something goes wrong, the experts can claim that they provided only the patent, information, or recommendations and thus could not control the ultimate implementation. Executives can claim that they relied on the experts' advice to make decisions about processes they might not have understood.

CORE CONCEPT 6 The growth of bureaucracies to coordinate the efforts of humans as well as machines and other technology is accompanied by alienation, a state of being in which human life is dominated by the forces of its inventions.

Karl Marx believed that humans' increased control over nature is accompanied by alienation, so that people are dominated by the forces of their inventions. Marx was specifically concerned about alienation in the workplace. He maintained that workers are alienated on four levels: (1) from the process of production, (2) from the product, (3) from the family and the community of fellow workers, and (4) from the self.

Resources on the Internet

Login to CengageBrain.com to access the resources your instructor requires. For this book, you can access:

Sociology CourseMate

Access an integrated eBook, chapter-specific interactive learning tools, including flash cards, quizzes, videos, and more in your Sociology CourseMate.

Take a pretest for this chapter and receive a personalized study plan based on your results that will identify the topics you need to review and direct you to online resources to help you master those topics. Then take a post-test to help you determine the concepts you have mastered and what you will need to work on.

CourseReader

CourseReader for Sociology is an online reader providing access to readings, and audio and video selections to accompany your course materials.

Visit **www.cengagebrain.com** to access your account and purchase materials.

Key Terms

alienation 147
bureaucracy 134
coercive organizations 133
control 137
efficiency 137
externality costs 141
formal dimension 135
formal organizations 132
industrial food system 131
ideal type 135
informal dimension 135
iron cage of rationality 138
McDonaldization of society 137
multinational corporations 139
oligarchy 145
predictability 137
professionalization 146
quantification and calculation 137
rationalization 136
secondary groups 132
statistical measures of performance 144
trained incapacity 143
utilitarian organizations 133
voluntary organizations 133

DEVIANCE, CONFORMITY, AND SOCIAL CONTROL

7

With Emphasis on THE PEOPLE'S REPUBLIC OF CHINA

The sociological contribution to understanding deviant and conforming behaviors goes beyond studying a person's character or motives. Instead, sociologists emphasize the social context in which behaviors occur and the mechanisms of social control that groups use to reward conformity and to punish behavior considered deviant. In fact, depending on the social context, any behavior can qualify as deviant or conforming. For example, these soldiers from the People's Liberation Army appear to exemplify conformity, but a close look shows that their conformity is not exact. In fact, in the context of the military, even the slightest deviation by one soldier can result in the entire unit being punished. Can you find any slight deviation for which a commanding officer might punish this group?

Why Focus On THE PEOPLE'S REPUBLIC OF CHINA?

In this chapter, we pay special attention to the People's Republic of China because it represents an interesting case for studying issues of deviance, conformity, and social control. Many behaviors that constituted deviance in China from 1966 to 1976, the period known as the Cultural Revolution, are no longer judged that way. During that time, any person who held a position of authority, worked to earn a profit, showed the slightest leaning toward foreign ways, or expressed academic interests was subject to interrogation, arrest, and punishment. Included in this group were scientists, teachers, athletes, performers, artists, writers, and owners of private businesses. The list of suspicious characters also included people who wore glasses, wore makeup, spoke a foreign language, owned a camera or a radio, had traveled abroad, or had relatives living outside China (Liao 2009).

Contrast the events of the Cultural Revolution with the fact that China has transformed itself to become a global center of manufacturing for everything from electronics to socks and toys. Consider that, in the late 1970s, when the people of Datang, a rice-farming village of 1,000 residents, took it upon themselves to stitch socks and sell them along a highway, the Chinese government ordered them to stop, branding the money-making venture as capitalist. Today, Datang and surrounding towns and villages is the socks capital of the world, producing eight billion socks per year (Crienglish 2008).

The changes described here speak to an unspoken deal, evolving since 1990, between the Chinese Communist Party and the people: Stay out of politics and the government will allow the people to "get on with the business of making money" and retreat from managing their everyday life (Fallows 2009). Prior to this "deal," the Chinese lived in tiny birdcages; now they live in an aviary. The people of China "cannot yet fly up to the clear blue sky" but there is more room in which to fly around (Gifford 2007, p. 15).

Online Poll

Indicate whether you have engaged in any of the following activities. Also indicate whether or not you were caught by a person with the authority to punish you:

Engaged in underage drinking

○ No

○ Yes, caught

○ Yes, not caught

Cheated on a test or school assignment

○ No

○ Yes, caught

○ Yes, not caught

Drove 20 or more mph over speed limit

○ No

○ Yes, caught

○ Yes, not caught

To see how other students responded to these questions, go to **www.cengagebrain.com.**

Video Tip: Show the author video introduction to Chapter 7, which can be found on the Power Lecture CD. A transcript of the video is included in the Instructor's Resource Manual.

Deviance, Conformity, and Social Control

CORE CONCEPT 1 The only characteristic common to all forms of deviance is that some social audience challenges or condemns a behavior or an appearance because it departs from established norms.

The topics of this chapter are deviance, conformity, and social control. **Deviance** is any behavior or physical appearance that is socially challenged or condemned because it departs from the norms and expectations of a group. **Conformity** comprises behaviors and appearances that follow and maintain the standards of a group. All groups employ mechanisms of **social control**—methods used to teach, persuade, or force their members, and even nonmembers, to comply with and not deviate from its norms and expectations.

Deviance and conformity are complex topics, because almost every behavior has at some time qualified as deviant or conforming. When sociologist J. L. Simmons (1965) asked 180 men and women in the United States from a variety of age, educational, occupational, and religious groups to "list those things or types of persons whom you regard as deviant," they identified a total of 1,154 items:

> The sheer range of responses included such expected items as homosexuals, prostitutes, drug addicts, beatniks, and murderers; it also included liars, democrats, reckless drivers, atheists, self-pitiers, the retired, career women, divorcées, movie stars, perpetual bridge players, prudes, pacifists, psychiatrists, priests, liberals, conservatives, junior executives, girls who wear makeup, and know-it-all professors. (Simmons 1965, pp. 223–224)

Although Simmons conducted this study more than 45 years ago, his conclusion remains relevant today: The only characteristic common to all forms of deviance is "the fact that some social audience regards" a behavior or person as deviant and treats it as such (p. 225). Consequently, it is difficult to generate a precise list of deviant behaviors and appearances, because something that some group considers deviant may not be considered deviant by another. Likewise, something considered deviant at one time and place may not be considered deviant at another. For example, wearing makeup is no longer considered a deviant behavior in China, as evidenced by the fact that the U.S.-based cosmetics company Avon has more than 6,300 stand-alone stores and more than 1,000 Avon counters inside department stores within the country (ConsumerAffairs.com 2005). As another example, cocaine and other now-illegal drugs once were legal substances in the United States. In fact, legality of cocaine is unwittingly acknowledged whenever someone asks for a Coke (Gould 1990). Originally Coca-Cola was marketed as a medicine to cure various ailments. One key ingredient used to make the drink came from the coca leaf, which is also used to produce cocaine (Henriques 1993). These examples alert us to the fact that deviance exists only in relation to norms in effect at a particular time and place.

Boni Li

At one time, wearing makeup was considered deviant in China. Today, there are an estimated 1,000 domestic suppliers of personal care products, from eye creams to shower gels. Foreign brands such as Lancôme number in the hundreds (Gerson Lehrman Group 2010).

Deviance: The Violation of Norms

CORE CONCEPT 2 Ideally, conformity is voluntary. When socialization fails to produce conformity, other mechanisms of social control—sanctions, censorship, or surveillance—may be used to convey and enforce norms.

In Chapter 3, we learned that norms give order and predictability to life. We also learned that some norms are considered more important than others (Field 2002). In that chapter, we highlighted two kinds of norms—folkways and mores—distinguished by sociologist

deviance Any behavior or physical appearance that is socially challenged or condemned because it departs from the norms and expectations of a group.

conformity Behavior and appearances that follow and maintain the standards of a group; also the acceptance of the cultural goals and the pursuit of those goals through means defined as legitimate.

social control Methods used to teach, persuade, or force a group's members, and even nonmembers, to comply with and not deviate from its norms and expectations.

Discussion Tip: In light of sociologist J. L. Simmons' study referenced on this page, ask students if anyone can name a behavior that was once deviant and now is no longer considered as such. The change in meaning may have occurred in the students' lifetime or it may be a behavior that their parents or grandparents considered deviant and is now no longer considered deviant OR even behavior that the student generation consider deviant and their grandparents or parents did not (like smoking in public).

William Graham Sumner. We learned that **folkways** are customary ways of handling the routine matters of everyday life—for example, how one should look, eat, greet another person, or express affection toward same-sex and opposite-sex people. **Mores** (pronounced môr'ā'z) are norms that people define as essential to the well-being of their group. People who violate mores are usually punished severely: They may be ostracized, institutionalized in prisons or mental hospitals, sentenced to physical punishment, or condemned to die. Unlike folkways, mores are considered unchangeable and regarded as "the only way" and "the truth" (Sumner 1907).

During the Cultural Revolution, the dominant mores rejected special social status and the accumulation of worldly possessions. Any person in a position of authority or with the slightest leaning toward foreign ways, including a farmer who planted extra crops, was considered suspect. If someone simply remarked that a foreign-made product, such as a can opener, was better than its Chinese counterpart, or if someone wrapped food or garbage in a piece of newspaper with then Communist Party Chairman Mao Zedong's picture in it, he or she was regarded with distrust (Mathews and Mathews 1983, Liao 2009). As Jung Chang writes in *Wild Swans: Three Daughters of China* (1991), such conditions reduced many people "to a state where they did not dare even to think, in case their thoughts came out involuntarily" (p. 6). The slightest misstep could make one a target of intense criticism.

Although mores are considered unchangeable and absolute, they do change. During the Cultural Revolution, people were sentenced to hard labor in the countryside for engaging in sex outside of marriage. Today, sex outside of marriage is acceptable. A number of factors, including the one-child policy instituted in 1979, helped to dissociate sex as an act that led to conception. This change in thinking helped to usher in a sexual revolution in the 1990s, making sex outside of marriage more acceptable (Hodges 2009, Farrer 2009).

Norms can vary according to whom they apply and according to whether people (1) know they exist, (2) accept them, (3) enforce them uniformly, (4) think them important, (5) back them up with the force of law, and (6) adhere to them in their public and/or private lives (Gibbs 1965). Consider speed limits, which are backed by the force of law. Most people know the speed limit from observing posted signs but, depending on the setting, may not follow it to the letter of the law. In fact, most drivers exceed posted limits by 10 or 15 miles per hour without getting caught and, when caught, are not always cited for the exact number of miles they were driving over that limit.

Most people abide by established norms because they accept them as "good and proper, appropriate and worthy" (Sumner 1907, p. 60). For the great majority of people, "the rule to do as all do suffices." Recall from Chapter 4 that *socialization* is the process by which most people come to learn and accept the ways of their culture as natural.

Socialization as a Means of Social Control

Because babies have no choice over the culture into which they are born, they also have little opportunity to avoid exposure to that culture's norms. If we compare the ways preschoolers are socialized in China and the United States, we can see that rules for behavior are incorporated into their daily activities. Even though it is impossible to make definitive generalizations about preschools in countries as large and diverse as the United States and China, we can identify some broad differences.

Three researchers from the University of Hawaii filmed daily life in Chinese and U.S. preschools to learn how teachers in each system socialize children to participate effectively in their respective societies. The researchers found that, compared to U.S. preschools, Chinese preschoolers are taught to give constructive critiques of their classmates' work and to learn from the critiques of their own and other's work. Chinese preschoolers are also taught to downplay interpersonal conflicts and play cooperatively. In contrast, American preschoolers are taught to expect praise for their work. They are also taught to turn to adults to mediate conflicts with peers, and to rely on adults to decide who is right and wrong. In addition, American preschoolers are encouraged to articulate their feeling about the conflict (Yi, Akiko, and Tobin 2007).

The following scene exemplifies the extent to which Chinese preschoolers are taught to give and accept critique and incorporate it into future assignments. Each day in a Shanghai preschool class, 22 children engage in a storytelling activity. One child is designated the "story king" and stands in front of the class to tell a story. Upon finishing, the teacher (Mrs. Wang) makes comments, asks students questions about the story, and then calls for a vote on whether today's storyteller earned the title story king. Eighteen children vote yes. Mrs. Wang looks to the children who voted "no" for reasons: "A child remarks, 'Some words I could hear, but some I couldn't.' 'Don't think his voice was loud enough' says another." The teacher turns to the storyteller and asks if he agrees with the critique, to which he nods yes. "At that point, the teacher comments, 'Next time, he will be loud and clear' (Yi, Akiko, and Tobin 2007, p. 7).

folkways Customary ways of handling the routine matters of everyday life.

mores Norms that people define as essential to the well-being of their group. People who violate mores are usually punished severely.

Student Activity: Ask students to read the descriptions of preschool in China and the United States under the heading "Socialization as a Means of Social Control." To what extent do they believe the researchers capture the American preschool experiences with regard to critique and the roles of adults in conflict. Consider asking students to write a one-page paper giving examples from their lives that support or contradict this research.

Nan Wylie

Would you allow or encourage this child's classmates to critique her work? If you live in the United States, is it unlikely that you would. But in Chinese preschools, such critique is encouraged and welcomed.

In the United States, preschoolers are not encouraged to critique each other's work, and especially not when that work is considered self-expressive or creative. Early childhood teachers in the United States tend to believe that their job is to protect and support children's self-esteem and that it is not "developmentally appropriate for a teacher to put a child on the spot by subjecting him to peer criticism" (Yi, Akiko, and Tobin 2007, p. 7). In fact, American teachers are reluctant to correct a child's mistakes in front of other students. When teachers in the United States do comment, it is often empty praise—"that's wonderful"—regardless of quality.

With regard to children's conflicts, Chinese preschool teachers do not try to sort out who is "right" or "wrong" or find out how the children feel about it. Instead, teachers down play any conflict simply because conflict is considered normal and inevitable. They tend to disfuse angry feelings and emotions by ignoring, downplaying, and redirecting them. From the Chinese point of view, there is really nothing to be mad about or to negotiate because, at this age, arguments are more often than not trivial and insignificant. In fact, why insist on finding out what really happened, as it is impossible to pinpoint blame? According to the Chinese Governmental Guidelines for Preschool Education, teachers should teach students "how to get along with each other, 'to be friendly to people,' to love parents, teacher, and peers and to love their hometown, and their motherland" (Yi, Akiko, and Tobin 2007, p. 8).

The researchers showed an audience of American teachers video clips of preschoolers (4-year-olds) in China critiquing each other and resolving conflicts. Some American teachers were bothered by the Chinese practice of allowing children to critique each other because they thought children were too young to do this kind of thing. Others were amazed at how well children gave and accepted critique. One teacher remarked, "I'm amazed how well that boy handled the criticism. I'm an adult and I think I would cry if people criticized me like that in front of a group!" (p. 7). The researchers pointed out that perhaps four-year-olds' self-esteem may not be as fragile as Americans assume.

With regard to conflict, some American educators thought the Chinese teachers should have addressed the conflict more directly and also should have addressed the children's feelings about it. The American educators tended to believe that adults acting as a mediator, encouraging children to confront conflicts, and allowing children to express heated emotions are appropriate ways to deal with and resolve conflict.

From a sociological point of view, both the American and Chinese approaches are intended to help preschoolers learn rules for behavior and to fit into the existing system. Ideally, conformity should be voluntary. That is, people should be internally motivated to maintain group standards and to feel guilty if they deviate. As noted earlier, during the Cultural Revolution, it was considered deviant to wear glasses, use makeup, speak a foreign language, or break or destroy items that displayed Mao Zedong's picture. Many Chinese conformed to these rules and felt guilty if they broke the rules, even if only by accident. The memories of one Chinese man illustrate this point:

> As a boy, I did not know what a god looked like, but I knew that Mao was the god of our lives. When I was six, I accidentally broke a large porcelain Mao badge. Fear gripped me. In my life until that moment, the breaking of the badge seemed the worst thing I had ever done. Desperate to hide my crime, I took the pieces and threw them down a public toilet. For months I felt guilty. (Author X 1992, p. 22)

In this case, the guilt is a sign that the person had internalized the expectations of the larger society. If conformity cannot be achieved voluntarily, however, people may employ mechanisms of social control to teach, persuade, or force others to conform.

Sanctions as Mechanisms of Social Control

Ideally, socialization brings about conformity and conformity is voluntary. When conformity cannot be achieved voluntarily, other mechanisms of social control may be used to convey and enforce norms. One such mechanism is **sanctions**—reactions of approval or disapproval to others' behavior or appearance. Sanctions can be positive or negative, formal or informal.

A **positive sanction** is an expression of approval and a reward for compliance; it may take the form of applause, a smile, or a pat on the back. In contrast, a **negative sanction** is an expression of disapproval for noncompliance; the punishment may consist of withdrawal of affection, ridicule, ostracism, banishment, physical harm, imprisonment, solitary confinement, or even death.

Informal sanctions are spontaneous, unofficial expressions of approval or disapproval that are not backed by the force of law. An example of an informal sanction is people making fun of a woman wearing a skirt when her legs are unshaven. Clearly no law requires women to shave their legs, but they are still penalized. **Formal sanctions**, by comparison, are expressions of approval or disapproval backed by laws, rules, or policies that specify (usually in writing) the conditions under which people should be rewarded or punished and the procedures for allocating rewards and administering punishments. Examples of formal positive sanctions include awarding medals, cash bonuses, and diplomas. Formal negative sanctions may take the form of fines, prison sentences, the death penalty, corporal punishment, or the firing of tear gas to disperse demonstrators (see Global Comparisons: "Incarceration Rates").

During the Cultural Revolution, it was common for students to apply negative sanctions to those in power without fear of consequences. Even elementary-age students took it upon themselves to target and punish those who held special social status or who were suspected of accumulating worldly goods:

> Some girls grabbed their female teachers and shaved half their hair off. . . . On the street, you would constantly see children carrying Chairman Mao's *Little Red Book* and a red sword made of wood. They would stop adults on the street, asking them to recite Chairman Mao's quotations. If they made a mistake, the children would stab their back with the wooden sword, and force them to start from the beginning. . . . It was very common to see students beat their teachers to death. (Liao 2009, pp. 197–198)

Censorship and Surveillance as Mechanisms of Control

In addition to sanctions, other mechanisms of social control include censorship and surveillance. **Censorship** is a method of preventing information from reaching an audience. That audience may consist of children, voters, employees, prisoners, or others. Censorship relies on **censors**—people whose job is to sift information conveyed through movies, books, letters, email, TV, the Internet, and other media. Censors try to remove or block any material considered unsuitable or threatening. A Harvard Law School study identified China as a country with the most extensive Internet censorship in the world. The study found that Chinese government censors, estimated to number between 30,000 and 50,000, policed the Internet and blocked access to sensitive material believed

There are millions of norms, too many to list. Some norms such as keeping pets on a leash are backed up by formal negative sanctions. In some cities, the fine for violating this norm can be as low as $25 (Boise, Idaho) or as high as $250 (Seattle, Washington).

sanctions Reactions of approval or disapproval to others' behavior or appearance.

positive sanction An expression of approval and a reward for compliance.

negative sanction An expression of disapproval for noncompliance.

informal sanctions Spontaneous, unofficial expressions of approval or disapproval that are not backed by the force of law.

formal sanctions Expressions of approval or disapproval backed by laws, rules, or policies that specify (usually in writing) the conditions under which people should be rewarded or punished and the procedures for allocating rewards and administering punishments.

censorship A method of preventing information from reaching an audience.

censors People whose job is to sift information conveyed through movies, books, letters, email, TV, the Internet, and other media and to remove or block any material that is considered unsuitable or threatening.

Video Tip: To learn more about the Cultural Revolution, Mao, and his influence on Chinese society today, consider showing a short video titled "The Cult of Mao Zedong." It was produced by PBS Online Newshour (www.pbs.org/newshour/) and can be accessed by using the video title as a search term.

Global Comparisons Incarceration Rates

This chart shows the top ten countries with the highest incarceration rate per 100,000 population. The United States tops the list with 756 sentenced prisoners per 100,000 population. Notice that China did not make the top ten list. Its incarceration rate is 118 per 100,000. If the 850,000 prisoners held in administrative detention are included, the rate is 181 per 100,000, still far below that of the United States.

There are many possible explanations for the high rate of incarceration in the United States, including the propensity of elected officials to pass strict crime legislation so they can present themselves as tough on crime. This propensity explains, in part, the long mandated prison sentences handed out to those convicted of drug possession and other nonviolent crimes. In addition, critics claim the United States has a high rate of repeat offenders in prisons because the system places little emphasis on rehabilitating prisoners. Finally, the **prison-industrial complex**—the corporations and agencies with an economic stake in building and supplying correctional facilities and in providing services—fuels an ongoing "need" for prisoners so that companies can maintain or increase profit margins. It should come as no surprise that these private corporations represent a significant lobbying force shaping legislation and correctional policy. Another incentive for maintaining a large prison population is that local, county, state, and federal governments have come to rely on prison labor. This dependency has increased the incentive to keep the prison population large. Many correctional institutions have short- and long-term contracts with local, city, county, and state government agencies to do roadwork and other routine maintenance (North Carolina Department of Correction 2009).

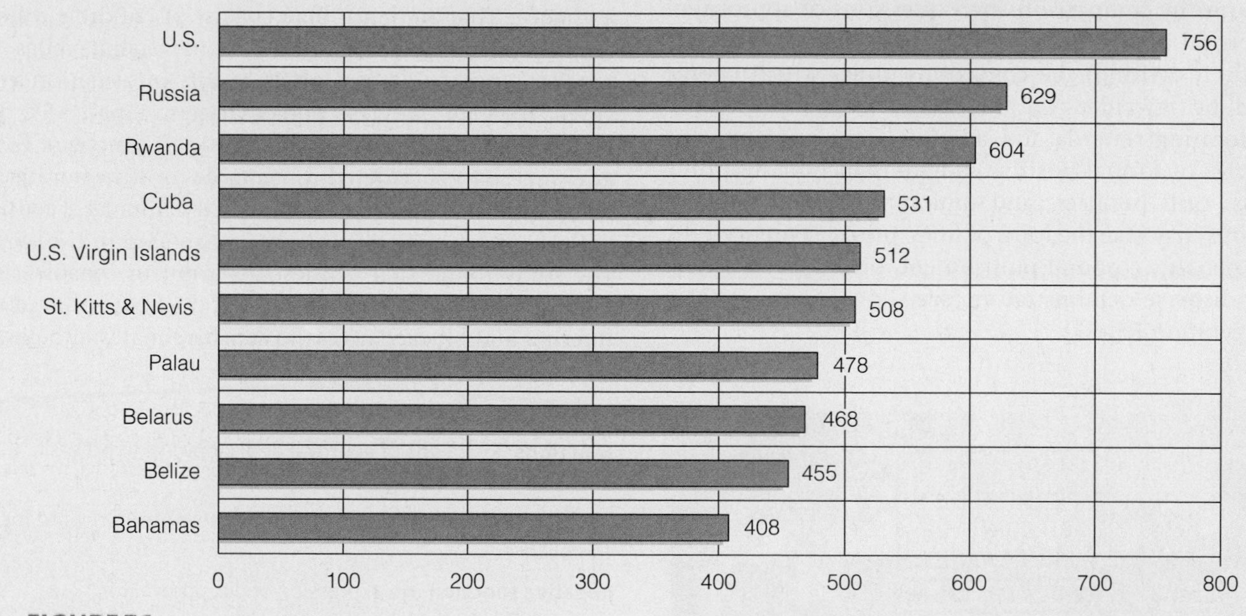

FIGURE 7.1 Prison Population Rates (per 100, 000)

Source: Data from International Centre for Prison Studies (2010)

to undermine the government—material related to topics such as "Tiananmen Square," "Falun Gong," "Tibet," "Taiwan," and "democracy" (Bristow 2010).

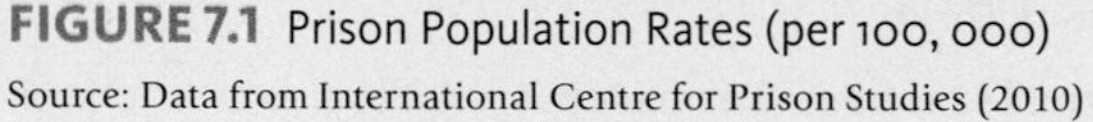

prison-industrial complex The corporations and agencies with an economic stake in building and supplying correctional facilities and in providing services.

Chinese censors in the recent past allowed no one to speak critically of the Communist leadership. Today, however, some criticism is allowed. Scholar and journalist Nicholas D. Kristof (2004) explains this new openness:

> You can't go online and say that President Hu is a turtle's egg (it sounds worse in Chinese), but you can gripe about local corruption or poor highway planning. I experimented on my last trip to China and tried various postings. My first version,

Student Activity: Spend some time looking at the bar graphs. Note that the U.S. incarceration rates far exceed that of any other country in the world. Ask students to use the "Google News" search engine to find news articles from around the U.S. and world on "incarceration rates." Do the articles offer any insights as to why U.S. rates are the highest in the world?

> which I sent to several chat rooms (in Chinese, pretending to be Chinese myself) was "Why is Prime Minister Wen Jiabao off in America kowtowing to the imperialists when he should be solving more important problems at home!" That was too tough and none of the chat rooms allowed it. But my third and mildest version was accepted: "Prime Minister Wen Jiabao's visit to America has been very successful, but I am wondering if perhaps he is wasting too much time abroad instead of focusing on our own important problems like unemployment." (p. 58)

Every government, not just the Chinese, engages in censorship in that they have procedures in place to block sensitive documents and other classified information from reaching all but those who have been cleared to view it. The practice gained notoriety in 2010, when the nonprofit organization known as WikiLeaks posted hundreds of thousands of State Department and Pentagon classified documents that had been leaked to them. Even after the documents were leaked, the Obama administration banned hundreds of thousands of federal employees from viewing the leaked documents on government computers, arguing that the material remained classified (MacAskill 2010).

Surveillance, another mechanism of social control, involves watching and otherwise monitoring the movements, activities, conversations, and associations of people to prevent them from engaging in wrongdoing, to catch those who are engaged in wrongdoing, and to ensure that the public is protected from wrongdoers. Surveillance activities include telephone tapping, interception of letters and email, electronic monitoring, and profiling certain groups believed most likely to engage in wrongdoing. It can also involve reviewing records of emails, text messages, tweets, credit card transactions, and Internet browsing histories. Surveillance is used by the military to monitor the actions of an enemy; by governments to monitor people defined as potential threats to national security; by employers to monitor employee job performance; by police to catch people breaking the law; and by businesses to monitor customer behavior, purchases, and preferences.

Most of us know that we are being watched at some point over the course of a typical day, if only by a store or an ATM surveillance camera. What does it mean to know that someone is or could be watching you at any time? How does that possibility shape behavior? These are the questions that interested French philosopher and psychologist Michel Foucault (1977), who wrote up the emergence of the disciplinary society.

The Disciplinary Society

Foucault (1977) sought to identify the turning points that make the society we live in today fundamentally different in structure from the societies that preceded it. In this regard, Foucault identified a historical shift or turning point in the way society punishes people from what he called a culture of spectacle to a carceral culture. A culture of spectacle is a social arrangement by which punishment for crimes—torture, disfigurement, dismemberment, and execution—is delivered in public settings for all to see. This very public way of punishing began to change around the time of the prison reform movements in Europe and in the United States (1775–1889), an era that ushered in what Foucault called a carceral culture, a social arrangement under which the society largely abandons physical and public punishment and replaces it with surveillance to control people's activities and thoughts. Foucault attributes this change not to a rise in humanitarian concern but to a transformation in the technologies (for example, cameras, computers, bureaucratic records) available to control others.

The prison reform movement coincides with the period of history in which "a whole set of techniques and institutions emerged for measuring, supervising, and correcting" those considered abnormal, including criminals (Johnston 2009, p. 401). One such invention was the Panopticon, designed by British philosopher Jeremy Bentham in 1785. Pan means a complete view and optic means seeing. The design represented his effort to create the most efficient and rational prison—the perfect prison. Foucault (1977) used it as a metaphor for the mentality driving nineteenth-century society.

The architectural plan had the following features: The guard tower was positioned in the center of the facility inside a circular gallery of cells. The front of each cell was barred, and the guard standing in the tower could see into each cell. The side and back walls of each cell were solid so that the prisoners could not see or interact with one another. Under this arrangement, one guard could watch the inmates housed in hundreds of cells. The design was such that the inmates could not see the guard in the central tower so that they were never sure when or if they were being watched. The threat of surveillance or the possibility of being observed pushed inmates to discipline themselves (Foucault 1977).

There is a larger lesson associated with this design that Foucault found especially applicable to today's society: When people believe that someone is watching, they will censor and police themselves. The Panopticon is a metaphor for what Foucault calls the **disciplinary society**, a social arrangement that normalizes surveillance,

surveillance A mechanism of social control that involves watching and otherwise monitoring the movements, activities, conversations, and associations of people to prevent them from engaging in wrongdoing; to catch those who are engaged in wrong doing; and to ensure that the public is protected from wrongdoers.

disciplinary society A social arrangement that normalizes surveillance, making it expected and routine.

Discussion Tip: Ask students to read the "Disciplinary Society" section. Can they recall a time when they altered their behavior because they believed someone was watching or they believed that someone at sometime in the future might be able to watch them?

©Mary Evans / Higginbotham Collection / The Image Works

Chris Caldeira

The Panopticon (top) is a metaphor for what Foucault calls the disciplinary society, a social arrangement that normalizes surveillance, making it expected and routine. Over the course of the day, countless numbers of cameras record our every move. We never know when someone is really watching or will want to watch what the camera records.

making it expected and routine. This disciplinary society that Foucault wrote about in the mid-1970s has been further magnified by the emergence of technologies that allow people to track their own and others' movements and behaviors. Those technologies include the Internet, cell phones, ATMs, credit cards, and surveillance cameras in public spaces, even in taxicabs. Surveillance has many applications—it can be used to reform prisoners, monitor the frail in their homes, follow teens as they drive, treat patients, instruct students, supervise workers, track Internet use, and monitor public spaces (Felluga 2009).

The People's Republic of China has a number of surveillance programs in place, including Project Golden Shield (with a goal of strengthening its control over the Internet) and Safe Cities, in which 660 cities are putting in high-tech surveillance systems, much the same way in which cities in the United States are installing such systems. In December 2010, the government-owned company, China Security and Surveillance Technology—which installs and operates surveillance systems used to monitor prisoners and customers in stores, banks, and Internet cafés—received approval to be listed on the New York Stock Exchange. By one estimate, the surveillance market in China is valued at $43.1 billion (per year), up from $500 million in 2003 (Bradsher 2007).

The Functionalist Perspective

CORE CONCEPT 3 It is impossible for a society to exist without deviance. Always and everywhere there will be some behaviors or appearances that offend collective sentiments.

Émile Durkheim (1901) argued that although definitions of what constitutes deviance vary by place, it is present in all societies. He defined *deviance* as acts that offend collective norms and expectations. The fact that always and everywhere some people will offend collective sentiments led him to conclude that deviance is normal as long as it is not excessive and that "it is completely impossible for any society entirely free of it to exist" (p. 99). According to Durkheim, deviance will be present even in a "community of saints" living in an "exemplary and perfect monastery" (p. 100). Durkheim used the analogy of the "perfect and upright" person who judges his or her smallest failings with a severity that others reserve for the most serious offenses. Likewise, even among the exemplary, some seemingly insignificant act or appearance will be greeted as deviant, even criminal, because "it is impossible for everyone to be alike if only because each of us cannot stand in the same spot" (p. 100).

Department of Defense

Photos such as this should not lead to the conclusion that China is a nation of robots who follow rules with no resistance. This photo does illustrate the lengths to which Chinese will go to present their country in a positive light. These performers practice endless numbers of hours to move in strict precision and may even stitch needles in shirt collars pointed at their neck to maintain a certain pose (La Franiere 2009). In such situations, even the slightest variation is considered deviant.

Durkheim believed that what makes an act or appearance deviant is not so much its character or consequences, but that a group has defined it as dangerous or threatening to its well-being. Wearing eyeglasses, for example, clearly does not harm others. As we have learned, however, during the Cultural Revolution, the behavior was a sign of "special status" or abandonment of revolutionary spirit—things that were not so easily observable.

According to Durkheim, deviance has an important function in society, for at least two reasons. First, the ritual of identifying and exposing the wrongdoing, determining a punishment, and carrying it out is an emotional experience that binds together the members of a group and establishes a sense of community. Durkheim argued that a group that went too long without noticing deviance or doing something about it would lose its identity as a group. In evaluating Durkheim's argument, consider that American identity is strengthened when U.S. media and public officials criticize China for any number of things: exploiting workers who earn 30 to 70 cents per hour; its one-child policy; or the country's control over "rare-earth" minerals needed in manufacturing iPods. Likewise, when Chinese media criticizes the United States for its national debt, its human rights record, unfair trading practices, and overconsumption, that criticism helps solidify Chinese identity. Second, deviance is functional because it helps bring about necessary change and prepares people for change. Nothing would change if someone did not step forward and introduce a new perspective or a new way of doing things. By definition, this "step forward" is considered deviant, as it departs from the normal way of thinking or of doing things.

Durkheim's theory offers an intriguing explanation for why almost anything can be defined as deviant. Yet, Durkheim did not address an important question: Who decides that a particular activity or appearance is deviant? Labeling theory provides one answer to this question.

Labeling Theory

CORE CONCEPT 4 Labeling theorists maintain that an act is deviant when people notice it and then take action to label it as a violation and apply appropriate sanctions.

In *Outsiders: Studies in the Sociology of Deviance*, sociologist Howard Becker states the central thesis of labeling theory:

> All social groups make rules and attempt, at some times and under some circumstances, to enforce them. When a rule is enforced, the person who is supposed to have broken it may be seen as a special kind of person, one who cannot be trusted to live by the rules agreed on by the group. He is regarded as an outsider. (1963, p. 1)

As Becker's statement suggests, labeling theorists are guided by two assumptions: (1) rules are socially constructed, and (2) these rules are not enforced uniformly or consistently. Support for the first assumption comes from the fact that because definitions of deviant behavior vary across time and place, people must decide what is deviant. The second assumption is supported by the fact that some people break rules and escape detection, whereas others are treated as offenders even though they have broken no rules. Labeling theorists maintain that whether an act is deviant depends on whether people notice it and, if they do notice, on whether they label it as a violation of a rule and subsequently apply sanctions.

Such contingencies suggest that violating a rule does not automatically make a person deviant. That is, from a sociological point of view, a rule breaker is not deviant (in the strict sense of the word) unless someone *notices* the violation and decides to take corrective action (see Figure 7.2). "The critical variable in the study of deviance, then, is the social audience rather than the individual actor, since it is the social audience [that] eventually determines whether or not any episode or behavior . . . is labeled deviant" (Erikson 1966, p. 11).

Labeling theorists suggest that for every rule a social group creates, four categories of people exist: conformists,

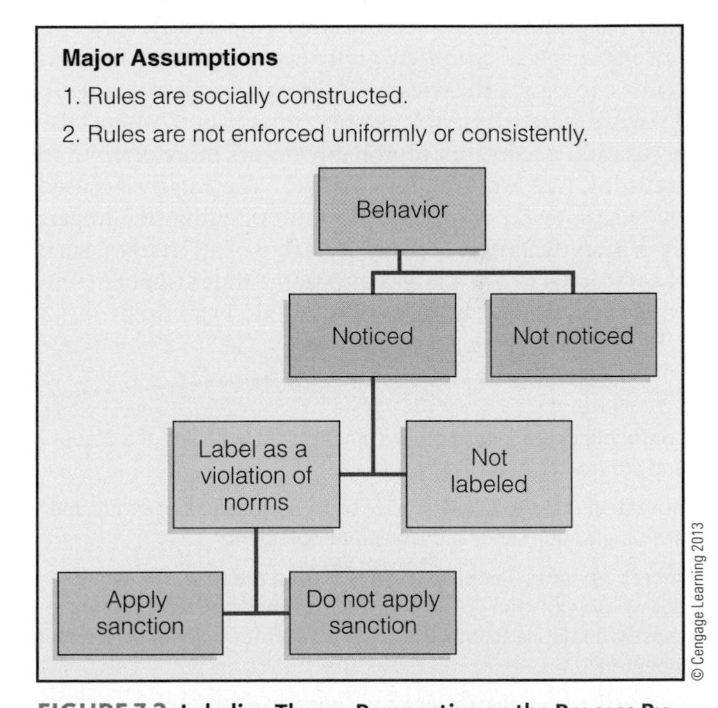

FIGURE 7.2 Labeling Theory Perspective on the Process By Which a Behavior is Noticed, Labeled and Punished
From the perspective of labeling theory, deviance occurs when a behavior is noticed and labeled as a violation of norms. Once labeled as such, sanctions (punishments) can be applied. The sanction may be as minor as a verbal reprimand or extreme such as a death sentence.

Discussion Tip: Figure 7.2 is a flowchart outlining the process by which a behavior is noticed, labeled, and punished. Ask students to write an account of a situation that follows the logic of this flowchart. Note, the situation may be about a behavior that was not noticed, or not labeled as a violation of norms.

pure deviants, secret deviants, and the falsely accused. The category to which one belongs depends on whether a rule has been violated and on whether sanctions are applied. **Conformists** are people who have not violated the rules of a group and are treated accordingly. **Pure deviants** are people who have broken the rules and are caught, punished, and labeled as outsiders.

Secret deviants are people who have broken the rules but whose violation goes unnoticed or, if it is noticed, prompts those who notice to look the other way rather than reporting the violation. Becker maintains that "no one really knows how much of this phenomenon exists," but he is convinced that the "amount is very sizable, much more so than we are apt to think" (1963, p. 20). A survey of crime victims in the United States found that 20.1 million crimes were committed against U.S. residents 12 years old and older. Of the victims, 39.5 percent did not report the crimes to police (U.S. Department of Justice 2010; see Table 7.1).

The **falsely accused** are people who have not broken the rules but are treated as if they have. The ranks of the falsely accused include victims of eyewitness errors and police cover-ups; they also include innocent suspects who make false confessions under the pressure of interrogation. For the book *In Spite of Innocence*, sociologist Michael L. Radelet (1994) and his co-author reviewed more than 400 cases of innocent people convicted of capital crimes and found that 56 had made false confessions. Apparently, some innocent suspects admitted guilt, even regarding heinous crimes, to escape the stress of interrogation (Jerome 1995). As with secret deviance, no one knows how often false accusation occurs, but it probably occurs more often than we think (see Working for Change: "The Falsely Accused on Death Row"). Moreover, the taint of guilt often lingers even after the falsely accused is cleared of all charges. Such cases lead us to ask a larger question: Under what circumstances are people most likely to be falsely accused?

Chris Caldeira

The Safe Drug Drop-Off Program (2011) provides an opportunity for people to "safely and anonymously surrender" any illegal drugs with no questions asked. In other words, participants can remain "secret deviants."

The Falsely Accused

Sociologist Kai Erikson (1966) identified a particular situation in which people are most likely to be falsely accused of a crime: when the well-being of a country or a group is threatened. The threat can take the form of an economic crisis (such as a depression or recession), a moral crisis (such as family breakdown), a health crisis (such as AIDS), or a national security crisis (such as war). At times like these, people need to identify a clear source of the threat. Thus, whenever a catastrophe occurs, it is common to blame someone for it. Identifying a threat gives an illusion of control. In a crisis, the person blamed is likely to be someone who is at best indirectly responsible, someone in the wrong place at the wrong time, or someone who is viewed as different.

This defining activity can take the form of a **witch hunt**—a campaign to identify, investigate, and correct behavior that has been defined as undermining a group. In actuality, a witch hunt rarely accomplishes these goals,

TABLE 7.1 Number of Victimizations by Crime Type and Percentage Reported to Police, 2009

Crime	Number (millions)	% Reported to Police
All crimes	20.1	39.5
Serious violent crimes	1.4	51.3
Other	4.3	48.6
Property crimes	15.6	39.4

Source: Data from U.S. Department of Justice, Bureau of Justice Statistics (2010)

conformists People who have not violated the rules of a group and are treated accordingly.

pure deviants People who have broken the rules of a group and are caught, punished, and labeled as outsiders.

secret deviants People who have broken the rules of a group but whose violation goes unnoticed or, if it is noticed, prompts those who notice to look the other way rather than reporting the violation.

falsely accused People who have not broken the rules of a group but are treated as if they have.

witch hunt A campaign to identify, investigate, and correct behavior that has been defined as undermining a group or country. Usually this behavior is not the real cause of a problem but is used to distract people's attention from the real cause or to make the problem seem manageable.

Discussion Tip: Ask students to study Table 7.1. Have they or someone close to them ever been the victim of a crime. Was the crime reported? If reported, was the "criminal" caught and punished?

Working for Change The Falsely Accused on Death Row

In September 1998, Anthony Porter was within 50 hours of his scheduled execution for a double homicide when the Illinois Supreme Court granted him a stay of execution. Porter had been defended by a lawyer who fell asleep in court, assigned a judge who later left the bench over a financial scandal, and convicted by a jury prejudiced by a witness's false testimony. After his appeals had failed, a lawyer volunteered his services and had Porter's IQ tested. When the lawyer learned that Porter had borderline mental retardation, a team of four other pro bono lawyers and journalism students agreed to take the case. The team interviewed two crime-scene witnesses.

One eyewitness, Inez Jackson, told the team that she had seen her then-husband, Alstory Simon, shoot both victims. Simon admitted his guilt, claiming that he killed one victim in self-defense while fighting over a drug deal and that the other victim's death was an accident (Center on Wrongful Convictions 2003).

George Ryan had just been inaugurated governor of Illinois in early 1999, when he saw Simon's videotaped confession. A proponent of capital punishment when elected, Ryan said this case left him feeling "jolted into reexamining everything I believed in" (Shapiro 2001). Weeks later, Andrew Kokoraleis, another Illinois prisoner, was scheduled to die. After agonizing over the decision, Ryan chose to sign off on the execution.

Later that year, Ryan learned that 13 death row inmates, some convicted 25 years before, had been found innocent after DNA evidence was discovered. Among them was an inmate who was within days of a scheduled execution. Ryan's views on capital punishment changed drastically. Although he never questioned the state's right to take a life, he argued that the sentencing process was so flawed that it must be shut down until it was repaired (*Christian Century* 2003). In January 2000, he ordered a moratorium on executions in Illinois.

Ryan then appointed a panel to investigate Illinois's capital punishment system. The panel recommended 85 changes, including videotaping all police questioning of capital suspects and revising the procedures for conducting lineups. Because the panel found that the death penalty was unevenly applied, they recommended that it should be applied only when the defendant had murdered two or more people, a police officer or firefighter, a prison officer or inmate, or a crime-scene witness. The panel also suggested that the death penalty should not be a sentencing option when only eyewitness evidence existed (Governor's Commission on Capital Punishment 2002).

In October 2002, Ryan pardoned four black men who, after serving 15 years on death row for the 1986 slaying and rape of a medical student, were exonerated by DNA evidence. Then in January 2003, after a three-year battle to reform the Illinois capital punishment system, Ryan announced that he was commuting the death sentences of another four black men tortured by Chicago police officers into confessing to crimes they did not commit. Ryan stated that these four men were "perfect examples of what is so terribly broken about our system" (Kelly 2003).

Two days before leaving office in January 2003, George Ryan commuted the death sentences of 167 inmates to life without parole. Because Illinois citizens were evenly divided on the issue of sparing prisoners and commuting death sentences to life (*The Economist* 2002), it should come as no surprise that Ryan's actions were both praised as courageous and scorned as irresponsible (Johnson 2003, p. 34). At a press conference, Ryan stated, "Our capital system is haunted by the demon of error—error in determining guilt, and error in determining who among the guilty deserve to die" (Ryan 2003).

Ryan's actions have raised public awareness about death penalty misuse and the plight of the wrongfully convicted. He has forced us to ask hard questions: How many of the 3,557 prisoners on death row in the United States were falsely convicted? How many of the 4,744 prisoners put to death since 1930 were innocent? (U.S. Department of Justice 2004). Ryan has won many awards recognizing his courage and conviction, and he was nominated for the 2003 Nobel Peace Prize. Ryan's efforts run parallel to those of the Innocence Project, a not-for-profit legal clinic that "only handles cases where post-conviction DNA testing of evidence can yield conclusive proof of innocence" (Innocence Project 2004). Students, supervised by a team of attorneys and clinic staff, investigate and handle the cases. Of the 144 inmates the clinic has exonerated, 23 of them (16 percent) were convicted in Illinois.

Source: Written by Missy Gish, Class of 2005, Northern Kentucky University, updated June 2007.

because the real cause of a problem is often complex, extending far beyond the behavior of those targeted. Often people who are labeled as the cause of a problem are simply being used to make the problem appear as if it is being managed. These dynamics help explain how, during the Cultural Revolution, the most seemingly insignificant acts—such as wearing makeup or eyeglasses—were classified as crimes against the country. The Cultural Revolution (1966–1976) was Chairman Mao Zedong's response to a specific crisis: the failure of the Great Leap Forward—Mao's

Technology Tip: Visit the Innocence Project website, www.innocenceproject.org, which offers profiles of 205 exonerations, a map that shows the number of exonerations by state, and audio/video interviews with some of the exonerated.

National Park Service

The U.S. government's internment of more than 110,000 people of Japanese descent (80 percent of whom were U.S. citizens) during World War II is an example of a witch hunt. Japanese Americans living on the West Coast were forced from their homes and taken to desert prisons surrounded by barbed wire and guarded with machine guns. None had been found guilty of anti-American activity. Nevertheless, wartime hysteria, combined with long-standing prejudice, led to this internment (Kometani 1987). Here we see Japanese American children tagged like luggage to be sent to various detention centers.

plan to mobilize the masses to transform China from a land of poverty into one of agricultural abundance in five short years (1958 through 1962). Under this plan, no household could claim private property, nor could people eat at home. They were to eat in community centers and dining halls (Deng 2008).

To meet the objective of the five-year plan, Mao mobilized hundreds of thousands of people for projects ranging from killing insects with flyswatters to building giant dams using shovels and wheelbarrows (Butterfield 1976). People were called upon to "donate every piece of metal they had in their homes including farm tools, cooking utensils, basins, locks, metal hoops, even women's hair clips, and to melt them down to produce steel and iron" (Deng 2008, p. 78). In reality, the Great Leap Forward was an ill-conceived, hastily planned, sweeping reorganization of Chinese society that created economic and environmental disruption on a massive scale, leading to the deaths of 30 to 50 million Chinese from human-induced famine. In one region, peasants stopped harvesting crops to dig tunnels in their fields to search for coal, which Communist Party officials believed was plentiful there. No coal was found, however, and the crops rotted.

In light of this crisis, Mao was particularly vulnerable to political attack. He blamed the failure of his plan on entrenched authority, which he loosely defined as the "Four Olds": old ideas, old culture, old customs, and old habits. Mao also blamed the failure on the abandonment of revolutionary spirit and on the "evils of special status and special accumulation of worldly goods" (Fairbank 1987, p. 319). He used the Cultural Revolution as an attempt to eliminate anyone in the Communist Party and in the masses who opposed his policies. Of course, such targeted behaviors as wearing eyeglasses or makeup could not possibly have been responsible for the failure of the Great Leap Forward. Nevertheless, targeting such behaviors diverted the public's attention from the failed plan and it united them behind a cause.

Of course, witch hunts are not confined to China. After the terrorist attacks of September 11, 2001, Muslim and Arab Americans were "caught up in the biggest criminal investigation in U.S. history" (Kaye 2001). Although the FBI did not keep statistics on the ethnicity or religious affiliation of the people questioned about the attacks, it is believed that most people interrogated were or appeared to be Muslim or Middle Eastern. In southern California alone, the FBI pursued more than 22,000 leads in the month following the attacks. Although many Arab and Muslim Americans expressed understanding about the real and perceived needs for such increased scrutiny, an unknown number of FBI and police interrogations went beyond questioning to include demands that women remove headscarves. We also know that many federal agents, haunted by the September 11 attacks, acted on "information from tipsters with questionable backgrounds and motives, touching off needless scares and upending the lives of innocent suspects" (Moss 2003, p. A1).

The Status of Deviant

The status of deviant can be primary or secondary in character. **Primary deviants** include those people whose rule breaking is viewed as understandable, incidental, or insignificant in light of some socially approved status they hold. For example, it is unlikely that employees who use a company-provided cell phone for personal calls or who take office supplies for personal use will be charged for theft. Similarly, a woman who kills a male partner because she fears for her physical safety has a greater chance of being labeled as suffering from battered person syndrome than being labeled a murderer. However, a male who kills a female partner claiming that he feared for his physical safety is likely to be labeled a cold-blooded murderer (Pfuhl and Henry 1993).

primary deviants Those people whose rule breaking is viewed as understandable, incidental, or insignificant in light of some socially approved status they hold.

Secondary deviants include those whose rule breaking is treated as something so significant that it cannot be overlooked or explained away. In this situation, the "secondary deviant is a person whose life and identity are organized around the facts of deviance" (Lemert 1967, p. 41). Secondary deviants assume a **master status of deviant,** an identification that "proves to be more important" than most other statuses that person holds, such that he or she is identified first and foremost as a deviant (Becker 1963, p. 33). A master status of deviant is linked to an expected set of auxiliary statuses. An abusive spouse (master status) is expected to be male and young to middle-aged (auxiliary statuses); the shoplifter (master status) is expected to be young (auxiliary status); criminals (master status) are expected to be black or Hispanic, or high school dropouts (auxiliary status); and prostitutes (master status) are expected to be young and women (auxiliary statuses). Expected auxiliary statuses are often what allow secret deviants to remain undercover. An 80-year-old shoplifter may escape detection because store security is focused on those who possess the expected auxiliary statuses of a shoplifter (Pfuhl and Henry 1993).

Sociologist Howard Becker (1973) recommends that, when studying deviance, researchers pay particular attention to who has the power to define how others "will be regarded, understood, and treated" (p. 204) and to who has the power to escape detection and punishment. The most powerful have the ability to create laws and policies that focus attention on some crimes and not others. They also have the ability to escape detection and to avoid punishment if caught (see Figure 7.3).

This emphasis suggests that sociologists are just as concerned with those who make, apply, and avoid rules as with those who are caught violating them. Sociologists consider who had the power to define deviance, influence the public to accept their definitions, and apply the recommended sanctions. The work of social psychologist Stanley Milgram provides some insights.

Gerald L. Nino

When sociologists study deviance, they place at least as much emphasis on the rule makers and rule enforcers as they do on those who get caught.

Obedience to Authority

CORE CONCEPT 5 The firm commands of a person holding a position of authority over a person hearing those commands can elicit obedient responses.

When Stanley Milgram (1974) conducted the research for his book *Obedience to Authority,* he wanted to learn how people in positions of authority persuade other people to accept an authority's definitions of deviance and to deliver sanctions. His study gives us insights into how events such as the Holocaust, the Cultural Revolution, and more recently, prisoner abuse at Abu Ghraib (Iraq) and other U.S.-run prisons, could have taken place. That such atrocities required the cooperation of many people raises important questions about people's capacity to obey authority:

> The person who, with inner conviction, loathes stealing, killing, and assault may find himself performing these acts with relative ease when commanded by authority. Behavior that is unthinkable in an individual who is acting on his own may be executed without hesitation when carried out under orders. (Milgram 1974, p. xi)

Milgram designed an experiment to see how far people would go before they would refuse to conform to an authority's orders. The participants in Milgram's experiment

secondary deviants Those whose rule breaking is treated as something so significant that it cannot be overlooked or explained away.

master status of deviant An identification that proves to be more important than most other statuses that person holds, such that he or she is identified first and foremost as a deviant.

Technology Tip: A famous study—as famous as Milgram's study—not covered in this chapter is the Zimbardo prison study. Listen to a National Public Radio interview with Zimbardo who conducted the Stanford Prison Experiment in which college students were randomly divided into prisoner and guard roles. In the interview, Zimbardo discusses the prison study's implications for Abu Ghraib, particularly how "institutional settings can override the internal dispositions of people in that setting." Go to www.npr.org, and use the search words "Lucifer Effect Asks Why Good People Go Bad."

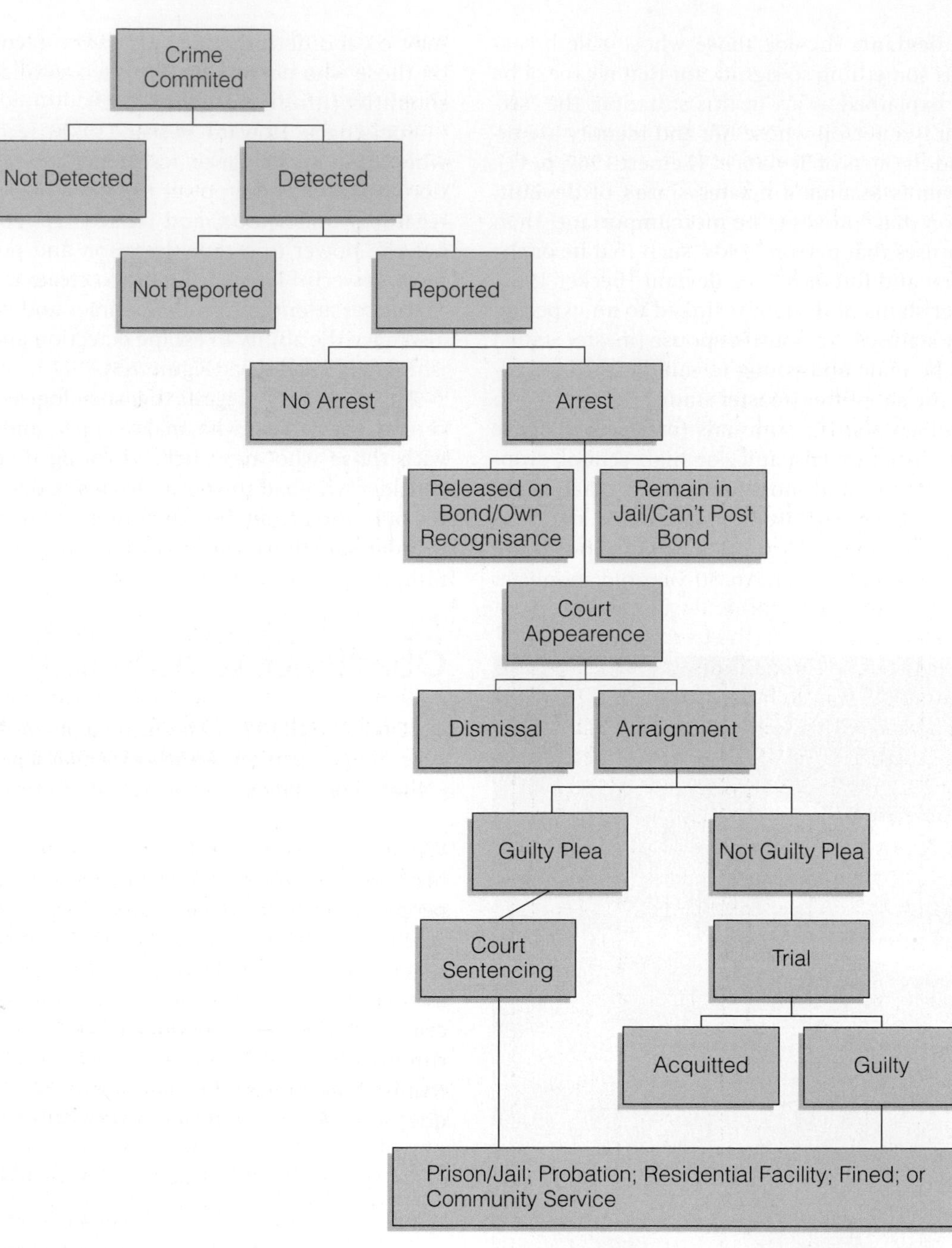

FIGURE 7.3 The Road to Prison
This flowchart shows the process by which people are arrested and then make their way through the criminal justice system. The prison population includes those who could not avoid one or more of the following: (1) detection, (2) someone reporting their offense, (3) being arrested, and (4) arraignment.
Source: U.S. Department of Justice

were volunteers who answered an ad he had placed in a local paper. When a participant arrived at the study site, a man in a laboratory jacket greeted that person and another apparent volunteer. The man in the lab coat explained that the study's purpose was to learn whether the use of punishment improves the ability to learn. (Unknown to each subject, the apparent "volunteer" was actually a confederate—someone working in cooperation with the investigator conducting the study.) The participant and the confederate drew lots to determine who would be the teacher and who would be the learner. The draw was fixed, however, so that the confederate was always the learner and the real volunteer was always the teacher.

The learner was strapped to a chair, and electrodes were placed on his wrists. The teacher, who could not see the learner, was placed in front of an instrument panel containing a line of shock-generating switches. The switches ranged from 15 to 450 volts and were labeled accordingly, from "slight shock" to "danger, severe shock." The researcher explained that when the learner made a first mistake, the teacher was to administer a 15-volt shock; the teacher would then increase the voltage with each subsequent mistake. In each case, as the strength of the shock increased, the learner expressed greater discomfort. One learner even called out that his heart was bothering him and then went silent.

When the volunteers expressed concern, the researcher firmly told them to continue administering shocks. Although many of the volunteers protested, a substantial number (65 percent) obeyed and continued on to eventually administer the highest level of shock—450 volts—"no matter how vehement the pleading of the person being shocked, no matter how painful the shocks seemed to be, and no matter how much the victim pleaded to be let out" (Milgram 1987, p. 567).

The results of Milgram's experiments are especially significant when one considers that the participants received no penalty if they refused to administer shocks. Obedience in this situation was founded simply on the firm command of a person with a status that gave minimal authority over the subject. If this level of obedience is possible under the circumstances of Milgram's experiments, one can imagine the level that is possible when disobedience brings severe penalties or negative consequences.

For the Cultural Revolution to have taken place, millions of Chinese must have cooperated to carry out Mao Zedong's mission of finding and purging those deemed responsible for the failure of the Great Leap Forward. Chinese author Wang Shuo (1997) described the Cultural Revolution as a time when "we were out of control. Everything was turned upside down. The teachers who used to do the educating were sent away to be reeducated. Children were allowed to correct their parents" (p. 51). Between 1966 and 1971, more than 36 million Chinese were persecuted in some way, with the most extreme forms of persecution being "enforced suicide" and being "hounded to death" (Spence 2006, MacFarquhar and Schoenhals 2006).

Mao initially assigned the Red Guards (his name for the youths of China between the ages of 9 and 18) the tasks of finding these culprits. In fact, Mao ordered classes suspended nationwide to free up 500,000 college students and 113 million primary and middle school students for political action (Spence 2006; MacFarquhar and Schoenhals 2006). (See The Sociological Imagination.)

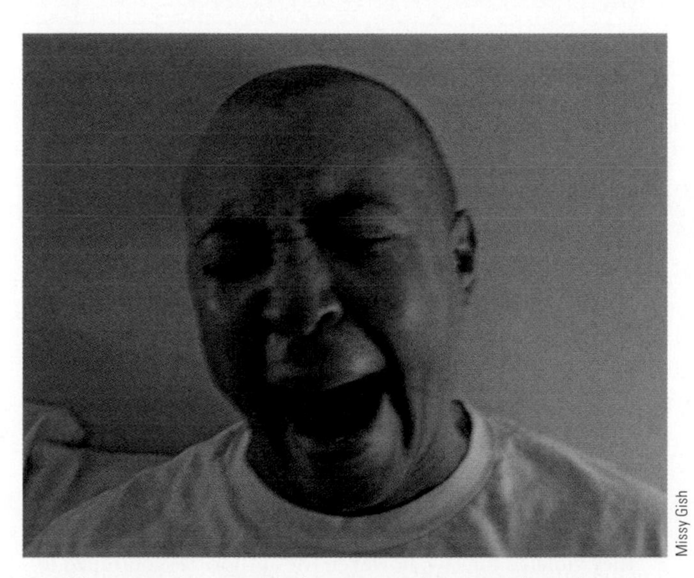

Missy Gish

Would you continue to shock someone if you could see that the level of shock was so intense it caused obvious pain? In Stanley Milgram's study, two-thirds administered the highest level of shock. In 2008, 45 years after the Milgram study, Professor Jerry Burger replicated the experiment with similar results (Cohen 2008).

The Constructionist Approach

CORE CONCEPT 6 In an effort to understand how deviance is defined, sociologists take a constructionist approach to study the role of claims maker and claims-making activities.

Regarding deviance, the **constructionist approach** focuses on the way specific groups (such as illegal immigrants and homosexuals), activities (such as child abuse), conditions (such as teenage pregnancy, infertility), or artifacts (such as song lyrics, guns, eyeglasses) become defined as problems. In particular, constructionists examine claims makers and claims-making activities. **Claims makers** are people who articulate and promote claims and who tend to gain in some way if the targeted audience accepts their claims as true. Claims makers include government officials, marketers, scientists, professors, and other special-interest groups. **Claims-making activities** are actions taken to draw attention to a claim—actions

constructionist approach A sociological approach that focuses on the way specific groups, activities, conditions, or artifacts become defined as problems.

claims makers People who articulate and promote claims and who tend to gain in some way if the targeted audience accepts their claims as true.

claims-making activities Actions taken to draw attention to a claim, such as "demanding services, filling out forms, lodging complaints, filing lawsuits, calling press conferences, writing letters of protest, passing resolutions, publishing exposés, placing ads in newspapers, . . . setting up picket lines or boycotts" (Spector and Kitsuse 1977, p. 79).

Teaching Tip: When presenting the constructionist approach, use the example of headline news regarding recalled products from China. Mention that the FDA posts product warnings and alerts involving products originating from hundreds of countries, including the United States, most of which never make the headlines. A list of recalls by country can be found at http://www.accessdata.fda.gov/cms_ia/countrylist.html. For what reasons might China be unfairly singled out for scrutiny?

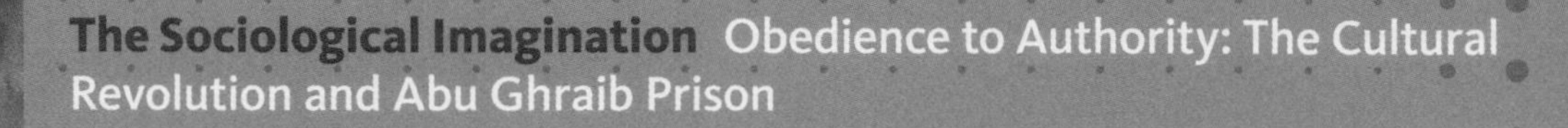

The Sociological Imagination Obedience to Authority: The Cultural Revolution and Abu Ghraib Prison

The reflections of a former Red Guard, some 15 years after the Cultural Revolution, show the intensity with which people were hunted down and persecuted: "I was very young when the Cultural Revolution began. . . . My schoolmates and I were among the first in Peking to become Red Guards; we believed deeply in Chairman Mao. I could recite the entire book of the Chairman's quotations backward and forward; we spent hours just shouting the slogans at our teachers." Hong remembered a particular winter day, with the temperature below freezing, when she and her faction of Red Guards put on their red armbands and made three of the teachers from their high school kneel on the ground outside without coats or gloves. "We had gone to their houses to conduct an investigation, to search them, and we found some English-language books. They were probably old textbooks, but to us it was proof they were worshipping foreign things and were slaves to the foreigners. We held a bonfire and burned everything we had found." After that, she recalled, the leader of her group—a tall, charismatic 18-year-old boy, the son of an army general, whose nickname was "Old Dog"—ordered them to beat the teachers. He produced some wooden boards, and the students started hitting the teachers on their bodies. "We kept on till one of the teachers start[ed] coughing blood," Hong said. "We felt very proud of ourselves. It seemed very revolutionary" (Butterfield 1982, p. 183).

Staff Sergeant Ivan L. Frederick II was caught up in the Abu Ghraib prison scandal. Abu Ghraib, one of the world's most notorious prisons under Saddam Hussein, was converted to a U.S. military prison after Hussein was removed from power. Frederick faced charges of conspiracy, dereliction of duty, cruelty toward prisoners, maltreatment, assault, and indecent acts. He was sentenced to eight years in prison. Letters and email messages that Frederick wrote to family members were presented in court to bolster his defense lawyer's assertion that he was simply carrying out orders (Hersh 2004). In January 2004, Frederick wrote "I questioned some of the things that I saw, . . . such things as leaving inmates in their cell with no clothes or in female underpants, handcuffing them to the door of their cell—and the answer I got was, 'This is how military intelligence [MI] wants it done.' . . . MI has also instructed us to place a prisoner in an isolation cell with little or no clothes, no toilet or running water, no ventilation or window, for as much as three days." Frederick also wrote that when he questioned his superior officer about this mistreatment, the officer said, "Don't worry about it." Frederick wrote about the situation of an Iraqi prisoner under CIA control: "They stressed him out so bad that the man passed away. They put his body in a body bag and packed him in ice for approximately twenty-four hours in the shower. . . . The next day the medics came and put his body on a stretcher, placed a fake IV in his arm and took him away" (Hersh 2004).

such as "demanding services, filling out forms, lodging complaints, filing lawsuits, calling press conferences, writing letters of protest, passing resolutions, publishing exposés, placing ads in newspapers, . . . setting up picket lines or boycotts" (Spector and Kitsuse 1977, p. 79).

With regard to the Cultural Revolution, some claims makers take issue with the charge that the 10-year period between 1966 and 1976 was a national disaster and that education, in particular, suffered. One such person is historian Dongping Han, author of *The Unknown Cultural Revolution: Educational Reforms and Their Impact on China's Rural Development*. Han points out that, during the Cultural Revolution, 17 million young urban youth volunteered to go to the countryside and work alongside farmers. Han uses the case of Jimo County to make the point that "during the Cultural Revolution, the Chinese government empowered Chinese farmers to set up their own schools." Han, a native of Jimo County, drew on his own firsthand experiences and gathered statistics to support his argument. At the start of the Cultural Revolution, there were 1,050 villages in Jimo County and only one high school and seven middle schools. In most of these villages, no one had been to high school. All that changed with the Cultural Revolution. During that time, 89 high schools were built and 242 middle schools. In addition, every village had its own primary school. Everyone was entitled to go to an education (Andreas 2010, Redmonde 2009, Han 2010).

Another example of a claims-making activity is the annual human rights reports that the U.S. Department of State (2010) releases on 190 countries, including one on the People's Republic of China. In that report, the United States makes a number of claims about China, including this one:

> [Chinese] government officials continued to deny holding any political prisoners, asserting that authorities detained persons not for their political or religious views but because they violated the law; however, the authorities continued to confine citizens for reasons related to politics and religion. Tens of thousands of political prisoners remained incarcerated, some in prisons and others in RTL (re-education through labor camps) or administrative detention. The government did not grant international humanitarian organizations access to political prisoners.

PVDE/RDA/Getty Images

REUTERS/Claro Cortes IV /Landov

Historian Dongping Han engages in claims-making activity when he challenges what is arguably an iconic images of the Cultural Revolution. The bottom photo shows the *Little Red Book*, a book of quotations and writing by Mao. During the Cultural Revolution people carried the book around and it was required reading in schools and workplaces. Critics of the Cultural Revolution point to this book as evidence that the Chinese people were brainwashed by the ideas of Mao. The top poster corresponds with the vision he believes should be celebrated; it shows Chinese eager to learn from a then young Mao.

Each year, the China Information Office (2010) responds by issuing a human rights report on the United States. In its most recent report, the office claims the following about the United States:

> The United States with its strong military power has pursued hegemony in the world, trampling upon the sovereignty of other countries and trespassing their human rights. As the world's biggest arms seller, its deals have greatly fueled instability across the world. . . . The wars of Iraq and Afghanistan have placed heavy burden on American people and brought tremendous casualties and property losses to the people of Iraq and Afghanistan. The war in Iraq has led to the death of more than 1 million Iraqi civilians, rendered an equal number of people homeless and incurred huge economic losses. In Afghanistan, incidents of the U.S. army killing innocent people still keep occurring.

The success of a claims-making campaign depends on a number of factors, including access to the media, available resources, and the claims maker's social status and skill at fund-raising, promotion, and organization (Best 1989). According to sociologist Joel Best, when constructionists study the process through which a group or behavior is defined as a problem to society, they focus on who makes the claims, whose claims are heard, and how audiences respond to them. Constructionists are guided by one or more of the following questions: What kinds of claims are made about the problem? Who makes the claims? Which claims are heard? Why is a claim made at a particular time? What are the responses to the claim? In essence constructionists examine how claims makers go about presenting a condition. Specifically, constructionists pay attention to any labels that claims makers attach to a condition, the examples they use to illustrate the nature of the problem, and their orientation toward the problem (describing it, for example, as medical, moral, genetic, or educational).

Labels, examples, and orientation are important because they tend to evoke a particular cause of a problem and a particular solution to it (Best 1989). Here, we consider the claims-making strategies Chinese leaders used to put the country on a new path when Mao died in 1976, and the Cultural Revolution ended. China's new leaders faced a great many problems, including how to undo the effects of this movement, which had taken place at the expense of China's economic, technological, scientific, cultural, and agricultural development and had drained the Chinese physically and mentally. It also created a 10-year gap in training, such that one leading Chinese surgeon claimed, "I can't honestly let any of the young doctors in my hospital operate on a patient. . . . They went to medical school. But they studied Mao's thought, planting rice, or making tractor parts. They never had to take exams and a lot of them don't know basic anatomy" (Butterfield 1980, p. 32).

To solve the problems resulting from the Cultural Revolution, the Communist Party, under the leadership of Deng Xiaoping, rallied the teachers, technicians, artists, and scientists whom the revolution had struck down. Deng Xiaoping claimed that the government's new policies were in the best interest of the country and that they did not promote individual self-interest, special status, or accumulation of wealth. These claims allowed Chinese leaders to send tens of thousands of students overseas to study in the capitalist West. They allowed farmers and factory workers to keep profits from surplus crops after meeting government quotas, and they permitted the government to establish special economic zones (SEZs), designated areas within China that could enjoy capitalist privileges. All of these activities were reframed as important to China's success.

Technology Tip: For images of the cultural revolution go to Google Images and use the search terms "Cultural Revolution propaganda" and/or "Cultural Revolution Red Guards."

To this point, we have examined several sociological concepts—socialization, norms (folkways and mores), and mechanisms of social control—and discussed how they relate to deviance. In addition, we have examined the functionalist perspective to gain insights about how any behavior or appearance can come to be defined as deviant. We have looked at labeling theory and the constructionist approach to gain insights into the role that rule makers play in shaping deviance. Next, we turn to the theory of structural strain, which helps us answer the following question: Under what conditions do people engage in behavior defined as deviant?

Structural Strain Theory

CORE CONCEPT 7 Deviant behavior is a response to structural strain, a situation in which a disconnect exists between culturally valued goals and legitimate means for achieving those goals.

According to sociologist Robert K. Merton (1957), **structural strain** is any situation in which (1) the valued goals of a society have unclear limits (that is, people are unsure whether they have achieved them), (2) people are unsure whether the legitimate means will allow them to achieve the goals, or (3) legitimate opportunities for reaching the goals remain closed to a significant portion of the population. The rate of deviance is likely to be high in any one of these situations. Merton uses the United States, a country where all three conditions exist, to show the relationship between structural strain and deviance.

Structural Strain in the United States

In the United States, most people place a high value on the culturally valued goal of economic success and upward mobility. Americans tend to believe that anyone, regardless of the circumstances into which they were born, can achieve such success. Such beliefs suggest that people have only themselves to blame if they fail. Merton argues that "Americans are bombarded on every side" with the message that economic success is achievable, "even in the face of repeated frustration" (1957, p. 137). Even when people do achieve such success, at no point do they feel secure because, no matter the income level "Americans want just about 25 percent more (but of course this 'just a bit more' continues to operate once it is obtained)" (p. 136).

Merton also maintains that structural strain exists in the United States because the legitimate means of achieving wealth do not always lead to its achievement. The individual's task is to choose a path that leads to success. That path might involve education, hard work, or development of a special talent. The problem is that schooling, hard work, and talent do not always guarantee economic success. Regarding education, for example, many Americans believe that a diploma (and especially a college diploma) in itself entitles a person to a high-paying job. In reality, a diploma is merely one of many components needed to achieve success.

Finally, structural strain exists in the United States because too few legitimate opportunities exist to achieve the goal of financial success. Although Americans are supposed to seek it, all cannot expect to achieve it legitimately. In addition, the opportunities for achieving success remain closed to many people, especially those in the lower classes. For example, many young black males living in poverty believe that one legitimate way to achieve success is through sports, but opportunities are severely limited. Consider that 3.1 percent of male high school basketball players go on to play at the college level, and that 1.2 percent of college players are eventually drafted by the NBA (National Collegiate Athletic Association [NCAA] 2010).

Merton believed that people respond in identifiable ways to structural strain and that their response involves some combination of acceptance and rejection of the valued goals and means (see Figure 7.4). He identified the following five responses—only one of which is not deviant:

- **Conformity** is the acceptance of the cultural goals and the pursuit of those goals through legitimate means.
- **Innovation** is the acceptance of the cultural goals but the rejection of legitimate means to achieve them. For the innovator, success is equated with winning the game rather than with playing by the rules (achieving a desired end by whatever means). After all, money may be used to purchase the same goods and services, whether it was acquired legally or illegally. According to Merton, when the life circumstances of the middle and upper classes are compared with those of the lower classes, the lower classes clearly face the greatest pressure to innovate, although no evidence suggests that they do so more than the middle and upper classes.
- **Ritualism** involves the rejection of the cultural goals but a rigid adherence to the legitimate means of achieving them. This response is the opposite of innovation: The game is played according to the rules despite defeat.

structural strain Any situation in which (1) the valued goals of a society have unclear limits, (2) people are unsure whether the legitimate means will allow them to achieve the goals, and (3) legitimate opportunities for reaching the goals remain closed to a significant portion of the population.

innovation The acceptance of cultural goals but the rejection of the legitimate means to achieve them.

ritualism The rejection of cultural goals but a rigid adherence to the legitimate means of achieving them.

Patrick Grieco

Robert K. Merton's theory of structural strain applies to the situation of those black athletes who seek to achieve financial success and mobility through sports, as only about one percent of college basketball players have the opportunity to join the NBA.

Merton maintains that this response can be a reaction to the status anxiety that accompanies the ceaseless competitive struggle to stay on top or to get ahead. Ritualism finds expression in clichés such as "Don't aim high and you won't be disappointed" and "I'm not sticking my neck out." It can also be the response of people who have few employment opportunities open to them. The laid-off worker may enroll in college simply because that is the only legitimate option open to him or her.

- **Retreatism** involves the rejection of both culturally valued goals and the legitimate means of achieving them. Retreatism is a response of those who have internalized the valued cultural goals but the legitimate means promising success are no longer available to them. According to Merton, retreatists face a mental conflict in that it is against their moral principles to use illegitimate means, yet the legitimate means have failed them. According to Merton, people who respond this way are the true aliens or the socially disinherited—the outcasts, vagrants, vagabonds, tramps, drunks, and addicts. They are "in the society but not of it."
- **Rebellion** involves the full or partial rejection of both the goals and the means of attaining them and the introduction of a new set of goals and means. When this response is confined to a small segment of society, it provides the potential for the emergence of subgroups as diverse as street gangs and the Old Order Amish. When rebellion is the response of a large number of people who wish to reshape the entire structure of society, a great potential for a revolution exists.

Mode of Adaptation	Culturally Valued Goals	Legitimate Means for Achieving Culturally Valued Goals
Conformity	Accept/Achieve	Accept/Follow
Innovation	Accept/Achieve	Reject/Do Not Follow
Ritualism	Reject/Cannot Achieve	Accept/Follow
Retreatism	Reject/Cannot Achieve	Reject/Do Not Follow
Rebellion	Reject/Establish New Goals	Reject/Establish New Means

FIGURE 7.4 Typology of Responses to Structural Strain
Merton believed that people respond to and are affected by structural strain in different ways.

Structural Strain in China

In China, one source of structural strain involves the number of legitimate opportunities for married couples to achieve the culturally valued goal of producing children, especially a son. Since 1979, China has worked to impose a limit of one child per couple in urban areas and a limit of two children per couple in rural areas in with the goal of slowing the population growth of the world's most populous country. This family-planning policy poses a problem, because a cultural preference for boys exists in China, especially among the people living in the countryside. One reason that sons are valued more than daughters is that sons and their families are expected to care for parents in old age. Thus, couples who produce a son can be confident that someone will care for them later in life. The legitimate means of starting a family include the following steps: Obtain permission to have

retreatism The rejection of both culturally valued goals and the means of achieving them.

rebellion The full or partial rejection of both the goals and the means of attaining them and the introduction of a new set of goals and means.

Culturally valued goal: One child per couple
Culturally valued means: One-child limit
Sources of structural strain: Preference for boys

Response	Goal Population control	Means One-child policy	Examples
Conformists	+	+	• Couples with no preference • "Ideologically sound" couples
Innovators	+	–	• Couples who abort female or unhealthy babies • Couples who abandon babies
Ritualists	–	+	• Couples who follow the rules but reject policies
Retreatists	–	–	• Couples who reject the idea of population control and hide the "extra" babies
Rebels	+/–	+/–	• Couples who replace official goals and means with new goals and means

+ Acceptance/achieve valued goals or means
– Rejection/fail to achieve valued goals or means

FIGURE 7.5 Merton's Typology Applied to China's One-Child Policy.

a child, accept the sex of the child (that is, do not abort female fetuses or kill a daughter), report the birth and sex of the child to appropriate agencies, and practice birth control to avoid conceiving other children.

We can apply Merton's typology of responses to structural strain to describe the reactions of Chinese couples to this one-child policy (Figure 7.5). Couples most likely to be conformists are those whose first child is a healthy son. Conformists would also include couples who have no preference as to the sex of their child and couples who are firmly committed to upholding the laws related to birth control because they see them as critical to China's quality of life (Bolido 1993, p. 6). Most people in urban China can be classified as conformists.

Innovators accept the culturally valued goal of one child per couple but reject the package of legitimate means to obtain this goal. Upon learning that she is expecting a child, a woman may undergo an ultrasound exam to learn the sex of the fetus. If it is female, the couple may decide to abort the fetus. Alternatively, upon the birth of a girl baby, the parents may kill her or have a midwife kill her. Such practices are blamed for the so-called "missing girls" problem. In response, many rural governments in China have launched "respect girls" campaigns backed by special incentives, such as free tuition to poor families with one or more girls (Yardley 2005).

A second category of innovators includes couples who abandon a baby considered unhealthy, a female child, or a second child born in violation of family planning regulations. These children fill the country's 67 state-run orphanages (Tyler 1996). (See No Borders, No Boundaries: "Immigrant Orphans Adopted by U.S. Citizens.")

Ritualists reject the one-child-per-couple goal of population control, but they adhere to the rules. They do not agree with the government policies, but they are afraid they will be punished if they do not follow them (Remez 1991).

Retreatists reject the one-child goal as well as the legitimate means open to them. This category of deviants include couples who continue having children until a son is born, adopt out girls, and hide the births of girls and second babies from party officials. In fact, Stirling Scruggs (1992) of the United Nations Population Fund argues that many of the so-called missing girls have just never been officially registered as having been born. Because of the high number of unreported births, some experts claim that it is impossible to know the actual size of China's population (Rosenthal 2000). In a sense, these retreatist parents are in society but, because of their secret, "not of it." So they can get a true picture of population size, the Chinese government has indicated that these undocumented children will be eligible for household registration cards—children must be registered to gain admission to schools and to find jobs as adults (China Daily 2010).

Rebels reject the culturally valued goal of population control as well as the legitimate means of achieving it; instead, they introduce new goals and new means. One

No Borders No Boundaries Immigrant Orphans Adopted by U.S. Citizens

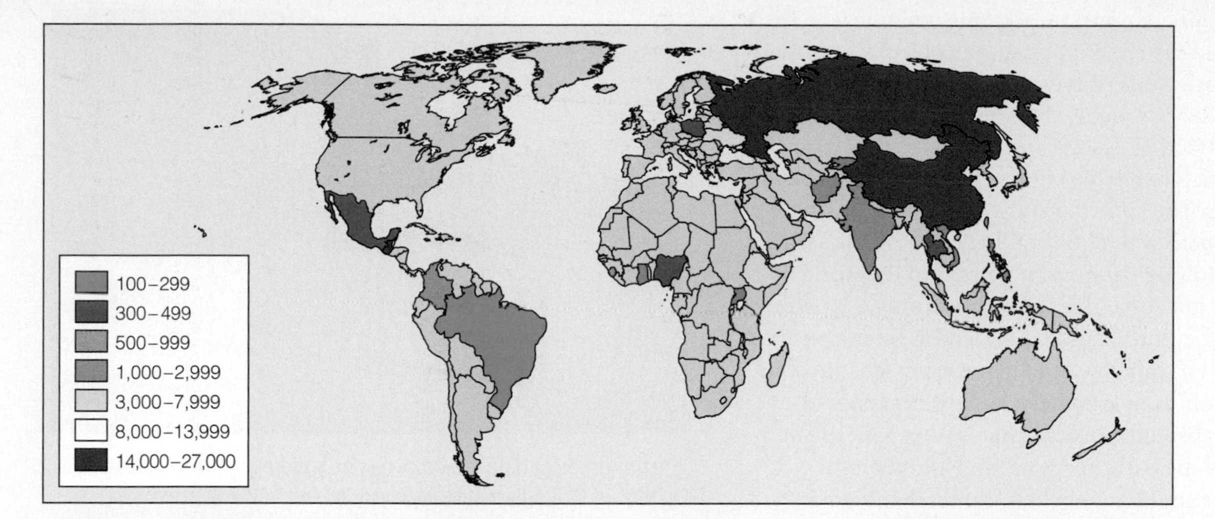

Country	# of Adoptions to U.S. 2005–2009
China	26760
Guatemala	17523
Russia	14079
Ethiopia	6428
South Korea	6084
Ukraine	3000
Kazakhstan	2565
Vietnam	2220
India	1658
Colombia	1484
Haiti	1366
Philippines	1349

Country	# of Adoptions to U.S. 2005–2009
Liberia	1104
Taiwan	984
Mexico	424
Nigeria	386
Poland	351
Thailand	308
Ghana	200
Brazil	187
Kyrgyzstan	132
Nepal	128
Uganda	123
Jamaica	116

FIGURE 7.6 Adoptions In U.S. Involving International Children by Country, 2005–2009
Study the list of countries from which Americans adopt international children. Notice that China leads the list. Why do you think Americans adopt children from abroad?
Source: Data from U.S. Department of State (2011)

could argue that this response applies to couples who belong to any of China's 55 ethnic minority populations, which make up 8.5 percent (114 million) of the total population (U.S. Central Intelligence Agency 2011). Most of these ethnic groups are exempt from the one-child policy. The government permits couples from such a group to have—depending on the group—two, three, or even four children. For these groups, the culturally valued goal is to increase the size of the minority populations, and the means of achieving that goal is exemption from the one-child policy. This option has prompted many couples to claim ethnic minority status (Tien et al. 1992). (See "The One-Child Policy in the Context of China's Population.")

Differential Association and Opportunities

CORE CONCEPT 8 Criminal behavior is learned; thus, criminals constitute a special type of conformist in that they conform to the norms of the group with which they associate.

Coined by sociologists Edwin H. Sutherland and Donald R. Cressey (1978), differential association explains how deviant behavior, especially juvenile delinquency, is learned. This theory states that exposure to criminal patterns and isolation from anticriminal influences put

The One-Child Policy in the Context of China's Population

The size of the Chinese population is one major reason for the country's rigid system of population control. More than 1.3 billion Chinese—one of every five people alive in the world—live in a space roughly the same size as the United States. After subtracting deserts and uninhabitable mountain ranges, China's habitable land area is about half that of the United States. The United Nations estimate that China's population will peak at 1.45 billion in 2030 (People's Daily Online 2010). Although almost 20 percent of the world's population lives in China, this country has only 6.3 percent of the world's agricultural land (U.S. Central Intelligence Agency 2011). Even though China manages to feed most of its population well, approximately 21.5 million people live in a state of absolute poverty; that is, they lack the resources to satisfy the basic needs of food and shelter. "Most Americans could not begin to comprehend what 21.5 million Chinese have to endure and what that level of deprivation is all about" (Piazza 1996, p. 47).

Boni Li

The hundreds of high-rise apartment buildings in the Chaoyang District of Beijing are one indicator of the housing pressures facing China's large population. Beijing's population is 15.8 million.

Another 150 million live in a state of substantial deprivation; that is, they live on less than $1.25 per day (China Daily 2010). It is believed that 240 million people from rural villages have migrated to the cities in search of work. "It is the largest migration in human history" (Gifford 2007, p. xvii, People's Daily Online 2010).

On average, 16.4 million births and 9.4 million deaths occur every year in China. If these patterns persist, the total population could increase by another 70 million people over the next 10 years. To complicate the situation, the population has expanded rapidly in the past 60 years, growing from approximately 500 million in 1949 to 1.33 billion in 2011 (Bureau of the Census 2011). Such rapid growth strains China's ability to house, clothe, educate, employ, and feed its people and has overshadowed its industrial and agricultural advancements. When one considers that approximately 1.3 billion people live under approximately 63 independent governments (not including island states) in the European Union and South America, it is easy to appreciate why the Chinese government is concerned (U.S. Central Intelligence Agency 2011). The one-child policy is associated (real or imagined) with a number of important changes in China, including the following: (1) the 4-2-1 problem when a child is cared for (and spoiled by) four grandparents and two parents, for whom the child must later care; (2) the Little Emperor/Empress syndrome, a situation in which only children who have been indulged become spoiled, rebellious, and self-centered; (3) a rise in childhood obesity and tooth decay as parents overfeed children; and (4) a rise in dog ownership as households acquire a dog to serve as a companion to only children and to people whose children have grown up (China Daily 2010, Wanli 2010).

people at risk of turning criminal. These criminal contacts take place within **deviant subcultures**, groups that are part of the larger society but whose members share norms and values favoring violation of that larger society's laws. People learn criminal behavior from closely interacting with those who engage in and approve of law-breaking activities. It is important to keep in mind, however, that contact with deviant subcultures does not by itself make criminals. Rather, there is some unspecified tipping point of exposure in which criminal influences offset exposure to law-abiding influences (Sutherland and Cressey 1978). If we accept the premise that behavior defined as criminal is learned, then criminals constitute a special type of conformist in that they are simply following the norms of the subculture with which they associate.

The theory of differential association does not explain how people make initial contact with a deviant subculture or the exact mechanisms by which people learn criminal behavior, except that individuals learn deviant subculture's rules the same way any behavior is learned. Sociologist

deviant subcultures Groups that are part of the larger society but whose members share norms and values favoring violation of that larger society's laws.

Technology Tip: Technology Tip: Visit the U.S. Bureau of the Census website (www.census.gov/ipc/www/idb/summaries.html) to find age and sex breakdowns of the Chinese population. You might compare China's population pyramid with that of the United States. To help students gain an understanding about the size of China's population, point out that China has 77 million children four years of age or younger. The United States has 21.3 million children in that age group.

Terry Williams (1989) offers one example of how teenagers can make contact with a deviant subculture. He studied a group of teenagers, some as young as 14, who sold cocaine in the Washington Heights section of New York City. These youths were recruited by major drug suppliers because, as minors, they could not be sent to prison if caught. Williams argues that the teenagers were susceptible to recruitment for two reasons: They saw little chance of finding high-paying jobs, and they perceived drug dealing as a way to earn money to escape their circumstances. Williams's findings suggest that once teenagers become involved in drug networks, they learn the skills to perform their jobs the same way everyone learns to do a job. Indeed, success in an illegal pursuit is measured in much the same way that success is measured in mainstream jobs: pleasing the boss, meeting goals, and getting along with associates.

Williams's research suggests that criminal behavior is not simply the result of differential association with criminal ways. There are other factors at work, including **illegitimate opportunity structures**—social settings and arrangements that offer people the opportunity to commit particular types of crime. In the case of Williams's study, drug suppliers recruited 14-year-olds because minors would not go to prison. The larger society offers minors an opportunity structure that allows them to engage in criminal activity without risking the full penalties of the law. Opportunities to commit crimes are shaped by the environments in which people live or work (Merton 1957). That is, for someone to embezzle money, another person has to have entrusted a would-be embezzler with a large sum of money; the act of entrusting money has to occur before the embezzler can set money aside for some unintended purpose.

Illegitimate opportunity structures figure into the type of crimes people commit. Working as a pharmacist offers the opportunity to steal prescription drugs to sell or to feed a personal or friend's addiction. For addicts without money, the only option available to them is to hold up a pharmacy. White-collar and corporate criminals also benefit from differential opportunity. **White-collar crime** consists of "crimes committed by persons of respectability and high social status in the course of their occupations" (Sutherland and Cressey 1978, p. 44). **Corporate crime** is committed by a corporation through the way that it does business as it competes with other companies for market share and profits. In the case of white-collar crime, offenders are part of the system: They occupy positions in the organization that permit them to carry out illegal activities discreetly. In the case of corporate crime, everyone in the organization contributes to illegal activities simply by doing their jobs. Both white-collar and corporate crimes are often aimed at impersonal—and often vaguely defined—entities such as the tax system, the environment, competitors, and so on. Neither kind of crime is aimed at a specific person who can report the offense to the police (National Council for Crime Prevention in Sweden 1985).

White-collar and corporate crimes—such as the manufacturing and marketing of unsafe products, unlawful disposal of hazardous waste, tax evasion, and money laundering—are usually handled not by the police but by regulatory agencies (such as the Environmental Protection Agency, the Federal Bureau of Investigation, and the Food and Drug Administration), which have minimal staff to monitor compliance. Escaping punishment is easier for white-collar and corporate criminals than for other criminals.

The concept of an illegitimate opportunity structure challenges the belief that the uneducated and people in certain minority groups are more prone to criminal behavior than are those in other groups. In fact, crime exists in all social strata, but the type of crime, the extent to which the laws are enforced, access to legal aid, and the power to sidestep laws vary by social strata (Chambliss 1974). In the United States, police efforts are largely directed at controlling crimes against individual life and property (crimes such as drug offenses, robbery, assault, homicide, and rape) rather than patrolling office buildings looking for white-collar and corporate criminals. Less than one percent of all people sentenced to U.S. federal prisons seem to fall under the category of white-collar criminals, whereas 51 percent are classified as drug offenders (Federal Bureau of Prisons 2011).

In China, notions of differential association are the basis of the philosophy underlying rehabilitation: A deviant individual becomes deviant because of "bad"—education or associations with "bad" influences. To correct these influences, society must reeducate deviant individuals politically, inspire them to support the Communist Party, and teach them a love of labor. These principles guided Communist Party leaders in their handling of the Chinese students who participated in a series of pro-democracy demonstrations in Tiananmen Square in 1989. The government eventually suppressed these demonstrations violently, accusing the students of "counterrevolutionary revolt" and "bourgeois liberalization." Although these terms have never been clearly defined, they suggest wanton expressions of individual freedom, which threatened the country's stability

illegitimate opportunity structures Social settings and arrangements that offer people the opportunity to commit particular types of crime.

white-collar crimes Crimes committed by those with high status, respectable positions as they carry out the duties and responsibilities of their occupation.

corporate crimes Crimes committed by a corporation through the way that it does business as it competes with other companies for market share and profits.

Theories of Deviance: Summary

Theory	Central Question	Answer
Functionalist	How does deviance contribute to order and stability?	Deviance—especially the ritual of identifying and exposing wrongdoing, determining a punishment, and carrying it out—is an emotional experience that binds together members of groups and establishes a sense of community.
Labeling theory	What is deviance?	Deviance depends on whether people notice it and, if they do notice it, on whether they label it as such and subsequently apply sanctions/punishment.
Obedience to authority	How do rule makers get people to accept their definition of deviance and to act on those definitions?	Behavior that is unthinkable in an individual acting on his or her own may be executed without hesitation when authority figures command such behavior.
Constructionist	How do specific groups, activities, conditions, or artifacts come to be defined as problems?	Claims makers with the ability to define something as a problem, to have those claims heard, and to shape public responses play important roles in defining deviance and responses to it.
Structural strain	Under what conditions do people engage in behavior defined as deviant?	People engage in behavior defined as deviant when valued goals have no limits or clear boundaries, when legitimate means do not guarantee valued goals, and when the number of legitimate opportunities is in short supply.
Differential association opportunity	How is behavior defined as deviant learned? What role does opportunity to commit crimes play?	People learn deviant behavior through close associations and interactions with those who engage in and approve of criminal behavior.

and unity. Such expressions had to be curbed. In the government's view, students who demonstrated led a sheltered life. As a result, they ignored larger collective interests and concerns and failed to grasp the complexities of government reforms (Kwong 1988, pp. 983–984).

The government undertook a number of measures to persuade the students to learn more about the complexities of life and resist subversive ideas. These measures included sending them "to rural areas to teach them to endure hardship, work hard and appreciate the daily difficulties faced by China's mostly rural population" (Kristof 1989, p. Y1). The rationale was that proper ideological commitment could be instilled through association with the masses and through manual labor. Other measures included limiting the number of students entering the humanities and social sciences. In the year following the Tiananmen Square incident, almost no students were admitted to study academic subjects that government officials considered "ideologically suspect," such as history, political science, sociology, and international studies (Goldman 1989).

Online Poll

Can you think of a time when you obeyed the "orders" given by someone in a position of authority even though you did not approve of what that person was asking you to do?

○ Yes

○ No

To see how other students responded to these questions, go to **www.cengagebrain.com.**

Summary of CORE CONCEPTS

In this chapter, we focused on changing conception of deviance in the People's Republic of China. We used the sociological concepts and theories related to deviance to understand how something deviant at one time and place is not deviant in another. When sociologists study deviance, they do not focus on deviant individuals per se but on the context in which deviance occurs and on the reactions and judgments of others, including the larger society, the group whose norms are broken, and rule makers and enforcers.

CORE CONCEPT 1 The only characteristic common to all forms of deviance is that some social audience challenges or condemns a behavior or an appearance because it departs from established norms.

Deviance is any behavior or physical appearance that is socially challenged or condemned because it departs from the norms and expectations of a group. Conformity comprises behaviors and appearances that follow and maintain the standards of a group. All groups employ mechanisms of social control—methods used to teach, persuade, or force their members, and even nonmembers, to comply with and not deviate from norms and expectations.

CORE CONCEPT 2 Ideally, conformity is voluntary. When socialization fails to produce conformity, other mechanisms of social control—sanctions, censorship, or surveillance—may be used to convey and enforce norms.

Because socialization begins as soon as a person enters the world, one has little opportunity to avoid exposure to the culture's folkways and mores. That exposure may take place in schools. For example, Chinese preschoolers are taught to give constructive critiques of their classmates' work and to learn from critiques of their own and others' work. Chinese preschoolers are also taught to downplay interpersonal conflicts and play cooperatively with other children. In contrast, American preschoolers are taught to express themselves and expect praise. They are also taught to seek an adult to mediate conflicts with peers and decide who is right and wrong. In addition, American preschoolers are encouraged to express in words their feeling about conflict.

When conformity cannot be achieved voluntarily, other mechanisms of social control may be used to convey and enforce norms. These mechanisms include sanctions, censorship, and surveillance. Sanctions can be positive (reward oriented) or negative (punishment oriented), informal (spontaneous and unofficial), or formal (official, backed by force of law).

CORE CONCEPT 3 It is impossible for a society to exist without deviance. Always and everywhere there will be some behaviors or appearances that offend collective sentiments.

Durkheim argued that although deviance does not take the same form everywhere, it is present in all societies. He defined *deviance* as acts that offend collective norms and expectations. Durkheim believed that deviance is normal as long as it is not excessive, and that no society can exist without deviance. First, the ritual of identifying and exposing wrongdoing, determining a punishment, and carrying it out is an emotional experience that binds together the members of a group and establishes a sense of community. Second, deviance helps bring about necessary change.

CORE CONCEPT 4 Labeling theorists maintain that an act is deviant when people notice it and then take action to label it as a violation and apply appropriate sanctions.

Labeling theorists maintain that violating a rule does not automatically make a person deviant. That is, a rule breaker is not deviant (in the strict sense of the word) unless someone *notices* the violation and decides to take corrective action. Labeling theorists suggest that for every rule a social group creates, four categories of people exist: conformists, pure deviants, secret deviants, and the falsely accused. Labeling theorists pay particular attention to power and authority to evade and create laws to punish crime.

CORE CONCEPT 5 The firm commands of a person holding a position of authority over a person hearing those commands can elicit obedient responses.

In *Obedience to Authority*, Stanley Milgram sought to explain how large numbers of people follow orders to carry out atrocities. He learned that this level of obedience can be founded simply on the firm command of a person with a social status that gives him or her even minimal authority over a subject.

CORE CONCEPT 6 In an effort to understand how deviance is defined, sociologists take a constructionist approach to study the role of claims maker and claims-making activities.

Claims makers are people who articulate and promote claims and who tend to gain in some way if the targeted audience accepts their claims as true. Claims-making activities draw attention to a claim and involve a range of activities, from filing lawsuits to holding signs. The success of a claims-making campaign depends on a number of factors such as access to the media. When constructionists study the claims-making process, they ask who makes the claims, whose claims are heard, how audiences respond, and so on.

CORE CONCEPT 7 Deviant behavior is a response to structural strain, a situation in which a disconnect exists between culturally valued goals and legitimate means for achieving those goals.

The theory of structural strain takes three factors into account: (1) culturally valued goals defined as legitimate for all members of society, (2) norms that specify the legitimate means of achieving those goals, and (3) the actual number of legitimate opportunities available to people to achieve the goals. Structural strain occurs when the valued goals have unclear limits, people are unsure whether the legitimate means will allow them to achieve the goals, or legitimate opportunities for meeting the goals remain closed to a significant portion of the population.

Merton believed that people respond in identifiable ways to structural strain and that their response involves some combination of acceptance and rejection of the valued goals and means. He identified the following five responses—conformity, innovation (such as taking illegal performance-enhancing drugs to achieve success in sports), ritualism, retreatism, and rebellion.

CORE CONCEPT 8 Criminal behavior is learned; thus, criminals constitute a special type of conformist in that they conform to the norms of the group with which they associate.

The theory of differential association explains how deviant behavior, especially juvenile delinquency, is learned. This theory states that it is exposure to criminal patterns and isolation from anticriminal influences that put people at risk of turning criminal. If we accept the premise that behavior defined as criminal is learned, then criminals constitute a special type of conformist. Other factors are at work beyond simply learning criminal behavior. One factor involved illegitimate opportunity structures—the social settings, and arrangements that offer people the opportunity to commit particular types of crime including white-collar and corporate crimes. In China, notions of differential association are the basis of the philosophy underlying rehabilitation: A deviant individual becomes deviant because of "bad"—education or associations with "bad" influences. To correct these influences, society must reeducate deviant individuals.

Resources on the Internet

Login to CengageBrain.com to access the resources your instructor requires. For this book, you can access:

Sociology CourseMate

Access an integrated eBook, chapter-specific interactive learning tools, including flash cards, quizzes, videos, and more in your Sociology CourseMate.

CENGAGENOW™

Take a pretest for this chapter and receive a personalized study plan based on your results that will identify the topics you need to review and direct you to online resources to help you master those topics. Then take a posttest to help you determine the concepts you have mastered and what you will need to work on.

CourseReader

CourseReader for Sociology is an online reader providing access to readings, and audio and video selections to accompany your course materials.

Visit **www.cengagebrain.com** to access your account and purchase materials.

Key Terms

censors 157
censorship 157
claims makers 167
claims-making activities 167
conformists 162
conformity 154
constructionist approach 167
deviance 154
deviant subcultures 174
disciplinary society 159
falsely accused 162
folkways 155
formal sanctions 157
informal sanctions 157
innovation 170
master status of deviant 165
mores 155
negative sanction 157
positive sanction 157
primary deviants 164
prison-industrial complex 158
pure deviants 162
rebellion 171
retreatism 171
ritualism 170
sanctions 157
secondary deviants 165
secret deviants 162
social control 154
structural strain 170
surveillance 159
witch hunt 162
white-collar crimes 175

SOCIAL STRATIFICATION

8

With Emphasis on THE WORLD'S RICHEST AND POOREST

This chapter focuses on the world's richest and poorest people. Among other things the chapter describes how wealth, income, and other valued resources are unequally distributed among the 7 billion people living on the planet. The inequalities are especially dramatic when we compare the lives of those living in the 22 richest and 50 poorest countries. What do you think it would be like to have grown up in the United States—one of the world's richest countries—and, after graduating from college, volunteered to go to Mauritania, which is among the world's poorest countries? That is what Scott McLaren, a student in one of my sociology classes, did. Scott is holding the child wearing the baseball cap.

Scott McLaren

Why Focus On THE WORLD'S RICHEST AND POOREST?

When sociologists study social stratification, they focus on the connection between social location and their life chances. A person's social location is a product of the categories humans have created. Those categories relate to nationality (an American, a Mauritanian, a Mexican), race (black, white, Asian), gender (male, female, transgender), age (under five, over 65), sexual orientation, social class, occupation, education, and other characteristics. A person's social location affects the chances he or she will survive the first year of life, will live beyond age 75, will play soccer or football, become literate, speak more than one language, and so on. One way to directly experience how social location affects life chances is to do what a student from one of my sociology classes did: Scott McLaren, a person who is considered white, male, American, a college graduate, 20-something, and from a solid middle-class community in the Midwest with a median household income of $62,000, joined the Peace Corps and was assigned to the African country Mauritania. He lived in villages where people survived on the equivalent of $1.00 per day.

On September 27, 2008, I received a letter from Scott. He wrote:

> I want to take a few minutes and share with you some thoughts regarding my first few months in Mauritania. Before I begin, I would like to say how appreciative I am of the fate that my last semester held within it the basics of sociology. That discipline has given me yet another set of eyes to view this experience. I have found that culture shock is but a mild symptom of travel and service in the Peace Corps. What is the most painful symptom is what I call self-death awareness—the self, being my understanding of who I am as revealed and shaped through my home culture and interactions with others in my society of origin. This awareness has hit me so very hard this week and I believe that it is at the epicenter of the repeated tidal waves of emotion within me. . . . I am now the barely-able foreigner who has to ask where to pee. I depend completely on others to sustain my needs and it is humiliating. The self-death shock has been debilitating this week and limited me to self-loathing and pity for my situation. . . . Self-death is painful; I am now beginning to deconstruct the person I had worked to be known as. I will be reconstructed into a person, not of my own making or choosing. My new self will be molded to the needs of survival.

Sociologists seek to understand the patterns of inequality that exist in the world. In that sense, they are interested in which countries the richest and poorest people tend to live and why some countries have larger percentages of poor and wealthy than others. Likewise, sociologists are interested in the patterns of inequality that exist within countries. They are obligated to ask the kinds of questions Scott faced head-on each day of his service in the Peace Corps:

- How do we explain the extremes of wealth and poverty in the world?
- Why should a very small percentage of the world's population enjoy an inordinate share of the income, wealth, and other valued resources, whereas so many others struggle to survive?
- Can we assume capitalism and globalization will correct these dramatic inequalities, or should we rethink the way wealth and other valued resources are distributed?

Note that Scott's experiences represent one person's experience in the Peace Corps. Peace Corp volunteers are assigned to many locations around the world, from Albania to Zambia. Scott's experiences do offer lived accounts of ways in which inequality is lived and experienced. It is also important to note that Scott's sensation of "self-death" can be a phase in an adjustment process. Eventually, Scott moved beyond that stage and came to enjoy his two-year assignment.

Online Poll

Because you could not afford it, do you do without something that could help you be successful in college, such as a textbook, computer, a printer, or Internet connection?

○ Yes

○ No

To see how other students responded to these questions, go to **www.cengagebrain.com.**

The Extremes of Poverty and Wealth in the World

It is not easy to define a condition of poverty except to say that it is a situation in which people have great difficulty meeting basic needs for food, shelter, and clothing. Poverty can be thought of in absolute or relative terms. **Absolute poverty** is a situation in which people lack the resources to satisfy the basic needs no person should be without. Absolute poverty is often expressed as a state of being that falls below a certain threshold or a minimum. In this regard, the United Nations has set the absolute poverty threshold in developing countries at the equivalent of US$1.00 per day. The World Bank (2009), on the other hand, believes that threshold should be set at US$1.25 per day. According to the United Nations (UN) threshold, 1.1 billion people live in a state of absolute poverty. Based on the World Bank threshold, that number is 1.4 billion people.

There are other criteria by which to determine the number of people living in absolute poverty. For example, if we use the lack of access to a toilet as a measure of absolute poverty, one-third of the world's people—2.6 billion—do not have a decent place to go to the bathroom. Some use plastic bags and then throw them into ditches and streets; others squat in fields, yards, and streams (Dugger 2006). Scott McLaren described the absolute poverty he observed in Mauritania in this way: Absolute poverty is

- eating the same meal every day;
- living in the same quarters as goats and cows;
- not having access to clean drinking water or enough water to bathe;
- sleeping on a plastic mat between your body and the sand; and
- no longer believing that one's life can be improved.

Relative poverty is measured not by some objective standard, but rather by comparing a person's situation against that of others who are more advantaged in some way. When thinking of poverty in relative terms, one thinks not just about an inability to meet basic needs, but about a *relative* lack of access to goods and services that people living in a particular time and place have come to expect as necessities. Today, in the United States, examples of such goods and services that people have come to "need" might be an automobile, a smart phone, satellite television service, and the Internet.

Extreme wealth, on the other hand, is the most excessive form of wealth, in which a very small proportion of people in the world have money, material possessions, and other assets in such abundance that a small fraction of it (if spent appropriately) could provide adequate food, safe water, sanitation, and basic health care for the 1 billion poorest people on the planet. About how many people in the world are excessively wealthy? The World Institute for Development Economics Research of the United Nations University (2006) released a groundbreaking study

absolute poverty A situation in which people lack the resources to satisfy the basic needs no person should be without.

relative poverty A situation measured not by some objective standard, but rather by comparing against that of others who are more advantaged in some way.

extreme wealth The most excessive form of wealth, in which a very small proportion of people in the world have money, material possessions, and other assets (minus liabilities) in such abundance that a small fraction of it (if spent appropriately) could provide adequate food, safe water, sanitation, and basic health care for the 1 billion poorest people on the planet.

Chris Caldeira

In an information society, owning a basic cell phone with no smart features may put someone at a disadvantage. The person with a basic flip phone may experience a kind of poverty relative to those who can afford smart phones.

Teaching Tip: For the latest list of the world's richest people, go to *Forbes* list of the World's Billionaires which can be accessed using google or some other search engine.

TABLE 8.1 The Distribution of Global Household Wealth

Researchers at the United Nations University have estimated how wealth is distributed among the adult population of the world. Of course, a significant percentage of the adult population have children or will have children who share in their wealth or poverty. We know that the world's poorest peoples have the greatest number of children. The table shows various income categories and the number of adults in each category. To be classified as extremely wealthy, a person must have a minimum wealth (assets minus liabilities) of $1 billion. Worldwide, only about 800 adults are categorized as "extremely wealthy." To be among the richest 1 percent, a person must have between $500,000 and $1 million (excluding the value of their home) in wealth. The richest 1 percent holds 40 percent of the world's wealth. Note that the poorest 50 percent of the world's adult population (1.9 billion people) possess less than 1 percent of the world's wealth.

Category	Estimated Number of Adults in Category	Minimum Wealth (Assets — Liabilities)*	Percent of All Household Wealth Held	Amount of Wealth Held
Extremely wealthy	1,200	$1 billion	Not known	Not known
Ultra rich	85,400	$30 million	Not known	Not known
Richest 0.025%	11.2 million	$1 million	Not known	Not known
Richest 1%	37 million	$500,000	40%	$49.6 trillion
Richest 10%	370 million	$61,000	85%	$105 trillion
Middle 40%	1.4 billion	$2,200	14%	$17 trillion
Poorest 50%	1.9 billion	<$2,200	<1%	$1.2 trillion

* Does not include the value of the house in which the person resides.

Source: Data from United Nations University 2006; *Forbes*. 2011. "The World's Billionaires." http://www.forbes.com/wealth/billionaires

estimating the world's total household wealth and describing how it was distributed. The study found that 1 percent of the world's adult population (or 37 million people) own more than 40 percent of the global household wealth (estimated to be $124 trillion). Contrast that with the poorest 50 percent of the world's adult population, who own less than 1 percent of global wealth (see Table 8.1).

CORE CONCEPT 1 When sociologists study systems of social stratification, they seek to understand how people are ranked on a scale of social worth and how that ranking affects life chances.

Social stratification is the systematic process of ranking people on a scale of social worth such that the ranking affects life chances in unequal ways. Sociologists define **life chances** as the probability that an individual's life will follow a certain path and will turn out a certain way. Life chances apply to virtually every aspect of life—the chances that someone will survive the first year of life after birth, complete high school and go on to college, see a dentist twice a year, work while going to school, travel abroad, be an airline pilot, play T-ball, major in elementary education, own 50 or more pairs of shoes, or live a long life. **Social inequality** describes a situation in which these valued resources and desired outcomes (that is, a college education, long life) are distributed in such a way that people have unequal amounts and/or access to them.

Lance Cpl. Chris Kutlesa

Lady Gaga is among the richest 85,400 people in the world. She earned $62 million between June 2009 and June 2010 (Telegraph 2011.)

social stratification The systematic process of ranking people on a scale of social worth such that the ranking affects life chances in unequal ways.

life chances The probability that an individual's life will follow a certain path and will turn out a certain way.

social inequality A situation in which these valued resources and desired outcomes (that is, a college education, long life) are distributed in such a way that people have unequal amounts and/or access to them.

Every society in the world categorizes and ranks its people. Almost any criterion can be used (and, at one time or another, probably has been used) to categorize people and assign them a status, whether it be based on hair color and texture, eye color, physical attractiveness, weight, height, occupation, sexual preference, age, grade point average, test scores, or many others. People's status in society can be ascribed or achieved.

Ascribed versus Achieved Statuses

Ascribed statuses are social positions assigned on the basis of attributes people possess through no fault of their own—those attributes are acquired at birth (such as skin shade, sex, or hair color), develop over time (such as height, weight, baldness, wrinkles, or reproductive capacity), or are possessed through no effort or fault of their own (such as the country into which one is born and religious affiliation if inherited from family). **Achieved statuses** are attained through some combination of personal choice, effort, and ability. In other words, people must act in some way to acquire an achieved status. Achieved statuses include a person's wealth, income, occupation, and educational attainment.

Ascribed and achieved statuses may seem clearly distinguishable, but that is not the case. One can always think of cases where people take extreme measures to achieve a status typically thought of as ascribed; they undergo a sex change operation, lighten their skin, or hire a plastic surgeon to look a different age. Likewise, one's ascribed statuses affect one's opportunities to achieve wealth, a college education, certain occupations, or high income. We can also raise questions as to what statuses children are able to achieve independent of their parents.

The various achieved and ascribed statuses hold **social prestige**, a level of respect or admiration for a status apart from any person who happens to occupy it. There is social prestige associated with a person's occupation, level of education, income, race, sex, age, and so on. The social prestige accompanying each of these characteristics can complicate the overall experience of prestige. As a case in point, the occupation of professional golfer—in the abstract—is a prestigious one. But that prestige can be complicated by the prestige assigned to race, sex, and age. Social prestige is further complicated by **esteem**, the reputation that someone occupying an ascribed or

Tim Hipps

Tiger Woods achieved the status of professional golfer. There is a level of prestige associated with that status that applies to any professional golfer. Woods's prestige as a golfer, however, is complicated by his other achieved and ascribed statuses. For example, Woods has achieved the statuses of a divorced father of two. His ascribed statuses include being male, classified as black in the U.S. and over 35 years of age. Taken together, the various statuses he holds enhance or detract from the prestige that comes with being a professional golfer. The esteem with which Woods was held, however, declined when his actions off the course led to a highly publicized divorce. As one measure of this decline, his 2010 earnings were $74.2 million, about $48.5 million less than in 2009, and his lowest earnings over the past decade (Myers 2010).

ascribed statuses Social positions assigned on the basis of attributes people possess through no fault of their own—those attributes are acquired at birth (such as skin shade, sex, or hair color), develop over time (such as height, weight, baldness, wrinkles, or reproductive capacity), or are possessed through no effort or fault of their own (such as the country into which one is born and religious affiliation "inherited" from parents).

achieved statuses Attained through some combination of personal choice, effort, and ability.

social prestige A level of respect or admiration for a status apart from any person who happens to occupy it.

esteem The reputation that someone occupying an ascribed or achieved status has earned from people who know and observe the person.

Scott McLaren

Scott McLaren

The top photo shows Scott on the day he graduated from college. The other shows him wearing a bubu. In the United States, there is considerable prestige associated with being a college graduate. In Mauritania, the quality of fabric or, in some cases, the color of a bubu corresponds to the position someone holds in the community and, by extension, signals some level of prestige. The average Mauritanian wears a white or light blue bubu (particularly in Moor culture) but will wear other colors to distinguish themselves during social events where people's position in the community is on display.

achieved status has earned from people who know and observe the person.

In a related vein, sociologists are also interested in the opportunities and constraints associated with ascribed and achieved statuses (white skin versus brown skin, blonde hair versus dark hair, single versus married, professional athlete versus high school teacher). The compensation guidelines for the September 11, 2001, attacks on the United States illustrate. The actual awards ranged from $250,000 (least valued life) to $7.1 million (most valued life). The "least valued" included single, childless adults age 65 and older with an annual income of $10,000. Under the guidelines, their relatives were awarded a one-time payment of $300,000. The "most valued" included married adults age 30 and younger with two children and an annual income of $225,000. Their relatives were awarded a one-time payment of $3,805,087. If the annual income had been $101,000 (rather than $225,000), the award would have been significantly less—$694,588 (Chen 2004; September 11 Victim Compensation Fund 2001).

Life Chances across and within Countries

Broadly speaking, what does it mean for a baby to be born in the United States as opposed to, say, Mauritania? For one thing, the country into which one is born has an incalculable effect on a person's aspirations about what they might accomplish in life. Scott McLaren has observed that Mauritanian boys, especially those who live in rural villages, "talk about herding large flocks of goats or owning lots of cattle. Cattle here are a sign of wealth and privilege. Many also talk about going to Nouakchott (the capital city) to open boutiques or become cab drivers. Very few really even mention going to university." By contrast, many American children no matter their situation in life are taught to believe they can be anything they want, however unrealistic that sentiment. And if they do not accomplish their dreams, it is largely their own fault.

We have no control over which of the world's 243-odd countries we are born in; in that sense, one's nationality is an ascribed status. Still, that country has important effects on life chances. The chances that a baby will survive the first five years of life depend largely on the country where he or she is born. Babies born in Sweden and Japan have some of the best chances of surviving their first five years, as fewer than 3 of every 1,000 babies born there die before reaching the age of 5. Babies born in Angola and Afghanistan have some of the worst chances of surviving that first year of life; some 175.9 babies die within the first five years of life (see Table 8.2).

One startling example of how life chances vary by country relates to consumption patterns. Table 8.3 shows countries with the highest and lowest known consumption on selected items. Note, on the whole, that people in

Technology Tip: For a list of the infant mortality rates by country go the *World Factbook*. It can be found at www.cia.gov/library/publications/the-world-factbook/index.html. Choose the "Country Comparison Link" to obtain these rankings.

TABLE 8.2 Selected Life Chances in the Country with the Lowest and the Highest Infant Mortality Rates

In the African country of Angola, 17.6 percent of babies—175.9 of every 1,000 born—die before reaching age 1. In Sweden, 0.0027 percent—2.7 of every 1,000 babies—die before reaching age 1. In Angola, the average woman has 6 children, compared to the average Swedish woman, who has 1.1 children. Largely because of the high mortality rate among children, the life expectancy is 38.8 years in Angola—some 43 years shorter than the life expectancy in Sweden.

Life Chance	Angola	Sweden
Under-1 mortality rate per 1,000	175.9	2.7
Fertility rate (average number of babies born to woman over lifetime)	6.0	1.1
Life expectancy at birth	38.8	82
Percentage of population living in poverty	40.5	essentially 0

Sources: Data from CIA 2011, UNICEF 2009

TABLE 8.3 Selected Types of Consumption: Countries Believed to Have Highest and Lowest Rates of Per Capita Consumption

Type of Consumption	Highest Known Consumption Per Capita	Lowest Known Consumption Per Capita
Per Capita Calories Consumed per Day	United States-3,754 calories per person	Democratic Republic of the Congo-1,606 calories per person
Per Capita Liters of Bottled Water Consumed per Year	Italy-155 liters per person	South Africa-2.4 liters per person
Personal Motor Vehicles per 1,000 People	United States-765 motor vehicles per 1,000 people	Afghanistan Less than 1 vehicle per 1,000
Oil Consumption Barrel per Day per 1,000 People	Singapore-189.9 barrels per 1,000 people	Chad-31.7 barrels per 1,000 people
Televisions per 10,000 People	United States-7,400 televisions per 10,000	Eritrea-2 televisions per 10,000

Source: Data from Nationmaster.com (Retrieved 2011).
Note: Statistics represent the most recent year data is available.

the United States have the highest access to a high-calorie diet, cars, and television. Those who live in Democratic Republic of the Congo consume the fewest calories on average. People in Afghanistan have almost no access to motor vehicles.

Ranking countries according to specific kinds of life chances and consumption captures only part of the story. That is because life chances vary within countries as well. In the United States, on average, 8 babies per 1,000 live births die before reaching age 5. But the chances of survival vary by racial and ethnic classification (see Table 8.4).

One way of gauging the inequalities that exist within individual countries is to compare the incomes of their richest and poorest residents. From a global perspective, the African country of Sierra Leone, a former British colony, has the greatest inequality between the richest and poorest 20 percent of its population, with the richest segment receiving 58 times more income than the poorest. Azerbaijan, a largely socialist country that was once part of the Soviet Union, has the greatest equality, with the richest 20 percent receiving 2.5 times the income of the poorest 20 percent (World Bank 2011).

Within the United States, the average 2007 after-tax income of the richest 20 percent living in the United States is $198,300, or 11.2 times that of the poorest 20 percent, who average $17,700. That is, for every $1,000 of taxed

caste system Any form of stratification in which people are categorized and ranked by characteristics over which they have no control and that they usually cannot change.

class system A system of social stratification in which people are ranked on the basis of achieved characteristics, such as merit, talent, ability, or past performance.

Discussion Tip: When reviewing the consumption table (Table 8.3), ask students to consider their consumption habits. For example, ask how many televisions are in the household in which they live. Do they have their own car or do they share with someone in their household?

TABLE 8.4 Infant Mortality Rates in U.S. by Race/Ethnicity

In the United States, an average of 6.8 babies per 1,000 live births die before reaching age 1. But the chances of survival vary by race and ethnic classification, with 13.7 babies classified as black and 9.2 babies classified as Native American dying in the first year of life for every 1,000 live births.

Race/Ethnicity	Under Age 1 Infant Mortality (per 1,000 live births)
American Indian/Alaska Native	9.2
Asian/Pacific Islander	4.8
Black/African American	13.7
White	5.6
Hispanic/Latino	5.9
Average, all groups	6.8

Sources: Data from U.S. Central Intelligence Agency 2011; Centers for Disease Control 2010.

income earned by the poorest one-fifth, the top one-fifth earns $11,203. When we compare the after-tax income of the top 1 percent with that of the bottom 20 percent, the inequality is even greater. That 1 percent's after-tax income is $1.3 million, or 73.4 times greater than the bottom 20 percent. To put it another way, for every $1,000 earned by the bottom 1 percent, the top 1 percent earn $74,559 (see Table 8.5).

To this point, we have shown that valued resources are distributed unequally both across countries and within countries. Next we will focus on the processes by which those resources are unevenly distributed.

Caste and Class Systems

Real-world stratification systems fall somewhere on a continuum between two extremes: a **caste system** (or "closed" system)—in which people's ascribed statuses (over which they have no control) figure most prominently in determining their life chances—and a **class system** (or "open" system)—in which merit, talent, ability, or past performance figure most prominently in determining their life chances.

> **CORE CONCEPT 2 Caste and class systems of stratification are opposite, extreme points on a continuum. The two systems differ in the ease of social mobility, the relative importance of achieved and ascribed statuses, and the extent to which those considered unequal are segregated.**

Most sociologists use the term *caste* to refer to any form of stratification in which people are categorized and ranked by ascribed characteristics over which they have no control. Whenever people are ranked and rewarded in this way, they are part of a caste system of stratification. A direct connection exists between caste rank and the opportunities to exercise power, acquire wealth, and secure valued opportunities. People in lower castes are labeled as innately inferior in intelligence, morality, ambition, and many other traits. Conversely, people in higher castes consider themselves to be superior in such traits. Moreover, caste distinctions are treated as if they are absolute; that is, the categories into which people are classified are viewed as unalterable and clear-cut. Finally, heavy restrictions constrain interactions among people in higher and lower castes. For example, marriage between people of different castes is forbidden. An excerpt from Scott McLaren's journal helps to clarify how

TABLE 8.5 Average After-Tax Income in the United States by Income Category, 1979 versus 2007 (in 2007 dollars)

The table compares after-tax income in the United States across six income categories at two points in time—1979 and 2007. Perhaps most striking is that the greatest financial gains within this time period have been made by those in the top fifth, including the top 1 percent. The financial gain made by those in the top 1 percent is 281 percent; for those in the top fifth, it is 95.0 percent.

Income Category	1979 Average After-Tax Income	2007 Average After-Tax Income	Percent Change	Dollar Change
Lowest Fifth	$15,300	$17,700	15.6%	$2,400
Second Fifth	$31,000	$38,000	22.6%	$7,000
Middle Fifth	$44,400	$55,300	25.4%	$11,200
Fourth Fifth	$57,700	$77,700	34.7%	$20,000
Top Fifth	$101,700	$198,300	95.0%	$96,600
Top 1 Percent	$346,600	$1,319,700	281%	$972,400

Source: Data from Congressional Budget Office 2010.

Discussion Tip: In reviewing Table 8.5 ask students to identify which of the six income categories the household in which they live falls. Has that household gained income in the past five years or so in line with the percent change listed in the table?

Lance Cpl. Jonathan G. Wright

Depending on where baby is born and to whom a baby is born, its chances of surviving to the first year of life varies dramatically. Almost 18 percent of babies born in Angola die before reaching age 1. In Sweden .0027 percent die.

caste systems in which gender is central operate in the rural Mauritanian village to which he has been assigned:

> There are very few girls in my village who can go to school. Our nearest school, which just opened this past year, is the first chance all of the kids in my area will have at getting an education. I'm praying that 2% literacy rate rises very soon. The girls are hard to get a handle on. Because of the cultural restrictions on men and women interacting, I can't really get close enough to any of them to really get to know them. The sisters in my family don't really talk much about what they'd like to do; they just talk about what they are doing in their daily chores.

social mobility Movement from one social class to another.

Scott McLaren

In Mauritania, girls who live in rural areas are married off at relatively young ages, in some cases as early as 15. Over the past few decades, girls have begun to choose their partners, but the parents still hold the final say. Theoretically, girls can move away from home if they choose, but their support network becomes very limited, and the challenges of finding ways to support themselves are often very great.

Theoretically, in class systems, "people rise and fall on the strength of their abilities" (Yeutter 1992, p. A13). Although class systems contain inequality, that inequality is not related to ascribed statuses such someone's sex, skin shade, hair texture, and age. In theory, the inequality that does exist results from differences in talent, ability, and past performance. Thus, in class systems, people assume that they can achieve a desired level of education, income, and standard of living through personal effort; that they can raise their class position during their own lifetime; and that their children's class position can differ from (and ideally be higher than) their own.

Social Mobility

Within a class system, movement from one social class to another is termed **social mobility** (see Chart 8.1). When thinking about mobility in the United States, we often think about the possibility that children's economic status will exceed that of their parents. Many Americans believe that they live in a country in which it is possible to move from rags to riches. But how many people born poor become wealthy? Although data to answer this question are hard to come by, one study conducted by economist Paul Hertz (2006) followed 4,004 children into adulthood to calculate the odds of changing or maintaining economic status. The researcher averaged the income of each of the 4,004

CHART 8.1 Types of Social Mobility

Many kinds of social mobility exist in class systems of social stratification. This chart offers a list of the various types along with specific examples.

Type of Social Mobility	Definition	Example
1. Horizontal	A change in social situation that does not involve a change in social status	A waitress moves into a customer service position for an insurance agency
2. Vertical	A change in a person's social situation that involves a gain or loss of social status	See examples for the four types of vertical mobility that follow.
2A. Upward	A change in a person's social situation that involves a gain in social status	A medical student moves up in rank and becomes a physician
2B. Downward	A change in a person's social situation that involves a loss of social status	A wage earner loses a job, goes on unemployment, or otherwise moves down in rank
2C. Intragenerational	A change in social situation that involves a loss or gain of social status over the course of an individual's lifetime	A laid-off factory worker takes a job with a lower salary/a bank teller is promoted to a bank manager
2D. Intergenerational	A change in social situation that involves a loss or gain of social status relative to a previous generation	A son or daughter goes into an occupation that is higher or lower in rank and prestige than a parent's occupation

children's households for the years 1967 through 1971, and compared it to their household income when they became 40-year-old adults (averaged over four years, 1996 through 2000). The study found that the chances of moving from the lowest-income category to the highest or from the highest to the lowest are actually quite low (see Table 8.6).

Hertz also found that children from high-income households (top fifth of household income) receive more education and are healthier as adults, factors that

TABLE 8.6 Chances of Mobility by Income Category of Household in Which People Are Born

The table shows the relationship between a person's household income as a child (parents' quintile) and their household income as an adult (adult children's quintile). The highlighted numbers along the diagonal represent the percentage of adult children who remained in the same income grouping as their parents. To interpret the data in this table, ask the following kinds of questions: What are the chances that someone born in the lowest household income category (lowest fifth) will achieve a household income that is among the top 5 percent? The answer is 1.1 percent. What are the chances that someone born in the top 5 percent will retain that income status into adulthood? The answer is 21.7 percent. What are the chances that a person born in the top 5 percent income category will be among the lowest fifth as an adult? The answer is 2.9 percent.

Childhood Home (4-Year Average Household Income, 1967–1971)	Household Income as an Adult (4-Year Average Household Income, 1997–2001)					
	Lowest Fifth	Second Fifth	Third Fifth	Fourth Fifth	Top Fifth	Top 5 Percent
Lowest Fifth	**41.5**	24	15.5	13.2	5.9	1.1
Second Fifth	22.6	**25.8**	23.1	18.5	10	1.5
Middle Fifth	18.7	25.8	**24.1**	19.6	16.9	1.8
Fourth Fifth	11.1	19	20.7	**25.1**	24	5.6
Top Fifth	6.1	11.1	17.2	23.7	**41.9**	14.2
Top 5 percent	2.9	9	15.5	21.5	51.1	**21.7**

Source: Data from Hertz 2006.

Student Activity: Ask students to review the types of mobility in Chart 8.1 above. Do any apply to someone in their family (including themselves)? Explain.

surely contributed to them maintaining their economic status. In addition, Hertz found that children classified as white have advantages over children classified as black with regard to financial mobility. Specifically, 63 percent of black children who grow up in lowest-income households retain that status as adults, compared to the 32.3 percent of poor whites. Black children from the lowest-income households have a 3.6 percent chance of moving into the highest 20 percent income category as adults, compared to a 14.2 percent for poor white children.

Conceptualizing Inequality

Sociologists draw upon the theoretical traditions of functionalist, conflict, and symbolic interaction to think about inequality—why it exists, who benefits from inequality, and how it is enacted in interaction with others.

Functionalist View of Social Inequality

CORE CONCEPT 3 Functionalists maintain that poverty exists because it contributes to overall order and stability in society and that inequality is the mechanism by which societies attract the most qualified people to the most functionally important occupations.

Sociologists Kingsley Davis and Wilbert Moore (1945) wrote what is now considered the classic functionalist argument about why social inequality exists. The authors argue that social inequality—the unequal distribution of social rewards—is the device by which societies ensure that the best-qualified people fill the most functionally important occupations. So, in the United States, garbage collectors earn an average of $40,000 per year and surgeons earn an average of $227,000 per year (U.S. Bureau of Labor Statistics 2011a). From a functionalist point of view, the $187,000 difference in average salary represents the greater functional importance of a physician relative to a garbage collector.

How do Davis and Moore define functional importance? They offer two indicators:

1. The degree to which the occupation is functionally unique (that is, few other people can perform the same function adequately)
2. The degree to which other occupations depend on the one in question

Davis and Moore argue that, because people need little training and talent to be a garbage collector, the position is not functionally unique and thus does not need to be highly rewarded. However, with regard to the second indicator—the degree to which other occupations depend on garbage collectors—we must acknowledge that virtually every occupation and area of life depends on garbage

From a functionalist point of view, sanitation workers are essential to the smooth operation of society, and yet they need not be rewarded highly because their job requires little training and skill.

collectors to maintain sanitary environments. Regardless, Davis and Moore argue that society still need not offer extra incentives to attract applicants for garbage collector because so many can do this job with little training. On the other hand, society does have to offer extra incentives to attract the most talented people to occupations such as physician that require long and arduous training and a high level of skills. Davis and Moore concede that the stratification system's ability to attract the most talented and qualified people is weakened when:

1. capable people are overlooked or denied access to the needed training;
2. elite groups control the avenues of training (by limiting admissions);
3. parents' influence and wealth (rather than the ability of their offspring) determine the status that their children attain.

Davis and Moore maintain, however, that society eventually adjusts to such shortcomings, as evidenced by the fact that medical schools, once dominated by white males, eventually began admitting people from groups previously denied access. Whenever there are shortages of applicants for occupations considered functionally important (such as teachers, nurses, and doctors), society adjusts by giving opportunities to those previously denied consideration. If such a step is not taken, the society as a whole will suffer and will be unable to meet its needs.

The Functions of Poverty

In another, now-classic essay, "The Functions of Poverty," written from a functionalist perspective, sociologist Herbert Gans (1972) asked, "Why does poverty exist?" He answered that poverty performs at least 15 functions, several of which are described here.

Fill Unskilled and Dangerous Occupations First, the poor have little choice except to take on the unskilled, dangerous, temporary, dead-end, undignified, menial work of society at low pay. In the United States, for example, there are 1.3 million residents in 17,000 certified nursing homes across the United States. Nursing home staff must lift patients, some of whom weigh more than they do, "help them in and out of baths, make beds, and take residents to and from the toilet" (Charney 2010). They have the highest rate of occupational-related injuries, especially to the back. They earn an average salary of $15,000 per year (U.S. Department of Health and Human Resources 2011).

Provide Low-Cost Labor for Many Industries The U.S. and many other economies depend on cheap labor from around the world and within its borders. Obviously, the lower the wage, the lower the associated labor costs to the hospitals, hotels, restaurants, factories, and farms that draw from the pool of laborers forced or "willing" to work at minimum wage or below. According to Pew Hispanic Center (2009) estimates, at least 12 million undocumented adults and children are living in the United States. Of these 12 million, 8.3 million are employed. Twenty-five percent of all farm workers, 17 percent of all construction workers, and 12 percent of all food preparation workers are believed to be undocumented. That is a "whole lot of cheap labor. Without it, fruits and vegetables would rot in the fields. Toddlers in Manhattan would be without nannies. Towels at hotels in states like Florida, Texas, and California would go unlaundered . . . bedpans and lunch trays at nursing homes would go uncollected" (Murphy 2004).

Serve the Affluent Affluent people contract out and pay low wages for many time-consuming activities, such as housecleaning, yard work, and child care. On a global scale, millions of poor women work outside their home countries as maids in middle- and upper-class homes. Consider that an estimated 460,000 Indonesian women from poor villages work as maids in Malaysia and Saudi Arabia. Many of these women must be trained in how to use toasters, vacuum cleaners, microwave ovens, refrigerators, and other appliances (Perlez 2004). Even the U.S. military depends on low-wage workers from the Philippines. Although only 51 Filipino troops served as part of the U.S.-led coalition in the Iraq War, more than 4,000 "serve food, clean toilets and form the backbone of the support staff for American forces. The military would be hard pressed to operate in Iraq without them" (Kirka 2004, p. 1A).

Volunteer for Drug Trial Tests The poor often volunteer for over-the-counter and prescription drug tests. Most new drugs, ranging from AIDS vaccines to allergy medicine, must eventually be tried on healthy human subjects to determine their potential side effects (such as rashes, headaches, vomiting, constipation, or drowsiness) and appropriate dosages. Money motivates people to volunteer as subjects for these clinical trials. Because payment is relatively low, however, the tests attract a disproportionate share of low-income, unemployed, or underemployed people (Morrow 1996).

Sustain Organizations and Employees Serving the Poor Many businesses, governmental agencies, and nonprofit organizations exist to serve poor people or to monitor their behavior, and, of course, the employees of these entities draw salaries for performing such work. The United States allocates about $1.6 billion toward food aid worldwide each year, but that money does not go directly to the poor; instead, it goes to corporations, agencies, and individuals who serve the poor. U.S. law mandates that American farmers must grow all government-donated food and that U.S.-flagged vessels must ship the food. Four agricultural corporations, five shipping companies, and seven food-aid charities receive a disproportionate share of food-aid monies. For example, $341 million of the $1.6 billion food-aid budget went toward paying packing, shipping, and storage costs. Critics argue that food should be grown in the countries where poor live. By one estimate, the United States is feeding 20 million fewer people a year because of costs lost to transportation (Dugger 2005b; Garber 2008).

Purchase Products That Would Otherwise Be Discarded Poor people use goods and services that would otherwise go unused and be discarded. Day-old bread, used cars, and secondhand clothes are purchased by or donated to the poor. In the realm of services, low-income communities purchase the labor of many professionals (such as teachers, doctors, and lawyers) who lack the competency to be hired in more affluent areas. Where do most of the estimated 307 million pieces of electronic equipment discarded each year such as cell phones, computer hard drives, and computer and TV monitors go? The Environmental Protection Agency (EPA) estimates that 50 to 80 percent is exported to countries like Ghana, China, Indonesia, and Pakistan (Frontline 2009). There, in some of the worst recycling facilities, people pick through e-waste, salvaging what they can by hand. Many are donated in the name of "bridging the digital divide" to poor countries. Each month, Nigeria alone receives 400,000 such computers, 75 percent of which are obsolete or nonfunctional and end up in landfills, where toxic materials pollute the surrounding environment, including groundwater (Dugger 2005c).

Gans (1972) outlines the functions of poverty to show how a part of society that everyone agrees is problematic

Teaching Tip: Listen to an NPR interview with Scott Carney, author of the *Red Market*, a book about trafficking in human body parts, including hair and eggs. In the interview Carney points out that "One of the very foundational concepts of the book is when people, say, give an organ ... it's always going to a richer person and, oftentimes, it's going to a person in another country... It's reduced to commerce so quickly." The interview can be found at www.npr.org/2011/06/10/136931615/blood-bones-and-organs-the-gruesome-red-market.

Scott McLaren

These boys live in the African country of Mauritania. Notice the little boy on the left is wearing a John Deere cap. Both are wearing clothes likely given away by Americans to a Goodwill store. The clothes come from what are called "dead toubab" stores (donated white people clothes). Given the racial and ethnic diversity in the United States, it is interesting that the clothes are seen as once belonging to white people.

and should be eliminated remains intact: It contributes to the supposed stability of the overall system. Based on this reasoning, the economic system as we know it would be strained seriously if we completely eliminated poverty; industries, consumers, and occupational groups that benefit from poverty would be forced to adjust.

A Conflict View of Social Inequality

CORE CONCEPT 4 Conflict theorists take issue with the premise that social inequality is the mechanism by which the most important positions in society are filled.

As you might imagine, conflict theorists challenge the fundamental assumption underlying the functionalist theory of stratification—that social inequality is a necessary device societies employ to ensure that the most functionally important occupations attract the best-qualified people. Sociologists Melvin M. Tumin (1953) and Richard L. Simpson (1956) point out that some positions command large salaries and bring other valued rewards even though their contributions to society are questionable. Consider the salaries of athletes. For the 2010–2011 season, the average NBA athlete earned $5.8 million, with the highest-paid athlete, Kobe Bryant, earning $24.8 million (Hooped Up 2010). We might argue that professional athletes deserve such enormous salaries because they generate income for owners, cities, advertisers, and media giants. The functionalist argument becomes less convincing, however, when we consider that U.S. school systems do not offer salaries high enough to attract the most qualified and gifted teachers. Consider that the median salary of a high school teacher is $52,200 (U.S. Bureau of Labor Statistics 2011b).

Tumin and Simpson maintain that the functionalist argument cannot explain why some workers receive a lower salary than other workers for doing the same job, just because they are of a different race, age, sex, or national origin. After all, the workers are performing the same job, so functional importance is not the issue. This question relates to issues of pay equity. For example, why do women working full-time as registered nurses in the United States earn a median weekly wage of $1,039, whereas their male counterparts earn $1,201? In fact, the U.S. Bureau of Labor Statistics (2010) data show only 8 of 300 occupational categories in which median weekly earnings for females exceed those of their male counterparts: counselors ($818 versus $808), occupational therapists ($1,094 versus $1,059), dental hygienists ($898 versus $897), food preparation and serving workers ($388 versus $369), nonfarm animal caregivers ($458 versus $455), bill and account collectors ($634 versus $612), file clerks ($583 versus $577), and stock clerks ($495 versus $482).

In addition to the issue of pay equity is the question of comparable worth: Should not women who work in predominantly female occupations (such as registered nurse, secretary, and day care worker) receive salaries comparable to those earned by men who work in predominantly male occupations that are judged to be of roughly comparable worth (such as those of a housepainter, a carpenter, and an automotive mechanic)? For example, assuming comparable worth, why should full-time workers at a child day care center (performing a traditionally female occupation) receive a median weekly salary of $398, whereas auto mechanics (performing a traditionally male occupation) earn $675 (U.S. Bureau of Labor Statistics 2010)?

Tumin and Simpson also ask how much inequality in salary is necessary to ensure that the best qualified people apply for what are considered the most important occupations. In the United States, the median base salary of the CEO of a large public (top 500) corporation is $9.6 million (Costello 2011). That salary is 190 times the median household income, which is $49,777 (U.S. Bureau of the Census 2009). If we compare CEO compensation with the wages of workers outside the United States, the inequality is even more dramatic.

Consider that the Wal-Mart CEO's total compensation package in fiscal year 2010 was $19 million, down from $28.2 million a year earlier (Reuters 2010). Notwithstanding the CEO's skills, the company's success can be partly attributed to the fact that it stocks its shelves with manufactured goods from the People's Republic of China. If the average Chinese factory worker earns about $3,600 per year, the Wal-Mart CEO earns about 5,277 times more than this

Discussion Tip: Note above that there are only 8 of 300 occupations in which median wage of full-time female employees exceeds that of their male counterparts. For a complete list of occupations and median wages for males and females go the U.S. Bureau of Labor Statistics website, www.bls.gov/cps/cpsaat39.pdf.

worker. In contrast, the average full-time Wal-Mart hourly employee earns $10.11 per hour, or $21,000 per year. The CEO earns about 904 times more than the average clerk (Barboza 2010).

Conflict theorists ask if such high salaries are really necessary to make sure that someone takes the job of CEO over, say, the job of a factory worker. Probably not. Nevertheless, these high salaries are justified as necessary to recruit and retain the most able people to run a corporation in the context of a global economy. In *Wealth and Commonwealth*, William H. Gates Sr. (father of Bill Gates) and Chuck Collins (2003) critique one CEO who justified his "enormous compensation package" by stating, "I created about $37 billion in shareholder value." The CEO made no mention of the role the company's 180,000 employees played in creating shareholder value. Gates and Collins argue that "the problem with this individualistic way of assessing one's own contribution is that it is inaccurate and dishonest" (p. 113).

Finally, Tumin and Simpson argued that in societies characterized by a complex division of labor, it is very difficult to determine the functional importance of any occupation, because the accompanying specialization and interdependence make every position necessary to the smooth operation of society. Thus, to judge that physicians are functionally more important than garbage collectors fails to consider the historical importance of sanitation relative to medicine. Contrary to popular belief, advances in medical technology had little influence on death rates until the turn of the twentieth century—well after improvements in nutrition and sanitation had caused dramatic decreases in deaths due to infectious diseases.

A Symbolic Interactionist View of Social Inequality

CORE CONCEPT 5 Symbolic interactionists emphasize how social inequality is communicated and enacted in everyday encounters.

When symbolic interactionists study social inequality, they seek to understand the experience of social inequality; specifically, they seek to understand how social inequality is communicated and how that inequality shapes social interactions—interactions that involve a self-awareness of one's superior or inferior position relative to others. Social inequality is also conveyed through symbols that have come to be associated with inferior, superior, and equal statuses. In addition, there is a negotiation process by which the involved parties reinforce that inequality in the course of interaction or they ignore, challenge, or change it.

In the tradition of the symbolic interaction, journalist Barbara Ehrenreich (2001) studied inequality in everyday life as it is experienced by those working in jobs that paid $8.00 or less per hour. Ehrenreich, a "white woman with unaccented English" and a professional writer with a PhD in biology, decided to visit a world that many others—as many as 30 percent of the workforce—"inhabit full-time, often for most of their lives" (p. 6). Her aim was just to see if she could "match income to expenses, as the truly poor attempt to do everyday" (p. 6). In the process, Ehrenreich worked as a "waitress, a cleaning person, a nursing home aid, or a retail clerk" (p. 9). The only "lie" she told in presenting herself to others was that she had completed three years of college. Yet no supervisor or coworker ever indicated to Ehrenreich that they found her "special in some enviable way—more intelligent, for example, or clearly better educated than most" (p. 8). Ehrenreich reflected on her lack of specialness in this way: "Low-wage workers are no more homogeneous in personality or ability than people who write for a living, and no less funny or bright. Anyone in the educated classes who thinks otherwise ought to broaden their circle of friends" (p. 8).

Ehrenreich's on-the-job observations show the many ways inequality is enacted. Working as a retail clerk in ladies' wear, one of Ehrenreich's jobs is to put away the returns—"clothes that have been tried on and rejected . . . there are also the many items that have been scattered by customers, dropped on the floor, removed from the hangers and strewn over the racks, or secreted in locations far from their natural homes. Each of these items, too, must be returned to its precise place matched by color, pattern, price, and size" (p. 154).

Ehrenreich tells of a colleague who becomes "frantic about a painfully impacted wisdom tooth and keeps making calls from our houses (we are cleaning) to try and locate a source of free dental care" (p. 80). She tells of a colleague who would like to change jobs but the act of changing jobs mean "a week or possibly more without a paycheck" (p. 136); then there is the colleague making $7.00 per hour at K-Mart thinking about trying for a $9.00-per-hour job at a plastics factory. Ehrenreich also tells of "single mothers who live with their own mothers, or share apartments with a coworker or boyfriend" and of a woman "who owns her own home, but she sleeps on a living room sofa, while her four grown children and three grandchildren fill up the bedrooms" (p. 79).

Explaining Inequalities across Countries

Figure 8.1 in the Global Comparisons box shows the poorest and the richest countries in the world. How did the poorest countries become so poor? To answer this question, sociologists draw upon two views: modernization theory and dependency theory.

Global Comparisons The World's 22 Richest and 50 Poorest Economies

The countries highlighted in orange represent the world's 50 poorest economies. Notice that most are concentrated in Africa. The world's 22 richest countries are highlighted in blue. In the sections that follow, we will try to understand possible reasons for the differences in wealth. There are 846 million people living in the 50 poorest countries. The combined gross domestic product (GDP) of these 50 countries is $429 billion or $507 per person. There are 1.24 billion living in the richest 22 countries. The combined GDP is $39.5 trillion or $31,854 per person.

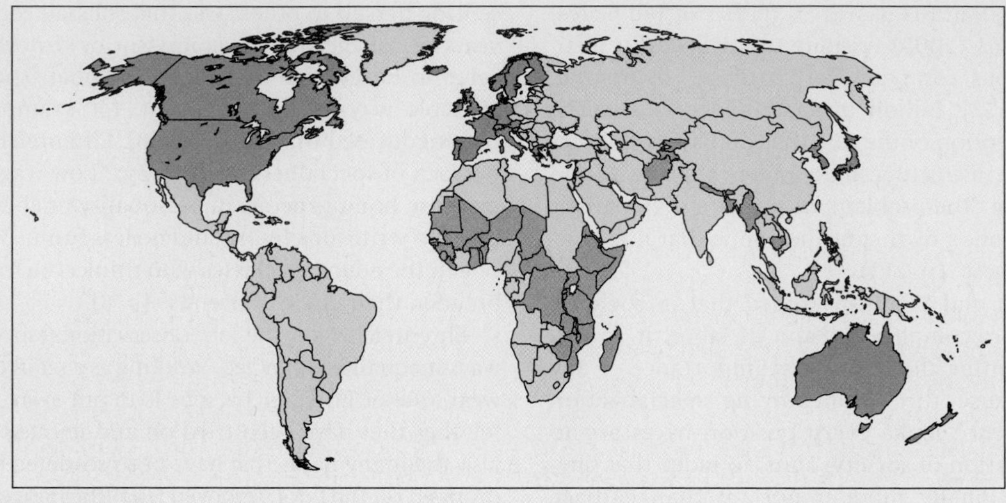

FIGURE 8.1

Source: Data from World Bank

Modernization Theory

CORE CONCEPT 6 Modernization theory holds that poor countries are poor because they have yet to develop into modern economies and that their failure to do so is largely the result of internal factors such as a country's resistance to free-market principles or to the absence of cultural values that drive material success.

Modernization is a process of economic, social, and cultural transformation in which a country "evolves" from preindustrial or underdeveloped status to a modern society in the image of the most developed countries (that is, western European and North American countries). A country is considered modern when it possesses the following eight characteristics (after each characteristic are comments from Scott McLaren about how the country to which he has been assigned—Mauritania—stands):

1. *A high proportion of the population lives in and around cities such that the society is urban-centered.* Scott notes that there has been a steady migration to the cities as infrastructure becomes more available. The number of new villages surrounding cities is growing. With the establishment of Nouakchott as the capital, rural people have migrated there looking to open boutiques or to find work so they can send money home.
2. *The energy to produce food, make goods, and provide services does not come primarily from physical exertion (human and animal muscle) but from inanimate sources of energy such as oil and electricity.* Scott notes that, in Mauritania, few areas have access to heavy machinery; however, much of the farming/gardening is done by hand. Government agencies sometimes provide large rice plantations with machines to help with the harvest.
3. *There is widespread access to goods and services, which are features of productive economies with high standards of living.* Scott observes that the capital city—Nouakchott—has some very wealthy families that can

modernization A process of economic, social, and cultural transformation in which a country "evolves" from preindustrial or underdeveloped status to a modern society in the image of the most developed countries.

afford many of the nuances we in the United States enjoy. The regional capitals have steady access to a broad range of products and services, although the quality or quantity of those services is far lower than those found in Nouakchott.

4. *People have a voice in economic and political affairs.* Scott has found that the people have very little voice. The country is dominated by a small elite, and although ideals of democracy have been planted, democracy does not exist in practice.
5. *Literacy is widespread and there is a scientific, rather than secular, orientation to solving problems.* Scott notes that although some government statistics report relatively high literacy, the reality in rural areas is that literacy is not widespread. There is a continually expanding school system that is striving to eventually include all people, but an infrastructure needs to develop.
6. *A system of mass media and communication is in place that offsets the influence of the family and local cultures.* Scott notes that the Mauritanian government controls the media. Little unapproved news is seen or heard. There is some access to outside news sources via radio, satellite TV, and the Internet.
7. *There are large-scale, impersonally administered organizations such as government, businesses, schools, and hospitals that reduce dependence on family for child care, education, and social security.* Scott believes that some government-funded organizations are set up to help, but their funding is limited and their reach is largely confined to the immediate areas around the capital.
8. *People feel a sense of loyalty to a country (a national identity), not to an extended family and/or tribe* (Naofusa 1999). Scott believes that, in Mauritania, loyalty to family is much stronger than to country. If Scott had to rank people's loyalties, people's sense of loyalty and connection to family is first, followed by a loyalty to culture, then ethnicity, and lastly country.

Modernization theorists seek to identify the conditions that launch underdeveloped countries on the path to modernization and to identify the stages through which those countries must pass to reach modernization. The road to modernization begins with a tradition-oriented way of life (stage 1) dominated by kinship-related obligations and loyalties that modernization theorists claim discourage change and personal mobility. Stage 1 is also characterized by a level of productivity limited by an inaccessibility to modern science, including its applications and frame of mind (Rostow 1960). W. W. Rostow (1960), an economic advisor to President John F. Kennedy and a proponent of modernization theory, described tradition-oriented cultures as possessing a long-run fatalism fueled by the "pervasive assumption that the range of possibilities open to one's grandchildren would be just about what it had been for one's grandparents.

Scott McLaren

This village school in Afghanistan enrolls more than 600 students. It has no modern conveniences, and these girls are allowed to attend on the condition that their father allows it. Modernization theorists would argue that a country will not modernize until the decision is out of the fathers' hands and becomes a government mandate.

According to Rostow's model of modernization, the next stages are the pre-takeoff (stage 2), the takeoff (stage 3), the drive to maturity (stage 4), and the age of high mass consumption (stage 5). Western countries can set the preconditions for takeoff by jump-starting modernization (stage 2) through foreign aid and investments that include technology transfers (for example, fertilizers, pesticides), birth control programs, loans, cultural exchange, and medical interventions (for example, inoculation programs). Ideally, these interventions "shock" the traditional society and hasten its undoing so that the country "takes off." Such interventions set into motion the ideas and sentiments by which a "modern alternative to the traditional society" evolves "out of the old culture" (Rostow 1960). The developing countries can hasten modernization through appropriate government reforms and policies. Eventually—perhaps as many as 60 years later—the developing country will reach a final state of modernization characterized by technological maturity and high mass consumption.

Tech. Sgt. Scott T. Sturkol

The U.S. government sent school buses to Afghanistan. How might this change the Afghan culture? Consider that before the school bus, schoolchildren walked to school with family members. What does it mean for family when children now spend time on a bus with just their peers?

According to Rostow, modernization involves a transformation of cultural beliefs and values away from those that supposedly support fatalism and collective orientation to those that support a work ethic, deferred gratification, future-orientation, ambition, and individualism (important attitudes and traits believed to be essential to the development of a free-market economy or capitalism). As the country modernizes, "the idea spreads, not merely that economic progress is possible, but that economic progress is a necessary condition for some other purpose . . . be it national dignity, private profit, the general welfare, or a better life for the children."

Dependency Theory

CORE CONCEPT 7 Dependency theory holds that, for the most part, poor countries are poor because they are products of a colonial past.

Dependency theorists challenge the basic tenet of modernization theory—that poor countries fail to modernize because they reject free-market principles and because they lack the cultural values that drive entrepreneurship. Rather, dependency theorists argue that poor countries are poor because they have been, and continue to be, exploited by the world's wealthiest governments and by the global and multinational corporations that are based in the wealthy countries. This exploitation began with colonialism.

Colonialism is a form of domination in which a foreign power uses superior military force to impose its political, economic, social, and cultural institutions on an indigenous population so it can control their resources, labor, and markets (Marger 1991). The age of European colonization began in 1492, with the voyage of Christopher Columbus.

By 1800, Europeans had learned of, conquered, and colonized much of North America, South America, Asia, and coastal parts of Africa, setting the tone of international relations for centuries to come (see Figure 8.2 in No Borders, No Boundaries). During this time, European colonists forced local populations to cultivate and harvest crops and to extract minerals and other raw materials for export to the colonists' home countries. When indigenous populations could not meet the colonists' labor needs, the colonists imported slaves from Africa or indentured workers from Asia and Europe. In fact, an estimated 11.7 million enslaved Africans survived their journey to the "New World" between the mid-fifteenth century and 1870 (Chaliand and Rageau 1995, Conrad 1996, Holloway 1996).

The scale of social and economic interdependence changed dramatically with the Industrial Revolution, which gained dramatic momentum in Britain around 1850, and then spread to other European countries and the United States. The Industrial Revolution even drew people from the most remote parts of the world into a process that produced unprecedented quantities of material goods, primarily for the benefit of the colonizing countries. Between 1880 and 1914, pursuit of and demand for raw materials and labor increased dramatically. This period, known as the Age of Imperialism, saw the most rapid colonial expansion in history. During this time, rival European powers (such as Britain, France, Germany, Belgium, Portugal, the Netherlands, and Italy) competed to secure colonies and influence in Asia, the Pacific, and especially Africa (see, again, No Borders, No Boundaries).

Consider as one measure of the extent of colonization that, during the twentieth century, 130 countries and territories gained political independence from their colonial masters. That process of gaining political independence is known as decolonization. **Decolonization** is a process of undoing colonialism such that the colonized country achieves independence from the so-called mother country. Decolonization can be a peaceful process by which the two parties negotiate the terms of independence, or it can be a violent disengagement that involves civil disobedience, insurrection, or armed struggle (war of independence). Once independence is achieved, civil war between rival factions often takes place as each seeks to secure the power relinquished by the colonizer. Some scholars argue that the Americas (which include the United States,

colonialism A form of domination in which a foreign power uses superior military force to impose its political, economic, social, and cultural institutions on an indigenous population so it can control their resources, labor, and markets.

decolonization A process of undoing colonialism such that the colonized country achieves independence from the so-called mother country.

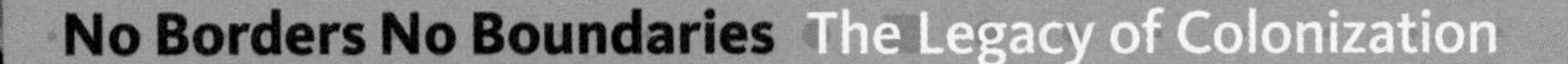

This map of Africa shows the decade in which each country gained independence from its "mother" country. The colonizing country exploited the labor and resources of the colony. After independence, the ties between the two countries do not end, however.

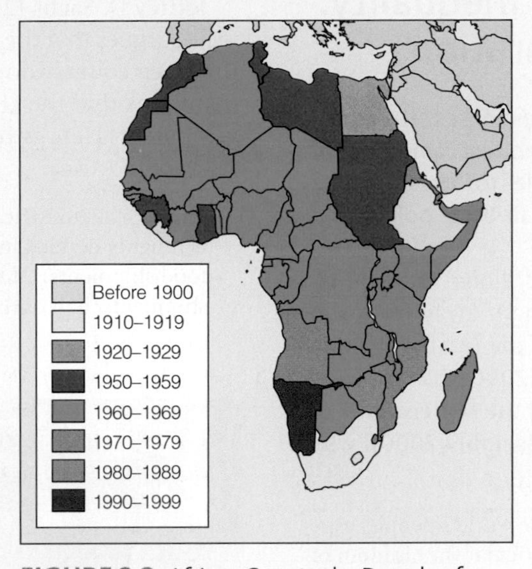

FIGURE 8.2 African Country by Decade of Independence

Source: Data from U.S. Central Intelligence Agency (2011)

Canada, and Central and South America) are technically still colonized lands because the indigenous peoples were not the ones to revolt and declare independence; rather, it was the colonists and/or their descendants who revolted and declared their independence. Those who took power simply continued colonizing and exploiting the land and resources belonging to indigenous peoples (for example, people now known as Native Americans) and others (that is, the enslaved and indentured peoples forced to immigrate) (Cook-Lynn 2008, Mihesuah 2008).

Gaining political independence does not mean, however, that a former colony no longer depends on its colonizing country. In *How Europe Underdeveloped Africa*, Walter Rodney argues that in the end, the African continent—90.4 percent of which was once controlled by colonial powers—has been "consigned to the role of producer of primary products for processing in the West" (Obadina 2000). Examples of primary products include products that are mined (gold) or extracted (oil) from the earth, as well as fish and agricultural products. Mauritania, a former colony of France, gained independence in the 1960s. The country has rich deposits of iron ore that account for 40 percent of that country's total exports, mostly to European Union countries and China. Its coastal waters are considered to be among the richest fishing areas in the world, but overexploitation by foreigners is threatening to deplete a major source of revenue (U.S. Central Intelligence Agency 2011).

This continuing economic dependence on former colonial powers is known as **neocolonialism**. In other words, neocolonialism is a new form of colonialism where more powerful foreign governments and foreign-owned businesses continue to exploit the resources and labor of the postcolonial peoples. Specifically, resources still flow from the former colonized countries to the wealthiest countries that once controlled them. Some critics would argue that the U.S. military presence in and around the continent of Africa is a form of neocolonialism.

In 2007, the U.S. Department of Defense put the continent of Africa under one military command, known as Africom. Prior to this, the command of the African continent was split between the European and Pacific Commands. The Pentagon's decision has faced resistance and criticism because "many African leaders questioned the formation of the command, calling it a U.S. grab for African resources—while others felt the command represented the

neocolonialism A new form of colonialism where more powerful foreign governments and foreign-owned businesses continue to exploit the resources and labor of the post-colonial peoples.

militarization of U.S. foreign policy." The official U.S position is that Africom "allows the U.S. military to help the Africans help themselves, provide security, and to support the far larger U.S. civilian agency programs on the continent" (Garacome 2008, U.S. African Command 2008).

A Response to Global Inequality: The Millennium Declaration

CORE CONCEPT 8 Structural responses to global inequality include transferring modest amounts of wealth from highest-income countries to lowest-income countries through foreign aid and fair-trade policies.

Clearly one obvious way to reduce global inequality is to redistribute wealth by transferring it away from those with the most wealth to those with the least. The United Nations has devised such a plan. In 2000, the 189 United Nations member countries endorsed the Millennium Declaration (United Nations General Assembly 2000), which states:

> As leaders we have a duty . . . to all the world's people, especially the most vulnerable and in particular the children of the world, to whom the future belongs. . . . We will spare no effort to free our fellow men, women, and children from the abject and dehumanizing conditions of extreme poverty, to which more than a billion are currently subjected. . . . We also undertake to address the special needs of the least developed countries including the small island developing states, the landlocked developing countries, and the countries of sub-Saharan Africa.

The Millennium Project set 18 targets and 60 measures of success to be reached by 2015, including these:

- Halve the proportion of people whose income is less than $1 a day.
- Halve the proportion of people who suffer from hunger.
- Reduce by three-quarters the maternal mortality ratio.

Clearly these are ambitious targets. Their success hinges on at least two major commitments from the world's 22 richest countries:

1. Increase current levels of foreign or development aid to 0.7 percent (seven-tenths of 1 percent) of their annual GNP in the Millennium Project.
2. Eliminate the subsidies, tariffs, and quotas that put the lowest income economies' products at a disadvantage in the global marketplace.

Increase Development Aid from Richest Countries

According to the UN the United States is the largest donor of foreign aid in absolute dollars ($26.3 billion). But that amount is deceiving when we consider that the population size of the United States is about 310 million. Per person spending on foreign aid translates into $85 per person. The European Union, by contrast, spends $145 per person. If we consider foreign aid as a percentage of gross national income (GNI), the United States is tied with Japan as the least generous (see Figure 8.3).

Jeffrey D. Sachs (2005), the UN Millennium Project director argues that the biggest myth most Americans hold is that their country donates a large amount of money. Sachs maintains that the United States spends very little on development. Here is how Sachs assesses U.S. financial assistance to Africa:

> The U.S. aid to Africa is $3 billion this year. That $3 billion is roughly divided into three parts: The first is emergency food shipments. Of the billion or so in emergency food shipments, half of that, roughly $500 million, is just for

Cpl. Thomas Childs

US NAVY

A review of U.S. State Department budget suggests that the bulk of the foreign aid assistance goes not toward development but toward other nondevelopment-related programs such as disaster and famine relief and military training apart from overall defense spending.

Teaching Tip: For the compete list of the 18 Millennium Development Project targets the United Nations hopes to reach by 2015 go to the www.unmillenniumproject.org/who/index.htm.

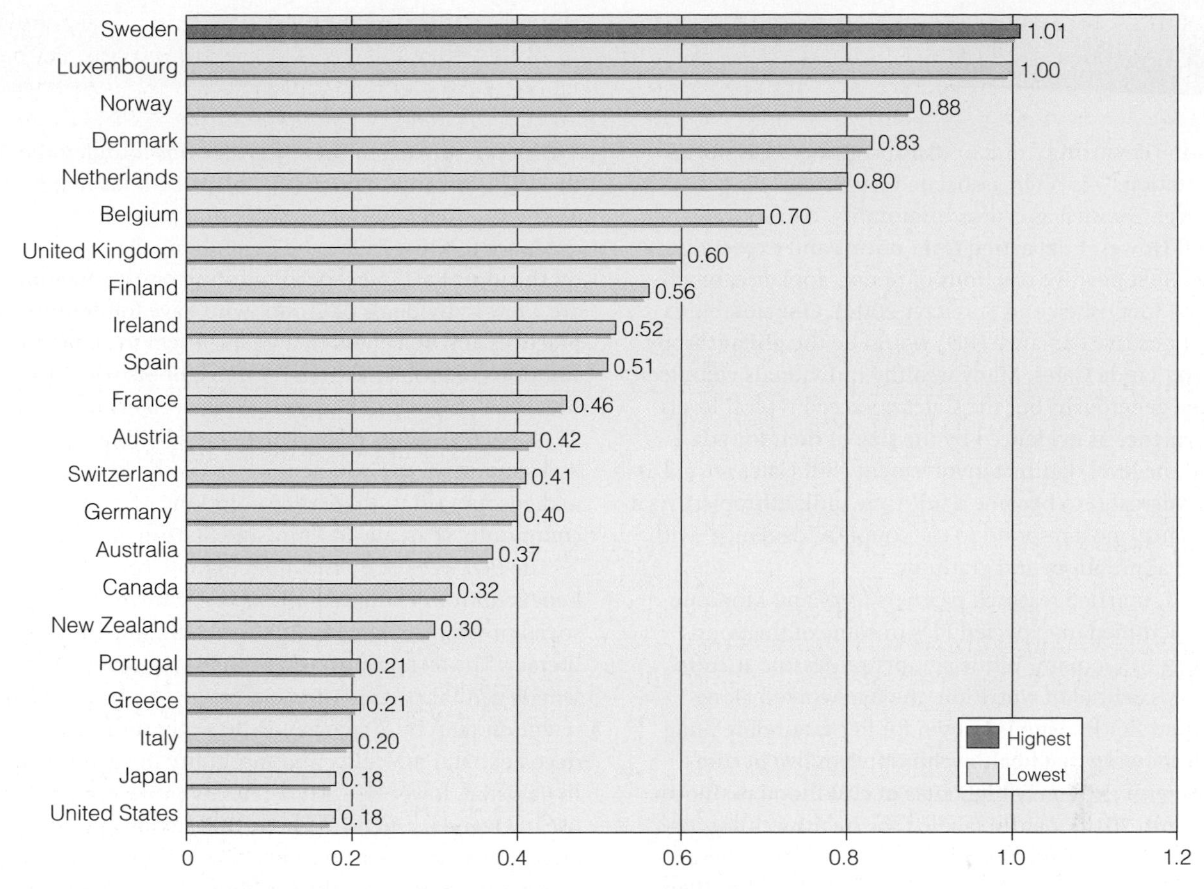

FIGURE 8.3 Foreign Assistance as a Percentage of Gross National Income, 2010
The bar lines show that the United States falls very short of meeting the 0.7 percent UN-recommended donation target. Given that the U.S. GDP is $14.62 trillion; 0.7 percent of that is $102 billion. Currently, the U.S. donates 0.18 percent, which is $26.3 billion, $75.5 billion short of the targeted amount.

Sources: Data from U.S. Department of State (2011), Central Intelligence Agency (2011), United Nations (2010)

transport costs. So the commodities are maybe half a billion dollars. That's not development assistance, that's emergency relief. The second billion is the AIDS program, now standing at about $1 billion. That, on the whole, is a good thing. I would call it a real program. It's providing commodities; it's providing relief. It started late and it's too small, but it's there. The third billion is everything else we do for child survival, maternal survival, family planning, roads, power, water and sanitation, malaria; everything is the third $1 billion. Most of that, approaching 80 percent, is actually for American consultant salaries. There's almost no delivery of commodities, for example. There's essentially zero financing to help a country build a school or build a clinic or dig a well.

Jeffrey Sachs's assessment contrasts starkly with the American public's belief that their government contributes about 20 percent of its $3.82 trillion federal budget (or $764 billion) in foreign aid (U.S. Office of Management and Budget 2011). Could the UN and Jeffrey Sachs be mistaken? According to U.S. Department of State data, they are not. A review of the State Department budget shows that $3.8 billion goes toward development assistance, and $8.5 billion goes toward global health and child survival. Other line items include contributions to military training ($5.4 billion), narcotics control ($2.1 billion), and to crisis intervention programs such as refugee assistance ($2.1 billion) and Pakistan Counterinsurgency Capability Fund ($1.2 billion) (U.S. Department of State 2011). It could also be that Americans count the $800 billion spent each year by the Department of Defense as foreign aid. Supporters of the U.S. level of giving argue that the United States gives assistance in other, less officially recognized forms, including private donations, wage remittances from immigrants working in the United States, and trade investments. Hundreds of creative and successful programs are aimed at reducing poverty (see Working for Change: "Positive Deviants as Change Agents").

Video Tip: Paul Solman of the PBS Online Newshour interviews two experts with opposing views about the effectiveness of foreign aid on reducing poverty. One expert is Jeffrey Sachs, author of *The End of Poverty*; the other author is William Easterly. The video can be found at www.pbs.org/newshour/bb/social_issues/july-dec06/foreignaid_09-21.html.

Working for Change Positive Deviants as Change Agents

Deviance—departing from, or disrupting a group's norms or expectations—is often associated with something that is bad or negative such as crime, immorality, corruption, and mischief. However departing from norms and expectations can also elicit positive reactions of praise, applause, or admiration (Sonenshen and Spreitzer 2004). One notable example of positive deviance (PD) would be the philanthropy of Bill and Linda Gates. Many wealthy individuals volunteer or donate generously, but the Gateses exceed typical levels of benevolence as evidenced by the size of their foundation and the level of direct involvement (Bill Gates retired as CEO of Microsoft to become a full-time philanthropist). As a consequence, most respond to the couple's "deviance" with applause, admiration, and gratitude.

In 1991, married research partners Jerry and Monique Sternin identified unexpected PDs in some of the poorest villages of Vietnam. While adjunct professors at Tufts University's School of Nutrition, the two worked alongside Marian Zeitlin who is known for her groundbreaking research showing that healthy children can live in communities with extremely high rates of childhood malnutrition (Sternin 2010). Zeitlin labeled the healthy children's caregivers positive deviants because, even though these caregivers were from impoverished households, they managed to accomplish something out of the ordinary. Zeitlin maintained that if she could identify the norms these caregivers were breaking, she would have the basis for a new health initiative (Sternin 2010).

After Jerry assumed the position of director of Save the Children, Vietnam, he and Monique moved to Vietnam, a country where 65 percent of children were malnourished, eager to test out Zeitlin's approach in four Hanoi villages. The couple collaborated with villagers to identify a handful of households with healthy-weight children. Eventually, the Zeitlins were able to determine what these families were doing. The mothers were feeding their children tiny shrimps and crabs found in rice paddies. Other families routinely discarded this food source because they assumed young children could not digest them (Sternin 2010). Because rice is Vietnam's primary agricultural crop, everyone in the villages had access to paddies so the challenge was to convince families with malnourished children to adopt the behavior of the positive deviants. Six months later, after several group sessions and a concerted effort to spread the word, many caregivers adopted the practice, resulting in a 74 percent reduction in number of malnourished children age 3 and younger (Positive Deviance Initiative 2011).

Upon returning to Tufts, the Sternins founded the Positive Deviance Initiative (PDI). Today, PDI has matured into an international, online network that provides resources and guidance to those interested in applying the model. PDI rests on the idea that "in every community or organization, there are a few individuals or groups who have found uncommon practices and behaviors that enable them to achieve better solutions to problems than their neighbors who face the same challenges and barriers" (Pascale, Sternin, and Sternin 2010, p. 206). Thus, PDI involves establishing a collaborative and supportive environment in which the PDs are identified and encouraged to share their solutions with others in their community (Pascale, Sternin, and Sternin 2010).

The PDI website boasts more than 41 countries that have benefited from PD-based initiatives to solve an array of social problems related to public health, nutrition, and illiteracy. The technique has been used to prevent 1,000 female genital circumcisions in Egypt, increase student retention rates by 50 percent in 10 Argentinean schools, reduce neonatal mortality and morbidity in Pashtun villages in Pakistan, lower HIV/AIDS rates by promoting condom use in Uganda, and decrease sex trafficking among young girls in East Java. Most recently, a U.S. hospital applied the concept in response to the 90,000 to 100,000 annual deaths in the United States caused by methicillin-resiliant Staphylococcus aureus (MRSA) (Gertner 2008). With support from the Veterans Administration (VA), the PDI model was applied. The end result was the discovery of the *Palmer method*, named for the hospital orderly identified as the positive deviant. Now universally taught in medical facilities across the country, the Palmer method involves taking gowns worn by the hospital staff who handle patients infected with MRSA, rolling them into a tight ball, and stuffing them inside their protective gloves, thereby reducing the chances that contaminated gowns lying around on floors and in baskets will facilitate the spread the infection (Gertner 2008). If PDI has not been employed to address MRSA outbreaks, Mr. Palmer's work habits would likely have been overlooked as simply eccentric. PDI has received international recognition and praise from reputable organizations such as USAID, UNICEF, NGOs, Peace Corp, and even the World Bank. The *New York Times* also recognized PDI in 2008, by highlighting it in its prestigious "Year in Ideas" magazine, an annual publication that pays tribute to the world's greatest social inventions and ideas (Gertner 2008).

Source: Written by Ashley Novogroski, Northern Kentucky University, Class of 2010.

End Subsidies, Tariffs, and Quotas

Even though the wealthiest countries have agreed to eliminate tariffs, subsidies, and quotas on products imported from the poorest countries, the wealthiest have resisted dismantling a system of trade structured to their advantage (Bradshear 2006). In particular, the United States, Japan, the European Union, and other high-income countries continue to subsidize agriculture and other sectors, such as steel so that producers in these countries are paid more than world market value for their products. Considerable attention has been given to agricultural subsidies, which give farmers in wealthy economies an estimated $376 billion in support (United Nations 2010). It is well documented that those subsidized are the large agricultural corporations, not small farmers. For example, Riceland Foods (the top recipient) received $554 million in subsidies between 1995 and 2009 (Environmental Working Group 2011).

In addition, the wealthiest countries apply tariffs and quotas to many imported items, thereby increasing their cost so those imports are higher or equal to the price of the domestic versions. Consider sugar. The European Union protects its sugar industry so that domestic producers earn double, sometimes triple, the world market price. Because of subsidies, 6 million tons of surplus sugar each year is dumped into the world market at artificially low prices. Of course, sugar is not the only protected commodity. The United States, although not a major exporter of sugar, applies tariffs and quotas on imported sugar cane and other sugars grown in Brazil, Vietnam, and elsewhere to protect its domestic sugar producers (Thurow and Winestock 2005). Subsidies, tariffs, and quotas are designed to keep products dumped onto the world market artificially low and prices on protected products artificially high.

Such policies affect not just workers in the poorest countries, but also workers in wealthy countries. For example, Brach and Kraft Foods closed their U.S.-based candy plants and outsourced more than 1,000 jobs to Argentina and Canada, where sugar can be purchased at lower, world-market prices (Kher 2002).

Ending subsidies, tariffs, and quotas may sound like a solution until one looks closely at real cases. For example, the United States imposed a 35 percent tariff on tires from China after a surge in tire imports from that country had the effect of lowing tire production in the United States, from 218.4 million to 160.3 million tires per year. The U.S. government argued that China was subsidizing domestic tire production by undervaluing its currency. Its low labor costs also gave China an unfair competitive advantage (Chan 2010). In this situation, one would hardly blame the United States for imposing tariffs. Despite these complications, as of 2010, 81 percent of the goods imported from the poorest countries by the richest countries now enter duty-free. The UN goal is 97 percent (United Nations 2010).

Progress Toward Reaching Millennium Goals (at Midpoint)

Recall that the UN Millennium goals were set in 2000, with the goal of achieving them by 2015. In 2008—the halfway point—the UN released a report highlighting the areas in which progress has been made and those in which greater efforts must be focused. Some areas of progress include the following:

- The Millennium Project is on track to reduce absolute poverty by half for the world as a whole.
- Deaths from measles have fallen from approximately 750,000 in 2000 to 250,000 in 2006, and an estimated 80 percent of children in developing countries receive measles vaccines.
- The use of ozone-depleting substances has been virtually eliminated.
- The private sector has increased access to some critical and essential drugs.
- Mobile phone technology has increased dramatically throughout the developing world. (UN 2009b, p. 4)

These successes notwithstanding, the UN (and, by extension, the world community) are failing to meet a number of goals that include the following:

- Reduce the proportion of people in sub-Saharan Africa living on less than $1 per day by 50 percent.
- Alleviate childhood undernourishment and its effects.
- Reduce maternal mortality.
- Improve sanitation of 2.5 billion people, or 50 percent of the developing world's population.
- Prevent carbon dioxide emissions from increasing. (United Nations 2009b, p. 4)

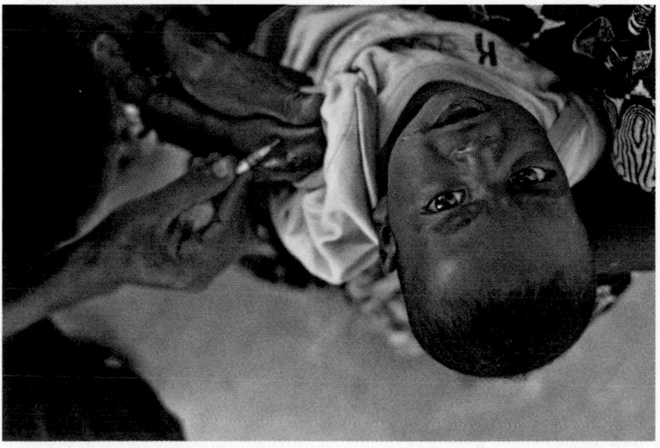

Mass Communication Specialist 2nd Class Jesse B. Awalt

The United Nations appears to be on track to meet its goal of vaccinating children against measles. It is not on track to meet a number of other goals, such as alleviating childhood malnutrition.

Criticism of the Millennium Declaration

Critics of the UN recommendation to increase aid and eliminate trade barriers say that is only a first step. For one, other factors make it difficult for poor economies to compete—one being that employers take advantage of desperate workers "willing" to work for less. As the factory worker's wages in China and elsewhere increased to about $150 per month, Vietnam became an attractive location as the minimum wage in its largest cities was $75 a month. In 2010, Intel moved semiconductor production from its facilities in China, Malaysia, and the Philippines to Ho Chi Minh City, Vietnam (Arnold 2010).

A second reason that increasing development and reducing trade barriers are not sufficient steps for reducing global inequality relates to **brain drain**, the emigration of the most educated and talented people from the poorest to richest countries. Brain drain encompasses those who are or who plan to be hospital managers, nurses, accountants, teachers, engineers, political reformers, and other skilled and educated segments. One estimate of brain drain shows that from 30 percent (Sri Lanka) to 84 percent (Haiti) of college-educated citizens from the poorest countries live abroad in high-income countries (Dugger 2005c).

The rich economies facilitate brain drain with immigration policies that give preference to educated, skilled foreigners. The British Medical Association has grown so concerned about the shortage of health care workers around the world and the migration of such workers from poor to rich countries that it has called for all countries to expand their capacity to train and retain their own physicians and nurses.

Analyzing Social Class

> **CORE CONCEPT 9 Social class is difficult to define. It depends on many factors, including people's relationship to the means of production, their sources of income (such as land, labor, or rent), their marketable abilities, their access to consumer goods and services, their status group, and their membership in political parties.**

Sociologists use the term **class** to designate a person's overall economic and social status in a system of social stratification. They see class as an important factor in determining life chances. We begin with the writings of Karl Marx and Max Weber, who represent the "two most important traditions of class analysis in sociological theory" (Wright 2004, p. 1).

Karl Marx and Social Class

In *The Communist Manifesto*, published in 1848 and written with Friedrich Engels, Marx observed that the rise of factories and mechanization as a means of production created two fundamental classes: those who owned the means of production (the bourgeoisie) and the largely propertyless workers (proletariat) who must sell their labor to the bourgeoisie (Allen and Chung 2000). For Marx, then, the key variable in determining social class is source of income.

In *Das Kapital*, Marx names three classes, each of which is comprised of people whose revenue or income "flow from the same common sources" (p. 1,032). For wage laborers, the source is wages; for capitalists, the source is profit; for landowners, the source is ground rent. In the *Class Struggles in France 1884–1850*, Marx named another class, the **finance aristocracy**, who lived in obvious luxury among masses of starving, low-paid, and unemployed workers. The finance aristocracy includes bankers and stockholders seemingly detached from the world of "work." Here is how Marx described the finance aristocracy's source of income: "it is a source of income created from nothing—without labor and without creating a product or service to sell in exchange for wealth." The finance aristocracy speculates or employs people who know how to speculate for them. "But while speculation has this power of inventiveness, it is at the same time also a gamble

Library of Congress Prints and Photographs Division Washington, D.C.

This 1883 political cartoon captures Karl Marx's vision of social class. It shows four of the wealthiest people who have ever lived—Cyrus Field, Jay Gould, Cornelius Vanderbilt, and Russell Sage. These men were wealthier in real dollars than those considered the world's richest today. The four are seated on bags of money atop a large raft, which is being held afloat by millions of workers.

brain drain The emigration from a country of the most educated and most talented people.

class A person's overall economic and social status in a system of social stratification.

finance aristocracy Bankers and stockholders seemingly detached from the world of "work."

Student Activity: For the complete text of the *Communist Manifesto* go to www.anu.edu.au/polsci/marx/classics/manifesto.html. Ask students to read and pick out one or two sentences that seem to describe today's economic situation.

and a search for the 'easy life'; as such it is the art of getting rich without work." According to Marx, the financial aristocracy appropriates to themselves "public funds or private funds without giving anything equivalent in exchange; it is the cancer of production, the plague of society and of states" (Marx 1856, Bologna 2008, and Proudhon 1847).

Max Weber and Social Class

Karl Marx clearly states that social class is based on people's relationship to the means of production, a relationship that determines the sources of their income. For Max Weber, the basis extends beyond someone's relationship to the means of production. According to Weber (1947), people's class standing depends on their marketable abilities (work experience and qualifications), their access to consumer goods and services, their control over the means of production, and their ability to invest in property and other sources of income. According to Weber, people completely lacking in skills, property, or employment, or who depend on seasonal or sporadic employment, constitute the very bottom of the class system. They form the **negatively privileged property class**.

Individuals at the very top—the **positively privileged property class**—monopolize the purchase of the highest-priced consumer goods, have access to the most socially advantageous kinds of education, control the highest executive positions, own the means of production, and live on income from property and other investments. Weber viewed class as a series of rungs on a social ladder, with the top rung being the positively privileged property class and the bottom rung being the negatively privileged property class. Between the top and the bottom of this social-status ladder is a series of rungs. He argued that a "uniform class situation prevails only among the negatively privileged property class." We cannot speak of a uniform situation regarding the other classes, because people's class standing is complicated by their occupation, education, income, group affiliations, consumption patterns, and so on.

Journalist 2nd Class Alexis R. Brown

Bodybuilders are a status group in that they have developed a lifestyle around maximizing the size and appearance of their muscles. They are held together by a shared way of living, including eating high-protein foods and sleeping at least eight hours of the day to help muscles recuperate and build efficiently after intense training.

Weber states that class ranking is complicated by the status groups and political parties to which people belong. He defines a **status group** as an amorphous group of people held together by virtue of a lifestyle that has come to be "expected of all those who wish to belong to the circle" and by the level of social esteem accorded them (Weber 1948, p. 187). This shared lifestyle can encompass leisure activities, eating, time devoted to sleeping, occupation held, and friendships.

Weber's definition suggests that wealth, income, and occupation are not the only factors that determine an individual's status group. Simply consider that some people possess equivalent amounts of wealth yet hold very different statuses due to their upbringing and education. In addition to status group, people can also belong to **political parties**—organizations "oriented toward the planned acquisition of social power [and] toward influencing social action no matter what its content may be" (Weber 1982, p. 68). Parties are organized to represent status groups and their interests. The means to secure power can include violence, vote canvassing, bribery, donations, the force of speech, and fraud. Examples of political parties include the Tea Party, National Organization for Women (NOW), Promise Keepers, the United Auto Workers (UAW), the National Rifle Association (NRA), and American Association of Retired Persons (AARP).

Income and Wealth as Indicators of Social Class

Although social class is a complex concept, we know that wealth and income are key components. When studying wealth and income, sociologists ask some key questions:

- *What distinguishes one social class from another?* Once sociologists settle on the number of class categories relevant to their analysis, they work to identify objective criteria by which to classify people into those

negatively privileged property class Weber's category for people completely lacking in skills, property, or employment or who depend on seasonal or sporadic employment; they constitute the very bottom of the class system.

positively privileged property class Weber's category for the people at the very top of the class system.

status group Weber's term for an amorphous group of people held together both by virtue of a lifestyle that has come to be expected of "all those who wish to belong to the circle" (Weber 1948, p. 187).

political parties According to Weber, "organizations oriented toward the planned acquisition of social power [and] toward influencing social action no matter what its content may be."

TABLE 8.7 Three Hypothetical Distributions of Wealth

In the Norton and Ariely (2011) study, 5,522 respondents were presented with three hypothetical distributions of wealth and asked to choose under which they would like to live. In hypothetical distribution #1, the richest 20 percent of households have 36 percent of all wealth; the poorest 20 percent have 11 percent. In hypothetical distribution #2, the wealthiest 20 percent of households have 84 percent of all wealth, and the bottom 20 percent have 0.1 percent. In hypothetical distribution #3, the wealth is divided evenly among all five household groups. Very few respondents chose hypothetical distribution #2, and virtually no one chose the third hypothetical. Almost everyone in the study chose distribution #1.

	Hypothetical Distribution #1	Hypothetical Distribution #2	Hypothetical Distribution #3
Richest 20 percent	36%	84%	20%
2nd 20 percent	21%	11%	20%
3rd 20 percent	18%	4%	20%
4th 20 percent	15%	.2%	20%
Poorest 20 percent	11%	.1%	20%

Source: Data from Norton and Ariely 2011.

categories. Should amount of income or accumulated wealth be used to determine one's social class? **Income** refers to the money a person earns usually on an annual basis from salary or wages. **Wealth** refers to the combined value of a person's income and other material assets such as stocks, real estate, and savings minus debt. If using wealth to divide the 113.6 million U.S. households into five classes consisting of 22.7 million households each, the top one-fifth controls 88 percent of the wealth (the equivalent of $43.6 trillion) and the bottom 22.7 million households hold no wealth after debt is paid out (Di 2007, U.S. Bureau of the Census 2009).

- *How much income or wealth qualifies someone to be upper, middle, or lower class?* The Pew Research Center (2008) defines social class in this way: A person is considered middle-income class if he or she lives in a household with an annual income that falls within 75 percent to 150 percent of the median household income. A person with a household income above that range is upper-income class; a person whose household income is below that range is the low-income class (see Figure 8.4). In 2009, the median household income in the United States was $61,082. Seventy-five percent of $61,082 is $45,765; 150 percent of $61,082 is $91,623. So a middle-class household is one with an annual income between $45,765 and $91,623. Of course, this represents just one way to conceptualize social class—in the 2008 presidential elections, then-candidate Barack Obama defined the upper limits of middle-class status as $250,000 with no lower limit specified.

  Pew researchers found that the "greater the income, the higher the estimate of what it takes to be middle class." Those with household incomes between "$100,000 and $150,000 a year believe, on average, that it takes $80,000 to live a middle-class life." Conversely, those with household incomes of "less than $30,000 a year believe that it takes about $50,000 a year to be middle class" (Pew Research Center 2008, p. 15).
- *How do people believe wealth is and should be distributed? How does that compare with reality?* Researchers Michael Norton and Dan Ariely (2011) asked a sample of 5,522 U.S. respondents a series of questions about how wealth is and should be distributed. The respondents shared a social and demographic profile that represented that of the United States. Before answering questions, respondents were given a definition of wealth—"net worth or the total value of everything someone owns minus any debt that he or she owes. A person's net worth includes his or her bank account savings plus the value of other things such as property, stocks, bonds, art collections, etc., minus the value of things like loans or mortgages." Respondents were then shown three hypothetical distributions of wealth and asked to choose under which one they would like to live. Ninety percent of respondents indicated that they did not want to live in a country where the top 20 percent controlled 84 percent of the wealth. Most people chose to live in a country where the top fifth controlled 36 percent of the wealth.

income The money a person earns, usually on an annual basis through salary or wages.

wealth The combined value of a person's income *and* other material assets such as stocks, real estate, and savings minus debt.

The Disadvantaged in the United States

One in eight people, or 14.3 percent of the U.S. population (43.6 million people), is officially classified as living in poverty (see Figure 8.4). To determine who lives in poverty, the U.S. Bureau of the Census sets a dollar-value threshold that varies depending on household size and age (under 65 and 65 and over). If the total household annual income is less than the specified dollar value, then that household is considered as living in poverty. The poverty threshold for a four-person family consisting of one adult and three children is $21,832. The poverty threshold for a single person under age 65 is $11,161. How does the U.S. government determine the various thresholds? The formula was set in 1963, and is based on the estimated daily cost per person of a nutritionally adequate diet; that estimate is then multiplied by 3. The resulting number is the amount of money (threshold) a person needs each day to live outside of poverty. That daily cost is multiplied by 365 to determine the yearly amount. Those living in poverty can be broadly classified into one of three geographic groups: inner city, suburban, or rural poor.

Inner-City Poor

What happens to people when a factory closes? What happens to the jobs in surrounding communities that serviced the people who worked at that factory? Detroit automobile plants, built in 1907, could employ as many as 40,000 people, enough employees to sustain a department store, two schools, and a grocery store on the premises. The Detroit plants began to close in 1957, laying off 130,000 autoworkers by 1967 as car companies restructured their operations, relocating plants to the suburbs and automating production facilities (Sugrue 2007). What happened to those who worked in the stores and schools? Of course, a second wave of restructuring and layoffs began in the 1970s and continues though today, as Detroit automakers steadily moved operations to overseas locations and downsized their operations in the United States. Beginning in 2008, the global economic crisis pushed Ford, General Motors, and Chrysler to restructure even further in response to foreign competition and declining car sales. GM closed 16 of 47 operating plants, laid off 23,000 production and 10,000 white-collar workers, and shut down 50 percent of its 6,200 dealerships (Goldstein 2009). This restructuring and downsizing was on the mind of sociologist William Julius Wilson when he wrote *The Truly Disadvantaged in the United States*.

CORE CONCEPT 10 Economic or occupational restructuring can devastate people, leaving them without jobs and disrupting the networks of occupational contacts crucial to moving affected workers into and up job chains.

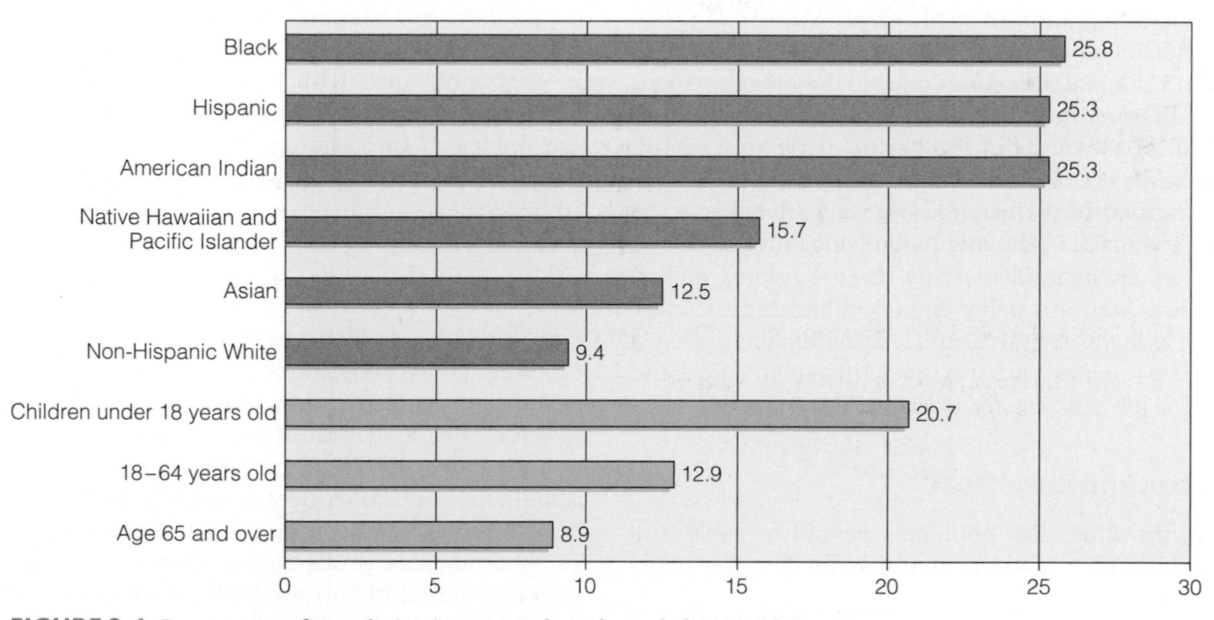

FIGURE 8.4 Percentage of Population in Poverty by Selected Characteristics, 2009
Poverty rates vary according to race, ethnicity, age, and sex. What percentage of non-Hispanic whites live in poverty? What percentage of Native Americans live in poverty? What percentage of children under 18 do?

Source: Data from U.S. Bureau of the Census (2010)

In *The Truly Disadvantaged* and other related studies, sociologist William Julius Wilson (1983, 1987, 1991, 1994) describes how structural changes in the U.S. economy beginning in the 1970s helped create what he termed the "ghetto poor," who are now known as the inner-city poor or **urban underclass**—diverse groups of families and individuals living in the inner city who are "outside the mainstream of the American occupational system and consequently represent the very bottom of the economic hierarchy" (Wilson 1983, p. 80). Those economic transformations include:

- The restructuring of the American economy from a manufacturing base to a service and information base.
- The rise of a labor surplus marked by the entry of women and the large "baby boom" segment of the population into the labor market.
- A massive exodus of jobs from the cities to the suburbs.
- The transfer of manufacturing jobs out of the United States.
- The transfer of customer service and information jobs out of the United States over the past decade (see Sociological Imagination).

Wilson (in collaboration with sociologist Loic J. D. Wacquant) studied Chicago to illustrate this point. (The same point applies to every large city in the United States.) In 1954, Chicago was at the height of its industrial power. Between 1954 and 1982, however, the number of manufacturing establishments within the city limits dropped from more than 10,000 to 5,000, and the number of jobs declined from 616,000 to 277,000. This reduction, along with the out-migration of stably employed working-class and middle-class families, which were fueled by access to new housing opportunities outside the inner city, profoundly affected the daily life of people left behind.

According to Wacquant (1989), the single most significant consequence of these historical economic events was the "disruption of the networks of occupational contacts that are so crucial in moving individuals into and up job chains." Inner-city residents "lack parents, friends, and acquaintances who are stably employed and can therefore function as diverse ties to firms . . . by telling them about a possible opening and assisting them in applying [for] and retaining a job" (Wacquant 1989, pp. 515–516).

Suburban and Rural Poor

Because the inner-city poor are the most visible and most publicized underclass in the United States, many Americans associate poverty with minority groups or urban areas. In fact, the suburban poor outnumber the urban poor by 1.2 million. Many of the suburban poor were pushed out of the city when factories and other businesses closed; they headed to the suburbs in search of jobs and low-cost housing (Jones 2006).

The rural poor in the United States are another population that needs attention. Demographers William P. O'Hare and Kenneth M. Johnson (2004) estimate that approximately 2.6 million rural children can be classified as underclass. In fact, 48 of the 50 counties with the highest child poverty rates are rural. Like their urban counterparts, members of the rural underclass are concentrated in geographic areas with high poverty rates. They, too, have felt the effects of economic restructuring, including the decline of the farming, mining, and timber industries and the transfer of routine manufacturing out of the United States.

Chris Caldeira

When factories shut down, the employees lose their jobs. Those who work for businesses that supported the factory workers lose their jobs as well.

The Indebted

Since the 1970s, credit has helped drive the U.S. and global economy, giving people money to spend that they did not have. Many people acquired unmanageable levels of debt, which created a division in society between the debt-free and the indebted. Simply put, *debt* is money owed to another party. Consumer debt is one way to fuel economic growth because credit puts money in the hands of consumers who purchase goods and services. Some of the most common sources of borrowed money are credit cards, payday loans, and other financing arrangements (two years same as cash, no payments for two years). Typically, these "short-term" credit sources are financed at higher interest rates than are mortgage, car, and student loans. Debt becomes a problem when borrowers cannot make payments

urban underclass The group of families and individuals in inner cities who live "outside the mainstream of the American occupational system and [who] consequently represent the very bottom of the economic hierarchy" (Wilson 1983, p. 80).

Video Tip: For an excellent case study of poverty in America among rural whites produced by PBS check out "Tammy's Story" at www.youtube.com/watch?v=Q8VXrHeLqBA.

The Sociological Imagination The Personal Impact of Economic Restructuring

Between December 2007 and April 2009, there were 5.7 million (net payroll) jobs lost in the United States. My students, many of whom are older adults or 18- to 26-year-olds working more than 20 hours a week, shared the experience of losing their job at this time:

- About a month ago, I found out my job was being eliminated. It was one of the worst days of my life. I had worked for my employer, an investment company, for 14 years. It was my first real job and I worked my way up in the company to a position that I truly loved. I was really in a great place, and even thought I would retire from that company! I was loyal, dedicated, and gave 100 percent each day. So needless to say, I was heartbroken when I found out I was part of the "RIF" (reduction in force). Not to mention the fact that my husband and I are in the process of trying to adopt two children. The timing couldn't have been worse.
- Today, before coming to class, I was called into the office and told I was to be laid off. I work for one of the largest banks in the United States. Already I have experienced a wide range of reactions from pretending to be totally confident about my future to what I can only describe as losing my mind. I even yelled at my husband, saying that I wished he would be more upset and stop telling me everything would be fine. My layoff wasn't totally unexpected, but to be told by my manager that the work I did is "above and beyond" that of other employees but that my services just aren't needed anymore is overwhelming. I have laughed, cried, yelled, and sat in silence. It feels like I am living through my own funeral—people stare or offer condolences.
- My boyfriend works as a driver for a major package delivery corporation that has cut out all domestic deliveries and now only delivers international. The company has dropped from 150 full-time drivers to 11. My boyfriend is number 12, which means he is on call when other drivers are overloaded or when someone is off or on vacation. So far, he has been called in to work every day, but every day he worries about whether he will be needed. He is on call day or night, so the company might call at 6:00 a.m. or 5:00 p.m. His life completely revolves around his job. He is very cautious about spending money. He needs a new car but is afraid to take on the payment. I feel sorry for him, because he's in a terrible situation.
- During the start of the economic crisis, I was working for an acrylic manufacturer when orders really slowed down due to the declines in new home sales. Fortunately, a job opportunity came up with the post office and I took it. Now my work hours have been reduced at the post office due to the decrease in mail volume. Within the past six months, I went from working 50-plus hours per workweek down to about 40 hours. I feel fortunate that I haven't lost full-time status.

or do not have the money to make payments large enough to reduce the overall amount owed. Although debt temporarily frees borrowers from their financial constraints in the short term, it can severely constrain their life chances if it becomes unmanageable. Often, the borrowers least able to afford credit and to pay off credit card debt each month are subjected to the highest interest rates.

The Pew Research Center conducted a nationally representative sample of 2,000 adults to learn the extent of debt problems in the United States. The survey found that one in seven adults (14 percent) have experienced a debt problem at some point in their lives that was so severe they used a debt consolidation service or declared bankruptcy. That percentage varies by income, with 8 percent of those with household incomes $100,000 or greater experiencing a debt problem and 19 percent of adults earning $30,000 or less experiencing such a problem (see Figure 8.5).

Americans who are late making credit card payments pay an estimated $15 billion in penalty fees a year. One in every five credit card holders carries over debt each month and pays interest rates of 20 percent or more (Baker 2009). President Barack Obama (2009) argues that Americans have a responsibility not to use credit cards to live beyond their means, but he also points out that "We're lured in by ads and mailings that hook us with the promise of low rates while keeping the right to raise those rates at any time for any reason—even on old purchases."

Payday loans represent a lending practice that can trap its users in a cycle of debt. Payday loan companies offer credit in the form of cash advances to be repaid when borrowers receive their next paycheck (usually one to two weeks later). Typically, the interest charged is equivalent to an annual percentage rate exceeding 400 percent. Borrowers who fail to repay the loan in full at the designated time can renew the loan for an added fee (plus interest). Although the research on payday loans is limited, existing data suggest that a large fraction of payday loan customers roll over their principal multiple times. Political scientist Robert Mayer (2009) sought to create a profile of the person who uses payday loan services. Mayer thought of an ingenious way to gain insight into this industry, its clients, and lending practices. He realized that when debtors file

Student Activity: Ask students if they have any personal examples to contribute to the Sociological Imagination box above on the personal impact of economic restructuring.

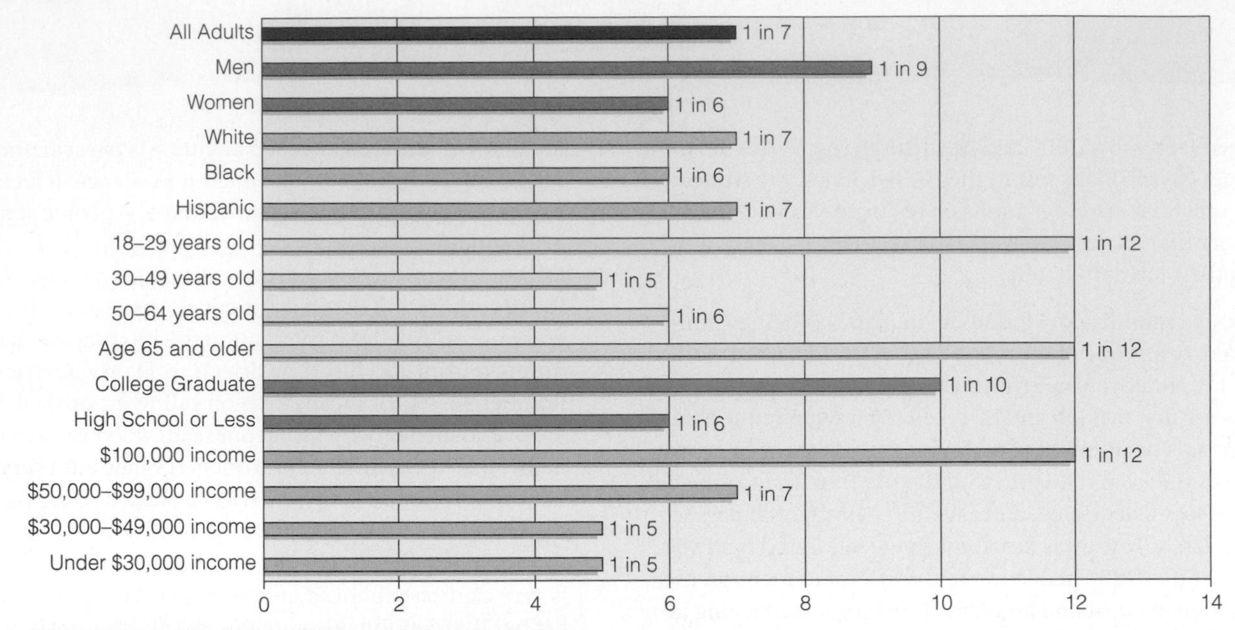

FIGURE 8.5 Chances of Ever Having a Debt Problem
The figure shows the chances of someone having a debt problem by selected population. Here, a debt problem was defined as debt so severe that a person has used a debt consolidation service or has filed for bankruptcy. Which category has the lowest chance of having a debt problem? Which category has the highest chance of having a debt problem?

Source: Data from PEW Research Center (2009)

for bankruptcy, they are required to list the names of creditors from whom they are seeking protection, including the amount of debt and the date the debt was incurred. Mayer examined a sample of 500 bankruptcy petitions filed by residents of one U.S. county—Milwaukee County—in 2004. It is worth noting that there are 66 licensed payday services in that county, the equivalent of one store for every 10,000 adults. Mayer found that 15.2 percent (n = 76) of petitions listed a debt owed to one payday loan company and 10.6 percent listed debts owed to two or more payday loan companies, with some petitions listing as many as nine loans. Overall, about 50 percent of the petitioners owed payday lenders more than the amount of their next paycheck. Mayer then created a profile of those filing for bankruptcy who list payday loans as a source of debt. The annual median income was $26,573, with an average pay day lenders debt of $928. Almost half were single mothers. Fifty three percent resided in a majority black neighborhood.

Online Poll

Look at Table 8.7. Under which hypothetical distribution of wealth would you prefer to live?

- ○ Hypothetical 1
- ○ Hypothetical 2
- ○ Hypothetical 3

To see how other students responded to these questions, go to **www.cengagebrain.com.**

Summary of CORE CONCEPTS

This chapter focuses on the world's richest and poorest people. Among other things, we followed the journey of Scott McLaren who, after graduating from college, joined the Peace Corp and was assigned to Mauritania. We learned how wealth, income, and other valued resources are unequally distributed among the 7 billion people on the planet. We learned that there is a pattern to inequality and we looked at sociological theories that seek to explain the extremes of wealth and poverty in the world and the efforts to correct that inequality.

CORE CONCEPT 1 When sociologists study systems of social stratification, they seek to understand how people are ranked on a scale of social worth and how that ranking affects life chances.

Every society in the world stratifies its people according to ascribed and achieved statuses. The various achieved and ascribed statuses hold social prestige. Sociologists give special attention to stratification systems in which ascribed statuses shape people's life chances and access to achieved statuses. The country into which we are born has important effects on our life chances. For example, the chances that a baby will survive the first year of life depend largely on the country where it is born. There are also variations within countries.

CORE CONCEPT 2 Caste and class systems of stratification are opposite, extreme points on a continuum. The two systems differ in the ease of social mobility, the relative importance of achieved and ascribed statuses, and the extent to which those considered unequal are segregated.

Real-world stratification systems fall somewhere on a continuum between two extremes: a caste system (or "closed" system), in which people are ranked by ascribed statuses (over which they have no control), and a class system (or "open" system), in which people are ranked by merit, talent, ability, or past performance.

CORE CONCEPT 3 Functionalists maintain that poverty exists because it contributes to overall order and stability in society and that inequality is the mechanism by which societies attract the most qualified people to the most functionally important occupations.

Functionalists see the unequal distribution of social rewards as the mechanism by which societies ensure that the best-qualified people fill the most functionally important occupations. In addition, functionalists maintain that poverty performs many functions that contribute to overall social order and stability. As one example, the poor have no choice but to take the unskilled, dangerous, temporary, dead-end, undignified, menial work of society at low pay.

CORE CONCEPT 4 Conflict theorists take issue with the premise that social inequality is the mechanism by which the most important positions in society are filled.

From a conflict point of view, inequality is an ineffective and flawed mechanism for filling the most important positions if only because many occupations that command large salaries and valued rewards contribute little to the good of the overall society. The issues of comparative work and pay equity remind us that some occupational categories command greater rewards for no apparent reason. Finally, there are many cases where the rewards offered exceed the amount likely needed to attract the best qualified people into a valued occupational category such as professional athlete or CEO.

CORE CONCEPT 5 Symbolic interactionists emphasize how social inequality is communicated and enacted in everyday encounters.

Social inequality is conveyed through symbols that have come to be associated with inferior, superior, and equal statuses. Symbolic interactionists focus on the process whereby inequality is enacted in daily life and interactions. In the tradition of the symbolic interactionist, journalist Barbara Ehrenreich worked at many different kinds of low-paying jobs as a way of learning about the work, family, and social lives of those who work in jobs with little status, benefits, and pay ($8.00 or less per hour).

CORE CONCEPT 6 Modernization theory holds that poor countries are poor because they have yet to develop into modern economies and that their failure to do so is largely the result of internal factors such as a country's resistance to free-market principles or to the absence of cultural values that drive material success.

Modernization is a process of economic, social, and cultural transformation in which a country "evolves" from underdeveloped status to a modern society in the image of the most developed countries (that is, western European and North American countries). A country is considered modern when it possesses certain characteristics including widespread literacy, an urban-centered environment, mechanized farming, and a system of mass communication.

CORE CONCEPT 7 Dependency theory holds that, for the most part, poor countries are poor because they are products of a colonial past.

Dependency theorists challenge the basic tenet of modernization theory. They argue that poor countries are poor because they have been, and continue to be, exploited by the world's wealthiest governments and by the global and multinational corporations that are based in the wealthy countries. This exploitation began with colonialism and continues today.

CORE CONCEPT 8 Structural responses to global inequality include transferring modest amounts of wealth from highest-income countries to lowest-income countries through foreign aid and fair-trade policies.

The United Nations' plan to reduce global inequality hinges on the world's 22 richest countries (1) investing 0.7 percent (seven-tenths of 1 percent) of their annual gross national income in foreign aid, and (2) implementing a trading system that eliminates the subsidies, tariffs, and quotas that put the poorest economies at a disadvantage in the global marketplace. To this point, some of the richest countries have exceeded the amount of foreign aid, but most have failed to deliver. Agricultural subsidies are a major problem, but tariffs have been eliminated for most products produced in the world's poorest countries.

CORE CONCEPT 9 Social class is difficult to define. It depends on many factors, including people's relationship to the means of production, their sources of income (such as land, labor, or rent), their marketable abilities, their access to consumer goods and services, their status group, and their membership in political parties.

Marx alerts us that the key variable in determining social class is source of income. For wage laborers, the source is wages; for capitalists, the source is profit; for landowners, the source is ground rent. The finance aristocracy's source of income is created without labor and without creating a product or service. For Weber, the basis for a person's class also depends on marketable abilities (work experience and qualifications), access to consumer goods and services, control over the means of production, and ability to invest in property and other sources of income. Social class spans a range of categories, with the "negatively privileged" property class at the bottom and the "positively privileged" property class at the top. Class ranking is also affected by the status group and political parties to which people belong.

CORE CONCEPT 10 Economic or occupational restructuring can devastate people, leaving them without jobs and disrupting the networks of occupational contacts crucial to moving affected workers into and up job chains.

Major changes in a society's economic or occupational structure—such as factory closings or a decline in farming—can have life-devastating consequences for the affected groups. Such structural changes in the United States help explain the situation of the inner-city, suburban, and rural poor, whose networks of occupational contacts (so crucial to moving them into and up job chains) have collapsed. We can also think of lending practices in structural terms. Since the 1970s, credit has helped drive the U.S. and global economy, giving people money to spend that they did not have. Many people acquired unmanageable levels of debt, which created a division in society between the debt-free and the indebted.

Resources on the Internet

Login to CengageBrain.com to access the resources your instructor requires. For this book, you can access:

Sociology CourseMate

Access an integrated eBook, chapter-specific interactive learning tools, including flash cards, quizzes, videos, and more in your Sociology CourseMate.

Take a pretest for this chapter and receive a personalized study plan based on your results that will identify the topics you need to review and direct you to online resources to help you master those topics. Then take a posttest to help you determine the concepts you have mastered and what you will need to work on.

CourseReader

CourseReader for Sociology is an online reader providing access to readings, and audio and video selections to accompany your course materials.

Visit **www.cengagebrain.com** to access your account and purchase materials.

Key Terms

9 RACE AND ETHNICITY

With Emphasis on BRAZIL

This is a photo of Brazil's soccer team. Study the physical features of the athletes. How many of the players appear to be black? How many appear to be white? You might be surprised to learn that few, if any, of these players would define themselves as black. In this chapter, we consider why this is the case. When sociologists study race, they study the process by which racial and ethnic categories are created and how people are assigned to them. They study how racial categories come to be, the meanings assigned to them, and their effects on life chances, race relations, and identity.

Why Focus On BRAZIL?

Like the United States, Brazil is considered a melting pot of culturally and racially diverse peoples. Brazil's ideas about race, however, are very different from those of the United States. Since 1600, the United States has worked hard to make everyone who has lived in and immigrated to the country fit into one of its official and ever-changing racial categories. Over 400 years, as many as 2,000 distinct groups of indigenous peoples were placed in the single category "Native American." The millions of immigrants from Europe eventually became "white." The peoples from all of Central and South America (except for Brazil) became "Hispanic." Those of African descent became "black." Those from the Far East, Southeast Asia, and the Indian subcontinent were lumped together into the category "Asian." The peoples of Hawaii and other Pacific Islands (such as American Samoa and Guam) were eventually lumped into the category of "Native Hawaiian and Pacific Islander." The guiding, yet erroneous, assumption was that everyone should fit neatly into one category. For most of its history, the United States was a country that discouraged sexual relationships and marriage between whites and nonwhites, but especially between whites and blacks. (Note: That does not mean that such relationships did not exist. In fact, they were quite common, especially during slavery.)

In contrast, the Brazilian government did not present race as categorical. From the beginning, the Portuguese colonizers were officially encouraged to "marry" the conquered indigenous and enslaved African peoples. As a result, the Brazilian idea of race held that Africans, native peoples, and Europeans had mixed to the point that race was no longer important. The interracial mixing, however, was driven by a broader purpose, and that purpose was to whiten its population. To achieve this goal, the Brazilian government officially recruited immigrants from Europe to whiten the gene pool. As a result of 500 years of policies supportive of whitening and racial mixing, most Brazilians do not see themselves as a particular race; rather, they see themselves on a continuum of color with black and white as endpoints (Telles 2004).

In 2000, the United States government, after hundreds of years of sorting people into clear-cut racial categories, now allows people to identify with more than one of 63 racial categories. Likewise, in 2001, after hundreds of years supporting multiracial identities, Brazilian public universities have instituted affirmative action policies that now require applicants to identify with one of two racial categories—white or black ("Negro").

Online Poll

In terms of race, how do you self-identify?

- ○ As one race, white
- ○ As one race, black
- ○ As one race, Native American
- ○ As one race, Asian
- ○ As one race, Hawaiian/Pacific Islander
- ○ As some other single race, please specify: ________
- ○ As being biracial or multiracial, please specify: ________

For the most part, does your self-identity match the race others see you as?

- ○ Yes
- ○ No
- ○ Don't know

To see how other students responded to these questions, go to **www.cengagebrain.com.**

Video Tip: Show the author's video introduction to Chapter 9, which can be found on the Power Lecture CD. The video focuses only on the U.S. system of racial classification.

Race

CORE CONCEPT 1 Sociologists define race as human-created or constructed categories that assume great social importance.

Although on some level we can say that **race** has something to do with skin shade, hair texture, eye shape, and geographical origins of ancestors, it is so much more than that. When sociologists study race, they study its social importance—the meanings assigned to physical traits, the rules for placing people into racial categories, and the effect race has on opportunities in life. We know that race is human created if only because racial categories vary across time and place. This variation suggests that it is people who "determine what the categories will be, fill them up with human beings, and attach consequences to membership" (Cornell and Hartmann 2007, p. 26). And it is people who embrace, resist, and change them.

To grasp the idea that race is human constructed, think about President Barack Obama, who is considered the first black president of the United States. Do you think that odd considering he described his father as a Kenyan immigrant who was "black as pitch" and his Kansas-born mother as "white as milk" (Obama 2004)? For Obama to be considered black, we decide that certain ancestors (those from Africa, specifically Kenya) are much more important than others (the Kansas-born ones). To call him black, we also have to discount that his skin shade is much lighter than that of his biological father and closer to that of his mother. Finally, we have to emphasize the African or black historical experience as more important that the European or white one in shaping Obama as a person.

In Brazil, it is highly unlikely that Barack Obama would be considered a member of a distinct racial group known as black. Brazilians very likely think of Obama as a cộr (color) along a white–black continuum. For administrative purposes, the Brazilian government uses three broad categories (more like segments on a continuum)—branco (white), pardo (brown), and preto (black), with branco and preto considered ends on that continuum. The three categories apply to 99 percent of the country's population. Two other categories that apply to the remaining one percent are amarelo (yellow) and indigena (indigenous). According to Brazilian point of view, Obama would be brown and perhaps white.

race Human-constructed categories that assume great social importance. Those categories are typically based on observable physical traits (for example, skin shade, hair texture, and eye shape) and geographic origin believed to distinguish one race from another.

Sgt. 1st Class JR Williams, 10th Combat Aviation Brigade

In the United States, because of his physical appearance and African ancestry, President Barack Obama is seen as belonging to the race of just his father. In Brazil, it is unlikely that Obama would be considered black; rather, he would likely be considered brown or perhaps white.

The differences in the way people in Brazil and the United States view Obama force us to think about the nature of racial categories. Although it may seem natural to divide people into racial categories, upon close analysis, it is illogical. First, there are no sharp lines to mark the physical boundaries that distinguish one race from another. In fact, it is difficult to specify the exact point at which some hair texture or skin shade marks a person as white and another as black. That is because no clear line separates so-called black from white skin or tightly curled hair from wavy or straight hair. Although the Brazilian system recognizes a continuum of hair textures and skin shades, it does not specify a place on the continuum that marks the point at which the white (branco) segment gives way to the brown (pardo) and brown gives way to the black (preto) segment.

Second, millions of people in the world are products of sexual unions between people of different races. Obviously, the offspring of such unions cannot be one biological race. Even if we devised rules for classifying each child as a single race, the biological reality does not support this conclusion. Third, the diversity of people within any one racial category is so great that knowing someone's race or color tells us little about him or her. For example, in the United States, people expected to identify as Asian include those who have roots in very different places: Cambodia, India, Japan, Korea, Malaysia, Pakistan, Siberia, the Philippines, Thailand, Vietnam, and dozens of other Far Eastern or Southeast Asian countries. Similar diversity exists within populations labeled as "black or African American," "white," or "American Indian and Alaska Native." Likewise the diversity of people within white (branco), brown (pardo), and black (preto) categories is too great to draw any meaningful conclusions about the people within each segment of the continuum.

Discussion Tip: Every 10 years the U.S. conducts a census of its population. The census bureau asks everyone seven questions—two of those questions relate to race and ethnicity. To review the seven questions go to http://2010.census.gov/2010census/pdf/2010_Questionnaire_Info.pdf.

Jason Eric Dustin, Courtesy of Joan Ferrante

These four brothers who live in the United States are offspring of the same biological parents pictured. Yet they do not appear to belong to the same race. In fact, it is difficult to specify the exact point or line at which hair texture or skin shade marks one brother as white and another as black. Likewise, if the brothers lived in Brazil, no line would mark the place where white becomes brown and brown becomes black.

Missy Gish

According to racial formation theory, people do not question basic assumptions that they hold about race. In the United States, most people would likely label one brother white and the other black even though they both come from the same genetic pool. Most Americans do not question the logic of this practice.

Finally, racial categories are problematic because they vary across time and place. We must remember that racial categories are not static; they shift over time. We have seen that the United States and Brazil employ different systems to divide humanity—one uses a continuum of racial categories; the other uses a clear-cut category scheme. Racial categories do not just vary by place, however, they vary over time within the same society. Over the past 200+ years, the United States has used as few as two and as many as 63 racial categories.. In addition, it has changed the labels assigned to racial categories (for instance, from "Negro" to "black"). The Brazilian Census has counted and used four racial categories since 1950: white (branco), brown (pardo), black (preto), and amarelo (yellow). In 1991, it added the category indigena (indigenous) (Telles 2004, Bailey 2008).

Racial Formation Theory

Sociologists are interested in how something that makes no logical sense has come to assume such great importance. Sociologists Michael Omi and Howard Winant (1986) offer racial formation theory as a way to understand the significance of race. The two theorists argue that anyone who lives in the United States (or elsewhere for that matter) must learn to "see" its racial categories—that is, they must learn to see arbitrary physical traits, such as skin color and hair texture, as meaningful and significant (see The Sociological Imagination). Moreover, they must develop what the two sociologists call **racial common sense,** shared ideas about each race believed to be so obvious or natural they need not be questioned. For most people in the United States, it is "common sense" that people can be placed in a racial category even in the face of clear evidence that they are not (for example, Barack Obama). In the United States, people must learn to "see" people with any discernable physical traits suggestive of African descent as black.

In contrast, there is a different kind of common sense in Brazil. In that country, it is common sense to see race not in terms of clear-cut categories, but as a continuum. It is also common sense to see people who have any discernable physical traits suggestive of European descent as evidence that that person is not black (Telles 2004).

Racial common sense extends beyond "seeing" racial categories as natural ways to divide humanity. It also involves unquestioned assumptions held about those associated with a specific racial category. Most people are reluctant to discuss commonsense thinking about race for fear that it will open a minefield of misunderstanding (Norris 2002). Through her comedy, Margaret Cho (2002) offers insights about racial common sense as it relates to those classified as Asian American. Specifically, for many in the United States, it is common sense to believe that people classified as Asian were born elsewhere. As Cho puts it, "when people say 'where are you from?' it's a really loaded question because when I answer 'Oh, I'm from

racial common sense Shared ideas believed to be so obvious or natural about racial groups that they need not be questioned.

The Sociological Imagination Learning to See Race

It is important to keep in mind that racial identity is something that is learned; it is not automatic that one is aware of or knows his or her race. In fact, a friend once told me that, when her daughter was about 6 years old, she was obsessed for a time about remembering her race. She would come home and say, "Mom, Mom, I can't remember, am I African American or Native American?"

The following statements come from interviews my students conducted with someone who appeared a different race than them. It is worth noting that white students selected primarily blacks to interview, whereas black students selected other nonwhites. I did not have a situation where nonwhite students chose to interview whites. What do you make of that pattern?

- I asked R. from India if she could tell me the story of when she first realized what her race was. She explained, "I came to USA at age 12. They gave me options to choose, and to me Indian was like American Indian. So I asked my uncle who told me to go with Asian. I remembered this and stuck with it. There were many options and at the advice of my family, I go by Asian."
- G. who appears "black" remembers that, although he was surrounded by whites, he never really saw himself as a different race. He thought of himself as just one of the kids playing on the playgrounds. He became more aware of his race in early elementary school. He remembered his father getting defensive when he told him about class modules on race relations.
- It must have been at a family event when T. was three or four years of age. He remembers a family reunion at a park. Everyone was enjoying themselves and each other's company. At the other part, he noticed a white family doing the same. He said he wondered why there weren't any white people with his family or in his family.
- When J. was young he remembers meeting his grandmother who lived in Alabama. He was confused when he first met her because she had very dark hair but she was also white. Both of J's parents appear black, so he was confused as to why his grandmother was white. He never really discussed the concept of race with his grandmother, although he did ask her what race she was because he was so confused.
- As a young child, K. did not pay attention to race. The idea of race presented itself to him in his teenage years. He recalled dating girls who appeared white. In particular, he remembers a girl who was a dancer for the school. She told him that she was not allowed to date black guys and if he had been white, it would be completely different.

San Francisco,' they always come back with 'No, uhm, I mean where are you really from?'"

Omi and Winant (2002) maintain that racial common sense understanding of race persists even when we meet people who defy expectations and assumptions. When that happens, we simply assume that they are exceptions to the rule. So an Asian born in the United States is an exception to the rule, thereby proving the rule exists.

Sociologist Charles A. Gallagher (2009) puts it this way: "race exists because we say it exists" (p. 2). Once racial labels and categories are put in place, it became easy to reify them. **Reify** means to treat them as if they are real and meaningful and to forget that they are made up. When we reify categories, we act as if people *are* those categories. When people do things or appear in ways that don't fit their assigned racial category, we act as if something is wrong with them or that they are the exceptions to the rule rather than questioning the category scheme.

reify Treating labels and categories as if they are real and meaningful and to forget that they are made up.

Racial Categories in the United States and Brazil

CORE CONCEPT 2 Most societies, if not all, have created racial categories and rules for placing people into those categories. Keep in mind that, when subjected to scrutiny, category schemes rarely, if ever, make sense.

Category schemes involve dividing people into racial categories that are implicitly or explicitly ranked on a scale of social worth.

U.S. Racial Categories

Today, the U.S. government recognizes five official racial categories (OMB 2011) plus a sixth category, "other race"—the category of last resort for those who resist identifying, or cannot identify, with one of the five official categories:

- American Indian or Alaskan Native—a person having origins in any of the original peoples of North, Central, or South America and who maintains tribal affiliation or community attachment

Discussion: Review the Sociological Imagination box above. Ask students if they have a story about how they learned what others considered their race to be.

- Asian—a person having origins in any of the original peoples of the Far East, Southeast Asia, or the Indian subcontinent
- Black or African American—a person having origins in any of the black racial groups of Africa
- Native Hawaiian or Other Pacific Islander—a person having origins in any of the original peoples of Hawaii, Guam, Samoa, or other Pacific Islands
- White—a person having origins in any of the original peoples of Europe, the Middle East, or North Africa

In critiquing this category scheme, notice that "Black or African American" is the only racial category that does not refer to original peoples. In fact, the words *original peoples* are replaced with *black racial groups of Africa*. If the words *original peoples* were included in the definition of black or African American, every person in the United States would have to claim this racial category. We know from archaeological evidence that all humans evolved from a common African ancestor.

As a further critique, ask if there is any group for which there appears to be no category. For example, where might people known as Hispanic/Latino and Arab fit? As we will learn, the U.S. government does not consider Hispanic to be a race; it considers it an ethnic group and maintains that Hispanics can be of any race. As for those of Arab ancestry, the U.S. government labels them white (see "Why Are People of Arab Ancestry Considered White?").

Until the 2000 census, the U.S. system of racial classification required that an individual identify with only one racial category. Although Americans have always acknowledged racial mixture unofficially by using (often derogatory) words like *mixed, mulatto, half-breed, mongrel,* and *biracial,* the government still insisted that everyone, including those with more than one racial background, identify with just one category. This practice changed with the 2000 census, when for the first time in its history, the United States allowed people to identify with two or more of its six official racial categories. This change represents a monumental shift in thinking about race. Still, when given a chance to identify with more than one race, very few people in the United States do so (see Table 9.1).

Because the U.S. government now allows people to identify with one or more race, there are six one-race categories and 57 permutations of those six. In other words, there are 15 two-race categories (for example, "Black-Asian"), 24 three-race categories (for example, "White-Black-Asian"), 10 four-race categories (for example, "White-Black-Native Indian/Alaska Native-Asian"), 7 five-race categories, and 1 six-race category. It is important to point out that, although the U.S. government has yet to decide what to call people who identify with more than one race, one thing is clear: the government has stated that it will not classify them as multiracial to date and it has never employed such a term in describing its population (OMB 2011).

TABLE 9.1 Number and Percentage of People in the United States By Race, 2009

What percentage of the U.S. population identifies as one race? What percentage identifies as two or more races? Are you surprised at how few identify with more than one race?

One race	299,501,383	97.60%
White	229,773,131	74.80%
Black	38,093,725	12.40%
American Indian and Alaska Native	2,457,552	0.80%
Asian	13,774,611	4.50%
Native Hawaiian and other Pacific Islander	454,001	0.10%
Some other race	14,948,363	4.90%
Two or more races	7,505,173	2.40%
White and Black	1,824,890	0.60%
White and American Indian/Alaska Native	1,776,923	0.60%
White and Asian	1,308,745	0.40%
Black and American Indian/Alaska Native	284,322	0.10%
Some other combination	852,996	0.30%

Source: Data from U.S. Bureau of the Census 2009.

Teaching Tip: Point out that there are two racial categories that contain less than 1% of the total population. The some "other race" category includes people who identify ethnically as Hispanic. Like Brazilians (who were once part of a Portuguese colony), Hispanics do not see race as categorical and thus have a difficult time identifying with one race only.

Why Are People of Arab Ancestry Considered White?

We have noted that the United States defines people of Arab ancestry as white. Yet, in light of the September 11, 2001, attacks on the United States, one must question whether people of Arab ancestries are really viewed and treated as white. The U.S. Bureau of the Census explored the idea of creating a separate racial or ethnic category for this group because it recognized that many people of Arab descent do not think of themselves as "white," nor are they treated as such. In the end, the bureau decided *against* creating a special racial or ethnic category. But it did issue a special report on this population. In fact, the bureau made history on December 3, 2003, when it released a report on the Americans of Arab *ancestry*. This report was historic because it was the first time the agency published a brief on a subpopulation not officially designated as a racial minority (Arab Institute 2003).

In the brief, the bureau defined *Arab* as anyone reporting their ancestry on the 2000 census to be Algerian, Alhuceman, Arab, Bahraini, Bedouin, Berber, Egyptian, United Arab Emirates, Iraqi, Jordanian, Kuwaiti, Kurdish, Lebanese, Libyan, Middle Eastern, Moroccan, North African, Omani, Qatari, Palestinian, Rio de Oro, Saudi Arabian, Syrian, Tunisian, or Yemeni. The census bureau pointed out that this definition of Arab includes some peoples, such as Kurds and Berbers, who do *not* necessarily identify themselves as Arab, while excluding other peoples who do identify themselves as Arab such as Mauritanians, Somalis, and Sudanese (U.S. Bureau of the Census 2003).

Here we might pause and ask: Why does the U.S. government classify people of Middle Eastern and Arab ancestry as white? Although this question has no clear answer, some critics argue that the Middle East holds important symbolic value that whites (or at least whites who had the power to make their classification) hope to associate with their racial group. For example, the Middle East is the birthplace of Christianity and the site of many important biblical cities (such as Jerusalem, in Israel and the Palestinian territories, and Babylon, in Iraq). The Middle East boasts the Egyptian pyramids, considered to be among the wonders of the world. Finally, the Middle East has renowned geographic landmarks associated with the cradle of civilization, including ancient Mesopotamia (the land between the Tigris and Euphrates Rivers, in what is now Iraq).

Some highlights from this report follow:

- Approximately 1.2 million people reported being of Arab ancestry.

Joe Seer/Shutterstock.com

According to the census bureau's definition of Arab, a number of celebrities in the United States would be classified as such, including Steve Jobs (cofounder, Apple, Inc., who has a Syrian father) and Marlo Thomas (actress, whose father is of Lebanese ancestry). Pictured here is Paula Abdul, former *American Idol* judge whose father is of Syrian ancestry.

- About half of the Arab population was concentrated in five states: California, Florida, Michigan, New Jersey, and New York.
- Arabs represented 30 percent of the population in Dearborn, Michigan.
- People claiming Lebanese, Syrian, and Egyptian ancestries account for about three-fifths of the Arab American population.
- An estimated 75 percent of Arab Americans are Christian. Many immigrants from Middle Eastern and Arab countries belonged to religious minorities in their home countries (Hertz 2003).

Technology Tip: For an interesting interview with a Arab-American/Muslim American comedian who is working to overcome discrimination and stereotyping through humor, go to www.npr.org and enter the title "Muslim Comedian Aims at Breaking Stereotypes" into the search engine.

To which racial categories would you assign these two people? The man on the left is considered Laotian, so under the U.S. system he would be classified as Asian. The girl on the right is considered Korean and black so she could be assigned to Asian and black categories. Before 2000, what race would she be? How do you think each would be classified under the Brazilian system?

Brazilian Racial Categories

To understand how Brazilians see race, we must consider three category schemes: the official categories used by the Brazilian Census Bureau (the IBGE), used in popular language, and promoted by the black consciousness movement (Telles 2004) and Bailey (2009).

The IBGE employs five categories: white (branco), brown (pardo), black (preto), yellow (amarelo), and indigenous (indîgena). Only about one percent of the Brazilian population is considered Asian (yellow) or indigenous. The remaining 99 percent are considered white, brown, or black (see Table 9.2). It is important to recall that Brazilians present race as segments on a continuum.

TABLE 9.2 Population of Brazil by Color or Race, 2009

What percentage of Brazilian population identifies as brown? What percentage as black? as white? Where might browns fit under the U.S. system of racial classification?

Color or Race	Number	Percentage
Total	193,733,795	100.00
White	92,992,221	48.43
Black	13,251,391	6.84
Brown	84,855,402	43.8
Yellow	1,123,656	0.58
Indian	542,454	0.28
No declaration	135,613	0.07

Source: Data from Instituto Brasileiro de Geografia e Estatística 2010.

A second system of racial classification relates to the popular language used to refer to race or color. Telles (2004) found that when presented with an open-ended question asking people their race, Brazilian answered with 135 distinct terms, 45 of which were used only once or twice. Ninety-seven percent of respondents used one of six popular terms to describe their color: branco/white (42 percent), moreno/no clear race (32 percent), pardo/brown (7 percent), moreno claro/light of no clear race (6 percent), preto/black (5 percent), Negro (3 percent), and claro/light (3 percent). Telles was intrigued by the fact that more than one-third (38 percent) used the term *moreno* or *moreno claro*. *Moreno*, a term not used by the Brazilian census, means a "colored person" of ambiguous or no clear race. *Moreno claro* means a person of light color.

The third system of racial classification is a two-category scheme employed by those in Brazil's black consciousness movement—someone is either negro or blanco. That movement seeks to dismantle ideas of race as a continuum, to destigmatize "blackness," and to challenge the unspoken assumption that brown is superior to black. Black consciousness movement activists argue that ambiguous racial identities have discouraged browns and blacks from mobilizing to fight well-documented discrimination and prejudices. Thus, the movement encourages all people who see themselves as moreno and pardo to identify as Negro.

Ethnicity

CORE CONCEPT 3 Like race, when sociologists study ethnicity, they are interested in studying the processes by which people make ethnicity important (or not).

An **ethnic group** consists of people within a larger society (such as country) who possess a group consciousnesses because they share or believe they share a common ancestry, a place of birth, a history, a key experience or some other distinctive social traits they have defined as the "essence of their peoplehood" (Schermerhorn 1978, p. 12; Cornell and Hartman 2007). The thing shared may be a religion, a style of dress, a language, a shared experience of persecution—anything that sets them apart from other ethnic groups or the society at large. Distinguishing between race and ethnicity is complicated because racial and ethnic identities are intertwined. In the United States, for example, people who consider themselves Korean or Chinese are assigned to the racial category "Asian."

It is also difficult to specify the unique markers that place people into a particular ethnic group. For example, does having a Chinese first name and last name make someone an ethnic Chinese? Or is it the ability to speak Mandarin or Cantonese that does? What if the person is bilingual? Does that make him or her less ethnic Chinese? Because markers of ethnicity are imprecise, one way to determine someone's ethnicity is to simply ask, "What is your ethnicity?" Self-identification, however, is also problematic because people's sense of ethnicity can range in intensity from nonexistent to all-encompassing (Verkuyten 2005).

In claiming ethnicity, people may point to ancestors they have never met (for example, "My great-grandfather was from Portugal.") or to a distinct community from their past (for example, "Growing up, I lived in Puerto Rico."). For some, ethnicity is based on a sentimental connection that may manifest itself in rooting for a particular soccer team (that is, the Brazilian soccer team). For others, ethnicity is a complete lifestyle that involves being born in a particular place, speaking the language, dressing a particular way, and interacting primarily with others in that ethnic group.

Ethnic identity is also affected by **selective forgetting**, a process by which people don't know about, forget, dismiss, or fail to pass on a connection to one or more ethnicities. Forgetting an ethnicity is affected by larger societal forces. For example, in the United States, some races have more freedom than others in claiming an ethnic identity. People in the United States classified as white have a great deal of freedom to claim a European ethnic identity. But it is unusual for those who appear white to claim a non-European ethnicity, such as Kikuyu, one of Kenya's many ethnic groups. People in the United States classified black have even less choice; they are expected to identify as simply "black" or as of African descent, even when they know their specific African and non-African ancestors (Waters 1994). In fact, most Americans almost never think of nonwhites as having a European ethnicity. For example, most Americans would likely dismiss as irrelevant the connections President Barack Obama has to his Swiss, German, or Irish ancestors (Dacey 2010).

People's sense of ethnicity can shift through a process known as **ethnic renewal**. This occurs when someone discovers an ethnic identity, as when an adopted child learns about and identifies with newly found biological relatives or a person learns about and revives lost traditions. Ethnic renewal includes the process by which people take it upon themselves to find, learn about, and claim an ethnic heritage (see The Sociological Imagination: "Selective Forgetting").

ethnic group People within a larger society (such as a country) who possess a group consciousnesses because they share or believe they share a common ancestry, a place of birth, a history, a key experience, or some other distinctive social traits they have defined as the "essence of their peoplehood" (Schermerhorn 1978, p. 12; Cornell and Hartman 2007).

selective forgetting A process by which people forget, dismiss, or fail to pass on a connection to one or more ethnicities.

ethnic renewal This occurs when someone discovers an ethnic identity, as when an adopted child learns about and identifies with newly found biological relatives or a person learns about and revives lost traditions.

involuntary ethnicity When a government or other dominant group creates an umbrella ethnic category and assigns people from many different cultures and countries to it.

ethnicity People who share, believe they share, or are believed by others to share a national origin; a common ancestry; a place of birth; distinctive concrete social traits (such as religious practices, style of dress, body adornments, or language); or socially important physical characteristics (such as skin color, hair texture, or body structure).

EVARISTO SA/AFP/Getty Images

The Macuxi are one of the estimated 230 indigenous ethnic groups in Brazil. The group lives in northeastern Brazil. Their ancestral land was confiscated by farmers some 30 years ago, and the group has struggled for at least 30 years to reclaim it. A supreme court decision ruled in Macuxi's favor, but farmers have armed themselves and have refused to leave the land (Amnesty International 2008).

The Sociological Imagination Selective Forgetting

Chris Caldeira

Chris Caldeira

For most of his life, Don Caldeira who was born and raised in the United States, celebrated his Portuguese ethnicity. To instill a sense of ethnic pride in his children, he did things like hang the Portuguese flag in the family room and teach his children to recognize other people who were Portuguese by noticing the spelling of their last name—(for example, "the *-eira* is what makes it. . . . Names like Meredith Vieira or Bobby Ferreira are Portuguese!"). Don would also tell his children that "we are the only Caldeira listed in the phone book." He made that fact a point of pride as it suggested that his family was special. When his daughter Chris moved to Massachusetts, she looked up the name *Caldeira* in the phone book and saw hundreds listed. She tore the page out to show her dad. Apparently, at some point a large Portuguese community had immigrated to the Cape Cod area.

It was not until Don was in his 70s, after his sister gave him a copy of their mother's birth certificate, that he learned his mother was classified as "Portuguese native Creole." Like most Americans, the process known as selective forgetting shaped his ethnic identity. For whatever reason, his mother and sister "forgot" to tell him. If he lived in Brazil, it is unlikely that he would have thought of himself as simply Portuguese, even if his sister and mother "forgot" to pass on that fact on. In Brazil, everyone is assumed multiracial. Now, in the spirit of ethnic renewal, Don makes a point of telling his grown children they are Portuguese *and* Creole.

Involuntary Ethnicity

Then there is the phenomenon of **involuntary ethnicity**. In this situation, a government or dominant group creates an ethnic category for a specific group. Often the people assigned to that category come from many different cultures and countries. In the United States, the ethnic category Hispanic is illustrative. Of the thousands of ethnic groups that live in the United States, the U.S. Bureau of the Census *officially* recognize just two—(1) "Hispanic or Latino" and (2) "Not Hispanic or Latino." The term *Hispanic*, created in 1970, applies to people from, or with ancestors from, 21 Central and South American countries that were once former colonies of Spain. Each of these 21 countries consists of peoples with distinct histories, cultures, and languages. To complicate matters even further, the history of Central and South America intertwined with that of Asia, Europe, the Middle East, and Africa. Because of this interconnected past, these 21 countries are populated not by one ethnic group known as "Hispanics," native- and foreign-born people, immigrants, nonimmigrant residents, and people from every conceivable ancestry, not just Spanish (Toro 1995). To those classified as Hispanic, the label *Hispanic* is likely very confusing because it forces them to identify with conquistadors and settlers from Spain, who imposed their culture, language, and religion on indigenous people and on the African peoples they enslaved.

With regard to ethnicity, the Brazilian government seeks to identify only the ethnicity of the 1 million or so indigenous peoples who live within its borders. After establishing that a person is racially indigenous (for example, Do you consider yourself indigenous?), the Brazilian census asked: (1) "What is your ethnic group or people you belong to? (2) Do you speak an indigenous language in your housing unit? and (3) Do you speak Portuguese in your housing unit?" (IBGE 2010). In Brazil, an estimated 230 indigenous ethnic groups speak 180 languages, representing one percent of the total population (Osava 2010).

In light of the information presented thus far, is it any wonder sociologist Max Weber (1922) argued that "The whole conception of ethnic groups is so complex and so vague that it might be good to abandon it altogether." So, why study ethnicity? One answer is that sociologists are interested in studying the processes by which people make ethnicity seem important or not important. For example, advantaged or dominant groups often do not think their ethnicity is relevant or important.

Dominant Group Ethnic Identity

Sociologist Ashley W. Doane (1997) defines **dominant ethnic groups** as the most advantaged ethnic group in a society; it is the ethnic group that possesses the greatest access to valued resources, including the political power. It is important to clarify that everyone who is part of the advantaged ethnic group does not hold a powerful or advantaged status. The term *dominant* or *advantaged* refers to the fact that European Americans are overrepresented among those holding such statuses. Doane (1997) refers to the dominant ethnic group as possessing a **hidden ethnicity**, a sense of self that is based on little to no awareness of an ethnic identity because its culture is considered normative, or mainstream.

In Brazil, the dominant ethnic groups are Portuguese and Italians. It was the Portuguese colonizers and political leaders who encouraged racial mixing with emphasis on whitening. As one measure of the extent to which Portuguese cultural traditions dominate the larger society, consider that the country is predominantly Catholic (75 percent). This religious tradition dominates because the Portuguese colonial government took measures to make it so, including recruiting Italian immigrants to bolster the number of Catholics and the religion's influence (Hudson 1997, U.S. Department of State 2010). As a result, the following holy days are observed as national or regional holidays: Saint Sebastian's Day, Ash Wednesday, Good Friday, Corpus Christi, Saint John's Day, Our Lady of Carmen ("Carmo"), Assumption Day, Our Lady Aparecida, All Souls' Day, Evangelicals Day, Immaculate Conception, and Christmas (U.S. Department of State 2010).

Dominant status is achieved over a long history that includes conquest, colonialism, and forced and invited labor migrations. Those who are part of an advantaged ethnic group, however, tend to dismiss that history is irrelevant to any of its advantages. In the United States, the dominant ethnic group began as Anglo-Americans, then expanded to encompass Protestant European Americans and eventually to encompass European Americans. Those in the advantaged ethnic group are also the least likely to recall incidents in which they personally faced prejudice, discrimination, or disadvantage because of their ethnicity or race. In other words, because their ethnicity is viewed as largely insignificant to their lives (or no longer significant), they believe that they don't have one.

Department of Defense

The Cristo Redentor (Christ the Redeemer) statue overlooks the city of Rio de Janeiro in Brazil. It is one symbol of the Catholic influence in the country. That influence can be traced to the fifteenth-century Spanish and Portuguese goal of spreading Christianity.

The hidden ethnicity of the dominant ethnic groups makes it difficult for those more visible ethnic groups to challenge the existing system. Specifically, those who seek to celebrate or hold on to their ethnicity are portrayed as unwilling to give up a "foreign" culture. This failure to let go is labeled as undesirable and divisive and as something that must be shed to become American or Brazilian.

The Roles of Chance, Context, and Choice

> **CORE CONCEPT 4 The racial and ethnic categories to which people belong are a product of three interrelated factors: chance, context, and choice.**

Chance is something not subject to human will, choice, or effort. We do *not* choose our biological parents, nor can we control the physical characteristics we inherit from them.

dominant ethnic group The most advantaged ethnic group in a society; it is the ethnic group that possesses the greatest access to valued resources, including the power to create and maintain the system that gives it these advantages.

hidden ethnicity A sense of self that is based on little to no awareness of an ethnic identity because its culture is considered normative, or mainstream.

chance Something not subject to human will, choice, or effort; it helps determine a person's racial and ethnic classification.

Discussion Tip: Ask students if any of them have parents, grandparents, or great grandparents who are of a different race than the one(s) with which they self-identify.

By Lance Cpl. Damany S. Coleman

By Lance Cpl. Jacob A. Singsank

Those in the dominant or advantaged ethnic groups do not see their own clothing, ways of styling hair, and many other things they do as "cultural." It is only others, such as these women pictured in the top photo wearing hand-loomed head wraps made by the Yoruba people of Southwest Nigeria, who possess culture.

Context is the social setting in which racial and ethnic categories are recognized, created, and challenged. **Choice** is the act of choosing from a range of possible behaviors or appearances. The choices one makes regarding racial/ethnic identity and behavior are constrained by chance and context (Haney Lopez 1994).

In evaluating the relative importance of chance, context, and choice, consider the case of a highly visible American: Tiger Woods who is by *chance* the son of a mother who is half Thai, a quarter Chinese, and a quarter "white." Woods's father is half "black," a quarter Chinese, and one-quarter American Indian (Page 1996, p. 285). Simply by *chance*, Woods inherited physical features that people in the United States associate with the category "black."

Tiger Woods could choose to make a point of announcing his white, specifically Dutch ethnic heritage, but Woods lives in a country (context) where few people would attribute any significance to that connection. Likewise, his Asian ties are viewed as much less significant than his African ancestry. When Woods first came on the golf scene, he tried to present himself as "Cablinasian"—a mixture of Caucasian, black, American Indian, and Asian—but as he has pointed out, context trumps choice: "In this country, I'm looked at as being black. When I go to Thailand, I'm considered Thai. It's very interesting. And when I go to Japan, I'm considered Asian. I don't know why it is, but it just is" (Woods 2006). If Tiger Woods lived in Brazil, people would likely assume that he is brown.

The Foreign-Born Population

CORE CONCEPT 5 Every country in the world has people living within its political boundaries who are immigrants and were born elsewhere. Often considerations of race and ethnicity figure into immigration policies.

Unless countries are severely underpopulated, most governments restrict the numbers of outsiders who are allowed to enter. Generally, no government welcomes just anyone. Historically, however, race- and ethnicity-related considerations have played major roles in any country's immigration policy. Legislation often focuses on the number and types of immigrants to allow into the country (for example, country of origin and labor needs of the country).

Three major immigration flows involving various racial and ethnic groups that occurred between 1600 and the early part of the twentieth century are significant to Brazilian and American history and race relations:

1. The massive exodus of European peoples to North, South, and Central America; Asia; and Africa to establish colonies and commercial ventures;
2. A relatively smaller flow of Asian migrants to East Africa, the United States (including Hawaii, which did not become a state until 1959), and Brazil, where they provided cheap labor for major transportation and agricultural projects; and
3. The forced migration of some 11 million Africans by Spanish, Portuguese, French, Dutch, and British slave traders to the United States, South America, the Caribbean, and West Indies.

context The social setting in which racial and ethnic categories are recognized, created, and challenged.

choice The act of choosing from a range of possible behaviors or appearances.

Teaching Tip: For interesting data on foreign born population admitted to the United States since 1900 see Yearbook of Immigration Statistics published by the Department of Homeland Security. The most recent yearbook can be found at www.dhs.gov/xlibrary/assets/statistics/yearbook/2009/ois_yb_2009.pdf.

U.S. Immigration Policy

Notable examples of efforts to curb immigrants of specific races or ethnicities from entering the United States include the Chinese Exclusion Act of 1882 and the Immigration Act of 1924. The Chinese Exclusion Act of 1882 prohibited the entry of Chinese laborers into the United States for ten years; it was then renewed in 1892, requiring Chinese immigrants already in the United States to carry resident permits. In 1943, legislation opened the door a crack by allowing 105 Chinese individuals to immigrate to the United States each year.

The Immigration Act of 1924 established a quota system that set numerical limits on immigration, based on national origin. The quota was set at 2 percent of the number of people from each nation already living in the United States at the time of the 1890 census. Note that the quota was not based on the most current census data at the time of this legislation, which was 1920. Because very few southern, central, and eastern Europeans—and virtually no Asians—had immigrated to the United States by 1890, people from these regions faced the greatest restrictions. In 1965, Congress abolished the discriminatory national origin quotas. This act opened the door to immigrants from Latin America and Asia.

Other immigration legislation has focused on specific racial and ethnic groups. The Bracero Program, which began in 1942, invited Mexican immigrants into the United States to work legally so as to relieve labor shortages in rural areas and to bolster the American workforce during World War II and Korean Wars. In 1954, a program titled "Operation Wetback" rounded up and deported about one million undocumented mostly Mexican immigrants living in southwestern United States.

Library of Congress

This photo from 1942 shows men standing in line outside a soccer stadium in Mexico City, seeking to sign up for work in the United States under the Bracero Program. Some stood in line for five days and nights.

Chris Caldeira

Since 2008—the start of the great recession—documented and undocumented immigrants to the United States, especially those who appear Hispanic, have not been welcomed as they had in past decades when jobs were plentiful and the economy was booming.

The Immigration Reform and Control Act of 1986 permitted illegal workers in the United States to apply for amnesty if they could prove they had worked there for at least 90 days between May 1, 1985 and May 1, 1986. Under this law, 1.3 million of undocumented workers (predominantly Hispanics) were granted amnesty and legal status (Kochhar 2006).

After the attacks of September 11, 2001, nationals from selected countries identified as presenting an elevated national security concern had to register with the Department of Homeland Security to verify their location, activities, and expected departure date. Those selected countries included places like Afghanistan, Algeria, Bangladesh, Egypt, Indonesia, Iran, Iraq, Jordan, Kuwait, Lebanon, Libya, Morocco, and North Korea. Before September 11, 2001, foreign nationals who had minor visa problems could, at the discretion of border or airport inspectors, enter the United States. Now such visitors are taken into custody and immediately deported. Under the old rules, foreign students who graduated from medical school in the United States could stay if they agreed to work in underserved areas. Now, after completing their studies, they must return to their home countries for at least two years before they can apply to return (About.com 2004, Madison 2002, U.S. Department of Homeland Security 2003).

Brazilian Immigration Policy

In 1550, when the Portuguese began their conquest of what was to become Brazil, an estimated 2.4 million Amerindians were living there. In the decades to follow, the king of Portugal sentenced exiles labeled *degredados* to Brazil as a punishment for crimes committed in Portugal. Until 1808, the Portuguese colonizers prohibited other Europeans from immigrating because the colonizers feared

No Borders No Boundaries Largest Immigrant Groups to the United States

Today, more than 38.5 million residents of the United States are counted as foreign-born. That number represents 12.5 percent of the total U.S. population and 15.5 percent of the civilian labor force. More than half (53 percent) of all foreign-born residents were born in a Central American, Caribbean, or South American country; another 28 percent were born in an Asian country (U.S. Bureau of Labor Statistics 2010, U.S. Bureau of the Census 2010). The six states with the largest percentage of foreign-born residents are California (26.8 percent), New York (21.7 percent), New Jersey (19.8 percent), Nevada (18.9 percent), Florida (18.6 percent), and Hawaii (17.8 percent). In some U.S. cities such as Miami, New York, and San Francisco, the foreign-born make up one-third or more of the population (U.S. Bureau of the Census 2011). However, if we take a long view of U.S. history (since 1820, when the U.S. government began keeping such records), we see that of the top ten countries from which people have immigrated to the United States, six are European. Of the 75.4 million people who have immigrated to the United States and obtained permanent legal status since 1820, 68.4 million (90.1 percent) were born in six European countries, whereas only 1.4 million (1.9 percent) were born in African countries.

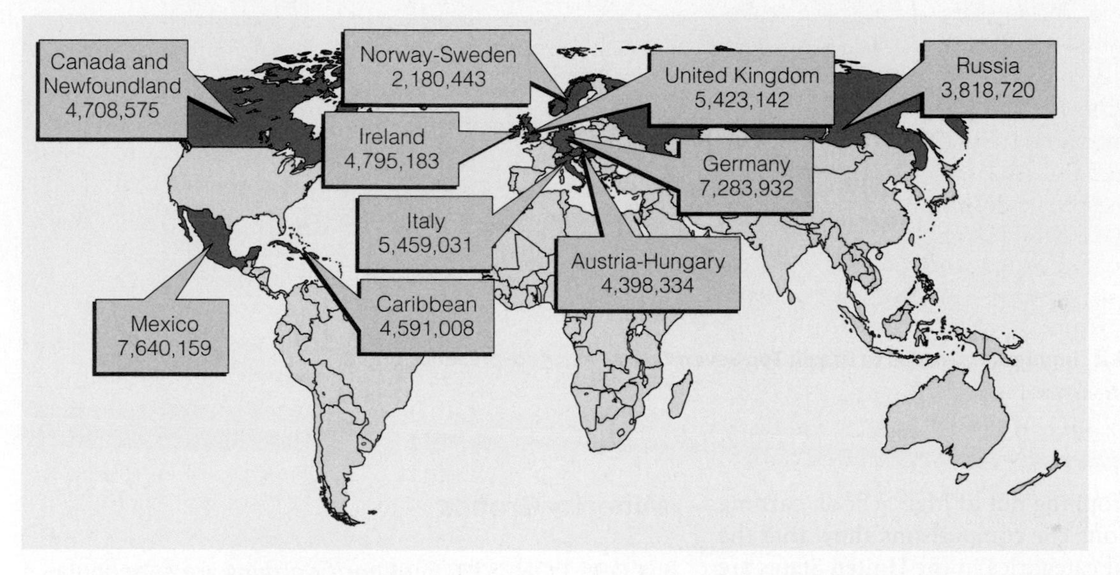

FIGURE 9.1
Source: Data from Department of Homeland Security (2010)

that they would try to claim territory within Brazil. Between 1550 and 1850, the Portuguese "imported" an estimated 4 million enslaved people out of Africa to work on sugarcane and coffee plantations. After slavery was abolished in 1888, the goals of finding an alternative to slave labor and of whitening the Brazilian population drove the country's immigration policy until 1960. Immigration policies were enacted to recruit European immigrants to populate the land, work in coffee plantations, and to "whiten" the Brazilian gene pool, which was about one-third brown and 20 percent black. Immigration policies restricted immigration from Asia until 1910, at which time Japanese immigrants were recruited to work on coffee plantations (Telles 2004).

In addition to recruiting immigrants from Portugal, the Brazilian government at various times recruited Italians, Spanish, and Germans to immigrate to Brazil under the condition they assimilate into Brazilian culture. The Brazilian government also recruited immigrants from Ukraine, Poland, Russia, Lithuania, Hungary, Armenia, China, and Korea. Because the Brazilian government feared that large immigrant communities would resist assimilation, it required that the immigrants learn Portuguese, prohibited them from organizing, and forbade them from publishing foreign-language magazines and newspapers (Migration Policy Institute 2011).

The Consequences of Racial and Ethnic Classification

Sociologists are particularly interested in the ways that race and ethnic categories affect life chances. Tables 9.3 and 9.4 show dramatic differences between racial groups in the United States and between racial groups in Brazil with regard to the chances of living a long life, surviving

No Borders No Boundaries Immigrant Groups to Brazil

According to the Brazilian Census 708,000 people are currently living in Brazil who are counted as foreign-born. About 72 percent have settled in the southeast. That number represents less than one percent (.36 percent) of Brazil's total population. The foreign-born include those from Lebanon, Palestine, Syria, Bosnia, Afghanistan, and West Africa (mostly Angolans and Nigerians), China, Korea, and other Latin American immigrants (most notably, Bolivians). If we take a long view of Brazilian history since 1550, we see that 4 million came to Brazil as slaves from the continent of Africa (IBGE 2010).

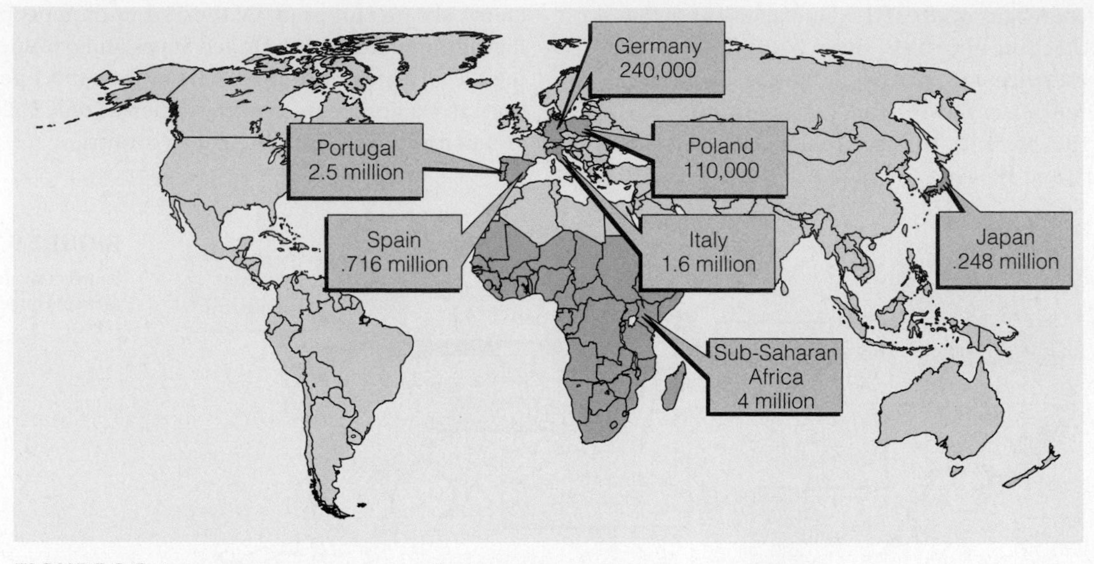

FIGURE 9.2 Immigrant Groups to Brazil: Top Seven Countries, 1500-present

Source: Data from World Lingo (2011).

the first year of life, dropping out of high school, earning a living wage, and so on. The comparisons show that the most advantaged racial categories in the United States are Asian and white, and the least advantaged are black and Native American. In Brazil, the most advantaged racial groups are Asian and white, and the least advantaged are brown, black, and indigenous.

In evaluating the information in Tables 9.3 and 9.4, keep in mind that the data apply to each country as a whole; it does not consider local, state, and regional variations. For example, in the United States, students classified as Asian have the lowest chance of dropping out of high school. But those chances vary by state where 1.2 percent of Asian high school students in Wisconsin and 22 percent in Maine drop out (National Center for Education Statistics 2009).

minority groups Subgroups within a society that can be distinguished from members of the dominant group by visible identifying characteristics, including physical and cultural attributes. These subgroups are systematically excluded, whether consciously or unconsciously, from full participation in society and denied equal access to positions of power, privilege, and wealth.

Minority Groups

CORE CONCEPT 6 ***Minority groups*** **are subpopulations within a society that are systematically excluded (whether consciously or unconsciously) from full participation in society and denied equal opportunities to access power, prestige, and wealth.**

Many groups can be classified as minorities, including some racial, ethnic, and religious groups; women; those in the LGBT community; the very old and the very young; and the physically impaired. Although we focus on ethnic and racial minorities, the concepts described here can apply to any minority. Sociologist Louis Wirth (1945) identified a number of essential traits that are characteristic of disadvantaged status.

First, membership in minority groups is involuntary. In fact, people are generally born into them. Wirth argues that as long as people are free to join or leave a group, they do not constitute a minority. Involuntary membership as a criterion for defining a minority group is controversial because the meaning of being free to join or leave is unclear. For example, one could argue that Muslim women who wear headscarves are not a minority because they can choose to remove

TABLE 9.3 Differences in Life Chances, United States

Chance of . . .	Highest Chance	Lowest Chance	Difference
living a long life (life expectancy)	Asian Female 86.7 years	Black Male 69.7 years	17.0 years
dropping out of high school	Black 39.1%	Asian 8.6%	30.5%
going to prison in lifetime	Black Male 32.5%	White Female 1%	31.50%
earning a high median weekly income (working full-time)	Asian Male $995	Hispanic Female $522	$473 per week
dying before reaching one year of age (per 100,000)	Black Male 1,448 per 100,000	Asian Female 427 per 100,000	1,021 babies per 100,000
living in poverty	Native American 24.5%	White 9.4%	15.1%
having no health insurance	Native American (not metro) 35%	White 12.0%	23.0%

Sources: Data from National Center for Education Statistics 2010, Centers for Disease Control 2010, U.S. Bureau of the Census 2010, Institute for Women's Policy Research 2010.

TABLE 9.4 Differences in Life Chances, Brazil

Chance of . . .	Highest Chance	Lowest Chance	Difference
living a long life (life expectancy)	Whites 74 years	Blacks 67.6 years	6.4 years
never going to school	Brown/black male 22.2%	White male 8.4%	13.8%
completing university	White 18%	Brown and Black 5%	13.0%
earning a high median monthly income (working full-time)	Asian $656.50 per month	Brown/Black $162.95 per month	$493.55
dying before reaching one year of age (per 100,000)	Brown/ Black 3,040 per 100,000	White 1,390 per 100,00	1,650 per 1,000
living in absolute poverty	Brown/ Black 18%	White 6%	27.3%
being literate	White Men 90%	Black Women 80%	10%

Sources: Data from Reuter 2007, Ikawa and Mattar 2009, Gradín 2007, Telles 2004, Matijasevich 2008, Gasnier 2009.

them. The problem is that removing the scarf for many also means violating some deeply held religious convictions.

Second, a minority may be the numerical majority in a society. The key to minority status relates not to size but to access and control over valued resources. In the United States, legally recognized racial/ethnic minorities are Hispanics, American Indian, Asian, black, and Native Hawaiian/other Pacific Islander. From a national perspective, all five are numerical minorities. However, there are communities in the United States in which a minority group is the numerical majority. In Brazil, blacks and browns constitute 51 percent of the population (see Figure 9.3). Under the country's new affirmative action policies—brown, black, and poor individuals are the minorities, along with high

Video Tip: For insights into Brazil's affirmative action policy, watch all or part of the Wide Angle documentary, Brazil in Black and White. It can be accessed through Google or other search engine using the terms "Wide Angle Brazil in Black and White." One episode in particular—Part 2, Affirmative Action in Brazil—is particularly relevant as it features high school students reflecting on the race they plan to use when applying to college.

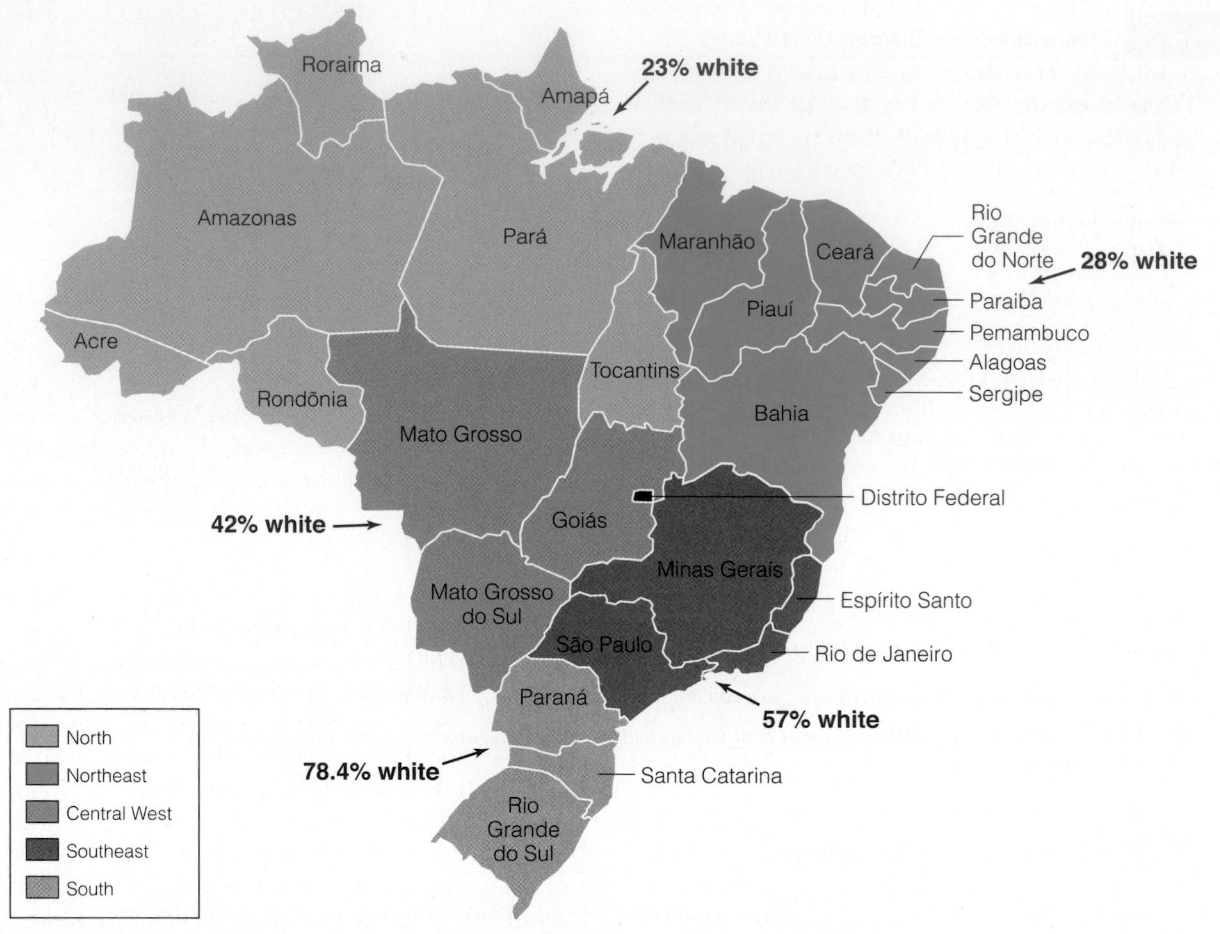

FIGURE 9.3 Map of Brazil Divided into Five Major Regions by % White
Brazil is the largest and most populated country in South America. It has the eighth largest economy in the world. Brazil can be divided into five very different regions: north, northeast, central south, southeast, and south. As you can see by the map, the white population is the numerical majority in two of the five regions of Brazil:

1. The north consists of the Amazon Basin covering half of the country, with vast reaches of largely uninhabited forest. The rate of migration to the Amazon region accelerated in the 1960s, after the government built a network of highways and roads to connect that region to the rest of the country. The network of roads opened the land to foreign and Brazilian investors and to landless and unemployed who clear the land for pasture and agriculture. The Amazon is also occupied by indigenous people, rubber tappers, nut gatherers, and others whose forest-centered livelihood has been disrupted by highway construction and migration. The forest dwellers' lives are disrupted by mining companies, lumber companies, cattle ranchers, and land-hungry migrants.
2. The northeast is semiarid scrubland prone to periodic drought and massive flooding; it is heavily settled and poor. About 27 percent of Brazil's population lives in the northeast. Most are descendants of slaves who worked the Portuguese sugarcane plantations between the sixteenth and nineteenth centuries, living on drought-stricken land. Even after slavery was abolished in 1888, the plantation agricultural system, which was oriented toward export, continued. Today, the most productive lands in the northeast are still used to grow sugarcane, soybeans, and other export crops.
3. The south consists of rich farmland, pasturelands, and large modern cities. It is a tourist attraction. After the southeast, it has the highest per capita income.
4. The southeast is a large densely populated urban center, including Rio de Janeiro and Sao Paulo, two of the world's largest cities and centers of multinational commercial, industrial, and agricultural activity. A significant portion of the population lives in what are known as favelas, concentrated populations living in makeshift dwellings constructed from cardboard, metal, or wood with inadequate sewers, running water, and electricity. It is the wealthiest of the five regions and contributes 60 percent of the country's GDP.
5. The central west is sparsely populated and home to some of the largest cattle ranches in South America. It is home to a satellite tracking station maintained by NASA.

school graduates from public schools. Indigenous people also qualify as minorities (Bailey 2009).

Third, minority groups are excluded from full participation in the larger society. That is, they do not enjoy the taken-for-granted advantages and immunities enjoyed by a dominant group including the following:

- Most of the time—when I am at school, work, or just out walking—I am in the company of people of my race or ethnic group.
- I feel confident that I can rent or purchase housing in any area in which I can afford to live.
- I can go shopping and not worry that I am being followed or targeted for surveillance by store detectives.
- I can do poorly on a test without worrying that my classmates or professor will attribute it to my race or ethnicity.
- Whether I use checks, credit cards, or cash, I can count on my skin color not to work against the perception that I am financially reliable (McIntosh 1992, pp. 73–75).

A fourth trait characteristic of minority status is social and spatial isolation. That isolation can manifest itself

- in segregated residential arrangements (ethnic neighborhoods and/or gated communities),
- in the portrayal of specific minorities as particularly dangerous,
- in laws prohibiting certain racial/ethnic groups from marrying those in dominant groups (miscegenation),
- in special surveillance (Wooddell and Henry 2005), and
- in underrepresentation of minorities in key political and economic positions.

With regard to the social and spatial isolation of minorities, Brazil stands apart from the United States in that it encouraged miscegenation and it did not create laws (for example, the Jim Crow laws) that prohibited marriage between whites and nonwhites or limited political or social opportunities. Still, there is no question that whites have the advantage in that country (Telles 2004). As one example, although half the Brazilian population is classified as black and brown, only about 3 percent of the 513 members of the national Chamber of Deputies is classified as such (Bailey 2009). Likewise, before university affirmative action policies (quotas) were implemented in 2003, only 3 percent of the .4 million incoming students to Brazilian universities identified themselves as black or mixed race (Jeter 2003).

The fifth trait is that minority status overshadows any accomplishments. As one example, black/brown students admitted under Brazil's quota system believe that no matter how well they do in school "people are going to look at me and say: 'Oh, he's an affirmative action student,' or 'He's an affirmative action hire.'" Few will consider the possibility that a black/brown student might have scored high enough on the entrance exam to be admitted regardless (Jeter 2003).

The five characteristics of minority group status apply especially to the situation of **involuntary minorities**, those

Library of Congress

Jim Crow laws (1876–1965) in the United States enforced so-called separate but equal segregation to the point of even requiring separate water fountains for whites and nonwhites. Brazil did not institute laws that enforced racial segregation.

who are members of racial or ethnic groups that did not choose to belong to a country. Rather, they or their ancestors experienced enslavement, conquest, or colonization. In the United States, those of Native American, African, Mexican, and Hawaiian descent are examples. In Brazil, those of indigenous and African descent would qualify. Unlike those who voluntarily immigrated to the United States or Brazil expecting to improve their way of life, involuntary immigrants had no such expectations. In fact, that forced incorporation involved a loss of freedom and status (Ogbu 1990). It is important to point out that not everyone who belongs to the dominant group category—white—in Brazil and the United States immigrated voluntarily. Many Europeans were forced to leave their home county and travel to the United States and Brazil as indentured servants.

The characteristics that Wirth identifies as associated with minority group status indicate that minorities stand apart from the dominant culture. Some people argue that minorities stand apart because they resist assimilation. To assess this claim, we turn to the work of sociologist Milton M. Gordon.

Assimilation

> CORE CONCEPT 7 **Assimilation is a process by which ethnic and racial distinctions between groups disappear because one group is absorbed into another group's culture or because two cultures blend to form a new culture.**

involuntary minorities Ethnic or racial groups that were forced to become part of a country by slavery, conquest, or colonization.

assimilation A process by which ethnic and racial distinctions between groups disappear because one group is absorbed into another group's culture or because two cultures blend to form a new culture.

Two main types of assimilation exist: absorption assimilation and melting pot assimilation.

Absorption Assimilation

In **absorption assimilation**, racial and ethnic minorities adapt to the point where they are completely "absorbed" into the dominant culture. That happens when they

1. abandon their own culture (language, dress, food, religion, and so on) for that of the dominant group,
2. gain access to the dominant group's social networks and institutions,
3. intermarry and have children with dominant group members,
4. identify with the dominant group's values,
5. encounter no widespread prejudice or discrimination, and/or
6. have no value conflicts with those of the dominant group.

Gordon maintains that when racial or ethnic minorities abandon their own culture (level 1), it does not automatically follow that they achieve other levels of assimilation. Of the six levels of assimilation, Gordon believes that gaining access to the dominant group's social networks and institutions (level 2) is the most important. Gordon proposes that if those in the dominant group allow minorities to join their social circles, clubs, and institutions on a large enough scale, interracial or interethnic marriages are bound to occur (level-3 assimilation):

> If children of different ethnic backgrounds belong to the same play group, later the same adolescent cliques, and at college the same fraternities and sororities; if the parents belong to the same country club and invite each other to their homes for dinner; it is completely unrealistic not to expect these children, now grown, to love and to marry each other, blithely oblivious to previous ethnic extraction. (Gordon 1978, pp. 177–178)

If we apply these six levels to Brazil, we see that level three—minorities intermarry and procreate with those in the dominant group—applies particularly well. The ideal of intermarriage is celebrated in Brazil, and as a result, there are significantly more interracial marriages in Brazil than in the United States where, even today, they are widely frowned upon. However, it is important to point out it is far more common for Brazilians to marry someone of their own race. And when whites, in particular, do marry across racial lines, it is most likely with someone considered mulatto or brown, not black (Telles 2004).

In practice, gaining such access to dominant group's networks and institutions is very difficult. Why? Because ethnic or racial minorities often experience **segregation,** the physical and/or social separation of people by race or ethnicity. Segregation may be legally enforced (de jure) or socially enforced without the support of laws (de facto). The segregation may be spatial or hierarchical. **Spatial segregation** occurs when racial or ethnic groups attend different schools, live in different neighborhoods, and use different public facilities, such as restaurants and even drinking fountains. It also occurs when people of different racial or ethnic groups occupy the same facilities but sit, work, socialize, or eat on different floors, in different rooms, or at separate tables.

In the United States, the Jim Crow laws enforced racial segregation between whites and nonwhites from 1880 to 1964. These laws resulted in the establishment of separate but unequal race-specific bathrooms, recreational facilities, hospitals, and drinking fountains. Although laws in the United States no longer support segregation in public spaces, we must acknowledge that segregation exists in fact. For most Americans, all of the important and meaningful primary relationships that are "close to the core of personality and selfhood"—including those with church members, classmates, and friends—are confined largely to people within the same racial/ethnic group (Gordon 1978, p. 204).

Segregation is hierarchical when those in advantaged racial and ethnic categories occupy the most prestigious positions while those in the disadvantaged categories are concentrated in the least prestigious ones, such as servants, maintenance workers, and laborers. In both the

absorption assimilation A process by which members of a minority group adapt to the ways of the dominant group, which sets the standards to which they must adjust (Gordon 1978).

segregation The physical and/or social separation of people according to their race or ethnicity.

spatial segregation A de facto or de jure situation in which racial or ethnic groups attend different schools, live in different neighborhoods, use different public facilities, or occupy the same facility but sit, work, or eat on different floors, in different rooms, or at separate tables.

Library of Congress

The 1816 illustration shows the nature of hierarchical segregation in Brazil. It shows two enslaved males carrying a white (Portuguese) woman in a sedan chair and an enslaved woman carrying baggage on her head as she follows the master who is on horseback.

United States and Brazil, hierarchical segregation occurred under slavery, where masters and enslaved were often in the same physical spaces but their statuses were very unequal. Today, hierarchical segregation exists when one racial or ethnic group is disproportionately represented in some occupations and not others. As an example, in the United States, 92.8 percent of aircraft pilots and flight engineers are classified as white (U.S. Bureau of Labor Statistics 2010). In Brazil, 81 percent of health care professionals are classified as white (Saboia and Saboia 2007).

Melting Pot Assimilation

Assimilation need not be a one-sided process in which a minority group disappears, or is absorbed, into the dominant group. Ethnic and racial distinctions can also disappear through **melting pot assimilation** (Gordon 1978). In this process, groups accept many new behaviors and values from one another. This exchange produces a new blended cultural system. The melting pot concept can be applied to the various African ethnic groups transported to the colonies, including the United States and Brazil. They were "not one but many peoples" who spoke many languages and came from many cultures (Cornell 1990, p. 376). Slave traders capitalized on this diversity: "Advertisements of new slave cargoes frequently referred to ethnic origins, while slave owners often purchased slaves on the basis of national identities and the characteristics they supposedly indicated" (Cornell 1990, p. 376; see also Rawley 1981). Although slave owners and traders acknowledged ethnic differences among Africans, they treated Africans from various ethnic groups as belonging to one category of people—the enslaved. As one example, slave owners tended to mix together the enslaved from different ethnic origins to decrease the likelihood that the enslaved would plot a rebellion. To communicate with one another, slaves invented pidgin and Creole languages.

In addition to developing new languages, the enslaved created a common and distinctive culture based on kinship, religion, food, songs, stories, and other features. The harsh conditions of enslavement, along with the mixing together of people from many ethnic groups, encouraged the enslaved to borrow aspects of one another's cultures and create a new, blended culture.

Although sociologists are interested in the assimilation processes, they also focus on the mechanisms people employ to preserve difference and inequality (Alba 1992). These mechanisms include racism, prejudice, stereotyping, and discrimination.

Racism

CORE CONCEPT 8 Racism is the belief that genetic or biologically based differences explain and even justify inequalities that exist between advantaged and disadvantaged racial and ethnic groups.

ISAAC and ROSA, Emancipated Slave Children, From the Free Schools of Louisiana, Photographed by KIMBALL, 477 Broadway, N.Y.

Library of Congress

This photo shows two emancipated slave children, one who appears white and the other black. In the context of slavery, sexual relationships (usually forced, sometimes willing) between enslaved "black" women and their "white" masters were commonplace. Those sexual relationships produced not only "mixed-race" offspring, but also sons and daughters, half-brothers and half-sisters, grandsons and granddaughters (Parent and Wallace 2002). Yet, the system of racial classification protected "white" racial purity by assigning the offspring of these unions (no matter their physical appearance) to the race and the enslaved status of the mother. This system allowed the master to own his offspring, thereby increasing the size of the enslaved population and his wealth.

Those alleged genetic differences—as manifested in skin color, hair texture, and eye shape—are deemed so significant that they are used to explain racial and ethnic differences as they relate to crime, graduation, teen pregnancy, and marriage rates. Physical traits are used to explain

melting pot assimilation Cultural blending in which groups accept many new behaviors and values from one another. This exchange produces a new cultural system, which is a blend of the previously separate systems.

Technology Tip: In 2008 President Obama made a major speech on race and racism. To listen and/or read that speech, go to www.npr.org and use search terms "Obama Speech on Race."

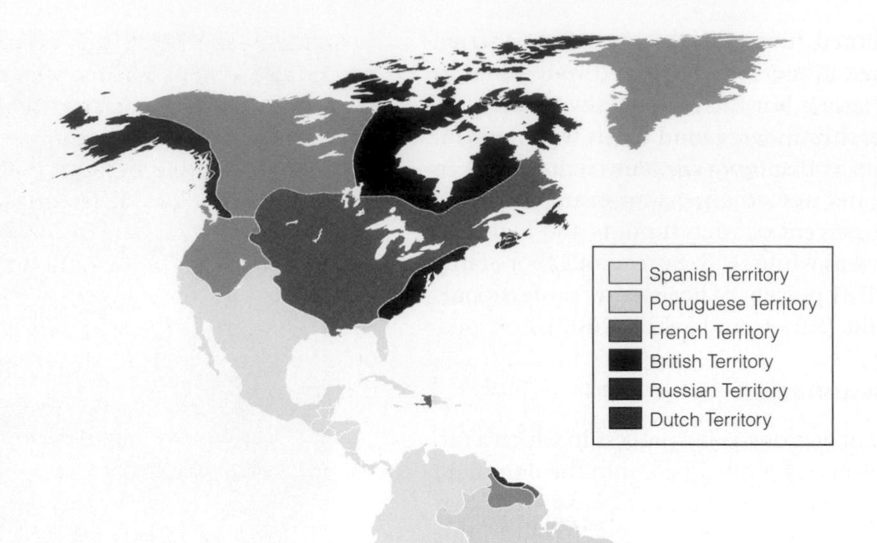

FIGURE 9.4 The map shows how North, Central, and South America were divided up by European and Russian powers in a process known as colonization. Colonization is a situation where a foreign power uses superior military force to impose its political, economic, social, and cultural institutions on an indigenous population to control their resources, labor, and markets (Marger 2012).
Source: Data from U.S. Central Intelligence Agency (2011)

differences in athletic ability, IQ scores, and taste in music. From a racist point of view, there is no other possible explanation for these inequalities.

Racism has probably always existed. Modern racism, however, emerged as a way to justify European exploitation of people and resources in Africa, Asia, and the Americas. Between 1492 and 1800, Europeans learned of, conquered, and colonized much of North America, South America, Asia, and Africa and set the tone for international relations for centuries to come. Among other things, this exploitation took the form of enslavement and colonialism (see Figure 9.4).

Under colonialism, local populations were forced to cultivate and harvest crops and to extract minerals and other raw materials for export to the colonists' home countries. Racism helped justify this exploitation of nonwhite peoples and their resources by pointing to the so-called superiority of the white race. More precisely, the exploitation was justified by **scientific racism**, the misuse of science to create findings that supported systems of racial rankings and theories of social and cultural progress that placed whites in the most advanced ranks and stage of human evolution.

The eugenics movement, popular during the early decades of the twentieth century, included racist elements. Eugenics was presented as an applied science with the purpose of identifying ways to improve the genetic composition of populations. With regard to race, eugenicists named and ranked racial groups, placing the white race at the apex of the hierarchy and black at the bottom. In addition, some eugenists maintained that racial mixing created degenerates (Telles 2004).

scientific racism The use of faulty science to support systems of racial rankings and theories of social and cultural progress that placed whites in the most advanced ranks and stage of human evolution.

In the United States, eugenic policies supported by scientific racism were behind laws created to protect white racial purity, including prohibiting sexual relationships between whites and nonwhites and banning interracial marriage. Eugenic thinking gave support to the Immigration Act of 1924 that sought to restrict inferior racial stocks from immigrating to the United States.

Eugenicists maintained that tropical climates contributed to mental and physical inferiority and, by extension, pointed to Brazil's population as an illustration of biological degeneracy dooming that country's fate to one of perpetual underdevelopment (Telles 2004). This assessment hit Brazil's political elite hard as many were from mixed-race ancestries. As a solution, Brazil's scientists, intellectuals, and political elite embraced whitening as a solution. While still embracing the doctrine of white superiority, they maintained that "black and mulatto inferiority could be overcome by miscegenation" and that "race mixture would eliminate the black population, eventually resulting in a white or mostly white Brazilian population" (Telles 2004, p. 28; see "Working for Change: Lester Ward").

Prejudice, Stereotyping, and Discrimination

> **CORE CONCEPT 9 Prejudice, stereotyping, and discrimination are tools that preserve the system that benefits advantaged race and ethnic groups.**

A **prejudice** is a rigid and usually unfavorable judgment about an out-group that does not change in the face of contradictory evidence. That judgment is applied to anyone who belongs to that out-group. Prejudices are based on **stereotypes**—simplistic generalizations about out-groups and applied to anyone who belongs to that out-group. Stereotypes interfere with a person's ability to recognize new or unexpected information that contradict that generalization. Stereotypes give the illusion that people are predictable and that one knows and has the right to construct images of "the other" (Crapanzano 1985).

Stereotypes are supported and reinforced in a number of ways. In **selective perception**, prejudiced people notice only those supposed facts that support their stereotypes. When subjected to close scrutiny, the facts prove unfounded. For example, many people use facts to support stereotypes that white men can't jump and are slow, based on the facts. After all, the facts show that only a small portion of professional basketball and track athletes are white. If one takes the time to look beyond the sport of basketball, it is easy to identify sports where the white athletes who dominate them possess extraordinary speed and leaping ability. Surprisingly, one such sport is weightlifting (see photos on p. 234).

Stereotypes persist in another way: When prejudiced people encounter someone who contradicts a stereotype, they see that person as an exception to the rule. In fact, such encounters merely reinforce the stereotype. Finally, stereotypes survive because prejudiced people evaluate the same behaviors differently depending on the race or ethnicity of the person involved (Merton 1957). For example, incompetence exhibited by racial or ethnic minorities is often attributed to their race or ethnicity. In contrast, incompetence exhibited by an advantaged race or ethnicity is almost always treated as an individual shortcoming.

Discrimination

In contrast to prejudice, **discrimination** is not an attitude but a behavior. It includes intentional or unintentional unequal treatment of individuals or groups based on attributes unrelated to merit, ability, or past performance. Discrimination denies people equal opportunities to achieve socially valued goals such as getting an education, finding employment, accessing health care, and living a long life.

Sociologist Robert K. Merton explored the relationship between prejudice (the attitude) and discrimination (the behavior). He argued that knowing whether people are prejudiced does not help to predict whether they will discriminate. Merton employed a four-part typology to show that both nonprejudiced people (who believe in equal opportunity) can discriminate and prejudiced people can refrain from discrimination.

---

prejudice A rigid and usually unfavorable judgment about an out-group that does not change in the face of contradictory evidence and that applies to anyone who shares the distinguishing characteristics of the out-group.

stereotypes Inaccurate generalizations about people who belong to an out-group. Stereotypes "give the illusion that one knows the other" and has the right to construct images of the other (Crapanzano 1985, pp. 271–272).

selective perception The process in which prejudiced people notice only those things that support the stereotypes they hold about an out-group.

discrimination An intentional or unintentional act of unequal treatment of individuals or groups based on attributes unrelated to merit, ability, or past performance. Discrimination denies people equal opportunities to achieve socially valued goals such as getting an education, finding employment, accessing health care, and living a long life. It is a behavior, not an attitude.

Working for Change Lester Ward (1841–1913)

Throughout his life, Lester Ward, the founder of American sociology, worked diligently to improve ethnic and racial relations. He vehemently opposed slavery, fought to have it abolished, and was seriously wounded in the Civil War doing so. After the war, both he and his wife worked to help educate emancipated slaves, and subsequently he was involved with the founding of Howard University. During the 1870s, as editor of *The Iconoclast*, he published the writings of the noted African American reformer Frederick Douglass, and he regularly addressed groups seeking to recognize the rights of African Americans.

In the early 1900s, the eugenics movement became popular in American society. Proponents contended that some groups were naturally or innately superior to others due to genetic or hereditary differences. Furthermore, they believed that the best way to improve society was to increase the birth rates of genetically superior peoples and decrease the rates of others. They held that unless steps such as mandated sterilizations were taken to reduce the birth rates of African Americans, southern Europeans, and other minority immigrant groups, there would be a steady deterioration of the fabric of American society.

Lester Ward worked tirelessly to resist the eugenics movement. He held that although there are indeed differences in ability *within* the respective groups, there are no significant genetic differences among the groups. He held that most differences observed with regard to intelligence, crime, and deviant behavior were rooted in differences of opportunity. In hindsight, one might say that Ward recognized that the proponents of eugenics were setting the stage for the emergence of racial superiority doctrines that were ultimately expressed in Nazism and genocide, that is, the elimination of groups on the basis of alleged hereditary traits.

In his final public lecture before his death, Ward called upon sociologists to vigorously challenge the *eugenics* movement and instead advocate for *euthenics*: a science seeking to improve society through the betterment of living conditions, such as the expansion of educational opportunity. He also challenged social scientists of his era who opposed ethnically and racially mixed marriages. Ward felt that such marriages should be encouraged and that they would ultimately lead to an improved and more tolerant society.

Source: Written by Gale Largey, professor emeritus of sociology, Mansfield University.

Which of the two athletes pictured relies on leaping ability to excel at his sport? Did you know the strongest person in the world could not lift heavy weights unless he or she also possesses extraordinary leaping ability? According to one professional weightlifter, "What you really need is speed and agility and balance. We can all spring up and slam-dunk a basketball from a dead standstill under the hoop" (Gore 2000).

Discussion Tip: Ask students if these two photos contrasting a weight lifter and basketball player help them to think more critically about athletic ability and race. Why or why not?

Nonprejudiced nondiscriminators (all-weather liberals) accept the creed of equal opportunity, and their conduct conforms to that creed. They not only believe in equal opportunity but also take action against discrimination.

Nonprejudiced discriminators (fair-weather liberals) believe in equal opportunity but discriminate because doing so gives them an advantage or because they simply fail to consider the discriminatory consequences of their actions. For example, white people, and even some nonwhites, decide to move out of their neighborhood after a certain number of black families moves in—not because they are prejudiced against blacks *per se*, but because they are afraid that property values might start to decline and they want to "get out" while time remains. The act of moving out contributes to lower property values for other neighbors left behind.

Prejudiced nondiscriminators (timid bigots) reject the creed of equal opportunity but refrain from discrimination, primarily because they fear possible sanctions or being labeled as racists. Timid bigots rarely express their prejudices and often use code words to camouflage their true feelings. An example of a prejudiced nondiscriminator is the parents of a minority college student who chooses a white professor as her mentor. The parents, who want to steer their child toward a same-race mentor, do not bring up the chosen mentor's race as the problem but find other faults with the white professor.

Prejudiced discriminators (active bigots) reject the notion of equal opportunity and profess a right, even a duty, to discriminate. They express with deep conviction that anyone from the in-group (including the village idiot) is superior to any members of the out-group (Merton 1976). Active bigots are most likely to believe that they "have the moral right" to destroy the people whom they see as threatening to their values and way of life. Of the four categories in Merton's typology, prejudiced discriminators are the most likely to commit hate crimes, actions aimed at humiliating people in the out-group, destroying their property, or ending their lives.

Individual versus Institutionalized Discrimination

Sociologists distinguish between individual discrimination and institutionalized discrimination. **Individual discrimination** is any individual or overt action aimed at someone in an out-group that depreciates, denies opportunities, or does violence to life or property. One example relates to teachers who decide against disciplining a student of a different race because they fear being called a racist. This decision denies the student the opportunity to learn from mistakes. Another example involves a person who wants to rent a room but, upon learning the potential renter's race, informs the person that no apartments are available.

Institutionalized discrimination is the established, customary way of doing things in society—the unchallenged rules, policies, and day-to-day practices established by advantaged groups that impede or limit the opportunities and achievements of those in disadvantaged groups. It is "systematic discrimination through the regular operations of societal institutions" (Davis 1978, p. 30).

Laws and policies that intentionally or unintentionally reward or punish some racial or ethnic groups and not others fall under the category of institutionalized discrimination. When discrimination is institutionalized, it is more difficult to identify, condemn, and punish than individual discrimination. That is because the discrimination results from simply following the law or adhering to existing policies that seem on the surface to be impersonal, fair, or just standard operating procedure. One example of institutional discrimination relates to federal sentences issued to those convicted of trafficking in crack cocaine versus powder cocaine (see photos and caption on page 236).

People who are the objects of prejudice and discrimination do not respond passively. History records countless examples of personal and collective responses to address, escape, and change the oppressive situations. In the United States, one collective response was the civil

nonprejudiced nondiscriminators (all-weather liberals) People who accept the creed of equal opportunity, and their conduct conforms to that creed. They not only believe in equal opportunity but also take action against discrimination.

nonprejudiced discriminators (fair-weather liberals) People who believe in equal opportunity but discriminate because doing so gives them an advantage or because they simply fail to consider the discriminatory consequences of their actions.

prejudiced nondiscriminators (timid bigots) People who reject the creed of equal opportunity but refrain from discrimination, primarily because they fear possible sanctions or being labeled as racists.

prejudiced discriminators (active bigots) People who reject the notion of equal opportunity and profess a right, even a duty, to discriminate. They express with deep conviction that anyone from the in-group (including the village idiot) is superior to any members of the out-group (Merton 1976).

individual discrimination Any individual or overt action aimed at someone in an out-group that depreciates, denies opportunities, or does violence to life or property.

institutionalized discrimination The established, customary way of doing things in society—the unchallenged rules, policies, and day-to-day practices established by advantaged groups that impede or limit the opportunities and achievements of those in disadvantaged groups. It is "systematic discrimination through the regular operations of societal institutions" (Davis 1978, p. 30).

Crack (right) and powder cocaine (left) have the same physiological and psychotropic effects but are handled very differently for sentencing purposes. On average, sentences for crack offenses are three to six times longer than those for offenses involving equal amounts of powder. Approximately 85 percent of defendants convicted of crack offenses in federal court are black, whereas 78 percent of defendants in powder cocaine cases are white; thus, the severe sentences are imposed "primarily upon black offenders" (Kimbrough v. United States 2007).

rights movement. In Brazil, one response was the black consciousness movement.

The Civil Rights Movement

Shortly after slavery was abolished in the United States, a state-sanctioned system of racial discrimination, known as Jim Crow was put into place. Under Jim Crow laws, blacks (and other minorities) were denied the right to vote and sit on juries; subjected to racial segregation (separate and unequal facilities); disadvantaged with regard to employment opportunities; and subjected to widespread, systematic discrimination, including violence against person and property. In many states, whites and nonwhites were denied the right to marry (see Table 9.5). Examples of such laws include the following:

- No person or corporation shall require any white female nurse to nurse in wards or rooms in hospitals, either public or private, in which Negro men are placed. (Alabama)
- It shall be unlawful for colored people to frequent any park owned or maintained by the city for the benefit, use, and enjoyment of white persons . . . and unlawful for any white person to frequent any park owned or maintained by the city for the use and benefit of colored persons. (Georgia)
- All marriages of white persons with Negroes, mulattos, Mongolians, or Malaya hereafter contracted in the State of Wyoming are and shall be illegal and void. (Wyoming)

The civil rights movement was a response to such systematic discrimination, not just in the South but also across the nation. The civil rights movement was waged by hundreds of thousands of people, many of whom put their lives on the line, demanding integrated schools, decent housing, and an end to racial bias. In the popular imagination, the civil rights movement involved

TABLE 9.5 Number and Percentage of U.S. Population Classified as Black and Mulatto, 1910

In the context of the United States between 1850 and 1910, unless people with white and African ancestries could pass as white, they were classified as mulatto, but still considered "Negro" or black and never "white." Although laws in the United States prohibited marriage and sexual relationships between whites and nonwhites, especially blacks, that does not mean sexual relationships were absent. Evidence of intermixing before 1967 (the year miscegenation laws were abolished) is reflected in U.S. census data from 1910. Notice that, in that year 20.9 percent of the "Negro" population was considered "mulatto," and yet, despite mixed ancestry, "mulattos" were still part of the "Negro" racial category, not the "white" category.

	"Negro" Population	Number and Percentage of Total "Negro" Population			
Census Year	Total	Black	Mulatto	% Black	% Mulatto
1910	9,827,763	7,777,077	2,050,688	79.1	20.9

Source: Data from U.S. Bureau of the Census 1910.

confronting white supremacists such as the Ku Klux Klan. However, activists also confronted institutional discrimination as embodied in local, state, and federal agencies, judicial systems, and legislative bodies, including police, the National Guard, judges, and all-white citizens' town/city councils. Most notably, police departments, especially in the South, arrested civil rights activists on false or trumped-up charges, and all-white juries found whites who murdered blacks not guilty. Some officials, such as Alabama Governor George Wallace, used the National Guard and state police to prevent school integration.

The black churches played a key role in the civil rights movement. In an atmosphere of profound discrimination and inequality, the black church had become not just a place to worship but also served as a community clearinghouse, a credit union, a support group, and center of political activism (National Park Service 2009). In fact, churches were the context for the emergence of key civil rights leaders such as reverends Martin Luther King Jr. and Fred Shuttlesworth and the emergence of key organizations such as the Southern Christian Leadership Conference (SCLC), the Student Nonviolent Coordinating Committee (SNCC) and the National Association for the Advancement of Colored People (NAACP).

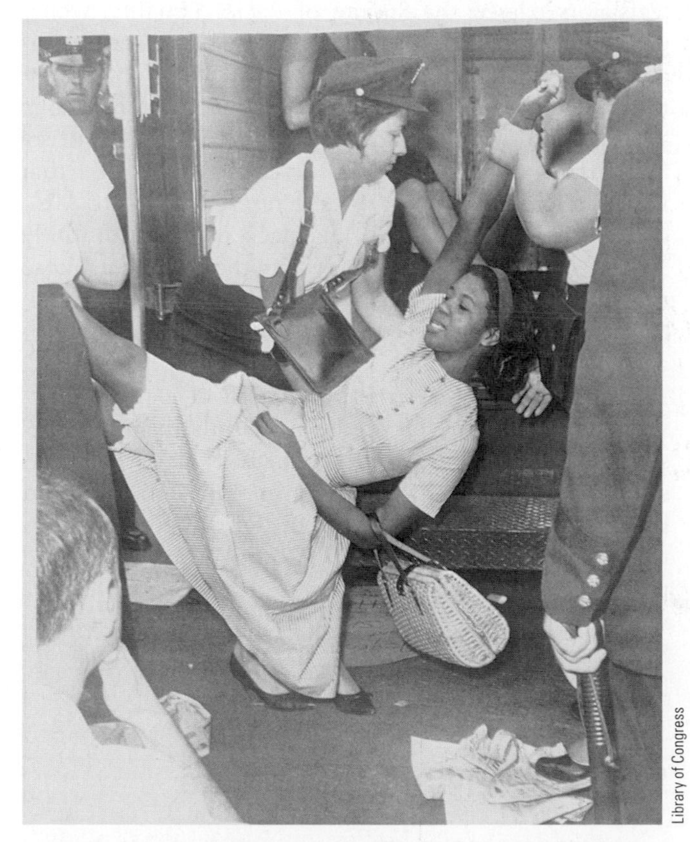

Library of Congress

College and high school students played key roles in the civil rights movements. They participated in bus boycotts, sit-ins, freedom rides, and school integration.

The Selma-to-Montgomery March was an especially significant moment for the civil rights movement, because it was the first event of the activist movement to be televised. What Americans saw created enough outrage to lend national support to the movement. The march began on what is known as Bloody Sunday, March 7, 1965, when state and local law enforcement agents stopped 600 demonstrators six blocks into the march and attacked them with clubs and tear gas. Civil rights leaders sought protection from the courts to march and it was granted. The escalating intensity of this movement pushed the federal government to become involved. Most notably, President John F. Kennedy used the power of his office to enforce desegregation in schools and public facilities. Attorney General Robert Kennedy filed suits against at least four states to secure the right to vote for blacks. When Congress passed the Civil Rights Act of 1964 and the Voting Rights Act of 1965, President Lyndon Johnson signed them into law knowing that it might cost him the next presidential election and severely weaken the Democratic Party's chance of winning in the next election cycle. Of course, federal and Supreme Court judges also played key roles in ruling against segregation and discrimination (National Park Service 2009).

The civil rights movement reached its most organized phase in the late 1950s and 1960s. It encompassed other related movements as well, including the American Indian Movement, La Raza Unida (the Unified Race), the antiwar movement (Vietnam), and the women's movement. After decades of struggle and resistance, that discrimination supported by law was overturned with the ratification of the Civil Rights Act of 1964, the Voting Rights Act of 1965, and the Fair Housing Act of 1968.

Black Consciousness Movement in Brazil

In the case of Brazil, we can say that the black consciousness movement came of age on May 11, 1988, two days before that country was to celebrate the 100th anniversary of the abolition of Brazilian slavery. On this day, 5,000 people marched through downtown Rio de Janeiro led by Frei Davi the leader of the Commission of Black Religious, Seminarians, and Priests. Davi yelled, "They say the good white masters gave us our freedom! Nonsense!" He reminded the participants and crowd that Brazilian blacks were still enslaved. Brazil's "racial democracy is a lie!" (Davi 1992).

This event was pivotal in pushing Brazilians to see that their country was a racial democracy. According to official ideology, race was deemed unimportant because Brazilians had a tradition of encouraging intermarriage and sexual relations across race. In addition, unlike the United States, Brazil had never created laws that enforced segregation. Brazil's traditions led many in and outside of Brazil to hold the country as a model of race relations. When the UN commissioned a series of studies in the 1950s, to understand Brazil's "secret of racial harmony in a world marked by horrors of racism and genocide" (Telles 2004, p. 42), the reports concluded that the ideal of racial democracy was a myth, that there was indeed widespread discrimination and prejudice against blacks and browns. The report also gave credibility to the claims made by those in the black consciousness movement.

In addition to the UN report, a number of other factors helped the black consciousness movement gain momentum, including a shift from military to democratic rule in 1985; widespread acknowledgement that racism, prejudice, and discrimination existed; and gradual efforts to implement policies that addressed racial discrimination. Is it worth mentioning that Fernando Henrique Cardoso, the Brazilian president from 1995 to 2003, was a prominent sociologist of race relations before assuming office. He was not afraid to admit that the country was racist and he endorsed racial quotas as a means of addressing racial inequality (Bailey 2008, Htun 2005).

Brazil's black consciousness movement pulled together hundreds of organizations ranging from church groups, university scholars, activists, dance companies, black women, and others. The overarching goals of the movement were to teach black and brown individuals to question the version of history they had been taught and the words they use to think about themselves. Specifically, browns and blacks should stop thinking of themselves as mulatto, or Moreno should reject the ideology of whitening and begin to call themselves "Negro." In fact, anyone with some discernable traits suggestive of African ancestry should considered themselves black or Negro.

The most political of the black consciousness movement—the Unified Negro Movement (MNU, for Movimento Negro Unificado) successfully lobbied for a constitutional amendment outlawing racial discrimination. MNU aligned with other left-of-center political parties and pushed for the creation of commissions to address racial issues, nominate blacks to run for office, appoint "Negros" to visible political positions, and to set up an office to address racist hiring practices. The MNU also pressured the Brazilian Census Bureau to collect data on the condition of the "Negro" population as it relates to employment, income, and education (Burdick 1992).

One key outcome of the black consciousness movement includes the implementation of affirmative action programs that address the racial inequality and discrimination in education. About 100 public universities and 1,000 private colleges have implemented a quota system in which a predetermined share of each class admitted are black, poor, or from public high schools. That share varies by university. By one estimate, 52,000 students admitted through this system have already graduated (Gasnier 2010).

AP Photo/Ioannis Androutsopoulos

This photo is of Brazil's women's soccer team. Study the faces. Imagine that each was applying to university under Brazil's new affirmative action program. Which athletes would qualify as black?

At the time of this writing, the Brazilian government had not mandated such quota programs nor had the Supreme Court ruled on their constitutionality. In July 2010, legislators passed the Statute of Racial Equality, which gives tax breaks to employees who hire blacks, and mandates that African and Brazilian black history be taught in elementary and middle schools. There is strong public support for affirmative action policies. The latest survey found that 45 percent of those surveyed *strongly agreed* that it is "fair for public universities to reserve spaces for Afro-descendants" (people who are black or mulatto). Only 18 percent disagreed *very strongly* with the statement. Those most likely to disagree with affirmative action in universities include the college educated and those with high incomes (Smith 2011).

We have looked at barriers that exist in society to prevent racial and ethnic groups from assimilating into mainstream society. These barriers include racist ideology, stereotypes, prejudice, and discrimination (individual and institutional). We have also looked at organized responses to institutional discrimination. Although we have viewed these barriers and responses in a general way, we have not examined how they operate in everyday interaction. Sociologist Erving Goffman (1963) offers us a framework for such an examination.

Social Identity and Stigma

CORE CONCEPT 10 Stigmas are attributes that are so deeply discrediting that they come to dominate social experiences and interactions.

Video Tip: Comedian Chris Rock's comedy-documentary, Good Hair, can be used to illustrate the concept of stigma and efforts to correct a perceived failing. The trailer to this film can be accessed at www.imdb.com/title/tt1213585/.

A **stigma** is a physical trait or other attribute that is deeply discrediting. A stigma can be physically evident—a certain skin shade, hair color, hair texture, condition (amputee)—or something feared will be uncovered (a sexual orientation, a certain religious affiliation). A stigma is discrediting because it focuses everyone's attention on one "tainted" status. As such, a stigma dominates social interactions and experiences. To illustrate how, Goffman refers to a letter written by a 16-year-old girl born without a nose. Although she is a good student, has a good figure, and is a good dancer, no one she meets seems able to get past the fact that she has no nose.

Goffman was particularly interested in social encounters known as **mixed contacts**—interactions between stigmatized persons and so-called normals. Note that Goffman did not use the term *normal* to mean "well-adjusted" or "healthy." Instead, he used it to refer to those people who possess no stigma. Note that normal and stigmatized status depends on the social context. A white athlete trying out for a basketball team consisting of black players may possess a stigma, as might the only black student walking into a class consisting of white students on the first day of school.

Goffman wrote that mixed contacts occur when the stigmatized and normals find themselves in the same social setting—whether they be "in a conversation-like encounter" or simply part of some "unfocused gathering" (Goffman 1963, p. 12). According to Goffman, when normals and stigmatized interact, the stigma dominates the interaction. Such dynamics can be applied to social settings where "race matters."

Patterns of Mixed Contact

A stigma can come to dominate interaction in many ways. First, the very anticipation of contact can cause normals and stigmatized to avoid one another. One reason they avoid contact is to escape anticipated discomfort, rejection, disapproval, and suspicion. Social psychologist Claude Steele (1995) offers this description:

> Imagine a black and a white man meeting for the first time. Because the black person knows the stereotypes of his group, he attempts to deflect those negative traits, finding ways of trying to communicate, in effect, "Don't think of me as incompetent." The white, for his part, is busy deflecting the stereotypes of his group: "Don't think of me as a racist." Every action becomes loaded with the potential of confirming the stereotype, and you end up with these phantoms they're only half aware of. The discomfort and tension [are] often mistaken for racial animosity. (p. A25)

One of my "white" students wrote about her experiences of trying to date and establish a relationship with a "black" classmate, against the disapproval of her father and many of her friends: "We tried to carry on a 'secret' relationship, but it just didn't work. We were always worried about who might see us out together. We both agreed it wasn't worth the trouble, so we called it off."

The response of avoidance is related to a second pattern that often characterizes mixed contacts: Upon meeting, normals and stigmatized people are unsure how the other views them or will act toward them. For the stigmatized, the source of the uncertainty is not that everyone they meet views them negatively and treats them accordingly; rather, they consider the chances high that they might encounter such treatment. Minorities may be wary of a white police officer, not because all white police officers are prejudiced and discriminate, but because they or their friends have had bad experiences in the past with some white officers.

A third pattern characteristic of mixed contacts is that normals often define accomplishments by the stigmatized—even minor achievements—"as signs of remarkable and noteworthy capacities" (Goffman 1963, p. 14) or as evidence that they have met someone who is an exception to the rule—someone who does not talk as expected, who possesses less athletic talent than expected, who works in a occupation not anticipated. In a fourth pattern, normals tend to attribute any major or minor failing on the part of the stigmatized—being late for a meeting, cashing a bad check, or leaving a small tip—to the stigma.

A fifth pattern common to mixed contacts is that the stigmatized are likely to experience invasion of privacy, especially when normals stare. Questions such as What are *they* doing in *our* neighborhood? Why are *they* crashing *our* party? and Why is she dating that white man? represent an invasion into the personal matters of the stigmatized person.

Responses to Stigmatization

Goffman describes five ways that the stigmatized respond when they are not accorded respect or treated as a category. First, they may attempt to "correct" the source of stigma. This response includes changing the visible markers believed to represent barriers to success and belonging. For example, a person may undergo plastic surgery to alter the shape of the nose, eyes, or lips; they may color or straighten their hair or wear tinted contacts. Often the stigmatized may feel like, or are considered, a traitor to their race or ethnicity. In addition, they may experience conflicting emotions. Lawrence Otis Graham (2001) experienced such emotions after he underwent plastic surgery on his nose:

> Did I have the operation in order to become less black—to have features that were more white? Had I bought into the white definition of beauty—the sharp nose, the thin lips, the straight hair? Did I think that my less Negroid-looking black friends were more attractive than me? (p. 36)

stigma A stigma is a physical trait or other attribute that is deeply discrediting. A stigma can be physically evident or something feared will be uncovered. A stigma is discrediting because it focuses everyone's attention on one "tainted" status.

mixed contacts Interactions between stigmatized persons and so-called "normals."

Technology Tip: The use of skin lightners illustrates a response to stigmatization—that response is to work to correct the perceived failing. Useful images to illustrate these products and how they are sold can be found though Google Images. Simply use search term "skin lighteners."

A second way the stigmatized respond involves devoting a great deal of time and effort to overcoming stereotypes or to appearing as if they are in full control of everything around them. The stigmatized may try to be perfect—to always be in a good mood, to be extra friendly, to outperform everyone else, or to master an activity not expected of them. This response is common among plumbers, electricians, building contractors, and other service workers who must make house calls in other race neighborhoods. One black contractor interviewed in the *New York Times* maintained that when doing business in white neighborhoods, he tries to "Avoid working at night or showing up at a job early in the morning. Never linger inside houses or gaze at a resident's possessions. And always keep your tools at hand to allay suspicion" (p. A1).

As a third response to being stigmatized, people may use their subordinate status for secondary gains, including personal profit, or as "an excuse for ill success that has come [their] way for other reasons" (Goffman 1963, p. 10). If an employee accuses an employer of discrimination and threatens to file a lawsuit when he or she has been justly sanctioned for poor work, then that person is using stigma for secondary gains. Keep in mind, however, that the person can use stigma this way only because discrimination is commonplace in the larger society.

A fourth response to being stigmatized is to view discrimination as a blessing in disguise, especially for its ability to build character or for what it teaches about life and humanity. Finally, a stigmatized person can condemn all the normals and view them negatively.

Online Poll

If given a chance to indicate your race on a survey, with how many official races will you identify?

- One race
- Two races
- Three or more races

To see how other students responded to these questions, go to **www.cengagebrain.com.**

Ester seng, Courtesy of Joan Ferrante

Summary of CORE CONCEPTS

The photo shows Brazilian students holding the flag of their country. In this chapter, we learned that Brazilian identity is built around the idea that everyone is multiracial and no racial group is distinct from others. This is in sharp contrast to the United States, where races are viewed as distinct categories. We used sociological concepts and theories to think about how ideas of race are constructed and the effects these categories have on life chances, race relations, and identity.

CORE CONCEPT 1 Sociologists define race as human-constructed categories that assume great social importance.

The shortcomings of racial and ethnic categories become evident when we imagine trying to classify the world's 7 billion people. This chapter identifies at lease three shortcomings: (1) There are no sharp dividing lines that distinguishes one racial category from an another. (2) Boundaries between races can never be fixed and clear, if only because males and females of any alleged race can produce offspring together. (3) Most classification schemes force diverse people who vary in ethnicity, language, generation, social class, or physical appearance under one umbrella category.

CORE CONCEPT 2 Most societies, if not all, have created racial categories and rules for placing people into those categories. Keep in mind that, when subjected to scrutiny, category schemes rarely, if ever, make sense.

The U.S. official system recognizes five race categories plus a sixth category, "other" race. Those categories are American Indian or Alaska Native, Asian, Black or African American, Native Hawaiian or Other Pacific Islander, and White. Until the 2000 census, the U.S. system of racial classification required individuals to identity with only one category. Now a person can identify with two or more categories. Only about 2 percent have done so.

The Brazilian Census Bureau employs five categories: white, brown, black, yellow, and indigenous. Only about one percent is considered Asian indigenous. Brazilians tend to use one of six popular terms; one-third use the term *moreno*, a term not employed by the census. The black consciousness movement seeks to divide populations into two categories, white and Negro.

CORE CONCEPT 3 Like race, when sociologists study ethnicity, they are interested in studying the processes by which people make ethnicity important (or not).

An ethnic group consists of people within a larger society (such as country) who possess a group consciousnesses because they share or believe they share a common ancestry, a place of birth, a history, a key experience, or some other distinctive social traits they have defined as the "essence of their peoplehood" (Schermerhorn 1978, p. 12). To capture ethnicity in all its complexity, sociologists employ a number of key concepts, including selective forgetting, ethnic renewal, involuntary ethnicity, and dominant ethnic groups. Dominant ethnic groups are the most advantaged ethnic groups. In Brazil and the United States, those dominant groups are of European ancestries.

CORE CONCEPT 4 The racial and ethnic categories to which people belong are a product of three interrelated factors: chance, context, and choice.

Chance is something not subject to human will, choice, or effort. We do *not* choose our biological parents, nor can we control the physical characteristics we inherit from them. Context is the social setting in which racial and ethnic categories are recognized, created, and challenged. Choice is the act of choosing from a range of possible behaviors or appearances. Individual choices are constrained by chance and context. Most blacks as well as many whites living in the United States would be classified as brown in Brazil. Likewise, everyone in Brazil is considered multiracial.

CORE CONCEPT 5 Every country in the world has people living within its political boundaries who are immigrants and were born elsewhere. Often considerations of race and ethnicity figure into immigration policies.

No government welcomes just anyone; often race, ethnicity, and skills figure into the probability that one will gain admission to a country legally or will have to enter illegally. Historically, race and ethnicity considerations have played a major role in U.S. and Brazilian immigration policies.

CORE CONCEPT 6 Minority groups are subpopulations within a society that are systematically excluded (whether consciously or unconsciously) from full participation in society and denied equal opportunities to access power, prestige, and wealth.

Membership in minority groups is involuntary, and a minority may be the numerical majority in a society. Minority groups are excluded from full participation in the larger society. That is, they do not enjoy the taken-for-granted advantages and immunities a dominant group enjoys. Often minority groups are subjected to social and spatial isolation. Minority status overshadows any accomplishments. These characteristics of minority group status apply especially to the situation of involuntary minorities.

CORE CONCEPT 7 Assimilation is a process by which ethnic and racial distinctions between groups disappear because one group is absorbed into another group's culture or because two cultures blend to form a new culture.

There are two types of assimilation: absorption and melting pot. In the first type, two or more racial and ethnic group minorities adapt to the point where they are completely "absorbed" into the dominant culture. In practice, this type of assimilation is difficult if only because disadvantaged racial and ethnic groups experience de jure or de facto segregation. The segregation may be spatial or hierarchical. The second type of assimilation is melting pot where racial and ethnic groups accept many new behaviors and values from one another. This exchange produces a new blended cultural system.

CORE CONCEPT 8 Racism is the belief that genetic or biologically based differences explain and even justify inequalities that exist between advantaged and disadvantaged racial and ethnic groups.

Those alleged genetic differences—as manifested in skin color, hair texture, and eye shape—are deemed so significant that they are used to explain racial and ethnic differences as they relate to crime, graduation, teen pregnancy, and marriage rates. From a racist point of view, there is no other possible explanation for these inequalities. Racism has probably always existed. Modern racism, however, emerged as a way to justify European exploitation of people and resources in Africa, Asia, and the Americas. More precisely, the exploitation was justified by scientific racism. In Brazil, eugenicists used scientific racism to justify policies aimed at "whitening" the population. In the United States, scientific racism justified laws aimed at preserving racial purity.

CORE CONCEPT 9 Prejudice, stereotyping, and discrimination are tools that preserve the system that benefits advantaged race and ethnic groups.

Both prejudiced and nonprejudiced people can discriminate. In contrast to prejudice, discrimination is not an attitude but a behavior. It is aimed at denying people equal opportunities to achieve socially valued goals (such as education, employment, health care, and long life) or blocking their access to valued goods and services. Prejudice does not necessarily predict discriminatory conduct.

CORE CONCEPT 10 Stigmas are attributes that are so deeply discrediting that they come to dominate social experiences and interactions.

A stigma is a physical trait or other attribute that is deeply discrediting. Sociologists examine social encounters between those deemed normal and stigmatized, known as mixed contacts. A stigma can come to dominate those contacts in many ways. For example, normals and stigmatized often take measures to avoid one another. The stigmatized respond in a variety of ways. They may attempt to "correct" the source of stigma or view it as a blessing in disguise.

Resources on the Internet

Login to CengageBrain.com to access the resources your instructor requires. For this book, you can access:

Sociology CourseMate

Access an integrated eBook, chapter-specific interactive learning tools, including flash cards, quizzes, videos, and more in your Sociology CourseMate.

Take a pretest for this chapter and receive a personalized study plan based on your results that will identify the topics you need to review and direct you to online resources to help you master those topics. Then take a posttest to help you determine the concepts you have mastered and what you will need to work on.

CourseReader

CourseReader for Sociology is an online reader providing access to readings, and audio and video selections to accompany your course materials.

Visit **www.cengagebrain.com** to access your account and purchase materials.

Key Terms

absorption assimilation 229
assimilation 229
chance 222
choice 223
context 223
discrimination 233
dominant ethnic group 222
ethnic group 220
ethnic renewal 220
ethnicity 220
hidden ethnicity 222
individual discrimination 235
institutionalized discrimination 235
involuntary ethnicity 220
involuntary minorities 229
melting pot assimilation 231
minority groups 226
mixed contacts 239
nonprejudiced discriminators (fair-weather liberals) 235
nonprejudiced nondiscriminators (all-weather liberals) 235
prejudice 232
prejudiced discriminators (active bigots) 235
prejudiced nondiscriminators (timid bigots) 235
race 214
racial common sense 215
reify 216
scientific racism 231
segregation 230
selective forgetting 220
selective perception 233
spatial segregation 230
stereotypes 233
stigma 238

GENDER

10 With Emphasis on AMERICAN SAMOA

When sociologists study gender they seek to understand the processes by which people learn behaviors and appearances expected of someone of their sex. They also are very interested in people who conform and defy expectations and how others react when they do. The two people pictured are American Samoan fa'afafines (pronounced fah-ah-fuh-fee-nay), someone not considered biologically female but who has taken on the "way of women" in dress, mannerism, appearance, and role. The two pictured are also international fa'afafine boxing champions. Fa'afafines are very diverse in the way they present themselves. The fa'afafines who live in cities tend to be more visible and dress flamboyantly, often performing in what are thought of as American-style drag shows. Those who live in rural areas or who are from devout Christian families are more discreet and tend not to flaunt sexuality (Tok Blong Pacifik 2008).

Why Focus On AMERICAN SAMOA?

In this chapter, the topic of gender is paired with American Samoa. Most Americans probably do not realize that American Samoa has been a territory of the United States since 1899, when the Samoan Islands were partitioned between Germany and the United States. Many Americans probably do know of an American Samoan who plays for their favorite NFL or Division I college football team, as at least 200 Samoans play at those levels. That number is truly amazing, given that the entire population of American Samoa is about 65,000, hardly large enough to fill a Super Bowl stadium (CBS 60 Minutes 2010).

In contrast to the rugged image of the football player, Samoans recognize a third gender that they call fa'afafine, people not considered biologically female but who have taken on the "way of women" in dress, mannerism, appearance, and role. The most visible fa'afafines dress as famous female celebrities such as Britney Spears, Madonna, or Kelly Clarkson. Their success in Samoan society comes from giving the most stunningly accurate imitation of these women. There is even a Miss Island Queen contest (since 1979) judged by very high-profile men and women outside the transgender community including U.S. military officers, writers, the reigning Miss American Samoa, and musicians (Matà afa 2006). One year, a second-grade teacher won. The winners are expected to engage in a range of community service projects that often involve the elderly, the local Red Cross chapter, and hospitals (Matà afa 2009).

Sociologists are fascinated by a society where both football players and fa'afafines are commonplace. They look for social forces that support the existence of both in such a tiny population. In addition, sociologists draw lessons about gender that go beyond American Samoa and inform a general understanding of gender.

Online Poll

If you were expecting a baby, would you want to know the sex of the baby in advance of its birth?

○ Yes

○ No

To see how other students responded to these questions, go to **www.cengagebrain.com.**

Phil Walter/Getty Images

Distinguishing Sex and Gender

In this chapter, we begin by examining a crucial distinction sociologists make between *sex* and *gender*. Although many people use those two words interchangeably, the two terms have very different meanings.

Sex as a Biological Concept

CORE CONCEPT 1 Sex is a biological concept, whereas gender is a social construct.

Sex is a biological distinction determined by primary sex characteristics or the anatomical traits essential to reproduction. Most cultures classify people in two categories—male and female—based largely on what are considered to be clear anatomical distinctions. Anatomical sex is not something that is clear-cut, however, if only because some

sex A biological concept based on primary sex characteristics.

Teaching Tip: Show the author's video introduction to Chapter 10, which can be found on the Power Lecture CD. A transcript of the video is included in the Instructor's Resource Manual.

babies are born **intersexed**. The medical profession uses this broad term to classify people with some mixture of male and female anatomy. Although we do not know how many intersexed babies are born each year, one physician who treats intersexed children estimated that number to be one thousand (Dreifus, 2005).

If some babies are born intersexed, why does society not recognize an intersexed category? Up until 2006, the American Academy of Pediatrics labeled the condition a "social emergency." Today, the academy labels this condition a disorder of sexual development (DSD) and recommends that children with DSD be treated by "an experienced multidisciplinary team consisting of pediatric subspecialists in endocrinology, surgery, and/or urology, psychology/psychiatry, gynecology, genetics, neonatology, and, if available, social work, nursing, and medical ethics" (Lee et al. 2006). Although the American Academy of Pediatrics no longer labels this condition a social emergency, the recommendation suggests that it should still be treated as such.

Determining biological sex becomes even more complicated when we consider that a person's anatomy may not match his or her sex chromosomes. Theoretically, two chromosomes determine one's sex. Each parent supposedly contributes one sex chromosome: The mother contributes an X chromosome, and the father contributes an X or a Y chromosome. If the chromosome carried by the sperm that fertilizes the egg is a Y, then the baby will be a male. Although it is not known how many people's sex chromosomes do not match their anatomy, the results of mandatory "sex tests" of female athletes competing in international competitions have shown that such cases exist. Indeed, a few women were disqualified from competitions because they "failed" the tests.

One of the most recent and highly publicized cases involved the South African runner Caster Semenya. Just hours before she was to compete in the 800 meters race at the 2009 international track and field world championships in Berlin, Germany, track officials announced that, because of her muscular build, husky voice, and superior athletic talent, she needed to submit to sex-determination testing. In spite of this announcement, Semenya went on to handily defeat her opponents. Although one might think it would be easy to determine whether Semenya is a man or woman, the test took several weeks to complete and involved a medical examination and reports from a gynecologist, an endocrinologist, a psychologist, an internal medicine specialist, and an expert on gender (Dreger 2009). Anonymous sources claimed that the tests showed that Semenya is both a woman and a man. No matter, the International Association of Athletics Federations cleared her to resume competition, which she did in July 2010 (Moore 2010).

FABRIZIO BENSCH/Reuters/Landov

The International Olympic Committee discontinued compulsory sex determination testing in 1999, claiming that such tests were "inconclusive, expensive, insensitive." However, female athletes must still submit to such tests when complaints are filed challenging their "femininity" and by extension their sex (Law 2007). Such a complaint was filed against South African runner Caster Semenya in 2009, during world competitions in Berlin. After undergoing testing and waiting 11 months for a verdict, Semenya was cleared to compete (Bearak 2009).

Why is there no clear line to distinguish male and female anatomy? One answer lies in the biological processes involved in creating males and females. In the first weeks after conception, the human embryo develops the potential to form a "female set of ovaries and a male set of testes." Approximately eight weeks into development, "a molecular chain of events orders one set to disintegrate." One week later, the embryo begins to develop an outer appearance that matches its external sex organs (Lehrman 1997, p. 49). This complex chain of events may not occur "perfectly"; instead, it may be affected by any number of factors, including exposure to medications taken by the mother.

In addition to anatomy and chromosomes, we also use **secondary sex characteristics** to distinguish one sex from

intersexed A broad term used by the medical profession to classify people with some mixture of male and female biological characteristics.

secondary sex characteristics Physical traits not essential to reproduction (such as breast development, quality of voice, distribution of facial and body hair, and skeletal form) that result from the action of so-called male (androgen) and female (estrogen) hormones.

Technology Tip: Play the NPR, This American Life program profiling the life of two transgender 8 year olds. The title of the program is "Somewhere Out There: Tom Girls" and it is 17 minutes in length. Simply go to This American Life website (www.thisamericanlife.org/radio-archives) and search the archives using "Tom Girls" as search terms.

another. These physical traits (such as breast development, quality of voice, distribution of facial and body hair, and skeletal form) are not essential to reproduction but result from the action of so-called male (androgen) and female (estrogen) hormones. We use the term *so-called* because, although testes produce androgen and ovaries produce estrogen, the adrenal cortex produces androgen and estrogen in both sexes (Garb 1991). None of the secondary characteristics are associated with a clear line by which to separate males from females.

Gender as a Social Construct

Whereas sex is a biological distinction, **gender** is a social distinction based on culturally conceived and learned ideals about appropriate appearance, behavior, and mental and emotional characteristics for males and females. *Ideal* in this context means a standard against which real cases can be compared. A gender ideal is at best a caricature, in that it exaggerates the characteristics that make someone the so-called perfect male or female. Keep in mind that very few people achieve a gender ideal; even those who do cannot usually sustain it, if only because they age. In fact, sometimes ideals may be so difficult to achieve that they may not exist in reality.

Consider that at one time the ideal foot length for Chinese women was 4 to 6 inches—an impossible standard that no females could achieve without enduring foot binding as young girls. This practice involved breaking the four smallest toes on each foot and binding them toward the heel so the feet could no longer grow. Likewise, few grown women have 18-inch waists, and yet, women in the United States and in other societies have worn corsets to achieve that impossible standard.

The terms **masculinity** and **femininity** signify the physical, behavioral, and mental and emotional traits believed to be characteristic of males and females (Morawski 1991). To grasp that gender is a culturally conceived "reality," we must note that no fixed line separates masculinity from femininity. The French painter Paul Gauguin pointed out this ambiguity in his observations about Tahitian men and women, which he recorded in a journal that he kept while painting in Tahiti in 1891. His observations were influenced by nineteenth-century Western ideals of femininity:

> Among peoples that go naked, as among animals, the difference between the sexes is less accentuated than in our climates. Thanks to our cinctures and corsets we have succeeded in making an artificial being out of woman. . . . We carefully keep her in a state of nervous weakness and muscular inferiority, and in guarding her from fatigue, we take away from her possibilities of development. Thus modeled on a bizarre ideal of slenderness . . . our women have nothing in common with us [men], and this, perhaps, may not be without grave moral and social disadvantages.

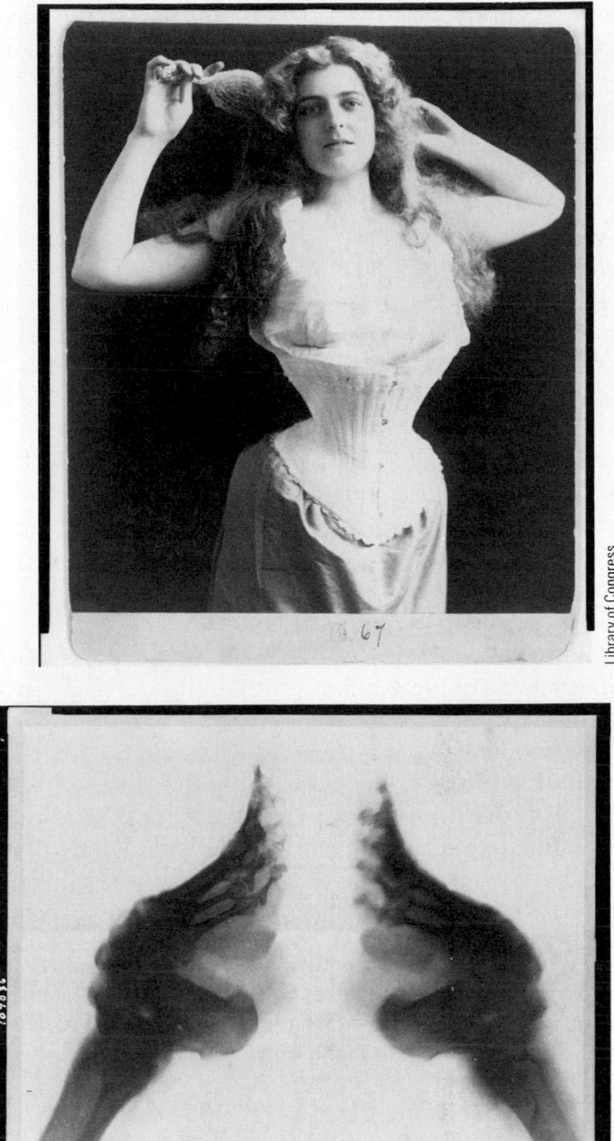
Library of Congress

Library of Congress

The two photos illustrate gender ideals with regard to waist and foot size that few, if any, people can achieve without taking extreme measures. Without the help of a corset, few women have an 18-inch waist. Without breaking the four smallest toes on each foot and binding them under the heel, few women have feet that are 4 inches in length. The X-ray shows the bone structure of a foot that has been subjected to binding. Both images were created between 1888 and 1920.

gender A social distinction based on culturally conceived and learned ideals about appropriate appearance, behavior, and mental and emotional characteristics for males and females.

masculinity The physical, behavioral, and mental and emotional traits believed to be characteristic of males.

femininity The physical, behavioral, and mental and emotional traits believed to be characteristic of females.

Teaching Tip: The Metropolitan Museum of Art put on an exhibition titled, "Extreme Beauty: The Body Transformed." Some images from this exhibition can be found at www.metmuseum.org/special/Extreme_Beauty/body_transformed_images.htm. Ask students if they know of any extreme measures people take today to achieve gender ideals (e.g., botox treatments, surgeries).

At the turn of the twentieth century, the French artist Paul Gauguin observed that differences between the sexes in Tahitian society were less accentuated than they were in Western society: There was "something virile in the women and something feminine in the men."

> On Tahiti, the breezes from forest and sea strengthen the lungs, they broaden the shoulders and hips. Neither men nor women are sheltered from the rays of the sun nor the pebbles of the sea-shore. Together they engage in the same tasks with the same activity. . . . There is something virile in the women and something feminine in the men. (1919, pp. 19–20)

Often we mistakenly attribute masculinity and femininity to biology, when in fact, they are socially created. In the United States, for example, norms specify the amount and distribution of facial and body hair appropriate for females. It is deemed acceptable for women to have eyelashes and well-shaped eyebrows but certainly not to have hair above their lips, under their arms, on their inner thighs (outside the bikini line), or on their chin, shoulders, back, chest, breasts, abdomen, legs, or toes. Many men, and even some women, do not realize that women work to achieve these cultural standards and that the women's compliance makes males and females appear more physically distinct in terms of hair distribution than they are in reality. We lose sight of the fact that normal biological events—puberty, pregnancy, menopause, stress—can change the balance between two hormones, androgen and estrogen, triggering hair growth that departs from societal norms about the appropriate amount and texture of hair for females. When women grow body hair because of these events, they tend to think something is wrong with them instead of seeing this development as natural. Both men and women work to achieve the ideal standards of masculine and feminine beauty, as portrayed in the media or as conveyed and reinforced elsewhere. On a personal level, these ideal standards are not viewed objectively—as something created— but as a violation of nature.

Consider also gender ideals regarding hair length. Like in the United States, long hair on Samoan women is the ideal. In fact, long hair does not simply *signify* feminine sexual attractiveness; it *is* feminine sexual attractiveness. Jeanette Mageo (1996) argues that ideal standards of beauty affect us personally because

> what has personal significance is at least in part a product of how we are regarded and treated by others. When a Samoan girl acts under constant threat of having her hair cut off or of being pulled home by her hair [because she is attracting male attentions], when her beauty is judged, at contests and elsewhere, by the length of her hair, the public symbol of hair cannot fail to touch her feelings. (p. 158)

Although Samoan women's femininity is judged according to the length of their hair, some Samoan men seek to acquire tattoos as a sign of masculinity. Before the Christianization of Samoa, the transition from boyhood to manhood was accompanied by a "long and painful process of body tattooing, from the waist to below the knees" (Cote 1997, p. 2). Tattooing or *tatau* (ta-TAH-oo) did not merely *signify* manhood; it *was* manhood:

> The man who was not tattooed . . . was not respected. . . . Until a young man was tattooed . . . he could not think of marriage, and he was constantly exposed to taunts and ridicule, as being poor and of low birth, and having no right to speak in the society of men. But as soon as he was tattooed, he . . . considered himself entitled to the respect and privileges of mature years. When a youth, therefore, reached the age of sixteen, he and his friends were all anxious that they should be tattooed. . . . On these occasions, six or a dozen young men would be tattooed at one time. . . . In two or three months the whole is completed. (Turner 1861, pp. 87–89)

To this point, we have drawn a distinction between sex and gender. Although sociologists maintain that there is no sharp line to distinguish males from females, they would never argue that there are no biological differences. Sociologists are, however, interested in the extent to which differences are socially induced. That is, they study the actions that men and women take to be different from one another and to accentuate biological differences.

Teaching Tip: Use the NPR search engine to find a program titled "The End of Gender." The webpage includes a photograph of an androgynous male model. The photograph can be treated as a contemporary representation of Gauguin's assessment that there was "something virile in the women and something feminine in the men."

Many Samoan males still choose to acquire the waste-to-knee tattoos. In fact, some Los Angeles–based Samoans on visits to American Samoa will get the painful body *tatau* to show they are men and responsible to family (Channell 2002).

Gender Polarization

Gender ideals shape practically every aspect of life—influencing, among other things, how people dress, how they express emotions, and what occupations they choose. **Gender polarization** is the organizing of social life around male–female ideals, so that someone's assigned sex influences every aspect of his or her life, including how to dress, the time to wake up in the morning, what to do before going to bed at night, the things to worry about, and even ways of expressing emotion and experiencing sexual attraction (Bem 1993). To understand how social life becomes organized around gender, we consider a classic research study in which Alice Baumgartner-Papageorgiou (1982) asked elementary and high school students how their lives would be different if they were the other sex. Their responses reflected culturally conceived and learned ideas about sex-appropriate behaviors and appearances and about the imagined and real advantages and disadvantages of being male or female (Vann 1995).

The boys generally believed that their lives would change in negative ways if they became girls. Among other things, they envisioned themselves as being less active and more restricted in what they could do. In addition, they believed they would become more conscious about tending to their appearance, finding a husband, and being alone and unprotected in the face of a violent attack:

- I would start to look for a husband as soon as I got into high school.
- I'd use a lot of makeup and look good and beautiful.
- I'd have to shave my whole body.
- I'd have to know how to handle drunk guys and rapists.
- I couldn't have a pocket knife.
- I would not be able to help my dad fix the car and truck and his two motorcycles. (Baumgartner-Papageorgiou 1982, pp. 2–9)

The girls, on the other hand, believed that if they became boys, they would be less emotional, their lives would be more active and less restrictive, they would be closer to their fathers, and they would be treated as more than "sex objects":

- I would have to stay calm and cool whenever something happened.
- I could sleep later in the mornings, since it would not take [me] very long to get ready for school.
- My father would be closer, because I'd be the son he always wanted.
- People would take my decisions and beliefs more seriously. (Baumgartner-Papageorgiou 1982, pp. 5–13)

Although the Baumgartner-Papageorgiou study was published almost 30 years ago, these beliefs about what it means to be male or female seem to hold up across time, even among the college students enrolled in the author's introductory sociology classes. These students were asked to take a few minutes to write about how their lives would change in positive and negative ways as members of the other sex. The men generally believed that they would be more emotional and more conscious of their physical appearance and that their career options would narrow considerably. Some responses illustrate:

- I would be much more sensitive to others' needs and what I'm expected to do.
- I wouldn't always have to appear like I am in control of every situation. I would be comforted instead of always being the comforter.
- People would put me down for the way I look.
- I would be more emotional.
- I would worry more about losing weight instead of trying to gain weight.

gender polarization The organizing of social life around male–female ideals, so that people's sex influences every aspect of their life, including how they dress, the time they get up in the morning, what they do before they go to bed at night, the social roles they take on, the things they worry about, and even the ways they express emotion and experience sexual attraction.

- If I stayed in the construction program, I would have to fight the belief that men are the only real construction workers.
- My career options would narrow.
- I would have to be conscious of the way I sit.

The women in the class believed that as men they would have to worry about asking women out and about whether their major was appropriate. They also believed, however, that they would make more money, be less emotional, and be taken more seriously. Some of their responses follow:

- I would worry about whether a woman would say yes if I asked her out.
- I would earn more money than my female counterpart in my chosen profession.
- People would take me more seriously and not attribute my emotions to PMS.
- My dad would expect me to be an athlete.
- I'd have to remain cool when under stress and not show my emotions.
- I think that I would change my major from "undecided" to a major in construction technology.

These comments show the extent to which life is organized and constrained in gendered ways. They reveal that decisions about how early to get up in the morning, which subjects to study, whether to show emotion, how to sit, and whether to encourage a child's athletic development are influenced by a society's gender ideals rather than by criteria such as self-fulfillment, interest, ability, or personal comfort. For example, one study found that almost 40 percent of women will wear uncomfortable shoes to be fashionable; 17 percent of men admit to buying the wrong size shoes, probably larger than needed (Daily Mail 2009).

coka/Shutterstock

Many women admit to wearing uncomfortable shows that are damaging to foot and body health just to be in fashion.

College students are influenced by gender ideals if they choose a major they believe is appropriate to their sex. Consider that 82 percent of bachelor's degrees in computer and information sciences are awarded to men, whereas 91 percent of bachelor's degrees in library sciences are awarded to females. Other majors dominated by women include education, health professions, family and consumer sciences/human sciences, and public administration/services (almost 80 percent of all bachelor's degrees awarded in these fields go to women) (*Chronicle of Higher Education* 2010).

To this point, we have shown that not everyone fits easily into two biological categories, that gender is a social construction, and that gender ideals are impossible to realize and maintain. So, it should be no real surprise that there are some societies such as American Samoa that accept a third gender. In Samoa, that third option is *fa'afafine*.

A Third Option

CORE CONCEPT 2 While all societies distinguish between male and female, some also recognize a third gender.

Jeannette Mageo (1992) begins her article "Male Transvestitism and Cultural Change in Samoa" by describing the guests attending a wedding shower in Samoa. Of approximately 40 "women," 6 were *fa'afafine*—people who are not biologically female but who have taken on the "way of women" in dress, mannerism, appearance, and role. Those who study *fa'afafine* maintain that to understand this third gender, we must set aside any cultural preconceptions we have about being male, female, gay, or transsexual (Fraser 2002).

During that wedding shower, the *fa'afafine* staged a beauty contest in which each sang and danced a love song. Such beauty contests are well known in Samoa, and the winner "is sometimes the 'girl' who gives the most stunningly accurate imitation of real girls, such that even Samoans would be at a loss to tell the difference; sometimes the winner is the most brilliant comic" (Mageo 1998, p. 213). Often the *fa'afafine* imitate popular foreign female vocalists, such as Whitney Houston, Britney Spears, Madonna, or Kelly Clarkson.

Mageo believes that *fa'afafines were* not common in pre-Christian Samoa (before 1830). If so, she believes that early Christian missionaries, preoccupied with documenting sexual habits of the Samoans would have mentioned it in their written accounts of that society. How, then, did assuming the role of *fa'afafine* become commonplace among males, especially in urban areas? Mageo (1992, 1998) argues that *fa'afafine* could not have become commonplace unless something about Samoan society supported gender

Student Activity: Ask students this question, "How would your life be different if you were members of the so-called opposite sex?" Ask students to break into groups of four or five to generate a list of responses. A spokesperson for the group can present the list to the class.

The Sociological Imagination Compliance and Resistance to Gender Ideals

If we simply think about the men and women we encounter every day, we quickly realize that most people fall short of society's gender ideals. This fact does not stop most people from using these ideals to evaluate their own and others' behavior and appearance. Some accounts of resistance, compliance, and the accompanying inner conflicts and social strains speak to the importance of gender ideals in shaping our lives.

Learning about and Accepting Gender Ideals. In high school, I began to realize how important my appearance and behavior were to being accepted. In the bathrooms, the juniors and seniors showed freshmen how to throw up after lunch in order to stay thin. Anorexia and bulimia were widespread, and we were very ruthless in our criticism of others. I began to practice walking with a sway in my hips and to flirt with my eyes lowered and head tilted. I started to wear makeup to accentuate my feminine features. I began to giggle, something I never really did growing up. Gender ideals have had their effects upon me. I work as an amateur model and actress, banking on the male–female distinction.

Attempting to Change the Behaviors that Deviate from Gender Ideals. There is something that drove me crazy. The feeling I experienced and the warmth I felt toward this woman were extraordinary, but so wrong. I didn't have anywhere to turn and no one to talk to. I did not want to tell anyone who or what I had done. Society said it was wrong to feel and act this way, but why did I feel so good and think about her so much? I nearly drove myself crazy and ran as far as I could. I joined the army to punish myself. Every day I hated what I had done and I wanted to hurt myself to make it go away. I hoped that by surrounding myself with men, I would forget what I had done and find some man that would help make me into a "normal" heterosexual woman.

Challenging Those Who Do Not Conform to Gender Ideals/ Refusing to Conform to Gender Ideals. I went on a blind date and met a girl who seemed too good to be true. Everything went well for the next three weeks. We hadn't been very intimate, so when she asked me to come over to her house and stay with her, I jumped at the opportunity. I entered her house to find candles lit and soft music playing. We began to kiss, and I noticed that she hadn't shaved her legs in a while. Disgusting, but under the circumstances I tried to block it out. As we got more involved I was surprised to find a lot of hair under her arms. I quickly pulled away. She asked what was wrong, and after I told her she laughed. Needless to say I felt like I was going to throw up. I put my clothes on and quickly left. On the way home I kept thinking how sick it made me that she didn't shave. I decided that I would never talk to her again. Sometime later she called me to explain. She told me that she didn't think women should have to shave and that she hadn't shaved for at least a year. She believed I should respect and even like her more for making a stand. Making a stand toward what, I thought? Anyway, I told her that I thought it was disgusting and I told her I didn't want to see her again.

blurring. She notes that "on a personal level Samoans do not distinguish sharply between men and women, boys and girls." For example, "boys and girls take equal pride in their skills in fights; pre-Christian personal names are often not marked for gender, and outside school little boys and girls still wear much the same clothing" (1998, p. 451).

Once Samoan boys reach the age of 5 or 6, they begin spending the majority of their time in the company of other boys; at this point, they are prohibited from flirting with girls. At the same time, "close and physically affectionate relations with same-sex people are established practices. In Samoa, as in much of the Pacific, boys may walk about hand-in-hand or with an arm draped around their comrade, and so may girls" (Mageo 1992, p. 452).

There are other historical factors that support the existence of *fa'afafine*. When the Christian missionaries observed girls engaged in sexualized forms of entertainment, they pressured the Samoans to change this practice and the girls to abandon this role. Mageo makes the case that this change opened the doors for *fa'afafine* to stand-in for the girls.

Another factor that may account for the widespread emergence of the *fa'afafine* relates to changes in the opportunities open to men in Samoa. Specifically, these changes are connected to the gradual decline in the importance of the *augama*, an organization of men without titles. At one time, the *augama* was considered the "strength of the village" (Mead 1928, p. 34), serving "as a village police force or an army reserve" (Mageo 1992, p. 444). It took responsibility for the heavy work, whether that be "on the plantation, or fishing, [or] cooking for the chiefs" (Mead 1928, p. 34).

The rise of compulsory education, the shift away from an agriculture-based to a wage-based economy, and the introduction of labor-saving technology contributed to the decline of the *augama*. That decline removed an important source of status for Samoan males. That loss of status has been compounded by an unemployment rate of 29.8 percent in American Samoa (U.S. Central Intelligence Agency 2011). Moreover, when we consider that the size of the Samoan labor force is just a little over 17,000 and that the largest employers are a tuna cannery (employing 2,282) and the Samoan government (employing 6,052), we can see the blows to status that many males might experience (U.S. Department of Interior 2010). This economic reality has left the average Samoan male without a clear sense of place. For some men, becoming a *fa'afafine* offered them an opportunity to step out of their lowered status and assume the status of well-known female impersonators. Other options for Samoan men include joining the military or becoming football players for the United States, Canadian, or European league.

In evaluating Mageo's research, keep in mind that she was writing about the social forces that push some fa'afafines to assume highly visible roles such as female impersonators. In reality, the fa'afafine population is very diverse. Keep in mind that Western labels—such as gay, transvestite, drag queen, or even transgendered—do not capture traditional Samoan conceptions of fa'afafine and their place in society. It is important to point out that fa'afafine do not define themselves as women in men's bodies. In fact, their mothers or other women close to the family decided they were fa'afafine based on the way they behaved or because there were not enough girls in the family to help with "women's work." In general, fa'afafine typically do not have children, and they often become teachers. They are thought to be devoted to family, caring for aging parents, keeping house, and babysitting (Tok Blong Pacifik 2008).

How do fa'afafines express themselves sexually? The answer is not a simple one. Many who consider themselves women "enter into clandestine, short-term relationships with men who see themselves as straight. Some fa'afafine, motivated by social pressure and the wish for children, leave their feminine identity behind and marry women, but many others don't. Occasionally they live openly with male partners" (Tok Blong Pacifik 2008).

Christina Douglas (9th Mission Support Command)

Economic opportunities are limited in American Samoa. After one of two tuna canneries closed in 2009, affecting one-third of all Samoan workers, many turned to the U.S. military. At this town hall meeting held in Pago Pago, the capital of American Samoa, attendees check with U.S. military personnel about plans to increase the number of Army Reserve positions in American Samoa.

sexual orientation "An enduring pattern of emotional, romantic, and/or sexual attractions to men, women, or both sexes. Sexual orientation also refers to a person's sense of identity based on those attractions, related behaviors, and membership in a community of others who share those attractions" (APA 2009).

Sexuality

We are bombarded daily with messages about sexuality. They may come from sex education classes that warn of the health dangers of unprotected sexual activities, from fairy tales, from song lyrics, or from commercials, movies, and news events. Other messages come from those close to us: friends who come out to us or parents who kidded us when we were toddlers about having a boyfriend or girlfriend. Finally, messages come from observing the treatment of people around us. For example, we notice uncomfortable reactions toward women who breast-feed their babies in public and toward men who appear feminine or women who appear masculine; we take notice of the boy and girl everyone wants to date or to not date; we take note of reactions and facial expressions when someone says they are from San Francisco.

CORE CONCEPT 3 Sexuality encompasses all the ways people experience and express themselves as sexual beings. The study of sexuality considers the range of sexual expressions and the social activities, behaviors, and thoughts that generate sexual sensations.

Sexuality is not an easy subject to present for several reasons. First, for most of us, sex/sexuality education focused on the dangerous consequences of sexuality (sexually transmitted diseases) uninformed by any discussions of what to make of sexual excitement, sexual attraction, or of the commercial uses of sexuality to sell products from cars to music. Second, people who have had difficult sexual experiences—those molested or raped as children, men who cannot achieve erections, and women and men who have been sexually assaulted—may be uncomfortable with the topic (Davis 2005). Third, it is very difficult to discuss human sexuality in all its dimensions when heterosexuality and all that it entails is presented as the norm and other expressions of sexuality are considered deviant and in need of fixing.

Sexual orientation is an expression of sexuality. Although sociologists are interested in the topic of sexual orientation, the American Sociological Association does not issue a statement about what sexual orientation means. According to the American Psychiatric Association (2009), sexual orientation refers to "an enduring pattern of emotional, romantic, and/or sexual attractions to men, women, or both sexes. Sexual orientation also refers to a person's sense of identity based on those attractions,

Discussion Tip: Ask students to comment on their memories of sex education classes they had in middle school and high school. In what ways were they effective or not effective?

related behaviors, and membership in a community of others who share those attractions." The word *enduring* suggests that one encounter does not make someone gay or lesbian. This caveat speaks to the fact that many people have experienced at least one same-sex sexual encounter at some point in their lives. Results from the most recent Centers for Disease Control (2002) survey found that 1 in 9 women and 1 in 18 men ages 15 to 44 have had a sexual experience with someone of the same sex.

Sexual orientation falls along a continuum, with its endpoints being exclusive attraction to the other sex and exclusive attraction to the same sex. In the United States, we tend to think of sexual orientation as falling into three distinct categories: heterosexual (attractions to those of the other sex), gay/lesbian (attractions to those of one's own sex), and bisexual (attractions to both men and women). It is important to realize that there are other labels that cultures apply to expressions of human sexualities (APA 2009).

Sexual orientation should not be confused with other related and intertwining terms, including the following:

gender identity—the awareness of being a man or woman, of being neither, or something in between (gender identity also involves the ways one chooses to hide or express that identity)

transgender—the label applied to those who feel that their inner sense of being a man or woman does not match their anatomical sex, so they behave and/or dress to actualize their gender identity (see Working for Change: "Transgender Day of Remembrance"). The *Diagnostic and Statistical Manual of Mental Disorders*, a reference book used by mental health practitioners, estimates that 1 in 30,000 people born male and 1 in 100,000 people born female have a "gender identity disorder" (Barton 2005). A revised edition of this manual is scheduled for release in 2012. Many practitioners are calling for the removal of gender identity disorder as a mental illness (Ault and Brzuzy 2009).

People enact sexual orientation in relationships with others. Thus, according to the APA (2009), "sexual orientation is closely tied to the intimate personal relationships that meet deeply felt needs for love, attachment, and intimacy." Based on what we know to date, the core attractions that emerge in middle childhood through early adolescence prior to sexual experiences are the foundation of adult sexual orientation. The experiences of coming to terms with sexual orientation vary. People can be aware of their sexual orientation even if they are celibate or have yet to engage in sexual activity. Others come to label their orientation after a sexual experience with a same-sex and/or other-sex partner. Still others ignore, suppress, or resist pulls toward those of the same sex because of widespread social disapproval (APA 2009).

Regardless of sexual orientation, every group has established **sexual scripts**, responses and behaviors that people learn, in much the same way that actors learn lines for a play, to guide them in sexual activities and encounters. The sexual scripts of the dominant culture call for behaviors and responses that support heterosexual ideals. Other sexual scripts, constructed by those in lesbian, gay, bisexual, and transgender and questioning (LGBTQ) communities, are dismissed as deviant. Even those who resist or reject the heterosexual scripts know that script and know they are ideally expected to follow them. As a result, those outside the heterosexual community often feel like they must account for deviating from the script. In this regard, most of my students have acknowledged knowing a same-sex person for whom they felt deep affection and attraction and who made them feel alive (descriptions we typically reserve for male–female attractions). Likewise, most if not all these students account for these feelings by emphasizing that they should in no way be interpreted as sexual.

Chris Caldeira

The Human Rights Campaign is a grass roots, not-for-profit, organization that claims one million supporters. HRC works to promote equal rights and a safe environment where LBGT can live an open, honest and safe life in their homes, workplaces and communities.

Socialization

CORE CONCEPT 4 Gender expectations are learned and culturally imposed through a variety of social mechanisms, including socialization, situational constraints, and commercialization of gender ideals.

Masculinity and femininity are not innate; children learn these characteristics. Once a child is labeled male or female, everyone who comes in contact with the child begins to treat him or her as such. With encouragement from others, children learn to talk, walk, and move in gendered

sexual scripts Responses and behaviors that people learn, in much the same way that actors learn lines for a play, to guide them in sexual activities and encounters.

Working for Change Transgender Day of Remembrance

Activist, writer and graphic designer Gwendolyn Ann Smith launched the Transgender Day of Remembrance (TDR) on November 20, 1999, as a tribute to Rita Hester who died in 1998. Hester was an African American transgendered female who was found stabbed to death at her apartment in Allston, Massachusetts. Although the crime against her was never solved, it was widely believed to be a hate crime. This small Internet project is snowballing into a worldwide movement to recognize the rights of the transgendered. Now on November 20 each year, Rita Hester's death, the deaths of other transgender people, and those who have suffered from gender-based intolerance and discrimination are remembered. According to the organization's website, the event's purpose is to raise public awareness about hate crimes against transgender people, stories that the mainstream media typically doesn't cover (St. Pierre 2007). "Day of Remembrance publicly mourns and honors the lives of our brothers and sisters who might otherwise be forgotten. Through the vigil, we express love and respect for our people in the face of national indifference and hatred. Day of Remembrance reminds non-transgender people that we are their sons, daughters, parents, friends, and lovers" (St. Pierre 2007).

Transgender people constitute a group that has endured discrimination and prejudice. In the United States, there are 315 documented cases of murders and suicides of transgender people that occurred between 1970 and 2010. For the most part, freedom of gender identity is not a recognized right, and politics and ideology play an important part in the way transgendered people are perceived and treated. But there have been some recent successes. On October 28, 2009, President Barack Obama signed the Matthew Shepard and James Byrd, Jr. Hate Crimes Prevention Act. In 1998, three men targeted Shepard, a University of Wyoming student, as gay. They tortured him, tied him to a fence post, and left him to die. In that same year, known white supremacists chained Byrd, an African American man, by his ankles to the back of a pickup truck and then dragged him for miles along a Jasper, Texas, road to his eventual death. Among other things, this federal law extends 1969 hate crime laws to cover crimes that target victims because of their actual or perceived gender, sexual orientation, gender identity, or disability (Robinson 2010).

In 2010, the annual Transgender Day of Remembrance marked its 12th anniversary. There were events in 200 cities in 20 different countries, including Malaysia, Minsk, Netherlands, New Zealand, Philippines, Poland, Switzerland, Germany, Greece, Israel, Italy, Ireland, Sweden, Australia, Canada, England, Finland, France, Scotland, and the United States (St. Pierre 2007). Each event is unique, but candlelit vigils are the most common. In Dublin, the St. Stephen's Green Unitarian Church honored the lives of 180 fellow Irish transgendered who died as a result of anti-transgender hate crimes with a candle-lighting ceremony and Irish song (Cedar Lounge Revolution 2010). In Santa Rosa, Australia, people gathered in the downtown courthouse square to light candles and remember the dead. Flyers listed the names of transgendered people who were murdered or committed suicide (Coffey 2010). In Vancouver, Canada, 120 people participated in a march from the Carnegie Community Center to SFU Harbour Center where they viewed the documentary *Isn't It Obvious*, listened to several readings, and sang songs to honor the dead (Starlight 2010). The Chicago Transgender Coalition sponsored two events. One, the Night of Fallen Stars, featured young transgendered speakers and a film about anti-transgender hate crimes and transgender people who have committed suicide. On the second night, 100 people gathered for a candlelit vigil. Although this was the first public celebration in Chicago, it is expected to occur annually (Sosin 2010). All events have the same mission, to honor and remember those transgendered who have suffered. If awareness and participation continue to grow, then the Transgender Day of Remembrance may become a celebration that reaches well beyond transgender and small sympathetic communities.

Source: Written by Brooke Goerman, Northern Kentucky University, Class of 2011.

ways (Lorber 2005). They also learn dominant gender roles, the behavior, and activities expected of someone who is male or female. These expectations channel children's energies in directions defined as sex-appropriate. As children learn to look and behave like boys or girls, most reproduce and perpetuate their society's version of how the two sexes should be. When children fail to behave in gender-appropriate ways, their character becomes suspect (Lorber 2005). At the minimum, people call girls who violate the rules tomboys and boys who do so sissies.

Gender Socialization

The gender socialization process may be direct or indirect. It is indirect when children learn gender expectations by observing others' words and behavior, such as the jokes, comments, and stories they hear about men and women or portrayals of men and women they see in magazines, books, and on television (Raag and Rackliff 1998). Socialization is direct when significant others intentionally convey the societal expectations to children.

Technology Tip: Visit the "Transgender Day of Remembrance" website (www.transgenderdor.org/). On that website is a list of people memorialized in 2010. A short profile, and in some cases photograph, of each transgendered person offers examples of the most extreme responses to those who do not fit gender ideals.

Terra Shultz, Courtesy of Joan Ferrante

If this little boy (center) showed up for a birthday party at your home as a princess, what would you say to him? Do you think other parents might get upset? How might other parents treat his mother?

Agents of socialization are the significant people, groups, and institutions that act to shape our gender identity—whether we identify as male, female, or something in between. Agents of socialization include family, classmates, peers, teachers, religious leaders, popular culture, and mass media. Child development specialist Beverly Fagot and her colleagues (1985) observed how preschool teachers shape gender identity. Specifically, the researchers focused on how toddlers, ages 12 and 24 months, in a play group interacted and communicated with one another and how teachers responded to the children's attempts to communicate. Fagot found no differences in the interaction styles of 12-month-old boys and girls: All of the children communicated by gestures, gentle touches, whining, crying, and screaming.

The teachers, however, interacted with them in gender-specific ways. They were more likely to respond to girls who communicated in gentle, "feminine" ways and to boys who communicated in assertive, "masculine" ways. That is, the teachers tended to ignore girls' assertive acts but respond to boys' assertive acts. Thus, by the time these toddlers were 2, they communicated in very different ways.

Fagot's research was conducted more than 25 years ago. A more recent study found that early childhood teachers are more accepting of girls' cross-gender behaviors and explorations than they are of boys'. According to this research, teachers believe that boys who behave like "sissies" are at greater risk of growing up to be homosexual and psychologically ill adjusted than are girls who behave like "tomboys." This finding suggests that although American society has expanded the range of behaviors and appearances deemed acceptable for girls, it has not extended the range for boys in the same way (Cahill and Adams 1997).

Children's toys and celebrated images of males and females figure prominently in the socialization process, along with the ways in which adults treat children. Barbie® dolls, for example, have been marketed since 1959, with the purpose of inspiring little girls "to think about what they wanted to be when they grew up." The dolls are available in 67 countries. An estimated 95 percent of girls between ages 3 and 11 in the United States have Barbie dolls, which come in several different skin shades and 45 nationalities (Mattel 2011). Then there are the estimated 26,000 Disney princess items on the market and merchandise for girls that "seems to come in only one color: pink jewelry boxes, pink vanity mirrors, pink telephones, pink hair dryers, pink fur stoles" (Paul 2011).

For boys, G.I. Joe was launched in 1964, as the first action figure toy on the market, and it was followed by a long line of action figures, including Transformers™, Micronauts™, Star Wars™, Power Rangers™, X-Men™, Street Fighter™, Bronze Bombers, and Mortal Kombat™. The popularity of these toys has generated comic books, motion pictures, and cartoons, and they appear on school supplies, video games, card games, lunch boxes, posters, and party supplies (Hasbro Toys 2011, Son 1998).

Learning to be male or female involves learning norms governing the way males and females present themselves; that includes learning the sex-appropriate norms governing body language. According to women's studies professor Janet Lee Mills (1985), norms governing male body language suggest power, dominance, and high status, whereas norms governing female body language suggest submissiveness, subordination, vulnerability, and low status. Mills argues that these norms are learned and that people give them little thought until someone breaks them, at which point everyone focuses on the rule breaker.

Mills describes how men hold power by taking an authoritative stance—often with a wide stance, one or both

Terra Shultz, Courtesy of Joan Ferrante

Parents and others buy children toys that channel their interests and behavior in masculine and feminine directions. Would you encourage this little boy to continue showing an equal amount of interest in his toy truck and his princess dress?

Discussion Tip: Ask students to study the photographs on this page and to consider the questions asked in each caption. Encourage students with opposing viewpoints to explain their position.

hands in pocket, straight posture, and head high. Women often suggest a submissive stance when they smile, cant their head, hold arms and hands close to their bodies, and assume an unstable stance. When talking to men who are shorter, women tend to slip into a scrunched up posture.

We might conclude that if we change socialization experiences, behavior will change accordingly. The Christian missionaries assigned to Samoa must have recognized this principle, as they sought to "destroy most of the social institutions that guided young Samoans through childhood to adulthood" (Cote 1997, p. 7). Among other things, these missionaries attempted to end the practice of tattooing, and they targeted the *aualuma*, a group of unmarried adolescent girls who "lived together," "supported one another emotionally," and carried out village work projects. As part of the missionaries' efforts, unmarried girls, instead of going to live with the *aualuma*, were brought to live with the pastors and their wives (Cote 1997, p. 8). By introducing mass education, the missionaries also changed the role of the *augama* (the organization of younger and older men without titles). Instead of learning skills as members of the *augama*, boys studied inside the classroom, which prepared them to work for wages instead of for the village as a whole.

Socialization of Samoan Boys

There are about 4,600 high school students (grades 9 to 12) in American Samoa. Of this number, about 400 males graduate from high school each year. Each year, about 46 graduates leave the Pacific island to play football in the United States at the collegiate level (Syken 2003). That figure translates into about one in every nine high school graduates. What socialization mechanisms channel young Samoan males' energies into a sport that may take them 4,150 miles or more from home?

First, for young Samoan boys to play football, the sport must be available in their society. Football was introduced to the island in 1969, after a U.S. government official decided that the public schools should field football teams. Second, the celebrity status of successful Samoan football players highlights for young Samoan males the rewards of pursuing a football career. For example, 120 football players of Samoan descent played at the University of Hawaii and Arizona State between 1997 and 2000, under Coach Dick Tomey. Today, 200 players of Samoan descent play on Division I college teams and about 20 play in the NFL. Others play in the Canadian Football League and NFL Europe (U.S. House of Representatives 2004, Ferguson 2005). Samoan youth hear and read praise from college and NFL coaches about Samoan players, which fuels their interest in the game and channels their choices toward football and not some other sport, such as golf or tennis:

- "They're so physical. Even in scrimmages they go all out." (Busch 2003)
- "There are no athletes that are, in my estimation, more competitive, more athletic, or more family-oriented, or who fit into a team concept as well as Samoan athletes. The more we could get on our team, the better I felt." (Tomey 2003)
- "Why not use what God gave you? You wouldn't mind putting a golf club in their hands, but you have to be realistic. I don't see a [Samoan] Tiger Woods out there. We're going to use what we know." (Malauulu 2003)

Third, high school football is very popular in American Samoa. The six high school football teams use the same 5,000-seat stadium to host all of their games. The schools play each other twice each season and meet again for playoffs. In addition to the fans who attend games, other fans listen to the games on the island's only radio station or watch them on TV (Saslow 2007, Ferguson 2005).

Finally, American Samoan males have relatively few career opportunities. Consider that one in every 50 people moves away each year. Surely this high rate is tied in part to the limited opportunities. As a case in point, consider that one-third of all Samoan jobs are connected to tuna fishing and processing. The importance of this industry to the economy is such that tuna represents 93 percent of American Samoa's total exports (U.S. Central Intelligence Agency 2011). In an interview three high school athletes reflected on football and their desire to leave the island that they call the "rock," a 54-square-mile volcanic island about 4,500 miles from mainland United States and approximately 2,300 miles from Hawaii (Saslow 2007):

- "The pride of the whole high school is football. That's the most important sport now . . . what ever part of the island has the best team, that part of the island celebrates all year."

BRIAN SNYDER/Reuters/Landov

Troy Polamalu is an NFL football player of Samoan ethnicity. He believes that football allows him to carry out his Samoan heritage in the way he runs, hits, and otherwise plays the game (CBS News 2010).

- "If you want to go the mainland, then you have to play football or go into the military. After high school everybody wants to leave, at least for awhile."
- "Everyone down here is just looking to get off 'the Rock.' That's what we call the island. It's just a rock in the middle of the ocean and we don't ever see anything else."

Commercialization of Gender Ideals

Commercialization of gender ideals is the process of introducing products into the market using advertising campaigns that promise consumers they can achieve masculine and feminine ideals if they buy and use the products. Keep in mind that sales depend on people buying a product. One way to convince people to buy products is to play on their insecurities about whether they measure up to gender ideals. Of course, achieving gender ideals requires a great deal of effort, and retailers offer products that can help in that effort. If we consider the strategies corporations employ to increase profits, we can see how commercialization of gender ideals supports profit-making goals. Those profit-making strategies include creating new products that consumers "need" to buy and creating new markets.

Creating New Products The list of products is endless, especially for women. From hair dye to toenail polish, products are available to improve almost every female body part or body function (from the top of the head to the tip of the toe). There are vaginal moisturizers, chin gyms (a mouthpiece that includes a miniature weight-lifting system to help those who use it avoid or lose a double chin), Botox, wrinkle creams, hair removers, and artificial fingernails. Relatively new products on the market for men include body washes, the erectile dysfunction drugs Viagra, Levitra, and Cialis, which are being advertised even to men who do not have the medical condition for which these drugs should be prescribed. Millions of men have tried these drugs to date, and the manufacturers hope to attract millions more "by suggesting that if men cannot have an erection 'on demand,' if they 'fail' even once, they are candidates for these drugs" (Tuller 2004).

Creating New Markets The female market is saturated with products. From a marketing perspective, the amount of discretionary money that female consumers have to spend on cosmetic products may have reached its limit. Thus, marketers must search for a new market—and one new market appears to be males. The problem for marketers is how to sell men products that have traditionally been viewed as "feminine." One strategy is to "masculinize" feminine products by selling them a "body wash that's not for sissies" or a revitalizing face cream that is "more evolved," playing on a hierarchy that puts men at the top of the evolutionary chain.

Structural Constraints

Structural constraints are the established and customary rules, policies, and day-to-day practices that affect a person's life chances. One example is the structural constraints that push men and women into jobs that correspond with society's ideals regarding sex-appropriate work. Women are pushed into work roles that emphasize personal relationships and nurturing skills or that pertain to family-oriented and "feminine" products and services. Men are pushed into jobs that emphasize decision making and control and that pertain to machines and "masculine" products and services.

Table 10.1 shows the top ten female-dominated occupations held by women who work full-time. Because women are 47.4 percent of the full-time labor force, we can see that they are very overrepresented in the secretaries/administrative assistant category. Notice that more than 3.0 million women in the United States work as secretaries or administrative assistants, filling 96.8 percent of such positions. Other occupational categories in which women make up 90 percent or more of the workforce include receptionists, bookkeepers, and child care workers. In Table 10.2, notice that almost 3 million men in the United States work as truck drivers. Men are 52.6 percent of the full-time labor force yet they are 94.2 percent of truck drivers. Other occupational categories dominated by men include construction laborers, carpenters, grounds maintenance workers, and electricians.

Sociologists consider the ways occupations deemed appropriate for one sex or the other channel behavior in stereotypically male and female directions. The point is that it is not the day care worker per se that is feminine; it is the skills needed for the job that makes the day care worker behave in ways we associate with femininity. Presumably anyone holding the job of day care worker will display "feminine" characteristics. Likewise, the skills we require of truck drivers means anyone holding that job behaves in ways we have come to associate with masculinity. This suggests that a person does not have to be an anatomical woman to be a day care worker or an anatomical man to be a truck driver, but they do have to possess the necessary skills.

commercialization of gender ideals The process of introducing products to the market by using advertising and sales campaigns that promise consumers they will achieve masculine and feminine ideals if they buy and use the products.

structural constraints The established and customary rules, policies, and day-to-day practices that affect a person's life chances.

Student Activity: Visit one of the websites that markets erectile dysfunction medicines to men such as viagra.com. Analyze the website for language or images that capitalize on male insecurities. Also visit the website for the prescription drug Botox (www.botoxcosmetic.com). Review that website for strategies the drug maker uses to convince women (and men) to undergo the procedure.

TABLE 10.1 Top 10 Female-Dominated Occupations, Full-Time Workers, 2009

Occupations	Total Women (in 1,000s)	% Workers Who Are Women	Women's Median Weekly Income	Men's Median Weekly Income
All women in workforce	66,208	47.4	$657	$819
Secretaries/administrative assistants	3,074	96.8	$619	$725
Elementary and middle school teachers	2,343	81.9	$891	$1,024
Registered nurses	2,612	92.0	$1,035	$1,201
Nursing, psychiatric, and home health aides	1,770	88.5	$430	$488
Bookkeeping, accounting, and auditing clerks	1,205	92.3	$627	$677
Receptionists and information clerks	1,168	91.5	$529	$547
Maids and housekeepers	1,282	89.8	$371	$455
Teacher assistants	921	91.6	$474	—
Child care workers	1,228	95.1	$364	—
Personal and home care aid	789	85.2	$406	$414

Source: Data from U.S. Department of Labor, Bureau of Labor Statistics 2010a.

TABLE 10.2 Top 10 Male-Dominated Occupations, Full-Time Workers, 2009

Occupations	Total Men (in 1,000s)	% Workers Who Are Men	Men's Median Weekly Income	Women's Median Weekly Income
All men in work force	73,669	52.6	$819	$651
Driver/sales workers and truck drivers	2,988	94.2	$691	$492
Construction laborers	1,389	97.3	$569	—
Carpenters	1,538	98.5	$624	—
Grounds maintenance workers	1,116	94.7	$433	—
Chief executive officers	782	75.1	$2,217	$1,598
Electricians	759	97.8	$890	—
Automotive service technicians and mechanics	785	98.2	$680	—
First-line supervisors of construction trades and extraction workers	707	96.3	$960	—
Police and sheriff's patrol officers	608	86.3	$992	$772
Industrial truck and tractor operators	472	93.1	$556	—
Construction manager	1,034	96.4	$1,189	—
Electronic home entertainment installers	1,244	98.4	—	—

Source: Data from U.S. Department of Labor, Bureau of Labor Statistics 2010b.

Student Activity: Ask students to write a paper on a dual working heterosexual couple they know very well such as parents, sibling and spouse, etc. Who makes the higher salary? What factors might explain the difference in salary? If the couple earns essentially the same income, why might that be the case?

Sexism

> **CORE CONCEPT 5** ***Sexism*** **is the belief that one sex—and by extension, one gender—is superior to another, and that this superiority justifies inequalities between sexes.**

Sexism revolves around four notions:

1. People can be placed into two distinct categories: male and female.
2. A close correspondence exists between a person's reproductive anatomy and other characteristics such as body movements, personality, intelligence, expression of sexual desire, and athletic ability.
3. Reproductive organs are so significant that they explain and determine behavior and the social, economic, and political inequalities that exist between the sexes.
4. People who behave in ways that depart from ideals of masculinity or femininity are considered deviant, in need of fixing, and subject to negative sanctions ranging from ridicule to physical violence.

This ideology is reflected in U.S. military policy toward gay men and lesbians, for example. Since the Revolutionary War, the U.S. military has had a policy of court-martialing, imprisoning, hospitalizing, and/or honorably discharging gay service members. According to the U.S. Department of Defense (1990), "the prohibition against homosexual conduct is a long standing element of military law. . . . The presence in the armed forces of persons who demonstrate a propensity or intent to engage in homosexual acts would create an unacceptable risk to high standards of morale, good order and discipline and unit cohesion that are the essence of military capability." (H.R.20401.E.H.1994). In December 2010, Congress passed legislation repealing the law (Don't Ask, Don't Tell) banning gays from openly serving in the military. While the repeal, signed into law by President Barack Obama, officially ended the policy on paper, the military can set the time table on when the repeal goes into full effect.

Staff Sgt. Stacy L. Pearsall

Whether taking part in training exercises or relaxing afterward, soldiers often make physical contact with other soldiers. Would the presence of gay men and lesbians in the military disrupt these activities? Might the presence of two men or a man and a woman who share a strong friendship or attraction also be disruptive?

Gender Inequality

> **CORE CONCEPT 6 When sociologists study inequality between males and females, they seek to identify the social factors that put one sex at a disadvantage relative to another.**

Social inequality exists between men and women when one category relative to the other (1) faces greater risks to physical and emotional well-being, (2) possesses a disproportionate share of income and other valued resources, or (3) is accorded more opportunities to succeed. There are many areas in which men are disadvantaged relative to women. One example is life expectancy. The average life expectancy for males living in American Samoa is 70.8 years. That is six years less than the life expectancy of females living there, which is 76.8 years (U.S. Central Intelligence Agency 2011). The average man in the United States can expect to live 75.6 years, 5.2 fewer years than the average life expectancy of women, which is 80.8. In this regard, some males are more disadvantaged than others and some groups of females are more advantaged. For example, females classified as Asian can expect to live 16.9 years longer than males classified as black.

There are also many areas in which women are disadvantaged relative to men. Notably, women as a group tend to earn less money than men. Table 10.3 shows a $169 per-week difference between the median incomes of males and females age 25 and older. It also shows that regardless of the level of education, men as a group earned more money than women. Income differences varied according to age, with the greatest inequality between men and women at ages 45 to 55 and the least inequality between men and women at ages 16 to 24.

Figure 10.2 shows that, in 2009, women ages 16 to 24 earned 93.1 cents for every dollar men earned, and that women, ages 45 to 54, earned 77 cents for every dollar. Notice also that the wage gap has steadily closed for all age groups since 1979. However, if we take a long view—and look at total earnings for men and women over a 15-year period—we find that the average woman earned about

sexism The belief that one sex—and by extension, one gender—is innately superior to another, justifying unequal treatment of the sexes.

Global Comparisons Countries that Allow Gays and Lesbians to Serve in the Military Openly

Since 1993, the Department of Defense discharged an estimated 13,000 servicemen and servicewomen for homosexuality under the "don't ask, don't tell" policy (Bumiller 2010, Stolberg 2010). Gay men and lesbians in 161 different occupations, including foreign-language specialists and infantrymen, have been discharged on the grounds that homosexuals create an unacceptable risk to military effectiveness (Online Newshour 2007). Yet little if any scientific evidence supports this policy. In fact, until 2010, the year Defense Secretary Robert Gates declared his intention to roll back this policy, whenever Pentagon researchers (with no links to the gay and lesbian communities and with no ax to grind) found evidence that runs contrary to this policy, high-ranking military officials have generally refused to release it or directed researchers to rewrite their reports. A 2007 Zogby poll found that 75 percent of U.S. soldiers returning from Iraq and Afghanistan indicated that they were comfortable interacting with gay colleagues; only 5 percent indicated that they were extremely uncomfortable (Shalikashvili 2007).

People who oppose the presence of gay men and lesbians in the military stereotype them as sexual predators just waiting to pounce on heterosexuals while they shower, undress, or sleep. Opponents seem to believe that *any* same-sex person is attractive to a gay man or lesbian. But as one gay ex-midshipman noted, "Heterosexual men have an annoying habit of overestimating their own attractiveness" (Schmalz 1993, p. B1). Supporters of gay men and lesbians in the military point out that almost 75 percent of troops say that they usually shower alone; only 8 percent say they usually take showers where others can see them (Zogby 2007). To date, 24 countries allow gays to serve openly. Those countries shown on the map are Australia, Austria, Belgium, Canada, Czech Republic, Denmark, Estonia, Finland, France, Germany, Ireland, Israel, Italy, Lithuania, Luxembourg, Netherlands, New Zealand, Norway, Slovenia, South Africa, Spain, Sweden, Switzerland, and the United Kingdom (Sosa 2010).

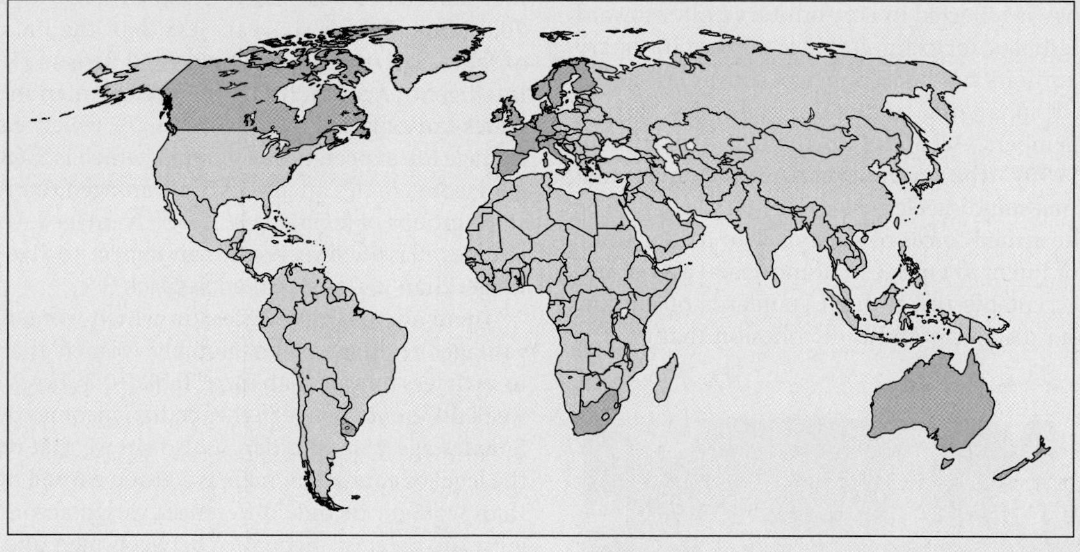

FIGURE 10.1

Source: Data from Palm Center (2010)

TABLE 10.3 Median Weekly Income of Full-Time Wage and Salary Workers Age 25 and Older by Education Level, 2010

	Overall	Less Than High School	High School Graduate	4-Year Degree	Graduate/ Professional Degree
Female	$709	$392	$539	$910	$1,126
Male	$878	$479	$718	$1,196	$1,559
Difference in Weekly Wages	$169	$87	$179	$286	$433

Source: U.S. Bureau of Labor Statistics (2010)

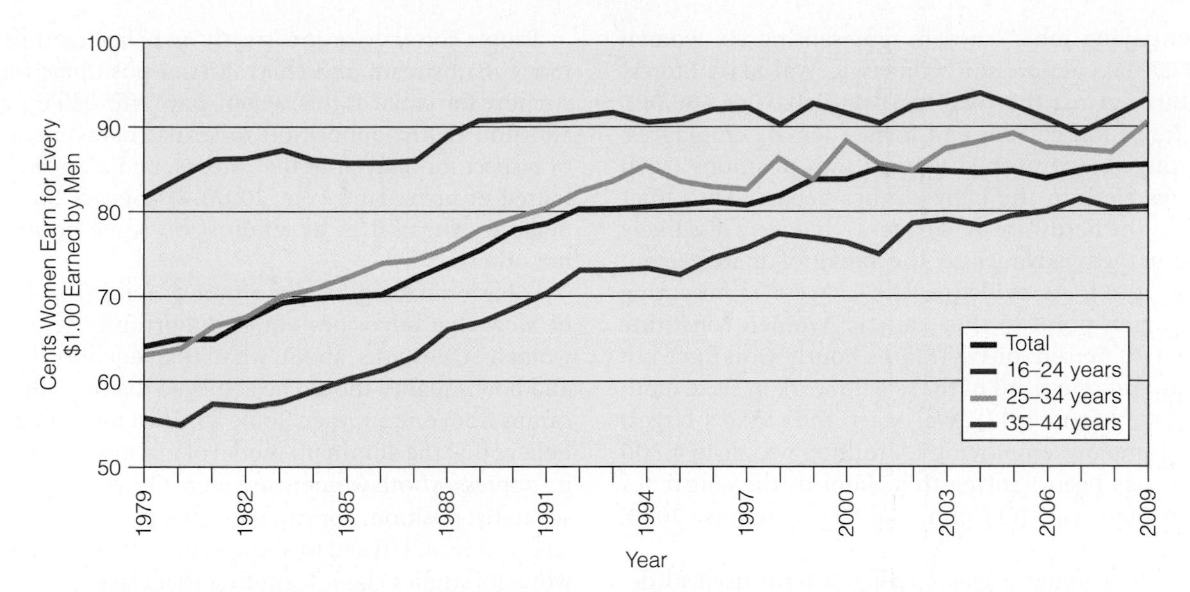

FIGURE 10.2 Cents Full-Time Female Wage and Salary Workers Earn for Every Dollar Earned by Men in 2009 dollars, 1979–2009

This graph shows year-by-year variations in money women earned relative to men. Which age group as a whole has the highest earning relative to men? Which age group has the lowest earning relative to men?

Source: U.S. Bureau of Labor Statistics (2010)

38 percent of what the average man did (Madrick 2004). Economists Stephen J. Rose and Heidi Hartman (2004) compared men's and women's total earnings between 1983 and 1998 and found that the average woman earned $273,592 whereas the average man earned $722,693.

Male–female income differences vary by occupation. Tables 10.1 and 10.2 show the top ten male- and female-dominated occupations and the percentage of males and females in each. Notice that for the ten occupations in which women dominated, their median weekly earnings ranged from a low of $364 (for child care workers) to a high of $1,035 (for registered nurses). Likewise, in the top ten male-dominated occupations, men's median weekly earnings ranged from a low of $433 (for grounds maintenance worker) to a high of $2,217 (for chief executive officers). Note that for all occupations considered in Tables 10.1 and 10.2, the median weekly income was always greater for males than for females, even when males worked in occupations that are female dominated.

There are many possible explanations for this income difference. They include the following:

- Women are disproportionately employed in lower-paying, lower-status occupations.
- Women choose or are forced into lower-paying positions that are considered sex-appropriate, such as teacher, secretary, and caregiver. Female-dominated occupations (day care worker) are valued less and thus pay than male-dominated occupations (such as auto mechanics and construction laborers).
- Women choose or are forced into positions that offer fewer, more-flexible hours to meet caregiving responsibilities.
- Women choose or are forced into lower-paying subspecialties within high-paying professions (for example, women tend to be divorce lawyers rather than corporate lawyers, and pediatricians rather than heart surgeons).
- Employers underinvest in the careers of childbearing-age women because they assume the women will eventually leave to raise children.
- Women leave the labor market to take care of children and elderly parents, and then they reenter it.
- Women choose or are forced into occupations that will not require them to relocate, work in unpleasant environments (such as mines), or take on hazardous assignments—three activities associated with higher pay (Sahadi 2006).
- Employers still view women's salary needs as less important than men's and pay women accordingly. Unfortunately, women's earnings are often considered supplemental to men's—earnings that can be used to buy "extras"—when in reality many women are heads of households.
- When negotiating for salaries, women underestimate their worth to employers and ask for less than their male counterparts.
- Some employers steer males and females into sex-appropriate assignments and offer them different training opportunities and chances to move into

Technology Tip: Listen to an NPR interview with sociologist Andrew Beveridge who talks about his research showing that women in large cities are bridging the income gap with men. Simply go to www.npr.org and enter search words "Women in Big Cities Bridging Income Gap."

better-paying jobs. Lawyers representing six women filed a class-action suit (Dukes v. Wal-Mart Stores) in 2001 against that Wal-Mart on behalf of 500,000 to 1.6 million current and former female employees, claiming that it pushed women into positions (such as sales clerk in the baby clothes department rather than in the hardware department) that were less likely to help them advance to the ranks of management (Love 2007). As evidence, the lawyers representing the women point to this statistic: Women constitute at least 70 percent of Wal-Mart's hourly workforce but account for one-third of those who work in store management (Mears 2011). Wal-Mart, the world's largest retail company, employing 1.4 million people in 4,300 stores, has been fighting this claim in the courts for the past ten years (O'Conner 2007, Greenhouse 2003, 2004).

- Women encounter a glass ceiling, a term used to describe a barrier that prevents women from rising past a certain level in an organization, especially when women work in male-dominated workplaces and occupations. The term applies to women who have the ability and qualifications to advance but who are not well connected to those who are in a position to advocate for or mentor them. With regard to men who work in female-dominated professions, they often encounter the glass escalator, a term that applies to the invisible upward movement that puts men in positions of power, even within female-dominated occupations. In this case, management singles out men for special attention and advancement such that men are encouraged to move from school teacher to assistant principal to principal or from social worker to program director.

Feminism

In its most basic sense, the feminist perspective advocates equality between men and women. When women living in the United States are asked, "Do you consider yourself a feminist or not?" only one in four or 25 percent of respondents answers yes. When asked the same question accompanied by a definition of *feminist* ("A feminist is someone who believes in social, political, and economic equality of the sexes. Do you think of yourself as a feminist or not?"), 65 percent of women answer yes. One possible explanation for the difference is that only 12 percent of women and 10 percent of men consider the label of *feminist* to be a compliment (CBS News Polls 2005).

People correctly or incorrectly associate feminists with many mainstream and controversial positions, including support for equal rights, equal pay, affordable day care, abortion rights, opposition to sexual harassment, a lack of respect for "stay-at-home" moms, and a dislike or even hatred of men (Time.com 2007). It appears that respondents see themselves as feminist on some positions and not others.

A basic sociological definition of **feminism** is a point of view that advocates equal opportunity for men and women. Questions about what that equality looks like and how equality should be achieved distinguish feminist camps from one another. Some feminist men, for example, believe that the dominant model of manhood or masculinity oppresses both women and men. Other feminists take a separatist position. For example, Mary Daly, a Boston College professor, refused to allow male students to attend her women's studies classes, arguing that class discussion was inhibited and "dumbed-down" by their presence. Apparently Daly believed that women were either intimated or said things to impress men. She did propose meeting individually with her male students but in an out-of-court settlement with the college, Daly agreed to retire (Daly 2006). Many feminists believe that any inequality between males and females, including that which gives females an advantage over males, needs to be addressed (see Working for Change: "Historic Events That Opened Opportunities for Women" on page 264). The following quotations from well-known feminists demonstrate the range of concerns and positions feminists hold:

> It's important to remember that feminism is no longer a group of organizations or leaders. It's the expectations that parents have for their daughters, and their sons, too. It's the way we talk about and treat one another. —*Anna Quindlen*

> If divorce has increased by one thousand percent, don't blame the women's movement. Blame the obsolete sex roles on which our marriages were based. —*Betty Friedan*

> Women do not have to sacrifice personhood if they are mothers. They do not have to sacrifice motherhood in order to be persons. Liberation was meant to expand women's opportunities, not to limit them. The self-esteem that has been found in new pursuits can also be found in mothering. —*Elaine Heffner*

> Women are systematically degraded by receiving the trivial attentions which men think it manly to pay to the sex, when, in fact, men are insultingly supporting their own superiority. —*Mary Wollstonecraft*

> No one sex can govern alone. I believe that one of the reasons why civilization has failed so lamentably is that it had one-sided government. —*Nancy Astor*

> I myself have never been able to find out precisely what feminism is: I only know that people call me a feminist whenever I express sentiments that differentiate me from a doormat, or a prostitute. —*Rebecca West*

feminism In its most basic sense, a perspective that advocates equality between men and women.

Courtesy Everett Collection

Feminists seek to give attention to women (and men) whose accomplishments are not recognized relative to the other gender. Remember, Ginger Rogers did everything Fred Astaire did, but she did it backwards and in high heels. —*Faith Whittlesey*

Sociologists take a feminist perspective when they emphasize in their teaching and research the following kinds of themes: the right to bodily integrity and autonomy, access to safe contraceptives, the right to choose the terms of pregnancy, access to quality prenatal care, protection from violence inside and outside the home, freedom from sexual harassment, equal pay for equal work, workplace rights to maternity and other caregiving leaves, and the inescapable interconnections between sex, gender, social class, race, culture, and religion. Important feminist concepts include those covered in this chapter—such as gender and sexism—and others not covered here—including patriarchy, sexual objectification, and oppression.

The Global-Scale Subordination of Women

CORE CONCEPT 7 Worldwide, females as a category are subordinate to males.

Sociologist Cynthia Fuchs Epstein (2007) points out that history is filled with examples of women doing what has been thought of as men's work; it is also filled with examples of women doing things that "no one, including themselves, thought they could, and they developed interests no one thought they had" (p. 10).

Epstein (2006) argues that the planet is characterized by a great many human-created divides—divides based on nation, wealth, race, religion, education, class, gender, sexuality, and so on. Of all the divides, Epstein considers gender to be the most basic, persistent, prevalent, and resistant to change. In fact, the minute babies are born, a glance at the genitals identifies them as male or female, and for the most part there is no definite place for those who do not fit into this seemingly clear-cut two-category scheme. That glance profoundly affects babies' life chances in unequal ways.

Epstein notes that, worldwide, females as a category are subordinate to males. Subordinate means that females are disproportionately assigned to statuses that are considered inferior to the statuses that are predominantly male. It also means that males make important decisions that affect females' lives. Simply consider that thrones and executive offices are overwhelmingly occupied by men and that "judges in courtrooms; priests, rabbis, and mullahs; leaders and members of unions and clubs" (p. 3) are most likely males who make policies and decisions that affect the lives of women and girls. The degree of subordination varies by society from situations of almost complete subordination to very little. But even in the most women-friendly societies, the gender divide is "always a lurking presence and it can easily become salient" (p. 4). This global-scale subordination is easily documented.

Although women as a group are disadvantaged relative to men, that does not mean that men live free of subordination or that some women are not advantaged relative to some men. For example, there is no question that society encourages men to take risks more than it does women. Risk-taking behavior might be celebrated, but it also increases the chance of doing permanent harm to the body. Men work almost 60 percent of all hours worked in the formal economy but suffer 92 percent of workplace fatalities. Men suffer disproportionately more workplace fatalities than women because they are employed in the most dangerous industries, including construction, mining, and logging. There is also evidence that males (relative to their female counterparts) fail to take preventive steps that would protect them from fatalities. Men also experience more nonfatal workplace injuries than females. For every 10,000 employed males, 142 are injured on the job each year. For every 10,000 employed females, 106.4 are injured on the job each year. Women's injuries are likely to be sprains and strains from lifting and otherwise overexerting muscles (lifting patients, picking up children, lifting mattresses). Men too suffer from sprains and bruises but are much more likely than women to suffer injuries related to falls, chemical and heat burns, severed limbs, and exposure to harmful chemicals (U.S. Bureau of Labor Statistics 2008).

Female subordination means that, relative to men as a category, women hold less power and control fewer resources. Simply consider the percentage of women who occupy political power at the national level. There are few, if

Teaching Tip: Point out that the United States is one of a handful of countries that does not offer maternity benefits. The other countries are Australia, Papua New Guinea, Western Sahara, Greenland, Oman, Estonia , Kazakhstan, Uzbekistan, and Turkmenistan. If someone from another country wondered why this is the case, ask students what answer they would give.

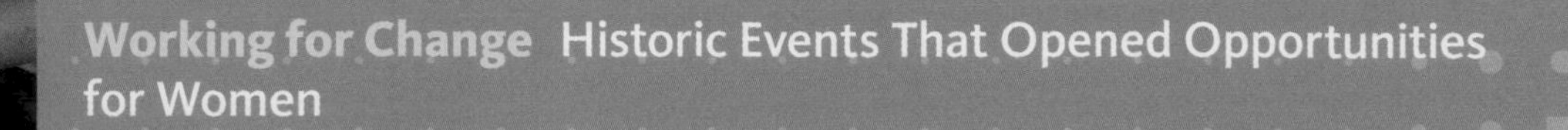

Working for Change Historic Events That Opened Opportunities for Women

Sgt. 1st Class Sheryl Lawry, 500th Military Intelligence Brigade

1848 A group of women and men assembled in Seneca Falls, New York, to discuss the status of women in American society. During this event, regarded as the beginning of the women's rights movement in the United States, Elizabeth Cady Stanton delivered the "Declaration of Rights and Sentiments" (a statement calling for women's rights, patterned after the Declaration of Independence).

1872 Susan B. Anthony and 15 other women were arrested and indicted for "knowingly, wrongfully, and unlawfully voting for a representative to the Congress of the United States." She appealed her conviction to the U.S. Supreme Court, but her conviction was upheld.

1920 The Nineteenth Amendment to the U.S. Constitution became law, guaranteeing women the right to vote.

1921 The American Birth Control League (which later became the Planned Parenthood Federation of America) was founded by Margaret Sanger and Mary Ware Dennett.

1938 Congress passed the Fair Labor Standards Act, prohibiting child labor in factories and mines. The law also established a minimum wage, a maximum workweek, and overtime pay, which benefited many working women.

1943 As more and more men enlisted during World War II, more and more women entered the civilian workforce. Over 6 million women held factory jobs as welders, machinists, and mechanics. About 310,000 women worked in the U.S. aircraft industry alone.

1963 The Equal Pay Act, signed by President Kennedy, prohibited the practice of paying women less money than men for the same job.

1964 President Lyndon B. Johnson signed the Civil Rights Act, outlawing discrimination in unions, public schools, and the workplace on the basis of race, creed, national origin, or sex.

1965 Under Title VII of the Civil Rights Act of 1964, the Equal Employment Opportunity Commission was established. Its function has been to enforce federal law prohibiting discrimination in the workplace on the basis of sex, religion, race, color, national origin, age, or disability.

1966 The National Organization for Women (NOW) was founded by Betty Friedan. It has challenged sex discrimination in the workplace through public demonstrations, lobbying, and litigation.

1972 The U.S. Senate approved the Equal Rights Amendment—49 years after it was first introduced in Congress. It was then sent to the state legislatures for ratification.

Title IX of the Education Amendments of 1972 made sex discrimination in schools that receive federal funding illegal. Title IX also requires that schools that receive federal funds give women and girls an equal opportunity to participate in sports and to receive millions of dollars in athletic scholarships.

1973 The U.S. Supreme Court ruled (7–2) that, according to a woman's right to privacy guaranteed in the Fourteenth Amendment, the Texas law restricting abortion in the first trimester was unconstitutional. As a result, antiabortion laws in nearly two-thirds of the states were declared unconstitutional, legalizing abortion nationwide.

1975 President Gerald Ford signed a defense appropriations bill to allow women to be admitted into U.S. military academies.

1978 The Women's Army Corps (WAC) as a separate military entity was dismantled, and women began integrating into the U.S. Army.

1993 President Bill Clinton signed the Family and Medical Leave Act. It allows eligible employees to take up to 12 weeks of leave for reasons of illness, maternity, adoption, or a child's serious health condition.

1996 U.S. women's successes in the Summer Olympics (19 gold medals, 10 silver, 9 bronze) are attributed to the Title IX legislation that supported and encouraged girls' participation in sports.

1997 The Supreme Court rules that college athletic programs must actively involve men and women in numbers that reflect the proportions of male and female students.

Source: Adapted from Barbara Boxer, U.S. senator from California, Historical Timeline for Women's History (2007).

Although males as a group disproportionately occupy the highest status position in the military (relative to females as a group), they also suffer the greater percentage of casualties. Males account for 97.5 percent of deaths among U.S. military personnel deployed to Iraq and Afghanistan (Fischer 2010).

any, places in the world in which women hold a majority share of political power that would allow them as a group to determine national policies (see Figure 10.3).

There also appear to be no societies in which women dominate the highest-paying, highest-status jobs, nor is there a society in which full-time working women earn the equivalent of male salaries. Even when women move into jobs traditionally assigned to men, such as manufacturing, with few exceptions their wages are significantly lower than that of their male counterparts.

These facts prompted Epstein to ask: Why does the subordination of women and girls persist even in female-friendly societies? How is it that males as a group are economically and politically advantaged relative to women virtually everywhere? Epstein proposes a very basic explanation for why gender inequality persists. Everywhere, women have been assigned the work that relates to "reproduction and gathering and preparation of food" (p. 15)—the work people must do to survive. For the most part, women carry and care for children and they gather and shop for food, cook, and work in factories that process and package food. The United Nations estimates that, in developing countries, women produce between 60 and 80 percent of food (Doss 2011). Epstein (2007) points out that "throughout the world, where water is a scarce commodity it is women who carry heavy buckets and vessels of water, usually on foot and over long distances, because this has been designated as a woman's job and men regard it as a disgrace to help them" (p. 10).

In addition, women are the day care workers, the elementary and secondary teachers, and the nurses and nurses' aides. Men's administrative support staffs are disproportionately women. As Epstein puts it, "This is a good deal—no, a great deal—for the men" (p. 15). Epstein asks, "Why do women agree to this?" In many places around the world, women's labor is controlled through force or by threats of punishment. There are also many countries in which laws are in place that deny women access to the same opportunities men enjoy, such as control over property and wealth, an education, a career, the right to walk the streets unaccompanied by males, and so on.

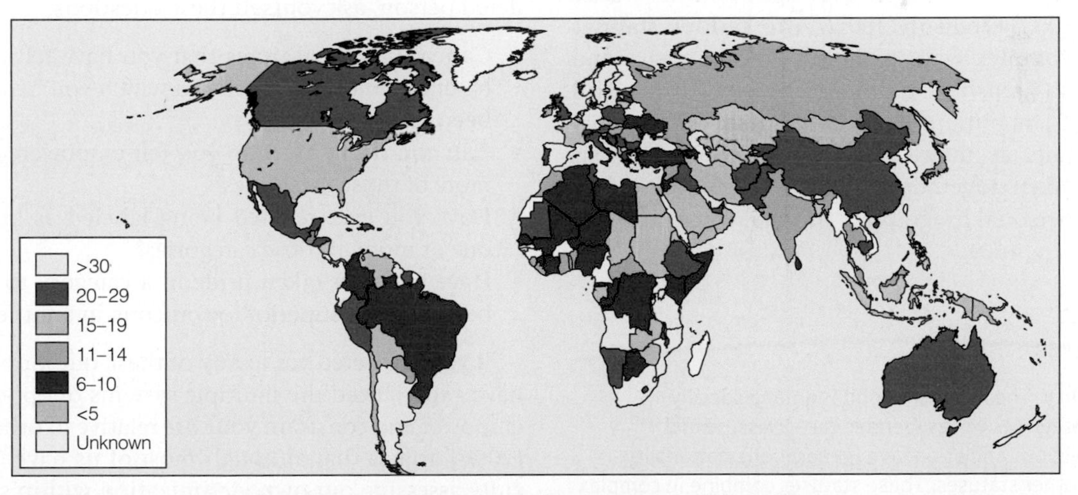

FIGURE 10.3 Percentage of Women Elected to National Level Political Offices
The map shows the percentage of women elected to a national level office (that is, equivalent in status to U.S. senator or congresswoman). There is only one country where women hold more than 50 percent of national political power. That country is Rwanda (56 percent). Study the map and identify some countries in which women hold 30 percent of national political positions. Identify a few countries in which women hold less than 5 percent of national political positions.

Source: Data from United Nations (2009)

But why is gender inequality everywhere, even in countries where women claim to be liberated? To answer this question, Epstein points to the cognitive mechanisms—the internalized and dominant cultural narratives—that support, sustain, and justify the gender inequalities. Those narratives are that men and women are different by divine design and/or nature, and that inequalities between them are natural. By extension, then, men are by nature dominant and women are submissive. This basic belief is supported by the many media stories highlighting gender differences. The media does not typically run stories featuring the many credible research studies showing very small or no differences between men and women on any number of traits. Nor does the media mention the methodological shortcomings of studies that might cast suspicion on findings (for example, that the subjects were college students "persuaded" to engage in experiments conducted in college laboratories and not in real world situations) (p. 8). Of course, academic journals are also to blame, because most will not publish studies that show statistically insignificant differences between men and women on some characteristic.

Intersectionality

Intersectionality, the interconnections among socially constructed categories of sex, gender, race, class, sexual orientation, religious affiliation, age (generation), nationality, disability and other statuses. To grasp the concept of intersectionality, keep in mind that we do not notice someone as just a particular sex, a specific race, a particular age, and so on. That person is everything at once—a lesbian black woman over age 65 from France who is Catholic (Ferguson 2001). The various statuses combine in complex ways to influence advantages and disadvantages (Crenshaw 1991). Sociologist Patricia Hill Collins (2000) maintains that sociologists must recognize these traits as interlocking categories of analysis that, when taken together, "cultivate profound differences in our personal biography" and the structure of our relationships (p. 460).

intersectionality The interconnections among socially constructed categories of sex, gender, race, class, sexual orientation, religious affiliation, age (generation), nationality, disability, and other statuses. These statuses combine in complex ways to influence advantages and disadvantages.

penalties Constraints on a person's opportunities and choices, as well as the price paid for engaging in certain activities, appearances, or choices deemed inappropriate of someone in a particular category.

privilege A special, often unearned, advantage or opportunity.

Discussion Tip: Ask students to name some unearned privileges and penalties that come with being male or female.

CORE CONCEPT 8 A gender category does not stand alone; it intersects with other socially significant and constructed categories, including social class, age, religious affiliation, sexual orientation, ethnicity, disability status, and nation.

The concept of intersectionality helps us to see that (1) no social category is homogeneous, (2) the categories to which some belong place them in a complex system of domination and subordination, and (3) the effects of the categories a person occupies cannot simply be added together to obtain some grand total.

Collins maintains that each of us derives varying amounts of penalty and privilege from the multiple systems of oppression that frame our lives. **Penalties** include constraints on a person's opportunities and choices, as well as the price paid for engaging in certain activities, appearances, or choices deemed inappropriate of someone in a particular category. That price may be rejection, ridicule, or even death. A **privilege** is a special, often unearned, advantage or opportunity. We know some categories of people have the privilege of "not being a suspect" when in fact they have committed a crime. A 75-year-old woman who shoplifts is less likely to be noticed because her age (and to some extent her sex) makes her largely invisible to store security.

A system of oppression is one that empowers and privileges some categories of people while disempowering other categories. The act of disempowering includes marginalizing, silencing, or subordinating another. We gain insights about these interlocking systems of oppression by thinking about the interlocking categories that shape our own life and interactions. As a male, female, or transgendered person, ask yourself these questions:

- Can you think of times that you have felt constrained by one or more categories to which you belong or have been assigned?
- Can you think of times you felt empowered by one or more of those categories?
- Have you ever resisted being labeled as belonging to one or more of those categories?
- Have you ever taken pride in a category to which you belong or felt superior to someone in another category?

If you answered yes to any of these questions, then you have experienced the multiple systems of oppression that empower and constrain your life relative to others. Collins (2006) argues that although most of us have "little difficulty assessing our own victimization within some major system of oppression, whether it be by race, religion, sexual orientation, ethnicity, age, or gender, we typically fail to see how our thoughts and actions uphold someone else's subordination" (p. 459). Many white feminists, for example, "routinely point with confidence to their oppression as women but resist seeing how much their white skin

To grasp the significance of intersectionality, think about the categories by which others know the people pictured. As you can see, the people are not just male or female. They are also people of a certain race, occupation, age, an inferred sexual orientation, social class, and ethnic descent. The experience of being male and females is complicated by the many ascribed and achieved statuses a person holds.

privileges them. African Americans who possess eloquent analyses of racism often persist in viewing poor white women as symbols of white power. . . . In essence, each group identifies the type of oppression with which it feels most comfortable as being fundamental and classifies all other types as being of lesser importance" (p. 459).

Collins believes that each of us must come to terms with the multiple ways the categories to which we belong shape our lives and relationships through institutionalized practices and symbolic representations. She maintains that each of us carries around the cumulative effects of these multiple structures of oppression and that we enforce that system in the personal choices we make about who to include or exclude in our lives and in the errors in judgment that we make about others who are not like us. One way to assess the extent to which you have been affected by these systems is to ask yourself: "Who are your close friends? Who are the people with whom you share your hopes, dreams, vulnerabilities, fears, and victories? How much are they like you?"

Online Poll

Have you ever decided not to pursue some activity or experience because you believed it was appropriate for someone of the other sex?

- ○ Yes
- ○ No

To see how other students responded to these questions, go to **www.cengagebrain.com**.

Molly Hayden, USAG Grafenwoehr

Summary of CORE CONCEPTS

When sociologists study gender, they focus on differences between males and females that are socially constructed and they focus on those behaviors and appearances that depart from gender ideals. To illustrate some of these important concepts, this chapter considers the case of fa'afafines and male football players in American Samoa.

CORE CONCEPT 1 Sex is a biological concept, whereas gender is a social construct.

Most cultures place people in two categories—male and female—based largely on what are considered to be clear anatomical distinctions. Biological sex is not a clear-cut category, however, if only because some babies are born intersexed. In addition, a person's primary sex characteristics may not match his or her sex chromosomes. The existence of transsexuals also challenges the practice of separating everyone into the two biological categories male and female. Gender is the socially created and learned distinctions that specify the ideal physical, behavioral, and mental and emotional traits characteristic of males and females and that make them masculine and feminine. Gender ideals are socially constructed standards that shape practically every aspect of life—influencing, among other things, how people dress, how they express emotions, and what occupations they choose.

CORE CONCEPT 2 While all societies distinguish between male and female, some also recognize a third gender.

The existence of *fa'afafine*—people who are not biologically female but who take on the "way of women" in dress, mannerism, appearance, and role in American Samoa and other Pacific island areas—challenges the two-gender classification scheme. Jeannette Mageo argues that *fa'afafine* could not have become commonplace unless something about Samoan society supports gender blurring.

CORE CONCEPT 3 Sexuality encompasses all the ways people experience and express themselves as sexual beings. The study of sexuality considers the range of sexual expressions and the social activities, behaviors, and thoughts that generate sexual sensations.

Sexual orientation is an expression of sexuality. It also refers to a person's enduring sense of identity, which can be based on to whom one is attracted, their behaviors, and membership in a group that shares similar attractions. Sexual orientation should not be confused with other related and intertwining terms that shape the experiences of sexuality and sexual orientation, including biological sex, gender role, gender identity, and transgender.

CORE CONCEPT 4 Gender expectations are learned and culturally imposed through a variety of social mechanisms, including socialization, situational constraints, and commercialization of gender ideals.

Socialization theorists argue that an undetermined yet significant portion of male–female differences is the product of the ways in which males and females are socialized. Another powerful mechanism for conveying gender expectations is the commercialization of gender ideals—the process of introducing products into the market by using advertising and sales campaigns that promise consumers they will achieve masculine and feminine ideals if they buy and use the products. Finally, structural constraints—the established and customary rules, policies, and day-to-day practices that affect a person's life chances—channel people's behavior in desired directions. Structural constraints push men and women into jobs that correspond with society's ideals for sex-appropriate work.

CORE CONCEPT 5 Sexism is the belief that one sex—and by extension, one gender—is superior to another, and that this superiority justifies inequalities between sexes.

Sexism revolves around four notions: (1) People can be placed into two categories: male and female; (2) a close correspondence exists between a person's primary sex characteristics and characteristics such as emotional activity, body language, personality, intelligence, the expression of sexual desire, and athletic capability; (3) primary sex characteristics are so significant that they explain and determine behavior and the social, economic, and political inequalities that exist between the sexes; and (4) people who behave in ways that depart from ideals of masculinity or femininity are considered deviant, in need of fixing, and subject to negative sanctions ranging from ridicule to physical violence.

CORE CONCEPT 6 When sociologists study inequality between males and females, they seek to identify the social factors that put one sex at a disadvantage relative to the other.

Social inequality exists between men and women when one category relative to the other (1) faces greater risks to physical and emotional well-being; (2) possesses a disproportionate share of income and other valued resources; and/or (3) is accorded more opportunities to succeed. In its most basic sense, the feminist perspective advocates equality between men and women. Sociologists take a feminist perspective when they emphasize in their teaching and research the following kinds of themes: the right to bodily integrity and autonomy, access to safe contraceptives, the right to choose the terms of pregnancy, access to quality prenatal care, protection from violence inside and outside the home, freedom from sexual harassment, equal pay for equal work, workplace rights to maternity and other caregiving leaves, and the inescapable interconnections between sex, gender, social class, race, culture, and religion.

CORE CONCEPT 7 Worldwide, females as a category are subordinate to males.

Of all the divides, gender seems to be the most basic, persistent, prevalent, and resistant to change. Worldwide, we can easily document that females as a category are subordinate to males. There are few, if any, countries in the world in which women hold political control or a majority share of power that allows them as a group to determine national policies. There also appear to be no societies in which women dominate the highest-paying, highest-status jobs, nor is there a society in which full-time working women earn the equivalent of male salaries. But why is gender inequality everywhere? One answer can be found in cognitive mechanisms that support, sustain, and justify the gender inequalities. Those narratives maintain that men and women are different by divine design and/or nature, and that inequalities between them are natural.

CORE CONCEPT 8 A gender category does not stand alone; it intersects with other socially significant and constructed categories, including social class, age, religious affiliation, sexual orientation, ethnicity, disability status, and nation.

The concept of intersectionality helps us to see that no social category is homogeneous; the categories to which someone belongs place them in a complex system of domination and subordination, and the effects of the categories a person occupies cannot simply be added together to obtain some grand total. Each of us derives varying amounts of penalty and privilege from the multiple systems of oppression that frame our lives.

Resources on the Internet

Login to CengageBrain.com to access the resources your instructor requires. For this book, you can access:

Sociology CourseMate

Access an integrated eBook, chapter-specific interactive learning tools, including flash cards, quizzes, videos, and more in your Sociology CourseMate.

Take a pretest for this chapter and receive a personalized study plan based on your results that will identify the topics you need to review and direct you to online resources to help you master those topics. Then take a posttest to help you determine the concepts you have mastered and what you will need to work on.

CourseReader

CourseReader for Sociology is an online reader providing access to readings, and audio and video selections to accompany your course materials.

Visit **www.cengagebrain.com** to access your account and purchase materials.

Key Terms

commercialization of gender ideals 257
feminism 262
femininity 247
gender 247
gender polarization 249
intersexed 246
intersectionality 266
masculinity 247
penalties 266
privilege 266
secondary sex characteristics 246
sex 245
sexual orientation 252
sexual scripts 253
sexism 259
structural constraints 257

11 ECONOMICS AND POLITICS

With Emphasis on INDIA

When sociologists study economic systems, they seek to understand systems of production and the way goods and services are distributed. When they study political institutions, they focus on the way power is acquired, distributed, and wielded. They also study how political and economic systems are interconnected. For example, India became positioned as a global information technology (IT) center because its government invested in five elite engineering universities in the 1970s. Another reason has to do with U.S. immigration policies over the past two decades that welcomed IT workers and students into the country from India.

Why Focus On INDIA?

In this chapter, we emphasize India. It is one of two rising powers (the other being China) expected to challenge the global power and influence of the United States. Many Americans associate India with outsourcing of business and IT services. For all its publicity, only about 2.5 million of India's labor force (out of 480 million) work in such outsourcing industries. India's economy is much more than that. India, the largest democracy in the world, has an extremely diverse economy that encompasses hunting-and-gathering societies, millions of village farms where oxen pull plows, modern manufacturing establishments, cottage industries, and a world-class business services and IT sector.

India, with a population of 1.2 billion people, has the second largest labor force in the world—480 million workers. As you might imagine, one of India's most pressing problems relates to employment. Of its 470 million workers, 430 million are part of the informal or unorganized economy doing things like milking the family cow, working at seasonal jobs, selling products such as incense sticks from street-side stalls, driving rickshaws, and doing work as maids (Luce 2007). India represents both a new market to which U.S. and other multinational corporations can sell their products, and it is also home to a huge labor force that "accepts" wages lower than those most American workers earn.

It is important to point out that government policies shape the economy of India. For example, in the 1970s, the government of India created five elite engineering universities whose graduates positioned India to assume a leading role in the global IT sector. As another example, the Indian government does not allow companies such as Wal-Mart to enter its retail sector for fear of what might happen to millions of "mom and pop" stores. On the other hand, it has allowed "single-brand" retailers such as Nike and Nokia to create outlets in India (Luce 2007).

Online Poll

As a college student, when you think about career possibilities, do you find yourself considering a career that you believe is safe from outsourcing?

- ○ Yes
- ○ No

To see how other students responded to these questions, go to **www.cengagebrain.com.**

The Economy

CORE CONCEPT 1 The ongoing agricultural, industrial, and information revolutions have profoundly shaped the world's economic systems.

A society's **economic system** is the social structure that coordinates human activity to produce, distribute, and consume goods and services. **Goods** include any product that is extracted from the earth, manufactured, or grown—such as food, clothing, petroleum, natural gas, automobiles, coal, and computers. **Services** include activities performed for others that result in no tangible product, such as entertainment, transportation, financial advice, medical care, spiritual counseling, and education. Three major, ongoing revolutions have shaped the world's economic systems and the goods and services a society produces and consumes: agricultural, industrial, and information revolutions. We consider how these revolutions changed the nature of human societies and their corresponding economic systems.

Types of Societies

We consider six broad types of human societies defined by the technologies each employs to produce food and exploit resources. The six societies are hunting and gathering, pastoral, horticultural, agrarian, industrial, and postindustrial. Each of the six is distinguished by the amount of surplus wealth that the people living in them are able to produce. **Surplus wealth** is a situation in which the amount of available food items and other products exceed that which is required to subsist, or to meet basic needs for human survival.

Hunting-and-Gathering Societies

Hunting-and-gathering societies do not possess the technology that allows them to create surplus wealth; people subsist on wild animals and vegetation. As the name suggests, hunters and gatherers do not reside in a fixed location; they are always on the move, securing food and other subsistence items. A typical hunting-and-gathering society is composed of 45 to 100 members related by blood or marriage. The institution of family is central to people's lives, and emphasis is placed on group welfare (Massey 2002). The division of labor is simple, and most people engage in activities related to achieving what they need to survive. The statuses people occupy revolve around gender, age, and kinship. Hunting-and-gathering societies do not view land and the natural resources as things individuals own but rather as a communal resource to be shared. Because almost no surplus wealth exists, there is little inequality.

Basic economic tasks for men might include carpentry, hunting, and fishing. For women, they might include weaving, cloth making, and oil making. Women also do routine fishing or hunting for small prey (Cote 1997). There is evidence that women work longer hours than do men and their direct contribution to subsistence surpasses that of men. Men are off hunting large animals, for example, while women gather most of the food and hunt smaller animals.

economic system A socially created institution that coordinates human activity in the effort to produce, distribute, and consume goods and services.

goods Any product that is extracted from the earth, manufactured, or grown, such as food, clothing, petroleum, natural gas, automobiles, coal, computers, and so on.

services Activities performed for others that result in no tangible product, such as entertainment, transportation, financial advice, medical care, spiritual counseling, and education.

surplus wealth Wealth beyond what is needed to meet basic human needs, such as food and shelter.

domestication The process by which plants and animals were brought under human control.

There are five hunting-and-gathering tribes living on the remote islands of Andaman and Nicobar off India's shores. Often when hearing such societies exist, many people think them primitive rather than respecting them for their skills at living without advanced technology and without a centralized government. However, the tribes on these islands anticipated the 2005 tsunami that killed several hundred thousand people and displaced 1.6 million in South and Southeast Asia. They knew to move to higher ground days before the tsunami occurred (U.S. Geological Survey 2011, *India Daily* 2005).

Sociologist Douglas Massey (2002) predicts that the last hunter-gatherers on the planet will cease to exist by 2020, ending six million years of dedication to "the most successful and long-persistent lifestyle in the career of our species" (Diamond 1992, p. 191). It may already be impossible to find a society today that meets all its needs from hunting, gathering, and fishing. For example, in India, there are an estimated 150,000 largely forest-dwelling peoples officially classified by the government as "primitive tribal groups." While these groups derive their subsistence from foraging, they also engage in some trade with outsiders to obtain products such salt, iron, or cooking utensils (Fortier 2009, Heitzman and Worden 1995).

Pastoral and Horticultural Societies

About 10,000 to 12,000 years ago, humans began domesticating plants and animals. **Domestication** is the process of bringing plants and animals under human control. Now instead of searching for and gathering wild grains and vegetation, people planted seeds and harvested crops. This change allowed for a more predictable food source and made it possible to produce more grain than people needed just to survive. Surplus food gave some people the freedom to spend time on pursuits other than securing subsistence, such as making vases to store food. The excess grain supported the domestication of cattle, oxen, and other animals, because enough food was available for animals as well as people. Domestication reduced the need to hunt for animals. Now, people captured, tamed, and bred them. Domesticated animals carried heavy loads, guarded sheep, and so on.

Domestication is the hallmark of two types of societies: pastoral and horticultural. Pastoral societies rely on domesticated herd animals to subsist. People living in deserts and other regions in which vegetation was limited adopted pastoralism. Those able to acquire and manage the largest herds assumed powerful statuses and passed their advantaged positions on to their children, creating hereditary-based political systems.

Most pastoral peoples are nomadic, moving their herds when grazing land and/or water sources are depleted. Even though they may be on the move, pastoralists are able to accumulate possessions such as tents, carpets, bowls, and other cultural artifacts, because now they have animals to carry those possessions. In the course of their travels, pastoralists encounter other nomads and settled peoples with whom they trade and/or fight to secure grazing land. The statuses people occupy revolve around gender, age, and kinship, but material possessions and success in conflicts are now also important to determining status.

People who live in horticultural societies rely on hand tools such as hoes to work the soil and digging sticks to punch holes in the ground into which seeds are dropped. Horticultural peoples grow crops rather than gather food and employ slash-and-burn technology in which they clear land of forest and vegetation to make fields for growing crops and grazing animals. When the land becomes exhausted, people move on, repeating the process. In contrast to pastoralists, horticultural societies are relatively settled, with their members migrating to new locations only after the soil is depleted. The horticultural system offers a level of predictability and residential stability that gives people the incentive and means to create surplus wealth, including houses, sculptures, and jewelry. The creation of surplus wealth is accompanied by conflict over available resources and by inequality with regard to its distribution.

Lt. Cmdr. Chuck Bell

© Ladi Kirn/Alamy

The major agricultural revolution that launched agrarian societies occurred around 5000 B.C., with the invention of the scratch plow (still used in some parts of the world); its forward-curving blade cut deep into the soil, bringing nutrients to the surface and turning weeds under. The plow was a great advance over hoes (top). The plow supported permanent settlements because farmers and their descendants could replenish the soil by turning it under year after year (Burke 1978, p. 9).

Barbara Houghton

In the context of contemporary India, pastoralists are defined as those groups in which at least 50 percent of their household consumption derives from the livestock they keep and breed. In addition at least 90 percent of what livestock consume comes from grazing in pastures (Sharma, Köhler-Rollefson, and Morton, 2011).

Agrarian Societies

The invention of the plow 6,000 years ago triggered a revolution in agriculture and marked the emergence of agrarian societies built on the cultivation of crops using plows pulled by animals to achieve subsistence. The plow made it possible to cultivate large fields and increase food production to a level that could support thousands to millions of people, many of whom lived in cities and/or were part of empires. Although the plow was a significant invention, planting and harvesting food still depended largely on human and animal muscle.

Agrarian societies are noted for dramatic inequality; power is concentrated in a hereditary monarch such as a king, queen, or emperor. Monarchs hold absolute power over their subjects, who for the most part do not question such power. In agrarian societies, there is a small number of landowning elites and large numbers of people known as serfs, peasants, or enslaved. There are also small numbers of merchants, traders, and craftspeople. In addition to dramatic inequality, agrarian societies are often engaged in wars to protect and/or expand their territory and to exercise control over resources.

Once the plow created surplus wealth, that wealth, along with a newfound ability to shape metal into weapons and blades, is believed to have changed the status of women relative to men in dramatic ways. As surplus wealth and populations increased in size, warfare between peoples fighting over land and resources became commonplace. The invention and proliferation of metal weapons supported empires, and military forces were created to advance and protect the interests of the political elite. The military excluded women, who spent much of their reproductive life pregnant or nursing, to offset the high death rates and low life expectancy (Boulding 1976).

Women's status was reduced in yet another way. The plow increased the amount of land that could be cultivated and by extension it increased the amount of food produced. It was men who operated the plows and managed heavy draft animals in fields away from home. Women's reproductive lives and caretaking responsibilities, in conjunction with the efficient technology men operated, made it difficult for women to outproduce men. As a result, women's share of the production diminished and their status eroded. Now women were left "with all the subsidiary tasks, including weeding and carrying water to the fields. The new fields were larger so women had to work just as many hours as they did before but at more secondary tasks" (Boulding 1976).

Much of India's agricultural sector qualifies as agrarian even after undergoing a Green Revolution, a plan to relieve chronic food shortages and help the country become self-sufficient in food production by constructing irrigation systems and investing in agricultural technologies, including hybrid seeds, pesticides, and fertilizers (Derdak 1988). The government encouraged chemical companies such as Union Carbide to locate in the country and to use local labor and regional raw materials, thereby creating other employment opportunities. The manufactured chemicals were used to prevent malaria and other insect-borne diseases and to protect crops and harvests from insects, rodents, and diseases. Agricultural yields were indeed impressive; India is now the second largest grain producer in the world, but ironically, India's farms still largely depend on manual labor.

colonization A form of domination in which a foreign power imposes its political, economic, social, and cultural institutions on an indigenous population to control their labor, resources, and markets.

Keith Farley

Today in India, 51 percent of the labor force is employed in the agricultural sector. Although this sector has been shaped by a number of agricultural revolutions, most notably the Green Revolution in the 1960s and 1970s, India has few highly mechanized farms or agribusinesses that can manage thousands of acres of food crops (Bajaj 2011).

Industrial Societies

Industrial societies rely on mechanization or on machines powered by burning wood and fossil fuels. Mechanization allowed humans to produce food, extract resources, and manufacture goods at revolutionary speeds and on an unprecedented scale. Eventually mechanization allowed a small percentage of the population to grow the food needed to sustain a society that could encompass hundreds of millions of people. Mechanization changed everything: how goods were produced, how people negotiated time and space, the relationships among geographically distant peoples, how people made their livings, the density of human populations, the relative importance and influence of the home in people's lives, and the proportion of people with access to formal education. The products of industrialization improved nutrition and living standards, which increased human life expectancy, decreased fertility, and lowered death rates (Massey 2002).

If we study patterns of conflict in the world, we can see that as countries industrialized they used their technological advantages and military strength to invade and control people they labeled as backward or primitive. In this regard, the Industrial Revolution cannot be separated from **colonization**. The Industrial Revolution and colonization forced people from even the most remote parts of the world into a production process that manufactured unprecedented quantities of material goods, primarily for the benefit of the colonizing countries. Consider as one measure of the extent of colonization that during the twentieth century, 130 countries gained independence from their "mother" countries. One of these countries was India, which was considered the "crown jewel" of the British Empire (see Global Comparisons).

Global Comparison World Map of the British Empire and Commonwealth

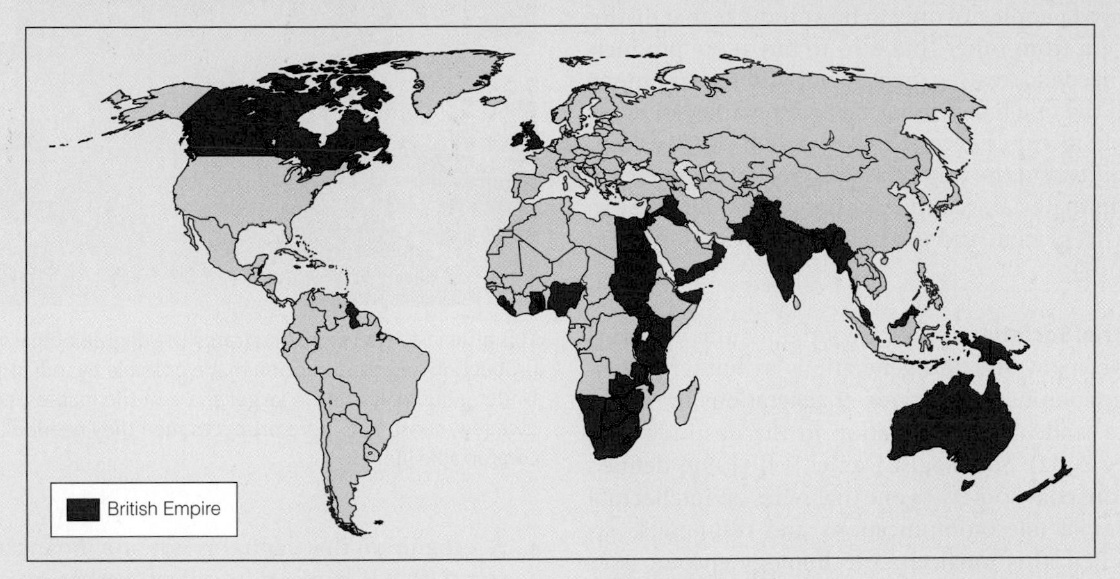

FIGURE 11.1 The territories the map shows in red were part of the British Empire and Commonwealth when it was at its peak in the 1930s. The British Empire lasted 350 years; at its peak, it controlled (on some level) 25 to 30 percent of the world's land and 25 percent of its population.

Source: Data from U.S. Central Intelligence Agency (2011)

Initially, the British Empire exploited India's raw materials, labor, and territory through the East India Company, a company so powerful that is possessed its own army that was larger in size than the British Army. But eventually the fortunes of the East India Company and Great Britain became so intertwined that nation and company moved in tandem with one another (Bowen 2000). The East India Company established its first factory in India in 1600. It was not until 1857 that the British government dissolved the company and took control of India until its independence in 1947. At independence, India was left with a population that was ranked among the poorest in the world, with an inadequate infrastructure, a failing industrial sector, an inability to grow enough food to sustain its large and rapidly increasing population, high illiteracy, and an unskilled labor force (Datt and Sundharam 2009).

The British Empire used its vast empire of colonies to supply the world with goods: "the gold and diamonds of South Africa; the wood, wheat, butter, and meat of Australia; the wheat, fish, and timber of Canada; the sugar of the West Indies; the rubber and tin of Malaysia; the wheat, cotton, jute, rice, and tea of India" (Demangeon 1925, p. 14).

The Industrial Revolution allowed people to create surplus wealth so large that it could support a diverse economy and many institutions, including education, medicine, sports, government, and so on. The mass production of goods allowed people not only to buy products that distinguished them from others but also to buy more products than they needed, creating great social differences among people. On the one hand, industrialization allowed many more people to experience a high standard of living and social mobility. On the other hand, it created dramatic inequalities in material wealth, especially between those in the richest 10 percent and the bottom poorest 20 percent (Massey 2002).

Postindustrial Societies Over the course of human history, people have spent 300,000 generations as hunter-gatherers, 500 generations as agrarians, 9 generations in the industrial era, and only 1 generation in the postindustrial era (Massey 2002). Sociologist Daniel Bell (1999) defined the **postindustrial society** as one that relies on intellectual technologies of telecommunications and computers. According to Bell, this intellectual technology encompasses four interdependent revolutionary innovations: (1) electronics that allow for incredible speed of data transmission and calculations, which can be made in nanoseconds; (2) miniaturization or the drastic reduction in size of electronic devices; (3) digitalization, which allows voice, text, image, and data to be integrated and transmitted with equal efficiency; and (4) software applications that allow people to perform a variety of tasks and generate a variety of simulated experiences. Intellectual technologies are driven by the microchip, the brain of many electronic products, including computers, cell phones, cameras, iPods, and televisions. Microchips run pacemakers and mechanical hearts. They are installed in microwave ovens and cars. Microchips control the deployment of air bags, the movement of artificial limbs, and much more.

According to Bell, postindustrial societies, built upon these intellectual technologies, are distinguished by

- A substantially greater share of the working population employed in service, sales, and administrative support occupations (in the United States, from 29 percent in 1950 to 41 percent in 2010);
- An increased emphasis on education as the avenue of social mobility (in the United States, in 1950, 6 percent of the population had at least a four-year college degree; in 2010, 28 percent did);

postindustrial society A society that is dominated by intellectual technologies of telecommunications and computers, not just "large computers but computers on a chip." These intellectual technologies have had a revolutionary effect on virtually every aspect of social life.

Chris Caldeira

This aisle in a retail store illustrates the degree of mass production and consumption made possible by industrialization. Under industrialization, a larger share of the masses, not just an elite few, consumed more products than they needed to live a comfortable life.

- A recognition that capital is not only financial but also social (that is, access to social networks serves as an important source of information and opportunity);
- The dominance of intellectual technology grounded in mathematics and linguistics that takes the form of what are known as apps;
- The creation of an electronically mediated global communication infrastructure that includes broadband, cable, digital TV, optical fiber networks, fax, email, and integrated system digital networks (ISDN); and
- An economy defined not simply by the production of goods but by applied knowledge and the manipulation of numbers, words, images, and other symbols.

What do these changes mean? In answering this question, keep in mind that Bell does not believe that technology determines the nature of any social change. Rather, it is the ways people choose to use and respond to the technology that shapes social change. Although it is virtually impossible to catalog all the changes associated with the intellectual technologies, they have (1) sped up old ways of doing things; (2) given individuals access to the equivalent of personal libraries, publishing houses, and production studios; (3) changed how people learn; and (4) permitted real-time exchange of information on a global scale. Although computer software and telecommunications technologies have increased the speed of information generation and exchange, people must still read, discuss, and contemplate the information to give it meaning. These activities are very slow compared with the speed at which the information is generated.

Relative to other types of societies, the postindustrial society presents its members with a distinct set of challenges. The communication infrastructure multiplies the interactions (however superficial and fleeting) between

Chris Caldeira

The distinguishing feature in the postindustrial society is "the enlargement of an individual's world" or the "tremendous change of scale" in the number of people one knows or can know (Bell 1976, p. 48). Although 351 friends may not seem an extraordinary number today, before Facebook and the Internet, few people could have imagined keeping track of the daily activities of 351 people.

people, making interpersonal relationships a primary focus of one's thoughts and actions. That focus is complicated by the fact that we leave records of most transactions, whether they are related to banking transactions or to the day and time of day a text message was sent.

The IT and business services sector of the Indian economy qualifies as postindustrial. India is the best known destination for European and American business process outsourcing (BPO) and IT services. By one estimate, 2.54 million people in India are employed by this sector (Ribeiro 2011). A large portion of the work outsourced falls under the category "low value," such as call center operators, a job that does no required specialized knowledge. However, some of the fastest growth involves work requiring graduate-level education in medicine, engineering, and the law. Law firms in the United States, for example, have already outsourced document review, legal research, and proofreading and are now moving toward outsourcing work to be performed by Indians with law degrees from some of the best U.S. and European universities (Ridge 2011). In evaluating the latest high-skill outsourcing trends, keep in mind that, after China, India sends the greatest number of students (105,000 in 2009) to the United States to study in its colleges and universities. Each year, the United States awards the largest number of new H1B visas to foreign workers from India. In 2010, that number was almost 30,000, about 20 percent of all such visas awarded (Homeland Security 2011).

In his book *Dead Ringers*, sociologist Shezad Nadeem (2011) described outsourcing as including international news agencies outsourcing basic business coverage; legal firms outsourcing draft patents; hospitals outsourcing X-rays, MRIs, and CT scans to be read; movie production companies outsourcing special effects scenes; insurance companies outsourcing insurance claims to be evaluated and processed; and much more. We also cannot forget medical services, including joint and heart valve replacements, dental work, and Botox injections, for wealthy tourists.

Major Economic Systems

CORE CONCEPT 2 The world's economic systems fall along a continuum whose endpoints are capitalism and socialism in most pure forms.

No economy fully realizes capitalist or socialist principles. The capitalist and socialist principles described here represent economic ideals, or the standards against which real economic systems can be compared.

Capitalism

Capitalism is an economic system in which the raw materials and the means of producing and distributing goods and services remain privately owned. This economic system is profit driven and free of government interference. Private ownership means that individuals (rather than workers, the government, or communal groups) own the raw materials, machines, tools, labor, trucks, buildings, and other inputs needed to produce and distribute goods and services. Profit-driven is the most important characteristic of capitalist systems. In such systems, those who own and manage the means of production and distribution are driven to continually increase and maximize profits. Profit motivates owners in their quest to maximize the return on their investment, to make the most efficient use of labor and resources. Theoretically, production and distribution are consumer-driven.

Capitalist systems are governed by the laws of supply and demand; that is, as consumer demand for a product or service increases, its price rises. Manufacturers and service providers respond to this demand by increasing production, which in turn "increases competition and drives the price down" (Hirsch, Kett, and Trefil 1993, p. 455). Although most economic systems in the world are classified as capitalist, in reality, no system fully realizes capitalist principles. Simply consider that 90 percent of home mortgage loans in the United States flow through two government-created corporations known as Fannie Mae and Freddie Mac, all backed by the U.S. federal government. To put it another way, the $1.5 trillion U.S. mortgage market is a taxpayer-owned industry (Blumberg 2011).

Karl Marx, who was considered a student of capitalism, believed that it was the first economic system that could

capitalism An economic system in which the raw materials and the means of producing and distributing goods and services remain privately owned.

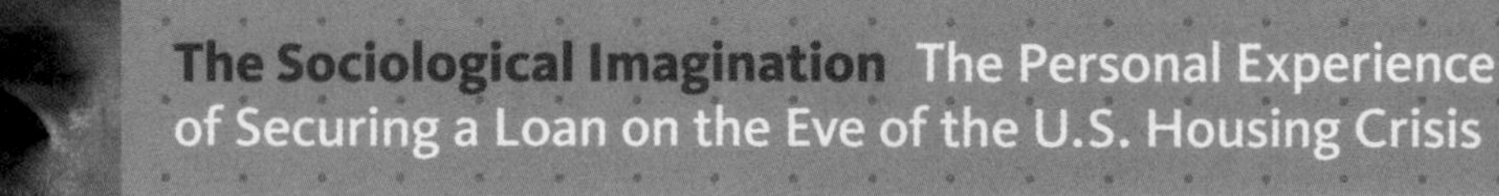

The Sociological Imagination The Personal Experience of Securing a Loan on the Eve of the U.S. Housing Crisis

Consider that greed ultimately fueled the mortgage crisis in the United States that came to light in 2008. At that time, about 1 in every 50 mortgage holders was late with house payments, and foreclosure proceedings were initiated on more than 1.5 million homes. The financial meltdown came about in part because so many, at all levels of the home-buying and lending process, made decisions based on profit and personal gain. What is the connection between the pursuit of profit and the housing crisis? The *Japan Times* (2008) described the connection in this way: "Banks gave mortgages to unworthy borrowers and failed to explain the terms of loans. Borrowers took loans that they knew they could not repay. Financial companies repackaged those loans and sold them, knowing that their value was uncertain at best. Companies bought those securities, not understanding their value. And regulators adopted a hands-off approach that facilitated the spread of toxic debt." My students shared their experiences with lenient lending practices during this time period.

- I took out a car loan in 2005. At that time I had no credit history, and the dealership asked me if I could find a cosigner; I explained that both my parents were deceased and I could absolutely not find a cosigner. Several hours later, I walked away with my brand new car and a loan for $17,000, with no money down and no cosigner. It was a bad deal for me; my interest rate was horrible and the length of the loan was long. I still look back and ask how the car company could give me a loan.
- We bought the house that we live in now in 2003. I was pregnant with our third child and thought that it was time to move to a bigger house. At the time, we made about $80,000 a year. We had several credit card bills as well and we were worried that we may not qualify for a loan. We had to show two weeks of pay stubs, W2s from the previous year, and any savings or 401(k) statements. That's it!!! We completed the application and, to our surprise, within two days the bank called and offered us more money than we had asked for. They were willing to give us $250,000 with no down payment. We needed $175,000, an amount we knew was going to be a stretch for our budget but, being naïve, we took $200,000.
- My family purchased three houses in the last seven years, all of which we bought without a down payment and after a minimal credit check. We sold two of the houses fairly easily. The last house, which we had built, cost us $200,000. Now, due to the economy and a housing slump, brand-new homes on our street are selling for between $160,000 and $180,000. This drop in prices means we have to sell this house for a price below what we paid to build it.
- When I was looking to buy a home in January 2007, I talked to a mortgage company and a local bank. The mortgage company rep (who worked on commission) approved me for an amount that I knew I couldn't afford. When I told that rep I couldn't afford it he responded that "on paper" I could definitely afford it. I told him that I didn't live on paper and I knew that I couldn't possibly make those monthly payments. He then offered me an interest-only loan (where I wouldn't have to pay on the principle) with an adjustable rate to make the monthly payments low enough. I told him thanks and I would get back to him. I went to a local bank (where the loan officers don't work on commission). After talking to them, they approved me for an amount I knew I could afford with a 30-year, fixed rate.

maximize the immense productive potential of human labor and ingenuity. He also felt, however, that capitalism ignored too many human needs and was driven by greed. (See the Sociological Imagination box: "The Personal Experience of Securing a Loan on the Eve of the U.S. Housing Crisis.")

Socialism

The term *socialism* was first used in the early nineteenth century in response to excesses of poverty and inequality that accompanied the capitalist-driven Industrial Revolution. In contrast to capitalism, **socialism** is an economic system in which raw materials and the means of producing and distributing goods and services are collectively owned. That is, public ownership—rather than private ownership—is an essential characteristic of this system. Socialists reject the idea that what is good for the individual and for privately owned businesses is good for society. Instead, they believe the government or some employee or community-oriented entity should play the central role in regulating economic activity on behalf of the people as a whole. Socialists maintain that things like water, oil, banks, medical care, transportation, and the media should be state owned. In socialism's most extreme form, the pursuit of personal profit is forbidden. In less extreme forms, profit-making activities are permitted as long as they do not interfere with larger collective goals. As with capitalism, no economic system fully realizes socialist

socialism An economic system in which raw materials and the means of producing and distributing goods and services are collectively owned.

Lisa Southwick

One could make the case that the housing foreclosure crisis in the United States represents a dramatic example of the pursuit of profit gone awry. Lenders issued loans without regard for the buyers' ability to afford them and passed the risk on to investors who also dodged risk through financial tools such as insurance policies that paid off if debts went sour.

principles. The People's Republic of China, Cuba, North Korea, and Vietnam are all officially classified as socialist economies, but they permit varying degrees of personal wealth-generating activities.

After India achieved independence in 1947, Jawaharlal Nehru became the country's first prime minister and held that position until 1964. The Nehru administration worked to create an economy that served the public interest, not profit-making interests of corporations. The government nationalized private businesses and created publicly owned finance, transportation, pharmaceutical, power, chemical, steel, and other companies (Luce 2007, p. 53). After Nehru left office in 1964, the country followed socialist policies until 1991, when India's largest trading partner, the Soviet Union, collapsed and the first Gulf War pushed oil prices to record levels. These events created an economic crisis for India, forcing it to turn to the International Monetary Fund for a $1.8 billion bailout loan. The request was granted on the condition that India implement economic liberalization policies that included dismantling government-sponsored monopolies, relaxing regulation over businesses, and easing terms of foreign investment. Since that time, India has continued on a path of economic liberalization. Still, the government of India maintains tight control over the economy, including more than 500 major companies it owns (Luce 2007).

We have seen that the economies of the United States and India do not fall clearly under one economic model. In reality, no economic system is purely capitalist or purely socialist. The **welfare state** is a term that applies to an economic system that is a hybrid of capitalism and socialism. In this economic model, the government (through taxes) assumes a key role in providing social benefits to some or all of its citizens including unemployment, child care, Social Security, medical care, transportation, education (including college), and housing. Under the welfare state model followed by the United States, such benefits are provided to those who meet certain criteria based on poverty-level income or age (62 and over). Under a second model, the benefits are awarded in a more comprehensive way to everyone in the population (for example, all families with children; all college-age students; universal health care). Most European countries follow the second model, as do oil revenue–rich countries such as Saudi Arabia, Kuwait, Qatar, Bahrain, Oman, and the United Arab Emirates.

India also follows a welfare-state model in that strives to balance the "economics of growth with the economics of equity" (Singh 2008). An example is government forgiveness loans aimed at ensuring opportunity for the "poorest of the poor," specifically an estimated 43 million small landholding farmers who took out loans between 1997 and 2007, but could not pay them back after crops failed several years in a row. The most tragic cases involved farmers who took out loans to purchase genetically modified seeds, 1,000 times more expensive than traditional seeds, yet designed in such a way that plants produce no viable seeds. Thus farmers are forced to buy new seeds each year. The loan program was instituted as a response to a high rate of suicides among indebted farmers (New Agriculturalist 2008, Malone 2008).

World System Theory

CORE CONCEPT 3 Capitalists' responses to economic downturns and stagnation have driven a 500-year-plus economic expansion, which has facilitated interconnections between local, regional, and national economies.

Immanuel Wallerstein (1984) is the sociologist most frequently associated with world system theory. He has written extensively about the ceaseless 500-year-plus expansion of a single market force—capitalism—that created the world economy. The world economy, which currently encompasses more than 200 countries and thousands of cultures, is interconnected by the division of labor. Although each government seeks to shape the global market in ways that benefit its interests, no single political structure such as a world government holds authority over the system of production and distribution.

How has capitalism come to dominate the global network of economic relationships? One answer to this question can be found in the strategies capitalists employ to increase profits during times of economic stagnation. Wallerstein

welfare state A term that applies to an economic system that is a hybrid of capitalism and socialism.

(1984) identifies six strategies: One response involves lowering labor costs by finding employees who will work for less; forcing people to work for little to no wages (enslavement, indentured servitude); and automating production.

A second response to economic stagnation capitalists use to generate profits is to secure at the lowest possible price the raw materials needed to make products; those products may be rubber, sugarcane, or coltan (an essential mineral for making cell phones). A third response is to create new markets that expand the boundaries of the world economy. The global expansion of fast food service corporations such as McDonald's and Domino's Pizza represents such a response. In addition to finding ways to lower labor-associated production costs, there are at least three other typical responses to economic stagnation:

- Creating new products that consumers feel they need to buy, such as the iPod, the BlackBerry, or even Viagra;
- Improving existing products to make previous versions obsolete (that is, create printers that print faster or make smart phones with more features); and
- Finding ways to help people purchase more products and services by offering higher wages or issuing credit, allowing people to spend beyond their means (that is, no payments for five years, no interest, home equity loans).

Because of these strategies, capitalism has spread steadily across the globe and facilitated connections between local, regional, and national economies. Wallerstein argues that the 200-plus countries that have become part of the world economy play one of three different and unequal roles in the global economy: core, peripheral, or semiperipheral.

Core Economies Core economies include the wealthiest, most highly diversified economies with strong, stable governments. Examples of core economies include the United States, Japan, Germany, France, Canada, and the United Kingdom.

These scooters deliver Domino's Pizza products in India. The pizza company opened its first store in India in 1996, and there are now more than 300 stores employing 9,000 people, making it the largest pizza chain in that country (Domino's Pizza India 2011).

The 20 percent of the world's population that constitutes the core economies accounts for 86 percent of total private consumption expenditures (World Bank 2008). Consequently, when economic activity weakens in core economies, the economies of other countries suffer, because exports to core economies decline and prices fall. In spite of their large size and relative stability, core economies have weaknesses, one of which is their dependence on foreign sources for raw materials, such as oil needed to fuel cars.

Peripheral Economies Peripheral economies are built on a few commodities or even a single commodity, such as coffee, peanuts, or tobacco, or on a natural resource, such as oil, tin, copper, or zinc (Van Evera 1990). At least 38 countries depend on one commodity for 50 percent or more of the revenues generated from exports (U.S. Central Intelligence Agency 2011). For example, coffee accounts for at least 50 percent of the revenue that Uganda and Burundi earn from their exports (U.S. Central Intelligence Agency 2011). Peripheral economies have a dependent relationship with core economies that traces its roots to colonialism. Peripheral economies operate on the so-called fringes of the world economy. Most of the jobs that connect their workers to the world economy pay little and require few skills. Amid widespread and chronic poverty, pockets of economic activity may exist, including manufacturing zones and tourist attractions.

The African country of Malawi represents one example of a peripheral economy as illustrated by this description in the *World Factbook*: "Landlocked Malawi ranks among the world's most densely populated and least developed countries. The economy is predominately agricultural with about 85 percent of the population living in rural areas. Agriculture accounts for more than one-third of GDP and 90 percent of export revenues. The performance of the tobacco sector is key to short-term growth as tobacco accounts for more than half of exports" (U.S. Central Intelligence Agency 2011).

Semiperipheral Economies Semiperipheral economies are characterized by moderate wealth (but extreme inequality) and moderately diverse economies. Semiperipheral economies exploit peripheral economies and are in turn exploited by core economies. According to Wallerstein, semiperipheral economies play an important role in the world economy because they are politically stable enough to provide useful places for capitalist investment if employee wage and benefit demands in core economies become too great such as when U.S. companies outsource manufacturing jobs to China or IT jobs to India. But India outsources work as well. India IT companies have established back offices in Mexico, Brazil, Chile, Uruguay, Canada, China, Portugal, Romania, Saudi Arabia, and many other strategic locations including lower-wage cities and towns within the United States (Giridharadas 2007).

Barbara Houghton

One problem with this three-tier classification scheme—core, semiperipheral, and peripheral—is that some countries such as India possess geographic areas within their borders that could qualify as any one of the three designations. Some agricultural regions in India revolve around human or animal muscles, suggesting the economy is peripheral. A call center, on the other hand, which services customers who have purchased products from U.S. multinational corporations qualifies as a semiperipheral economy.

The countries known as big emerging market (BEM) economies qualify as semiperipheral economies. They are Brazil, China, Egypt, India, Indonesia, Mexico, Philippines, Poland, Russia, South Africa, South Korea, and Turkey. One critical feature of these emerging economies is that they are quickly being integrated into the information society, even as their industrial sector remains limited or underdeveloped.

Two Economies Compared

CORE CONCEPT 4 The United States qualifies as a core economy; India represents an example of a semi-peripheral economy.

As measured by the GDP, the United States has the largest economy in the world at $14.72 trillion (U.S. Central Intelligence Agency 2011); India has the fifth largest in the world at $1.43 trillion. In per capita or per person terms, the United States has the tenth largest gross domestic product in the world—$47,400 per person—after Qatar ($145,300), Liechtenstein ($122,100), Luxembourg ($81,800), Bermuda ($69,900), Norway ($59,100), Singapore ($57,200), Jersey ($57,000), Kuwait ($51,700), and Brunei ($50,300). India's per capita GDP is $3,400, making it the 163rd largest economy in the world (U.S. Central Intelligence Agency 2011).

The U.S. national debt is $14.2 trillion, which is 97 percent of the country's GDP. About $5.4 trillion of the $14.2 trillion in debt is held by other U.S. government entities, including the Social Security Trust Fund. Foreign investors and governments hold an estimated $4.8 trillion of the debt. Other holders of national debt include U.S. state and local governments ($511 billion), individual investors ($1.46 billion), and public and private pension funds ($706 billion) (CNBC 2011, U.S. Department of Treasury 2011). India's national debt is $295.8 billion, which is about 20 percent of its total GDP (Rediff 2011).

In addition to the national debt, total U.S. personal debt stands at $16.1 trillion, with $13.8 trillion in mortgage debt and $804 billion in credit card debt (U.S. Debt Clocks 2011). Each month, 1 in every 15 credit card holders (6.5 percent) misses a credit card payment (Streitfeld 2009). The large consumer debt has been building since the mid-1980s, and indicates that U.S. consumption fueled by debt has played a key role in driving the growth of the domestic and global economy (see Table 11.1).

Trade Deficit Driven by Dependence on Oil Imports

The United States imported $2,329.7 billion in goods and services in 2010, and it exported $1,831.8 billion. The overall U.S. trade deficit—the difference between the dollar value of goods and services imported and exported—was $497 billion in 2010. That is, the United States imported $497 billion more goods and services than it exported. The country with which the United States had the largest trade deficit is China (−$273 billion), as Americans exported $91 billion of goods and services to China while importing $364.9 billion from China. The United States' trade relationship with India is very small by comparison. The United States exported $19.2 billion of goods and services to India while importing $29.5 billion from India for a trade deficit of −$10.3 (U.S. Bureau of the Census 2011).

TABLE 11.1 Total Consumption and Per Capita Consumption by United States Relative to the European Union, Japan, China, and India

U.S. personal consumption averages $32,577 for every man, woman, and child in the country. Per capita personal consumption in the United States is much greater than that of the European Union and Japan and far exceeds that of China and India.

Country	Total Personal Consumption	Per Capita Personal Consumption
United States	$9.7 trillion	$32,577
European Union	$8.9 trillion	$18,126
Japan	$2.5 trillion	$19,685
China	$1.2 trillion	$2,199
India	$0.6 trillion	$1,610

Sources: Data from *New York Times* 2008, U.S. Bureau of Economic Analysis 2009, *Financial Times* 2011.

Working for Change Measuring Happiness

The government of Bhutan, informed by the country's deeply rooted Buddhist tradition, has offered the world a new measure by which to quantify national well-being. In 1972, Bhutan's King Jigme Singye Wangchuck, realizing that the country's Buddhist spiritual values were threatened by the forces of globalization, established the Gross National Happiness Index (GNH), a measure that challenges the assumption that economic indicators of monetary wealth and consumption such as GDP measure well-being. The GNH Index was conceived and aligned with Buddhist spiritual values to guide the economic and development goals of the country. GNH is not a utopian dream but a recognition that humanistic and holistic principles should guide government policies (Thinley 2011).

Gross domestic product, the most widely used measure of economic success, is the total dollar value of all goods and services produced annually by a country. Presumably the larger the GDP, and the greater the increase in GDP from one year to the next, the healthier a country's economy and the higher its standard of living. But GDP does not take into account how income, goods, and services are distributed within that economy. High GDP only tells us that some of a country's residents are doing well economically (Schell 2002). In 1968, Robert F. Kennedy gave a speech that eloquently expresses the shortcomings of the GDP measurement which

> counts air pollution and cigarette advertising and ambulances to clear our highways of carnage. It counts special locks for our doors and the jails for the people who break them. It counts the destruction of the redwoods and the loss of our natural wonder in chaotic sprawl. It counts napalm and it counts nuclear warheads, and armored cars for the police to fight riots in our cities. It counts Whitman's rifle and Speck's knife, and the television programs which glorify violence in order to sell toys to our children.
>
> Yet the Gross [Domestic] Product does not allow for the health of our children, the quality of their education, or the joy of their play. It does not include the beauty of our poetry or the strength of our marriages, the intelligence of our public debate or the integrity of our public officials. It measures neither our wit nor our courage, neither our wisdom nor our learning, neither our compassion nor our devotion to our country; it measures everything, in short, except that which makes life worthwhile.

In contrast to GDP, gross national happiness is calculated by using measures of well-being and happiness that are more subjective and focused on quality of life. The Bhutan government asks a random sample of 1,000 householders to fill out a 290-question survey and to keep a diary about daily activities. The survey includes questions about mental states and emotional balance, opportunities for spiritual growth, exercise, the total number of hours working and sleeping, exposure to pollution, ties to others in the community,

Chris Caldeira

Missy Gish

The gross national happiness index captures nonmaterial qualities of life that affect well-being. Notice that the child in Laos has few, if any, material objects with which to play, whereas the child in the United States has many material objects at his fingertips. Which child do you think might have a happier life? Explain.

family relations, feelings about personal safety, health status, proximity to medical care, and much more. Examples of questions asked include: How often is someone there to help you when you have problems? Do you plant trees around your farm or houses? (National Statistics Bureau 2007).

Over the past 40 years, Bhutan's gross national happiness index has received considerable attention throughout the world. It has opened a dialogue among policy makers about what factors best capture national well-being. The most recent Gallup World Poll surveyed people in 155 countries, asking them questions about their day-to-day experiences. Based on answers, Gallup calculated an overall life satisfaction score. Denmark ranked first, along with neighbors Finland, Norway, and Sweden, and the United States ranked 14th. Bhutan was not included in the poll (Levy 2010).

Source: Written by Victoria Michell, Northern Kentucky University, Class of 2011.

If we break the total trade deficit of the United States into two parts—goods and services—we find that the United States runs a surplus (+$148.7 billion) in services and a deficit in goods (−$646.5 billion). Petroleum imports accounted for 41 percent of the overall trade deficit (U.S. Bureau of the Census 2011). The fact that 41 percent of the U.S. trade deficit is related to oil imports points to a major weakness or vulnerability—the U.S. dependence on foreign sources for raw materials. According to the U.S. Department of Energy (2011), the United States produces approximately 9.1 million barrels of crude oil each year. This amount meets approximately 49 percent of the country's crude oil needs. The United States must import the remaining 51 percent—about 9.7 million barrels per day (see Table 11.2). India by contrast imported $327 billion in goods and services and exported $210 billion for a trade deficit of −$117. Of that $117 deficit, 98.1 billion is the cost of importing oil; that is, oil accounts for almost 84 percent of India's deficit (U.S. Central Intelligence Agency 2011).

The extent of U.S. dependence on foreign oil becomes evident when we consider that it has an estimated 19.1 billion barrels of proven oil reserves—less than 3 percent of the world's total proven reserves (see Figure 11.2). At the current rate of domestic production (49 percent of need per year), these reserves will last about six years. If the United States could produce and refine 100 percent of its crude oil needs, it would deplete those reserves in less than 2.8 years. When we compare the domestic oil production in the United States, oil consumption, and proven reserves with India and China, we can see that the three countries will increasingly depend on foreign sources to meet their needs (see Table 11.2).

Although most Americans likely know about their country's dependence on oil, they are less likely to know of the country's dependence on imported minerals. Simply consider that the automobile we drive contains at least 32 minerals, including aluminium, carbon, copper, silicon, lead, and zinc. If that car is a Toyota Prius or other hybrid car, it needs about 2.2 pounds of neodymium for its motor magnets. By one estimate, each year, Americans use 25,000 pounds of minerals per person to sustain their current standard of living as it relates to food production, shelter, the infrastructure, health care, and information and communication. Even a green economy depends on minerals. As one example, wind power turbines require more than 700 pounds of neodymium per megawatt of energy generating capacity. Currently, that mineral can only be acquired from China. There are at least 18 other strategic mineral commodities on which the United States has a 100 percent dependence, including arsenic and indium needed to make semiconductors and strontium needed to make fuel cells. The competition for these minerals is likely to dramatically increase as China's and India's economies continue to grow at recording-setting paces (International College of the Armed Forces 2010).

Union Membership

Of all workers in the United States, 11.9 percent (or 14.7 million) are union members. Union affiliation varies by state. In four states, 20 percent or more of the workers belong to unions: Hawaii (21.8 percent), New York (24.2 percent), Alaska (22.9 percent), and New Jersey (20.1 percent). Four states record union affiliation of less than 4 percent of the workforce: North Carolina (3.2 percent),

TABLE 11.2 United States, India, and China: Selected Oil Statistics

How large is the U.S. population relative to India and China? Which country consumes the most oil per day? How long will it take the United States to deplete domestic oil reserves? Can the United States continue to consume 25 percent of all oil produced in the world?

	United States	India	China
Population Size	311 million	1.2 billion	1.3 billion
Percentage of World Population	4.5%	17.4%	18.8%
Oil Consumption Per Day	18.8 million barrels/day	3.1 million barrels/day	8.3 million barrels/day
Percentage of World Oil Consumption	25%	4.1%	11.6%
Oil Imported from Foreign Sources	9.7 million barrels/day	2.2 million barrels/day	4.3 million barrels/day
Oil Produced Domestically	9.1 million barrels/day	.9 million barrels/day	4.0 million barrels/day
Known Reserves of Oil (in millions of barrels)	19,100	5,600	20,300
Time to Deplete Known Reserves at Current Levels of Domestic Consumption	2.8 years	4.9 years	6.7 years

Source: U.S. Energy Information Administration 2011.

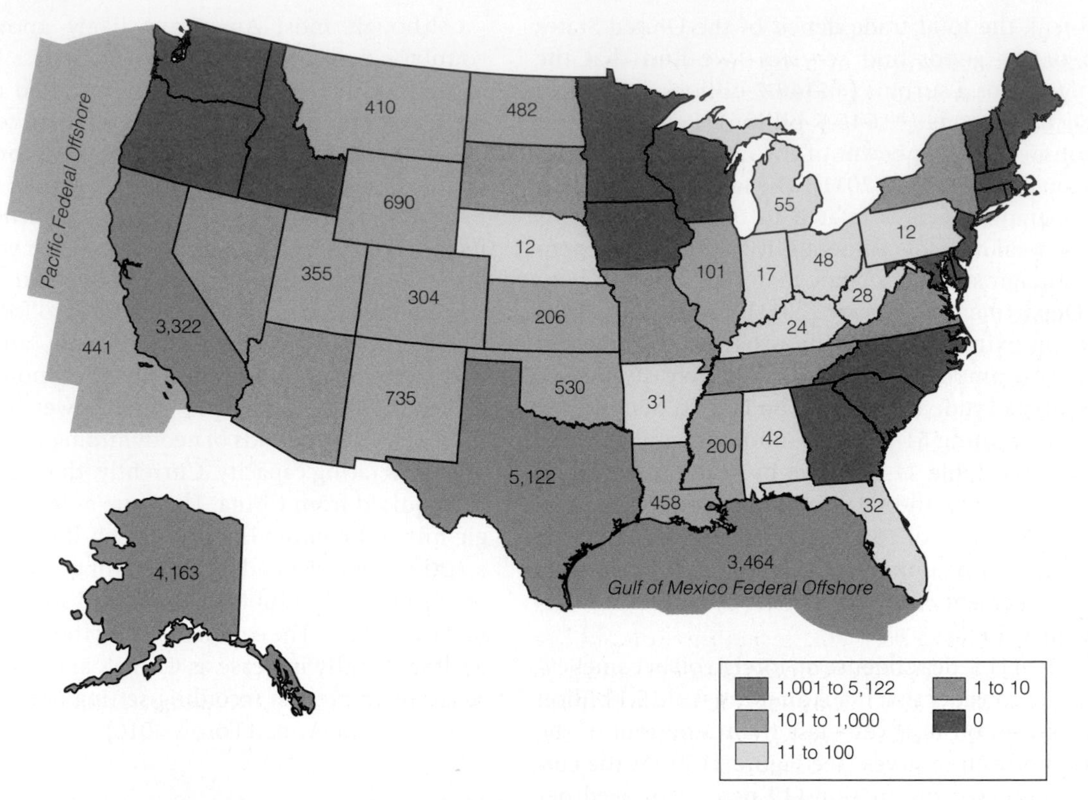

FIGURE 11.2 Amount of Proven Reserves of Crude Oil (in millions of barrels)
The map shows that there are 4.2 million barrels of known crude oil in the state of Alaska. Texas has 5.1 billion barrels within its borders. How can we use these numbers to assess the claim that drilling for oil in Alaska will help the United States achieve oil independence? One way is to place this figure in the context of annual consumption. The United States consumes 20 million barrels of oil per day; that translates to 7.3 billion barrels per year. Alaska, with 4.2 billion barrels, contains enough oil to satisfy six months of oil demand. The Arctic National Wildlife Refuge (ANWR) is believed to contain about 1.9 billion barrels of known oil, the equivalent of about three months of oil consumption. Some government geologists believe that there could be an additional 10 billion barrels of oil waiting to be discovered, an amount equivalent to 1.5 years of consumption.
Source: U.S. Energy Information Administration (2011)

Chris Caldeira

When we think of green technologies, we think independence from foreign oil producers. We don't think about a new kind of dependence on foreign sources for minerals such as neodymium needed to construct wind turbines.

Arkansas (4.0), Georgia (4.0 percent), and Louisiana (4.3 percent) (U.S. Department of Labor 2011). Unions, or organized labor, seek to at least maintain and sometimes improve workers' pay, benefits, and working conditions. Ideally, unions also strive to ensure that wages, benefits, and working conditions remain secure for future generations of workers.

Union membership in the United States has declined from a high of 35 percent of the workforce in the 1950s, to 20.1 percent in 1983, to just under 12 percent today (U.S. Department of Labor 2011). The steady drop in union membership, especially over the past 30 years, has been connected to many factors, including the following:

- The declining significance of the manufacturing sector (the traditional base of union membership) in the overall economy.
- Increasing percentages of females in the workforce (who have tended to work in nonunion positions).
- Increasing global competition (which has added pressure to keep wages down and minimize union influence).

In the United States, about 43 percent of public sector employees belong to unions. Among the most unionized occupations are teachers, police officers, and fire fighters. Only about 7 percent of private sector employees are unionized with the highest unionization rates among employees in transportation (airlines), utilities, and construction. For the most part, there are no significant differences in union membership rate for men versus women or across race. Workers aged 55 to 64 years old are more likely (15.7 percent) to be union members than those ages 16 to 24 (4.3 percent). In the United States, unions (as a group) are visible supporters of Democratic candidates—as evidenced by the $50 million they contributed during the 2008 presidential election cycle, an amount greater than any other category of contributors (U.S. Department of Labor 2011, Center for Responsive Politics 2009).

In India, according to the Trade Unions Act 2001, a registered trade union in India must have at least 10 percent or 100 workers (whichever is smaller) at the workplace as members. Nonemployees can be union members and hold office. In India, there are unions specific to a workplace and there are centralized unions that represent an entire profession. In India, political parties play crucial roles in forming unions and in leading collective bargaining. Often trade union leaders are affiliated with a particular political party, not with a workplace or a specific profession per se.

In India, about one in three nonagricultural workers are union members. This percentage varies by state. In the state of Mizoram, almost everyone (91 percent) belongs to a union. In the state of Delhi, the percentage is 19.1. In India, union membership is highest among males, full-time workers, those near retirement age, members of communist parties, and those who have engaged in political activism. Also, those who belong to scheduled castes or tribes are more inclined to join unions compared to others (Pal 2008).

Relative Importance of the Three Sectors

We can think of an economy as being comprised of three sectors: primary, secondary, and tertiary. The **primary sector** includes economic activities that generate or extract raw materials from the natural environment. Mining, fishing, growing crops, raising livestock, drilling for oil, and planting and harvesting forest products are examples. The **secondary sector** consists of economic activities that transform raw materials from the primary sector into manufactured goods. The **tertiary sector** encompasses economic activities related to delivering services such as health care or entertainment and those activities related to creating and distributing information. One way to identify the relative importance of each sector of an economy is by determining how much it contributes to the GDP (see Table 11.3).

TABLE 11.3 Sector Contribution to GDP and Employment

Study the following three charts. Look at the contribution of industry to each country's economy. Which of the three countries' industrial sectors contributes the greatest percentage of GDP? Are you surprised that the U.S. industry sector is so much larger than that of India and China? Although the United States does not manufacture clothes, toys, and cheap electronic products, it is the world's leader in the manufacture of high-value products such as airplanes and semiconductors (*Planet Money* 2011).

China		
Sector	% Contribution to GDP $5.75 trillion	% of Labor Force Employed 819.5 million
Agriculture	9.6%	39.5%
Industry	46.8%	27.2%
Services	43.6%	33.2%

Source: Data from U.S. Central Intelligence Agency 2011.

India		
Sector	% Contribution to GDP $1.43 trillion	% of Labor Force Employed 480 million
Agriculture	15.7%	52.1%
Industry	28.0%	14.0%
Services	56.3%	34.0%

Source: Data from U.S. Central Intelligence Agency 2011.

United States		
Sector	% Contribution to GDP $14.2 trillion	% of Labor Force Employed 153.1 million
Agriculture	1.2%	.7%
Industry	22.2%	20.3%
Services	76.7%	79.0%

Source: Data from U.S. Central Intelligence Agency 2011.

primary sector Economic activities that generate or extract raw materials from the natural environment.

secondary sector Economic activities that transform raw materials from the primary sector into manufactured goods.

tertiary sector Economic activities related to delivering services such as health care or entertainment and those activities related to creating and distributing information.

Employment

The United States has a labor force of 153.1 million people. India's labor force is 480 million and China's is 819.5 million. As you might imagine, India's and China's most pressing issues have to do with finding work for such a large number of people. We will focus on the U.S. job market with these statistics in mind. Between December 2007 and April 2009, 6.5 million *net* jobs were lost in the United States. The extent of the economic crisis cannot be measured only by job loss. Since April 2009, the number of jobs have increased each year but at very modest levels. In January 2011, 25.1 million Americans—16.4 percent of the workforce—were looking for work, working fewer hours than they would like, or so discouraged that they gave up looking for work. Putting this many people back to work will take years, even in the event of a recovery (Uchitelle 2009). In assessing unemployment statistics, it is important to consider which occupational categories have been most and least affected by the economic downturn. According to the U.S. Bureau of Labor Statistics (2011), the occupational category most affected by job loss as measured by percentage of people unemployed was construction with an unemployment rate of 20.0%. The job category most insulated from unemployment was health care practitioner and technical occupations with an unemployment rate of just 1.8%. Table 11.4 shows that some demographic groups have been more affected by the downturn in the economy than others.

TABLE 11.4 Selected Unemployment Statistics for March 2011

The data in this table is for one month only, but it gives insights about job loss, gains, and dissatisfaction with current job situation. How many people in the United States lost their jobs in March 2011? How many part-time workers wanted full-time work? What percentage of black teenagers who wanted to work were unemployed?

Overall Employment Rate	8.8%
Total Unemployed	13.9 million
Number Who Lost a Job	9.4 million
Number Who Left Job	.896 million
Number Who Reentered Job Market	3.3 million
Number Who Entered Job Market for First Time	1.4 million
Part-Time Workers Who Wanted Full-Time Work	8.4 million
Unemployed Teenagers (all)	26.0%
Unemployed Teenagers (black)	43.5%
Less than High School Diploma (age 25+)	15.1%
Number in Labor Force	153.4 million

Source: Data from U.S. Bureau of Labor Statistics 2011.

Outsourcing

The United States has lost a total of 8 million factory jobs since mid-1979, the year the number of manufacturing jobs peaked at 19.6 million (American Press 2011). We cannot offer precise accounts of where those 8 million factory jobs went. Some factory jobs were automated out of existence. Other jobs were outsourced to foreign countries, and some factory jobs just disappeared because the products manufactured went out of fashion. The outsourcing of factory jobs from the United States to elsewhere has been going on for almost 50 years now. For example, RCA was the first U.S.-based corporation to outsource jobs to Mexico in 1965 (Barrio 1988). Advances in digital technologies, however, have led to a second stage of outsourcing that has put a wider range of jobs up for international competition—those jobs are in the areas of office and IT. At first, the outsourced jobs involved routine office work that required little training, or little direct or face-to-face contact with customers or coworkers—such as bill processing, bookkeeping, data entry, and payroll. But then, the not-so-routine, high-skilled jobs became targets for outsourcing, including work done by architects, radiologists, and lawyers.

It is impossible to know the number of office and information jobs that have been outsourced to foreign countries. First, the U.S. Bureau of Labor Statistics does not collect data on jobs outsourced; second, corporations rarely share outsourcing plans with the public or government policymakers. Finally the United States does not collect data on the impact of outsourcing, positive or negative (Hira and Hira 2008).

When we think of outsourcing, we often think of China as the destination for manufacturing jobs and India for technology and service jobs. Although these two countries are the best known, manufacturing and service jobs are outsourced to just about every country in the world. French corporations, for example, outsource call center operations to Tunisia (Cusi 2011). As mentioned earlier, India was positioned to be a leader in IT and BPO outsourcing because its government invested in elite universities in the 1970s. In addition, India's dominance in BPO and IT services, starting in the late 1990s, could not have happened if a large Indian population had not been living in the United States going to college and working in the IT sector (see Figure 11.3). This human link between India and the United States gave India an advantage. In the mid-1980s, Silicon Valley corporations short on talent began using large numbers of engineers from India and China. Eventually, these foreign-born engineers formed their own start-ups. By the late 1990s, Chinese and Indian

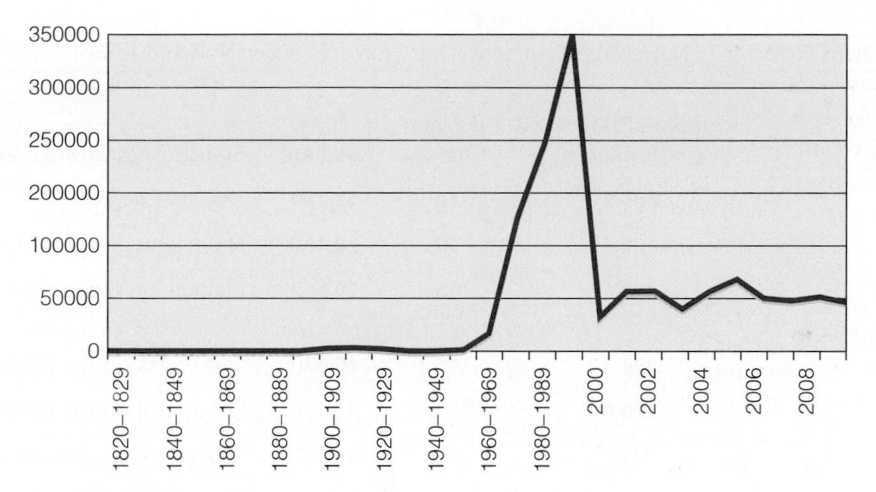

FIGURE 11.3 Persons From India Obtaining Legal Permanent Resident Status Fiscal Years 1820–2009

Source: Data from U.S. Department of Homeland Security (2010)

immigrants were behind 29 percent of all Silicon Valley high-tech start-up companies. By one estimate, Indian CEOs were heading 778 firms. Some Indians outsourced work in their home country to give them a competitive edge. Others set up businesses in their home countries while still maintaining a presence in the United States (Hira and Hira 2008).

In light of the global competition for low-cost labor, almost any analysis of jobs in the United States must be considered in light of the potential to be outsourced in the future. Table 11.5 shows the 20 occupations projected to have the largest numerical growth between now and 2018. The table also shows the type of education and training needed for each job. Of the 25 jobs, six involve working with data or information—customer service reps, accountants and auditors, bookkeeping, management analysts, computer software engineers, receptionists, and information clerks. Only six jobs require college degrees (for example, associates to doctorate).

Chris Caldeira

Among the 20 occupations with the fastest growth are food preparation and serving workers. Between now and 2018, the U.S. economy is projected to add 394,300 such jobs.

Political Systems and Authority

A society's **political system** is the institution that regulates the use of and access to the power that is essential to articulating and realizing individual, local, regional, national, international, or global interests and agendas. **Power** is the probability that an individual can achieve his or her will, even against another individual's opposition (Weber 1947). That probability increases if the individual can force people to obey his or her commands or if the individual has authority over others.

> CORE CONCEPT 5 **When people believe that power differences are legitimate, those with power possess authority.**

Authority is legitimate power—power that people believe is just and proper. A leader has authority to the extent that people view him or her as being entitled to give orders. Max Weber identified three types of authority: traditional, charismatic, and legal-rational. **Traditional authority** relies on

political system A socially created institution that regulates the use of and access to power that is essential to articulating and realizing individual, local, regional, national, international, or global interests and agendas.

power The probability that an individual can achieve his or her will even against another individual's opposition.

authority Legitimate power in which people believe that the differences in power are just and proper—that is, people view a leader as being entitled to give orders.

traditional authority A type of authority that relies on the sanctity of time-honored norms that govern the selection of someone to a powerful position (chief, king, queen) and that specify responsibilities and appropriate conduct for the individual selected.

TABLE 11.5 Occupations Projected to Have Largest Numerical Job Growth Between Now and 2018.

Occupations	Number of New Jobs (*in thousands*)	Percent Change	Wages (median)	Education/Training Category
Registered nurses	581.5	22	$62,450	Associate degree
Home health aides	460.9	50	20,460	Short-term on-the-job training
Customer service reps	399.5	18	29,860	Moderate-term on-the-job training
Food preparation and serving workers	394.3	15	16,430	Short-term on-the-job training
Home care aides	375.8	46	19,180	Short-term on-the-job training
Retail salespersons	374.7	8	20,510	Short-term on-the-job training
Office clerks, general	358.7	12	25,320	Short-term on-the-job training
Accountants/auditors	279.4	22	59,430	Bachelor degree
Nursing aides, orderlies, and attendants	276	19	23,850	Postsecondary vocational award
Postsecondary teachers	256.9	15	58,830	Doctoral degree
Construction laborers	255.9	20	28,520	Moderate-term on-the-job training
Elementary school teachers	244.2	16	49,330	Bachelor degree
Truck drivers	232.9	13	37,270	Short-term on-the-job training
Landscaping and groundskeeping workers	217.1	18	23,150	Short-term on-the-job training
Bookkeeping, accounting, and auditing clerks	212.4	10	32,510	Moderate-term on-the-job training
Administrative assistants	204.4	13	40,030	Work experience in a related occupation
Management analysts	178.3	24	73,570	Bachelor or higher degree, plus work experience
Computer software engineers	175.1	34	85,430	Bachelor degree
Receptionists	172.9	15	24,550	Short-term on-the-job training
Carpenters	165.4	13	38,940	Long-term on-the-job training

Source: U.S. Bureau of Labor Statistics 2010.

the sanctity of time-honored norms that govern the selection of someone to a powerful position (such as chief, king, or queen). People comply with a leader because they believe they are accountable to the past and have an obligation to perpetuate it. (Their reasoning is apt to be, "It has always been like that.") To give up past ways of doing things is to renounce a heritage and an identity (Boudon and Bourricaud 1989).

Legal-rational authority derives from a system of impersonal rules that formally specify the qualifications for occupying a powerful position. These rules also specify the scope of that power and appropriate conduct. In cases of legal-rational authority, people comply with commands, decisions, and directives because the power belongs to the position, and by extension, to the person occupying the position.

Charismatic authority derives from the exceptional and exemplary qualities of the person who issues commands. That is, charismatic leaders are obeyed, because their followers believe in and are attracted irresistibly to the leaders' vision. These leaders, by virtue of their special qualities, can unleash revolutionary changes; they can persuade their followers to behave in ways that depart from rules and traditions.

legal-rational authority A type of authority that rests on a system of impersonal rules that formally specifies the qualifications for occupying a powerful position.

charismatic authority A type of authority that derives from the exceptional and exemplary qualities of the person who issues the commands.

Charismatic leaders often emerge during times of profound crisis (such as economic depressions and wars), because in these situations, people are most likely to be drawn to someone with exceptional personal qualities who offers them a vision of a new order. A charismatic leader is more than popular, attractive, likable, or pleasant. A merely popular person, "even one who is continually in our thoughts" (Boudon and Bourricaud 1989, p. 70), is not someone for whom we would break all previous ties and give up our possessions. Charismatic leaders successfully persuade their followers to make extraordinary personal sacrifices, cut themselves off from ordinary worldly connections, or devote their lives to achieving a vision that the leaders have outlined.

The source of a charismatic leader's authority, however, does not rest with the ethical quality of the command or vision. Mohandas Gandhi, Adolf Hitler, Franklin D. Roosevelt were all considered charismatic leaders. Each assumed leadership of a country during turbulent times. Likewise, each conveyed a powerful vision (right or wrong) of his country's destiny. (See Working for Change: "Mohandas Gandhi.")

Charismatic authority is grounded in the intense relationships between leaders and followers. From a relational point of view, then, charisma is a highly unequal relationship between "an inspired guide and a cohort of followers" who believe wholeheartedly in the guide's promises and visions (Boudon and Bourricaud 1989, p. 70).

Over time, charismatic leaders and their followers come to constitute an "emotional community" devoted to achieving a goal and sustained by a belief in the leaders' special qualities. Weber argues, however, that the followers must eventually be able to return to a normal life and to develop relationships with one another based on something other than their connections to the leader. Attraction and devotion cannot sustain a community indefinitely, if only because the object of these emotions—the charismatic leader—is mortal.

Forms of Government

> CORE CONCEPT 6 ***Government* is an organizational structure that directs and coordinates human activities in the name of a country or some other territory, such as a city, county, or state. That structure may be democratic, authoritarian, totalitarian, or theocratic.**

Democracy

Sir Winston Churchill, the prime minister of the United Kingdom during World War II, once said that "democracy is the worst form of government except for all others that have been tried" (wordiq.com 2004). **Democracy** is a system of government in which power is vested in the citizens or "the people." Usually, the size of the citizenry makes direct participation impossible. Therefore, voters elect representatives to make decisions for them. In democracies, candidates from different political parties run for office. When a majority of citizens votes to change the party in power, an orderly and peaceful transition in government occurs. In democracies, elected representatives make laws and vote on taxes and the budget. They also debate, criticize, support, and oppose government policies.

Democratic forms of government extend basic rights to all citizens and legal residents. These rights include freedom of speech, movement, religion, press, and assembly (that is, the right to form and belong to parties and other associations) as well as freedom from "arbitrary arrest and imprisonment" (Bullock 1977, pp. 210–211). According to its constitution, India is a "sovereign, socialist, secular, democratic republic" (U.S. Department of State 2011). Like the United States, India has a federal form of government. However, the central government in India has greater power over its states, and has adopted a British-style parliamentary system (U.S. Department of State 2011). In India, 714 million Indians were eligible to vote and, in the last general election, 417 million or 58 percent did so. In that election, votes were cast in 828,804 polling stations for over 5,000 candidates from seven national political parties and several regional parties. Because so many of the country's voters are illiterate, India makes use of party symbols, so that voters who cannot read candidates' names can still vote. Symbols include the open palm of the Indian National Congress, representing the lotus of the Bharatiya Janata Party, and the hammer and sickle representing the communist parties (Tharoor, 2009).

The United States is classified as a democracy. As in India not everyone who is eligible to vote does. In the 2008 presidential election, 64.9 percent of those eligible to vote actually voted. Barack Obama received 52.9 percent of all votes actually cast but only 33.4 percent of all votes that Americans were eligible to cast. The percentages of voting-age Americans who reported being registered to vote varies dramatically by age and racial or ethnic classification. It is striking that only 54.9 percent of people classified as Hispanic or Latino and 58.5 percent of those aged 18 to 24 reported being registered. In contrast, 72 percent of voting-age people classified as white and 78.1 percent of those aged 65 and older reported being registered (U.S. Bureau of the Census 2009).

In light of these statistics, we might question whether elected officials represent everyone or just those groups who are likely to vote. We might also question whether

government The organizational structure that directs and coordinates people's involvement in the political activities of a country or other territory (city, county, state) within that country.

democracy A system of government in which power is vested in the citizen or "the people," and in which the citizenry participates directly or indirectly in making decisions.

Working for Change Mohandas Gandhi

Mahatma Gandhi, born in Porbandar, India, is a key spiritual and political leader in India and world history. Mahatma, which means "great soul," is a name bestowed on Gandhi, not at birth, but later by the people of India. After obtaining a law degree in London, Gandhi traveled to South Africa in 1893, to work as a lawyer, where he encountered the humiliation and discrimination of the South African apartheid system that privileged whites and severely disadvantaged African, Indians, and other nonwhite people. He remained in South Africa until 1915, working for political change. He returned to India as activist and leader of the country's independence movement. Among other things, he encouraged Indians to boycott British-made goods and buy Indian-made products as a way to revitalize local economies and undermine a British-dominated economy that exploited Indian labor and natural resources. Over the course of his life, Gandhi was imprisoned and, even in prison, undertook hunger strikes that attracted international attention and proved effective in pushing change. He is perhaps most famous for a 240-mile walk to the Arabian Sea to make salt, an act of treason under British rule. Keep in mind that humans and animals require salt to live. Under British rule, it was illegal for people to harvest salt. This law allowed Britain to maintain an unchallenged monopoly on the sale and production of salt.

Gandhi developed and conceived of a strategy of nonviolent resistance known as *satyagraha*—"the force of truth" or "the firmness of truth." The philosophy and strategy guided his work in South Africa and later the Indian independence movement. Among others, Gandhi's thinking and methods had a great influence on Nelson Mandela in his struggle to end South Africa's system of apartheid and on the way Martin Luther King Jr. organized campaigns for civil rights in the United States. Gandhi wrote that truth (satya) involves love and firmness (agraha), qualities that require actions and persistence. Satyagraha treats means and goals as inseparable. The means one follows to achieve some goal deeply affects that which is achieved. If unjust means are employed to achieve even a just end, the result is injustice. One can never claim that a goal, however lofty, justifies using dishonest means. The means are, in the end, everything, as this example illustrates: "If I want to deprive you of your watch, I shall certainly have to fight for it; if I want to buy your watch, I shall have to pay for it; and if I want a gift, I shall have to plead for it; and, according to the means I employ, the watch is stolen property, my own property, or a donation" (Gandhi 1909, p. 287).

Barbara Houghton

Gandhi is an important figure who led a largely nonviolent struggle against British rule. Gandhi's accomplishment was "an extraordinary feat of personal magnetism," in which he inspired the participation of the illiterate and poor in the independence movement (Luce 2007).

The application of satyagraha requires that people be up front and not secretive. So before embarking on the salt walk, Gandhi send a letter that he made public to Lord Irwin, the viceroy of India, asking for an end to the salt tax and outlining his plan to collect salt in the sea. Gandhi followed through on his plan to encourage Indians to break the law. In the end, thousands of Indians were arrested; their acts of civil disobedience helped to undermine the power of British colonizers.

Gandhi is without a doubt the most famous Indian in the world and is considered the country's founding father. His image is on the currency of India. India gained independence from Britain in 1947, but the country was partitioned into India (Hindus) and Pakistan (Muslims). As Hindus and Muslims rioted, eventually resulting in deaths of millions and the migration of 12 million across the newly drawn borders, Gandhi advocated for a united India in which the people of two religions could live in peace, with Muslims having equal rights. He began to fast and, after five days, the two sides ended their fighting. Unfortunately a Hindu fanatic assassinated Gandhi, ending his life in 1948, at the age of 78.

elected officials represent all voters or whether they simply serve the powerful constituents who donate generously to their campaigns. In assessing whether a form of government is a true democracy, it is important to consider who has the right to vote. At one time or another, many governments classified as democratic have—on the basis of race, sex, income, property, criminal status, mental health, religion, age, or other characteristics—excluded portions of their populations from decision making (Creighton 1992, pp. 430–431).

Totalitarianism

Totalitarianism is a system of government characterized by (1) a single ruling party led by a dictator, (2) an unchallenged official ideology that defines a vision of the "perfect" society and the means to achieve that vision, (3) a system of social control that suppresses dissent, and (4) centralized control over the media and the economy. Ideological goals vary but may include overthrowing capitalist and foreign influences (as in China under Mao Zedong), creating the perfect race (as in Germany under Hitler), or meeting certain economic and development goals (as during China's Great Leap Forward). Whatever the government's goals, the political leaders, the military, and the secret police intimidate and mobilize the masses to help the state meet the goals.

Totalitarian governments are products of the twentieth century, because by that time, technologies existed that allowed a few people in power to control the behavior of the masses and the information the masses could hear. Many of the governments labeled as totalitarian have followed communist principles. Traditionally, communist governments instituted polices that outlawed private ownership of property, supported the equal distribution of wealth, and offered status and power to the working class (proletariat). Communist leaders mobilized the masses to help them realize communist principles and to bring about economic changes that benefited everyone, not just the upper and middle classes.

The Soviet Union under the leadership of Joseph Stalin provides one example of how communist ideals were put into practice and helps to explain why most communist governments eventually collapsed. Stalin believed that if the Soviet Union did not become industrialized, it could not compete with European nations that were expanding their territories and fighting to gain influence. He maintained that the Soviet Union was 50 years behind these countries and that the gap must be closed within 10 years. To accomplish this goal, Stalin conducted a reign of terror. He forced millions of peasants to work in factories, seized millions of private landholdings, and created massive state-owned agricultural collectives. In addition, he controlled a brutal system of repression (characterized by secret police, forced labor camps, mass deportations, and purges) as means of controlling or eliminating anyone who opposed him, or was even suspected of opposing him. This system was so relentless and brutal that it caused the death of more than 20 million people. Because Stalin controlled and censored all mass media, Soviet people learned only about his vision of socialism and heard only good things about his policies. In addition, Stalin strengthened the government's control over the economy so that state bureaucrats decided what should be produced, how much should be produced, how much the products should cost, and where they should be distributed.

Authoritarianism

Under **authoritarian government**, no separation of powers exists; a single person (a dictator), a group (a family, the military, a single party), or a social class holds all power. No official ideology projects a vision of the "perfect" society or guides the government's political or economic policies. Indeed, authoritarian leaders do not seek to mobilize the masses to help realize a vision or meet ideological goals. Instead, the government functions to serve those in power, who may or may not be interested in the general welfare of the people. Common to all authoritarian systems is the "leader's freedom to exercise power without restraint, unencumbered by a commitment to law, ideology, or values" (Chehabi and Linz 1998).

How does a single person, a group, or a social class gain control of an entire country? The political culture must be amenable to personal leadership. Authoritarian leaders typically receive support from a foreign government that expects to benefit from their leadership (Buckley 1998). During the Cold War, for example, the United States supported anticommunist dictators, and the Soviet Union supported anticapitalist dictators. Between 1945 and 1989, the foreign and domestic policies of the United States and the Soviet Union were shaped largely by Cold War dynamics. Virtually every U.S. policy—from the 1949 Marshall Plan to the covert aid given to the Contra guerrillas during the Reagan administration—was shaped in some way by America's professed desire to protect the world from Soviet influence and the spread of communism, even to the point of supporting antidemocratic, brutally repressive authoritarian regimes (McNamara 1989).

Making a clear-cut distinction between totalitarian and authoritarian governments is difficult. In the early 1980s, the U.S. Ambassador to the United Nations, Jeanne Kirkpatrick, distinguished between totalitarian and authoritarian governments by using a "lesser of two evils" principle. That principle holds that authoritarian dictatorships are likely to be anticommunist and not "ideology" driven, whereas communist dictatorships are likely to be totalitarian. Both control and punish those who oppose them, but totalitarian dictatorships go even further, in that they seek to control thoughts and beliefs. Kirkpatrick maintained that authoritarian regimes are the lesser

totalitarianism A system of government characterized by (1) a single ruling party led by a dictator, (2) an unchallenged official ideology that defines a vision of the "perfect" society and the means to achieve that vision, (3) a system of social control that suppresses dissent and opposition, and (4) centralized control over the media and the economy.

authoritarian government A system of government in which there is no separation of power and a single person (dictator), group (family, military, single party), or social class holds all power.

of two evils, because they are not ideologically driven and because they do not engage in thought control. Kirkpatrick also argued that, in its effort to defeat communism, the United States could support authoritarian regimes because they posed less of a danger to the American way of life and were more capable of reform.

Theocracy

Theocracy, which means "rule of the deity," is a form of government in which political authority rests in the hands of religious leaders or a theologically trained elite group. The primary purpose of a theocracy is to uphold divine laws in its policies and practices. Thus, it recognizes no legal separation of church and state.

Government policies and laws correspond to religious principles and laws. Contemporary examples of theocracies include the Vatican under the pope, Afghanistan under the Taliban, and Iran under Ayatollah Ali Khamenei. In other forms of theocracy, power is shared by a secular ruler (such as a king) and a religious leader (such as a pope or an ayatollah), or by secular government leaders who are devoted to the principles of the dominant religion. At one time, England was dominated by the Anglican Church, France by the Roman Catholic Church, and Sweden by the Lutheran Church. Today, Saudi Arabia is a monarchy whose head of state and government is a king, not a religiously trained leader; its constitution and legal system, however, are grounded in Islamic laws and principles.

Government Laws and Policies

No matter the form of government or the scope of its jurisdiction, all make **laws**, formal rules that mandate people to behave in specified ways or to refrain from behaving in some specified way. Laws are created by those in power and enforced by regulatory institutions such as police, military, or other bodies (for example, the FDA or EPA). Laws govern almost every area of life. When sociologists study laws, they consider questions of fairness and justice in their creation, interpretation, enforcement, and consequences. Many laws in the United States were not fair or just, such as don't ask don't tell, the Jim Crow laws (mandating racial segregation), and the Chinese Exclusion Act (banning Chinese immigration to the United States, from 1822 to 1943). Sociologists also study intended and especially unintended consequences of laws. The United States passed the Food, Conservation, and Energy Act of 2008—a $288 billion bill that subsidizes specific agricultural crops such as corn. Among other things, this act also issues grants to states that make fresh fruit and vegetables available to elementary school children and that establish community gardens for high-poverty schools as a tool to teach children about agriculture practices and diet. The subsidy portion of this law has been especially criticized because subsidies disproportionately benefit large corporate farmers. In addition, when a government subsidizes farmers for certain crops, it pays them more than market value for certain agricultural products. Farmers in poor countries cannot compete against subsidized products. In that sense, subsidies contribute to and perpetuate inequalities.

In India, the government has passed laws that give farmers higher prices for their products than the market pays. While these subsidies did increase agricultural output, the infrastructure—roads, temperature-controlled warehouses—was such that it could not support the movement of increased amounts of produce and grains. As a result a considerable amount rots before reaching consumers. The Indian government also offers free or subsidized electricity, but only the wealthiest farmers can afford to install the electrical connections, to sink wells, and to buy the machines such as pumps that can be powered by this electricity (Luce 2007). In addition, only the wealthiest Indian farmers are able to purchase the chemicals and hybrid seeds even though subsidized. To complicate matters chemicals, such as the herbicide Roundup, killed weeds but also increased unemployment as workers who pulled weeds are out a job (Christian Aid 2005).

Power-Sharing Models

> **CORE CONCEPT 7 There are two major models of power: the power elite and pluralistic models. The two models help us to evaluate whether an elite few hold the power in society or whether power is dispersed among competing interest groups.**

The Power Elite

Sociologist C. Wright Mills wrote about the connection between government, industry, and the military in *The Power Elite* (1956). The **power elite** are those few people who occupy such lofty positions in the social structure of leading institutions that their decisions affect millions, even billions, of people worldwide. For the most part, the source of this

theocracy A form of government in which political authority rests in the hands of religious leaders or a theologically trained elite. Under this system, there is no separation of church and state.

laws Formal rules that mandate people to behave in specified ways or to refrain from behaving in some specified way. Laws are created by those in power and enforced by regulatory institutions such as police, military, or other bodies.

power elite Those few people who occupy such lofty positions in the social structure of leading institutions that their decisions have consequences affecting millions, even billions, of people worldwide.

power is legal-rational—residing not in the personal qualities of those in power, but rather in the positions that the power elite have come to occupy. "Were the person occupying the position the most important factor, the stock market would pay close attention to retirements, deaths, and replacements in the executive ranks" (Galbraith 1958, p. 146).

The power elite use their positions, and the tools of their positions, to rule, control, and influence others. These tools might include weapons, surveillance equipment, and specialized modes of communication. According to C. Wright Mills, since World War II, rapid advances in technology have allowed power to become concentrated in the hands of a few; those with access to such power exercise an extraordinary influence over not only their immediate environment, but also millions of people, tens of thousands of communities, entire countries, and the globe.

In writing about the power elite, Mills does not focus on any single individual, but rather on those who occupy the highest positions in the leading U.S. institutions. According to Mills, these leading institutions are the military, corporations (especially the 200 or so largest), and the government. "The power to make decisions of national and international consequence is now so clearly seated in political, military, and economic institutions that other areas of society seem off to the side and, on occasion, readily subordinated to these" (Mills 1963, p. 27).

The origins of these institutions' power can be traced to World War II, when the political elite mobilized corporations to produce the supplies, weapons, and equipment needed to fight the war. U.S. corporations, which were left unscathed by the war, were virtually the only institutions in the world that could offer the services and products war-torn countries needed for rebuilding. The interests of the U.S. government, the military, and corporations became further intertwined when the political elite decided that a permanent war industry was needed to contain the spread of communism. Thus, over the past 65 years, these three institutions have become deeply and intricately interrelated in hundreds of ways.

Consider that each year the U.S. Department of Defense awards more than 60 million contracts to more than 2,000 businesses. The value of these contracts ranges from less than $25,000 to $21.9 billion. In evaluating these amounts, think about Lockheed Martin's dependence on the military-industrial complex. In 2009, 85 percent of its sales were to the U.S. Department of Defense, the Department of Homeland Security, and nongovernment agencies. For fiscal year 2009, the company received $11.9 billion in DOD contracts. Department of Defense and other government contracts support 132,000 Lockheed employees working in 522 facilities in 500 cities in 46 states and 75 countries and territories (Lockheed Martin 2009, 2011).

Lockheed Martin's board of directors includes a former undersecretary of defense, a retired U.S. admiral and commander, and a former vice chairman, Joint Chiefs of Staff (Lockheed Martin 2011). Lockheed Martin's loyalty does not simply lie with the United States. It has an office in New Delhi, India, which according to the website has "aggressively pursued opportunities to sell military hardware" to all three branches of the Indian military (navy, army, and air force). As one example, Lockheed Martin has not only produced F-16 fighters for India but has produced 4,400 F-16s for 25 governments around the world (Lockheed Martin 2011).

Because the military, government, and corporations are so interdependent and because decisions made by the elite of one sector affect the elite of the other two sectors, Mills believes that everyone has a vested interest in cooperation. Shared interests cause those who occupy the highest positions in each sector to interact with one another. Out of necessity, then, a triangle of power has emerged. We should not assume, however, that the alliance among the three sectors is untroubled, that the powerful in each realm share the same mind-set, that they know the consequences of their decisions, or that they are joined in a conspiracy to shape the fate of a country or the globe:

> At the same time it is clear that they know what is on each other's minds. Whether they come together casually at their clubs or hunting lodges, or slightly more formally at the Business Advisory Council or the Committee for Economic Development or the Foreign Policy Association, they are definitely not isolated from each other. Informal conversation elicits plans, hopes, and expectations. There is a community of interest and sentiment among the elite. (Hacker 1971, p. 141)

Mills acknowledges that the power elite are not free agents. A chief executive officer of a major corporation is answerable to regulatory bodies. Pentagon officials are subject to congressional investigations and budget constraints. Defense contractors must be aware of the federal False Claims Act, which rewards any employee who can prove that the contractor has defrauded the government (Stevenson 1991). The president of the United States is constrained by bureaucratic "red tape" and by the judicial and legislative branches. A pluralist model of power acknowledges these constraints and offers an alternative vision of how power is distributed.

Pluralist Models

Pluralist models of power view politics as a plurality of special interest groups competing, compromising, forming alliances, and negotiating with each other for power. Special interest groups consist of people who share an interest

pluralist models of power A view that sees politics as a plurality of special interest groups competing, compromising, forming alliances, and negotiating with each other for power.

in a particular economic, political, or social issue and who form an organization or join an existing organization to influence public opinion and government policy. Some special interest groups form political action committees (PACs), which raise money to be donated to the political candidates who seem most likely to support their special interests. Examples of the more than 4,500 registered PACs listed among the top 20 contributors to the 2009–2010 U.S. political campaigns included the National Association of Realtors ($3.8 million), Honeywell International ($3.6 million), International Brotherhood of Electrical Workers ($3.0 million), AT&T ($3.3 million), American Bankers Association ($2.8 million), National Beer Wholesalers Association ($3.0 million), National Auto Dealers Association ($2.4 million), and International Association of Fire Fighters ($2.4 million) (Center for Responsive Politics 2011).

Another kind of special interest group is the **527 group**. This is a tax-exempt advocacy organization that seeks to influence federal elections by running issue-related advertisements criticizing the record of a candidate or by mobilizing voters to register and vote. Prominent 527 groups in the 2010 election cycle included Emily's List ($9 million), College Republican National Committee ($8.0 million), and Gay and Lesbians Victory Fund ($3.4 million) (Center for Responsive Politics 2011).

According to the pluralist model, no single special interest group dominates a political system. Rather, competing groups thrive and can express their views through opinion polls, organizing, emails, and PACs. "If a variety of interest groups are able to exercise power and influence in the system through a variety of means, then the system, with all its flaws, can be considered democratic" (Creighton 1992). One problem with the pluralist model is that, even though there are a countless number of interest groups, we cannot conclude that every special interest group has enough resources to organize or to influence policies and laws.

The pluralist model prompts us to consider the provisions the Indian government makes to give a voice to groups considered disadvantaged. The Constitution of India mandates that the government "shall promote with special care the educational and economic interests of the weaker sections of the people, and, in particular the Scheduled Castes and Scheduled Tribes, and shall protect them from social injustice and all forms of exploitation" (The Constitution of India 2011). Together, the 1,108 Scheduled Castes (SCs) and 744 Scheduled Tribes (STs) comprise 24 percent of India's population and are recognized in the Constitution of India as in need of special programs and protections. The terms *scheduled caste* applies to "untouchable" castes, and the term *scheduled tribes* to indigenous people. Historically, under the now abolished caste system, untouchable status was given to those working in occupations considered to be impure (for example, leatherwork, butchers, garbage collectors, manual labor, street/latrine/sewer cleaners). People doing such work were considered polluted and so were those with whom they came in contact. As a result, untouchable castes were segregated from those in higher castes and were objects of discrimination. Although the caste system has been abolished, the inequality and discrimination perpetuated by that system still exists. The government distinguishes between scheduled classes/tribes and the forward classes, groups who do not currently qualify for a special protection and benefits, most notably, quotas for university admissions, scholarships, government jobs, and political representation.

In 1992, the Indian government amended the constitution to mandate that one-third of local government seats at three levels (village, block, and district) be reserved for women, but not in national and state legislatures (Htun 2004) (see Global Comparisons: "Countries in Which Representation of Minorities and Women is Mandated").

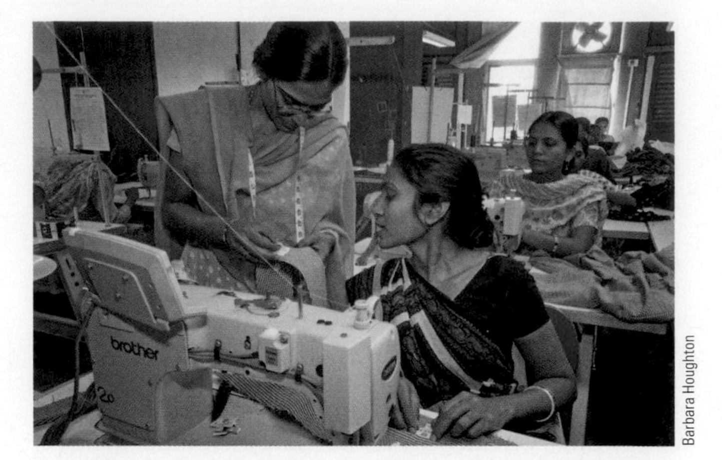

Barbara Houghton

The Indian government supports village cooperatives and cottage industries through grants. The photo shows women who are part of the Self-Employed Women's Association. These cooperatives support local employment and self-reliance.

Imperialism and Related Concepts

> CORE CONCEPT 8 **Empire, imperialism, hegemony, and militarism are concepts that apply to political entities such as governments that can exercise their will over other political entities.**

An **empire** is a group of countries under the direct or indirect control of a foreign power or government, which shapes

527 group A tax-exempt advocacy organization that seeks to influence federal elections by running issue-related advertisements criticizing the record of a candidate or by mobilizing voters to register and vote.

empire A group of countries under the direct or indirect control of a foreign power or government, which shapes their political, economic, and cultural development.

Global Comparisons Countries in Which Representation of Minorities and Women is Mandated

This map shows countries in which minorities and gender are guaranteed representation in local, regional, and/or national elected bodies. Countries in orange mandate representation for both women and minorities; countries in green mandate representation for women; and countries in light green mandate for groups designated as minorities.

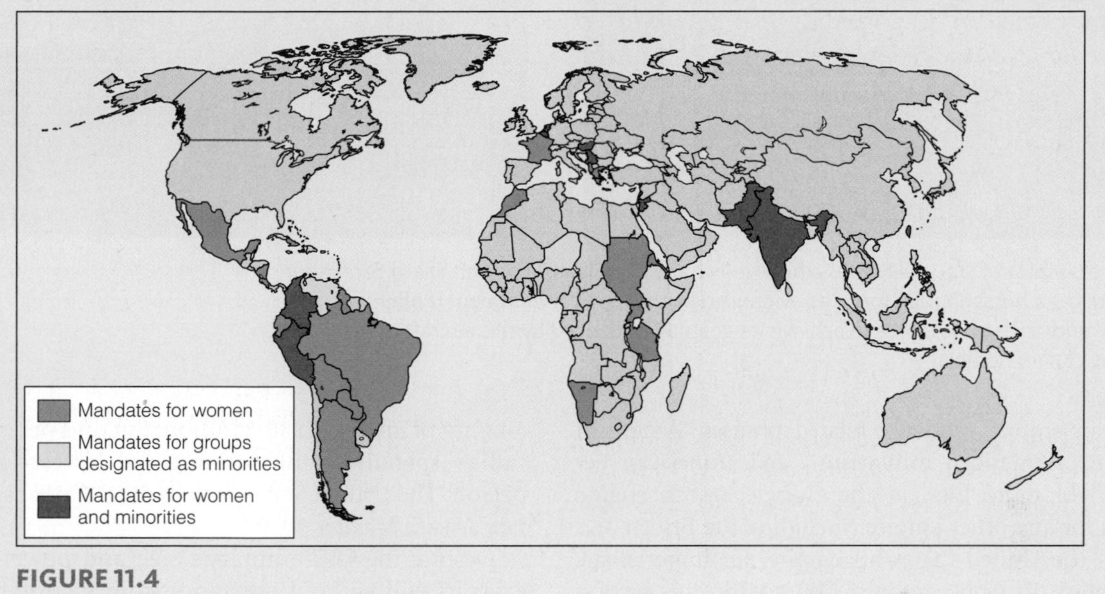

FIGURE 11.4

Source: Data from Htun (2004)

their political, economic, and cultural development. An **imperialistic power** exerts control and influence over foreign entities either through military force or through political policies and economic pressure. Imperialists believe that their cultural, political, or economic superiority justifies control over other entities, and they maintain that such control is for the greater good of all humankind.

Hegemony is a process by which a power maintains its dominance over foreign entities. Those in power use institutions (such as the World Bank and the United Nations) to formalize their power; work through bureaucratic structures "to make power seem abstract (and therefore, not attached to any one individual)"; use advertising, education, television, music, movies, and other forms of media to influence the foreign populace; and mobilize a military or police force to intimidate and subdue opposition forces (Felluga 2002).

A **militaristic power** believes that military strength, and the willingness to use it, is the source of national and even global security. Usually a "peace through strength" doctrine—peace depends on military strength and force—is cited to justify military buildups and interventions on foreign soil.

Is the United States an Imperialistic Power?

> Throughout the history of mankind, certainly no country has existed that so thoroughly dominates the world with its policies, its tanks, and its products as the United States does today. (*Der Spiegel* 2003)

> Talk of "empire" makes Americans distinctly uneasy . . . and yet though the rest of the world is under no illusion, in the United States today there is a sort of wishful denial. We don't want an empire, we aren't an empire—or else if we are an empire, then it is one of a kind. (Judt 2004, p. 38)

imperialistic power A political entity that exerts control and influence over foreign entities either through military force or through political policies and economic pressure.

hegemony A process by which a power maintains its dominance over foreign entities.

militaristic power One that believes military strength, and the willingness to use it, is the source of national—and even global—security.

Department of Defense

Mass Communication Specialist 3rd Class Joshua Valcarcel

We can find examples of U.S. military as a benevolent and a militaristic power. The U.S. military often operates as a humanitarian force, as evidenced by the medical treatment it offers people around the world. It also uses force to achieve its goals as evidenced by this aircraft in the midst of unleashing cluster bombs.

"American empire" and the related phrases "American imperialism," "American militarism," and "American hegemony" yield more hits on the Google search engine than terms for any other empire (including the British and Roman). Is the United States an empire, an imperialistic power, militaristic, or hegemonic? Our goal in this section is *not* to assess whether the United States is an evil or a benevolent empire. Rather, we simply wish to assess the United States' world influence and power in light of these concepts.

Of course, the ability to exercise power over foreign entities requires a strong military, the ability to put weapons into the hands of allies, and the ability to keep those same weapons out of the hands of adversaries (see No Borders, No Boundaries: "Countries in Which the United States Intervened to Support Regime Change, Support Dictators, or Oppose Reactionary Movements, 1902–2011"). Between 2002 and 2009, the United States delivered $166.3 billion worth of arms to foreign countries. This figure represents 40 percent of all arms delivered, whose value was $415.8 billion. After the United States, the top arms suppliers during that seven-year period were Russia ($73.9 billion), France ($35.1 billion), the United Kingdom ($29.4 billion), and China ($13.7 billion). Of all arms delivered, 66 percent went to developing nations, including India ($58.4 billion), Saudi Arabia ($49.4 billion), China ($31.4 billion), United Arab Emirates ($26.9 billion), Pakistan ($26.9 billion), Egypt ($22.5 billion), and Israel ($17.9 billion) (Shah 2010, Grimmett, 2010).

In terms of its ability to invest in its military, the United States accounts for almost 57 percent of all military spending worldwide. In 2009, worldwide military expenditures totalled $1.5 trillion. The United States budgeted $663.3 billion, followed by the People's Republic of China ($98.8 billion), the United Kingdom ($69.2 billion), France ($67.3 billion), and Russian Federation ($53.5 billion) (Global Security.org 2009). India spends the ninth highest amount of money—$36.3 billion. But on a per capita basis, India's spending ranks among the lowest—$30.40 per person. The United States spends $2,132 per capita (*Christian Science Monitor* 2010).

Despite the U.S. military's size and power, it cannot exert its will without resistance from **insurgents,** groups who participate in armed rebellion against an established authority, government, or administration with the hope that those in power will retreat or pull out. From an occupier's point of view, insurgents have no legitimate cause; from an insurgent's point of view, the authority of the occupier or liberator is illegitimate. Resistance to U.S. military presence in Iraq and Afghanistan has been both violent and nonviolent. Violent strategies have included the use of improvised explosive devices placed in garbage, on telephone poles, and hidden beside roads; ambushes; suicide bombings; kidnappings; beheadings; and other attacks on military and civilian targets (Wordiq.com 2004).

Online Poll

If you could vote, would you vote to increase, decrease, or sustain the size of the U.S. military budget?

○ Increase

○ Decrease

○ Stay the same

To see how other students responded to these questions, go to **www.cengagebrain.com**.

insurgents Groups who participate in armed rebellion against some established authority, government, or administration with the hope that those in power will retreat or pull out.

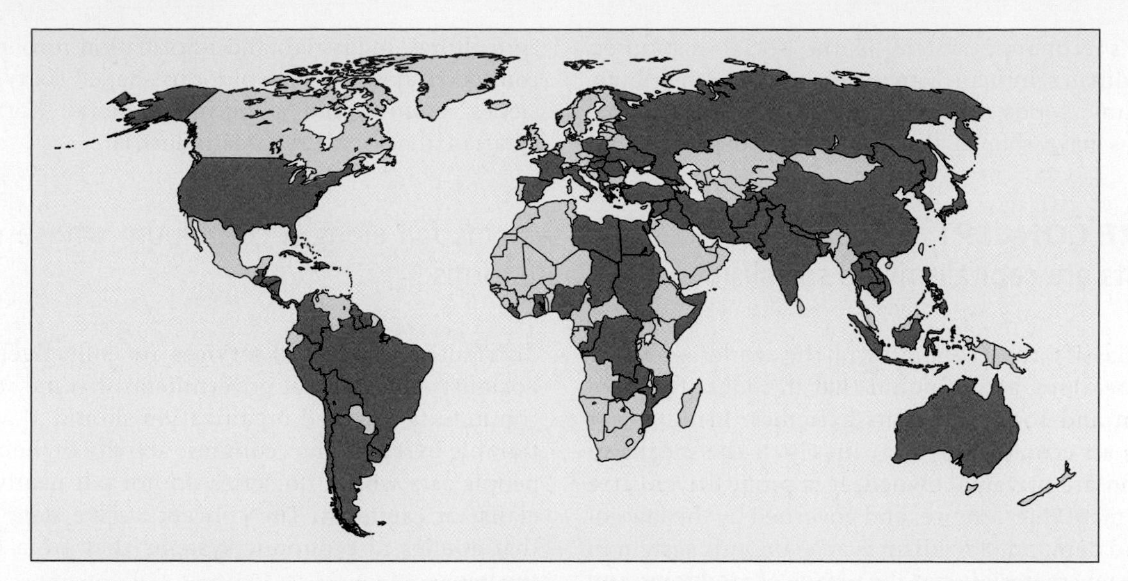

FIGURE 11.5 Countries in Which the United States Intervened to Support Regime Change, Support Dictators, or Oppose Reactionary Movements, 1902–2011

Consider as one indicator of American power the countries (highlighted in orange) in which the United States intervened to support regime change, support dictators, or oppose reactionary movements during the period 1902–2011. These interventions took a variety of forms: overt force, covert operations, and subverted elections. This map is not intended to judge a decision to intervene, as each intervention has a specific history. Before making such judgments, the reader must study the reasons for and events leading up to each intervention.

Source: Data from U.S. Central Intelligence Agency (2011)

Barbara Houghton

Summary of CORE CONCEPTS

In this chapter we compared U.S. and India's economic and political systems to gain insights about each country's economic and political status in the world. The fact that India is a leading destination for outsourced IT and customer service jobs gives the impression that its economy is becoming service oriented. However, we have learned that India's economy is weighed down by the staggering size of its labor force, much of which toils in the agricultural sector.

CORE CONCEPT 1 The ongoing agricultural, industrial, and information revolutions have profoundly shaped the world's economic systems.

A society's economic system is the social institution that coordinates human activity to produce, distribute, and consume goods and services. Three major, ongoing revolutions have shaped the world's economic systems: agricultural, industrial, and information revolutions. We considered how these revolutions shaped six types of societies: hunting and gathering, pastoral, horticultural, agrarian, industrial, and postindustrial.

CORE CONCEPT 2 The world's economic systems fall along a continuum whose endpoints are capitalism and socialism in most pure forms.

We can classify the economies of the world as falling somewhere along a continuum that has ideal forms of capitalism and socialism as its extremes. Ideally, capitalism is an economic system in which the means of production are privately owned. It is profit-driven, free of government interference, and governed by the laws of supply and demand. Socialism is an economic system in which the raw materials and the means of producing and distributing goods and services are collectively owned. Socialists believe that government or some worker- or community-oriented organization should play the central role in regulating economic activity on behalf of the people as a whole. Societies do not fall neatly into socialist or capitalist. The concept *welfare state* is a term that applies to economic systems that are a hybrid of the two.

CORE CONCEPT 3 Capitalists' responses to economic downturns and stagnation have driven a 500-year-plus economic expansion, which has facilitated interconnections between local, regional, and national economies.

World system theory focuses on the forces underlying the development of economic transactions that transcend national boundaries. In particular, world system theorists identify profit-generating strategies that have caused capitalism to dominate and facilitate a global network of economic relationships. As a result, capitalism has spread steadily throughout the globe. In addition, every country of the world has come to play one of three different and unequal roles in the global economy: core, peripheral, or semiperipheral.

CORE CONCEPT 4 The United States qualifies as a core economy; India represents an example of a semiperipheral economy.

The United States and India have the largest and fifth largest economies in the world, respectively. When measured by per capita GDP, the United States has the tenth largest economy, and India has the 163rd largest. Both countries depend on oil from foreign sources. The Indian economy is dominated by agriculture, whereas the U.S. economy is dominated by the information and service sector. The U.S. workforce is 153 million compared to India's workforce of 470 million—436 of which work in the informal sector. India is a destination for many IT and customer service jobs once done by Americans.

CORE CONCEPT 5 When people believe that power differences are legitimate, those with power possess authority.

Authority is legitimate power—power that people believe is just and proper. A leader has authority to the extent that people view him or her as being entitled to give orders. Authority can be of three types: (1) traditional, (2) charismatic, and (3) legal-rational, which derives from a system of impersonal rules that formally specify the qualifications for occupying a powerful position.

CORE CONCEPT 6 Government is an organizational structure that directs and coordinates human activities in the name of a country or some other territory, such as a city, county, or state. That structure may be democratic, authoritarian, totalitarian, or theocratic.

No matter the form of government or the scope of its jurisdiction, all make laws, formal rules that move people to behave in specified ways or to refrain from behaving in some specified way. Laws are created by those in power and enforced by regulatory institutions such as police, military, or other bodies. Laws govern almost every area of life. When sociologists study laws, they consider questions of fairness and justice in their creation, interpretation, enforcement, and consequences.

CORE CONCEPT 7 There are two major models of power: the power elite and pluralistic models. The two models help us to evaluate whether an elite few hold the power in society or whether power is dispersed among competing interest groups.

The power elite consists of people whose positions in the military, the government, and the largest corporations are so high that their decisions affect the lives of millions, even billions, of people. For the most part, the source of this power is legal-rational. In writing about the power elite in the United States, sociologist C. Wright Mills focused on those who occupy the highest positions in the leading institutions: the military, the 200 largest corporations, and the government. Pluralist models view politics as a plurality of special interest groups competing, compromising, forming alliances, and negotiating with each other for power. A pluralist model views power as something dispersed among special interest groups.

CORE CONCEPT 8 Empire, imperialism, hegemony, and militarism are concepts that apply to political entities such as governments that can exercise their will over other political entities.

A government is an empire when it controls the political, economic, and cultural development of a group of countries. An imperialistic power controls foreign entities through military force or through political policies and economic pressure. Imperialists justify their control by claiming that they have cultural, political, or economic superiority and that they are using it for the greater good of all humankind. Hegemony is a process by which a power formalizes its dominance over foreign entities—using established institutions, bureaucratic structures, the mass media, and military or police force. A militaristic power believes that military strength, and the willingness to use it, is the source of national and even global security.

Resources on the Internet

Login to CengageBrain.com to access the resources your instructor requires. For this book, you can access:

Sociology CourseMate

Access an integrated eBook, chapter-specific interactive learning tools, including flash cards, quizzes, videos, and more in your Sociology CourseMate.

Take a pretest for this chapter and receive a personalized study plan based on your results that will identify the topics you need to review and direct you to online resources to help you master those topics. Then take a posttest to help you determine the concepts you have mastered and what you will need to work on.

CourseReader

CourseReader for Sociology is an online reader providing access to readings, and audio and video selections to accompany your course materials.

Visit **www.cengagebrain.com** to access your account and purchase materials.

Key Terms

527 group 296
authoritarian government 293
authority 289
capitalism 279
charismatic authority 290
colonization 276
democracy 291
domestication 274
economic system 274
empire 296
goods 274
government 291
hegemony 297
imperialistic power 297
insurgents 298
laws 294
legal-rational authority 290
militaristic power 297
pluralist model 295
pluralist models of power 295
political system 289
postindustrial society 278
power 289
power elite 294
primary sector (of the economy) 287
secondary sector (of the economy) 287
services 274
socialism 280
surplus wealth 274
tertiary sector (of the economy) 287
theocracy 294
totalitarianism 293
traditional authority 289
welfare state 281

FAMILY

12 With Emphasis on JAPAN

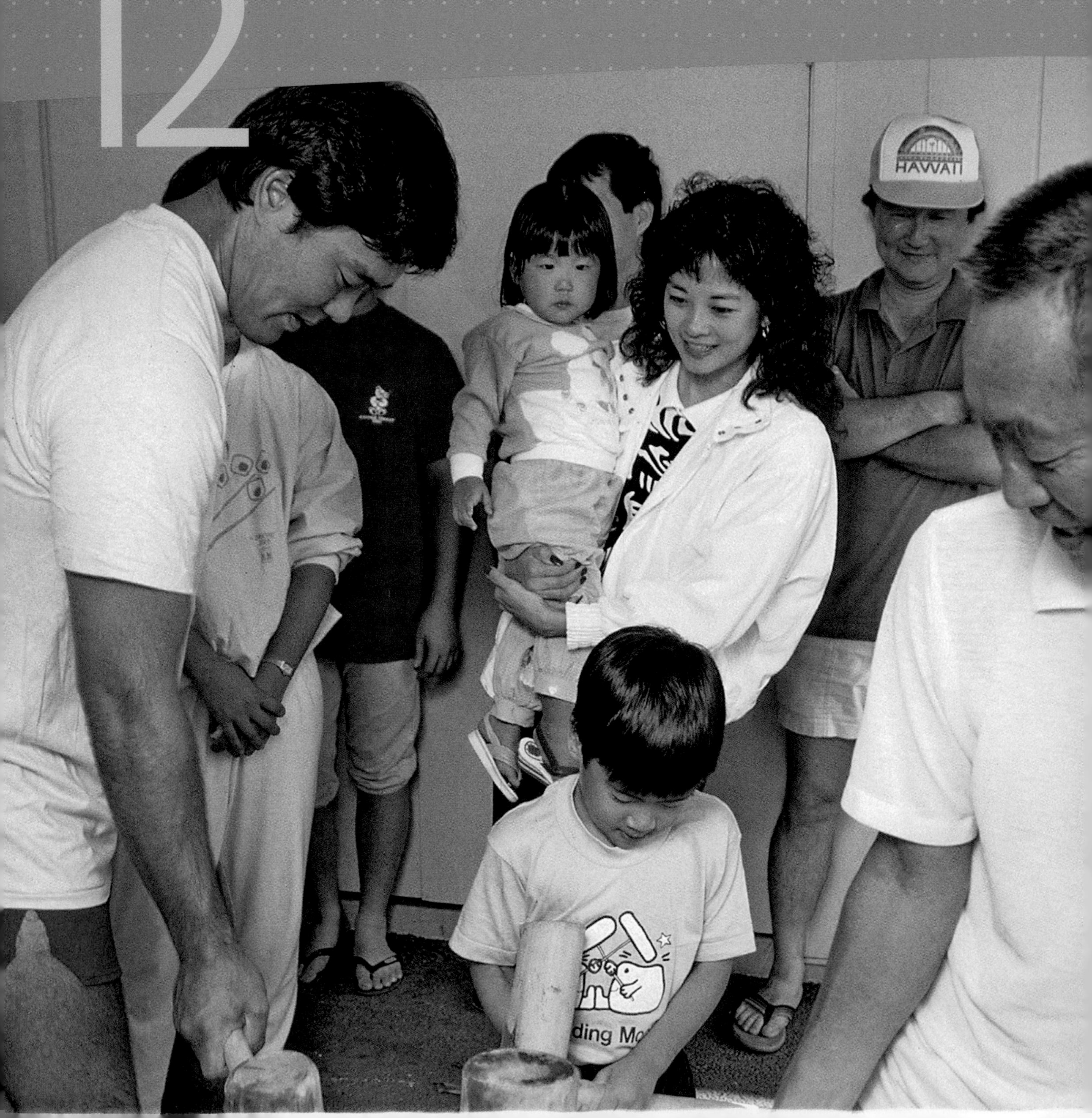

When sociologists study the family, they focus on the many factors that affect its structure and composition. In Japan, an aging population and low fertility rate are dramatically shaping the structure of family life. That is, people age 65 and older are increasing relative to other age groups. In addition, the number of children born each year is not enough to replace the population as its members die. For example, in 2010, there were 925,000 births and 1.3 million deaths in Japan (U.S. Central Intelligence Agency 2011).

Why Focus On JAPAN?

The family is an ever-changing entity. Millions of seemingly personal decisions influence the variety of family arrangements that exist in any country—decisions about whether to (1) have children, and if so, how many to have, when to have them, and how to space them; (2) marry, and if so, when; (3) work for pay; and (4) become a caregiver to dependent relatives. As we will see, these decisions are shaped and constrained by several larger forces, including average life expectancy, employment opportunities, and social norms.

In this chapter, we compare family life in Japan and in the United States. Based on indicators that seem to be associated with family well-being and stability, Japan appears to do better than the United States. The country has lower infant mortality than the United States; it has a lower teen birth rate (4.6 live births per 1,000 females age 15 to 19 versus 41.9 births per 1,000 females age 15 to 19), and a much smaller percentage of single-parent households. In addition, Japan has much fewer reported cases of domestic and child abuse than the United States (see Figure 12.1).

On the other hand, people in the United States seem more "optimistic" about having children than people in Japan; the United States has a higher **total fertility rate**; the average number of children that a woman bears in her lifetime is 2.1 versus Japan's rate, which is 1.2. The United States has a lower abortion rate, a higher teen birth rate, and a greater percentage of births to unmarried mothers (see Figure 12.1).

Both the United States and Japan have an **aging population**, one where the percentage of those age 65 and older is increasing relative to younger age groups. Currently, 13.0 percent of the U.S. population and 22.8 percent of the Japanese population are 65 years old or older. In 2020, 30 percent of Japan's population will be 65 and older, compared to 17.6 percent of the U.S. population (U.S. Bureau of the Census 2011).

Japan's low total fertility rate, combined with its long life expectancy and low immigration rate, means that the country has one of the oldest populations in the world. The low fertility rate is a major national concern, and it has prompted a variety of responses, including condemning young people for being selfish, delivering urgent appeals to couples to have babies, and initiating policies that make it easier on women to pursue a career and raise children (Yoshida 2008).

In the United States, the decline in the number of households occupied by married parents and their children has grabbed headlines along with a high teen birth rate and high percentage of single-parent households. In this chapter, we seek to understand the major social forces shaping family life in such different ways in the United States and Japan.

Online Poll

How many generations are a part of your family?

- ○ Two generations
- ○ Three generations
- ○ Four generations
- ○ Five generations
- ○ More than five generations

To see how other students responded to these questions, go to **www.cengagebrain.com.**

Defining Family

CORE CONCEPT 1 An amazing variety of family arrangements exists in the world. This variety makes it difficult to define family.

total fertility rate The average number of children that a woman bears in her lifetime.

aging population A population in which the percentage that is age 65 and older is increasing relative to other age groups.

Joe Carini/The Image Works

Video Tip: Show the author's video introduction to Chapter 12, which can be found on the Power Lecture CD. A transcript of the video is included in the Instructor's Resource Manual.

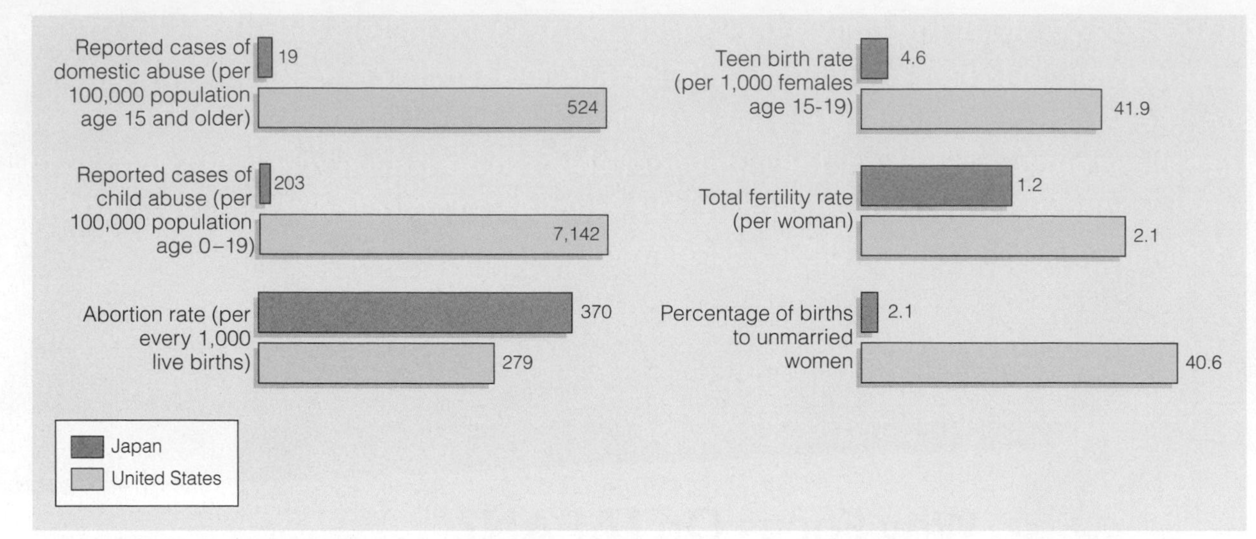

FIGURE 12.1 Selected Indicators of Family Structure, Composition, and Well-Being: Japan and United States

Sources: Data from NationMaster.com 2011; U.S. Bureau of Census (2009, 2011a, 2011b); Lah, 2011; Population Reference Bureau 2009; U.S. Department of Health and Human Services 2009

Family is a social institution that binds people together through blood, marriage, law, and/or social norms. Family members are generally expected to care for and support each other. This definition is very general because even though everyone is born into a family, there is no structure common to the amazing variety of family arrangements that exist worldwide. That variety is captured in the numerous norms that specify how two or more people can constitute a family. Among other things, these norms govern who can marry, the number of partners people can have, and the ways people trace their ancestry (see Table 12.1). In light of this variability, we should not be surprised that when people think of family, they often emphasize different dimensions, such as kinship, ideal members, or legal ties.

Kinship

Definitions of *family* that emphasize kinship view the family as comprising members who are linked together by blood, marriage, or adoption. Based on this definition, the size of any given person's family network is beyond comprehension, because one person has an astronomical number of living and deceased kin. Keep in mind that to calculate the number of a person's relatives, one would have to count primary kin (mother, father, sister, brother), secondary kin (mother's mother, mother's father, sister's son, brother's daughter), tertiary kin (brother's daughter's son, mother's sister's son), and beyond (brother's daughter's son's son).

Given that it is virtually impossible to keep track of even one's living relatives, let alone maintain social relationships with them, every society finds ways to exclude some kin from their idea of family. For example, some societies trace family lineage through the maternal or the paternal side only. Selective forgetting and remembering is

Missy Gish

Most of the people in this photo are connected to one another by blood or marriage. Yet the family shown represents only a fraction of all those who share the status of relative.

family A social institution that binds people together through blood, marriage, law, and/or social norms. Family members are generally expected to care for and support each other.

TABLE 12.1 Norms Governing Family Structure and Composition

Number of Marriage Partners	
Monogamy	One husband, one wife
Serial monogamy	Two or more successive spouses
Polygamy	Multiple spouses at one time
Polygyny	One husband, multiple wives at one time
Polyandry	One wife, multiple husbands at one time
Choice of Spouse	
Arranged	Parents select their children's marriage partners (sometimes in collaboration with children)
Romantic	Self-selected partner based on love
Endogamy	Marriage within one's social group
Exogamy	Marriage outside one's social group
Homogamy	Marriage to a partner whose social characteristics—such as class, religion, and level of education—are similar to one's own
Authority	
Patriarchal	Male dominated
Matriarchal	Female dominated
Egalitarian	Equal authority between sexes
Descent	
Patrilineal	Traced through father's lineage
Matrilineal	Traced through mother's lineage
Bilateral	Traced through both mother's and father's lineage

Household Type	
Nuclear	Husband, wife, and their immediate children
Extended	Three or more generations living together under one roof
Single-parent	Mother or father living with children
Nonfamily household	People who share the same residence but are not considered family
Domestic partnership	People committed to each other and sharing a domestic life but not joined in marriage or civil union
Civil union	A legally recognized partnership providing same-sex couples with some of the rights, benefits, and responsibilities associated with marriage
Family Residence	
Patrilocal	Wife living with or near husband's family
Matrilocal	Husband living with or near wife's family
Neolocal	Wife and husband live apart from their parents

another way of excluding some kin. That is, people make conscious or unconscious decisions about which kin they will acknowledge as family and which they will "forget" to mention to their children (Waters 1990).

Membership

Some popular definitions of *family* include specific ideas about who should count as family. In this regard, one of the broadest definitions of *family* is "anyone who lives under one roof and expresses love and solidarity" (Aguilar 1999). Organizations such as the World Congress of Families (2011) argue that the ideal or natural family is one "centered around the voluntary union of a man and a woman in a lifelong covenant of marriage," that is, welcoming of children. An **ideal** is a standard against which real cases can be compared. If we simply think about the living and procreation arrangements we observe every day, we quickly realize that many do not match that ideal. This fact does not stop people from using their ideal to judge their own and others' living arrangements, and from labeling families that do not fit their ideal as nontraditional, dysfunctional, immoral, or at-risk (Cornell 1990).

ideal A standard against which real cases can be compared.

Discussion Tip: As part of the Deficit Reduction Act of 1995, the U.S. federal government spends $150 million each year to fund "The Healthy Marriage Initiative." To review the initiative, visit the U.S. Department of Health and Human Services Web site at www.acf.hhs.gov/healthymarriage/about/mission.html#notabout. Among other things, the Web site lists the benefits of a healthy marriage. In assessing these benefits, run down the list and ask if each applies only to committed heterosexual relationships or if they might apply to committed same-sex relationships.

Legal Recognition

When legal recognition is the defining criterion, a family is defined as two or more people whose living and/or procreation arrangements are recognized *under the law* as constituting a family. U.S. federal laws define *spouse* as "a person of the opposite sex who is a husband or wife" and *marriage* as "a legal union between one man and one woman as husband and wife" (Defense of Marriage Act 1996, section 7). Legal recognition of family and marriage arrangements means that laws enforce any awarded benefits, responsibilities, and rights. Some state and local governments within the United States formally recognize family relationships that are in violation of federal law such as same-sex marriages, domestic partnerships, and civil unions. This recognition acknowledges that many people (including gay, lesbian, and heterosexual couples) form lasting, committed, caring, and faithful relationships—and that they are entitled to the legal protections, benefits, and responsibilities associated with marriage. Without these benefits and protections, such people might suffer numerous obstacles and hardships. As a case in point, the U.S. General Accounting Office (2004) identified 1,138 federal statutory provisions in United States Legal Code "in which marital status is a factor in determining or receiving benefits, rights, and privileges."

Functionalist View of Family Life

> **CORE CONCEPT 2** **Family can be defined in terms of the social functions it performs for society.**

Because of the debate over what constitutes family, some sociologists argue that *family* should be defined in terms of valued social functions. In this regard, the family performs at least five functions: (1) regulating sexual behavior, (2) replacing the members of society who die, (3) socializing the young, (4) providing care and emotional support, and (5) conferring social status.

Regulating Sexual Behavior Marriage and family systems generate norms (which can take the form of laws) that regulate sexual behavior. These norms may prohibit sex outside of marriage, or they may specify the social characteristics of partners. Such norms may prohibit marriage and sexual relationships between certain relatives (such as first cousins), specified age groups (such as an adult and a

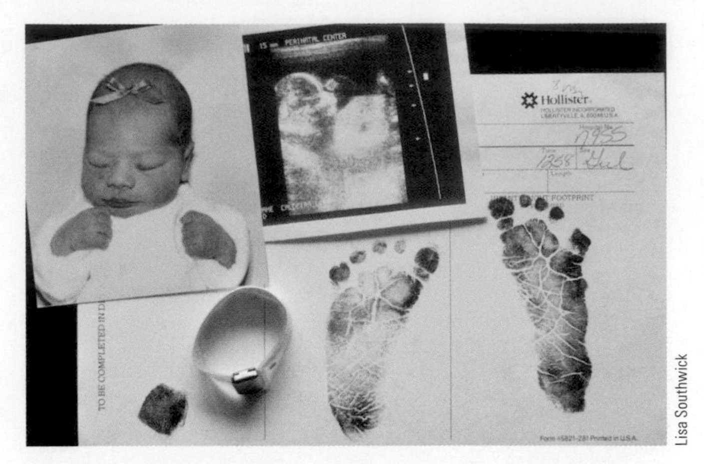

Lisa Southwick

Families function to replace the members of society who die, by providing a legally or socially sanctioned arrangement that can bring new members into the world.

minor), and different racial or ethnic groups. Other norms regulate the number of partners (such as monogamy, serial monogamy, and polygamy).

Replacing the Members of Society Who Die All people eventually die. Thus, for humans to survive as a species, we must at least replace those who die. Marriage and family systems provide a socially and legally sanctioned environment into which new members can be born and nurtured.

Socializing the Young Recall that socialization is a learning process that begins immediately after birth. The family is the most significant agent of socialization, because it gives society's youngest members their earliest exposure to relationships and the rules of life.

Providing Care and Emotional Support A family is expected to care for the emotional and physical needs of its members. No matter how old, all humans require meaningful social ties to others. Without such ties, people deteriorate both physically and mentally. The human life cycle is such that we all experience at least one stage of extreme dependency (infancy and childhood). Unless we die suddenly, we are also likely to experience some level of mental and/or physical deterioration in adulthood, accompanied by varying degrees of dependency.

Conferring Social Status We cannot choose our family, the quality of the relationship between our parents, or the economic conditions into which we are born. Among the things we inherit from our parents are a genetic endowment and a social status. For example, the physical characteristics we inherit affect the racial category to which we are assigned. Parents' occupations and incomes are also important predictors of **life chances**—a critical set of

life chances A critical set of potential social advantages, including the chance to survive the first year of life, to live independently in old age, and everything in between.

Teaching Tip: For a quick overview of the legal definition of family, see the Free Dictionary synopsis (http://legal-dictionary.thefreedictionary.com/Family+Law). You will see that "family law has become entwined with national debates over the structure of the family, gender bias, and morality."

Global Comparisons Countries with Highest and Lowest Total Fertility Rates

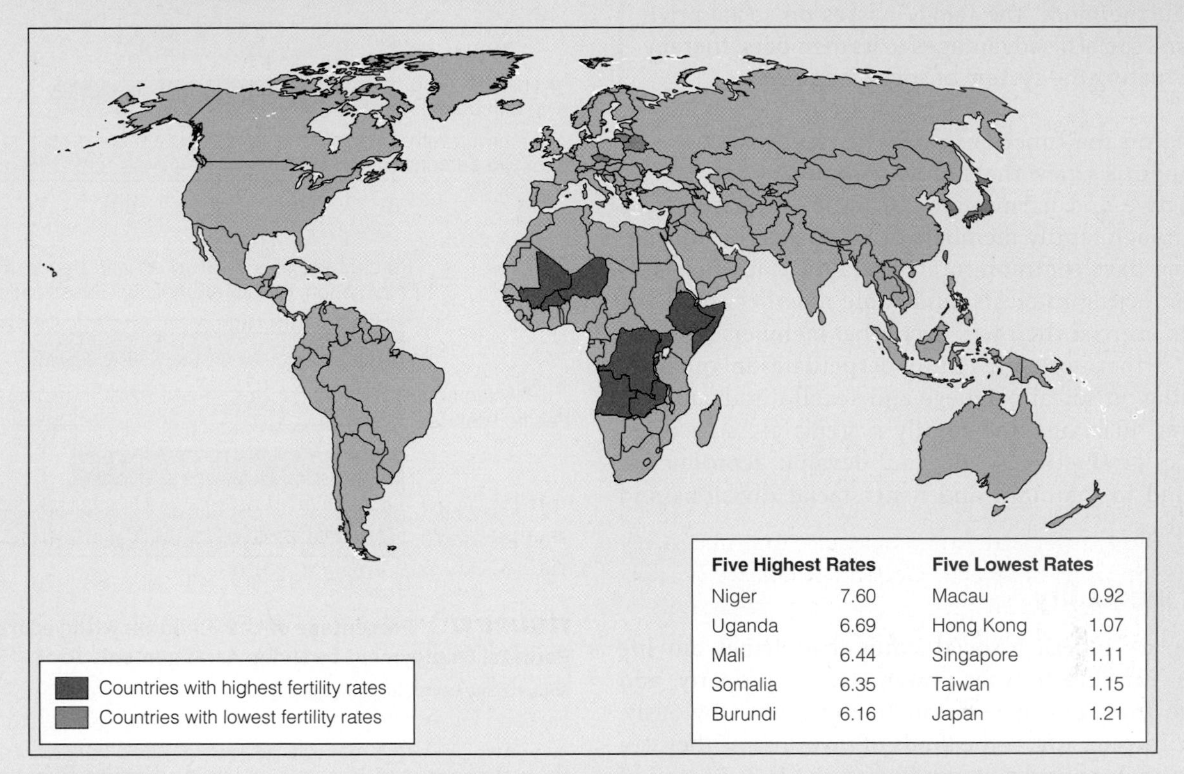

Five Highest Rates		Five Lowest Rates	
Niger	7.60	Macau	0.92
Uganda	6.69	Hong Kong	1.07
Mali	6.44	Singapore	1.11
Somalia	6.35	Taiwan	1.15
Burundi	6.16	Japan	1.21

FIGURE 12.2 The map shows the 10 countries with the highest and lowest total fertility rates; the table shows data for the five countries with highest and lowest rates. Macau has the lowest total fertility rate, at .92; Niger has the highest total fertility rate, at 7.60. That is, the average woman in Macau bears .92 children in her lifetime, whereas the average woman in Niger bears 7.60 children. The total fertility rate for the United States is 2.06. What part of the world has the highest fertility rates? Note that the countries with lowest fertility rates are islands or physically small making it difficult to see them on any map.

Source: Data from World Factbook (2011)

potential social advantages, including the chance to survive the first year of life, to live independently in old age, and everything in between.

Although everyone might agree that families should fulfill these five functions, we must acknowledge that families often fail to achieve one or more of them, as evidenced by the following facts:

- Family systems do not always succeed at regulating sexual activity so that it is confined to a husband and wife or legal partners. Based on tests for organ tissue typing, physicians estimate that between 5 to 20 percent of the donors are genetically unrelated to the men that they believed to be their biological fathers (Anderlik and Rothstein 2002).
- Marriage and family systems do not always succeed in replacing the members of society who die. In at least 96 countries, the total fertility rate is below 2.1—the minimum number of live births needed to replace the members who die (U.S. Central Intelligence Agency 2011). Why a minimum of 2.1 and not 2? Not all babies survive to replace their biological parents. Of course, in societies that have high childhood mortality, the total fertility rate must be more than 2.1. (See Global Comparisons: "Countries with Highest and Lowest Total Fertility Rates.")
- Family members do not always care for one another in positive ways. Domestic and child abuse is a problem in both the United States and Japan. Although the number of *reported* cases of such abuse in Japan is very low compared with the number reported in the United States, many cases go unreported. In one survey taken by the Japanese Cabinet Office's Gender Equality Bureau, 33 percent of women and 17.4 percent of men reported that their partner abused them physically, mentally, or sexually. About 10 percent of women and 2.6 percent of men said they suffered repeated abuse (*Japan Times* 2006).

Teaching Tip: The map highlights the 10 countries with highest and lowest fertility rates. You might mention that of the 266 countries profiled in the *World Factbook*, 105 have a fertility rate that is below 2.1 (below replacement level) and 40 countries have a fertility rate that is above 4.0.

Conflict View of Family Life

CORE CONCEPT 3 Family life is not always harmonious. Furthermore, the family passes on social privilege and social disadvantages to its members, thereby perpetuating the system of social inequality.

Focusing on the functions of family and marriage systems supports a view that family relationships are largely constructive and harmonious. Conflict theorists argue that although family members often do support one another and have common interests, family members also have competing interests, and some members have the power to exercise their will over other members (Cornell 1990). Furthermore, the family perpetuates inequalities by passing on social privilege and social disadvantages. Moreover, marriage and family systems are structured to value productive work and devalue reproductive work, and to maintain and foster racial divisions and boundaries.

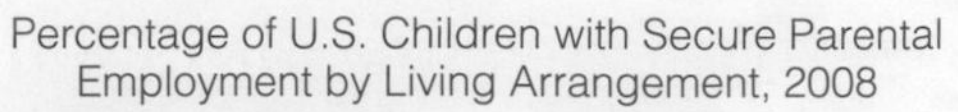

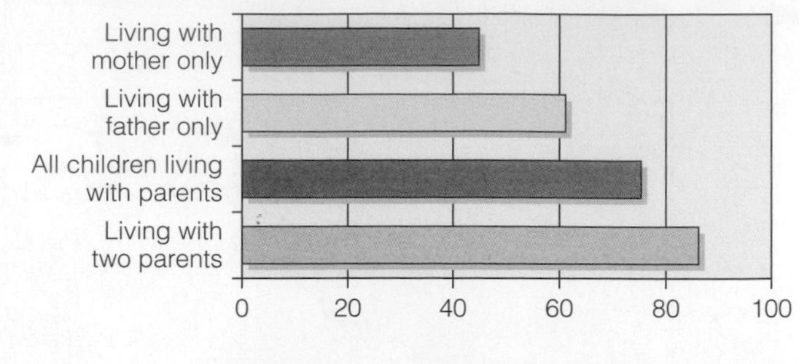

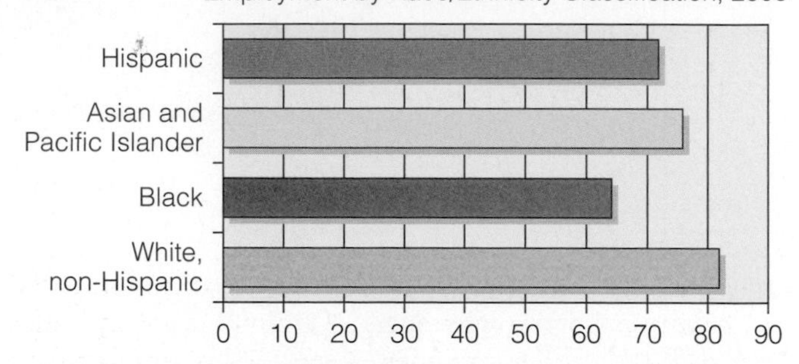

FIGURE 12.3 Percentage of U.S. Children with Secure Parental Employment by Living Arrangement, 2008

Source: Data from Child-Stats.gov (2010)

Social Inequality

At birth, we inherit a social status that shapes our life chances. Families transfer power, wealth, property, and privilege from one generation to the next. Obviously, parents' income affects the kinds of investments they can make in their children. According to the U.S. Bureau of the Census, 75 percent of children in the United States live in a household with **secure parental employment**. That is, they reside with at least one parent or guardian who was employed full-time (35 or more hours per week for at least 50 weeks in the past year). The percentage varies by racial classification and living arrangement (see Figure 12.3). Note that it drops to 45 percent for children living with their mothers only and increases to 86 percent for children living with both parents. Children classified as living in white households are more likely than others to live in secure parental employment households, whereas children classified as black are least likely to live in such households. As we might expect, parents or guardians who are securely employed are less likely than those not to live in poverty and more likely to have access to adequate housing and health care (ChildStats .gov 2010).

Productive and Reproductive Work

Friedrich Engels (1884) distinguished between productive and reproductive work. **Productive work** involves the creation of what humans need to exist (food, clothing, and shelter); **reproductive work** involves the creation of human beings —the "propagation of the species" (pp. 71–72). Reproductive work includes not only bearing children, but caregiving, managing households, and educating children. Both types of activities—production and reproduction—are work: "Renewing life is a form of work, a kind of production, as fundamental to the perpetuation of society as the production of things" (Laslett and Brenner 1989). Although we say that reproductive work is valued, it is not usually rewarded highly on an economic level. In addition, women perform reproductive work disproportionately, even when pay is involved (see Figure 12.4). In addition to low wages, reproductive labor often involves poor working conditions, little or no training, and few benefits, such as health insurance and retirement packages.

If we compare housework sharing between husbands and wives in Japan, we see that men spend 33 minutes per

secure parental employment A situation in which at least one parent or guardian is employed full-time (35 or more hours per week for at least 50 weeks in the past year).

productive work Work that involves "the production of the means of existence, of food, clothing, and shelter and the tools necessary for that production" (Engels 1884, pp. 71–72).

reproductive work Work that involves bearing children, caregiving, managing households, and educating children.

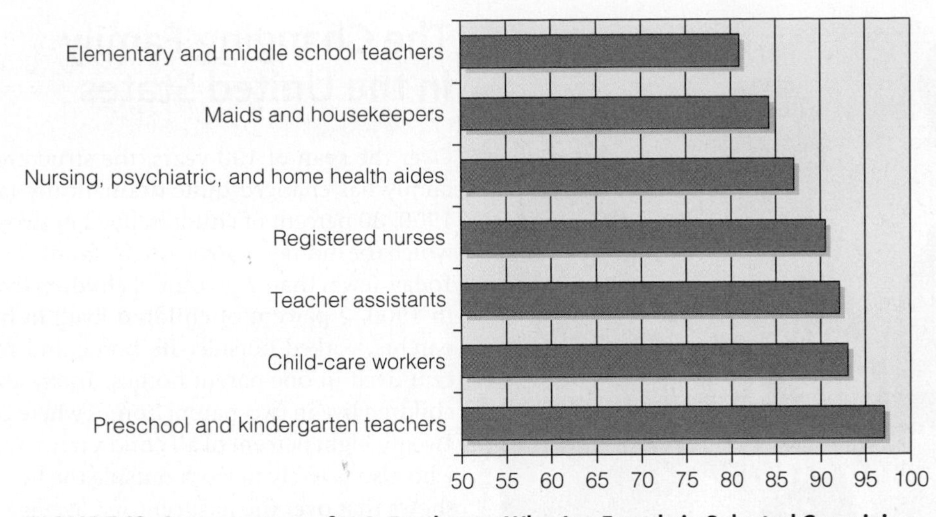

FIGURE 12.4 Percentage of U.S. Employees Who Are Female in Selected Caregiving Occupations

Source: Data from U.S. Bureau of Labor Statistics (2011)

day doing housekeeping and child care activities compared to Japanese women who spend 3 hours and 45 minutes per day doing such activities. Regardless of employment status, Japanese women contribute more hours than their male counterparts to housework and child care (Statistics Bureau, Ministry of Internal Affairs and Communications [Japan] 2007).

It is difficult to compare United States and Japan with regard to how housework and child care responsibilities are shared, if only because homes in the United States tend to be larger and because the two governments employ different measures. Nevertheless, it does seem that men living in the United States are more willing to share domestic responsibilities with women than men living in Japan. On average, American men who work full-time report spending 101.4 minutes a day compared to women who spend 212 minutes per day (U.S. Bureau of Labor Statistics 2010).

In *Having It All*, Francine M. Deutsch (1999) concludes that "men and women can decide to share in reproductive work but doing so involves costs for both parties." Deutsch cites the example of a husband, a wife, and their young son Ollie traveling together by plane. The husband is holding Ollie, who is screaming. A male passenger sitting behind them asks, "What's wrong with the child's mother? Why doesn't the mother take care of the baby?" The husband answers, "Because I'm his father and I am perfectly capable of taking care of him." The husband's decision not to hand his son over to his wife and his wife's decision not to grab Ollie away represent this couple's commitment to share in the reproductive work. Such decisions come at a price, however. Despite informal and subtle (and probably even hostile) pressures from passengers for the wife to intervene and the husband to hand the child over, the couple stood their ground. This scenario illustrates how even well-intentioned couples committed to equality might give in to societal pressures (Gerson 1999).

Racial Divisions and Boundaries

In the United States, we assume that people choose a partner based on love. Upon investigating who marries, however, we find that people's choices are guided by other considerations as well: a potential partner's age, height, weight, income, education, race, sex, social class, and religion, among other things. When the conditions are right, we "allow" ourselves to fall in love. All societies have norms defining who may date or marry whom. These norms may be formal (enforced by law) or informal (enforced by social pressure).

Exogamy refers to norms requiring or encouraging people to choose a partner from a social category other than their own—for example, a partner outside the immediate family and not a partner of the same sex. **Endogamy** refers to norms requiring or encouraging people to choose a partner from the same social category as their own—for example, a partner of the same sex, race, religion, or social class. In the United States, most people marry partners whom they believe belong to their own ethnic or racial category. At one time, the United States had laws forbidding people to do otherwise. (See Working For Change: "Dismantling a Big Lie" on page 313.)

exogamy Norms requiring or encouraging people to choose a partner from a social category other than their own.

endogamy Norms requiring or encouraging people to choose a partner from the same social category as their own.

Rob Williams, Courtesy of Joan Ferrante

Most people in Japan practice endogamy; that is, they choose partners in the same racial category as their own. Still, about 6 percent break from the practice and choose partners considered to be a different ethnicity, such as Chinese or Korean. Very few Japanese marry across racial lines as did this Japanese woman and African American man.

In Japan, 94 percent of all marriages involve brides and grooms both classified as Japanese. Of the 44,701 marriages between a Japanese and non-Japanese partner that took place in one year, 35,993—80 percent of the marriages—involved a Japanese groom marrying a non-Japanese woman (Japan Ministry of Health, Labor and Welfare 2008). One reason endogamy is so predominant is that Japan's immigration policies have allowed few foreigners into the country. Thus, Japan is a homogenous society, described by its education minister as "one nation, one civilization, one language, one culture and one race" (Burgess 2007). In Japan, 98.2 percent of residents are classified as Japanese (Japan Ministry of Justice 2009). In the past 10 years, only 50,000 work visas per year have been issued to foreigners. This number is very low when we consider that demographers have stated that Japan needs to issue 640,000 visas per year just to prevent its population from shrinking (Burgess 2007, Brooke 2004).

CORE CONCEPT 4 Family structures are not static; they change in response to larger economic, cultural, historical, and social forces. Sociologists track changes in family structure over time and seek to identify triggers of change.

The Changing Family in the United States

Over the span of 100 years, the structure of the American family has changed quite dramatically (see Table 12.2). In 1900, 80 percent of children lived in two-parent families in which the mother worked on the family farm or in the home. Today, fewer than 2 percent of children live in farm families. In 1900, 2 percent of children lived in homes where both parents worked outside the home and fewer than 10 percent lived in one-parent homes. Today about 60 percent of children live in two-parent homes where both parents work. Twenty-eight percent of all children live with a single parent, who also is likely to work outside the home. Table 12.4 also shows that over the past century, average life expectancy at birth has increased by almost 30 years for men and by about 33 years for women. Infant mortality has dropped from 99.9 deaths to 6.0 deaths per 1,000 live births.

In "Wives and Work: The Sex Role Revolution and Its Consequences," sociologist Kingsley Davis (1984) identified "as clear and definite a social change as one can find" (p. 401). Between 1900 and 1980, the percentage of women in the work force rose from less than 20 percent to 60 percent, and the percentage of married women in the labor force rose from 15.4 percent to 53.1 percent. Davis links women's entry (and especially married women's entry) into the paid work force to a number of interrelated factors including (1) the rise and fall of the breadwinner system, (2) declines in total fertility, (3) increased life expectancy, (4) higher divorce rates, and (5) increased employment opportunities for women.

The Rise of the Breadwinner System

Before industrialization—that is, for most of human history—the workplace comprised the home and the surrounding land. Under these circumstances, the division of labor was based on sex. In nonindustrial societies (which include both hunting-and-gathering and agrarian societies), men provided raw materials through hunting or agriculture, and women processed these materials and took care of the young. This division of labor was not always clear-cut; women also worked in agriculture and provided raw materials by gathering food and hunting small animals.

The Industrial Revolution separated the workplace from the home and altered the division of labor between men and women. It destroyed the household economy by removing economic production from the home and taking it out of women's hands.

> The man's work, instead of being directly integrated with that of his wife and children in the home or on the surrounding land, was integrated with that of nonkin in factories, shops, and offices. In one sense, the man's

Working for Change Dismantling a Big Lie

Why do people laugh when someone suggests that a black person and a white person are relatives? This account by Mike Morgan, a black student from my intro class, illustrates. Mike was invited to the front of the classroom to draw the name of a fellow student out of a hat full of names. Coincidentally, he drew the name of a white female whose last name was also Morgan.

©AP Photo/Richmond Times-Dispatch, Bob Brown

After Mike called out the name, he said without hesitation, "Perhaps we are related." The class broke into laughter, as if it seemed impossible. The belief that it is impossible for blacks and whites to be brothers, sisters, cousins, parent and child, and so on speaks to a great American tragedy—the 400-year practice of dividing biologically related people (parents and children, grandparents and grandchildren, brothers and sisters) into distinct racial categories based on physical appearance. In the United States, this practice of dividing family members along racial lines began with slavery.

Although the story of race in America is a story of family tragedy, it is almost never cast in that light. One person who has told the story in that light is Shannon Lanier. When he was a 21-year-old student at Kent State, he published (with photographer Jane Feldman) *Jefferson's Children: The Story of One American Family* (2000). The book is marketed to young readers.

Lanier (who appears black) begins the book by announcing that he is a descendant of Thomas Jefferson—the third president of the United States—and Sally Hemings—an enslaved woman. According to Lanier, Jefferson was his great-great-great-great-great-great-grandfather. Lanier grew up knowing this. His mother told him, and "she had learned [it] from her mama as her mama had learned from hers, and so on, from lips to ears, down through the generations" (Lanier and Feldman 2000, p. 11). Lanier recalls that as a first grader, he tried to share his family history with his classmates on President's Day but his teacher reprimanded him for lying. After all, nowhere in the history books of the time was Jefferson's relationship with Hemings mentioned. Although Lanier dreamed of someday meeting relatives from both sides of his family, he did not believe it could happen.

In 1998, a team of geneticists tested Y-chromosomal DNA evidence and concluded that a male carrying the Jefferson Y chromosome fathered Eston Hemings—the last child born to Sally Hemings, in 1808. Because some 25 Jefferson males were living in Virginia at that time, the DNA evidence alone could not confirm Thomas Jefferson as the father. The Thomas Jefferson Foundation appointed a research committee to look into the matter further. It eventually concluded that the "DNA study, combined with multiple strands of currently available documentary and statistical evidence,[1] indicates a high probability that Thomas Jefferson fathered Eston Hemings, and that he most likely was the father of all six of Sally Hemings's children" (Thomas Jefferson Foundation 2000).

On May 15, 1999, Lanier traveled to the Monticello estate in Virginia to meet descendants of both Martha Jefferson (Thomas Jefferson's wife) and Sally Hemings.[2] He also met photographer Jane Feldman, who was there to document this historic gathering. The two decided to travel around the country to meet and photograph probable descendants of the Thomas Jefferson–Sally Hemings relationship. Young readers who encounter this family's tale will come to learn that the true story of race in America is a family story.

1. Documentary evidence listed in the Thomas Jefferson Foundation's report includes the following: "Sally Hemings's birth patterns match Thomas Jefferson's Monticello visitation patterns. . . . Several people close to Jefferson or the Monticello community believed he was the father of Sally Hemings's children. . . . Sally Hemings's children had unique access to freedom. Jefferson gave freedom to no other nuclear slave family. . . . Sally Hemings's children bore a striking resemblance to Thomas Jefferson."

2. Sally Hemings was the half-sister of Jefferson's wife, Martha. In fact, Martha Jefferson had five other half-siblings, the offspring of sexual relationships between her father and enslaved women (PBS 2005).

economic role became more important to the family, for he was now the link between the family and the wider market economy, but at the same time, his personal participation in the household diminished. His wife, relegated to the home, still performed the parental and domestic duties that women had always performed. She bore and reared children, cooked meals, washed clothes, and cared for her husband's personal needs, but to an unprecedented degree her economic role became restricted. She could not produce what the family consumed, because production had been removed from the home. (Davis 1984, p. 403)

Technology Tip: Listen to a National Public Radio report on "white" and "black" descendants of slave, slaves owners, and traders. Go to www.npr.org, and enter the title "Descendents Gather to Heal Wounds of Slavery."

Technology Tip: Listen to National Public Radio commentary by Shannon Lanier, the author of *Jefferson's Children: The Story of One American Family,* who speaks on the struggles and rewards of bringing family members of different racial classifications together. Go to www.npr.org and enter "Shannon Lanier" into the search engine.

TABLE 12.2 U.S. Households: 100 Years of Change

Living Arrangement	1900	1950	2009
Average household size (persons)	4.8	3.4	2.6
Percent of households with 7 or more people	20.4	4.9	1.0
Living arrangements of children by family status			
% Two-parent farm family	41	17	2
% Two-parent nonfarm family	45	79	64
% Father breadwinner, mother homemaker	43	56	32
% Dual-earner parents	2	13	60
% Single-parent	9	8	28
Not living with parent	5	6	4
Median age at first marriage			
Men	25.9	22.8	27.5
Women	21.9	20.3	25.6
Life expectancy at birth (years)			
Males	46.3	65.6	76.0
Females	48.3	71.1	81.0
Infant mortality rate (deaths per 1,000 live births)	99.9	29.2	6.0
Life expectancy at age 65			
Men	11.7	12.9	17.0
Women	12.4	15.2	20.0
Percent age 65 and older	4.1	8.1	13.0
Total fertility rate (children born over woman's lifetime)	3.6	3.1	2.1

Source: Data from U.S. Central Intelligence Agency 2011, U.S. Bureau of the Census 2009, Centers for Disease Control 2010.

Davis calls this new economic arrangement the breadwinner system. Historically, this system was not typical. Rather, it was peculiar to the middle and upper classes and was associated with a particular phase of industrialization. In the United States, its heyday dates from about 1860 to 1920. This system has been in decline ever since. Davis asks, "Why did the separation of home and workplace lead to the breadwinner system?" The major reason, he believes, is that women had too many children to engage in work outside the home. His answer is supported by the fact that family size, as measured by the number of living members, reached its peak in the period from the mid-1800s to the early 1900s. During this period, infant and childhood mortality declined but the old norms favoring large families persisted.

The Decline of the Breadwinner System

The breadwinner system did not last long because, for one thing, it placed too much strain on husbands and wives. The strains stemmed from several sources. Never before had the roles of husband and wife been so distinct. Never before had women played less than a direct, important role in producing what the family

Discussion Tip: Ask students to look at numbers in Table 12.2 above and to select out what they consider the most dramatic changes to family structure since 1900. Have they ever heard a parent, grandparent, or great grandparent talk about a live experience that gives concrete insights about a particular structural arrangement (e.g., households with 7 or more people, high infant mortality).

Lithograph by J. Keppler

This 1887 drawing depicts an image we have come to associate with the breadwinner system. As the breadwinners, men did not work at home or on surrounding land but worked with nonkin in factories, shops, and offices. The wife stayed home and took care of the children and house.

consumed. Never before had men been separated from the family for most of their waking hours. Never before had men been forced to bear the sole responsibility of supporting the entire family. Davis regards these events as structural weaknesses in the breadwinner system. Given these weaknesses, the breadwinner system needed strong normative controls to survive: "The husband's obligation to support his family, even after his death, had to be enforced by law and public opinion. Illegitimate sexual relations and reproduction had to be condemned; divorce had to be punished, and marriage had to be encouraged by making the lot of the 'spinster' a pitiful one" (p. 406).

Davis maintains that the normative controls eventually collapsed not only because of the strains in the breadwinner system, but also because of demographic and social changes that accompanied industrialization. These changes included decreased total fertility rates, increased life expectancy, increased divorce rates, and increased opportunities for employment perceived as suitable for women.

Declines in Total Fertility

The decline in total fertility (number of children born over the average woman's lifetime) began before married women entered the labor force in large numbers. Davis attributes the decline to two sources: the forces of industrialization, which changed children from economic assets to economic liabilities, and a desire to "advance one's own and one's children's status in a rapidly evolving industrial society" (p. 408). Davis concluded that a decline in total fertility changed women's lives so that they had the time to work outside the home, especially after their children entered school. Not only did the number of children born in the average family decrease, but the age at which women had their last child decreased (the mother's median age at the time of her last child's birth was 40 in 1850; by 1940, it had fallen to 27.3). In addition, the births were spaced more closely together.

Increased Life Expectancy

Given her relatively short life expectancy and the relatively late age at which she had her last child (age 40), the average woman in 1860 was dead by the time her last child left home. By 1980, given the changes in family size, spacing of children, and age of last pregnancy, the average woman could expect to live 33 years after her last child left home. As a result, the time devoted to child care came to occupy a smaller proportion of a woman's life. In addition, women could expect to live longer than men. In 1900, women outlived men by about 1.6 years, on average. Today, the average woman outlives the average man by 5 years. And because brides tend to be younger than their grooms, the average married woman can expect to live approximately 8 to 10 years beyond her husband's death. In addition, the distorted sex ratio caused by males' earlier death decreases the probability of remarriage later in life. Although few women would probably mention their husbands' impending death as a reason for working, the difference in male–female life expectancy may be a background consideration.

Increased Divorce Rate

Davis traces the rise in the divorce rate to the breadwinner system, and specifically to the shift of economic production outside the home:

> With this shift, husband and wife, parents and children, were no longer bound together in a close face-to-face division of labor in a common enterprise. They were bound, rather, by a weaker and less direct mutuality—the husband's ability to draw income from the wider economy and the wife's willingness to make a home and raise children. The husband's work not only took him out of the home but also frequently put him into contact with other people, including young unmarried women who were strangers to his family. Extramarital relationships inevitably flourished. Freed from rural and small-town social controls, many husbands either sought divorce or, by their behavior, caused their wives to do so. (pp. 410–411)

As Davis notes, an increase in the divorce rate preceded married women's entry into the labor market by several decades. He argues that once the divorce rate reached a certain threshold (a 20 percent or greater chance of divorce), more married women seriously considered seeking employment to protect themselves in case of failed marriage. When both husband and wife participate in the labor force, the chances of divorce increase even more. In such a scenario, both partners interact daily with people who are strangers to the family.

Increased Employment Opportunities for Women

Davis believes that married women are motivated to seek work because of changes in the childbearing experience, the increase in life expectancy, the rising divorce rate, and the inherent weakness of the breadwinner system. However, women can act on these motivations only if their opportunities to work increase. With improvements in machine technology, the physical labor required to produce goods and services decreased. As industrialization matured, it brought a corresponding increase in the kinds of jobs perceived as suitable for women beyond nursing, clerical and secretarial work, and teaching. As women filled these jobs, they increased their economic self-sufficiency and transformed gender roles. There is "nothing like a checking account to decrease someone's willingness to be pushed into marriage or stay in a bad one" (Kipnis 2004).

Davis helps us to understand forces behind the decline of the breadwinner system. He does not say that the present system is free of problems, however. First, it "lacks normative guidelines. It is not clear what husbands and wives should expect of each other. It is not clear what ex-wives and ex-husbands should expect, or children, cohabitants, friends, and neighbors. Each couple has to work out its own arrangement, which means in practice a great deal of experimentation and failure" (Davis 1984, p. 413).

Keith Farley

Women have demonstrated that they are capable of doing very physical work, but they have often been constrained by the kinds of jobs society perceived them as capable of doing.

Second, even if she works, the woman tends to remain primarily responsible for domestic matters. Davis maintains that women will bear this responsibility until men and women are unequal in the labor force. (At the time Davis wrote his study, women earned 66 cents for every dollar men earned. Today, they earn about 82.8 cents for every dollar men earn [U.S. Bureau of Labor Statistics 2011].)

The problems of the post-breadwinner system are evident when we consider psychosocial costs to women—costs that include the stress of juggling family and career, finding reliable day care, and anxiety over making those choices. The tensions can be summarized as follows: If women work and have no children, they are often considered selfish. If they stay home and raise a family, they are considered underemployed at best. If they work and raise a family, people wonder how they can possibly do either job right. The following comments from students in my introduction to sociology classes speak to this dilemma:

- I have felt pressured since I was little to go to college and have a career, and all I have ever wanted was to be a housewife and mother. Now that I have been in college for three years, I still have no major because my interests are with homemaking—that does not require a degree. It just kills me that people think that if women want to stay at home they are living in the past and that women should be career-driven.
- After I was born, my mother faced the tensions between being a mother and working outside the home. I was her second child, and she felt pressured to choose between her job and her two children. She quit her job and had two more kids. Later on, when she was ready to go back and get a job, she got a job at Arby's. However, the only reason she worked there was so she could be home to help us get ready for school, and meet us when we got home from school.
- I worked part-time for years, and once my youngest child entered school my husband kept asking when I was going to work full-time. There always was the power issue in our family—who makes the most money gets to make the big decisions. Truthfully, that played a part in my going to work full-time—so I could have some more power in the decision making.

The Changing Family in Japan

For at least two decades, the Japanese government had sought to increase the birth rate. Since 1991, there have been four five-year plans: Angel Plan (1994 to 1999), New Angel Plan (2000 to 2004), Support Plan for Parents and Children (2005 to 2009), and the current plan (2010 to 2014) (Sutton 2010). These five-year plans represent national initiatives specifically aimed at reversing the low total fertility rate and encouraging working women to

Student Activity: Ask students to read bullet-point items on this page in which college students reflect on tensions between career and raising families. Do these reflections capture their views on this. If yes, how so? If not, why not?

have children (Fukue and Daimon 2010). Maternity leave and after-school programs are examples of the kinds of initiatives put in place to encourage childbearing. In addition to national plans each municipality must establish an action plan to support the development of the next generation (Iwasawa and Kaneko 2010).

Over the span of 100 years, the structure of the Japanese family has changed drastically (see Table 12.3). Infant mortality declined sharply during the last century, from 155 deaths to 3 deaths per 1,000 births. The average number of children that Japanese women bear over their lifetime dropped from 5.11 to 1.2. The percentage of males age 25 to 29 who have never married increased from 18.7 to 64.3. For women, that percentage increased from 8 percent in 1900 to 56.3 percent. Over the past 100 years, average life expectancy increased by 35 years for men and by about 42 years for women.

In Japan, the pressing social issues revolve around increasing life expectancy and declining fertility rates. Japan's fertility has declined to 1.2 births per woman, and the population over age 65 is 22.7 percent. This decline in fertility is critical given that there are now more deaths than births each year. This means the population of Japan is now entering a phrase of ongoing decline (Toru 2010). As we will see, the drop in total fertility is intertwined with a number of historical forces, including the fall of the multigenerational household system, the rise of a breadwinner system, the decline in the number of arranged marriages, the rise of the so-called "parasite single," and increased employment opportunities, especially for single women.

TABLE 12.3 Japan's Households: 100 Years of Change

Item	1900	1950	2010
Average household size (in persons)	4.8	3.4	2.6
Percent age 65 and older	5.5	4.9	22.8
Infant mortality rate (deaths per 1,000 live births)	155	60.1	3.0
Mean age at first marriage			
Women	23	23	28.6
Men	27	25.9	30.4
Mean age at first birth	—	—	29.7
Total fertility rate (average number of children born over a woman's lifetime)	5.11	3.65	1.2
Life expectancy at birth (years)			
Males	44.25	59.57	79.6
Females	44.83	62.97	86.4
Life expectancy at age 65 (projected years)			
Males	10.14	11.35	18
Females	11.35	13.36	23
Percentage never married (age 25 to 29)			
Men	18.7	—	64.3
Women	8.0	—	56.3
Percentage never married (age 30 to 34)			
Men	—	—	39.4
Women	—	—	28.1
Percentage of population engaged in agriculture	53.8	41.1	6
Percentage of one-person households	6	3.4	10

Sources: Data from Statistics Bureau, Ministry of Internal Affairs and Communications 2011, Nishioka et al. 2010.

Student Activity: Visit the newspaper *Japan Times Online* at www.japantimes.co.jp. Search the archives for three or four articles about fertility, specifically declining fertility in Japan. In particular, look for information that relates to the consequences of declining fertility or the efforts to increase fertility.

The Fall of the Multigenerational Household and the Rise of the Breadwinner System

In 1898, the Japanese government established the Domestic Relations and Inheritance Law. Under this law, everyone belonged to a multigenerational household system (known as an *ie*) and was required to register in an official family registry. Even if families of the same ancestor lived apart, they still registered as one *ie* (Takahashi 1999). Legally the household head held authority over other family members and was responsible for the household's management and well-being. Relationships between family members were shaped by the Confucian values of filial piety, faith in the family, and respect for elders. Ideally, women obeyed men, the young obeyed the old, and daughters-in-law obeyed mothers-in-law (Hashizume 2000). Firstborn sons held privileged status. As future heads of the household, they were the heirs to all of the family's assets. Younger sons were expected to establish their own livelihoods and residences apart from the main household. Even so, the wives of younger sons were expected to help care for their husbands' parents, despite the fact that their parents-in-law lived in a separate household.

Under the *ie* system, a daughter was viewed as a temporary family member until marriage, at which point she moved in with her husband's family and assumed his surname (Takahashi 1999). A bride—especially the bride of the oldest son—was known as the "bride of the family." She served and obeyed her husband, his parents, and the household heir. She was responsible for domestic work, including caring for her parents-in-law in their old age. If a household head and his wife produced no children, the couple adopted a child (preferably a male). If the couple had no biological or adopted son, they adopted a son-in-law to marry a daughter, take on the family name, and assume the role of household head. Legally, women could not choose their spouses or own property.

Soon after U.S. forces dropped atomic bombs on the Japanese cities Hiroshima and Nagasaki in 1945, World War II ended; U.S. troops occupied Japan until 1952. Under the direction of General Douglas MacArthur, the occupational authority imposed sweeping changes on Japan's economic, education, legal, and family systems. The *ie* system ended. New laws granting equal rights to women, ending arranged marriage, and abolishing primogeniture were instituted. Women were given the right to vote, to initiate divorce, and to retain custody of children. The Ancestry Registration Law was abolished, and the nuclear family replaced the *ie* as the legal family unit (Takahashi 1999).

The U.S. government gave economic assistance to its former foe, helped Japan to rebuild, and established a democratic and capitalistic system. Japan literally rose from the ashes of World War II to become one of the top economies in the world and a top trading partner of the United States.

Department of Defense

In 1945, during World War II, U.S. forces dropped atomic bombs on the Japanese cities Nagasaki and Hiroshima. The bombs' physical and psychological devastation hastened Japan's surrender that same year. U.S. troops then occupied Japan until 1952, and the occupational authority imposed sweeping changes on Japan's family system.

The rise of capitalism moved productive functions away from the home. Men assumed the role of breadwinners, working outside the home; women assumed the role of homemakers, responsible for reproductive work, including the care of children and the elderly.

Despite these changes to the family structure, the belief that problems should be managed within the family has persisted. This persistence is evident in the structure of Japan's social welfare system: It has only been in recent years that the Japanese government has supported public services to the elderly, until then relying on the caregiving tradition in which daughters-in-law cared for their husband's parents. Japan's efforts have focused on policies that make it easier for them to work and take care of children. As one example, Japan has a maternity leave policy that grants women 14 weeks leave at 67 percent of their salary (World Economic Forum 2010). To date, however, the government has not granted men paternity leave or help balancing work and family life, even as men are assuming caregiver roles in relation to elderly parents. Without such initiatives aimed at men, the caregiving burden continues to fall disproportionately on women (Makita 2010).

About 23 percent of the population in Japan—almost one in four people—is age 65 or older. That percentage is expected to increase to 30 percent—one in three—by 2020. How do you think an aging population affects family life?

The Decline of Arranged Marriages

Between 1955 and 1998, the proportion of all marriages in Japan that were arranged fell from 63 percent to 7 percent. Today, about 6.3 percent of marriages are believed to be arranged (Masami 2009). The shift away from arranged marriages helps to account for an increase in the median age at first marriage. When parents no longer arranged marriages, love became a private matter and young people were left to their own devices. As a result, the Japanese marriage market is not as well developed as the U.S. market. Unlike the United States, Japan does not have a "couple's culture." As one young Japanese woman commented, "In the U.S., you are supposed to be with your boyfriend or husband all the time. . . . In Japan, women have their ways of having fun and men have their ways. You're not expected to bring a date everywhere and you don't feel excluded if you're not involved with someone" (Ornstein 2001, p. 34).

The Rise of the "Parasite Single"

In Japan, a high percentage of working single adults (age 22 and older) live with their parents while contributing little to household expenses. An estimated 90 percent of single women in their twenties and 60 percent of single men in their thirties live with their parents (Retherford, Ogawa, and Matsukura 2001, Yamada 2000, Zielenziger 2002). In the United States, 20 percent of 25- to 34-year-olds live with a parent or someone from an older generation (Pew Research Center 2010). These rates in both countries are exacerbated by the tight job market for new college graduates.

Sociologist Masahiro Yamada (2000) coined the phrase "parasite singles" to describe young adults pursuing the "new single concept," enjoying a comfortable life free of the financial and emotional pressures associated with parenting (especially mothering). Among the most stressful pressures that these singles wish to avoid is that of guiding children through Japan's highly competitive educational system.

This competitiveness can be traced to top corporations' and government ministries' practice of recruiting career employees from a handful of elite universities. Admission to these universities is tied to high scores on very difficult entrance exams. The intense competition is a key factor behind the use of *juku* (cram schools). These are educational programs where Japanese children go to study and learn after the regular school day, on weekends, and during vacation periods. Approximately 39 percent of all public elementary students (first through sixth grades) and 75 percent of public middle school students attend one of the 50,000 *juku* (Sato 2005). The *juku* phenomenon places tremendous financial pressure on the parents who must pay tuition, purchase supplementary textbooks, and employ tutors (Brasor 1999). In fact, many mothers work part-time to pay juku-related expenses, which can average $2,888 a year for kindergarteners to $5,691 for high school seniors. Parents with children in private schools pay an average of $15,533 per year (*Japan Times* 2005).

Such pressures are reflected in Japanese parents' answers to survey questions about the disadvantages of having children. The top two drawbacks cited are the financial costs and psychological stresses associated with the juku system. The juku pressure is particularly stressful for mothers, who almost single-handedly guide children through the process. Many working fathers are

In Japan, in addition to going to school during the day, many students also enroll in what are known as juku or cram schools. This practice places tremendous financial pressure on the parents as well as emotional pressure. Parents, especially the mother, feel emotional pressure, because their child's success or failure is a reflection on them.

Student Activity: Pressures associated with *juku* (Japanese cram schools) are particularly stressful for Japanese mothers and are cited as one of the disadvantages of having kids. Visit the newspaper *Japan Times Online* (www.japantimes.co.jp), and plug in search term "juku" to learn more about this phenomenon. Write two to three paragraphs elaborating on these pressures.

largely absent from the home, because the workplace is governed by a mentality of work over family, such that "employees feel obligated to work long hours (including weekends), forgo needed time off, and accept sudden job transfers without consideration of family needs" (Makita 2010, Newport 2000).

Entrenched Barriers to Employment

In Japan, women make up approximately 42 percent of the paid labor force. On average, women in Japan earn 53 cents for every dollar men earn (World Economic Forum 2010). Although women account for 42 percent of Japan's labor force, they compose just 9 percent of those occupying senior leadership positions. Japanese women hold 11 percent of all national-level elected government positions, whereas American women hold 17 percent of such positions and 43 percent of all senior-level leadership positions (World Economic Forum 2010). One Japanese government report suggests that "Japan is still a developing country in the sense of gender equality" (Bando 2003), as evidence by the World Economic Forum (2010), which ranked Japan 94th out of its 134 member countries in its ability to empower women; it ranked the United States 19th.

For the most part, Japanese women are expected to quit working when they marry or have children. The latest survey data shows that 73.5 percent of women are employed one year before their children's birth; 6 months after childbirth, 67 percent of women have left their place of employment (Japan Ministry of Internal Affairs and Communication 2008). When mothers do work, they tend to accept low-paying and insecure employment in exchange for the flexibility needed to meet household and caregiving responsibilities. Although this situation is beginning to change, many corporations still allow women only one of two choices: devote their lives to the company or quit upon getting married and having children (Boling 1998).

Sociologist Kaku Sechiyama argues that the key to establishing a work environment that supports married women, mothers, and women who plan to marry and have children is to create a system that imposes housework, child-rearing, and elder care duties on men. Then, "employers know that there will be a certain disadvantage regardless of whether they hire men or women" (Takahara 2000). See The Sociological Imagination: "Going Back to Japan after Living in the United States" on pages 322–323.

low-technology tribal societies Hunting-and-gathering societies with technologies that do not permit the creation of surplus wealth.

Key Forces Changing Family Structures

CORE CONCEPT 5 **Over the past 100 years, fundamental shifts in the economy, a decline in parental authority, the changing status of children, and dramatic increases in life expectancy have changed the family structure.**

Fundamental Shifts in the Economy

Sociologist Randall Collins (1971) offers a theory of sexual stratification to explain the changing relations between men and women, and by extension changes in family life. Collins's theory is based on three assumptions. First, people use their economic, political, physical, and other resources to dominate others. Second, any change in the distribution of resources across a society alters the structure of domination. Third, ideology is used to support and justify one group's domination of another.

In the case of males and females, males tend to be physically stronger than females. Collins argues that because of this physical difference, the *potential* for male domination exists in every encounter between males and females. He maintains that the ideology of sexual property, the "relatively permanent claim to exclusive sexual rights over a particular person" (1971, p. 7), lies at the heart of sexual stratification. Collins points out that when women are viewed and treated as men's sexual property, they are by definition considered less equal.

According to Collins, the extent to which women are viewed as sexual property and subordinate to men has historically depended—and still depends—on two important interdependent factors: women's access to agents of violence control (such as the police) and their position relative to men in the economy. Based on these factors, Collins identifies four historical economic arrangements that shape relationships between men and women: (1) low-technology tribal societies, (2) fortified households, (3) private households, and (4) advanced market economies.

Low-technology tribal societies include hunting-and-gathering societies with technologies that do not permit the creation of surplus wealth. In such societies, the emphasis is on collective welfare so all members must work to ensure the group's survival. Evidence suggests that women in hunting-and-gathering societies perform more menial tasks and work longer hours than men do. Men hunt large animals, for example, while women gather most of the food and hunt smaller animals. The women might perform routine agricultural work (weeding, transplanting, and gathering crops). Women also do routine fishing or hunting for small prey (Cote 1997).

Because almost no surplus wealth exists, marriage does little to increase a family's wealth or political power. Consequently, daughters are not treated as "property" to be bargained away. Thus, women in low-technology tribal societies have more "freedom of self-determination, more social value, and higher-status economic roles" (Cote 1997, p. 8).

Fortified households are preindustrial arrangements characterized by no police force, militia, national guard, or other protective bodies. Instead, the household acts as an armed unit, and the head of the household acts as the commander. Fortified households "may vary considerably in size, wealth, and power, from the court of a king or great lord . . . down to households of minor artisans and peasants" (Collins 1971, p. 11). All fortified households, however, share one characteristic: the presence of slaves or servants. In the fortified household, "the honored male is he who is dominant over others, who protects and controls his own property, and who can conquer others' property" (p. 12). Men treat women as sexual property in every sense: Daughters are bargaining chips for establishing economic and political alliances with other households; males have sexual access to female slaves and servants; and women (especially in poorer households) bear many children, who eventually become an important source of labor. Under this system, women's power depends on their relationship to the dominant men.

Private households emerge in conjunction with a market economy and the rise of government-controlled police and military forces that alleviate the need for citizens to take the law into their own hands. Under this household arrangement, men monopolize the most important economic and political positions. Although men are considered heads of household who control the property, they assume a new role as breadwinner. Women remain responsible for housekeeping and child rearing. Until 1848 in the United States, for example, a married woman's legal position was such that any wages she earned and any property she had acquired before or after her marriage belonged to her husband. In the event of divorce, husbands were awarded custody of children. Married women could not sign business contracts, sue, or be sued. Husbands, in turn, were responsible for any debts that their wives assumed (PBS 2000). Similarly, in Japan until the end of World War II, women lacked property rights under the *ie* system.

The decline of the fortified households, the separation of the workplace from the home, smaller family size, and the rise of a police force (an impersonal body to which women could potentially appeal for protection) gave rise to the notion of romantic love as a key ingredient in marriage. In the marriage market associated with private households, men offer women economic security, because they dominate the important, high-paying positions. Women offer men companionship and emotional support and strive to be attractive—that is, to achieve the ideal version of femininity, which might include possessing an 18-inch waist. At the same time, women try to act as sexually inaccessible as possible, because they offer sexual access to men in exchange for economic security.

Advanced market economies offer widespread employment opportunities for women. Although women remain far from being men's economic equals, some can enter into relationships with men by offering more than an attractive appearance; they can provide an income and other personal achievements. Because they have more to offer, these women can make demands on men to be sensitive and physically attractive, to meet the standards of masculinity, and to help with reproductive work. In the United States today, about one-fourth (22 percent) of all married women in dual-earner households where both partners work full-time earn more money than their male partner (Fry and Cohn 2010). Moreover, young women in Japan and the United States are the female group whose average income comes closest to equaling that of their male counterparts. This situation may explain why increasing commercial attention has been given in the past decade to women who are evaluating men's appearances—as evidenced by advertisements related to guy watching, bodybuilding, hairstyles, and male skin and cosmetic products.

Decline in Parental Authority

Around the beginning of the twentieth century, children still learned from their parents and other relatives the skills needed to make a living. As the pace of industrialization increased, jobs moved away from the home and into factories and office buildings. Parents no longer trained their children, because the skills they possessed were becoming obsolete.

Children came to expect that they would not make their living in the same way their parents did. As the economic focus shifted from agriculture to manufacturing, the opportunities for parents and children to work together disappeared and, as a result, parents and their children moved in different social spheres. Education, work, social, and leisure activities became largely age-segregated experiences, to the point that intergenerational activities needed to be planned.

Gradually values and norms developed that supported privacy and intergenerational independence (for example, the ideas that elders should not interfere in the lives of their adult children and that a healthy living arrangement is one in which parents and children reside in separate households). Popular opinion pushed governments to establish social security and health insurance programs supporting the elderly. These policies further reinforced what Ogawa and Retherford (1997) labeled as "intimacy at a distance."

fortified households Preindustrial arrangements characterized by no police force, militia, national guard, or other peacekeeping organization. Instead, the household acts as an armed unit, and the head of the household acts as its military commander.

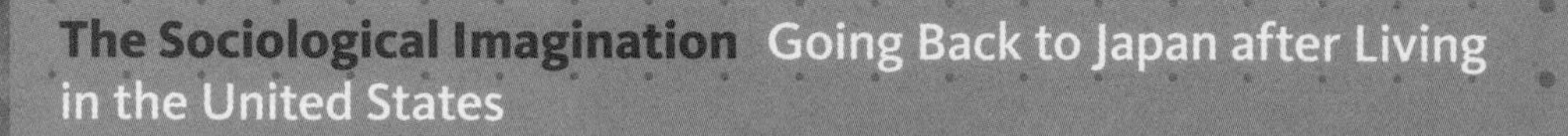

The Sociological Imagination Going Back to Japan after Living in the United States

Perhaps the best way to determine the ways the society in which one lives shapes biography is to live in two societies and compare/contrast the corresponding opportunities and constraints. Noriko Ikarashi moved from Japan to the United States with her husband and children and stayed for four years and then returned to home. In the essay that follows, she reflects on that experience and how living in each place shapes her life:

In 2000, my children and I moved to the United States with my husband. Six months later, one of my friends asked "Why don't you go to Northern Kentucky University to study?" I did not want to miss this chance, because at my age I could never consider being a college student when I returned to Japan. So in the fall of 2000, my life as a college student began. I took an Introduction to Anthropology course, and one of my first homework assignments was to define who I am. I wrote: "I am Japanese. I am a wife. I am a mother. I am a woman. I am 35. I am a student at NKU." Many American students listed personal characteristics: "I am cheerful," "I am optimistic," and "I am tall." However, I did not think to add such characteristics to my list. Why? "Because I am Japanese." The Japanese tend to identify themselves in terms of a social context rather than by personal characteristics. In other words, one's role in relation to others is more important than individual, personal, and physical characteristics. Now, a year is left until my family returns to Japan, and my friends ask me, "Do you want to go back to Japan?" My answer is, "Well, no I don't," because many social obligations and social pressures that I do not feel in the United States await me there.

First of all, "I am the wife" of the oldest son in the Ikarashi family. In Japan, that means my husband and I have to take care of his parents. To meet this obligation, we started to live with them a year before coming to the United States. They expect economic, mental, and physical support from us, especially when they get really old. When I return to Japan, I will have to live with my parents-in-law. In some ways, living with extended family is good, especially for my children. The presence of grandparents at home is beneficial, because grandparents are usually gentle and loving with grandchildren, while it is difficult for parents to be nice and gentle to them all the time. Grandparents and grandchildren play, talk, care for, and influence each other. My parents-in-law are helpful to me, too, because they provide some help with child care and housework. However, the biggest concern revolves around the time my parents-in-law get very old and become disabled. In Japan, nursing homes are not common like in the United States. So I, being the oldest son's wife, have to or am expected to take care of his parents. Deep down, I would rather take care of my own parents, not my in-laws, but that is a social obligation that I am expected to fulfill. If I did not, I would feel very guilty and be accused of being selfish and dishonest.

Norikio Ikarashi, Courtesy of Joan Ferrante

"I am a mother." In most Japanese families, the mother is almost exclusively responsible for child care. I have heard that women in younger generations tend to share this task with their husbands, but still the Japanese men are not equal partners with their wives. Ideally, mothers should take close care of their children at least until they are 3 or 4 years old. If a mother asks somebody to take care of the child from a very young age, and the child's behavior is terribly bad, the mother is often criticized for not taking care of the child by herself.

At the same time, it is difficult to get a husband's help with child care because of men's work schedules. For example, in Japan, we rarely see fathers at parent–teacher conferences. I have never seen men attend a school field trip. While in the United States, my husband, Triesto, tried to come to our children's activities like many American fathers do, although he did not come often. In Japan, driving back and forth for after-school activities, including juku, a private supplemental school, is primarily the mother's work. In addition to these domestic obligations, the mental pressure in everyday life is enormous for Japanese mothers, even though more fathers come to pick up their children from after school activities and come to more school events that in the past.

Since the Japanese value uniformity, to be too proud of one's own children is a taboo. In reality, mothers are proud of their children, but they avoid expressing it. If someone praises their child—"Your child got 100 percent on the last exam. He is very smart, isn't he?"—the ideal response would be "No, he is not so smart. He was just lucky on the test." Even though you think your child is smart, you should not say it. Although everyone wants to be better than the others, being looked at as such is not helpful in Japan. Being proud of something and expressing that pride to others leads to negative consequences. More often than not, such a person has difficulty maintaining good relationships with others.

Therefore, returning to Japan with children who are used to self-expression in the United States is a source of anxiety for me. The Japanese maintain their relationships with others by being the "same as others." My 11-year-old daughter, Anna, told me after visiting Japan, "It was tiring living in Japan because I had to think about how my friends think about my words and actions." Anna explained, "When in Japan I just mentioned to a girl 'You have the best outfit on today.'" However, the girl thought Anna was making fun of her. The word "best" suggests she stood out from the others. My daughter's words hurt the girl's feelings because most Japanese do not value standing out among their friends. Then, the girl told her friends what Anna said, so all of her friends glared at Anna. During socialization, the Japanese learn empathy, so even children try to read how others feel. Anna should have anticipated how the girl would feel before she talked to her. Since the Japanese try to be the same as others, mothers tend to have their children do the same thing as other children do. If her child's friends take English lessons after school, the mother believes that her child should do so as well.

I am 37 now. From the Japanese point of view, I am already too old to have a good job. In the Japanese workplace, age as well as gender discrimination are very common. Therefore, I am in a double-bind situation in trying to get a job when I go back. If you look at job advertisements, they clearly mention an age limit. Usually, well-paying jobs for women limit the age to 35 or younger. For women older than 35, the job market is very cold; they are considered as *oba-san*, misses or lady. The word has a negative connotation, which adds to the image of "old lady." At 37, I am already in the category of "old woman" in Japan.

There is a tendency in the Japanese job market to value young women. Women who give up good careers for a time because of marriage or pregnancy usually find it hard to reenter the workplace unless they have a specialized skill such as nursing. This is one reason that many Japanese women marry at an older age than their American counterparts and that the birth rate is low. Being a wife and mother is still regarded as an obstacle to a successful career.

Moreover, government policy limits married women's job opportunities. Generally speaking, if a woman earns less than about $10,000 annually, she does not have to pay income tax and can remain as a husband's dependent. In addition, husbands can get a family allowance and dependents' tax credit. If the woman earns $15,000 or more, she has to pay income tax and pay into the social security pension system, and her husband is not entitled to family benefits.

Consequently, her contribution to total family earning will be less than when she earned $10,000 annually. Therefore, many married women "choose" low-paying part-time jobs. If a woman chooses a full-time job, there is no benefit unless she earns more than $20,000 per year. The Japanese government is working to reform this dependent tax credit now, but the progress is slow.

For women who do not have special skills, and who are also doing domestic work, earning that amount of money is not so easy. Even though I will return to Japan college-educated, I am very anxious about whether I can get a well-paying job given my age and domestic status. To complicate matters, Japanese men tend to dislike well-educated older women. Men regard such women as assertive, a quality not associated with the ideal woman.

"I am a student at NKU." Until I came to the United States, I never thought that I would be a college student. That rarely happens in Japan. Many mothers of my generation are busy bringing up children. I have to save money for my children instead of using it for my education. A 37-year-old married woman who has two children and goes to a university is ridiculous by the Japanese standard, even though some Japanese women might wish to do this. I have almost finished my undergraduate degree, and I want to go to graduate school in Japan. However, going to college, including graduate school, seems simply too difficult for me. I have parents-in-law and children to take care of, and there are many domestic tasks connected with that. Tuition is relatively high. In addition, I have to consider how my female friends, especially neighbors of the same age, see me. If I go to graduate school, they might say, "Wow, that is wonderful," but many of them would really feel uneasy about that. Some of them may think that I am being ridiculous or selfish. Doing something very different from others affects the social relationship that I have with them.

"I am Japanese," so I know I will adapt to the Japanese way again soon. However, I also know that there are many social obstacles in Japan, as I explained. Those obstacles do not necessarily apply to everyone. For instance, right now more than 70 percent of my friends do not live in an extended family. However, many expect to eventually care for parents-in-law.

Epilogue: Noriko returned to Japan at the end of December 2003, with her husband and two children. In 2010, she returned again to the United States with her husband whose employer assigned him to work in the United States. Noriko reflected on how things have changed in Japan since 2003. She believes that Japanese society is moving slowly toward gender equality. However this movement is too slow to catch up with society's needs. Regarding Japanese values, even if government policy changes, Noriko believes that values fundamental to Japanese will not change that much. Noriko put it this way: "The Japanese way has developed over a long period of time to adapt to our environment and unique historical challenges."

Source: Written by Noriko Ikarashi, Class of 2003, Northern Kentucky University, Updated May 2011.

Farm Security Administration - Office of War Information Photograph Collection, Library of Congress Prints and Photographs Division

DoD photo by Petty Officer 2nd Class Susan Cornell, U.S. Navy.

In primarily agriculture-based economies, children represent an important source of free unskilled labor for the family. In market and advanced market economies, the motives for having children change to emphasize intangible, emotional rewards.

Although intergenerational programs do exist in the United States, "a rich array of intergenerational initiatives exists in Japanese schools (public and private), community settings, and institutional facilities" (Kaplan and Thang 1997, p. 302). These initiatives are designed with the goal of increasing interaction between youth 21 years old and younger and those 60 and over (Kaplan et al., 1998, Intergenerational Programs and Aging 2006). Such programs include Rent-a-Family, which enables seniors with limited or unsatisfactory family ties to "rent the services of actors to play the part of children and grandchildren and share family-like experiences." Other programs integrate senior and youth services (for example, children's libraries and playgrounds are located in or near the open spaces of retirement homes).

Intergenerational programs in Japan are structured with the goals of offering seniors meaningful and productive roles, combating ageism, fostering intergenerational understanding, drawing on the talents and energies of youth and elderly to solve problems, and fostering an environment of mutual support and understanding (Kaplan and Thang 1997).

Status of Children

As noted earlier, the technological advances associated with the Industrial Revolution and the shift away from an agriculture-based economy not only changed relationships between adult children and parents, but also changed the status of children from economic assets to liabilities. Mechanization decreased the amount of physical effort and time needed to produce food and other commodities. Consequently, children lost their economic value. In agriculture, children represent an important source of free unskilled labor for the family. This fact may partly explain why the highest fertility rates in the world occur in places like Afghanistan, Somalia, the Democratic Republic of the Congo, and Niger—places where labor-intensive production remains common (see The Sociological Imagination: "The Economic Role of Children in Labor-Intensive Environments").

The shift away from labor-intensive production has stripped children of whatever economic contribution they might have made to the family (Johansson 1987). People in market and advanced market economies who choose to have children bring them into the world to meet intangible needs for love and companionship, as an outlet for nurturing feelings or to enhance some dimension of adult identity.

In the United States, an advanced market economy, children have become expensive to rear. Today, depending on income, American parents spend between $205,960 (average for lowest income) and $475,680 (average for highest income) to house, feed, clothe, transport, and supply medical care to a child until he or she is 18 years old.

Technology Tip: For historical images of child labor, visit the Library of Congress, Prints and Photograph Division at www.loc.gov/pictures/. Use the search term "child labor" to yield thousands of images (many of which can be enlarged for easy viewing). Simply click on the photograph for a larger image.

The Sociological Imagination The Economic Role of Children in Labor-Intensive Environments

Children are often an important source of cheap labor, especially for labor-intensive, nonmechanized industries. The childhood experiences of Chico Mendes, the son of an Amazon rubber tapper, illustrate the economic role children can take in such an environment:

> Childhood for Chico Mendes was mostly heavy work. . . . If all his siblings had lived to adulthood, Chico would have had 17 brothers and sisters. As it was, conditions were so difficult that by the time he was grown, he was the oldest of six children—four brothers and two sisters.
>
> When he was 5, Chico began to collect firewood and haul water. A principal daytime occupation of young children on the seringal [rubber estate] has always been lugging cooking pots full of water from the nearest river. . . . Another chore was pounding freshly harvested rice to remove the hulls. A double-ended wooden club was plunged into a hollowed section of tree trunk filled with rice grains, like an oversize mortar and pestle. Often two children would pound the rice simultaneously, synchronizing their strokes so that one club was rising as the other descended.
>
> By the time he was 9, Chico was following his father into the forest to learn how to tap. . . . Well before dawn, Chico and his family would rise. . . . They would grab the tools of their trade—a shotgun, . . . a machete, and a pouch to collect any useful fruits or herbs found along the trail. They left before dawn, because that was when the latex was said to run most freely. . . . As they reached each tree, the elder Mendes grasped the short wooden handle of his rubber knife in two hands, with a grip somewhat like that of a golfer about to putt. . . . It was important to get the depth [of the cut] just right. . . . A cut that is too deep strikes the cambium [generative tissue of the tree] and imperils the tree; a cut that is too shallow misses the latex producing layer and is thus a waste. . . .
>
> Chico learned how to position a tin cup, or sometimes an empty Brazilian nut pod, just beneath the low point of the fresh cut on a crutch made out of a small brand. . . . The white latex immediately began to dribble down the slash and into the cup. . . . Chico quickly adopted the distinctive, fast stride of the rubber tapper. . . . The pace has evolved from the nature of the tapper's day. The 150 and 200 rubber trees along an estrada [trail] are exasperatingly spread out. A simple, minimal bit of work is required at each tree, but there is often a 100-yard gap between trees. Thus, a tapper's morning circuit can be an 8- to 11-mile hike. And that is just the morning. . . . Then, they would retrace their steps on the same trail, to gather the latex that had flowed from the trees during the morning. Only rarely would they return home before five o'clock. By then they would be carrying several gallons of raw latex in a metal jar or sometimes in a homemade, rubber-coated sack.
>
> The very best rubber is produced when this pure latex is immediately cured over a smoky fire. . . . Chico would ladle the latex onto a wooden rod or paddle suspended over a conical oven. . . . As the layers built up on the rod, the rubber took on the shape of an oversize rugby football. The smoking process would continue into the evening. After a day's labor of fifteen hours or more, only six or eight pounds of rubber were produced.
>
> The tappers often developed chronic lung diseases from exposure to the dense, noxious smoke. Toward December, with the return of the rainy season, the tappers stopped harvesting latex and began collecting Brazil nuts. During the rainy season, the Mendeses often crouched on their haunches around a pile of Brazil nut pods, hacking off the top of each one with a sharp machete blow, then tossing the loose nuts onto a growing pile. . . . When the Mendeses were not harvesting latex or nuts, they tended small fields of corn, beans, and manioc.

Chico Mendes was an important Brazilian grassroots environmentalist and union activist dedicated to preserving the Amazon rain forest and to improving rubber tappers' economic standard of living as compared with that of cattle ranchers and rubber barons. He was murdered in 1988 by Amazon cattle ranchers. Indians and rubber tappers are now working together against those who misuse or otherwise destroy the resources of the forests.

Source: From *The Burning Season* by Andrew Revkin, pp. 69–76.

Annual expenses for child rearing will range from $8,330 to $39,640 (U.S. Department of Agriculture 2010). These costs cover only the basics; when we include extras, such as summer camps, private schools, sports, and music lessons, the costs go even higher. Even if children go to work when they reach their teens, most generally spend their earnings on personal goods and services and do not contribute to paying household expenses.

Of course, for many parents, the cost of raising children does not stop when they reach age 18. About 70 percent of U.S. high school graduates enroll in college. The College Board (2010) estimated that the average annual cost of in-state tuition and fees was $7,020 and $26,273 at a 4-year private school. Room and board ranged from $8,193 at 4-year public colleges and $9,363 at 4-year private colleges. The high cost of raising children may be one reason that, in a recent national survey of 2,200 adults, children were among the least cited contributors to a successful marriage. Faithfulness, a good sexual relationship, household chore sharing, income, good housing, shared religious beliefs, and similar tastes and interests were cited more often than children (St. George 2007).

The cost of raising children in Japan is also high. The Japanese government expanded the subsidies it awards to

Student Activity: Since 1960, the USDA has calculated estimates of annual expenses associated with raising children from birth through age 17 for two-parent and single parent families. The USDA posts a calculator at www.cnpp.usda.gov/calculator to assist in calculating costs. Ask students to make the basic calculation for the number of children they have or plan to have. Perhaps students could interview their parents about the cost of raising them.

TABLE 12.4 Percentage of U.S. Deaths by Age Cohort, 1900, 1950, 2005

In 1900, 1950, and 2005, what percentage of all deaths involved infants under age five? Which age groups accounted for the greatest percentage of all deaths in 2005?

Age	1900	1950	2005
less than 1	20.72	7.15	1.16
1 to 4	9.44	1.25	0.19
5 to 14	4.27	1.01	0.27
15 to 24	6.34	1.95	1.40
25 to 34	8.31	2.92	1.71
35 to 44	8.18	5.30	3.46
45 to 54	8.25	10.20	7.50
55 to 64	9.94	17.50	11.25
65 to 74	11.57	23.61	16.27
75 to 84	9.48	21.06	28.05
85+	3.19	8.02	28.72
All ages	100.00	100.00	100.00

Source: Data from U.S. Centers for Disease Control 2010

parents with children 12 years of age and under and who have annual incomes under $104,000. Qualified parents receive $60 to $120 per month depending on income. The subsidies represent one response to the low birth rate in Japan that is tied, at least in part, to the high financial cost of raising children (Minoru 2010).

Dramatic Increases in Life Expectancy

Since 1900, the average life expectancy at birth has increased by 30 years in the advanced market economies and by 20 years (or more) in developing countries. Table 12.4 shows that, in 1900, death was something people in every age group, especially infants, experienced. In fact, 20 percent of all deaths in that year involved infants. As late as 1950, 20 percent of deaths (one in every five) involved people under age 45. By 2005, that percentage dropped to about 8 percent. Today, death is something we have come to associate primarily with people of older ages as those 55 and older account for 85 percent of all deaths.

In *The Social Consequences of Long Life*, sociologist Holger Stub (1982) describes at least four ways gains in life expectancy altered family relationships in the last century. First, the chance that a child will lose one or both parents before he or she reaches 16 years of age has decreased sharply. In 1900, the chance of such an occurrence was 24 percent; today it is less than 1 percent. At the same time, parents can expect their children to survive infancy and early childhood.

Ray Elfers

In the United States, at the turn of the twentieth century, 30 percent of all deaths involved children under 5 years of age.

Second, the potential length of the average marriage has increased. Given the mortality patterns in 1900, newly married couples could expect their marriage to last 23 years before one partner died (assuming they did not divorce). Today, if they do not divorce, newly married couples can expect to be married for 53 years before one partner dies. This structural change may be one factor underlying the currently high divorce rates. At the turn of the last century, death ended relationships. But today the thought of living decades beyond retirement age in an unsatisfying relationship leads many to divorce (Dychtwald and Flower 1989, p. 213). According to Stub, divorce dissolves today's marriages at the same rate that death did 100 years ago.

Third, people now have more time to choose and get to know a partner, settle on an occupation, attend school, and decide whether they want children. In fact, nearly all of these areas of experience are occurring later in life than they did in past generations. Some sociologists are labeling the years 18 to 35 as "transitional adulthood"—a life stage between childhood and adulthood (Lewin 2003). Moreover, an initial decision made in any one of these areas is not final. The amount of additional living time enables individuals to change partners, careers, or educational and family plans—a luxury not available to their counterparts of a century ago. Stub (1982) argues that the so-called midlife crisis is related to long life, because many people "perceive that there yet may be time to make changes and accordingly plan second careers or other changes in lifestyle" (p. 12).

Finally, the number of people surviving to old age has increased. Thus, an increasing percentage of people in their 50s and 60s have surviving parents and other older relatives (United Nations 2010). The elderly are a heterogeneous group; they differ by gender, age (a difference of 30 years or more may separate people aged 65 from those in their 90s), social class, and health status. Although most elderly are not institutionalized, a major issue even the closest of families face is how to meet the needs of disabled

Student Activity: Direct students to http://calculator.livingto100.com/calculator to answer a series of questions the answers to which help project their life expectancy. Ask them to reflect on the age they are projected to live.

and frail elderly so as not to constrain investments in children or impose too great a psychological, physical, or time burden on caregivers.

Caregiving

CORE CONCEPT 6 The aging of the population has no historical precedent. The family must find ways to adapt to this situation and to balance the caregiving needs of the elderly against others who need care.

Caregivers are those who provide services to people who, because of a disability or physical impairment, cannot do certain activities without assistance (Day 2009). The caregiving that family members, neighbors, and friends provide in a home setting is informal care. Caregiving provided, usually for a fee, by credentialed professionals (whether in the person's home or some other facility) is formal care. Here we focus on the informal dimension of care, because most caregiving in the United States is provided on an informal basis (Day 2009).

Caregiving for an Aging Population

There has always been a very small number of people who lived to age 80 and beyond but there is "there is no historical precedent" for a significant proportion of the population researching that age today (Soldo and Agree 1988). Although most people 65 and over in the United States do not live in nursing homes, one in four do require assistance with daily activities such as bathing, walking, dressing, and eating. An estimated 19 percent of adults (43.5 million) in the United States provide some kind of informal care to a person age 50 or older. Sixty-seven percent of caregivers are women; 33 percent are men. That percentage holds across racial categories, with the exception of Asian American households. Of those Asian Americans who give care, 48 percent are male and 52 percent are female. The typical caregiver is a 50 years old, female, working full-time, and caring for a 77-year-old mother, who lives nearby, for an average of 19 hours per week. The average person who cares for a senior does so for four years (National Alliance for Caregiving 2009).

As we have learned, Japan has a tradition of caring for aging parents. The most recent data shows that 71 percent of those age 85 and older, 56.6 percent of those 80 to 84 years of age, and 43 percent of those 74 to 79 years of age live with their children (Hachiro et al. 2010). Government survey data show that about 30 percent of those 75 and over (10.6 million) need care (Akiko 2009). In Japan, there are 5,900 nursing homes serving 400,000 residents and an estimated 400,000 on a waiting list. The 400,000 people in nursing homes currently represent 7.5 percent of the 10.6 million people age 75 and older

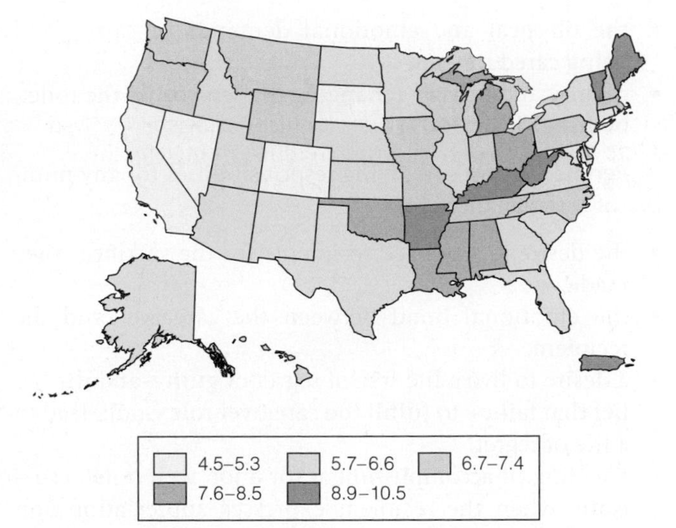

FIGURE 12.5 Percentage of Non-Institutionalized Persons Age 5 to 15 Reporting a Physical, Mental, or Sensory Impairment, 2007
Generally when one thinks of disabled and impaired populations, those age 65 and over come to mind; 14.5 million in that age group are disabled in the United States. But significant numbers of disabled and impaired are age 5 to 15. Which states have the highest percentage of youth age 5 to 15 with an impairment? Which states have the lowest percentages? Notice that in some states as many as 1 in 10 youth ages 5 to 15 has a physical or mental impairment. The total number of people age 5 to 15 with an impairment is 2.8 million.

Sources: U.S. Census Bureau, American Community Survey 2005–2007

who need care. Costs are covered by the nursing care insurance program for those elderly who have been certified as in need of care (Kyodo News 2009).

But there are others beside the elderly who need care. In the United States, for example, an estimated 26.6 million people age 5 to 64 have a physical or mental impairment. This estimate comes from the U.S. Bureau of the Census (2007), which counts those who have serious difficulties (1) hearing and/or seeing (even when wearing glasses); (2) concentrating, remembering, and/or walking or climbing stairs; and (3) dressing, bathing, and doing errands alone, such as shopping and going to a doctor. Figure 12.5 shows just the percentage of 5- to 15-year-old children by state with an impairment.

Caregiving, especially when it is long-term or ongoing, creates strain and tension for both the provider and receiver of care. The relationship between provider and receiver is subject to any number of strains and stresses related to

- the amount of time the caregiver is able to devote and the time those receiving care need or require,
- balancing the demands of caregiving with the caregiver's other commitments, including job and family,

Technology Tip: It is easy to create population pyramids for any country of the world simply by going to Census Bureau, International Division at www.census.gov/population/international/data/idb/informationGateway.php. Create a pyramid for the country with the highest fertility and the lowest fertility in the world. Comparing the two pyramids will help illustrate the dynamics of an aging population.

- the physical and emotional demands of caring and being cared for, and
- dignity and privacy (changing diapers, using the toilet, bathing) (Day 2009).

People take on caregiving responsibilities for any number of reasons, including

- the desire to pay back recipients for the sacrifices they made,
- the emotional bond between the caregiver and the recipient,
- a desire to live a life free of regret or guilt—and the belief that failure to fulfill the caregiver role would lead to a life of regret,
- a feeling of accomplishment for a job well done, especially when the recipient expresses appreciation and satisfaction, and
- personal growth derived from the caregiving experience (Yamamoto and Wallhagen 1997).

To gain insights about caregiving, I routinely ask my students to describe anyone in their family, including themselves, who needs care. The last time I asked my students to write on this topic, 85 students wrote about a total of 109 family members. Three examples follow:

- My mother has severe arthritis. Her bones are deteriorating in her wrist and her ankles. My mother used to be a hairdresser but four years ago she was no longer able to move her hands and stand on her feet. My mom has had two wrist replacements and one ankle operation. She has been on disability for four years and it's time to reapply. My mom takes many pills every morning and every night, about 20 each time. She often uses her wheelchair. She's able to take care of herself but if she pushes herself too much, she needs help and becomes stiff.
- My younger brother is 19 and was born with several problems. He is mentally retarded, has scoliosis and a clubfoot. He could not walk until he was 4; he cannot talk other than making simple sounds and he has had one major surgery to correct his scoliosis (he had a metal rod put into his back) and will have another next year after he graduates high school. . . . He uses a handheld computer to communicate, and he just got his first job at Kroger. Growing up with him I have come to know many disabled people. . . . It's unbelievable how many disabilities exist and their seriousness.
- I have epilepsy. I cannot drive. I cannot consume certain foods that cause migraines, which trigger seizures. When I get a migraine, I have so much pressure on my head my sight blurs and it is hard to see or want to move. . . . It's scary because you don't know when you are going to have one and it's embarrassing when you do. I get sick easily. I would be stuck if it weren't for my friends and family who drive me places.

Impairment and Disability

Sociologists make a distinction between impairment and disability. An **impairment** is a physical or mental condition that interferes with someone's ability to perform an activity that the average person can perform without technical or human assistance. For example, the average person needs no technical or human assistance to run down a street. So a person who is born without legs has an impairment.

A **disability** is something society has imposed on those with certain impairments because of how inventions were designed and social activities organized to exclude them and to accommodate others. In this vein, one might argue that humans invented bicycles to assist those with legs in overcoming barriers to how fast they could travel by foot. The point is that bicycles were designed to remove barriers for only those who can pedal with their legs.

Disability is imposed when the emphasis is placed on the loss of some mental or physical capacity and no consideration is given to ways of reducing barriers to full participation (Barton 1991). Those with impairments often experience what many have called the **tyranny of the normal**—a point of view that assumes those who are impaired with regard to

Robert Bechtel

Clearly, people paralyzed from the waist down or who have no legs cannot pedal a traditionally constructed bike, but they can pedal with their hands and arms. The point is when the guiding assumptions about who will use bikes change, the design changes and the new design can open up opportunities for those once excluded.

impairment A physical or mental condition that interferes with someone's ability to perform an activity that the average person can perform without technical or human assistance.

disability Something society has imposed on those with certain impairments because of how inventions were designed and social activities organized to exclude them and to accommodate others.

tyranny of the normal A point of view that assumes those who are impaired with regard to some activity such as walking, are also impaired in other areas that do not involve walking.

Video Tip: The Online Newshour report "Caregivers Struggle with the Needs of Alzheimer's Patients" considers the financial, physical, and emotional demands of caring for people with Alzheimer's disease. Simply enter the show title in the search engine at www.pbs.org/newshour.

some activity, such as walking, are also impaired in other activities that do not involve walking. A person confined to a wheelchair is often thought incapable of cooking. However, if the stove was designed to accommodate those who sit, and not just stand, cooking would present no problem for the wheelchair-bound person.

Pam Evans (1991), a wheelchair-bound woman, clarifies further this tyranny by outlining common assumptions held about the life of impaired individuals:

- That our lives are a burden to us, barely worth living.
- That we crave to be normal and whole.
- That any able-bodied partner we have is doing us a favor and that we bring nothing to the relationship.
- That if we are particularly gifted, successful, or attractive before the onset of disability our fate is infinitely more tragic than if we were none of these things.
- That our need and right to privacy isn't as important. . . .

Although it would be naive to believe that these kinds of thoughts never occur to those with impairments, these common assumptions capture the indirect and direct messages leveled against individuals with impairments.

Online Poll

Are you or someone in your immediate family a caregiver to someone with an impairment or disability?

○ Yes

○ No

To see how other students responded to these questions, go to **www.cengagebrain.com**.

Katie Englert

Summary of CORE CONCEPTS

In this chapter, we focused on the many factors that affect family structure and composition. We gave special attention to the structure of the family in Japan, a structure that is dramatically shaped by an aging population and low fertility rate. We compared the structure of Japanese and American households over time to gain insights about the many factors that shape family life and relationships.

CORE CONCEPT 1 An amazing variety of family arrangements exists in the world. This variety makes it difficult to define family.

The most basic definition of family is a social institution that binds people together through blood, marriage, law, and/or social norms. Family members are generally expected to care for and support each other. This definition is very general because even though everyone is born into a family, there is no single structure that applies to the amazing variety of family arrangements that exist worldwide.

CORE CONCEPT 2 Family can be defined in terms of the social functions it performs for society.

Some sociologists argue that *family* should be defined in terms of social functions, or its contributions to order and stability in the larger society. Such functions include regulating sexual behavior, replacing the members of society who die, socializing the young, providing care and emotional support, and conferring social status.

CORE CONCEPT 3 Family life is not always harmonious. Furthermore, the family passes on social privilege and social disadvantages to its members, thereby perpetuating the system of social inequality.

Conflict theorists argue that the family perpetuates existing inequalities by passing on social privilege and social disadvantages to its members. Moreover, marriage and family systems are structured to value productive work and devalue reproductive work, and to maintain and foster racial divisions and boundaries.

CORE CONCEPT 4 Family structures are not static; they change in response to larger economic, cultural, historical, and social forces. Sociologists track changes in family structure over time and seek to identify triggers of change.

One of the most important changes affecting the structure of families in the United States relates to the percentage of women working in the paid labor force. Between 1900 and 1980, the percentage rose from less than 20 percent to 60 percent, and the percentage of married women in the labor force rose from 15.4 percent to 53.1 percent. Women's entry (and especially married women's entry) into the paid work force can be connected to at least five factors: (1) the rise and fall of the breadwinner system, (2) declines in total fertility, (3) increased life expectancy, (4) higher divorce rates, and (5) increased employment opportunities for women.

In Japan, declining fertility rates, along with an aging population, are having a major impact on family structures. Japan's fertility has declined to 1.2 births per woman, and the population over age 65 is 22.7 percent. The drop in total fertility is intertwined in a number of historical forces, including the fall of the multigenerational household system, the rise of a breadwinner system, the decline in arranged marriages, the rise of the so-called "parasite single," and increased employment opportunities, especially for single women.

CORE CONCEPT 5 Over the past 100 years, fundamental shifts in the economy, a decline in parental authority, the changing status of children, and dramatic increases in life expectancy have changed the family structure.

Four economic arrangements affect the family and relationships among its members: low-technology tribal societies, fortified households, private households, and advanced market economies. Because of economic forces that accompanied industrialization and the rise of private households and advanced market economies, children no longer learned from their parents and other relatives the skills needed to make a living. Parental authority over adult children lost its economic and legal supports.

The technological advances associated with the Industrial Revolution and the shift from an agriculture-based economy to a manufacturing-based altered the status of children from economic assets to liabilities. Increases in life expectancy have also changed the family in fundamental ways. Parents can expect their children to survive infancy and early childhood, children can expect their parents to live a long life, couples can count on a long marriage, and people have more time to settle on a partner, an occupation, and whether to have children.

CORE CONCEPT 6 The aging of the population has no historical precedent. The family must find ways to adapt to this situation and to balance the caregiving needs of the elderly against others who need care.

Finding ways to care for the elderly population is among the greatest challenges. In both the United States and Japan, caregivers are overwhelmingly female. Although most elderly do not live in nursing homes, many do need care with daily activities, such as bathing, walking, dressing, and eating. There are others who need care besides the elderly, and the family must find ways to balance the needs of its elderly members against others who also need care.

Resources on the Internet

Login to CengageBrain.com to access the resources your instructor requires. For this book, you can access:

Sociology CourseMate

Access an integrated eBook, chapter-specific interactive learning tools, including flash cards, quizzes, videos, and more in your Sociology CourseMate.

CENGAGENOW™

Take a pretest for this chapter and receive a personalized study plan based on your results that will identify the topics you need to review and direct you to online resources to help you master those topics. Then take a posttest to help you determine the concepts you have mastered and what you will need to work on.

CourseReader

CourseReader for Sociology is an online reader providing access to readings, and audio and video selections to accompany your course materials.

Visit **www.cengagebrain.com** to access your account and purchase materials.

Key Terms

aging population 305
disability 328
endogamy 311
exogamy 311
family 306
fortified households 321
ideal 307
impairment 328
life chances 308
low-technology tribal societies 320
productive work 310
reproductive work 310
secure parental employment 310
total fertility rate 305
tyranny of the normal 328

EDUCATION

13 With Emphasis on THE EUROPEAN UNION

This chapter emphasizes formal education or the ways in which societies structure the educational experience. We consider how educational experiences shape successes and failures among advantaged and disadvantaged populations. As one example, European college students experience an advantage over their American counterparts in that taxpayers cover a greater share of the tuition costs. In light of the economic downturn, that advantage is in jeopardy. Here, students in France protest proposed cuts to higher education.

Why Focus On THE EUROPEAN UNION?

The European Union (EU) is an economic and political alliance that began in 1952, with six member countries. Today, that alliance includes 27 member countries. We focus on the European Union in this chapter for several reasons. First, the EU is investing heavily in education and research to boost its international competitiveness and to ensure that Europeans have the skills necessary to thrive in the twenty-first century. The EU is also offering scholarships to attract the world's super-scholars, and has opened its higher education institutions to the rest of the world, thereby challenging the United States' dominance as a host country to international students (European Commission 2011, Lee 2004).

Second, the U.S. Department of Education routinely compares its students and education system with foreign, especially European, counterparts on a host of attributes, including teachers' salaries, reading scores, scientific literacy, per capita spending on education, and access to educational opportunities. This comparative analysis allows an assessment of U.S. strengths and weaknesses relative to the world's wealthier economies.

Online Poll

How much debt do you expect to acquire over the course of your college career?

- No debt
- Under $5,000
- $5,000 to $9,999
- $10,000 to $14,999
- $15,000 to $19,999
- $20,000 to $29,999
- More than $30,000

To see how other students responded to these questions, go to **www.cengagebrain.com.**

Education

CORE CONCEPT 1 In the broadest sense education includes the formal and informal experiences that train, discipline, and shape the mental and physical potentials of the maturing person.

An experience that educates may be as commonplace as reading a sweater label and noticing that the sweater was made in China or as intentional as performing a scientific experiment to learn how genetic makeup can be modified deliberately through the use of viruses. In view of this definition and the wide range of experiences it encompasses, we can say that education begins when people are born and ends when they die.

Sociologists make a distinction between informal and formal education. **Informal education** occurs in a spontaneous, unplanned way. Experiences that educate informally occur naturally; they are not designed by someone to stimulate specific thoughts or to impart specific skills. Informal education takes place when a child puts her hand inside a puppet and then works to perfect the timing

education In the broadest sense, the experiences that train, discipline, and shape the mental and physical potentials of the maturing person.

informal education Education that occurs in a spontaneous, unplanned way.

Formal education occurs when someone designs the educating experience with an outcome in mind, as when city officials display a wrecked van to teach the dangers of drinking and driving.

between the words she speaks for the puppet and the movement of the puppet's mouth.

Formal education is a purposeful, planned effort to impart specific skills or information. Formal education, then, is a systematic process (for example, military boot camp, on-the-job training, or smoking cessation classes) in which someone designs the educating experiences. We tend to think of formal education as an enriching, liberating, or positive experience, but it can be an impoverishing and narrowing experience (such as indoctrination or brainwashing). In any case, formal education is considered a success when those being instructed internalize the skills, thoughts, and information that those designing the experience seek to impart.

This chapter is concerned with a specific kind of formal education: schooling. **Schooling** is a program of formal, systematic instruction that takes place primarily in classrooms but also includes extracurricular activities and out-of-classroom assignments. In its ideal sense, "education must make the child cover in a few years the enormous distance traveled by mankind in many centuries" (Durkheim 1961, p. 862). More realistically, schooling represents the means by which instructors pass on the values, knowledge, and skills that they or others have defined as important for success in the world. What constitutes an ideal education—in terms of learning objectives, material, and instructional techniques—varies according to time and place.

formal education A purposeful, planned effort aimed at imparting specific skills and information.

schooling A program of formal, systematic instruction that takes place primarily in classrooms but also includes extracurricular activities and out-of-classroom assignments.

Social Functions of Education

CORE CONCEPT 2 Schools perform a number of important social functions that, ideally, contribute to the smooth operation of society.

These functions include transmitting skills, facilitating personal growth, contributing basic and applied research, integrating diverse populations, and screening and selecting the most qualified students for what are considered the most socially important careers.

Transmitting Skills Schools exist to teach children the skills they need to adapt to their environment. To ensure that this end is achieved, society reminds teachers "constantly of the ideas, the sentiments that must be impressed" on students. Educators must pass on a sufficient "community of ideas and sentiments without which there is no society." These ideas and sentiments may relate to instilling a love of country, training a skilled labor force, or encouraging civic engagement. Without some agreement, "the whole nation would be divided and would break down into an incoherent multitude of little fragments in conflict with one another" (Durkheim 1968, pp. 79, 81).

Facilitating Personal Growth Education can be a liberating experience that releases students from the blinders imposed by the accident of birth into a particular family, culture, religion, society, and time in history. Education can broaden students' horizons, making them aware of the conditioning influences around them and encouraging them to think independently of authority.

Contributing to Basic and Applied Research Universities employ faculty whose job descriptions require them to do basic and applied research (in addition to teaching and sometimes in lieu of teaching). The following examples of university-based research centers or institutes suggest that universities add to society's knowledge base and influence policy in a variety of fields: the Center for Aging Research at Indiana University, the Artificial Intelligence Center at the University of Georgia, the Institute for the Study of Planet Earth at the University of Arizona, and the Institute for Drug and Alcohol Studies at Virginia Commonwealth University.

Integrating Diverse Populations Schools function to integrate (for example, to Americanize or Europeanize) people of different ethnic, racial, religious, and family backgrounds. In the United States, schools play a significant role in what is known as the melting-pot process. Recall that the "peopling of America is one of the great dramas in all of human history" (Sowell 1981, p. 3). Among other things, it involved the conquest of the native peoples, the annexation of Mexican territory along with many of its inhabitants (who lived in what is now New Mexico, Utah, Nevada, Arizona, California, and parts of Colorado and Texas), and the voluntary and involuntary immigration of millions of people from practically every country in the world. Early American school reformers—primarily those of Protestant and British backgrounds—saw public education as the vehicle for Americanizing a culturally and linguistically diverse population, instilling a sense of national unity and purpose, and training a competent workforce.

The European Union is relying on its schools to facilitate smooth relationships and interactions among 492.4 million people in 27 member states speaking 23 official languages (U.S. Central Intelligence Agency 2011). Among other things, the EU Commission recommends that schools prepare EU residents to be conversationally proficient in at least two languages beyond the mother tongue. (See Figure 13.1).

Screening and Selecting Schools use tests and grades to evaluate students and reward them accordingly by conferring or withholding degrees, assigning students to academic tracks, rejecting or admitting students into programs, and issuing grades. Thus the schools channel students toward different career paths. Ideally, they channel the best skilled into the most desirable and important careers and the least skilled into careers believed to require no special talents.

Solving Social Problems Societies use education-based programs to address a variety of social problems, including parents' absence from the home, racial inequality, drug and alcohol addictions, malnutrition, teenage pregnancy, sexually transmitted diseases, and illiteracy. Although all countries support education-based programs that address social problems, the United States is probably unique in the emphasis it places on education as the *primary* solution to many problems, including childhood obesity, illegal drug use, poverty, hunger, unwanted pregnancy, and so on.

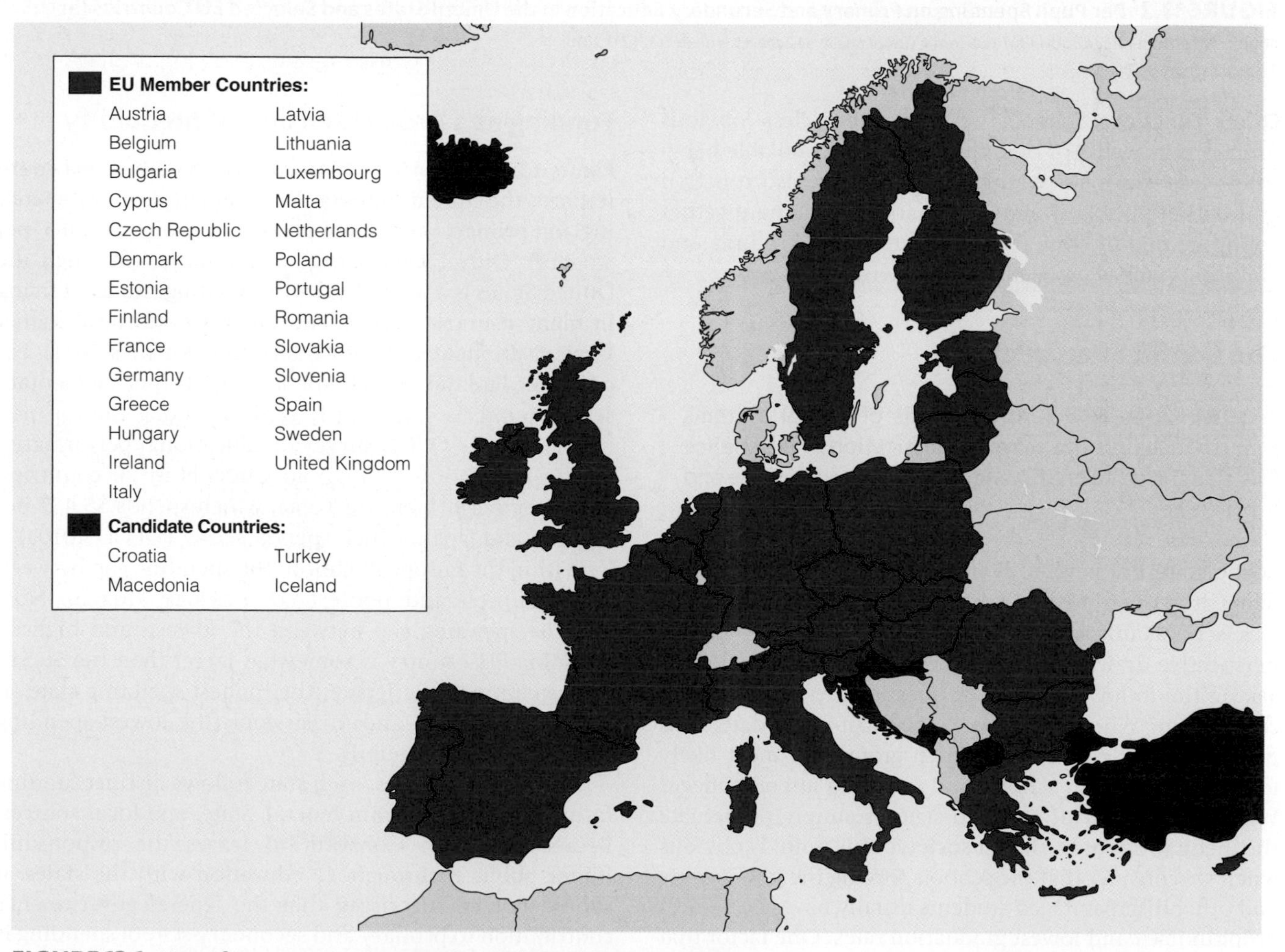

FIGURE 13.1 Map of European Union Member and Candidate Countries
Source: Data from World Factbook

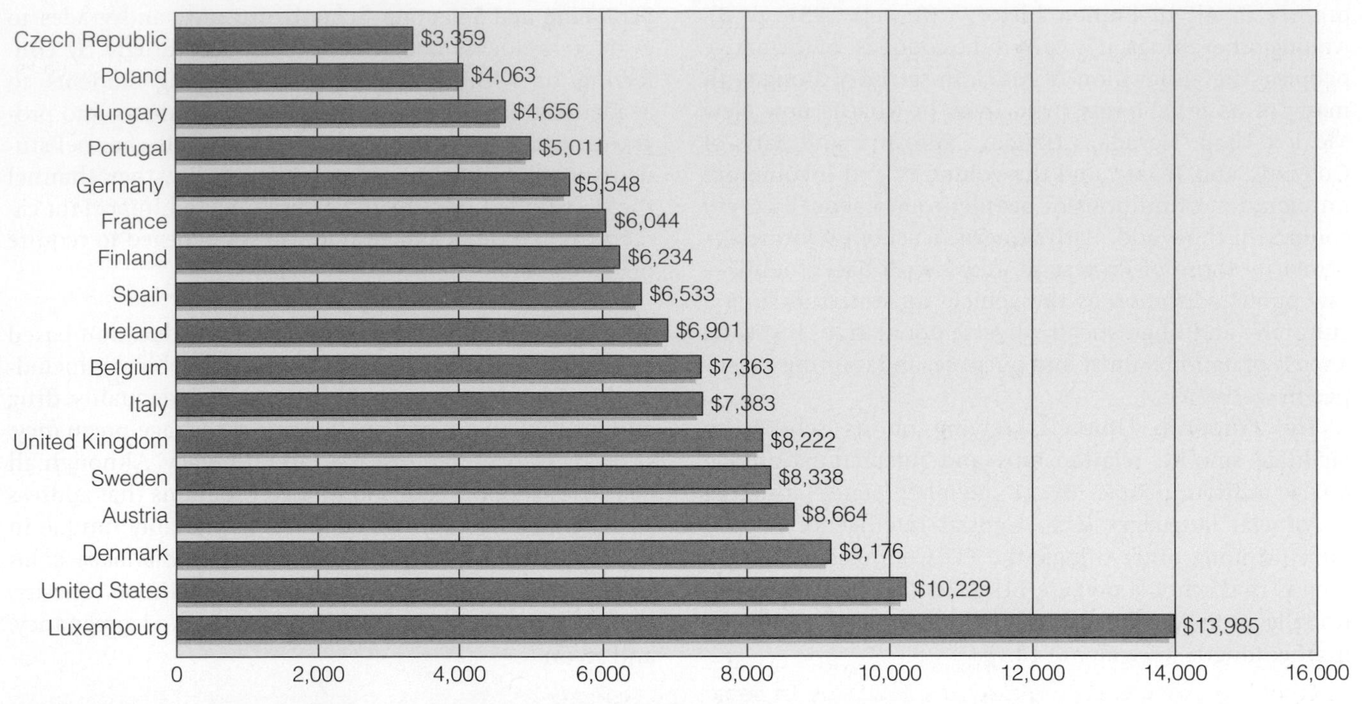

FIGURE 13.2 Per Pupil Spending on Primary and Secondary Education in the United States and Selected EU Countries (in U.S. $)
Source: Data from Organization for Economic Cooperation and Development (OECD) 2010a.

Other Functions Schools perform other, less obvious functions as well. For one, they function as reliable babysitters, especially for young children. They also function as a dating pool and marriage market, bringing together young people of similar and different backgrounds and ambitions whose paths might otherwise never cross.

The Conflict Perspective

CORE CONCEPT 3 Any analysis of school systems must focus on the ways the educational experience is structured to create and perpetuate advantage and privilege.

Schools are not perfect: Not all minds are liberated; students drop out, refuse to attend, or graduate with deficiencies; schools misclassify students; and so on. The conflict perspective draws our attention to issues of inequality by asking the following kinds of questions: Who writes the curriculum? Who has access to the most up-to-date computer or athletic facilities? Which groups are most likely to drop out of high school, and which to attend college? Who studies abroad? How do schools simply perpetuate the inequalities of the larger society? This point is obvious when we consider that the schools serving the low-income and other disadvantaged students usually have the highest dropout rates and lowest graduation rates. One factor that contributes to this inequality is, of course, differences in funding.

Funding as a Broad Measure of Inequality

Figure 13.2 shows that, when compared with its EU counterparts, the United States ranks second in per-pupil spending for primary and secondary education ($13,985 per student). Only Luxembourg spends more. Although the United States is a world leader in spending, students living in many countries that spend far less perform at higher levels (National Center for Education Statistics 2011). For example, Finland, which spends $6,234 per elementary school pupil, is consistently ranked among the top performers on the OECD survey of educational performance that tests 500,000 15-year-old students in 70 countries. Other top performers are Korea, which spends $5,437 per student, and Japan, which spends $7,247 (OECD 2010a).

Within the European Union, the spending gap between the wealthiest and poorest countries is $10,626. Note that the spending gap between the lowest- and highest-spending EU country is somewhat larger than the $9,515 gap separating New Jersey (the highest-spending state, at $16,163 per pupil) and Mississippi (the lowest-spending state, at $6,648 per pupil).

In the United States, each state follows distinct funding formulas that draw from federal, state, and local sources. Because the U.S. Constitution leaves the responsibility for public K through 12 education with the states, it should not be surprising that the federal government's contribution to primary and secondary school spending is 10.8 percent of the total cost. The federal contribution includes funding for the Head Start program, the School

Lunch Program, and the Race to the Top fund. The states contribute 45.6 percent, and 43.6 percent comes from local and other intermediate sources (U.S. Department of Education 2011, National Center for Education Statistics 2011). Such a heavy reliance on state and local revenue is problematic, because less wealthy states and local communities generate less tax revenue than do wealthier ones.

One way to evaluate areas in which U.S. school systems fall short or succeed at educating their students is by comparing those systems with EU education systems, using criteria that sociologists have identified as critical to profiling and evaluating education systems. Most of the data for our comparative analysis comes from the Organization for Economic Cooperation and Development (OECD) education-related reports. We begin this comparative analysis by comparing the percentages of the populations in the United States and selected EU countries that are considered functionally illiterate.

Illiteracy In the most general and basic sense, **illiteracy** is the inability to understand and use a symbol system, whether it is based on sounds, letters, numbers, or some other type of symbol. In the United States (as in all countries), some degree of illiteracy has always existed, but conceptions of what people need to know to be considered literate have varied over time. At one time, Americans were considered literate if they could sign their names and read the Bible. At another time, completing the fourth grade made someone literate. The National Literacy Act of 1991 defines literacy as "an individual's ability to read, write, and speak English and compute and solve problems at levels of proficiency necessary to function on the job and in society, to achieve one's goals, and to develop one's knowledge and potential" (U.S. Department of Education 1993, p. 3).

This point suggests that illiteracy is a product of one's environment. Today, people may be considered functionally illiterate if they cannot use a computer, read a map to find a destination, make change for a customer, read traffic signs, follow instructions to assemble an appliance, fill out a job application, and comprehend the language others are speaking.

Among other things, the OECD (2010a) report focuses on three kinds of literacy: reading, mathematical, and scientific. It seeks to determine how successful school systems are at developing these literacies. For example, in the area of mathematical literacy—defined as "an individual's capacity to identify and understand the role that mathematics plays in the world, to make well-founded judgments, and to use and engage with mathematics in ways that meet the needs of that individual's life as a constructive, concerned, and reflective citizen" (p. 72)—the OECD classifies 28.1 percent of U.S. students as illiterate. In comparison to selected EU countries listed in Table 13.1, the United States has the greatest percentage of 15-years-old students classified as illiterate, followed by Italy.

TABLE 13.1 Percentage of 15-year-olds in the United States and EU Countries Whom the OECD Classified as Mathematically Illiterate

Students who take the OECD math test are classified into one of seven levels: below 1, level 1, level 2, level 3, level 4, level 5, and level 6. Those who are classified as level 1 or below are universally considered illiterate. Individual countries, however, have different criteria for mathematical literacy. To be considered literate in the Netherlands, for example, students must be classified at level 4 or better (de Lange 2006). The percentages in the table show percentages classified as below level 1 or level 1. Which country has the smallest percentage of students classified as illiterate? Which has the largest percentage?

Country	% Illiterate
Finland	4.1
Netherlands	13.0
Denmark	13.6
Hungary	15.0
Germany	15.4
Ireland	15.5
Czech Republic	15.6
Sweden	16.4
Poland	17.0
Belgium	17.0
Spain	19.6
Slovakia	20.0
Austria	20.0
France	21.2
Luxembourg	22.1
Portugal	24.3
Italy	25.3
United States	28.1

Source: Data from OECD 2010.

Foreign Language Illiteracy If we focus on languages, of which there may be as many as 9,000, we can see that the potential number of illiteracies is overwhelming, as people cannot possibly be literate in every language. If a person speaks, writes, and reads in only one language, by

illiteracy The inability to understand and use a symbol system, whether it is based on sounds, letters, numbers, pictographs, or some other type of symbol.

definition he or she is illiterate in as many as 8,999 languages. For most people, such a profound level of illiteracy rarely presents a problem until they find themselves in a setting (such as a war or a business negotiation) that puts them at a disadvantage for not knowing the language others around them are speaking. Both United States and European Union leaders acknowledge the societal benefits that accompany literacy in a language other than the mother tongue. In fact, the European Commission put forth an action plan, calling for every citizen to "have a good command of two foreign languages together with the mother tongue" (Binder 2006). For its part, the U.S. Department of Education (2006) laments that other nations "have an edge in foreign language instruction, a key to improved national security and global understanding."

In European countries, foreign language instruction is compulsory and can start as early as age 5. In the United States, by contrast, 44 percent of high school students study a foreign language (usually for about two years) and only 8 percent of undergraduates take foreign language courses. Study abroad is one way to immerse oneself in a foreign language and culture. Yet, even when Americans study abroad, many of the most popular destinations are English-speaking (International Institute of Education 2010; see No Borders, No Boundaries: "Study Abroad Destinations").

Because of the European Union's greater emphasis on foreign language instruction, 50 percent of people in EU countries indicate that they can speak at least two languages well enough to carry on a conversation. In the United States, however, only 18 percent report an ability to speak a language other than English. It is very likely that the United States is the only country in the world where it is possible to complete high school and college without studying a foreign language. In fact, only ten states require foreign language study as a prerequisite for high school graduation. To exacerbate the situation, upon entering college, most students do not continue on with language studies. When American students do study languages, they are predominantly European languages—most notably Spanish, French, or German—rather than languages named as critical to U.S. national security such as Arabic and Mandarin Chinese, Urdu and Farsi, Pashto and Dari (U.S. Department of Education 2010).

Christopher Brown

This is one of about 500 U.S. students who choose to study abroad in Egypt each year (Lindsey and Labi 2011). Great Britain is the number one choice for U.S. students.

Chris Caldeira

Look at the writing on this sign. If you can only read the top line and not the bottom line, then you are illiterate in the symbol system known as English.

Education critic Daniel Resnick (1990) argues that the absence of serious foreign language instruction contributes to the parochial nature of American schooling. The almost exclusive attention paid to a single language has deprived students of the opportunity to appreciate the connection between language and culture and to see that language is a tool that enables them to think about the world. According to Resnick, the focus on a single language "has cut students off from the pluralism of world culture and denied them a sense of powerfulness in approaching societies very different from their own" (1990, p. 25; see Global Comparisons: "The Legacy of European Colonization on Language Instruction.").

The Availability of College

Only a handful of countries in the world give a significant share of the population the opportunity to attend college. The United States and EU countries represent places in the world where the college-educated constitute

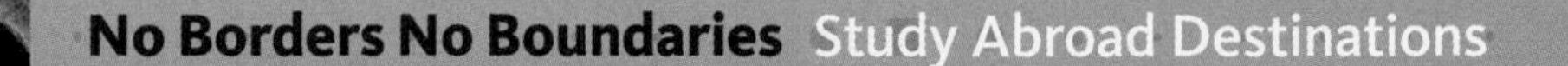

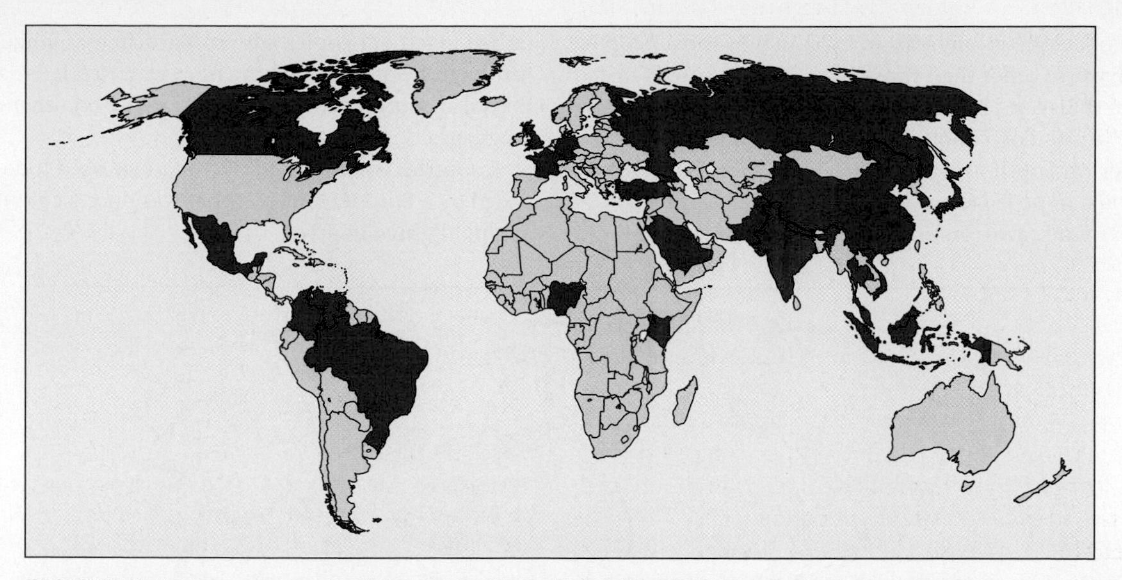

FIGURE 13.3 Top 25 Countries (Highlighted in Red) Sending Students to the United States, 2009–2010 School Year

Over 500,000 international students attend college in the United States. Figure 13.3 shows the top 25 countries sending students to the United States in 2009. China ranked number 1, sending 127,628, followed by India, which sent 104,897, and South Korea, which sent 72,153. Russia, the country ranked 25th, sent 4,827.

Source: Data from International Institute of Education (2010)

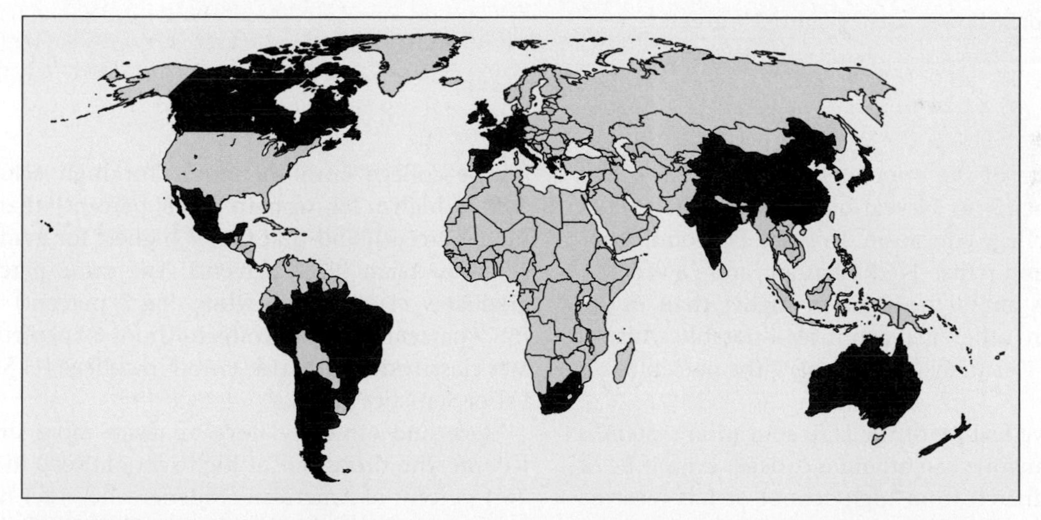

FIGURE 13.4 Top 25 Countries (Highlighted in Blue) to Which the United States Sent Students, 2009–2010 School year

Approximately 260,000 U.S. students studied in a foreign country in 2009. Of the 25 most popular destinations, 11 are EU countries. In fact, 141,953 or 55 percent of American students who study abroad each year go to EU countries. The number one destination was the United Kingdom, with 31,342 students or 12 percent of all students who studied abroad, followed by Italy (27,362) and Spain (24,169). The 25th most popular destination was South Korea (2,062).

Source: Data from International Institute of Education (2010)

Global Comparisons The Legacy of European Colonization on Language Instruction

The legacy of colonization helps to explain why most people around the world other than those born in the United States speak more than one language. Beginning as early as 1492, Europeans learned of, conquered, or colonized much of North America, South America, Asia, and Africa. In doing so, Europeans imposed their languages on the colonized peoples. In many cases, Europeans created countries that pulled together peoples who spoke different languages. Although people learned the new, imposed languages, they also continued to speak their own and other native languages.

Countries where the *official* language used today was imposed by a European nation that was once a colonial power are highlighted in green.

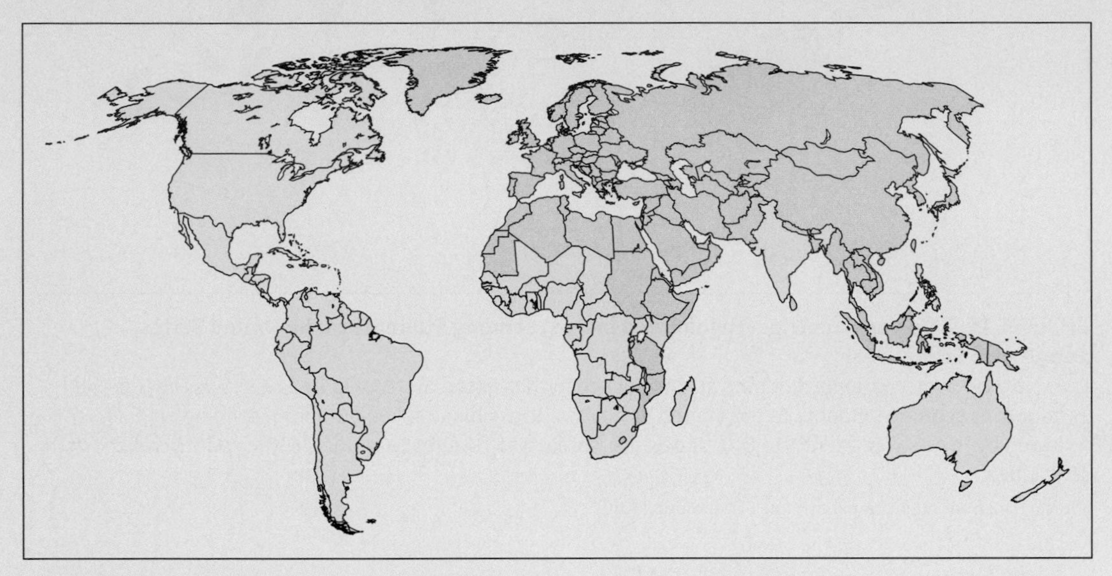

FIGURE 13.5 Countries where the *official* language was imposed by a European nation that was once a colonial power are highlighted in green.

Source: Data from U.S. Central Intelligence Agency (2011)

a significant share of the population. Figure 13.6 shows that 32 percent of 25- to 34-year-olds in the United States have at least a college education. In some EU countries—Denmark, Finland, the Netherlands, and Sweden—the percentage is about the same or higher than in the United States. In other EU countries—notably, Austria (13 percent) and Germany (17 percent)—the percentage is much smaller.

One distinctive feature of the U.S. education system is that, in theory, anyone can attend a college, even if he or she has not graduated from high school or has received a general equivalency diploma (GED). A U.S. Department of Education study found that 400,000 students—2 percent (1 in 50) of all college students—did not have a high school diploma or GED (Arenson 2006). Among those who do graduate from high school, almost 70.1 percent enroll in college the following year (U.S. Bureau of Labor Statistics 2010). The share of *all* 18-year-olds who enroll in college is about 40 percent (U.S. Department of Education 2010).

The college enrollment rate for high school graduates is higher for women (73.8 percent) than for men (66.0 percent), and that rate is highest for graduates classified as Asian (92.2 percent). The same percentages of graduates classified as white (69.2 percent) and black (68.7 percent) go on to college. About 60 percent of graduates classified as Hispanic enroll in college (U.S. Bureau of Labor Statistics 2010).

Race and ethnicity have an even more dramatic effect on who drops out of high school. Keep in mind that 26.1 percent of American students who enter ninth grade in any given year do not graduate from high school four years later. But that dropout rate varies for students classified as Asian (21 percent), white (24 percent), Native American (43 percent), black (45 percent), and Hispanic (47 percent) (U.S. Department of Education 2010).

As another indicator of the relatively easy access to college found in the United States, consider that many U.S. four-year colleges and universities accept students regardless of deficiencies or poor grades in high school coursework, or

FIGURE 13.6 Postsecondary Education Statistics, 2009

The chart shows that 32[1] percent of Americans between the ages of 25 and 34 have the equivalent of a college degree. The table also shows that, in the United States, one-third (31.6 percent) of college costs are subsidized with public expenditures. In some EU countries, 80 percent or more of college costs are subsidized with public expenditures. Over the past five or so years, some European governments have reduced the public (taxpayer) contribution. As one example, in 2003, the UK taxpayer paid for 67.7 percent of the costs of college. That percentage has been reduced to 35.8. Other countries that have reduced public contributions by at least 10 percent since are Austria and Slovak Republic. Recently France has also reduced its contribution, but that reduction is not reflected in this table, which shows 2009 data, the most current data available.

Country	Per student cost of tertiary education (in US$)	% of 25- to 34-year-olds who have obtained the equivalent of at least a college degree	Percentage of public expenditure relative to total cost of postsecondary education
Austria	12,845	13	85.4
Belgium	11,860	23	90.3
Czech Republic	6,826	18	83.8
Denmark	15,890	35	96.5
Finland	12,983	33	95.7
France	10,657	24	84.8
Germany	NA	17	84.7
Ireland	10,540	31	85.4
Italy	5,531	20	69.6
Netherlands	11,246	38	72.4
Portugal	NA	23	70.0
Slovak Republic	4,153	18	76.2
Spain	9,740	26	79.0
Sweden	15,774	32	89.3
United Kingdom	5,352	31	35.8
United States	20,154	32	31.6

[1] Twenty percent of American college students attend four-year institutions where they pay less than $6,000 per year to attend school. 13.2 percent attend four-year institutions where they pay $30,000 or more per year in tuition and fees.

Sources: Data from OECD 2010a, U.S. Department of Education 2010, College Board 2010.

low scores received on the ACT or SAT. In fact, ACT scores suggest that only 25 percent of students taking them are prepared for college-level work (Lewin 2005). Almost 80 percent of colleges and universities offer remedial courses for students who lack the skills needed to do college-level work. An estimated 28 percent of entering freshmen take one or more remedial courses in reading, writing, or mathematics (National Center for Education Statistics 2004).

Although the United States makes it easier for people to enroll in college in spite of academic deficiencies, it places more of the funding burden on the private sector. Compared with its EU counterparts, the United States ranks last in the percentage of postsecondary education costs paid by public funds or taxpayer dollars. In the 16 EU countries for which we have data, with the exception of the UK and Italy, at least 70 percent of postsecondary education costs is paid by public funds. In the United States, that share is 31.6 percent (OECD 2010a). The U.S. system relies more heavily on private sources—such as scholarships, tuition reimbursement from employers, and bank loans—to offset personal costs. As a result, 66 percent of U.S. college students borrow money to pay for college. Upon graduation, the average debt burden is $23,186 (Chalker 2009). Given this high level of private investment, one should not be surprised to find that American students (and their parents) are preoccupied with the return on this investment.

Despite the debt burden, the U.S. way of funding higher education may have some advantages. Claude Allègre, a former French education minister and reformer, argues that the U.S. university system drives American prosperity

Missy Gish

Unlike European counterparts, American students have come to expect more amenities of their universities because they pay more. Most U.S. colleges and universities offer apartment living, gyms, food courts, smart classrooms, and services such as Early Alert, a support program that helps students form an action plan when they encounter obstacles that interfere with college success.

Missy Gish

Imagine that this employee works as a customer service rep at a bank and spends 90 percent of her workday talking to clients, fielding basic questions about their retirement accounts. Her answers follow a script from which she must not deviate. Do you think a college degree is needed for this job?

and that the French government simply does not invest in higher education. It promises a college education to any high school graduate who passes the baccalaureate exam, but the government does not deliver the facilities, which are considered to be run-down, crowded, and uninspiring (Sciolino 2006). Americans, on the other hand, expect more because they are paying more: "comfortable student residences, gyms with professional exercise equipment, better food of all kinds, more counselors, . . . more high-tech classrooms and campuses that are spectacularly handsome" (Chace 2006).

Credential Society

Sociologist Randall Collins (1961) is associated with the classic statement outlining the credential society. Collins points out that it is difficult to assess the role education plays in occupational success because there have been few, if any, systematic studies of how much of a particular job's skills are learned on the job, through job training, or acquired through something learned in school. In addition, it is the rare study that examines "what is actually learned in school and how long it is retained" (p. 39). In spite of the untested role education plays in job success, Collins points to the steady increase in educational requirements for employment throughout the last century that has created what he calls a **credential society.**

credential society A situation in which employers use educational credentials as screening devices for sorting through a pool of largely anonymous applicants.

> CORE CONCEPT 4 **The credential society is a situation in which employers use educational credentials as screening devices for sorting through a pool of largely anonymous applicants.**

Employers have come to view applicants with college degrees as having demonstrated responsibility, consistency, and presumably, basic skills. In addition, employers often require a degree for promotion and advancement, even among those who have an excellent work record and have demonstrated a high level of competence. Likewise, employers use a high school diploma as a screening device for hiring low- and mid-level employees who are viewed (relative to high school dropouts) as people "who have acquired a general respect" for cultural values and styles (Collins 1961, p. 36).

Collins asked what historical factors contributed to the emergence of a credential society in the United States. This is what he discovered:

1. The emergence *cannot* be traced to technological advancements associated with full-scale industrialization because the vast majority of jobs created as a result of industrialization do not require advanced knowledge beyond that of an eighth-grade education.
2. The emergence *can* be traced to a long-standing association between high economic status and advanced degrees. Collins argues that, beginning with the colonial era, the high visibility of a relatively small group of educated elite in high-status positions fueled public

demand in the United States that educational opportunities be available "on a large scale" (p. 37).

3. The emergence of the credential society *can* also be traced to the fact that the United States has always left decisions about what to teach to state and local communities. In addition, the country maintains a separation between church and state (no national church). These two characteristics set the stage for various religious groups to establish their own schools and a very large number of them. Collins argues that it was this large number of schools and colleges in the United States that helps explain, in part, the emergence of the credential society. More specifically, religious rivalry helped produce the Catholic and Lutheran school systems and even the public school system. Collins maintains that white Anglo-Saxon Protestant (WASP) elites founded the public school system in response to large-scale Catholic immigration from Europe. Of course, once the system of public mass education was established, the elite founded private schools for their children as a "means of maintaining cohesion of the elite culture itself" (p. 38). These rivalries set the stage for religious and elite groups to establish universities as well. As a result, Collins believes the opportunities for education at all levels expanded faster in the United States than anywhere else in the world, so that today there are an estimated 4,301 colleges in the United States (National Center for Education Statistics 2008).

Collins argues that it was this large number of schools and colleges in the United States that helped explain the emergence of the credential society. The employer's demand for credentials in turn has fueled and perpetuated a widely held belief that a person must go to college to be successful. The ever-increasing supply of college-educated people, in turn, has made a college degree increasingly a requirement for many jobs. With regard to this demand, surveys show that at least 80 percent of the American public believes that a "young person is best advised to pursue a college education rather than take even a good job out of high school." And 91 percent believe that "employers are less likely to hire people without degrees even though they could do the job" (National Center for Public Policy and Higher Education 2008). In other words, the American public sends the message that a college degree is virtually the only option for obtaining a well-paying job, even though skilled electricians and plumbers, for example, can earn more than many college-educated professionals (Reuters 2006).

The emphasis on a college degree may explain why fewer than 10 percent of American high school students are enrolled in vocational programs and why 60 to 70 percent are enrolled in the college preparatory track. In contrast, 35.6 to 80.7 percent of EU high school students enroll in what those in the United States would call vocational programs (see Figure 13.7). Such programs prepare students for direct entry into a specific occupation (OECD

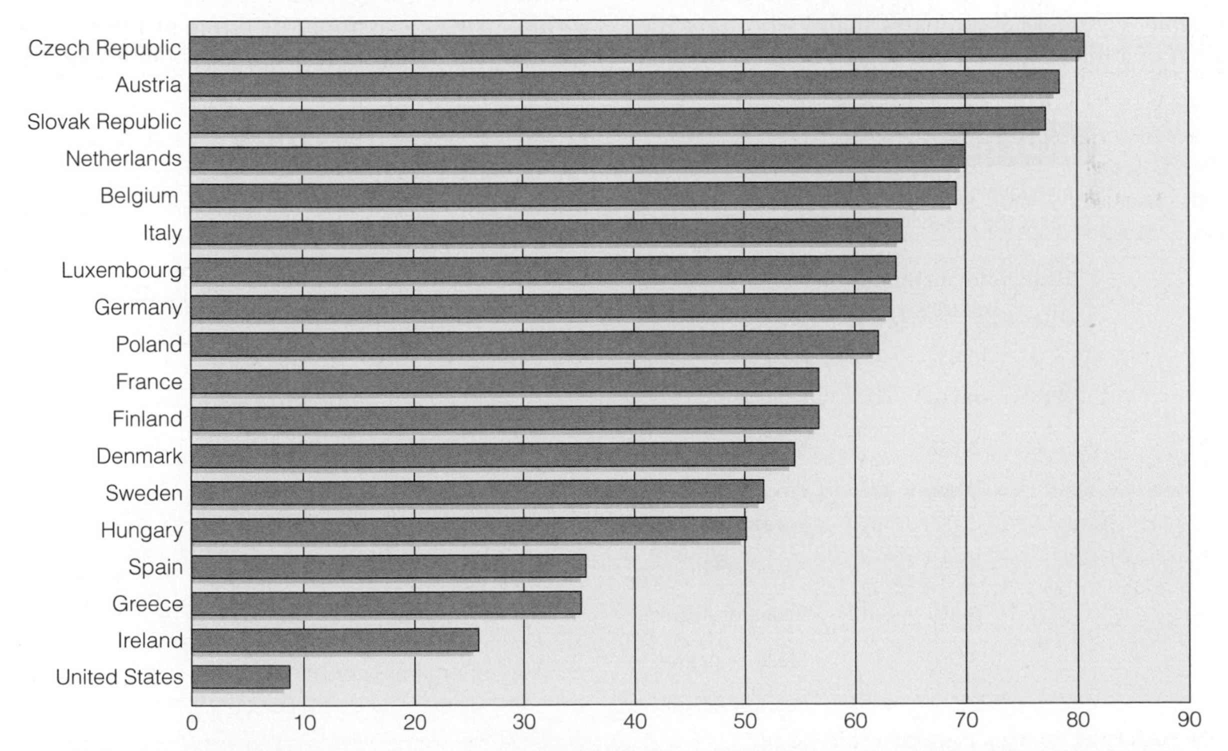

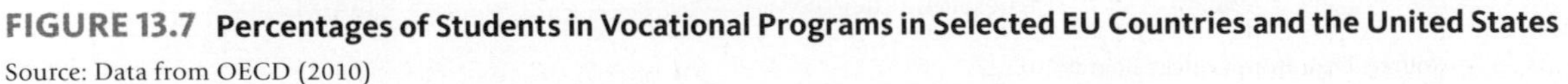
FIGURE 13.7 Percentages of Students in Vocational Programs in Selected EU Countries and the United States

Source: Data from OECD (2010)

2009). In thinking about vocation schooling in the EU, we should not apply our ideas of U.S. vocational education. According to Richard Owen (2000), a Sacramento high school principal who visited ten European countries to learn about their education systems, most vocational programs are equivalent in rigor to U.S. college preparatory programs.

The Promise of Education

Collins has outlined the core elements of credential society. His idea that a college education is not required for many jobs is supported by the 40 percent of college graduates working in the United States who claim that their degree is not needed to do the job they currently hold. Although a college degree is not necessary for many jobs, it is still important to point out that education pays. Table 13.2 shows that income rises and risk of unemployment declines with the level of education obtained.

Sociologist John Reynolds points out that American parents and high school counselors send the message that a college degree is the only option for obtaining a well-paying job, when in fact skilled electricians and plumbers earn more than many college-educated professionals (Reuters 2006). In the United States and elsewhere, the promise that a college education will lead to job opportunities and higher salaries is not always realized on a personal level. To complicate matters, many workers with a high school degree earn more than some college graduates. For example, Figure 13.8 compares males who have the equivalent of a high school degree against those with the equivalent of a 4-year college degree for selected European countries and the United States. Notice that 4 percent of men in Austria with a high school degree earn more than twice the median income compared to 50.3 percent of college educated. In the United States, we see that 11.7 percent of men with a high school degree earn twice the median income. The point is that those without a college degree can be economically successful.

Curriculum

CORE CONCEPT 5 Most, if not all, educational systems sort students into distinct instructional groups according to similarities in past academic performance, performance on standardized tests, or even anticipated performance.

Curriculum encompasses subject content, assessment methods, and activities involved in teaching and learning for a specific course, grade, or degree. When sociologists study a curriculum, they focus on at least two questions: (1) Are students tracked or exposed to different kinds of curricula? (2) As students learn the curriculum, what other lessons do they learn?

Tracking

Under this system, known as tracking or ability grouping, students may be assigned to separate instructional groups within a single classroom or different programs such as college preparatory versus general studies or advanced

TABLE 13.2 Earnings and Unemployment Rate for People 15 and Over, United States

Which levels of education are associated with unemployment rates of 5.2 percent or less? What is the mean income of those with bachelor degrees? With high school, no college?

Unemployment rate in 2009	Level of education completed	Mean (average) earnings in 2009
14.6%	Less than high school diploma	$28,496
9.7%	High school graduate, no college	$40,352
8.6%	Some college, no degree	$46,800
7.0%	Occupational program (trade/ vocational school)	$46,696
6.8%	Associate degree	$48,308
5.2%	Bachelor degree	$71,552
3.9%	Master's degree	$82,628
2.5%	Doctoral degree	$113,308
2.3%	Professional degree	$114,712

Source: Data from College Boards 2011.

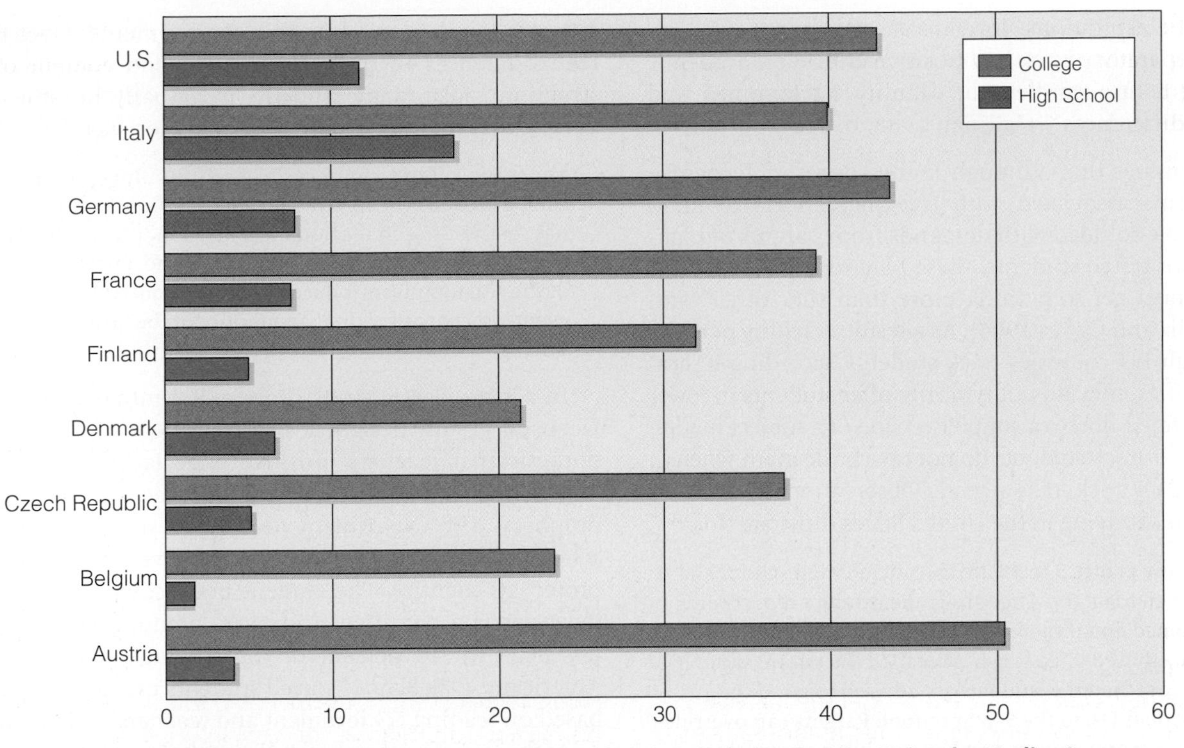

FIGURE 13.8 Percentage of the 25- to 64-Year-Old Male Population Earning Twice the Median Income for Males (College vs. High School Graduates)
This chart shows the percentage of 25- to 64-year-old men who earn salaries at least twice the median income for men. In which country do male high school graduates do best and worst?
Source: Data from OECD (2010b)

placement versus remedial classes. Advocates of tracking offer the following rationales in support of the practice:

- Students learn better when they are grouped with those who learn at the same rate. Slower learners hold back the quickest learners, and slower learners receive the extra time and special attention needed to correct academic deficiencies.
- Slow learners develop more positive attitudes when they do not have to compete with those deemed academically capable.
- Groups of students with similar abilities are easier to teach than groups of students with differing abilities.

There is little evidence to indicate that placing students in remedial or basic courses contributes to their intellectual growth, corrects their academic deficiencies, prepares them for success in higher tracks, or increases their interest in learning. In fact, the special curricula to which advanced-track students are exposed actually helps widen differences between them and students in different tracks (Oakes 1986a, 1986b).

In a now-classic study, sociologist Jeannie Oakes (1985) investigated how tracking affected the academic experiences of 13,719 middle school and high school students in 297 classrooms and 25 schools across the United States. "The schools themselves were different: some were large, some very small; some in the middle of cities; some in nearly uninhabited farm country . . . but the differences in what students experienced each day in these schools stemmed not so much from where they happened to live and which school they happened to attend but rather, from differences within each school" (Oakes 1985, p. 2). Oakes's findings are consistent with the findings of other studies that assess tracking:

Placement: Poor and minority students were placed disproportionately in the lower tracks.

Treatment: The different tracks were not treated as equally valued instructional groups. Clear differences existed in classroom climate and in the quality, content, and quantity of instruction, as reflected in the teachers' attitude, in student–student relationships, and in teacher–student relationships. Low-track students were consistently exposed to inferior instruction—watered-down curricula and endless repetition—and to a more rigid, more emotionally strained classroom climate.

Self-image: Low-track students did not develop positive self-images because they were publicly identified and treated as educational discards, damaged merchandise, or even as unteachable. Among average- and low-track groups, tracking seemed to foster lower self-esteem and promote misbehavior, higher dropout rates, and lower academic aspirations. In contrast, placement in a college preparatory track had positive effects on academic achievement regardless of "family background and ability differences" (Hallinan 1988, p. 260).

Oakes argues that although many educators recognize the problems associated with tracking, efforts to undo tracking have collided with demands from parents of high-achieving or gifted students; these parents insist that their children must get something more than the "other" students (Wells and Oakes 1996). As a result, tracking persists.

Although EU countries track students according to academic abilities, they do not typically offer students in lower tracks a watered-down or simpler version of a subject matter. That is, lower-track students do not take basic math whereas those in higher tracks take algebra. Observations from a German student studying in the United States illustrate this:

> In Germany grades 5 to 13 are considered high school and 1 to 4 are elementary. After 4th grade, student report cards are evaluated and if they are comprised of As and Bs, students are advised to go to what is called the gymnasium. If there are Cs, then the students are advised to go to the 10-year school; if Ds, to the 9-year school. Parents can override that advice everywhere except Bavaria, but a gymnasium headmaster can always override a parent. In my class of 21 students, 13 went to the gymnasium (a very high proportion). After the first year, those who had been advised to go to 9- or 10-year schools left because they were failing. While failing students are not forced to leave they must repeat grades in order to stay. Everyone takes the same math in high school and you have to take math every year; there is no option. There is no difference in math classes within schools.

Self-Fulfilling Prophecies

Tracking can create self-fulfilling prophecies by affecting teachers' expectations of the academic potentials and abilities of students placed in each track. The idea of a self-fulfilling prophecy is a deceptively simple yet powerful one that originated from an insight by William I. and Dorothy Swaine Thomas: If people "define situations as real, they are real in their consequences" (1928, p. 572). A **self-fulfilling prophecy** begins with a false definition of a situation. The false definition is assumed to be accurate, however, and people behave as if it were true. In the end, the misguided behavior produces responses that confirm the false definition (Merton 1957). A self-fulfilling prophecy in education can occur if teachers and administrators assume that some students are "fast," "average," or "slow" learners and consequently expose them to "fast," "average," and "slow" learning environments. Over time, real differences in quantity, quality, and content of instruction cause many students to actually become (and believe that they are) "slow," "average," or "fast."

> The tragic, often vicious, cycle of self-fulfilling prophecies can be broken. The initial definition of the situation which has set the circle in motion must be abandoned. Only when the original assumption is questioned and a new definition of the situation is introduced, does the consequent flow of events [show the original assumption to be false]. (Merton 1957, p. 424)

In a now classic study, Robert Rosenthal and Lenore Jacobson (1968) designed an experiment to test the hypothesis that teachers' positive expectations about students' intellectual growth can become a self-fulfilling prophecy. The experiment took place in an elementary school called Oak School, a name given the school to protect its identity. The student body came mostly from lower-income families and was predominantly white (84 percent); 16 percent of the students were Mexican Americans. Oak School sorted students into ability groups based on reading achievement and teachers' judgments.

At the end of a school year, Rosenthal and Jacobson gave a test, purported to be a predictor of academic "blooming," to the students who were expected to return the next year. Just before classes began in the fall, all full-time teachers were given the names of the white and Hispanic students in "fast," "average," and "slow" groups who had supposedly scored in the top 20 percent. The teachers were told that these students "will show a more significant inflection or spurt in their learning within the next year or less than will the remaining 80 percent of the children" (Rosenthal and Jacobson 1968, p. 66). Teachers were also told not to discuss the scores with the students or the students' parents. Actually, the names given to teachers were

NationalService.org

When you look at these two students, do you think one could be better at math or science than the other? Or might one be better at sports than the other? When teachers approach students with such preconceived notions, they can set into motion the dynamics surrounding the self-fulfilling prophecy.

self-fulfilling prophecy A concept that begins with a false definition of a situation. Despite its falsity, people assume it to be accurate and behave accordingly. The misguided behavior produces responses that confirm the false definition.

chosen randomly; the differences between the children earmarked for intellectual growth and the other children existed only in the teachers' minds. The students were retested after one semester, at the end of the academic year, and after a second academic year.

Overall, intellectual gains, as measured by the difference between successive test scores, were greater for the students who had been identified as "bloomers" than for the students not identified as such. Although "bloomers" benefited in general, some benefited more than others: First- and second-graders, Mexican American children, and children in the middle track showed the largest increases in test scores. The "bloomers" received no special instruction or extra attention from teachers; the only difference between them and the other students was the teacher's belief that the "bloomers" bore watching. Rosenthal and Jacobson speculated that this belief was communicated to "bloomers" in very subtle and complex ways, which they could not readily identify:

> To summarize our speculations, we may say that by what she said, by how and when she said it, by her facial expressions, postures, and perhaps by her touch, the teacher may have communicated to the ["bloomers"] that she expected improved intellectual performance. It is self-evident that further research is needed to narrow down the range of possible mechanisms whereby a teacher's expectations become translated into a pupil's intellectual growth. (p. 180)

Formal and Hidden Curricula

> **CORE CONCEPT 6 Schools and teachers everywhere and at all levels of education teach two curricula simultaneously: a formal one and a hidden one.**

The essential content of the various academic subjects—mathematical formulas, science experiments, key terms, and so on—make up the **formal curriculum**. Students do not learn in a vacuum, however. As teachers deliver key content, they also teach a **hidden curriculum** embedded in the examples used, the test questions, teaching style, assignments, and readings that convey important messages to students unrelated to subject content per se.

To illustrate, consider the different lessons the two math problems that follow convey. One problem asks students to think about a candy corporation that produced 30 million pieces of candy last year but sold only 13 million. What percentage of the candy is sold? The answer is 13/30 or 43 percent. A second problem informs students there are 30 million people living in Afghanistan, 13 million of whom are age 14 and under. What percentage of population is under age 14? The answer is 13/30 or 43 percent. While students calculate percentages, they learn other lessons as well. The candy problem might send the following message: "A company should not produce more candy than it can sell." The Afghanistan problem might cause students to think "I didn't know there were so many young people in Afghanistan affected by war." The point is that math problems are not just about solving the problem. The thoughts math problems generate unrelated to math skills deliver a lesson that is part of the hidden curriculum.

Hidden curriculum is also conveyed in other ways: through the tone of the teacher's voice, attitudes of classmates, the frequency of teacher absences, and specific requests made of students. To illustrate, on the surface, a teacher requesting students go to the blackboard to work through a math problem as classmates watch, seems to offer students the chance to demonstrate math skills. But this learning strategy also teaches students "to fear failure" and "envy success." That is, if they get the problem wrong, a classmate will be asked to identify and correct the mistake; hence, students likely learn that one's success is achieved at the expense of another's failure (Henry 1965). (See The Sociological Imagination: "Hidden Lessons Across Cultures.")

Economic and Cultural Capital

Look at the black-and-white photograph focusing on the hands of an older worker. Imagine that a professor

If a professor asked you to write about this image, would you have difficulty thinking of something to say? Sociologist Pierre Bourdieu used this line of questioning to document the perceptual schemes students bring to the classroom.

formal curriculum The essential content of the various academic subjects—mathematical formulas, science experiments, key terms, and so on.

hidden curriculum Important messages conveyed to students unrelated to subject content per se.

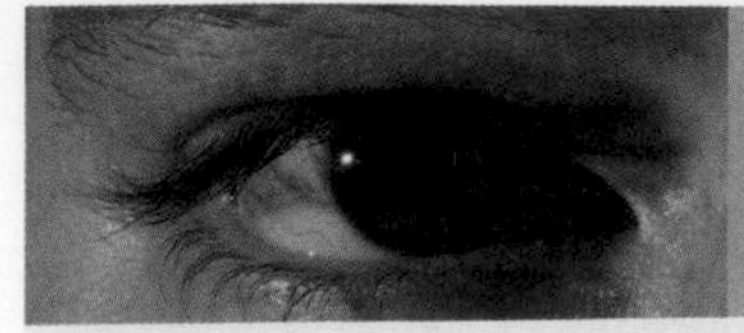

The Sociological Imagination European Students Studying in the United States Comment on American Teachers, Tests, and Study Habits

Three European students attending college in the United States offer insights about the hidden curriculum as it relates to lessons learned about college professors, tests, and study habits. That is, by observing professors—their behavior, tone of voice, body language, interactions with other students—they draw conclusions about the expectations those professors hold. In addition, the number of tests and types of tests convey larger lessons about what type of learning matters and the best ways to study.

College Professors

Germany: American teachers do not seem to ask their students to do as much work as German teachers do. In the United States, the homework is more like busy work such as a scavenger hunt on a website or looking at a catalog to find out what the requirements are for a particular major. These are things that I would do on my own but the students here need to be told to do them.

In Germany, we are taught to be independent and in the United States it is the opposite. In the beginning, it was nice being a college student in the U.S. because I got straight "As" and it helped with my confidence but now I want to be more challenged. In Germany, I was an OK student but in the United States I am a straight-A student. American teachers are very supportive and helpful with keeping students up with the lessons. I feel like I can ask my American teachers anything and they will do whatever they can to help. It's not so much that I would not ask a German teacher something but here I never feel that I ask a stupid question.

Poland: American teachers are more helpful, more approachable, and they seem more equal to students. You would never ask a professor in Poland how they are or call them by their first name. Here you can walk in and talk to a professor about personal things such as what you did over the weekend; that would never happen in Poland. I feel I can ask American teachers for help and I will get it.

Spain: American teachers are more friendly and accessible. They are always asking about personal things like what happened over the weekend. American teachers talk to students like they are kids, not adults. In the United States, professors seem to want to be friends with the students; in Spain, they are just professors, not friends too.

Tests

Germany: In Germany, it was essay only. Here the tests are too easy with multiple choice and true/false. At first it was a good feeling that I was always doing well but now I just want to be more challenged.

Poland: Tests are a different format here. In Poland, they were all essay questions, no multiple choice. We also would have one test at the end of the semester that covered everything. Here we have three or four tests.

Spain: In my entire education in Spain, I have only taken one multiple-choice test. They are not very common. Even essay tests are very easy in the United States. If American students write something even remotely related to the answer, teachers give them some points just for their effort.

Study Habits

Germany: American students are all about memorizing. My roommate memorizes her flash cards the night before the test. At home it is more about understanding the subject, not just a specific date that something happened. We read other books beside the textbook so we can understand the material but American students just study their notes.

Poland: American students spend less time studying than students in Poland. Polish students discuss serious topics for fun. I guess fun is the wrong word. We talk about serious topics because they are serious and need attention. When American students get together to talk, it is more about what was on the headline news or what was going on in class. We don't get into groups and do assignments or have discussions. We are more independent in Poland.

Spain: It's easier in the United States. In Spain, students cannot study two days and expect to do well on a test. . . . In Spain we study almost a month before taking exams and have a week of tests every few months. Even in September when school starts we have a week of exams so we have to study over the summer. In high school, we take ten subjects over the course of a school year and if someone fails two or three exams, he or she has to take the whole year again. American students eat, sleep, and listen to music while they study. I might listen to some music when I study but it would be relaxing music like classical, but not rock.

Sources: Missy Gish, Northern Kentucky University, Class of 2005 (interviewer); Isabell Haage, Class of 2007 (Germany); Anna Nowak, Class of 2005 (Poland); and Cristina Gonzalez, Class of 2004 (Spain).

projected this photograph onto a screen and asked you to comment about it in writing. What would you write? Sociologist Pierre Bourdieu used this line of questioning to document the perceptual schemes that individuals draw upon to think about and react to the world around them. He found that working-class respondents tend to use plain, concrete language to describe the woman's hand (for example, "This man looks like he's got arthritis. His hands are all knotted. I feel sorry seeing that poor old man's hands.") Respondents from more advantaged classes tend use abstract, aesthetic language that transcends the situation of the particular woman pictured: "This photograph is a symbol of toil. It puts me in mind of Flaubert's old servant-woman. . . . It's terrible that work and poverty are so deforming" (Bourdieu 1984). Bourdieu was interested in how these perceptual schemes or points of view come into being. He found that the schemes people draw upon are shaped in large part by their social position. The social position someone occupies depends on the amount of economic and cultural capital upon which they can draw (Appelrouth and Edles 2007).

Economic capital refers to a person's material resources—wealth, land, money. Cultural capital refers to a person's nonmaterial resources, including educational credentials, the kinds of knowledge acquired, social skills, and aesthetic tastes. Both forms of capital are distributed unequally throughout society.

CORE CONCEPT 7 When people locate themselves relative to others, they gain a sense of their place in society, and of what is objectively possible.

According to Bourdieu's theory, high school dropouts come to know and internalize what is objectively possible for someone with their educational credentials. As a result, they are not likely to expect or aspire to a high income. They are also likely to assume that higher incomes are out of reach and to feel that they are just a step away from poverty. Someone with a college or graduate degree, on the other hand, will likely expect to live free of poverty and to earn a relatively high salary. Such assumptions match an objective reality. Figure 13.8 shows that people with college degrees or higher in United States and EU countries have a much better chance of earning twice the median income than those with a high school education.

The **habitus** is the objective reality internalized. That internalized reality becomes the mental filter through which people understand the social world and their place in it. The habitus guides behavior and interpretations of others' actions. Bourdieu believed that the habitus even affects how people physically hold themselves and move about the world (that is, posture, facial expressions, gestures).

The habitus plays a vital role in a process sociologists call **social reproduction**, the perpetuation of unequal relations such that almost everyone, including the disadvantaged, come to view this inequality as normal and legitimate and tend to shrug off or resist calls for change. According to Bourdieu, no institution does more to ensure the reproduction of inequality than education (Appelrouth and Edles 2007). He argues that the system of education is widely misperceived as meritocratic—that grades are awarded according to demonstrated academic abilities and not family connections or class privilege. Upon close scrutiny, however, educational systems actually perpetuate preexisting inequalities. For example, we accept tests as an objective measure of academic achievement. Bourdieu, however, views examinations as one of the most powerfully effective ways of impressing upon students the dominant culture and its values. In fact, tests dominate the educational experience in that students' mental energies are organized around taking them and their grades are largely determined by test scores.

Bourdieu maintains that the purpose of exams cannot just be to measure academic progress. He argues that

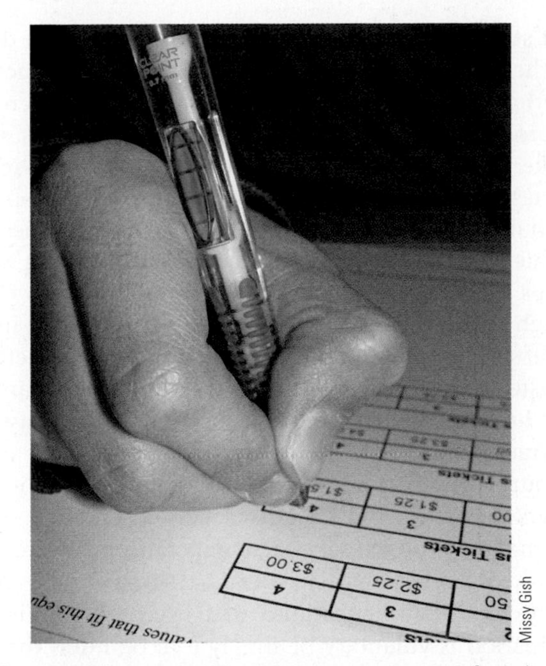
Missy Gish

Bourdieu sees the exam as the "clearest expression of academic values" (1984, p. 142). Tests are treated as a valid measure of knowledge. Thus, test performance is the socially accepted, largely unchallenged way to demonstrate that a specified body of knowledge has been acquired.

habitus Objective reality internalized. That internalized reality becomes the mental filter through which people understand the social world and their place in it.

social reproduction The perpetuation of unequal relations such that almost everyone, including the disadvantaged, come to view this inequality as normal and legitimate and tend to shrug off or resist calls for change.

most students who drop out make the decision to do so, not the school system. For most students, the education experience revolves around studying for tests. Therefore, the prospect of failing tests and studying for tests, and a dislike for the kinds of knowledge one must possess to pass tests, spurs them to "voluntarily" drop out. Bourdieu maintains that we can learn about the inequalities perpetuated by the educational system by identifying which groups are most likely to drop out by declining to return to high school after summer breaks, not enrolling in college after high school, or dropping out of college between semesters. Bourdieu urges us to grasp the significance of what he calls the differential educational mortality rate, illustrated in Figure 13.9.

Bourdieu (1977) argues that the kind of relationships students establish with their teachers, peers, and others who make up the school system depends on the probability that someone from their social background will survive the system. Bourdieu argues that even when this self-elimination is voluntary or simply a recognition that one lacks the academic ability to go on, that act places the student in a devalorized category. In addition, the act of dropping out both reflects and sustains the preexisting hierarchy. The subjective belief that one will not make it or that "school is not for me" results from internalizing the objective chances of success relevant to one's position. Thus, to give a full account of the process by which students are sorted, selected, and eliminated within the educational system, we must consider not only the judgments of educators, which they support with test scores, but also the convictions that disadvantaged individuals hold about themselves.

In evaluating Bourdieu's ideas, it is important to keep in mind that he did not say that no one from a disadvantaged background "survives" the educational system—he did say the probability of surviving is much lower relative to advantaged students. The OECD has collected data on the proportion of high-achieving students (top one-third) who are from disadvantaged backgrounds. That data show that 8.9 percent (Norway) to 15.4 percent (Portugal) of the highest-achieving students (the top one-third) are from backgrounds that are disadvantaged or of high risk for failure. In the United States, the percentage is 13 percent (OECD 2011).

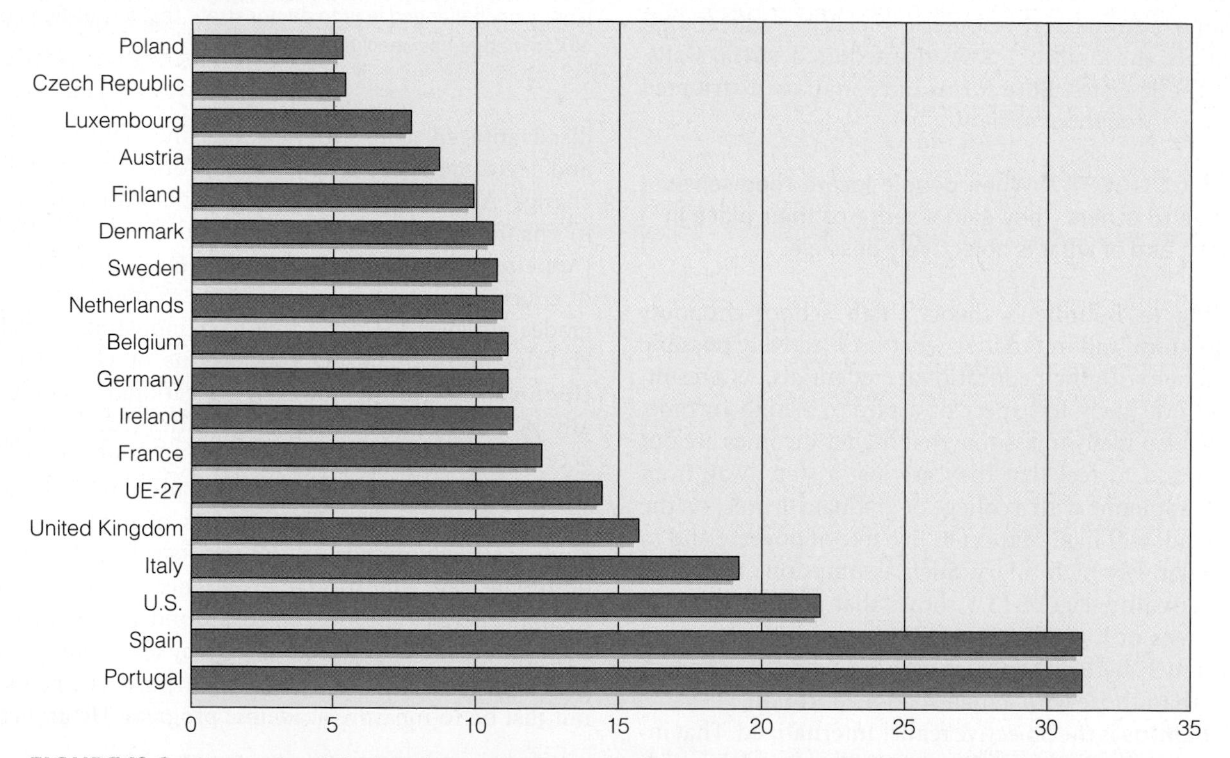

FIGURE 13.9 Percentage of the Population Aged 18–24 with Less Than High School Education and Not in Education or Training (2009)

The graph shows the percentage of 18- to 24-year-olds by selected EU countries with less than a high school education but who are not enrolled in school of any kind or training. As you can see, Portugal and Spain have a very high "mortality" rate of almost one-third whereas Poland and the Czech Republic have rates of less than 6 percent. EU studies show that, as in the United States, those from low-income households, those raised in systems of public care (for example, foster care), those with immigrant backgrounds, and those with physical and mental disabilities and other speech needs have the greatest probabilities of dropping out.

Source: Data from European Commission (2011)

Demands on Schools and Teachers

CORE CONCEPT 8 Schools are a stage on which critical issues and concerns are voiced and addressed.

Every government seems to think its education system is failing in major ways. Singapore, which boasts some of the best math students in the world, believes it needs to improve before others catch up; Japan worries that its exam system puts too much pressure on students; India and China worry that their growing armies of engineers and customer sales forces have not had enough humanities courses (Friedman 2006). The United States is no exception. Throughout U.S. history, it seems as if public education has always been in a state of crisis and under reform. Between 1880 and 1920, for example, the public was concerned about whether schools were producing qualified workers for the growing number of factories and businesses and whether the schools were instilling an American identity in immigrant and ethnically diverse populations. When the United States became involved in major wars—World War I, World War II, the Korean conflict, and the Vietnam War—the public voiced concerns about whether the schools were turning out recruits physically and mentally capable of defending the American way of life.

When the Soviet Union launched its Sputnik satellites in the mid-1950s, Americans were forced to consider the possibility that their public schools were not educating students in mathematics and sciences as well as the Soviet schools were. In the 1960s, civil rights events forced Americans to question whether they were offering children from less advantaged ethnic groups and social classes the knowledge and skills that would allow them to compete economically with children from more advantaged groups.

Beginning in the late 1970s and continuing throughout the 1980s and 1990s, many critics both at home and abroad maintained that the U.S. system of education was inadequate for meeting the challenges of competing in a global economy. The system was deemed so inadequate that this warning was issued: "If an unfriendly foreign power had attempted to impose on America the mediocre education performance that exists today, we might well have viewed it as an act of war" (National Commission on Excellence in Education 1983, p. 5). Many employers claimed that they were unable to find enough workers with the level of reading, writing, mathematical, and critical thinking skills needed to function adequately in the workplace. Reform efforts focused on increasing "seat time," the amount of time students devoted to academic activities, either in school or at home. The rationale came from findings that U.S. students devoted considerably less time to their academic activities than did their foreign counterparts.

In the twenty-first century, the focus has been on leaving no child behind (Bush administration) and on the race to the top (Obama administration), which emphasizes preparing students to succeed in college and to compete in a global economy (U.S. Department of Education 2011). There is also an emphasis on accountability or measuring effectiveness. Given that emphasis, testing is presented as the most cost-effective method of holding students, schools, and parents accountable to a specified standard.

The ongoing nature of the educational "crises" in the United States and elsewhere suggests that schools are a "stage on which a lot of cultural crises get played out" (Lightfoot 1988, p. 3). Inequality, racial segregation, poverty, chronic boredom, family breakdown, unemployment, and illiteracy are "crises" that transcend the school environment. Yet, we confront them whenever we go into the schools (Lightfoot 1988). Consequently, the schools seem to be both a source of and a solution for our problems. Of course, this relentless focus on schools invites a corresponding focus on teachers.

Teachers' jobs are complex; teachers are expected to undo learning disadvantages generated by inequalities in the larger society and to handle an array of discipline problems. An EU report on teacher workload pointed out that "stress seems to be intrinsic to teaching." The report named 45 sources of stress, including stress generated by mandated changes in curriculum, inadequate salaries, increased class size, lack of parental involvement, excessive paperwork, and lack of student motivation, attention, or interest. High stress is connected to absenteeism, turnover, and poor teaching Likewise, U.S. teachers name uncompleted homework assignments, cheating, stealing, drugs and alcohol, truancy, and absenteeism as very serious or fairly serious problems in their school. Compared with their counterparts in Germany, U.S. teachers more often name "uninterested students," "uninterested parents," "low student morale," "tardiness," and "intimidation or verbal abuse of teachers/staff" as problems that limit teaching effectiveness and disrupt the learning environment (Education International and European Trade Union Committee for Education 2007).

Equality of Educational Opportunity

CORE CONCEPT 9 Not all racial and income groups experience educational success or failure at the same rates. Sociologists seek to understand why this is the case.

More than 45 years ago, sociologist James Coleman was the principal investigator behind the congressionally mandated report *Equality of Educational Opportunity*, popularly known as the Coleman Report. Coleman and his colleagues surveyed 570,000 students and 60,000 teachers, principals, and school superintendents in 4,000 schools across the United States. Coleman found that a

Thomas J. Halloran/Library of Congress

Brown v. Board of Education declared unconstitutional state laws that established separate public schools for black and white students on the grounds that such an arrangement denied black children equal access to educational opportunities. This 1955 photograph taken shortly after the decision shows a newly integrated class at Barnard Elementary School in Washington, DC.

Gideon Mendel

These students attend a government-funded faith-based Muslim religious school in London founded by Yusuf Islam (formerly known as Cat Stevens). The school serves 210 students and has a waiting list of 3,500 children.

decade after the 1954 Supreme Court's famous desegregation decision (Brown v. Board of Education), U.S. schools were still largely segregated: 80 percent of white children attended schools that were 90 to 100 percent white, and 65 percent of black students attended schools that were more than 90 percent black. Furthermore, almost all students in the South and the Southwest attended schools that were 100 percent segregated. The Coleman Report also found that white teachers taught black children, but that black teachers did not teach white children. In his study, approximately 60 percent of the teachers who taught black students were black, whereas 97 percent of the teachers who taught white students were white.

Today, almost 50 years after the Coleman Report was published, school-based racial segregation is still a problem, even though the percentage of nonwhite and Hispanic students has increased from 12 to 40 percent. Regardless, 70 percent of blacks attend schools that are 90 percent black and 76 percent of Hispanics or Latinos attend schools that are 90 percent minority. Illinois, Michigan, New York, and California have been identified as the most segregated states; more than 50 percent of their schools are composed of 90 to 100 percent minority students (Celis 1993, Harvard Civil Rights Project 2006, Schemo 2001).

Segregating minority student populations is not unique to the United States. In the European Union, first- and second-generation immigrants—who are likely to be Muslims from Africa, the Middle East, or Asia—"often attend schools with economically, socially, and culturally disadvantaged student populations." In fact, 25 percent of second-generation immigrant students are enrolled in schools in which at least 50 percent of the student body is second-generation (OECD 2006).

Test Scores Coleman's study also looked at test scores and did find sharp differences across racial groups with regard to verbal ability, nonverbal ability, reading comprehension, mathematical achievement, and general knowledge as measured by the standardized tests. The white students scored highest, followed by Asian Americans, Native Americans, Hispanics (Mexican Americans and Puerto Ricans), and African Americans. For the most part, these sharp differences across racial groups still persist more than a half-century later. The latest data show that, as a group, Asian students tend to score highest, followed by whites. Hispanics, blacks, and Native Americans retain their disadvantaged positions (see Table 13.3). As in the United States, not all groups experience educational success or failure at the same rates. One group that is disadvantaged in the EU includes students with first- and second-generation immigrants (see Figure 13.10).

Neighborhood Coleman determined that academic success as measured by test scores was affected by neighborhood. The average minority student was likely to come from an economically and educationally disadvantaged household located in a disadvantaged neighborhood. Thus, significantly fewer of his or her classmates complete high school, maintain high grade point averages (GPAs), enroll in college preparatory curricula, or are optimistic about their future. As in the 1960s, today black and other minority students are significantly more likely than white students to find themselves in school environments characterized by high levels of poverty and low levels of academic achievement. Consider the following:

- Among those schools with a student population that is 0 to 10 percent black/Hispanic, 11.7 percent of the schools serve a student body where 50 percent or more of the student body is classified as poor.

TABLE 13.3 Percentage of U.S. Fourth-, Eighth-, and Twelfth-Grade Students Considered Proficient to Advanced in Writing by Race

What percentage of Asian students in fourth, eighth, and twelfth grade are considered proficient to advanced in writing achievement? What percentage of black students in those same grades is considered proficient to advanced in writing? Notice, however, that for no racial group are a majority of students considered proficient.

Racial Classification	Percentage of 4th Graders	Percentage of 8th Graders	Percentage of 12th Graders
Asian	42%	42%	26%
American Indian	16%	18%	Unknown
Black	15%	13%	9%
Hispanic	18%	17%	13%
White	35%	39%	28%

Source: Data from U.S. Department of Education 2007.

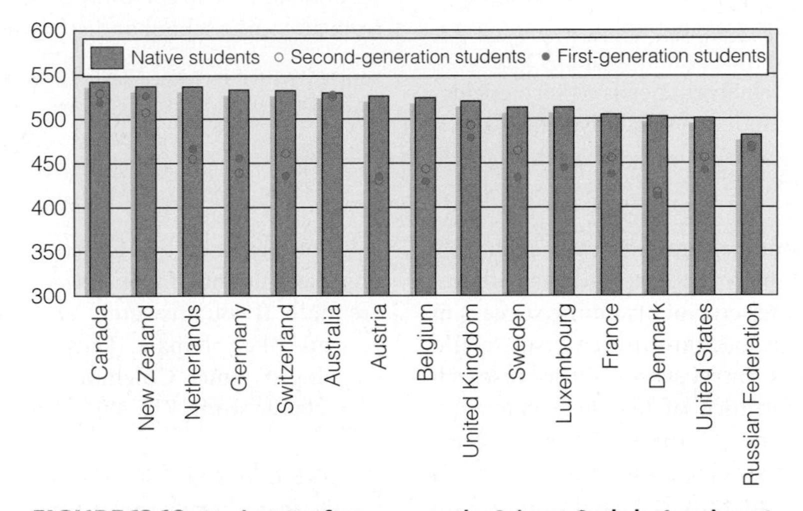

FIGURE 13.10 Student Performance on the Science Scale by Immigrant Status (2006)

As a group, immigrant students in EU countries tend to perform below that of native students. Overall, first-generation migrant children score 58 points lower than native children. To put it another way, first-generation immigrants are about 1.5 years of schooling behind. Notice, however, immigrant students in some countries do better than in other countries.

Source: Data from Organization for Economic Cooperation and Development (OECD) (2010c)

- Among those schools with a student population that is 90 or more percent black/Hispanic, 86 percent of the schools serve a student body where 50 percent or more of the student body is classified as poor (Frankenberg 2006).

Among other things, the Coleman Report also examined the progress of disadvantaged blacks who had participated in school integration programs and found that their test scores were higher than those of their disadvantaged counterparts who did not participate. Clearly, then, the important variable in determining academic success is not race. If race was the factor, test scores would remain unchanged even when black students changed schools. Rather, Coleman attributed this newfound academic success to neighborhood and peer environment, both of which affect the social context in which learning occurs.

The Role of Family Background Coleman maintained that neighborhood and the peer environment are closely intertwined with family background. After all, a family's economic standing determines the housing it can afford and by extension the neighborhood in which it lives (see Working for Change: "Care to Learn"). That

Working for Change Care to Learn

In 2007, when Doug Pitt, younger brother of the famous actor Brad Pitt, learned of the widespread child poverty in his hometown of Springfield, Missouri, he was shocked and ashamed that very little was being done to help these children. Doug contacted his brother Brad and a local businessman Jim Morris and the three worked together to create the Care to Learn Foundation, a nonprofit organization dedicated to changing the lives of low-income schoolchildren in Springfield, Missouri schools. This foundation targets the 36 percent of students who qualify for free or reduced lunch, many of whom live in households that cannot afford clothing, hygiene products, or even food. Brad Pitt and partner Angelina Jolie agreed to match through the Jolie-Pitt Foundation any donations that Care to Learn received. Doug also used his connections to bring this cause to the attention of other celebrities, as well as the general public.

By 2008, they had created the "Brad Pitt-Jim D. Morris Fund" to provide "funds for emergent needs of Springfield students in the areas of health, hunger, and hygiene (care)." Among other things, the men hoped to put an end to students missing school for reasons such as a girl who cannot afford feminine hygiene products or a boy who has only his mother's old jeans to wear. In addition, the three men addressed other small but important needs such as providing toothbrushes to two siblings who were sharing one. They wanted to give hope to a girl who was embarrassed because she had to wear her mother's old high heels to school as they were the only shoes she had that fit her. In 2009, Care to Learn created four more chapters in areas adjacent to Springfield, Missouri. The chapters collaborate to collect donations from all over the country to purchase food, clothing, and hygiene products. The goal is to help the children who are living in poverty change their outlook on life and school and to help solve any problem that is keeping a child from attending school or distracting a child from learning.

Source: Written by Jessica Ezell, Class of 2011, Northern Kentucky University.

does not mean that students are trapped by their family background. Although family background was identified as the most important factor of academic success in the Coleman study, family background by itself could not account for differences in test scores. Other research studies confirm the importance of family background to educational achievement (Hallinan 1988). For example, the International Association for the Evaluation of Educational Achievement (2003) tested students in 22 countries on six subjects. That study found that home environment is the key factor in determining the level of academic achievement, interest in learning, and years of schooling. Still, even through it was the key factor, family background defined in terms of parents' race, income, education, and occupation explained only about 30 percent of the variation in student academic performance. Clearly, factors other than home background must also be involved.

Peer Groups

Think back to your high school days; how would you most like to be remembered by your classmates—as an athlete, as a brilliant student, as a leader in extracurricular activities, as attractive to the opposite sex, or as the most popular student? If you answered "athlete," it is likely you are male. If you answered "attractive to the opposite sex," you are likely female. These are the kinds of questions sociologist James Coleman and colleagues asked in the now-classic study, *The Adolescent Society.*

CORE CONCEPT 10 The adolescent society or subculture is a "small society, one that has most of its important interactions within itself, and maintains only a few threads of connection with the outside adult society" (Coleman, Johnstone, and Jonassohn 1961).

The emergence of an **adolescent society** can be traced to industrialization. Around the turn of the twentieth century—the early decades of late industrialization—fewer than 10 percent of teenagers attended high school in the United States. Young people attended elementary school to learn reading, writing, and arithmetic, but they learned the skills needed to make a living from their parents or neighbors. As the pace of industrialization increased, jobs began to move away from the home and the neighborhood and into factories and office buildings. Parents no longer trained their children, because the skills they knew were becoming obsolete.

Children came to expect that they would not make a living in the same way as their parents. As the economic focus in the United States shifted from predominantly farm and small-town work environments to the factory

adolescent society Or subculture is a "small society, one that has most of its important interactions within itself, and maintains only a few threads of connection with the outside adult society."

Library of Congress

This 1910 photograph shows an Italian American family in which everyone worked as berry pickers. The children were between ages 3 and 11. Imagine the extent to which the family influenced day-to-day activities. How might relationships be different if the children were in school for six or seven hours each day?

and the office, and opportunities for parents and children to work together disappeared, the family became less involved in children's lives. Under this new arrangement, family occasions became events that were consciously arranged to fit everyone's work schedule.

According to Coleman, this shift in training from the family to the school cut adolescents off from the rest of society and forced them to spend most of the day with those of their own age group. Adolescents came "to constitute a small society, one that has most of its important interactions within itself, and maintains only a few threads of connection with the outside adult society" (Coleman, Johnstone, and Jonassohn 1961, p. 3).

Coleman surveyed students from ten high schools in the Midwest to learn about the adolescent status system, a classification system in which participation in some activities results in popularity, respect, acceptance, and praise, and participation in other activities results in isolation, ridicule, exclusion, disdain, and disrespect. He selected schools representative of a wide range of environments: Five schools were in small towns, one in a working-class suburb, one in a well-to-do suburb, and three in cities of varying sizes. Also, one was an all-male Roman Catholic school. Coleman asked students questions similar to the following:

- How would you like to be remembered—as an athlete, as a brilliant student, as a leader in extracurricular activities, or as the most popular student?
- Who is the best athlete? The best student? The most popular? The boy the girls go for most? The girl the boys go for most?
- Which person in the school would you most like to date? To have as a friend? What does it take to get in with the leading crowd in this school?

Based on the answers to these and other questions, Coleman identified a clear pattern common to all ten schools. "Athletics was extremely important for the boys." For girls "social success with boys" accomplished through being a cheerleader or being good-looking was "extremely important for girls" (Coleman 1960, p. 314).

Coleman also found that the peer group had more influence over and exerted more pressure on adolescents than did their teachers. In fact, a significant number of

Lance Cpl. Shelby R. Shields

Lance Cpl. Jared J. Butler

Coleman found that popular boys might be those who were good students, dress well, or had enough money to meet social expenses, but to be *truly* admired he also had to be a good athlete. Girls, on the other hand, gave the highest value to social success with boys, which could be achieved through good looks and/or becoming a cheerleader.

adolescents were influenced more by the peer group than by their parents. Coleman wondered why the adolescent society penalized academic achievement. He maintained that the manner in which students are taught is a factor. When teachers prescribe assignments and students take tests at a teacher's command, there is no room for creativity, only conformity. Students show their discontent by choosing to become involved in things they can call their own: athletics, dating, clothes, cars, and extracurricular activities. This reaction is inevitable, given the passive roles that students play in the classroom: Athletics is one of the major avenues open to adolescents, especially males, in which they are considered important to the school and the community. Others support this effort, identify with the athletes' successes, and console athletes when they fail. Athletic competition between schools generates an internal cohesion among students as no other school-sponsored event can. For this reason, male athletes gain so much status.

Coleman argues that because athletic achievement is so widely admired, everyone with some athletic ability will try to develop it. In contrast, because academic pursuits go unrewarded relative to athletics, those who have the ability to perform well in school may not be motivated to do the hard work of developing their intellectual potential. This reward structure suggests that the United States does not draw into the competition everyone who has academic potential. Coleman's findings should deliver the message that the peer group represents a powerful influence on learning, but they should not leave the impression that the family and school have no influence.

Online Poll

Who were the most popular male students in the high school you attended?

- ○ Athletes
- ○ Band members
- ○ The top students academically
- ○ Other

Who were the most popular female students in the high school you attended?

- ○ Athletes
- ○ Band members
- ○ The top students academically
- ○ Cheerleaders
- ○ Other

To see how other students responded to these questions, go to **www.cengagebrain.com.**

©Age Fotostock

Summary of CORE CONCEPTS

This chapter emphasizes formal education or the ways in which societies structure the educational experience. We considered how educational experiences in the United States and EU shape successes and failures among advantaged and disadvantaged populations.

CORE CONCEPT 1 In the broadest sense, education includes the formal and informal experiences that train, discipline, and shape the mental and physical potentials of the maturing person.

Sociologists make a distinction between formal and informal education. Informal education occurs in a spontaneous, unplanned way and formal education encompasses a purposeful, planned effort aimed at imparting specific skills or information.

CORE CONCEPT 2 Schools perform a number of important social functions that, ideally, contribute to the smooth operation of society.

Schools perform a number of important functions that serve the needs of society and contribute to its smooth operation. These functions include transmitting skills, liberating minds, facilitating personal change and reflection, performing basic and applied research, integrating diverse populations, solving social problems, and screening and selecting the most qualified students for the most socially important careers. Schools perform other, not so obvious functions; they function as reliable babysitters and as dating pools and marriage markets.

CORE CONCEPT 3 Any analysis of school systems must focus on the ways the educational experience is structured to create and perpetuate advantage and privilege.

The conflict perspective inspires this kind of focus. In this regard, conflict theorists examine a wide range of issues, including differences in school funding, functional illiteracy, and access to college.

CORE CONCEPT 4 The credential society is a situation in which employers use educational credentials as screening devices for sorting through a pool of largely anonymous applicants.

The college degree has become a requirement for jobs that arguably do not need it. Employers have come to view applicants with college degrees as having demonstrated responsibility, consistency, and presumably basic skills. In addition, employers often require a degree for promotion and advancement. Likewise, employers use a high school diploma as a screening device for hiring low- and mid-level employees. Although a college degree is not necessary for many jobs, it is still important to point out that income rises and risk of unemployment declines with the level of education obtained.

CORE CONCEPT 5 Most, if not all, educational systems sort students into distinct instructional groups according to similarities in past academic performance, performance on standardized tests, or even anticipated performance.

The practice of storing students into distinct instructional groups is known as tracking or ability grouping. Advocates of tracking argue that students learn better when they are grouped with those who learn at the same rate; slow learners develop more positive attitudes when they do not have to compete with the more academically capable; and groups of students with similar abilities are easier to teach than students of various abilities. Research suggests that tracking has a positive effect on high-track students, a negative effect on low-track students, and no noticeable effects on middle-track or regular track students.

CORE CONCEPT 6 Schools and teachers everywhere and at all levels of education teach two curricula simultaneously: a formal one and a hidden one.

The content of the various academic subjects—mathematical formulas, science experiments, key terms, and so on—make up the formal curriculum. As teachers deliver the content, they also teach a hidden curriculum that conveys lessons unrelated to the subject matter per se. Hidden curriculum is presented through things like the tone of the teacher's voice, attitudes of classmates, the number of students absent, the frequency of teacher absences, and specific requests made of students.

CORE CONCEPT 7 When people locate themselves relative to others, they gain a sense of their place in society, and of what is objectively possible.

Economic and cultural capital are distributed unequally throughout society. When people locate themselves relative to others, they gain a sense of their place in society, and of what is objectively possible. Habitus is objective reality internalized. We can learn about the inequalities perpetuated by the educational system by identifying the differential educational mortality rate, the rate at which various groups are likely to "voluntarily" drop out of school. The kind of relationships students maintain with their teachers, peers, and others who make up the school system depends on the probability that someone from their social background will survive the system.

CORE CONCEPT 8 Schools are a stage on which critical issues and key concerns are voiced and addressed.

Every government seems to think its education system is failing in major ways. The United States is no exception. Throughout U.S. history, it seems as if public education has always been in a state of crisis and under reform. The ongoing nature of the educational "crises" in the United States and elsewhere suggests that schools are a "stage on which a lot of cultural crises get played out" (Lightfoot 1988, p. 3). Inequality, racial segregation, poverty, chronic boredom, family breakdown, unemployment, and illiteracy are "crises" that transcend the school environment. Yet, we confront them whenever we go into the schools (Lightfoot 1988). Consequently, the schools seem to be both a source of and a solution for our problems.

CORE CONCEPT 9 Not all racial and income groups experience educational success or failure at the same rates. Sociologists seek to understand why this is the case.

Sociologist James Coleman's research, known as the Coleman Report, represents a classic example of how sociologists study inequalities in schools. Coleman determined that the average minority student was likely to come from an economically and educationally disadvantaged household located in a disadvantaged neighborhood. Coleman also found that disadvantaged blacks who had participated in school integration programs scored higher on tests than their disadvantaged counterparts who did not. Clearly, then, the important variable in determining academic success is not race. If race was the factor, test scores would remain unchanged even when black students changed schools. Although family background was identified as the most important factor in the Coleman study, the effects of family background could not be easily separated from the effects of neighborhood and peer groups.

CORE CONCEPT 10 The adolescent society or subculture is a "small society, one that has most of its important interactions within itself, and maintains only a few threads of connection with the outside adult society" (Coleman, Johnstone, and Jonassohn 1961, p. 3).

The emergence of an adolescent society can be traced to industrialization. Around the turn of the twentieth century—the early decades of late industrialization—jobs began to move away from the home and the neighborhood and into factories and office buildings. Parents no longer trained their children, because the skills they knew were becoming obsolete. This shift in training from the family to the school cut adolescents off from the rest of society and forced them to spend most of the day with those of their own age group. Adolescents came to constitute a subculture with great influence over its members and that penalized academic achievement. For adolescent boys, athletic success was extremely important, and for girls, social success with boys is highly valued.

Resources on the Internet

Login to CengageBrain.com to access the resources your instructor requires. For this book, you can access:

 Sociology CourseMate

Access an integrated eBook, chapter-specific interactive learning tools, including flash cards, quizzes, videos, and more in your Sociology CourseMate.

CENGAGENOW™

Take a pretest for this chapter and receive a personalized study plan based on your results that will identify the topics you need to review and direct you to online resources to help you master those topics. Then take a posttest to help you determine the concepts you have mastered and what you will need to work on.

CourseReader

CourseReader for Sociology is an online reader providing access to readings, and audio and video selections to accompany your course materials.

Visit **www.cengagebrain.com** to access your account and purchase materials.

Key Terms

adolescent society 354
credential society 342
education 333
formal curriculum 347
formal education 334
habitus 349
hidden curriculum 347
illiteracy 337
informal education 333
schooling 334
self-fulfilling prophecy 346
social reproduction 349

RELIGION

14 With Emphasis on THE ISLAMIC REPUBLIC OF AFGHANISTAN

What do you make of this U.S. Air Force sergeant stationed in Afghanistan putting on his taqiyah, a round cap Muslim men wear during worship? He is part of a worship service in Afghanistan marking the end of the Hajj, an annual Muslim pilgrimage to Mecca. When sociologists study religion, they do not study whether God or some other supernatural force exists, whether certain religious beliefs are valid, or whether one religion is better than another. Instead, they focus on the social aspects of religion, such as the characteristics common to all religions and the ways in which people use religion to justify almost any kind of action.

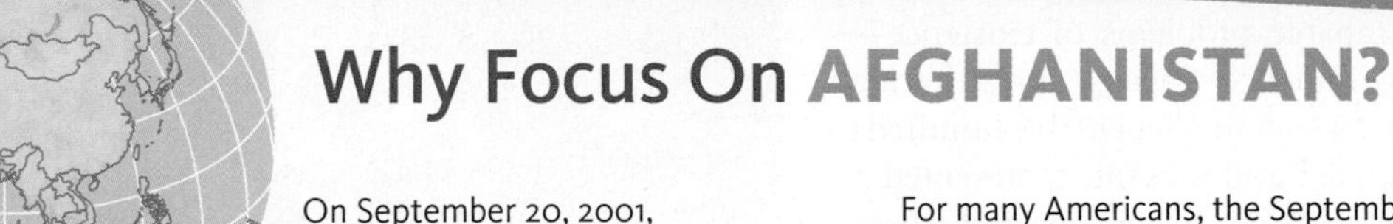

Why Focus On AFGHANISTAN?

On September 20, 2001, nine days after the September 11 terrorist attacks on the United States, then President George W. Bush answered a question many Americans were asking: Who attacked the United States? He identified those who hijacked the commercial aircraft and turned them into "cruise missiles" as belonging to a collection of loosely affiliated terrorist organizations led by Osama bin Laden and known as al-Qaida. Al-Qaida members, believed to be scattered across more than 60 countries, learned the tactics of terrorism in Afghanistan. That night, Bush demanded that the Taliban (an Islamic fundamentalist group that took control of Afghanistan in 1996) close all terrorist training camps, turn over any al-Qaida leaders in Afghanistan, and grant the U.S. government full access to the camps (Bush 2001a). The demands were not met, so on October 7, 2001, the United States began air strikes on Taliban military installations and al-Qaida training camps.

For many Americans, the September 11 attacks represented the most devastating in a long line of attacks by radical Islamists. When radical Islamists become the focus, the attacks are dismissed as simply resulting from the actions of religious fanatics driven by "primitive and irrational" religious conviction. This perspective fails to recognize that "lurking behind every terrorist act is a specific political antecedent. That does not justify either the perpetrator or his political cause. Nevertheless, the fact is that almost all terrorist activity originates from some political conflict and is sustained by it as well" (Brzezinski 2002).

Recognizing political antecedents—more specifically struggles for power—allows us to realize that religious affiliation per se explains little about the causes behind acts considered terrorist. Rather people draw upon religion to justify responses made to political situations. The sociological perspective is useful because it allows us to step back and view in a detached way an often emotionally charged subject. Detachment and objectivity are necessary if we wish to avoid making sweeping generalizations about the nature of religions, such as Islam, that are unfamiliar to many of us.

Online Poll

Is there a mosque in the area in which you live?

○ Yes

○ No

Have you ever visited it?

○ Yes

○ No

To see how other students responded to these questions, go to **www.cengagebrain.com.**

What Is Religion?

CORE CONCEPT 1 When sociologists study religion, they are guided by the scientific method and by the assumption that no religions are false.

When sociologists study religion, they do not investigate whether God or some other supernatural force exists, whether certain religious beliefs are valid, or whether one religion is better than another. Sociologists cannot study such questions, because they adhere to the scientific method, which requires them to study only observable and verifiable phenomena. Instead, they investigate the social

SrA Daryl Knee

aspects of religion, focusing on the characteristics common to all religions, the functions and dysfunctions of religion, the conflicts within and between religious groups, and the way religion shapes people's behavior and their understanding of the world. We begin with a definition of religion. Defining religion is a surprisingly difficult task, one with which sociologists have been greatly preoccupied.

What is a religion? In the opening sentences of *The Sociology of Religion,* Max Weber (1922) states, "To define 'religion,' to say what it is, is not possible at the start of a presentation such as this. Definition can be attempted, if at all, only at the conclusion of the study" (p. 1). Despite Weber's keen interest in, and extensive writings about, religious activity, he could offer only the broadest of definitions: Religion encompasses those human responses that give meaning to the ultimate and inescapable problems of existence—birth, death, illness, aging, injustice, tragedy, and suffering (Abercrombie and Turner 1978). To Weber, the hundreds of thousands of religions, past and present, represented a rich and seemingly endless variety of responses to these problems. In view of this variety, he believed that no single definition could hope to capture the essence of religion.

Like Max Weber, Émile Durkheim believed that *religion* is difficult to define. In the first chapter of his book, *The Elementary Forms of the Religious Life,* Durkheim (1915) cautions that when studying religions, sociologists must assume that "there are no religions which are false" (p. 3). Like Weber, Durkheim believed that all religions are true in their own fashion; all address the problems of human existence, albeit in different ways. Consequently, he said, those who study religion must first rid themselves of all preconceived notions of what religion should be. We cannot study religion using standards that reflect our own personal experiences and preferences.

Consider that many critics view the *hijab,* the traditional head covering of Muslim women, as the primary evidence that these women are severely oppressed. Although women in Islamic countries certainly do not have the same rights as men, critics should not be so quick to assume that the *hijab* is the *source* of oppression (Kristof 2002), especially when we consider the view that some Muslim women hold toward American dress customs:

> If women living in Western societies took an honest look at themselves, such a question [as why some Muslim women wear hijab] would not arise. They are the slaves of appearance. . . . Every magazine and news medium (such as television and radio) tells them how they should look and behave. They should wear glamorous clothes and make themselves beautiful for strange men to gaze and gloat over them. So the question is not why Muslim women wear hijab, but why the women in the West, who think they are so liberated, do not wear hijab. (*Mahjubah* 1984)

The discussion of the *hijab* shows that preconceived notions of what constitutes religion and uninformed opinions about the meaning of religious symbols and practices can close people off to a wide range of religious beliefs and experiences.

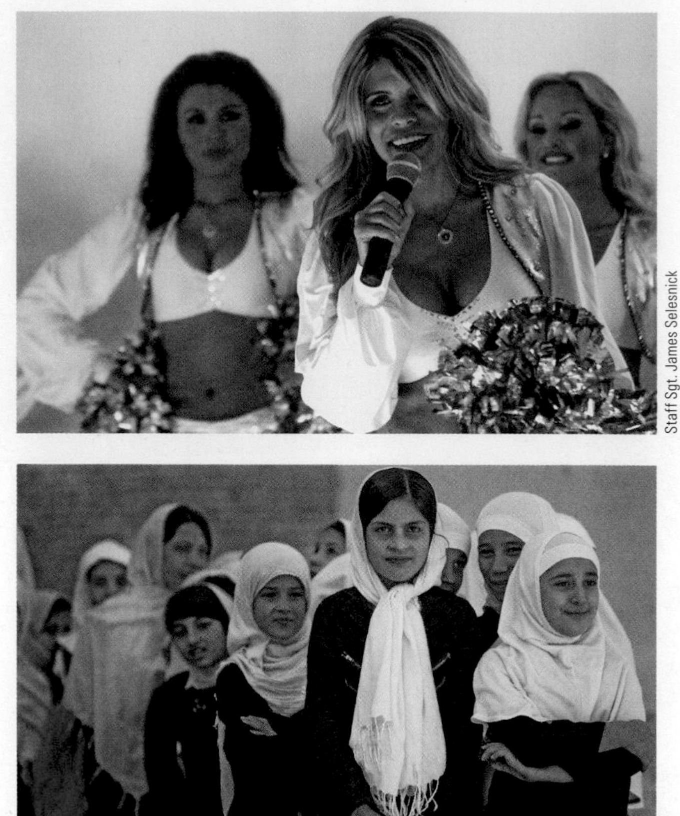

Staff Sgt. James Selesnick

G. A. Volb

It is a challenge to see through one's own preconceptions about what is "right" in everyday life. A Western woman may look on the traditional Muslim women's head covering, the hijab, as a sign of sexual oppression. A Muslim woman may look on a Western woman's garb as oppression of women imposed by media pressures to display themselves as sex objects.

Essential Features of Religion

CORE CONCEPT 2 Durkheim defined religion as a system of shared rituals and beliefs about the sacred that bind together a community of worshippers.

In formulating his ideas about religion, Durkheim remained open to the many varieties of religious experiences throughout the world (see Global Comparisons: "The World's Predominant Religions"). He identified three essential features that he believed were common to all religions, past and present: (1) beliefs about the sacred and the profane, (2) rituals, and (3) a community of worshippers.

Beliefs about the Sacred

At the heart of all religious belief and activity stands a distinction between two domains: the sacred and the profane. The **sacred** includes everything that is regarded

Global Comparisons The World's Predominant Religions

The map shows which of the world's major religions predominates in each country. Keep in mind that other religions are also practiced in each country, some by many people. In the United States, for example, the population is believed to be 52 percent Protestant, 24 percent Roman Catholic, 1.7 percent Mormon, 1.7 percent Jewish, .6 percent Muslim, 4.7 percent some other religion, and 16 percent no affiliation (PEW Research Center 2008). Likewise, Latin American countries have many Protestants, although the predominant religion is Roman Catholicism. The term *syncretism* refers to compatible combinations of belief systems, such as Confucianism, Buddhism, Taoism, and Shinto in Japan.

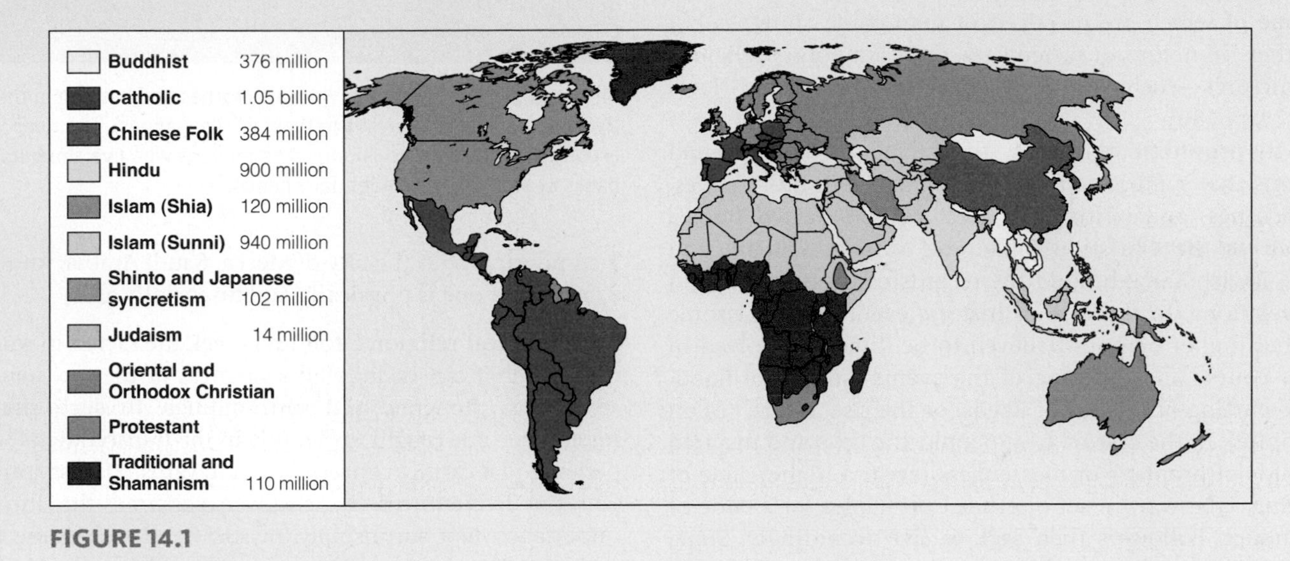

FIGURE 14.1

Source: Data from U.S. Central Intelligence Agency (2011).

as extraordinary and that inspires in believers deep and absorbing sentiments of awe, respect, mystery, and reverence. These sentiments motivate people to safeguard what is sacred from contamination or defilement. To find, preserve, or guard what they consider sacred, people have gone to war, sacrificed their lives, and performed other life-endangering acts (Turner 1978).

Definitions of what is sacred vary according to time and place. Sacred things may include objects (such as chalices, scriptures, and statues), living creatures (such as cows, ants, and birds), elements of nature (such as rocks, mountains, trees, the sea, the sun, the moon, and the sky), places (such as churches, mosques, synagogues, and birthplaces of religions or their founders), days that commemorate holy events, abstract forces (such as spirits), key figures (Jesus Christ, the Buddha, Moses, Muhammad, Zarathustra, and Nanak), states of consciousness (such as wisdom and oneness with nature), past events (such as the crucifixion and resurrection of Jesus, the escape of Hebrews from Egypt, and the birth of the Buddha), ceremonies (such as baptism, marriage, and burial), and other activities (holy wars, just wars, confession, fasting, and pilgrimages).

Durkheim (1915) maintains that sacredness springs not from the item, ritual, or event itself, but rather from its symbolic power and from the emotions that people experience when they think about the sacred thing or when they are in its presence. These emotions can be so strong that believers feel part of something larger than themselves and become outraged when other people behave inappropriately in the presence of the sacred thing. Ideas about what is sacred are such important elements of religious activity that many researchers classify religions according to the type of phenomenon that their followers consider sacred. One such typology of religion includes three categories: sacramental, prophetic, and mystical (Alston 1972).

sacred A domain of experience that includes everything regarded as extraordinary and that inspires in believers deep and absorbing sentiments of awe, respect, mystery, and reverence.

Sacramental, Prophetic, and Mystical Religions

In **sacramental religions**, followers seek the sacred in places, objects, and actions believed to house a god or a spirit. These locations may include inanimate objects (such as relics, statues, and crosses), animals, trees or other plants, foods, drink (such as wine and water), places, and certain processes (such as the way people prepare for a hunt or perform a dance). Sacramental religions include many forms of Native American spirituality, none of which are documented in holy books such as the Bible or Koran, and none of which are practiced in man-made churches but rather "in nature, at sacred sites, or in temporary religious structures—such as a tepee or sweat lodge" (Echo-Hawk 1979, p. 280).

In **prophetic religions**, the sacred revolves around items that symbolize historic events or around the lives, teachings, and writings of great people. Sacred books, such as the Christian Bible, the Muslim Qur'an, and the Jewish Tanakh, hold the records of these events and revelations. In the case of historic events, God or some other higher being is believed to be directly involved in the course and outcome of the events (such as a flood, the parting of the Sea of Reeds, or the rise and fall of an empire). In the case of great people, the lives and inspired words of prophets or messengers reveal a higher state of being, "the way," a set of ethical principles, or a code of conduct. Followers then seek to live accordingly. Some of the best-known prophetic religions include Judaism, as revealed to Abraham in Canaan and to Moses at Mount Sinai, Confucianism (founded by Confucius), Christianity (founded by the earliest followers of Jesus Christ), and Islam (founded by Muhammad). The set of ethical principles may include the Ten Commandments of Judaism and Christianity or the Five Pillars of Islam. Muslim tenets include the following:

- The declaration of faith known as the *shahadah* ("There is no god but Allah, and Muhammad is his messenger.")
- Obligatory prayer known as *salah* (performed five times per day)
- Almsgiving (Each year, devout Muslims set aside a percentage of their accumulated wealth to assist the poor and sick.)

Barbara Houghton

The people in this photo are washing clothes and bathing in the river Ganga (also known in the West as the Ganges). The river is considered sacred to Hindus. The millions who live along its banks depend on it to meet daily needs.

- A pilgrimage to the city of Mecca, Saudi Arabia, known as *hajj* (if one is physically and financially able)

In **mystical religions**, followers seek the sacred in states of being that can exclude all awareness of their existence, sensations, thoughts, and surroundings. In such states, mystics become caught up so fully in the transcendental experience that earthly concerns seem to vanish. Direct union with the divine forces of the universe assumes the utmost importance. Not surprisingly, mystics tend to become involved in practices such as fasting or celibacy to separate themselves from worldly attachments.

In addition, they meditate to clear their minds of worldly concerns, "leaving the soul empty and receptive to influences from the divine" (Alston 1972, p. 144).

Sgt. 1st Class Mark Bruce, 8th Theater Sustainment Command

Founded in the sixth and fifth centuries BC by the Buddha, Siddhartha Gautama, Buddhism has an estimated 376 million followers. Buddhism teaches that suffering is an inevitable part of human existence; desires and feelings of self-importance cause suffering; nirvana is achieved through meditation, karma, and righteous actions, thoughts, and attitudes (BBC 2009).

sacramental religions Religions in which the sacred is sought in places, objects, and actions believed to house a god or spirit.

prophetic religions Religions in which the sacred revolves around items that symbolize significant historical events or around the lives, teachings, and writings of great people.

mystical religions Religions in which the sacred is sought in states of being that, at their peak, can exclude all awareness of one's existence, sensations, thoughts, and surroundings.

Buddhism and philosophical Hinduism are two religions that emphasize physical and spiritual discipline as a means of transcending the self and earthly concerns.

Keep in mind that the distinctions between sacramental, prophetic, and mystical religions are not clear-cut. In fact, most religions in each of these categories incorporate or combine elements of the other categories. Consequently, most religions cannot be assigned to a single category.

Beliefs about the Profane

According to Durkheim (1915), the sacred encompasses more than the forces of good: "There are gods of theft and trickery, of lust and war, of sickness and of death" (p. 420). Evil and its various representations are, however, generally portrayed as inferior and subordinate to the forces of good: "In the majority of cases we see the good victorious over evil, life over death, the powers of light over the powers of darkness" (p. 421). Even so, Durkheim considers superordinary evil phenomena to fall within the category of the sacred, because they are endowed with special powers and serve as the objects of rituals (such as confession to rid one of sin, baptism to purify the soul, penance for sins, and exorcism to rid one of evil) designed to overcome or resist the negative influences of such phenomena.

The **profane** encompasses everything that is not considered sacred, including things opposed to the sacred (such as the unholy, the irreverent, and the blasphemous) and that stand apart from the sacred (such as the ordinary, the commonplace, the unconsecrated, and the bodily) (Ebersole 1967).

Contact between the sacred and the profane is viewed as dangerous and sacrilegious. Consequently, people take action to safeguard sacred things by separating them from the profane. For example, some refrain from speaking the name of God when they feel frustrated; others believe that a woman must cover her hair or her face during worship and that a man must remove his hat during worship.

Sgt. Martin Downs

Removing shoes before entering a mosque is an act that separates the profane (ordinary and unconsecrated) from the sacred (holy place of worship).

Rituals

In the religious sense, **rituals** are rules that govern how people behave in the presence of the sacred. These rules may take the form of instructions detailing an appropriate place to engage in worship, the roles of various participants, acceptable dress, and the precise wording of chants, songs, and prayers. Participants engage in rituals with a goal in mind, whether it be to purify the body or soul (as through confession, immersion, fasting, or seclusion), to commemorate an important person or event (as by making a pilgrimage to Mecca or celebrating Passover or the Eucharist), or to transform profane items into sacred items (for example, changing water to holy water and human bones to sacred relics) (Smart 1976, p. 6).

Rituals can be as simple as closing one's eyes to pray or having one's forehead marked with ashes. Alternatively, they can be as elaborate as fasting for three days before entering a sacred place to chant, with head bowed, a particular prayer for forgiveness. Although rituals are often enacted in sacred places, some are codes of conduct aimed at governing the performance of everyday activities, such as sleeping, walking, eating, defecating, washing, and dealing with members of the opposite sex.

According to Durkheim, the nature of the ritual is relatively insignificant. Rather, the important element is that the ritual is shared by a community of worshippers and evokes certain ideas and sentiments that help individuals feel themselves to be part of something larger than themselves.

Community of Worshippers

Durkheim uses the word **church** to designate a group whose members hold the same beliefs regarding the sacred and the profane, who behave in the same way in the presence

profane A term describing everything that is not sacred, including things opposed to the sacred and things that stand apart from the sacred, albeit not in opposition to it.

rituals Rules that govern how people must behave in the presence of the sacred to achieve an acceptable state of being.

church A group whose members hold the same beliefs about the sacred and the profane, who behave in the same way in the presence of the sacred, and who gather in body or spirit at agreed-on times to reaffirm their commitment to those beliefs and practices.

Student Activity: After reading about Durkheim's definition of *church*, ask students to browse Google News for articles about the activities of *churches*, in the broadest sense of the word. Use key words, such as "church," "synagogue," "temple," or "mosque" to find an interesting article that describes some practice, belief, or shared identity of a "moral community." Ask students to write a one-page essay reflecting on what they have read.

TSgt. Michele A. Desrochers

Kneeling with forehead touching the floor in prayer facing Mecca five times a day constitutes a ritual.

Chris Caldeira

Chris Caldeira

Many religious denominations have churches in the United States. Above is a Hindu temple in San Francisco. Below is a small Christian church located in rural community of the United States.

of the sacred, and who gather in body or spirit at agreed-on times to reaffirm their commitment to those beliefs and practices. Obviously, religious beliefs and practices cannot be unique to an individual; they must be shared by a group of people. If not, then the beliefs and practices would cease to exist when the individual who held them died or if he or she chose to abandon them. The gathering and the sharing create a moral community and allow worshippers to share a common identity. The gathering need not take place in a common setting, however. When people perform a ritual on a given day or at given times of day, the gathering may be spiritual rather than physical.

Sociologists have identified at least five broad types of religious organizations or communities of worshippers: ecclesiae, denominations, sects, established sects, and cults. As with most classification schemes, these categories overlap on some characteristics because the classification criteria for religions are not always clear.

Ecclesiae

An **ecclesia** is a professionally trained religious organization, governed by a hierarchy of leaders, that claims everyone in a society as a member. Membership is not voluntary; it is the law. Consequently, considerable political alignment exists between church and state officials, so that the ecclesia represents the official church of the state. Ecclesiae formerly existed in England (the Church of England [Anglican], which remains the official state church), France (the Roman Catholic Church), and Sweden (the Church of Sweden [Lutheran]). The Afghan constitution signed in 2004 declares the country to be an Islamic republic, makes Islam the official religion, and announces that "no law can be contrary to the sacred religion of Islam." The Afghan government, however, guarantees non-Muslims the right to "perform their religious ceremonies within the limits of the provisions of law" (Feldman 2003).

Individuals are born into ecclesiae, newcomers to a society are converted, and dissenters are often persecuted.

ecclesia A professionally trained religious organization, governed by a hierarchy of leaders, that claims everyone in a society as a member.

Those who do not accept the official religious view tend to emigrate or to occupy a marginal status. The ecclesia claims to be the one true faith and often does not recognize other religions as valid. In its most extreme form, it directly controls all facets of life.

Denominations

A **denomination** is a hierarchical religious organization in a society in which church and state usually remain separate; it is led by a professionally trained clergy. In contrast to an ecclesia, a denomination is one of many religious organizations in society. For the most part, denominations tolerate other religious organizations; they may even collaborate with other such organizations to address problems such as poverty or disaster relief in society. Although membership is considered to be voluntary, most people who belong to denominations did not choose to join them. Rather, they were born to parents who were members. Denominational leaders generally make few demands on the laity (members who are not clergy), and most members participate in limited and specialized ways.

For example, members may choose to send their children to church-operated schools, attend church on Sundays and religious holidays, donate money to the church, or attend church-sponsored functions Although laypeople vary widely in lifestyle, denominations frequently attract people of particular races, ethnicities, and social classes.

Major denominations in the world include Buddhism, Christianity, Confucianism, Hinduism, Islam, Judaism, Shinto, and Taoism. Each is predominant in different areas of the globe. For example, Christianity predominates in Europe, the Americas, and Australia and Oceania; Islam predominates in the Middle East and North Africa; and Hinduism predominates in India.

Sects and Established Sects

A **sect** is a small community of believers led by a lay ministry; it has no formal hierarchy, or official governing body, to oversee its various religious gatherings and activities. Sects are typically composed of people who broke away from a denomination because they came to view it as corrupt. They then created the offshoot in an effort to reform the religion from which they separated.

All of the major religions encompass splinter groups that have sought at one time or another to preserve the integrity of their religion. In Islam, for example, the most pronounced split occurred about 1,300 years ago, approximately 30 years after the death of Muhammad. The split related to Muhammad's successor. The Shia maintained that the successor should be a blood relative of Muhammad; the Sunni believed that the successor should be selected by the community of believers and need not be related to Muhammad by blood. After Muhammad's death, the Sunni (encompassing the great majority of Muslims) accepted Abu Bakr as the caliph (successor). The Shia supported Ali, Mohammad's first cousin and son-in-law, and they called for the overthrow of the existing order and a return to the pure form of Islam. Today, Shiite Islam predominates in the Islamic Republic of Iran (95 percent), whereas Sunni Islam predominates in the Islamic Republic of Pakistan (77 percent) and Afghanistan (80 percent) (U.S. Central Intelligence Agency 2011a).

SrA Daryl Knee

Muslim men at a prayer service in Afghanistan. All work for the International Security Assistance Force in Afghanistan. Muslims are not a monolithic group. In Afghanistan, 20 percent are Shia and 80 percent are Sunni. Muslims also have ties with major ethnic groups such as Pashtun (followers of Sunni Islam) and Hazara (Shiite). The most puritanical are Sunni Taliban whose followers are Pashtun. Obviously, all Pashtuns are not Taliban.

The divisions within Islam have existed for so long that Sunni and Shia have become recognized as **established sects**—groups that have broken from denominations or ecclesiae and have existed long enough to acquire a large following and widespread respectability. As you might expect, divisions can form within established sects, creating splinter groups. Sects exist within the Sunni branch (Wahabis) and the Shiite branch (the Assassins, the Druze).

Similarly, several splits have occurred within Christianity. During a period from about the eleventh century to the

denomination A hierarchical religious organization, led by a professionally trained clergy, in a society in which church and state are usually separate.

sect A small community of believers led by a lay ministry, with no formal hierarchy or official governing body to oversee its various religious gatherings and activities. Sects are typically composed of people who broke away from a denomination because they came to view it as corrupt.

established sects Religious organizations, resembling both denominations and sects, that have left denominations or ecclesiae and have existed long enough to acquire a large following and widespread respectability.

Technology Tip: For an excellent discussion of the Sunni-Shia divide, see the Fareed Zakaria (host of the show *Foreign Exchange*) interview with Vali Nasr, author of *The Shia Revival*. Among other things, Nasr draws parallels to the Catholic-Protestant divide. The interview is available at http://being.publicradio.org/programs/2009/sunni-shia/transcript.shtml.

early thirteenth century, for example, the Greek-language Eastern churches (then centering on Constantinople) and the Latin-language Western church (centering on Rome) gradually drifted apart over issues such as the papal claim of supreme authority over all Christian churches in the world. The Protestant churches owe their origins largely to Martin Luther (1483–1546), who also challenged papal authority and protested against many practices of the medieval Roman Catholic Church.

Cults

Generally, **cults** are very small, loosely organized religious groups, usually founded by a charismatic leader who attracts people by virtue of his or her personal qualities. Because the charismatic leader plays such a central role in attracting members, cults often dissolve after the leader dies. Consequently, few cults last long enough to become established religions. Even so, a few manage to survive, as evidenced by the fact that the major world religions began as cults. Because cults form around new and unconventional religious practices, outsiders tend to view them with considerable suspicion.

Cults vary in terms of their purpose and the level of commitment that their leaders demand of converts. They may draw members by focusing on highly specific but eccentric interests, such as astrology, UFOs, or transcendental meditation. Members may be attracted by the promise of companionship, a cure for illness, relief from suffering, or enlightenment. In some cases a cult leader may require members to break all ties with family, friends, and jobs and thus to rely exclusively on the cult to meet all of their needs.

Durkheim's definition of *religion* highlights three essential characteristics: beliefs about the sacred and the profane, rituals, and a community of worshippers. Critics argue that these characteristics are not unique to religious activity. This combination of characteristics, they say, applies to many gatherings (for example, sporting events, graduation ceremonies, reunions, and political rallies) and to many political systems (for example, Marxism, Maoism, and fascism). On the basis of these characteristics alone, it is difficult to distinguish between an assembly of Christians celebrating Christmas, a patriotic group supporting the initiation of a war against another country, and a group of fans eulogizing James Dean or Elvis Presley. In other words, religion is not the only unifying force in society that incorporates the three elements defined by Durkheim as characteristic of religion. Civil religion represents another such force that resembles religion as Durkheim defined it.

Chief Photographer's Mate Johnny Bivera

The three essential characteristics of religion also apply to other events such as a football game when people engage in pregame rituals such as praying. The school colors take on a sacred quality, and a community of worshippers gathers to watch the game, often believing "God" is on their side.

Civil Religion

CORE CONCEPT 3 Civil religion is an institutionalized set of beliefs about a nation's past, present, and future and a corresponding set of rituals that take on a sacred quality and elicit feelings of patriotism.

Civil religion forges ties between religion and a nation (Bellah 1992, Hammond 1976, Davis 2002). A nation's values (such as individual freedom and equal opportunity) and rituals (such as parades, fireworks, singing the national anthem, and 21-gun salutes) often assume a sacred quality. Even in the face of division, national beliefs and rituals can inspire awe, respect, and reverence for the country. These sentiments are most evident during times of crisis and war, on national holidays that celebrate important events or people (such as Thanksgiving, July 4th), and in the presence of national monuments or symbols (the flag, the Capitol, the Lincoln Memorial, the Vietnam Memorial).

In times of war, presidents offer a historical and mythological framework that morally justifies the country's involvement in the war and offers the public a vision and an identity. Sociologist Roberta Cole (2002) argues that America's civil religion found its voice in a nineteenth-century political doctrine known as *manifest destiny*. Although the term

cults Very small, loosely organized groups, usually founded by a charismatic leader who attracts people by virtue of his or her personal qualities.

civil religion An institutionalized set of beliefs about a nation's past, present, and future and a corresponding set of rituals. Both the beliefs and the rituals take on a sacred quality and elicit feelings of patriotism. Civil religion forges ties between religion and a nation's needs and political interests.

Discussion Tip: Ask students if they can think of nonreligious gatherings or events that have a religious quality as outlined by Durkheim.

was first used in 1845, it expressed a long-standing ideology that the United States, by virtue of its moral superiority, was destined to expand across the North American continent to the Pacific Ocean and beyond (Chance 2002). Manifest destiny included the beliefs that the United States had a divine mission to serve as a democratic model to the rest of the world, that the country was a redeemer exerting its good influence upon other nations, and that it represented hope to the rest of the world (Cole 2002). In 1835, Alexis de Tocqueville observed this long-standing belief among Americans that their country was unique:

> For 50 years, it has been constantly repeated to the inhabitants of the United States that they form the only religious, enlightened, and free people. They see that up to now, democratic institutions have prospered among them; they therefore have an immense opinion of themselves, and they are not far from believing that they form a species apart in the human race.

Farm Security Administration and Office of War Information Collection, Library of Congress Prints and Photographs Division

In 1941, the year when these children were reciting the Pledge of Allegiance with hand over heart, they said "one nation indivisible, with liberty and justice for all." They did not say the words "under God" because those words were not part of the oath until the 1950s, during the cold war. At that time, the U.S. government also started stamping "In God We Trust" on its coins.

Civil Religion and the Cold War

The cold war (1945 to 1989) included an arms race, in which the Soviet Union and the United States competed to match and then surpass any advances made by each other in the number and technological quality of nuclear weapons. Although the United States and the Soviet Union fell short of direct, full-scale military engagement, they took part in as many as 120 proxy wars fought in developing countries. In many of these conflicts, the United States and the Soviet Union supported opposing factions by providing weapons, military equipment, combat training, medical supplies, economic aid, and food. Three of the best-known proxy wars were fought in Korea, Vietnam, and Afghanistan (1979 to 1989). Soviet and American leaders justified their direct or indirect intervention on the grounds that it was necessary to contain the spread of the other side's economic and political system, to protect national and global security, and to prevent the other side from shifting the balance of power in favor of its system.

Library of Congress Prints and Photographs Division Washington, D.C.

The painting portrays those who participated in the United States' westward expansion as fulfilling an almost divine mission, represented by the guardian angel-like figure watching over them. Of course, westward expansion was not the peaceful process depicted here.

From 1945 through 1989, the foreign and domestic policies of the United States were largely shaped by cold war dynamics—specifically, a professed desire to *save*, even *redeem*, the world from Soviet influence and the spread of communism. Robert S. McNamara (1989), U.S. Secretary of Defense under Presidents Kennedy and Johnson, remarked that "on occasion after occasion, when confronted with a choice between support of democratic governments and support of anti-Soviet dictatorships, we have turned our backs on our traditional values and have supported the antidemocratic," brutally repressive, and totalitarian regimes (p. 96). President George W. Bush (2003) agreed with McNamara's assessment when he acknowledged in a speech to the British people that

> we must shake off decades of failed policy on the Middle East. Your nation and mine in the past have been willing to make a bargain to tolerate oppression for the sake of stability. Long-standing ties often led us to overlook the faults of local elites. Yet this bargain did not bring stability or make us safe. It merely bought time while problems festered and ideologies of violence took hold.

The United States and Muslims as Cold War Partners

The cold war between the United States and the Soviet Union made Afghanistan a focus of those two countries' conflict (see Figure 14.2). When the Soviet Union invaded Afghanistan in 1979, and put its Afghan supporters in charge, the United States supported Islamic guerrillas, known as the *mujahideen*, by funneling money through Pakistan. At that time, Pakistani president Zia's goals were to turn Pakistan into the leader of the Islamic world and to cultivate an Islamic opposition to Soviet expansion into central Asia. Zia's aims fit well with the United States' cold war goals of containing the Soviet Union. If the United States could show the Soviet Union that the entire Muslim world was its partner, then the United States would indeed be a force to fear (Rashid 2001).

The U.S. Central Intelligence Agency (CIA) worked with its Pakistani equivalent, the Inter-Services Intelligence Agency, on a plan to recruit radical Muslims from all over the world to fight with their Afghan brothers against the Soviet Union. An estimated 35,000 Muslims from 43 countries—primarily in central Asia, North and East Africa, and the Middle East—heeded the call. Thousands more came to Pakistan to study in *madrassas* (Muslim schools) in Pakistan and along the Afghan border (Rashid 2001).

Military training camps staffed with U.S. advisors helped train the guerrillas, and the *madrassas* offered a place for the most radical Muslims in the world to meet, exchange ideas, and learn about Islamic movements in one another's countries. Among those who came to Afghanistan was Osama bin Laden. At that time, the pressing question for the United States, as asked by national security advisor Zbigniew Brzezinski (2002), was, "What was more important in the world view of history? The possible creation of an armed, radical Islamic movement or the fall of the Soviet Empire? A few fired-up Muslims or the liberation of Central Europe and the end of the Cold War?" These Pakistani- and U.S.-supported recruiting and military centers would eventually evolve into al-Qaida ("the base"). In 1989, the year the term *al-Qaida* was first used, Osama bin Laden had taken over as the centers' leader. That same year, Soviet troops withdrew from Afghanistan, leaving behind

> an uneasy coalition of Islamist organizations intent on promoting Islam among all non-Muslim forces. [They also] left behind a legacy of expert and experienced fighters, training camps and logistical facilities, elaborate trans-Islam networks of personal and organizational relationships, a substantial amount of military equipment, . . . and most importantly, a heavy sense of power and self-confidence based on what [they] had achieved, and a driving desire to move on to other victories. (Huntington 2001, p. A12)

To help measure the legacy of U.S.-supported training camps, consider that "key leaders of every major terrorist attack, from New York to France to Saudi Arabia, inevitably turned out to be veterans of the Afghan War" (Mamdani 2004).

Civil Religion and the Gulf War I

In 1990, at the request of the Saudi government, the United States government sent 540,000 troops to the Persian Gulf region after Iraqi troops invaded Kuwait. In a presidential address, George H. W. Bush (1991) fused country and religion together when he described the United States in sacred terms:

> I come to this House of the people to speak to you and all Americans, certain that we stand at a defining hour. Halfway around the world, we are engaged in a great struggle in the skies and on the seas and sands. We know why we're there: We are Americans, part of something larger than ourselves. For two centuries, we've done the hard work of freedom. And tonight, we lead the world in facing down a threat to decency and humanity. . . . Yes, the United States bears a major share of leadership in this effort. Among the nations of the world, only the United States of America has both the moral standing and the means to back it up. We're the only nation on this Earth that could assemble the forces of peace. This is the burden of leadership and the strength that has made America the beacon of freedom in a searching world.

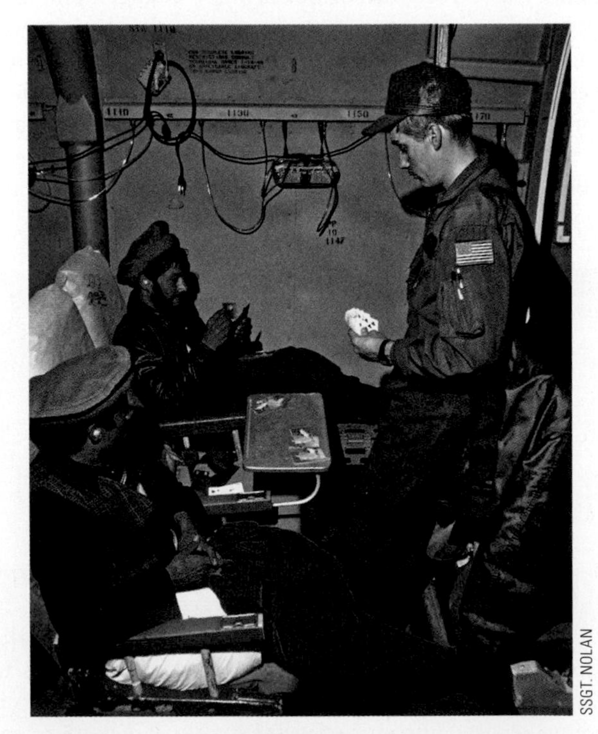
SSGT. NOLAN

The United States offered medical treatment and other assistance to mujahideen who were wounded fighting the Soviet Union. Here, a U.S. medic plays cards with two wounded "freedom fighters," the term the American government used to characterize the anticommunist guerrillas, en route to a U.S. airbase in Germany for specialized medical care.

The Historical Context of Afghanistan

Afghanistan is a mountainous and landlocked county. Its neighbors are Pakistan, Iran, China, and three countries once part of the Soviet Union—Turkmenistan, Uzbekistan, and Tajikistan. Afghanistan connects the Middle East with Central Asia and the India. Afghanistan's borders, especially with Pakistan, have always been in dispute, and great empires and dynasties have fought to control the country, its peoples, and resources, beginning with Alexander the Great in 330 B.C. Here we focus on the nineteenth and twentieth centuries, when Britain invaded Afghanistan twice—the First Anglo-Afghan War of 1838 to 1842 and the Second Anglo-Afghan War of 1878 to 1880—with the goal of limiting Russian influence. Russia invaded in 1979, to support a secular government. The United States supported Afghanistan's military resistance to the Soviets, which was mobilized in large part by proclaiming a "holy war." The Soviet Union eventually pulled out in 1989, leaving a country ravaged and full of rival factions fighting for control. When the Taliban government took power in 1996, it justified many of its new policies on Islamic grounds. Westerners tend to see such policies as simply fanatical and irrational and to overlook the history that led up to them.

In October 2001, the United States and its European allies launched a bombing attack against what was called the epicenter of international terrorism. In October 2011, the campaign marked the tenth-year anniversary.

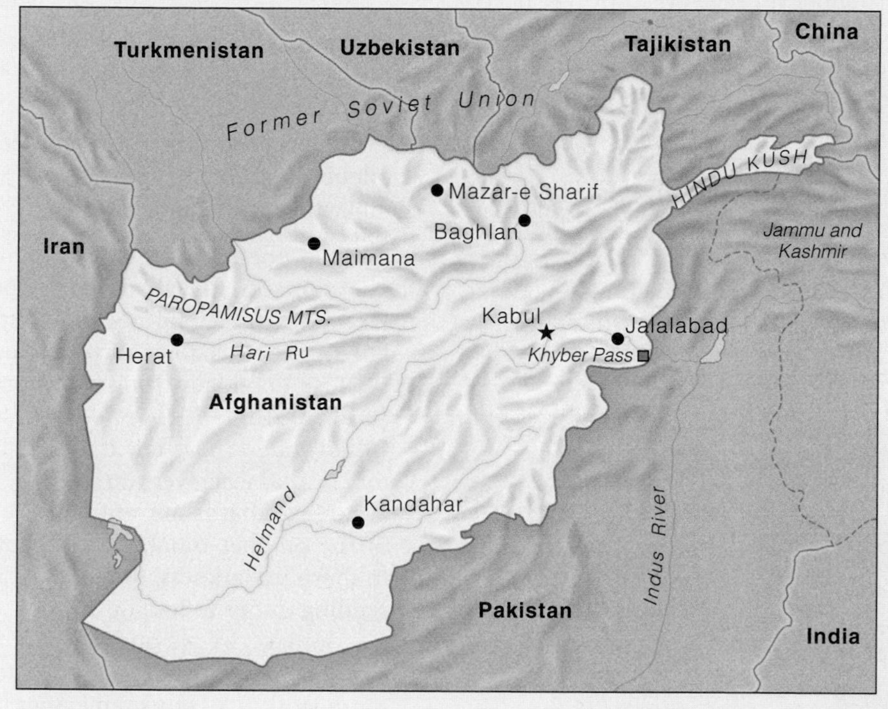

FIGURE 14.2

Source: Map from U.S. Central Intelligence Agency 2011

Osama bin Laden, who had hoped to raise a force composed of veterans of the Afghan War to fight Iraq, was infuriated with the Saudi royal family for calling upon the United States for help. He appealed to Muslim clerics to issue a *fatwa* (ruling or decree) condemning the stationing of non-Muslim troops in Saudi Arabia. His request was denied, and eventually the Saudi royal family, tired of bin Laden's incessant criticism, revoked his citizenship.

According to bin Laden (2001a), the "U.S. knows that I have attacked it, by the grace of God, for more than ten years now. . . . Hostility toward America is a religious duty and we hope to be rewarded for it by God. I am confident that Muslims will be able to end the legend of the so-called superpower that is America." Osama bin Laden claimed credit for the 1993 World Trade Center bombings and attacks on U.S. soldiers in Somalia, the 1998 attacks on U.S. embassies in East Africa, and the 1998 attack on the USS *Cole*. Although not formally claiming credit for the September 11, 2001, attacks on the United States, bin Laden (2001b) condoned them with the following religiously charged words: "Here is America struck by God Almighty in one of its vital organs, so that its greatest buildings are

Teaching Tip: The map above shows that Afghanistan is very mountainous. The country's rugged terrain disadvantages those who have tried to control the country. The U.S. Department of Defense has posted photographs of the Afghan mountains that you may wish to share with students. Go to www.defense.gov/multimedia/multimedia.aspx; choose one of the photo options (e.g., Army, Navy, etc.) and enter search terms "Afghanistan mountain," "Afghanistan mountains," or "Afghan terrain" for hundreds of images from which to choose.

destroyed. Grace and gratitude to God. America has been filled with horror from north to south and east to west, and thanks be to God."

Civil Religion and the War on Terror

On September 20, 2001, President George W. Bush indicated that a global war on terror would begin with air strikes against al-Qaida and Taliban strongholds in Afghanistan. The enemy was larger than Afghanistan, however; it was a "radical network of terrorists" and the governments (as many as 60) that supported them. Bush (2001a) indicated that the war would not end "until every terrorist group has been found, stopped, and defeated."

On March 22, 2003, Bush announced the beginning of Operation Iraqi Freedom. He described the mission as clear: "to disarm Iraq of weapons of mass destruction, to end Saddam Hussein's support of terrorism (it has aided, trained, and harbored terrorists, including operatives of al-Qaida), and to free the Iraqi people." We know now that Iraq had no weapons of mass destruction and no substantiated links to al-Qaida. Our purpose here is *not* to address the question of whether the wars in Iraq and Afghanistan have been just or whether the war effort has succeeded. Rather, we continue to focus on the language that presidents use to justify war and to articulate a national identity in time of war. Usually during such times, the nation assumes a sacred quality and the president projects a moral certitude that some critics liken to "a kind of fundamentalism" and a "dangerous messianic brand of religion, one where self-doubt is minimal" (Hedges 2002). The following are examples of such statements:

- "We did not ask for this mission, but we will fulfill it. The name of today's military operation is Enduring Freedom. We defend not only our precious freedoms, but also the freedoms of people everywhere." (George W. Bush upon launching attack on Afghanistan, 2001) (Bush 2001b)
- "All of you . . . have taken up the highest calling of history . . . and wherever you go, carry a message of hope—a message that is ancient and ever new. In the words of the prophet Isaiah, to the captive 'come out,' and to those in darkness, 'be free.'" (George W. Bush upon sending troops to Iraq in 2003)
- ". . . tonight, we are once again reminded that America can do whatever we set our mind to. That is the story of our history . . . Let us remember that we can do these things not just because of wealth or power, but because of who we are: one nation, under God, indivisible, with liberty and justice for all." (Barack Obama on the death of Osama Bin Laden)

TSGT CEDRIC H. RUDISILL, USAF

Five members of al-Qaida hijacked American Airlines Flight 77 and then crashed the aircraft into the Pentagon, killing 64 passengers onboard and 125 people on the ground. The Pentagon was one of three targets on September 11, 2001, the other being the twin towers of the World Trade Center and presumably the White House (which was spared when passengers brought their aircraft down in a Pennsylvania field).

Department of Defense

Consider the legacy of the U.S.-supported training camps in Afghanistan during the cold war: Key leaders behind every major terrorist attack on U.S. interests since then were veterans of the Afghan War.

The Functionalist Perspective

> **CORE CONCEPT 4 The functionalist perspective maintains that religion serves vital social functions for individuals and for the group.**

Some form of religion appears to have existed for as long as humans have lived (at least 2 million years). In view of this fact, functionalists maintain that religion must serve

Student Activity: Ask students to search for presidential speeches that were made at times of war. The speeches might be made on occasions of launching, escalating, or ending a war.

some vital social functions for individuals and for the group. On the individual level, people embrace religion in the face of uncertainty; they draw on religious doctrine and ritual to comprehend the meaning of life and death and to cope with misfortunes and injustices (such as war, drought, and illness).

Life would be intolerable without reasons for existing or without a higher purpose to justify the trials of existence (Durkheim 1951). Try to imagine, for example, how people might cope with the immense devastation and destruction resulting from decades of war. When Soviet troops invaded Afghanistan in 1979, they attacked civilian populations, burned village crops, killed livestock, used lethal and nonlethal chemical weapons, planted an estimated 10 million mines, and engaged in large-scale high-altitude carpet bombing. "In the countryside it was standard Soviet practice to bombard or even level whole villages suspected of harboring resistance fighters. Sometimes women, children, and old men were rounded up and shot" (Kurian 1992, p. 5).

Even after the Soviets withdrew from Afghanistan in 1989, the civil war continued, as various political parties competed to fill the power vacuum. Table 14.1 summarizes the tragic results of more than 20 years of war in this country. In light of this situation, is it any wonder that Afghan people might turn to religion to cope with the devastation and restore a sense of order out of chaos?

Besides turning to religion in the face of intolerable circumstances, people rely on religious beliefs and rituals to help them achieve a successful outcome (such as the birth of a healthy child or a job promotion) and to gain answers to questions of meaning: How did we get here? Why are we here? What happens to us when we die? According to Durkheim, people who have communicated with their God or with other supernatural forces (however conceived) report that they gain the inner strength and the physical strength to endure and to conquer the trials of existence:

> It is as though [they] were raised above the miseries of the world. . . . Whoever has really practiced a religion knows very well . . . these impressions of joy, of interior peace, of serenity, of enthusiasm, which are, for the believer, an experimental proof of his beliefs. (Durkheim 1915, pp. 416–417)

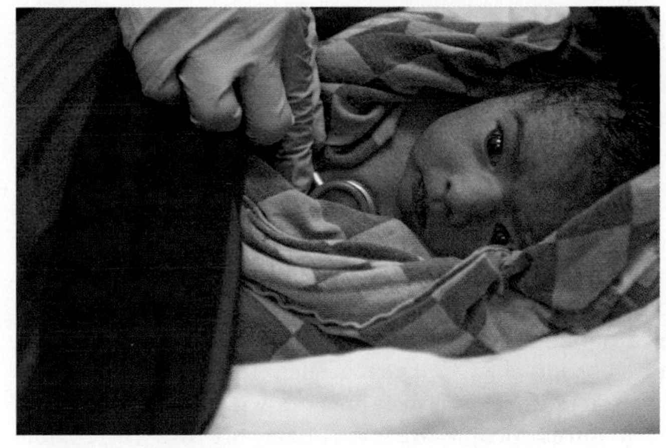

Staff Sgt. Arthur Hamilton

This baby in Afghanistan, born at a hospital staffed with U.S. military doctors, has a 16 percent chance of dying before reaching age 5.

TABLE 14.1 Profile of the Islamic Republic of Afghanistan

Before the United States began its military attacks on Afghanistan in 2001, the country was already devastated. Barnett Rubin (1996) argues that no one paid more for the U.S. cold war victory than did Afghanistan and its people: "Millions of unknown people sacrificed their homes, their land, their cattle, their health, their families, with barely hope of success or reward, at least in this world" (p. 21). Following the Soviet withdrawal, the country experienced a decade of civil war, Taliban rule, and severe drought (1999 to 2001), and then, in 2001 to present, the U.S.-led Afghanistan war. One has to go back to the early 1800s, to find a time when Afghanistan could be considered a unified country (Halloran 2004).

Population	29.8 million
People dependent on food aid	6.0 million
Deaths as a result of war	500,000 military, 1.5 million civilian (since 1979)
Life expectancy at birth	Males: 44.7 years; females: 45.3 years
Malnutrition	49.3% of infants to five-years olds are underweight for their age
Access to drinking water	83% of households have no safe drinking water
Literacy rate	Males: 43.1%; females: 12.6%
Maternal mortality	1,600 per 100,000 pregnancies
Infant mortality	161 babies per 1,000 live births before age 5
Birth rates	39.8 births per 1,000 people

Sources: Data from U.S. Central Intelligence Agency 2011a, United Nations 2009, World Bank 2011

Religion functions in several ways to promote group unity and solidarity. First, shared doctrines and rituals create emotional bonds among believers. Second, religions strive to raise individuals above themselves—to help them achieve a life better than they would lead if left to their own impulses. When believers violate moral codes of conduct, they feel guilt and remorse. Such feelings, in turn, motivate them to make amends. Third, religious rituals reinforce and renew social relationships—thereby binding individuals to a group. Finally, religion functions as a stabilizing force in times of severe social disturbance and abrupt change. During such times, many regulative forces in society may break down. In the absence of such forces, people are more likely to turn to religion in search of a force that will bind them to a group. This tie helps people think less about themselves and more about some common goal whether that goal is to work for peace or to participate more fervently in armed conflict (Durkheim 1951).

That religion functions to meet individual and societal needs, and that people create sacred objects and rituals, led Durkheim to reach a controversial but thought-provoking conclusion: The "something out there" that people worship is actually society.

Society as the Object of Worship

CORE CONCEPT 5 The variety of religious responses is endless, because people play a fundamental role in determining what is sacred and how they should act in its presence.

If we operate under the assumptions that all religions are true in their own fashion and that the variety of religious responses is virtually endless, we find support for Durkheim's conclusion that people create everything encompassed by religion—gods, rites, sacred objects. That is, people play a fundamental role in determining what is sacred and how to act in the presence of the sacred. Consequently, at some level, people worship what they (or their ancestors) have created. This point led Durkheim to conclude that the real object of worship is society itself—a conclusion that many critics cannot accept (Nottingham 1971).

Let us give Durkheim the benefit of the doubt, however, and ask the following: Is there anything about the nature of society that makes it deserving of such worship? In reply to this question, Durkheim maintained that society transcends the individual life, because it frees people from the bondage of nature (as in "nature versus nurture"). How does it accomplish this task? We know from cases of extreme isolation, neglect, and limited social contact that "it is impossible for a person to develop without social interaction" (Mead 1940, p. 135). In addition, studies involving psychologically and socially sound people who experience profound isolation—astronauts orbiting alone in space and prisoners of war placed in solitary confinement—show that when people are deprived of contact with others, they lose a sense of reality and personal identity (Zangwill 1987). The fact that we depend so strongly on society for our humanity supports Durkheim's view of society as "a reality from which everything that matters to us flows" (Durkheim, cited in Pickering 1984, p. 252). Durkheim argued that people create religion that reflects their strongest convictions—those convictions may have to do with the place of women in society, who we can love, and how we treat animals. In fact, Durkheim observed that whenever any group of people has strong conviction, that conviction almost always takes on a religious character. Religious gatherings and affiliations become ways of affirming convictions and mobilizing the group to uphold them, especially when the group is threatened.

A Critique of the Functionalist Perspective of Religion

To claim that religion functions as a strictly integrative force is to ignore the long history of wars between different religious groups and the many internal struggles between factions within the same religious group. For example, although the Afghan mujahideen united to oppose the Soviet occupation and its secular government, many competing factions existed within the mujahideen. After the Soviets withdrew from Afghanistan, the former mujahideen commanders became the major power brokers, and each took control of different cities outside Kabul. At this point, as had happened in the past, the same rugged terrain that made it impossible for the Soviets to gain control over the entire country likewise made it difficult for any one internal

Chris Caldeira

Durkheim believed that the variety of religious responses is endless. This is because people create the churches in which they worship. What clues does this sign offer about the people who are members of this church?

Discussion Tip: Ask students for examples of churches (including their own) where the culture of the worshippers is reflected in the rituals, sacred symbols, and physical surroundings.

The Sociological Imagination: Personal Images of Jesus

The religious painter and illustrator Warner Sallman (pictured on the right) created the image of Jesus Christ (in the background) in 1940. The number of times this image has been reproduced on "church bulletins, calendars, posters, book marks, prayer cards, tracts, buttons, stickers and stationery" is more than 500 million (Grimes 1994). As a result, many people in the United States have come to think of Jesus's physical appearance as such. Given that Jesus was born in Bethlehem (according to the Christian Bible), a town in the Middle East, is the Sallman image the most accurate representation of how Jesus might have looked? Archaeological evidence suggests that the average man at the time of Jesus was 5 feet, 3 inches tall and weighed approximately 110 pounds (Gibson 2004). Student comments suggest that many accept Sallman's image but others have come to question it:

AP Photo

- Whenever I think about what Jesus looks like, I always see Sallman's image. However, I believe that Jesus cannot look like that because of the geographic region in which he was born. I like to think that maybe God is female.
- I really can't believe that my image of Jesus is a man-made one. Warner Sallman's image has been in my head so long I cannot even comprehend another image.
- It is shocking to me to learn that Jesus probably had dark skin, hair, and facial features, because I have always imagined Jesus to look like Sallman's paintings.
- My image of Jesus used to be that of a Caucasian male, but I remember reading in the Bible that he had "hair like sheep's wool and dark skin."
- The Bible does not give an exact physical description of Jesus, but it does say that he was "unattractive to the eye." People think that he was beautifully pale with long wavy brown hair, when really he was unattractive. Now, no one really knows what he looks like. That's why I belong to a church that's Christian nondenominational and that doesn't display or worship pictures of Jesus.

group to consolidate its power. Tribal elders and religious students, in turn, tried to wrestle control from rebel commanders (U.S. Central Intelligence Agency 2001).

Eventually, the Taliban, with the help of the Pakistani government, rose to power and came to control 90 percent of the country. Its ultimate aim was to establish a pure Islamic state. At first, the Taliban seemed a welcome relief to the chaos of decades of war. Later, its strict interpretation of Islamic laws, which were enforced by amputations and public executions, created widespread resentment among the Afghan people.

This point is that religion is not entirely an integrative force. If it were, then it could not be used as the justification for destroying people who did not follow a particular version of a religion. An Amnesty International (1996c) document, *Afghanistan: Grave Abuses in the Name of Religion*, outlines numerous human rights violations committed by the Taliban in the name of religion. Those abuses included "indiscriminate killings, arbitrary and unacknowledged detention of civilians, physical restrictions on women for reasons of their gender, the beating and ill-treatment of women, children and detainees, deliberate and arbitrary killings, amputations, stoning and executions."

The Conflict Perspective

CORE CONCEPT 6 Conflict theorists focus on ways in which people use religion to repress, constrain, and exploit others.

Scholars who view religion from the conflict perspective focus on how religion turns people's attention away from social and economic inequality. This perspective stems from the work of Karl Marx, who believed that religion was the most humane feature of an inhumane world and that it arose from the tragedies and injustices of human experience. He described religion as the "sigh of the oppressed creature, the heart of a heartless world, and the soul of soulless conditions. It is the opium of the people" (Marx 1976). According to Marx, people need the comfort of religion to make the world bearable and to justify their existence. In this sense, he said, religion is analogous to a sedative.

Even though Marx acknowledged the comforting role of religion, he focused on its repressive, constraining, and exploitative qualities. In particular, he conceptualized religion as an ideology that justifies existing inequities or

Teaching Tip: Durkheim argued that, at some level, people worship what they or their ancestors have created—with emphasis on "at some level." The millions of images that have been created of Jesus illustrate this point. Go to Google Images, and enter the search term "Jesus." Almost 80 million images are noted. Take a few minutes during class to browse through these images, which offer insights about the infinite ways people have chosen to portray Jesus.

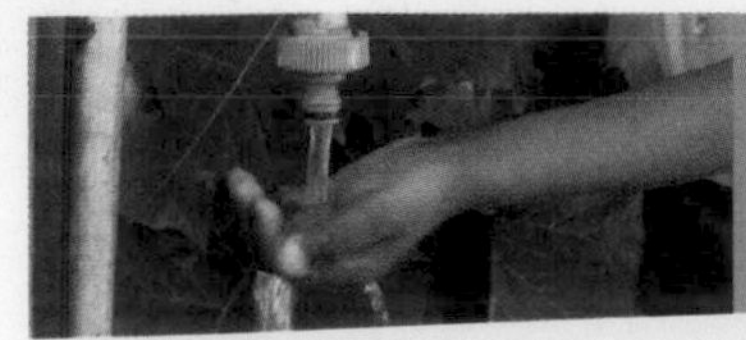

Working for Change Faith-Based Organizations in the United States

Basic statistics suggest that faith-based organizations operate as significant agents of change in American life:

- Faith ministers to the less fortunate. Eighty percent of the more than 300,000 religious congregations in America provide services to those in need.
- Faith shapes lives. Over 90 percent of urban congregations provide social services, ranging from preschool to literacy programs to health clinics.
- Faith shepherds communities. Polls estimate that between 60 and 90 percent of America's congregations provide at least one social service, and about 75 percent of local congregations provide volunteers for social service programs.
- Faith nurtures children. One out of every six child care centers in America is housed in a religious facility. The nation's largest providers of child care services are the Roman Catholic Church and the Southern Baptist Convention.

And perhaps most significantly, faith inspires the faithful to love their neighbors as they'd love themselves. Nearly one-quarter of all Americans volunteer their time and effort through faith-based organizations. Many of America's best ideas—and best results—for helping those in need have come not from the federal government but from grassroots communities, private and faith-based organizations of people who know and care about their neighbors. For years, America's churches and charities have led the way in helping the poor achieve dignity instead of despair, self-sufficiency instead of shame.

Sources: Excerpted from "President Bush's Faith-Based and Community Initiative," www.whitehouse.gov/fbci (August 1, 2004); prepared remarks of Attorney General John Ashcroft, White House Faith-Based and Community Initiative Conference (June 13, 2004).

downplays their importance. In particular, religion is a source of false consciousness in that religious teachings encourage the oppressed to accept the economic, political, and social arrangements that constrain their chances in this life because they are promised compensation for their suffering in the next world. This promise serves to rationalize the political and economic interests of the advantaged social classes.

SSGT JEREMY T. LOCK, USAF

Ironically, in its quest to recruit and support groups that would fight against the Soviet occupation of Afghanistan, the United States supported producers of opium poppies. Thus, as mujahideen insurgents pushed the Soviets out, they ordered peasants to plant opium. U.S. support helped to turn Afghanistan into the world's largest producer of opium and processed heroin. Today, the Afghan economy depends on opium, and profits from its production fund Taliban operations against the United States (Judah 2001, U.S. Central Intelligence Agency 2011).

This kind of ideology led Marx to conclude that religious teaching inhibits protest and revolutionary change. He went so far as to claim that religion would be unnecessary in a truly classless or propertyless society. In the absence of material inequality and exploitation, there are no injustices that cause people to turn to religion. Consider one extreme example of religion-inspired injustice. After the Taliban took control of Afghanistan, they placed, in the name of Islam, severe restrictions on women and the population in general. Women were required to appear covered from head to toe; they had to stay home unless accompanied by a close male relative and could not work outside the home or go to school. Nonreligious schools were closed; music, television, and other forms of entertainment were banned; homosexuals were killed. The Taliban's funding came from two major sources: Osama bin Laden and revenue from the production of opium for heroin (Judah 2001).

A Critique of the Conflict Perspective of Religion

The major criticism leveled at Marx and the conflict perspective of religion is that, contrary to that perspective, religion is not always a sign or tool of oppression. Sometimes religion has been used as a vehicle for protesting or working to change social and economic inequities (see Working for Change: "Faith-Based Organizations in the United States").

Liberation theology represents one such approach to religion. Liberation theologians maintain that Christians have a responsibility to demand social justice for the

Student Activity: Ask students to identify a faith-based organization in their community that serves a population in need. That need may be related to homelessness, addiction, disaster relief, and so on. Write a paper describing the service offered.

PH2 ANTHONY J. PUGLIANI

This Buddhist monk sits outside Kadena Air Base in Afghanistan in protest of U.S. military intervention. He is playing a drum to console the spirits of those who have died in that war.

marginalized peoples of the world, especially landless peasants and the urban poor, and to take an active role at the grassroots level to bring about political and economic justice. Ironically, this interpretation of Christian faith and practice is partly inspired by Marxist thought, in that it advocates raising the consciousness of the poor and teaching them to work together to obtain land and employment and to preserve their cultural identity.

Sociologist J. Milton Yinger (1971) identifies at two interrelated conditions under which religion can become a vehicle of protest or change. In the first condition, a government or other organization fails to deliver on its ideals (such as equal opportunity, justice for all, or the right to bear arms). In the second condition, a society becomes divided along class, ethnic, or sectarian lines. In such cases, disenfranchised groups may form sects or cults and "use seemingly eccentric features of the new religion to symbolize their sense of separation" and to rally their followers to fight against the establishment, or the dominant group (p. 111). In the United States, one religion that emerged in reaction to society's failure to ensure equal opportunity to disenfranchised blacks was the Nation of Islam.

In the 1930s, black nationalist leader Wallace Fard Muhammad founded the Nation of Islam and began preaching in the Temple of Islam in Detroit. (When Fard disappeared in 1934, he was replaced by his chosen successor, Elijah Muhammed.) According to Fard, the white man was the personification of evil, and black people, whose religion had been stripped from them upon enslavement, were Muslim. In addition, he taught that the way out did not entail gaining the "devil's" or white man's approval but by exercising self-discipline and gaining an education. Members received an X to replace their "slave name" (hence, Malcolm X). In the social context of the 1930s, this message was very attractive:

> You're talking about Negroes. You're talking about "niggers," who are the rejected and the despised, meeting in some little, filthy, dingy little [room] upstairs over some beer hall or something, some joint that nobody cares about. Nobody cares about these people. . . . You can pass them on the street and in 1930, if they don't get off the sidewalk, you could have them arrested. That's the level of what was going on. (National Public Radio 1984a)

The Nation of Islam is merely one example of a religious organization working to improve life for African Americans. Historically, African American churches have reached out to millions of black people who have felt excluded from the U.S. political and economic system (Lincoln and Mamiya 1990). For example, African American churches did much to achieve the overall successes of the civil rights movement. Indeed, some observers argue that the movement would have been impossible if the churches had not become involved (Lincoln and Mamiya 1990).

NYWT&S Photograph Collectgion, Library of Congress Prints and Photographs Division

Elijah Muhammad, the man who succeeded the founder of the Nation of Islam, is shown here addressing his followers in 1964, at the height of the civil rights movement. One of his best-known followers is in attendance: Cassius Clay, who later changed his name to Muhammad Ali.

liberation theology A religious movement based on the idea that organized religions have a responsibility to demand social justice for the marginalized peoples of the world, especially landless peasants and the urban poor, and to take an active role at the grassroots level to bring about political and economic justice.

Teaching Tip: When presenting Marx's vision of religion as the "sigh of the oppressed creature, the sentiment of a heartless world, and the soul of soulless conditions; it is the opium of the people," mention the recent revelations that Mother Teresa, who spent her life working with the poor in the slums of Calcutta, had a similar view. Some quotes from her letters include (1) "Where is my faith? Even deep down... there is nothing but emptiness and darkness... If there be God—please forgive me." (2) "What do I labor for? If there be no God, there can be no soul. If there be no soul then, Jesus, You also are not true."

The Interplay between Economics and Religion

Max Weber wanted to understand the role of religious beliefs in the origins and development of **modern capitalism**—an economic system that involves careful calculation of costs of production relative to profits, borrowing and lending money, accumulating all forms of capital, and drawing workers from an unrestricted global labor pool (Robertson 1987).

> **CORE CONCEPT 7 Modern capitalism emerged and flourished in Europe and the United States because Calvinism supplied an ideologically supportive spirit or ethic.**

In his book *The Protestant Ethic and the Spirit of Capitalism*, Weber (1958) asked why modern capitalism emerged and flourished in Europe rather than in China or India (the two dominant world civilizations at the end of the sixteenth century). He also asked why business leaders and capitalists in Europe and the United States were overwhelmingly Protestant.

To answer these questions, Weber studied the major world religions and some of the societies in which these religions were practiced. Based on his comparisons, Weber concluded that a branch of Protestant tradition—Calvinism—supplied a "spirit" or a work ethic that supported profit-oriented behavior and motivations. Unlike other religions that Weber studied, Calvinism emphasized **this-worldly asceticism**—a belief that people are instruments of divine will and that God determines and directs their activities. Consequently, Calvinists glorified God when they worked hard and did not indulge in the fruits of their labor (that is, when they did not use money to eat, drink, or otherwise relax to excess). In contrast, Buddhism, a religion that Weber defined as the Eastern parallel and opposite of Calvinism, "emphasized the basically illusory character of worldly life and regarded release from the contingencies of the everyday world as the highest religious aspiration" (Robertson 1987, p. 7). Calvinists, who believed God to be all powerful and all knowing, emphasized **predestination**—the belief that God has foreordained all things, including the salvation or damnation of individual souls. According to this doctrine, people could do nothing to change their fate and only a small portion of people was destined to attain salvation.

modern capitalism An economic system that involves careful calculation of costs of production relative to profits, borrowing and lending money, accumulating all forms of capital, and drawing labor from an unrestricted global labor pool.

this-worldly asceticism A belief that people are instruments of divine will and that God determines and directs their activities.

predestination The belief that God has foreordained all things, including the salvation or damnation of individual souls.

Weber maintained that this-worldly asceticism and predestination created a crisis prompting Calvinists to search for some concrete sign that they were among God's chosen people, destined for salvation. Accumulated wealth became that concrete sign. At the same time, this-worldly asceticism "acted powerfully against the spontaneous enjoyment of possessions; it restricted consumption, especially of luxuries" (Weber 1958, p. 171). Frugal behavior encouraged people to accumulate wealth and make investments—important actions for the success of capitalism.

For Weber, the Protestant ethic was a significant ideological force; it was not the sole cause of capitalism but one force underlying the rise of "*certain aspects* of capitalism" (Aron 1969, p. 204). Unfortunately, many who read Weber's ideas overestimate the importance that he assigned to the Protestant ethic for achieving economic success, drawing a conclusion that Weber himself never reached: The reason that some groups and societies are disadvantaged is simply that they lack this ethic.

In assessing Weber's ideas about the origins of industrial capitalism, keep in mind Weber was not writing about the form of capitalism that exists today, a form that places high value on consumption and self-indulgence. Weber maintained that, once established, capitalism would generate its own norms and become a self-sustaining force. In fact, Weber argued, capitalism came to support a production system "without inner meaning or value and in which men operate almost as mindless cogs" (Turner 1974, p. 155). At that point, religion becomes an increasingly insignificant factor to maintaining the capitalist system.

THE EMPIRE BUILDERS
"Those Christian men to whom God in his infinite wisdom has given control of the property interests of the country."

Library of Congress Prints and Photographs Division

This print, whose setting is New York City's Trinity Church, shows men who were considered empire builders in U.S. history: James J. Hill, Andrew Carnegie, Cornelius Vanderbilt, John D. Rockefeller, J. Pierpont Morgan, Jay Cooke or Edward H. Harriman, and Jay Gould. Notice the caption below the image: "Those Christian men to whom God in his infinite wisdom had given control of the property interests of the country."

Secularization and Fundamentalism

CORE CONCEPT 8 Secularization and fundamentalism fuel each other's growth in that secularization invites a fundamentalist response.

Some sociologists argue that industrialization and scientific advances that accompany the rise of capitalism cause **secularization**—a process in which religious influences on thoughts and behavior become increasingly irrelevant. Thus, in the face of uncertainty, people are less likely to turn to religion or to a supernatural power to intervene; rather, they rely on scientific explanations and technological interventions. As one example, illness is not a product of God's will. Instead, science explains illnesses, and technology is employed to cure illness.

Secularization invites a fundamentalist response, a belief in the timelessness of sacred writings and a belief that such writings apply to all areas of one's life. Fundamentalists believe sacred principles have been abandoned, and they aim to revive them as the definitive and guiding blueprint for life.

Americans and Europeans tend to associate secularization with an increase in scientific understanding and in technological solutions to everyday problems of living. From a Muslim perspective, secularization is a Western-imposed phenomenon—specifically, a result of exposure to what many people in the Middle East consider the most negative of Western values. This point is illustrated by the following observation by a Muslim student attending college in Great Britain:

> If I did not watch out [while I was in college], I knew that I would be washed away in that culture. In one particular area, of course, was exposure to a society where free sexual relations prevailed. There you are not subject to any control, and you are faced with a very serious challenge, and you have to rely upon your own strength, spiritual strength to stabilize your character and hold fast to your beliefs. (National Public Radio 1984b)

The Complexity of Fundamentalism

In its popular usage, the term *fundamentalism* is applied to a wide array of religious groups around the world, including the Moral Majority in the United States, Orthodox Jews in Israel, and various Islamic groups in the Middle East. Religious groups labeled as fundamentalist are usually portrayed as "fossilized relics . . . living perpetually in a bygone age" (Caplan 1987, p. 5). Americans frequently employ this simplistic analysis to explain events in the Middle East, especially the causes of political turmoil that threatens the interests of the United States (including its demand for oil).

Fundamentalism is a more complex phenomenon than popular conceptions would lead us to believe. It is

SPC LESLIE ANGULO

U.S.-led troops distribute dolls and other toys to orphaned Afghan girls. What does it mean to receive such toys, which challenge Islamic beliefs about modest dress and other aspects of life?

impossible to define a fundamentalist in terms of age, ethnicity, social class, political ideology, or sexual orientation, because this kind of belief appeals to a wide range of people. Perhaps the most important characteristic of fundamentalists is their belief that a relationship with God, Allah, or some other supernatural force provides answers to personal and social problems. In addition, fundamentalists often wish to "bring the wider culture back to its religious roots" (Lechner 1989, p. 51).

Caplan (1987) identifies a number of other traits that seem to characterize fundamentalists. First, fundamentalists emphasize the authority, infallibility, and timeless truth of sacred writings as a "definitive blueprint" for life (p. 19). This characteristic does not mean that a definitive interpretation of sacred writings actually exists. Indeed, any sacred text has as many interpretations as there are groups that claim it as their blueprint. Even members of the same fundamentalist organization may disagree about the true meaning of the texts they follow.

Second, fundamentalists usually conceive of history as a "cosmic struggle between good and evil": a struggle between those dedicated to principles outlined in sacred scriptures and those who digress. To fundamentalists, truth is not a relative; it does not vary across time and place. Instead, truth is unchanging and knowable through the sacred texts.

Third, fundamentalists do not distinguish between the sacred and the profane in their day-to-day lives. Religious principles govern all areas of life, including family, business, and leisure. Religious behavior, in their view, does not just take place in a church, a mosque, or a temple.

Fourth, fundamentalist religious groups emerge for a reason, usually in reaction to a perceived threat or crisis,

secularization A process by which religious influences on thought and behavior are reduced.

Video Tip: The textbook points out that fundamentalists in their day-to-day lives do not distinguish between the sacred and profane. That is, religious principles govern all areas of life, including family, business, and leisure. For two examples of religious principles governing interactions with the public, see the online Newshour reports "Islamic Community in Minnesota Faces Growing Pains," profiling Muslim cab drivers who refuse to serve customers behaving in "unIslamic" ways, and "Morning-After Pill Protest" profiling Christian pharmacists. Simply enter titles into the Newshour search engine at www.pbs.org/newshour.

whether real or imagined. Consequently, any discussion of a particular fundamentalist group must include some reference to an adversary.

Fifth, one obvious concern for fundamentalists is the need to reverse the trend toward gender equality, which they believe is symptomatic of a declining moral order. In fundamentalist religions, women's rights often become subordinated to ideals that the group considers more important to the well-being of the society, such as the traditional family or the "right to life." Such a priority of ideals is regarded as the correct order of things.

Islamic Fundamentalism

In *The Islamic Threat: Myth or Reality?*, professor of religious studies John L. Esposito (1992) maintains that most Americans' understanding of fundamentalism does not apply very well to contemporary Islam. The term *fundamentalism* has its roots in American Protestantism and the twentieth-century movement that emphasized the literal interpretation of the Bible.

Fundamentalists are portrayed as static, literalist, retrogressive, and extremist. Just as we cannot apply the term *fundamentalism* to all Protestants in the United States, we cannot apply it to the entire Muslim world, especially when we consider that Muslims make up the majority of the population in at least 45 countries. Esposito believes that a more appropriate term is **Islamic revitalism** or *Islamic activism*. The form of Islamic revitalism may vary from one country to another but it involves a disenchantment with, and even rejection of, the West; soul-searching; a quest for greater authenticity; and a conviction that Islam offers a viable alternative to nationalism, socialism, and capitalism (Esposito 1986).

Esposito (1986) believes that Islamic revitalism represents a "response to the failures and crises of authority and legitimacy that have plagued most modern Muslim states" (p. 53). Recall that after World War I, France and Great Britain carved up the Middle East into nation-states, drawing the boundaries to meet the economic and political needs of Western powers. Lebanon, for example, was created in part to establish a Christian tie to the West. For example, Israel was envisioned as a refuge for persecuted Jews when no country seemed to want them; the Kurds received no state; Iraq became virtually landlocked; and resource-rich territories were incorporated into states with very sparse populations (for example, Kuwait, Saudi Arabia, the United Arab Emirates). Their citizens viewed most of the leaders who took control of these foreign creations "as autocratic heads of corrupt, authoritarian regimes . . . propped up by Western governments and multinational corporations" (p. 54).

When Arab armies from six states lost "so quickly, completely, and publicly" in a war with Israel in 1967, Arabs were forced to question the political and moral structure of their societies (Hourani 1991, p. 442). Had the leaders and the people abandoned Islamic principles or deviated too far from them? Could a return to a stricter Islamic way of life restore confidence to the Middle East and give it an identity independent of the West? Questions of social justice also arose. Oil wealth and modernization policies had led to rapid increases in population and urbanization and opened up a vast chasm between the oil-rich countries, such as Kuwait and Saudi Arabia, and the poor, densely populated countries, such as Egypt, Pakistan, and Bangladesh. Western capitalism, which was seen as one of the primary forces behind these trends, seemed blind to social justice, instead promoting unbridled consumption and widespread poverty. Likewise, the Marxist socialism

Islamic revitalism Responses to the belief that existing political, economic, and social systems have failed—responses that include a disenchantment with, and even a rejection of, the West; soul-searching; a quest for greater authenticity; and a conviction that Islam offers a viable alternative to secular nationalism, socialism, and capitalism.

SSGT CECILIO R CARDO, USAF

An Afghan child holds up a leaflet warning against picking up unexploded ordinance. The warning extends to unexploded ordinance that has accumulated over the last 25 years of war. In light of history, is it any wonder that Afghans have rejected nationalism, socialism, and capitalism in favor of Islam?

Student Activity: Ask students to read an Online Newshour interview with "four Biblical translators about their differing translations of the holy book." The differing interpretations lend support to Durkheim's conclusion that people play a fundamental role in creating religion. The interview is not available in audio or video but the text is available at http://www.pbs.org/newshour/bb/religion/bible_4-04.html.

No Borders No Boundaries Countries with Significant Percentages of Muslims

The prophet Muhammad's first recitations of the Qur'an occurred in Arabia around AD 610. Islam's spread has made it one of the world's major religions. The map shows countries where a significant percentage of people practice Islam. Here, *significant percentage* is defined as "at least 2 percent of the population (or 1 in every 50 persons)."

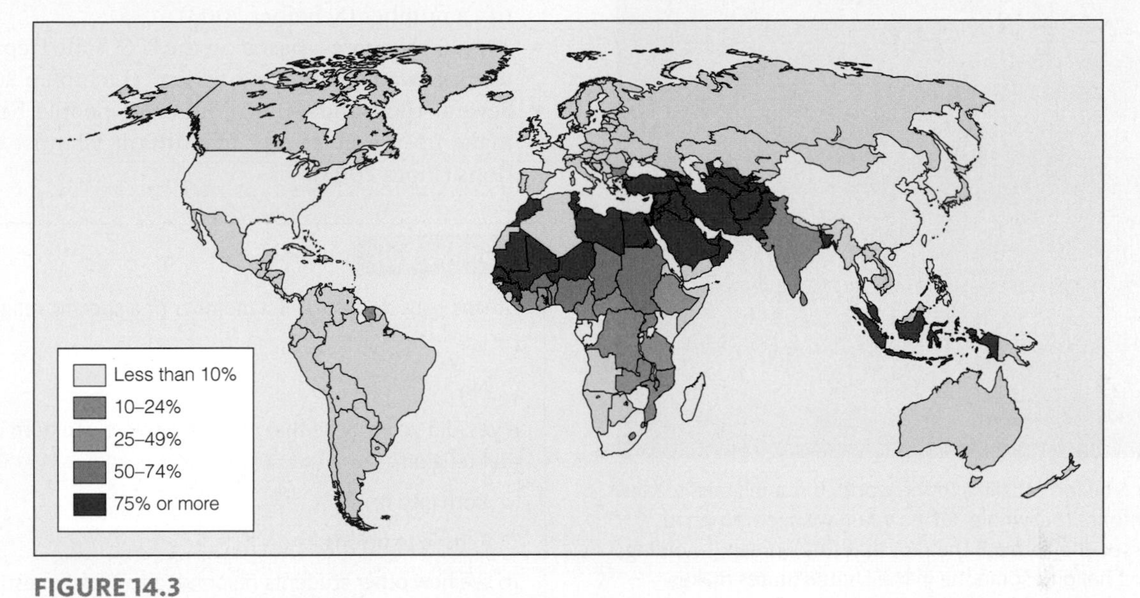

FIGURE 14.3

Source: Data from U.S. Central Intelligence Agency (2011)

(a godless alternative) of the Soviet Union had failed to produce social justice. It is no wonder that the Taliban and other Muslim groups in Afghanistan rejected nationalism, Western capitalism and Marxist socialism. After all, the disintegration of Afghanistan was a direct product of the cold war between the United States and the Soviet Union.

For many people, Islam offers an alternative vision for society. According to Esposito (1986), five beliefs guide Islamic activists (who follow many political persuasions, ranging from conservative to militant):

1. Islam is a comprehensive way of life relevant to politics, law, and society.
2. Muslim societies fail when they depart from Islamic ways and follow the secular and materialistic ways of the West.
3. An Islamic social and political revolution is necessary for renewal.
4. Islamic law must replace laws inspired or imposed by the West.
5. Science and technology must be used in ways that reflect Islamic values, to guard against the infiltration of Western values.

Muslim groups differ dramatically in their beliefs about how quickly and by what methods these principles should be implemented. Most Muslims, however, are willing to work within existing political arrangements; they condemn violence as a method of bringing about political and social change.

Jihad and Militant Islam

In thinking about the meaning of jihad, it is important to distinguish between religious and political jihad. Many Islamic scholars have pointed out that in the religious sense of the word, true *jihad* is the "constant struggle of Muslims to conquer their inner base instincts, to follow the path to God, and to do good in society" (Mitten 2002). But as Daniel Pipes (2003) points out in *Militant Islam Reaches America*, jihad as used by those who lead political organizations such as Egyptian Islamic Jihad, Islamic Jihad of Yemen, and International Islamic Front for Jihad against Jews and Christians means "armed struggle against non-Muslims" and against "Muslims who fail to live up to the requirements of their faith" (p. 264). Militant Islam is an "aggressive totalitarian ideology that ultimately discriminates barely, if at all, among those who stand in its path" (p. 249). In other words, non-Muslims as well as Muslims (who do not share the militants' outlook or who happen to be in the wrong place at the wrong time) can be targets of attack.

Courtesy of Bob Nabor

There are 1.6 billion Muslims in the world. It is a mistake to view them as a monolithic whole. Often when we see women in burkas, we see the "other." The fact that this woman is holding a sign saying hello to someone in the United States makes us wonder about her life and personality; the simple act of wondering releases this woman from the designation "other."

How many militant Islamist political *jihadists* exist in the world today in which there are 1.6 billion Muslims (Pew Research 2009)? Some estimates follow:

- 15,000—based on the number believed to have been trained in al-Qaida training camps
- 5,000 living in the United States—based on FBI figures created in response to pressure from Congress to identify a number (Scheiber 2003)
- 100,000 or more—based on the U.S. State Department's terrorist watch list or "no-fly list" (Lichtblau 2003)
- Several thousand—the number of people believed to make up the *inner core* of militant Islamist organizations (Pipes 2003)

Online Poll

Do you consider yourself a member of a specific religion?

○ Yes

○ No

If yes, did you choose that religion or were you born into that religion?

○ Born into it.

○ I chose to belong.

To see how other students responded to these questions, go to **www.cengagebrain.com.**

TECH SGT CECILIO M. RICARDO JR

Summary of CORE CONCEPTS

CORE CONCEPT 1 When sociologists study religion, they are guided by the scientific method and by the assumption that no religions are false.

Sociologists studying religion adhere to the scientific method, which requires them to study only observable and verifiable phenomena. When studying religions, sociologists must rid themselves of all preconceived notions of what religion should be.

CORE CONCEPT 2 Durkheim defined religion as a system of shared rituals and beliefs about the sacred that bind together a community of worshippers.

Religions can be classified into three categories depending on the type of phenomenon their followers consider sacred: sacramental, prophetic, or mystical. There are at least five broad types of religious organizations: ecclesiae, denominations, sects, established sects, and cults.

CORE CONCEPT 3 Civil religion is an institutionalized set of beliefs about a nation's past, present, and future and a corresponding set of rituals that take on a sacred quality and elicit feelings of patriotism.

Civil religion forges ties between religion and a nation's needs and political interests. Even in the face of internal divisions, national beliefs and rituals can inspire awe, respect, and reverence for country. In times of war, presidents draw upon a selected historical and mythological framework to justify military engagement, offer the public a hoped-for outcome, and instill patriotism. America's civil religion can be traced to a nineteenth-century political doctrine known as *manifest destiny*—the belief that the United States had a divine mission to serve as a democratic model to the rest of the world, to exert its good influence upon other nations, and to instill hope to the rest of the world.

CORE CONCEPT 4 The functionalist perspective maintains that religion serves vital social functions for individuals and for the group.

That some form of religion appears to have existed for as long as humans have lived encourages functionalists to maintain that religion must serve some vital social functions for individuals and the group. On the individual level, people embrace religion in the face of uncertainty, in intolerable circumstances, and to achieve a successful outcome. Religion can function in several ways to promote group unity and solidarity, including forging emotional bonds among believers; instilling a broader purpose that raises individuals above themselves; and working as a stabilizing force in times of severe social disturbance and abrupt change.

CORE CONCEPT 5 The variety of religious responses is endless, because people play a fundamental role in determining what is sacred and how they should act in its presence.

If we operate under the assumptions that all religions are true in their own fashion and that the variety of religious responses is virtually endless, we must realize the role people play in creating religion and in determining what is sacred and how to act in the presence of the sacred. Consequently, at some level, people worship what they (or their ancestors) have created.

CORE CONCEPT 6 Conflict theorists focus on ways in which people use religion to repress, constrain, and exploit others.

Conflict theorists focus on how religion turns people's attention away from injustices and on religion's repressive, constraining, and exploitative qualities. From this point of view, religion is used to rationalize existing inequities. Religion is not always a sign or tool of oppression; it has been used as a vehicle for protesting or working to change social and economic inequities. In particular, liberation theologians maintain that they have a responsibility to demand social justice for the marginalized peoples of the world, especially landless peasants and the urban poor, and to take an active role at the grassroots level to bring about political and economic justice.

CORE CONCEPT 7 Modern capitalism emerged and flourished in Europe and the United States because Calvinism supplied an ideologically supportive spirit or ethic.

Max Weber focused on understanding how norms generated by different religious traditions influenced adherents' economic orientations and motivations. Based on his comparisons, Weber maintained that this-worldly asceticism and predestination created a crisis prompting Calvinists to search for some concrete sign that they were destined for salvation. Accumulated wealth became that concrete sign. At the same time, this-worldly asceticism discouraged excessive consumption and encouraged people to accumulate wealth and make investments—important actions for the success of capitalism.

CORE CONCEPT 8 Secularization and fundamentalism fuel each other's growth in that secularization invites a fundamentalist response.

Secularization is a broad term used to describe the decline of religious influences over everyday life. In the face of uncertainty, people are less likely to turn to a supernatural power to intervene; rather, they rely on scientific explanation and technological interventions. Secularization invites a fundamentalist response. Fundamentalists believe sacred principles have been abandoned and they aim to revive them as the definitive and guiding blueprint for life. Fundamentalism is a more complex phenomenon than popular conceptions would lead us to believe. It is impossible to define a fundamentalist in terms of age, ethnicity, social class, political ideology, or sexual orientation, because this kind of belief appeals to a wide range of people.

Resources on the Internet

Login to CengageBrain.com to access the resources your instructor requires. For this book, you can access:

Sociology CourseMate

Access an integrated eBook, chapter-specific interactive learning tools, including flash cards, quizzes, videos, and more in your Sociology CourseMate.

Take a pretest for this chapter and receive a personalized study plan based on your results that will identify the topics you need to review and direct you to online resources to help you master those topics. Then take a posttest to help you determine the concepts you have mastered and what you will need to work on.

CourseReader

CourseReader for Sociology is an online reader providing access to readings, and audio and video selections to accompany your course materials.

Visit **www.cengagebrain.com** to access your account and purchase materials.

Key Terms

church 365
civil religion 368
cults 368
denomination 367
ecclesia 366
established sects 367
Islamic revitalism 380
liberation theology 377
modern capitalism 378
mystical religions 364
predestination 378
profane 365
prophetic religions 364
rituals 365
sacramental religions 364
sacred 363
sect 367
secularization 379
this-worldly asceticism 378

15 BIRTH, DEATH, AND MIGRATION

With Emphasis on EXTREME CASES

How many children do you think you would have if, in a given year, there is a one in 50 chance of dying in childbirth? These odds apply to Sierra Leone. You might be surprised to learn that women at the greatest risk of dying in child birth also have the most children; on average, as many as seven or eight. But what if the odds of dying in childbirth were virtually zero, as is the case in Ireland and Sweden? How might you feel about having children? Chances are you would have two or fewer children. Moreover, the chances that an Irish or Swedish woman between the ages of 40 and 44 is childless ranges from 15 and 30 percent (OECD 2010). The point is that knowing the chances of surviving childbirth offers broader insights about how people, especially women, see themselves and plan their futures.

Why Focus On EXTREME CASES?

Births, deaths, and migration are key experiences, not just for individuals but also for societies. Births represent the entry of new members into society; deaths represent their exit. Migration involves leaving one society for another. In this chapter, we focus on these three key experiences and pay special attention to countries where births, deaths, and migration occur at the highest and lowest rates. Specifically, we compare the countries that experience the highest and the lowest

- birth rates, including the teen birth rate;
- death rates including infant, maternal, and overall death rates; and
- migration rates, including the rates of migration into and out of the country.

We emphasize extreme cases because doing so allows us to frame the end points on the continuum of human experience. Generally, being at the extreme ends of an experience suggests vulnerability and sometimes special advantage. As one example, the teen birth rate in Niger is 199 of 1,000 teens and that rate is 1.2 in 1,000 teens in South Korea. On the surface, these birth rates might just seem like numbers with little human significance. But actually, knowing these rates allows us to think deeply about what personal lives are like and how a society is organized. For example, if we know the teen birth rate in Niger is 199 per 1,000 teens, we know that *each year* there are 199 births for every 1,000 teen females. To put it another way, each year, 20 percent or 1 in 5 teens have a baby. If we know that the teen birth rate in South Korea is 1 in 1,000, we know that each year there is 1 birth for every 1,000 teen females. What do these rates suggest about the lives of females who are teenagers in each country? If you were a teenage girl, how might you think about the future if you lived in Niger versus South Korea? The point is that knowing rates allows us to think more deeply about our own and others' lives.

Online Poll

How many children do you think you would have if you knew that 1 in 50 mothers die in childbirth each year?

○ None

○ One

○ Two

○ Three or more

To see how other students responded to these questions, go to **www.cengagebrain.com.**

The Study of Population

CORE CONCEPT 1 Demography, a subspecialty within sociology, focuses on births, deaths, and migration—major factors that determine population size and rate of growth.

Demography focuses on human populations and their characteristics, including size and rate of growth. Most organizations—private, public, and governmental—have an interest in knowing population characteristics, if only for planning purposes. For example, school officials need to know the size of the school-age population and whether,

Teaching Tip: For comparative data on the three major life events—births, deaths, and migration—see United Nations Population Division, World Population Prospects (www.un.org/esa/population/).

on the basis of births and in-migration, it is projected to decline or increase in coming years. These projections will affect decisions to expand or consolidate the number of schools. Health care planners need to know the size of the population age 65 and older and whether it is projected to decline or increase, as this age group has some of the greatest health care needs (see Working for Change).

The size and growth of a population depend on three key events—births, deaths, and migration. In the pages that follow, we will consider these population-related characteristics and how each is expressed as rates, giving special attention to extreme cases as endpoints on the continuum of human experiences (for example, the teen birth rate range from a low of 1.2 in 1,000 teens in South Korea to a high of 199 per 1,000 teens in Niger). Later in the chapter, we will learn the reason for very low and very high rates.

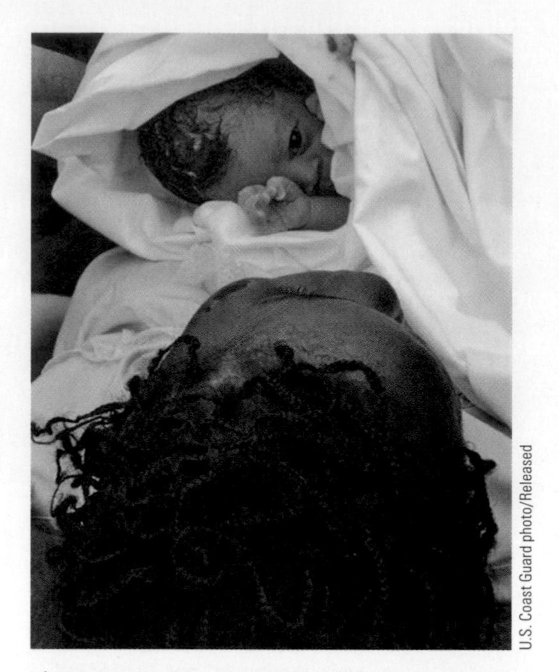
U.S. Coast Guard photo/Released

The average woman in the world bears 2.5 children over her lifetime. But the total fertility rate for a country ranges from 1.15 in China to 7.7 children in Niger.

Births

Births add new people to a population. Each year, the world adds approximately 134 million people. For comparison, demographers often convert the number of births into a crude birth rate. The **crude birth rate** is the annual number of births per 1,000 people in a designated area. From a global perspective, the crude birth rate is 19.5 births for every 1,000 people in the world. The country with the highest crude birth rate is the African country of Niger, where each year there are approximately 51.4 births for every 1,000 people. The country with the lowest crude birth rate is Japan, with an annual birth rate of 7.3 births per 1,000 people. To calculate the birth rate, we divide the number of births in a year by the size of the population living in the geographic area of interest at the onset of that year and then multiply that figure by 1,000.

Sometimes demographers want to know age-specific rates for a specific age cohort within the population. Of particular interest is the teenage birth rate, the number of babies born each year to women who are in their teens. We have already learned that the country with the highest teen birth rate is Niger (199 babies for every 1,000 teens). So over the course of a year, 19.9 percent of teens give birth to a baby. We have also learned that South Korea has the lowest teen birth rate, which is 1.2 babies per every 1,000 teens.

In addition to the birth rate, demographers are interested in the **total fertility rate**, which states the average number of children that women bear over their lifetime. The average woman in the world bears 2.5 children over the course of her reproductive life. The country with the highest total fertility rate is Niger with 7.7 children; the country of China has the lowest rate (1.15 children).

Deaths

Deaths reduce the size of a population. Each year, the planet loses about 56.2 million people to death. This loss is often expressed as a rate. The **crude death rate** is the annual number of deaths per 1,000 people in a designated area. Like the crude birth rate, it is calculated by dividing the number of deaths in a year by a designated area's population size at the onset of that year and then multiplying that number by 1,000. The country with the highest death rate in the world is Angola with 23.4 deaths per 1,000 population, and the country with the lowest death rate is United Arab Emirates with a death rate of 2 deaths per every 1,000 people.

As with birth rates, we can calculate the death rates for specific segments of the population, such as for men, for women, or for specific age categories such as 1 year olds or younger. The death rate among those 1 year old or younger is called the **infant mortality rate**. Infant mortality is calculated by dividing the number of deaths among those 1 year old or younger by the total number of births in that year and then multiplying that result by 1,000. The

demography A subspecialty within sociology that focuses on the study of human populations and their characteristics, including size and rate of growth.

crude birth rate The annual number of births per 1,000 people in a designated geographic area.

total fertility rate The average number of children that women in a specific population bear over their lifetime.

crude death rate The annual number of deaths per 1,000 people in a designated geographic area.

infant mortality rate The annual number of deaths of infants 1 year old or younger for every 1,000 such infants born alive.

Working for Change U.S. Bureau of the Census

The U.S. Bureau of the Census serves as the leading source of quality data about the nation's people and economy. In collecting that data, the census bureau honors privacy, protects confidentiality, shares its expertise globally, and conducts its work openly. Among other things, the information gathered allows us to know how many people were born since the last census, moved from one location to another within the United States, and moved into the United States from a foreign country, as well as the age-sex composition of the population. The Bureau of the Census normally employs nearly 12,000 people, but it temporarily expands its workforce by about 800,000 when the census is taken every ten years. Some of its most important data products are:

- Population and Housing Census—every 10 years
- Economic Census—every 5 years
- Census of Governments—every 5 years
- American Community Survey—annually

The data collected has many uses, including to determine the distribution of congressional seats to states as mandated by the U.S. Constitution; to apportion seats in the U.S. House of Representatives; to define legislature districts, school district assignment areas, and other important functional areas of government to make decisions about services for the elderly; to define where to build new roads and schools; and where to locate job training centers. Census data affects how funding is allocated to communities' neighborhood improvements, public health, education, transportation, and much more.

Source: U.S. Bureau of the Census 2011.

infant mortality rate for the world is 41.6 deaths before age 1 for 1,000 babies born. The highest infant mortality in the world is Angola, with 175.9 deaths per 1,000 babies born; the lowest infant mortality is in Sweden where 2.7 babies die per 1,000 born before reaching age 1. The maternal mortality rate is also an important indicator of well-being. **Maternal mortality** is the death of a woman, while pregnant or within 42 days of a termination of pregnancy, from any cause related to or aggravated by pregnancy or the way it is managed (World Health Organization 2011). The country with the highest maternal mortality rate is Sierra Leone, with 199 deaths per 1,000 pregnancies. Sweden has the lowest rate, 5 deaths per 1,000 pregnancies.

Migration

Migration is the movement of people from one residence to another. Demographers use the term **in-migration** to denote the movement of people into a designated area and the term **out-migration** to denote the movement of people out of a designated area. That movement increases population size if the people are moving in, or reduces the population size if they are moving out. Sociologists calculate the **net migration**, the difference between the number moving into an area and the number moving out. This difference is typically converted into a rate by dividing that difference by the size of the relevant population, and then multiplying the result by 1,000. We can calculate the **migration rate** for towns, cities, counties, states, countries, or any other region of the world. The country with the highest net migration rate in the world is Zimbabwe; its rate is +24.8 per 1,000 residents, which means that 24.8 more people moved into the country than moved out for every 1,000 residents who lived there. The country with the lowest net migration is Jordan with a rate of −14.3, which means that 14.3 more people moved out of the country than moved in for every 1,000 residents.

Migration results from two factors. **Push factors** are the conditions that encourage people to move out of an area. Common push factors include religious or political persecution, discrimination, depletion of natural resources, lack of employment opportunities, and natural disasters (droughts, floods, earthquakes, and so on). A dramatic example of a push factor was the 2005 Hurricane Katrina, which pushed 60 percent of New Orleans's population out of the city, changing the city's size from 454,863 to

maternal mortality rate The death of a woman while pregnant or within 42 days of a termination of pregnancy from any cause related to or aggravated by pregnancy or the way it is managed (World Health Organization).

migration The movement of people from one residence to another.

in-migration The movement of people into a designated area.

out-migration The movement of people out of a designated area.

net migration The difference between the number moving into an area and the number moving out.

migration rate A rate based on the difference between the number of people entering and the number of people leaving a designated geographic area in a year. We divide that difference by the size of the relevant population and then multiply the result by 1,000.

push factors The conditions that encourage people to move out of a geographic area.

Teaching Tip: Take some time to show students the U.S. Bureau of the Census website, specifically the wealth of national, and even international data, available at www.census.gov/.

The Sociological Imagination Moving to the United States from Liberia

Photo by Lance Cpl. Dorian Gardner, USMC

More than 33,000 non-U.S. citizens are serving in the U.S. military, which means that each immigrated to the United States at some point in life. One among the 33,000 is a Liberian native named Nimley Tabue. Tabue's parents came from different tribes. He said his parents' tribal differences did not affect his family until a war between the tribes erupted in 1989. "My father refused to kill, so (rebels) tried to kill him," Tabue said.

Tabue remembers fleeing through the country for three days as a child. "We stopped by a river once to get some water," said Tabue, who was with his mother and siblings at the time. "I held my 4-month-old brother in my arms as he died." According to Tabue, his father, Aloysius Tabue, traveled to America searching for ways to improve his family's life, and he called home often. "I learned about the Marines from my father," Tabue said. "He would say, 'If you guys come over here, make sure you do something with your life. The Marines will give you something no other service can.'"

Because of the ongoing war around him, school became less of a priority, and Tabue was taken out of school following the second grade. He, along with his mother and sister, came to Chicago to live with his father. At 12 years old, Tabue jumped back into the school swing. But after four years without touching a book, school presented a new challenge. "I forgot how to do math, and my English was bad," Tabue said. "I had to go to school over the summer and take extra classes."

After years of extra classes, Tabue's name was added to the high school honor roll. Tabue had not planned on leaving Chicago, but he remembered what his father had always told him about the Corps. "He told me, 'This is where they separate the men from the boys,'" Tabue said. Adjusting to boot camp was harder than any English class. "The first day was horrible. I almost lost my temper when the drill instructor got in my face . . .. But I told myself it was just a mind game . . .. I had trouble speaking in third person (as required in boot camp). Instead of saying 'This recruit requests permission to use the head,' I would say, 'I would like to use the head.' Drill instructors didn't really like that." When the Crucible—the grueling 54-hour field exercise that is the culmination of boot camp—came, Tabue found his role in the platoon. "He stepped up," Nofziger said. "He wasn't a squad leader, but he acted as one." After Marine Corps recruit training, Tabue will become a mortarman in the Marine Corps Reserve. He said he'll be ready to fight.

From: "West African Immigrant Heeds Father's Words, Joins U.S. Marines" by Lance Cpl. Dorian Gardner, USMC Special to American Forces Press Service.

187,525 overnight (U.S. Department of Homeland Security 2006). If we consider the entire Gulf Coast population, the number of people pushed out of the area exceeds one million (Nossiter 2006).

Pull factors are the conditions that encourage people to move into an area. Common pull factors include employment opportunities, favorable climate, and tolerance for a particular lifestyle. Migration can be placed into two broad categories: international and internal (see The Sociological Imagination: "Moving to the United States from Liberia").

International Migration International migration involves the movement of people between countries. In reference to international migration, demographers use the term **emigration** to denote the act of *departing* from one country to take up residence elsewhere, and the term **immigration** to denote the act of entering one country after leaving another. Most governments restrict the numbers of people who can immigrate. Sometimes governments encourage the immigration of certain categories of people, such as nurses, to fill occupations characterized by a shortage of workers.

pull factors The conditions that encourage people to move into a geographic area.

emigration The act of departing from one country to take up residence elsewhere.

immigration The act of entering one country after leaving another.

Pull factors are those qualities that draw people into a geographic area to live. San Francisco has established a reputation of being a gay-friendly city. That friendliness is symbolized by the prevalence of colors associated with gay pride.

Internal Migration In contrast to international migration, **internal migration** involves movement of people within the boundaries of a single country—from one state, region, or city to another. One major type of internal migration is the rural-to-urban movement (urbanization) that accompanies industrialization.

The United States is a country characterized by high rates of internal migration. Consider that each year about 37.1 million Americans move (change residences). About 67 percent of that number moves from one residence to another within the same county. Approximately 17 percent move from one county to another within the same state. Another 12.6 percent (4.7 million people) move from one state to another (U.S. Bureau of the Census 2010).

Population Size and Growth

The population size of a geographic area constantly changes, depending on births, deaths, and migration flows. About 7 billion people live on planet Earth, and the world's population is distributed unevenly (see Table 15.1). Table 15.1 shows the ten most populous countries in the world. Two countries, China and India, top the list. Taken together, the two countries account for 36 percent of the world's population. The United States in the third most populous country in the world, with 313 million people.

Demographers calculate annual growth in population size according to the following formula: (number of births − number of deaths) + (in-migration − out-migration). Each year the planet increases its population size by approximately 77.8 million. That is, there is 77.8 million more births than deaths. Migration is not a factor in figuring *world* population growth because people cannot move off the planet unless we count the handful of people working in outer space who will eventually return to Earth.

To determine the rate of world population growth, simply divide the amount of change in population size over the course of a year by the population size at the beginning of the year. Using this formula, the annual growth rate for the planet is 1.1 percent. The country with the highest annual growth rate is Zimbabwe; its population size increased by 4.3 percent. The country with the lowest growth rate is Bulgaria; its population size declined by −.78 percent. Keep in mind that the growth rate is relative to the size of an existing population so often the country with the highest growth rate is not the country that adds the greatest number of people to its population over the course of a year. The country that adds the largest number of people per year is India—it adds about 15.9 million people per year. Given the size of India's population, that country's population growth rate is 1.3 percent.

Doubling time is the estimated number of years required for a country's population to double in size. India, with a population growth rate of 1.3 percent, will double its population of 1.2 billion in about 51 years. The United States, with a natural growth rate of 1.0 percent, will double its population in about 78 years. Figure 15.1 shows world population growth since A.D. 1. Note that the population has doubled five times in the last 2,000 years, and that the time between the doublings has decreased dramatically, even alarmingly.

Each year, India loses almost 9 million people through deaths for a net gain of 15 million people. India has 352 million children age 14 and under—that number is larger than the entire U.S. population. Each year, the country adds 24 million babies to its population (U.S. Bureau of the Census 2011).

internal migration The movement of people within the boundaries of a single country—from one state, region, or city to another.

doubling time The estimated number of years required for a country's population to double in size.

Student Activity: Ask students to think about the town or city in which they live. Have them write a short paper describing what features might "pull" people to live or visit and the features that might "push" people out or away.

Global Comparisons The 10 Countries With Largest Populations

TABLE 15.1 The World's Most Populous Countries, 2011

Rank	Country or Area	Population	% of World's Population
1	China	1,336,718,015	19.1
2	India	1,189,172,906	16.9
3	United States	313,232,044	4.5
4	Indonesia	245,613,043	3.5
5	Brazil	203,429,773	2.9
6	Pakistan	187,342,721	2.7
7	Bangladesh	158,570,535	2.3
8	Nigeria	155,215,573	2.2
9	Russia	138,739,892	2.0
10	Japan	126,475,664	1.8

Source: Data from U.S. Bureau of the Census 2011.

TABLE 15.2 Population Size and Growth: The Role of Birth, Death and Migration.

This table shows the population size at two points in time; midyear 2010 and midyear 2011 for three countries: (1) India, the country that added the greatest number of people to its population between 2010 and 2011; (2) Zimbabwe, the country that increased its population size by the greatest percentage; and (3) Bulgaria, the country with the greatest percentage decrease in population size. How many births occurred in each country? How many deaths? How many people did each country gain or lose through migration?

		India	Zimbabwe	Bulgaria
Population (Midyear)	2010	1,173,190,000	11,563,000	7,038,000
Births		+24,937,000	+385,000	+66,000
Deaths		−8,895,000	−164,000	−102,000
Net Migration		−59,000	+300,000	−20,000
Population (Midyear)	2011	1,189,173,000	12,084,000	7,094,000
Growth Rate		1.3%	4.3%	−0.8%
Doubling Time		51 years	11.6 years	92.5 years country will disappear

Source: Data from U.S. Bureau of the Census 2011; U.S. Central Intelligence Agency 2011.

Age-Sex Composition

CORE CONCEPT 2 The age-sex composition of a population helps demographers predict birth, death, and migration rates.

A population's age and sex composition is commonly depicted as a **population pyramid**, a series of horizontal bar graphs, each representing a different five-year age cohort. A **cohort** is a group of people born around the same time—in this case, within a five-year time frame—who

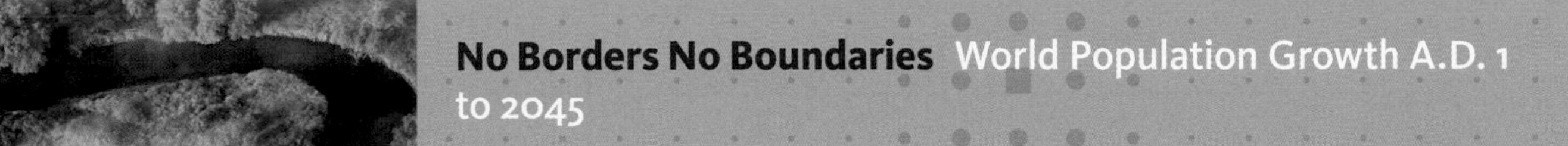

No Borders No Boundaries World Population Growth A.D. 1 to 2045

The graph shows that it took approximately 1,150 years for the world's population to double from 170 million in A.D. 1 to 340 million in 1150. Around 1930, the world's population reached 2 billion people, taking less than 100 years to double from 1 billion in 1850. By the 1960s, the world's population reached 3.04 billion, and it took just 30 years to double to 6.26 billion.

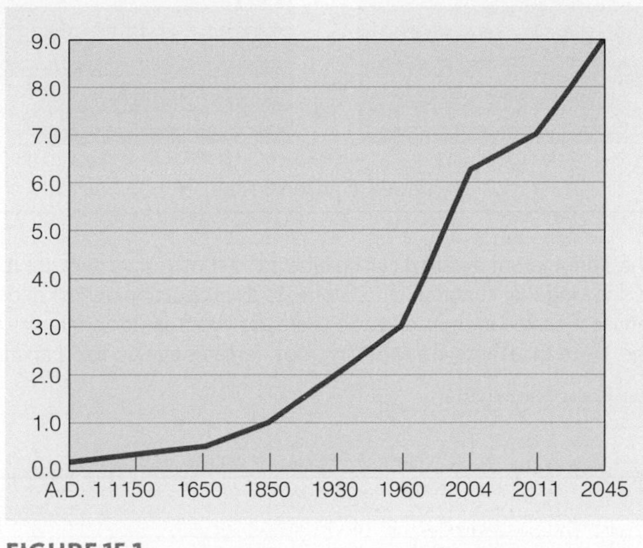

FIGURE 15.1

Source: Data from U.S. Bureau of the Census (2011)

share common experiences and perspectives by virtue of the time they were born. To create a population pyramid, we construct two bar graphs for each cohort—one for males and the other for females. We place the bars end to end, separating them by a line representing zero. Typically, the left side of the pyramid depicts the number or percentage of males that make up each cohort, and the right side depicts the number or percentage of females. We stack the bar graphs according to age—the age 0 to 4 cohort forming the base of the pyramid and the age 100+ cohort forming the apex. The population pyramid allows us to compare the sizes of the cohorts and to compare the numbers or percentages of males and females in each cohort.

The population pyramid offers a snapshot of the number of males and females in the various cohorts at a particular time. Generally, a country's population pyramid approximates one of three shapes: expansive, constrictive, or stationary. An **expansive pyramid** is triangular; it is broadest at the base, and each successive bar is smaller than the one below it. The relative sizes of the cohorts in expansive pyramids show that the population is increasing and consists disproportionately of young people. A **constrictive pyramid** is narrower at the base than in the middle. This shape shows that the population consists disproportionately of middle-aged and older people. A **stationary pyramid** is similar to a constrictive pyramid, except that all cohorts other than the oldest are roughly the same size (see Figure 15.2).

Knowing age-sex composition can help demographers predict a country's birth, death, and migration rates. Bulgaria's population pyramid shows that there are few people age 14 and under relative to the size of the age cohorts that could be their parents. This suggests that many women of reproductive ages 15 to 54 are not having children or a small number of children.

population pyramid A series of horizontal bar graphs, each representing a different five-year age cohort, that allows us to compare the sizes of the cohorts.

cohort A group of people born around the same time (such as a specified five-year period) who share common experiences and perspectives by virtue of the time they were born.

expansive pyramid A triangular population pyramid that is broadest at the base, with each successive cohort smaller than the one below it. This pyramid shows that the population consists disproportionately of young people.

constrictive pyramid A population pyramid that is narrower at the base than in the middle. It shows that the population consists disproportionately of middle-aged and older people.

stationary pyramid A population pyramid in which all cohorts (except the oldest) are roughly the same size.

Student Activity: The U.S. Census Bureau has created population pyramids for all 50 states and territories of the U.S. Simply use the search terms "2010 Census Population Profile Maps" in Google or another search engine. Ask students to write a short profile of their state using only the information gleaned from the population pyramid.

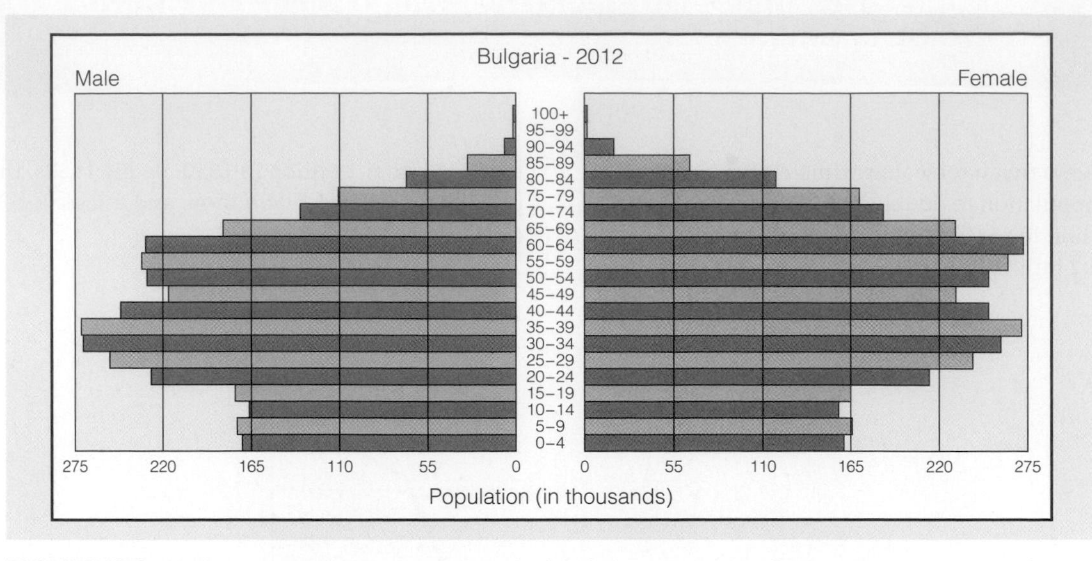

FIGURE 15.2a Bulgaria's population pyramid can be labeled as constrictive because it is narrower at the base than in the middle, showing that the population consists disproportionately of middle-aged and older people. Notice that the base is scaled in thousands. So there are about 165,000 females age 0 to 4 and about 171,000 males of that age. Note that there are about 275,000 females age 60 to 64 and about 231,000 males.

Source: Data from U.S. Bureau of the Census (2012)

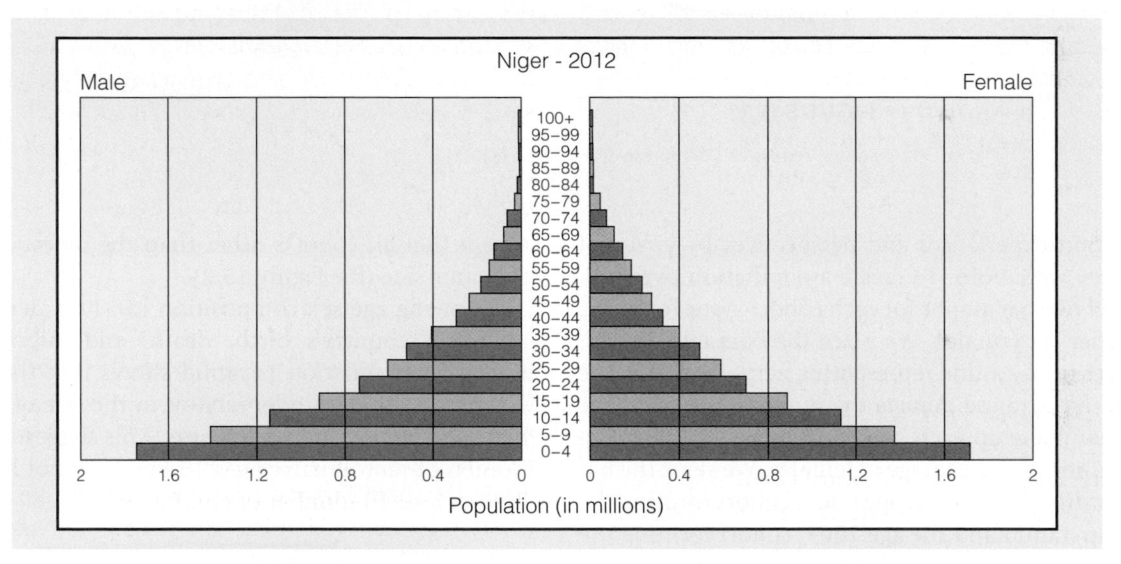

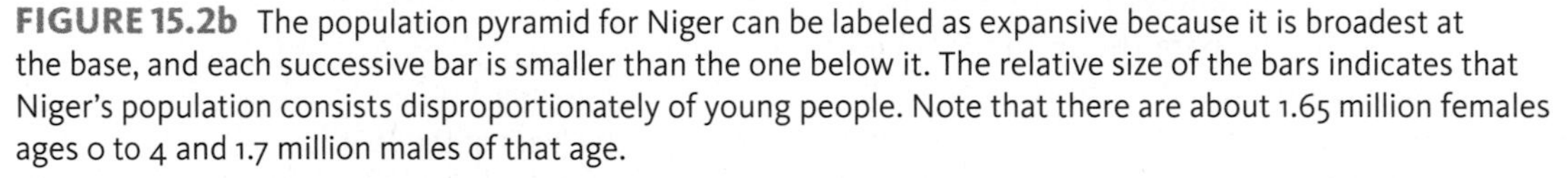
FIGURE 15.2b The population pyramid for Niger can be labeled as expansive because it is broadest at the base, and each successive bar is smaller than the one below it. The relative size of the bars indicates that Niger's population consists disproportionately of young people. Note that there are about 1.65 million females ages 0 to 4 and 1.7 million males of that age.

Source: Data from U.S. Bureau of the Census (2012)

When we know age-sex composition, we can calculate the **sex ratio**—the number of males for every 100 females (or another preferred constant, such as every 10, 100, or 10,000 males). The country of United Arab Emirates has the greatest imbalance in favor of males relative to females with 219 males for every 100 males. The country Russia has the greatest imbalance in favor of females: 86 males per 100 females (U.S. Central Intelligence Agency 2011).

The Theory of Demographic Transition

CORE CONCEPT 3 The demographic transition links the birth and death rates in western Europe and North America to the level of industrialization and economic development.

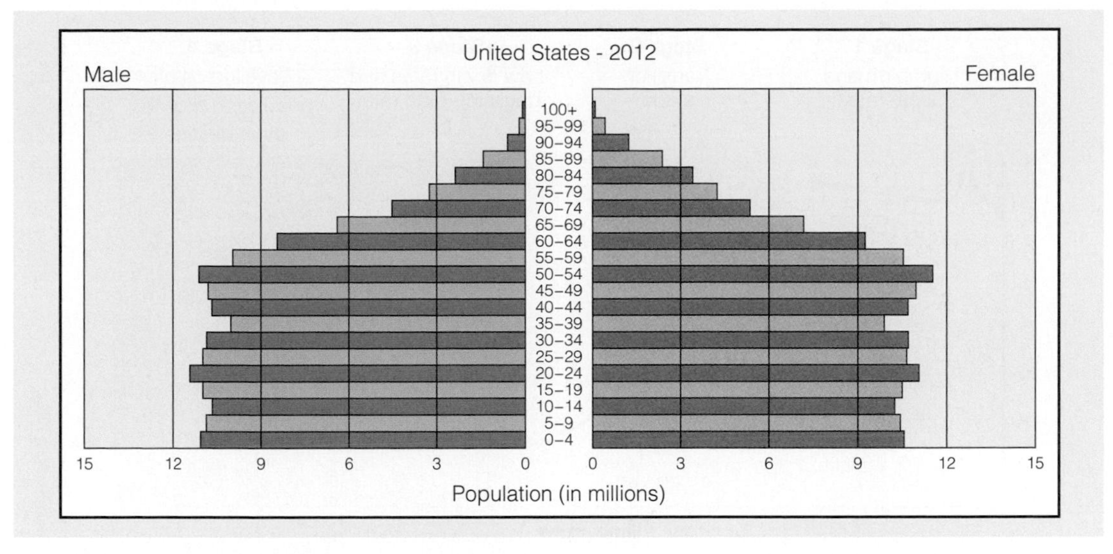

FIGURE 15.2c The population pyramid of the United States yields a near stationary pyramid, because, except for the older age categories, each cohort is roughly the same size. In the United States, there are about 10 million females age 0 to 4 and 10.5 million males of that age.

Source: Data from U.S. Census Bureau (2012)

In the 1920s and early 1930s, demographers observed birth and death rates in various countries. They soon noticed that both birth and death rates were high in Africa, Asia, and South America. In eastern and southern Europe, death rates were declining and birth rates remained high. In western Europe and North America, birth rates were declining and death rates were low. At that time, demographers observed that western Europe and North America had the following sequence of birth and death rates:

1. Birth and death rates remained high until the mid-eighteenth century, when death rates began to decline.
2. As the death rates decreased, the population grew rapidly, because more births than deaths occurred. The birth rates began to decline around 1800.
3. By 1920, both birth and death rates had dropped below 20 per 1,000 (see Figure 15.3).

Based on these observations, demographers put forth the theory of the demographic transition. They proclaimed that the characteristics of a country's birth and death rates are linked to its level of industrial or economic development, and they hypothesized that the less economically and industrially developed countries would follow the pattern of western Europe and North America.

Note that this four-stage model documents the general situation; it should not be construed as a detailed description of the experiences of any single country. Even so, we can say that for the most part the countries of the world have followed the essential pattern of the demographic transition, although they have differed in the timing of the declines and the rates at which their populations have increased since death rates began to fall. The theory of the demographic transition also sought to explain the events that caused birth and death rates to drop in western Europe and North America, and to predict when these declines would occur in the rest of the world.

Stage 1: High Birth and Death Rates

For most of human history—the first 2 to 5 million years—populations grew very slowly, if at all. The world population remained at less than 1 billion until around A.D. 1850, when it began to grow explosively. Demographers speculate that growth until that time was slow because **mortality crises**—violent fluctuations in the death rate, caused by war, famine, or epidemics—were a regular feature of life. Stage 1 of the demographic transition is often called the stage of high potential growth: If something happened to cause the death rate to decline—for example, improvements in agriculture, sanitation, or medical care—the population would increase dramatically. In this stage, life is short and brutal; the death rate almost always exceeds 50 per 1,000. When mortality crises occur, the death

sex ratio The number of females for every thousand males (or another preferred constant, such as 10, 100, or 10,000).

mortality crises Violent fluctuations in the death rate, caused by war, famine, or epidemics.

Teaching Tip: The population pyramid allows people to make rough estimates of the size of various age-sex groups. More precise estimates are available at www.census.gov/population/international/data/idb/informationGateway.php. Simply download the Excel sheet below the requested population pyramid.

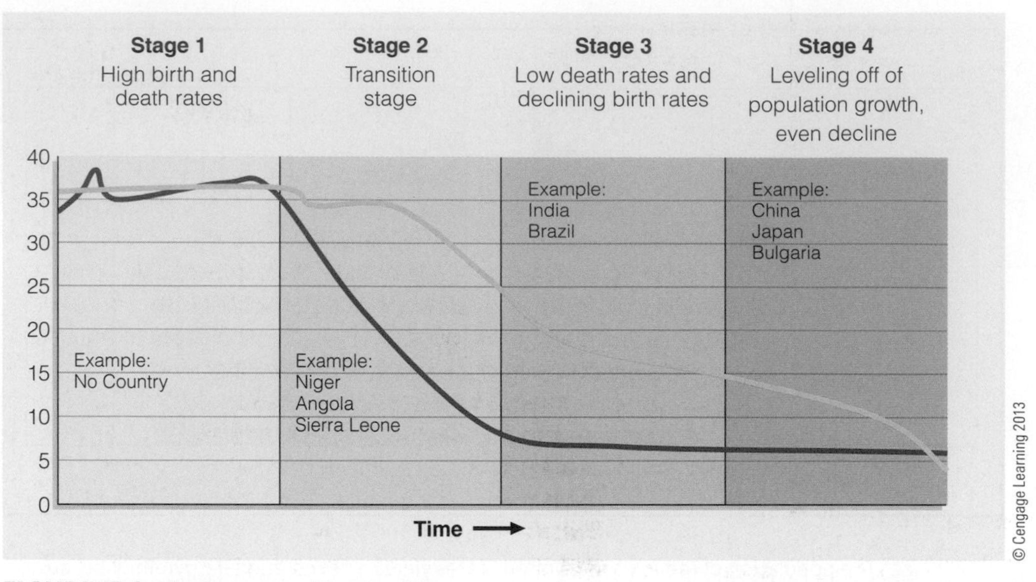

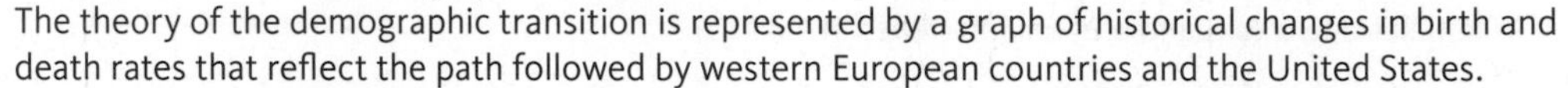
FIGURE 15.3 The Demographic Transition
The theory of the demographic transition is represented by a graph of historical changes in birth and death rates that reflect the path followed by western European countries and the United States.

rate seems to have no limit. Sometimes half the population is affected, as when the Black Death struck Europe, the Middle East, and Asia in the mid-fourteenth century (the plague recurred periodically for approximately 300 years). Within 20 years of its onset, the plague killed an estimated three-fourths of all people in the affected populations.

Another mortality crisis—but one that has not received as much attention as the Black Death—affected the indigenous populations of North America when Europeans arrived in the fifteenth century. A large proportion of the native population died because they had no resistance to diseases such as smallpox, measles, tuberculosis, and influenza, which the colonists brought with them. Historians continue to debate what proportion of the native population died because of this contact; estimates range from 50 to 90 percent.

The plague known as the Black Death hit Europe, the Middle East, and Asia in the mid-fourteenth century, recurring periodically for approximately 300 years. The plague's name came from one of its symptoms: gangrene.

In stage 1, then, average life expectancy at birth remained short—perhaps 20 to 35 years—with the most vulnerable groups being women of reproductive age, infants, and children younger than age 5. It is believed that women gave birth to large numbers of children and that the crude birth rate was about 50 per 1,000—the highest rate recorded, and thus believed possible, for humans. Families remained small, however, because one of every three infants died before reaching age 1, and another died before reaching adulthood. If the birth rate had not remained high, the society would have become extinct. Demographer Abdel R. Omran (1971) estimates that in societies where life expectancy at birth is 30 years, each woman must have an average of seven live births to ensure that two children survive into adulthood. Theoretically, she must bear six sons to ensure that at least one son survives into adulthood. In western Europe before 1650, high mortality rates were associated closely with food shortages and famines. Even when people did not die directly from starvation, they died from diseases that preyed on their weakened physical state.

Thomas Malthus (1798), a British economist and an ordained Anglican minister, concluded that "the power of population is so superior to the power in the earth to produce subsistence for man, that premature death must in some shape or other visit the human race" (p. 140). According to Malthus, **positive checks** served to keep population size in line with the food supply. He defined *positive checks* as events that increase deaths, including epidemics of infectious and parasitic diseases, war, famine, and natural disasters. In

Department of Defense, U.S. Navy Photo

The March 11, 2011 earthquake in Japan registered a 9.0 magnitude. An estimated 30,000 people died, and more than 250,000 people lost their homes and were moved to evacuation shelters.

2010, 373 natural disasters worldwide killed about 300,000 and affected 208 million (Centre for Research on the Epidemiology of Disasters 2011). In terms of human life lost, two disasters stand out—the January 12 earthquake in Haiti in which 222,500 people died, and the Russian summer heat wave that resulted in 56,000 deaths. In addition to disasters, Malthus believed that the only moral ways to prevent populations from growing beyond what the food supply could support were delayed marriage and celibacy.

Stage 2: Transition

Around 1650, mortality crises became less frequent in western Europe; by 1750, the death rate there had begun to decline slowly. This decline was triggered by a complex array of factors associated with the onset of the Industrial Revolution. The two most important factors were (1) increases in the food supply, which improved the nutritional status of the population and increased its ability to resist diseases, and (2) public health and sanitation measures, including the use of cotton to make clothing and new ways of preparing food. The following excerpt elaborates on these trends:

> The development of winter fodder for cattle was important; fodder allowed the farmer to keep his cattle alive during the winter, thereby reducing the necessity of living on salted meats during half of the year. . . . [C]anning was discovered in the early nineteenth century. This method of food preservation laid the basis for new and improved diets throughout the industrialized world. Finally, the manufacture of cheap cotton cloth became a reality after mid-century. Before then, much of the clothes were seldom if ever washed, especially among the poor. A journeyman's or tradesman's wife might wear leather stays and a quilted petticoat until they virtually rotted away. The new cheap cotton garments could easily be washed, which increased cleanliness and fostered better health. (Stub 1982, p. 33)

Library of Congress Prints and Photographs Division

Preserving foods in airtight jars, cans, or pouches and then heating to destroy contaminating microorganisms improved the nutritional status of the population in industrialized societies, leading to lower death rates.

Contrary to popular belief, advances in medical technology had little influence on death rates until the turn of the twentieth century—well after improvements in nutrition and sanitation had caused dramatic decreases in deaths due to infectious diseases. Over a 100-year period, the death rate fell from 50 per 1,000 to less than 20 per 1,000, and life expectancy at birth increased to approximately 50 years of age. As the death rate declined, fertility remained high. Fertility may even have increased temporarily, because improvements in sanitation and nutrition enabled women to carry more babies to term. With the decrease in the death rate, the **demographic gap**—the difference between the birth rate and the death rate—widened, and the population grew substantially.

Accompanying the unprecedented growth in population was **urbanization**, an increase in the number of cities and

positive checks Events that increase deaths, including epidemics of infectious and parasitic diseases, war, famine, and natural disasters.

demographic gap The difference between a population's birth rate and death rate.

urbanization An increase in the number of cities in a designated geographic area and growth in the proportion of the area's population living in cities.

Teaching Tip: The International Disaster Database, Center for Research on Epidemiology of Disaster posts a weekly list of natural and technological disasters around the world. Malthus labeled these disasters "positive checks" on population growth.

growth in the proportion of the population living in cities. (As recently as 1850, only 2 percent of the world's people lived in cities with populations of 100,000 or more.) Around 1880, fertility began to decline. The factors that caused birth rates to drop are unclear and continue to inspire debate among demographers. But one thing is clear: The decline was not caused by innovations in contraceptive technology, because the methods available in 1880 had been available throughout history. Instead, the decline in fertility seems to have been associated with several other factors.

First, the economic value of children declined in industrial and urban settings, as children no longer represented a source of cheap labor but rather became an economic liability to their parents. Second, with the decline in infant and childhood mortality, women no longer had to bear a large number of children to ensure that a few survived. Third, a change in the status of women gave them greater control over their reproductive life and made childbearing less central to their life.

Stage 3: Low Death Rates and Declining Birth Rates

Around 1930, both birth and death rates fell to less than 20 per 1,000, and the rate of population growth slowed considerably. Life expectancy at birth surpassed 70 years—an unprecedented statistic. The remarkable successes in reducing infant, childhood, and maternal mortality rates permitted accidents, homicides, and suicide to become the leading causes of death among young people. The reduction of the risk of dying from infectious diseases ensures that people who would have died of infectious diseases in an earlier era can survive into middle age and beyond, when they face an elevated risk of dying from degenerative and environmental diseases (such as heart disease, cancer, and strokes). For the first time in history, people age 50 and older account for more than 70 percent of annual deaths. Before stage 3, infants, children, and young women accounted for the largest share of deaths (Olshansky and Ault 1986).

As death rates decline, disease prevention becomes an important issue. The goal is to live not merely a long life but a "quality life" (Olshansky and Ault 1986, Omran 1971). As a result, people become conscious of the link between health and lifestyle (sleep, nutrition, exercise, and drinking and smoking habits). In addition to low birth and death rates, stage 3 is distinguished by an unprecedented emphasis on consumption (made possible by advances in manufacturing and food production technologies).

Since the time the demographic transition was first proposed, a fourth stage has been added in which both birth rates and death rates are low. Birth rates drop to levels that fall below that needed to replace those who die. Although death rates are low, there is an increase in lifestyle diseases caused by lack of exercise, poor nutrition, and obesity. Birth rates fall below replacement when the average woman has fewer than two children over the course of her reproductive life. Italy and Japan are examples of countries in which this is the case.

When the theory of the demographic transition was put forth, a hypothesis was also put forth that the so-called developing countries would follow this model. In some ways, most of the developing countries have followed the broad overall pattern but with some differences that we will discuss.

TABLE 15.3 Percentage of Total U.S. Deaths by Age Cohort, 1900, 1950, 2005

At one time in the United States—1900—death was something people in every age group experienced, but especially those less than 1 year of age. Twenty percent of all deaths in 1900 involved infants less than 1 year old. As late as 1950, 20 percent of deaths (one in every five) involved people under age 45. By 2005, that percentage dropped to about 8 percent. Today, death is something we have come to associate primarily with people of older ages as those 55 and older account for 85 percent of all deaths.

Age	1900	1950	2005
less than 1	20.72	7.15	1.16
1 to 4	9.44	1.25	0.19
5 to 14	4.27	1.01	0.27
15 to 24	6.34	1.95	1.40
25 to 34	8.31	2.92	1.71
35 to 44	8.18	5.30	3.46
45 to 54	8.25	10.20	7.50
55 to 64	9.94	17.50	11.25
65 to 74	11.57	23.61	16.27
75 to 84	9.48	21.06	28.05
85 plus	3.19	8.02	28.72

Source: Data from U.S. Centers for Disease Control and Prevention 2009.

Industrialization in Developing Countries: An Uneven Experience

CORE CONCEPT 4 Industrialization was not confined to western Europe and North America. It pulled people from across the planet into a worldwide division of labor and created long-lasting, uneven economic relationships between countries.

The Industrial Revolution was not confined to western Europe and the United States. In fact, during this revolution, people from even the most seemingly isolated and remote regions of the planet became part of a worldwide division

TABLE 15.4 Demographic Differences between Selected Labor-Intensive Poor Economies and Core Economies

Labor-intensive poor economies differ markedly from core economies on a number of important indicators, including doubling time, infant mortality, total fertility, and per capita income.

	Population Doubling Time (years)	Infant Mortality (per 1,000)	Total Fertility	Per Capita Income ($U.S.)
Labor-Intensive Poor Economies				
Afghanistan	20.7	149.2	5.39	1,000
Haiti	41.9	54.02	3.07	1,200
India	51	47.57	2.62	3,400
Core Economies				
United States	78	6.06	2.06	47,400
Japan	636	2.78	1.21	34,200
Germany	1,750	3.54	1.41	35,900

Source: Data from U.S. Central Intelligence Agency 2011.

of labor. Industrialization's effects were not uniform; they varied according to country and region of the world.

With regard to industrialization, the countries of the world are commonly placed into two broad categories, such as developed and developing. Comparable but equally misleading terms for this dichotomy include *industrialized/industrializing* and *first world/third world*. These terms are misleading because they suggest that a country is either industrialized or not industrialized. The dichotomy implies that a failure to industrialize is what makes a country poor, and it camouflages the fact that as Europe and North America plunged into industrialization, they took possession of Asia, Africa, and South America—establishing economies there that served the industrial needs of the colonizers, not the needs of the colonized. The point is that countries we label as "developing" or "industrializing" were actually part of the Industrial Revolution from the beginning.

The World Bank, the United Nations, and other international organizations use a number of indicators to distinguish between so-called developed and developing countries, including the following: doubling time, infant mortality, total fertility, per capita income, percentage of the population engaging in agriculture, and per capita energy consumption. Instead of the term *developing, industrializing,* or *third world*, it might be more accurate to think in terms of **labor-intensive poor economies**. Instead of the term *developed, industrialized,* or *first world,* we will use the term **core economies.** Table 15.4 shows how labor-intensive poor economies differ from core economies on a number of important indicators, such as per capita electricity consumption and doubling time.

The Demographic Transition in Labor-Intensive Poor Economies

CORE CONCEPT 5 Labor-intensive poor economies differ from core economies in several characteristics: In particular, they have experienced relatively high birth rates despite declines in their death rates, resulting in more rapid population growth and unprecedented levels of rural-to-urban migration (urbanization).

Birth and Death Rates in Labor-Intensive Economies

Sociologists Bernard Berelson (1978) and John Samuel (1997) have identified some important "thresholds" associated with declines in fertility:

1. Less than 50 percent of the labor force is employed in agriculture. (The economic value of children decreases in industrial and urban settings.)

labor-intensive poor economies Economies that have a lower level of industrial production and a lower standard of living than core economies. They differ markedly from core economies on indicators such as doubling time, infant mortality, total fertility, per capita income, and per capita energy consumption.

core economies Economies that have a higher level of industrial production and a higher standard of living than labor-intensive poor economies. They include the wealthiest, most highly diversified economies in the world.

Student Activity: Ask students to select a labor-intensive poor country and a core economy country from Table 15.4. Use Google News to check out and compare headline news for each of the two countries. Write a one page paper comparing those headlines and what they say about life (that makes the news) in each country.

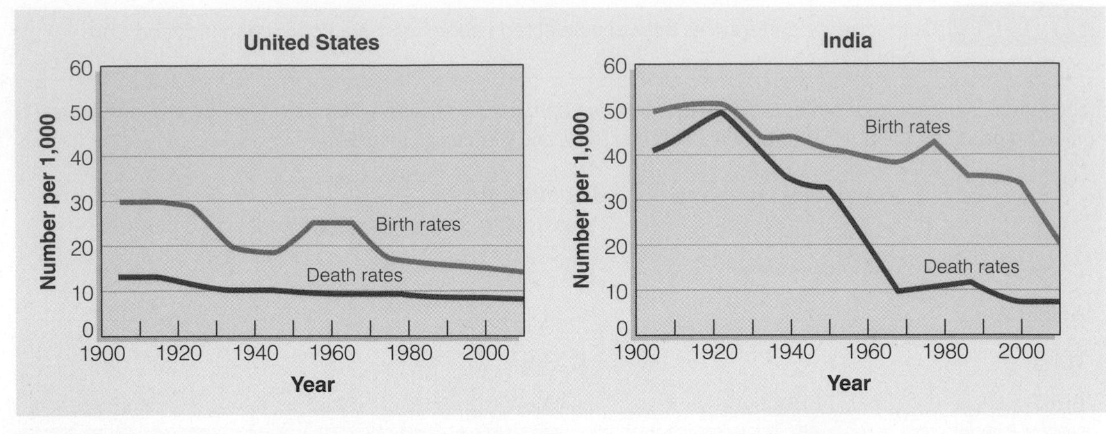

FIGURE 15.4 Birth and Death Rates in the United States and India, 1900–2010
Study the two graphs. What does it mean when the gap between birth rate and death increases? The answer explains why India's population is growing at a much faster pace than the U.S.

Source: Data from U.S. Bureau of the Census (2011)

2. At least 50 percent of people between the ages of 5 and 19 are enrolled in school. (Especially for women, education "widens horizons, sparks hope, changes status concepts, loosens tradition, and reduces infant mortality" (Samuel 1997).)
3. Life expectancy is at least 60 years. (With increased life expectancy, parents can expect their children to survive infancy and early childhood.)
4. Infant mortality is less than 65 per 1,000 live births. (When parents have confidence that their babies and children will survive, they limit the size of their families.)
5. Eighty percent of the females between the ages of 15 and 19 are unmarried. (Delayed marriage is important when it is accompanied by delayed sexual activity or protected premarital sex.)

Death rates in the labor-intensive poor economies, such as India, have declined much more rapidly than they did in the core economies, such as the United States. Demographers attribute the relatively rapid decline to cultural diffusion. That is, the labor-intensive poor economies imported Western technology—such as pesticides, fertilizers, immunizations, antibiotics, sanitation practices, and higher-yield crops—which caused an almost immediate decline in the death rates. Figure 15.4 shows that the death rate in India was so high at the beginning of the twentieth century that the gap between the birth rate and the death rate was relatively small. Around 1920, the death rate began to steadily decline because of medical advancements, especially mass inoculations. But the birth rates have remained high relative to death rate.

The swift decline in death rates and relatively slower decline in birth rates has caused the populations in India and other labor-intensive poor economies to grow very rapidly. Some demographers believe that such countries may be caught in a **demographic trap**—the point at which population growth overwhelms the environment's carrying capacity:

> Once populations expand to the point where their demands begin to exceed the sustainable yield of local forests, grasslands, croplands, or aquifers, they begin directly or indirectly to consume the resource base itself. Forests and grasslands disappear, soils erode, land productivity declines, water tables fall, or wells go dry. This in turn reduces food production and incomes, triggering a downward spiral. (Brown 1987, p. 28)

International agencies such as the World Food Programme (WFP) and World Health Organization reject the

Barbara Hougton

India's death rate has declined dramatically over the 50 to 60 years but its birth rate has lagged, declining at a much slower pace. Today, the birth rate is 20.97 per 1,000, and the average woman has 2.6 children over the course of her lifetime. Of course, average means that there are women who have more or fewer children than the average number for the women of the country.

demographic trap The point at which population growth overwhelms the environment's carrying capacity.

Missy Gish

Many people who are overweight do not have resources to buy nutritious food—food low in salt and sugar, for example. This bottle of apricot juice costs about $4.00. The bottle of Mountain Dew costs $1.50. For people who earn minimum wage, the apricot juice takes more than 30 minutes to earn before taxes. The Mountain Dew takes 12.5 minutes to earn.

idea that rapid population growth, by itself, overwhelms the environment's carrying capacity. In fact, enough food is produced each year to nourish the estimated 800 million people in the world who are chronically hungry or that go to bed hungry each night. There is also enough food produced to meet the needs of the 2 billion who suffer from food insecurity—that is, they do not have the financial resources to secure food that is consistently safe, sufficient, and nutritious. The simple fact is that these 2.8 million people simply do not have the income to buy the food they need. That is because the world economy is structured so that access to sufficient amounts of food remains highly uneven across the globe.

Urbanization

CORE CONCEPT 6 Urbanization is a transformative process by which people migrate from rural to urban areas and change the way they use land, interact, and make a living.

Urbanization encompasses (1) the process by which a population becomes concentrated in urban areas and (2) the corresponding changes in land use, social interaction, economic activity, and landscape. What constitutes an urban area varies by country. The U.S. Bureau of the Census (2010)

Chris Caldeira

The U.S. Bureau of Census defines all areas not considered urban as rural. To be rural, the density or number of people per square mile must be fewer than 1,000.

defines an urban area as a densely settled core with at least 1,000 people per square mile and adjacent territory containing nonresidential urban land uses. In addition, there are outlying densely settled territories that are considered part of the urban area. Greater San Francisco, for example, includes the downtown but extends its influence and reach to surrounding cities and suburbs.

The world has 483 **agglomerations**, urban areas with populations of 1 million or more. Of these, 80 are in China, 48 are in India, and 53 are within the United States. Within the agglomeration category is the **megacity**, cities in which at least 10 million people reside. According to this definition, 26 megacities exist in the world. Two lie in the United States: New York (22.2 million) and Los Angeles (17.9 million). The largest megacity in the world is Tokyo with 32.4 million people (Brinkhoff 2011).

Urbanization in Labor-Intensive Poor Economies versus Core Economies

Urbanization in labor-intensive poor economies differs in several major ways from urbanization in core economies. At comparable points in the demographic transition, the rate of urbanization in labor-intensive poor economies far exceeds that of the core economies. Consider that during the 25 years of its most rapid growth, New York City increased its population by 2.3 million. As one contrasting example, consider that during the 25 years of its most rapid growth, Bombay, India, added 11.2 million people (Brinkhoff 2011).

agglomerations Urban areas with populations of 1 million or more.

megacity An agglomeration of at least 8 million (UN definition) or 10 million (U.S. definition) people.

Teaching Tip: Read about the People's Republic of China's plan to create the world's largest city with 42 million people. Simply use a search engine to find any number of articles about this historical plan.

Why such a difference? For one thing, "new worlds" existed to siphon off the population growth of Europe (Light 1983). Millions of Europeans who were pushed off the land were able to migrate to sparsely populated places, such as North America, South America, South Africa, New Zealand, and Australia. If the people who fled Europe for other lands in the eighteenth and nineteenth centuries had been forced to make their living in the European cities, the conditions there would have been much worse than they actually were:

> Ireland provides the most extreme example. The potato famine of 1846–1849 deprived millions of peasants of their staple crop. Ireland's population was reduced by 30 percent in the period 1845–1851 as a joint result of starvation and emigration. The immigrants fled to industrial cities of Britain, but Britain did not absorb all the hungry Irish. North America and Australia also received Irish immigrants. Harsh as life was for these impoverished immigrants, the new continents nonetheless offered them a subsistence that Britain was unable to provide. (Light 1983, pp. 130–131)

In India, for example, the problem of urbanization is compounded by the fact that many people who migrate to the cities come from some of the most economically precarious sections of India. In fact, most rural-to-urban migrants are not pulled into the cities by employment opportunities; rather, they are forced to move there because they have no alternatives. When these migrants come to the cities, they face not only unemployment, but also a shortage of housing and a lack of services (electricity, running water, waste disposal). One distinguishing characteristic of cities in labor-intensive poor economies is the prevalence of slums and squatter settlements, which are much poorer and larger than even the worst slums in the core economies.

> It is a familiar sight in so-called underdeveloped countries to find somewhere, in the midst of great poverty, . . . a gleaming, streamlined new factory, created by foreign enterprise . . .. Immediately outside the gates you might find a shanty town of the most miserable kind teeming with thousands of people, most of whom are unemployed and do not seem to have a chance of ever finding regular employment of any kind. (Schumacher 1985, p. 490)

Sociologist Kingsley Davis uses the term **overurbanization** to describe a situation in which urban misery—poverty, unemployment, housing shortages, and insufficient infrastructure—is exacerbated by an influx of unskilled, illiterate, and poverty-stricken rural migrants who have been pushed into cities out of desperation. In this regard, the United Nations estimates that one billion people worldwide live in slums lacking essential services such as water and sanitation (Dugger 2007).

U.S. Navy photo by Mass Communication Specialist 3rd Class Matthew

Chris Caldeira

Missy Gish

This chapter has focused on key experiences of human life, not just for individuals but also for societies. Those experiences are births, deaths, and migration. Specifically, we compared the countries that experience the highest and the lowest related rates. We emphasize extreme cases because they capture end points on the continuum of human experience. We learned how knowing a country's birth, death, and migration rates allows us to think deeply about the human experience and the way a society is organized.

Extreme Cases

To this point, we have reviewed key concepts and processes related to three key human experiences: birth, death, and migration. We have also identified countries with highest and lowest rates related to these human experiences (see Table 15.5). We now consider each country listed in Table 15.5.

United Arab Emirates

The most noticeable feature of the United Arab Emirates (UAE) population pyramid is that, with the exception of those 19 and under, males outnumber females in all age categories. This is because about 80 percent of the 5 million people who live in UAE are not citizens of the country. They are people who migrated to UAE in search of work. About 25 percent of UAE's population is from surrounding Arab countries and the Persian country, Iran. About 50 percent is from South Asian countries, most notably India, Pakistan, and Bangladesh. There are also significant numbers from the Philippines and Sri Lanka. The large influx of labor explains why the UAE is the highest positive net migration rate in the world.

TABLE 15.5 Key Demographic Indicators for Extreme Cases and the United States

This table includes countries we have named in this chapter as extreme cases; that is, they have a birth, death, and migration rate that is particularly high or low. In the pages that follow we consider some reasons why each country named in this table is an extreme case.

	Highest	Lowest	United States
Crude Birth Rate	Niger 51.4 per 1,000	Japan 7.3 per 1,000	14 per 1,000
Teen Birth Rate	Niger 199 per 1,000	South Korea 1.2 per 1,000	41 per 1,000
Fertility Rate Average # children per female	Niger 7.7	China 1.15	2.1
Crude Death Rate	Angola 23.4 per 1,000	United Arab Emirates 2 per 1,000	8 per 1,000
Infant Mortality Rate	Angola 175.9 per 1,000	Sweden 2.7 per 1,000	6.0 per 1,000
Maternal Mortality	Sierra Leone 2,000 per 100,000 live births	Sweden 5 per 100,000 live births	17 per 100,000 live births
Migration Rate	United Arab Emirates +22 per 1,000	Jordan −14.3 per 1,000	+4 per 1,000 residents
Population Growth Rate	Zimbabwe 4.3%	Bulgaria −0.78%	1.1%
Male to Female Sex Ratio	United Arab Emirates 219 males per 100 females	Russia 86 males per 100 females	97 males per 100 females
Life Expectancy (at birth)	Japan 82.3	Angola 38.7	78.4
% of population 14 and under	Niger 49.6%	Japan 13.1%	20.1%
% of population 65 and older	Japan 22.9%	United Arab Emirates .9 %	13.1%
Median Age	Japan 44.8 years	Niger 15.2 years	36.9 years
% working in agriculture	Niger 90%	Sweden 1.1%	1.6%

Source: Data from U.S. Bureau of the Census 2011, U.S. Central Intelligence Agency 2011.

Student Activity: Ask students to select any country in the world not covered in the extreme cases section of this chapter. Create a population pyramid and data table covering the indicators in listed in Table 15.5. The data for this table can be obtained from World Factbook (www.cia.gov/library/publications/the-world-factbook/) the pyramid can be created by going to the Census Bureau webstite (www.census.gov/population/international/data/idb/informationGateway.php).

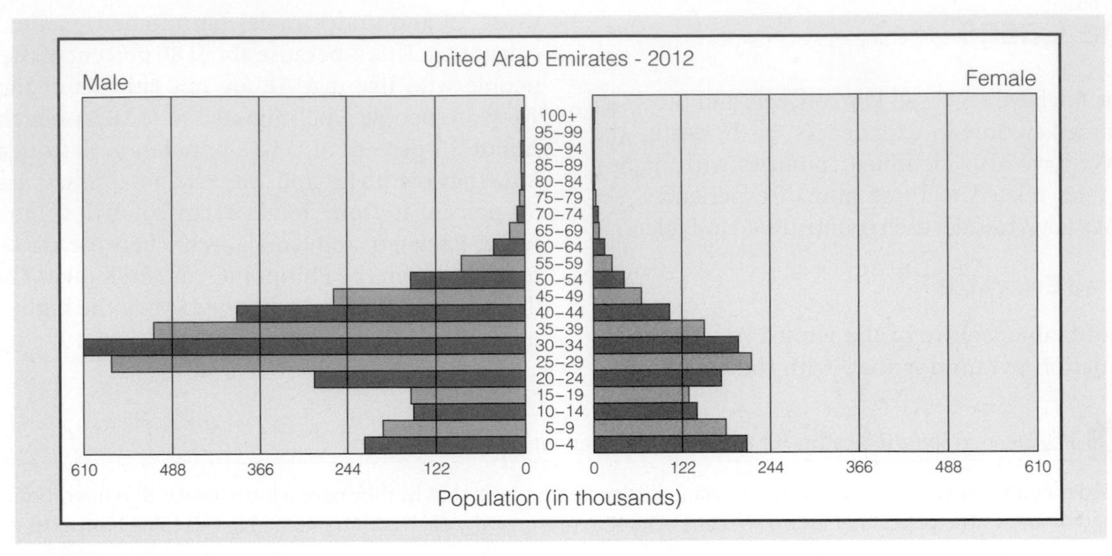

United Arab Emirates

Lowest percentage of population 65 and over: 0.9%
Lowest crude death rate: 2 per 1,000
Highest male to female sex ratio: 219 males per 100 females
Highest net migration: +22 per 1,000

Source: Data from U.S. Census Bureau (2012)

The UAE, with the third highest per capita income in the world, needs people to work in petroleum and natural gas sectors, which account for 80 percent of the country's wealth. In addition, UAE has a number of ambitious construction and tourism-oriented projects under way: The country is building the world's tallest building, a world-class international airport, the largest artificial islands in the world, Dubailand (which will be twice the size of Disney Land), the Dubai Sports City, and Dubai Mall, billed as the world's largest mall. The population pyramid suggests that when migrants' work life ends or when jobs end, they leave UAE to return home. The crude death rate and the percentage of the population 65 and older are low because the large migrant population remains young due to turnover and constant flux.

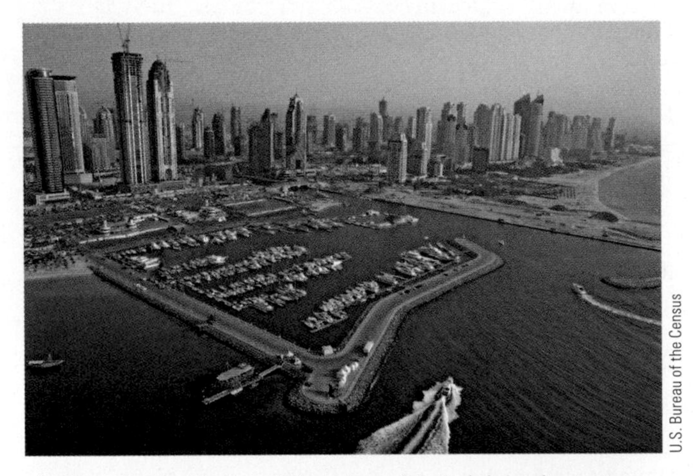

U.S. Bureau of the Census

The city of Dubai in the UAE has been labeled the richest city in the world. It has built many attractions for tourists. Migrants from outside the country work in the hotels, restaurants, and tourist destinations.

overurbanization A situation in which urban misery—poverty, unemployment, housing shortages, insufficient infrastructure—is exacerbated by an influx of unskilled, illiterate, and poverty-stricken rural migrants who have been pushed into cities out of desperation.

Bulgaria

Study the population pyramid for Bulgaria. Can you determine the year that Bulgaria's population began its decline? The age 0- to 19-year-old cohorts are dramatically smaller than most of the older cohorts. So the question becomes what happened 20 years ago, in the late 1980s and early 1990s? Bulgaria, being part of Eastern Europe, was under Soviet Union control from 1946 until 1989, the year the Berlin Wall fell and the Soviet Union collapsed. After Bulgaria held its first elections, it embarked on the long, hard transition of moving away from a communist government and centrally planned economy to a political democracy and market economy. In the process, Bulgarians experienced inflation, unemployment, corruption, and crime.

Recall that population decline occurs when the birth rate is lower than the death rate and when more people leave the country than enter it. The collapse of the Soviet Union allowed Bulgarians the opportunity to emigrate. In addition, hard economic times and stresses associated with dramatic economic and political change contributed to the low birth rate and total fertility. Finally, Bulgaria joined the European Union in 2007, which likely opened up further opportunities for people to emigrate.

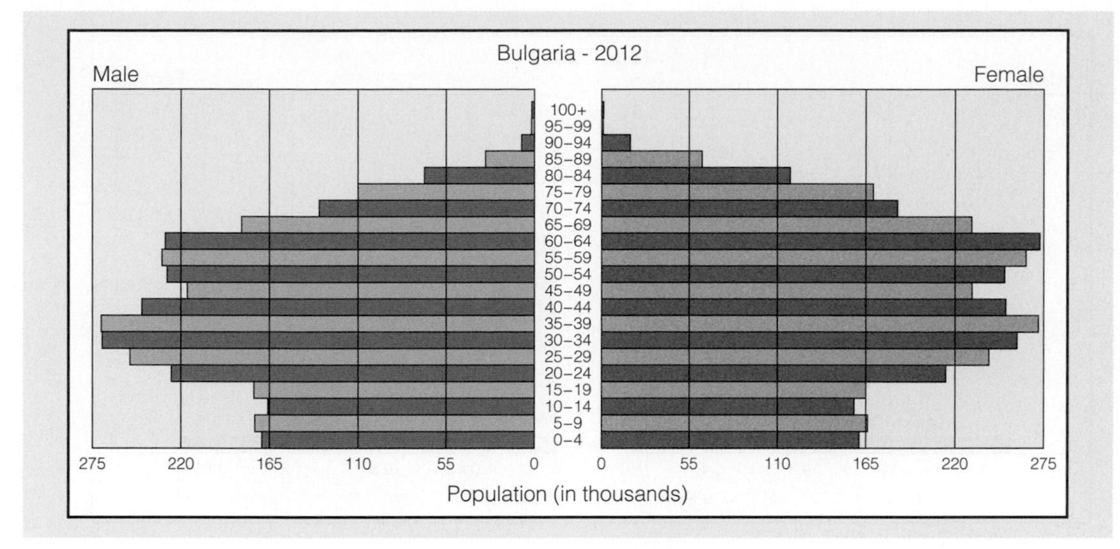

Bulgaria

Lowest growth rate: –.78

Source: Data from U.S. Census Bureau (2012)

Japan

What about the population pyramid tells you that Japan has the highest median age, the greatest percentage of people age 65 and older, the highest life expectancy at birth, the lowest percentage of people 14 and under, and the lowest crude birth rate? Perhaps one of the most striking features is that the number of 80- to 84-year-olds (4.3 million) is almost as large as the number of children aged 4 and under (4.9 million). In addition, each of the cohorts that make up the 35- to 74-year-old tiers are larger in size than any of the 19 and under cohorts. We should not be surprised that Japan's average life expectancy and median age are the highest in the world.

We can explain Japan's situation by noting that it is in stage 4 of the demographic transition. But we might also note that Japan is a stressful place for men, women, and children. Men must work long hours at companies where the expectation is that the jobs comes first and family life should not interfere. Women are expected to quit their jobs when they have children, and children must participate in the competitive examination system. These factors, along with the high cost of raising children, contribute to the low birth rate.

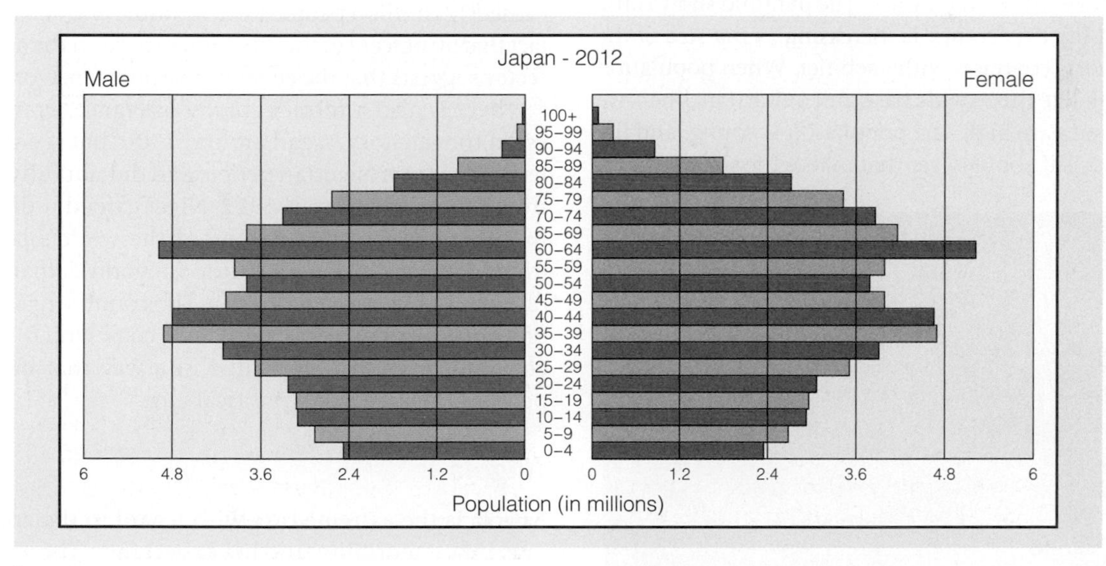

Japan

Highest median age: 44.8

Highest percentage of population age 65 and over: 22.9%

Highest live expectancy at birth: 82.3

Lowest percentage of population age 14 and under: 13.1%

Lowest crude birth rate: 7.3 per 1,000

Source: Data from U.S. Census Bureau (2012)

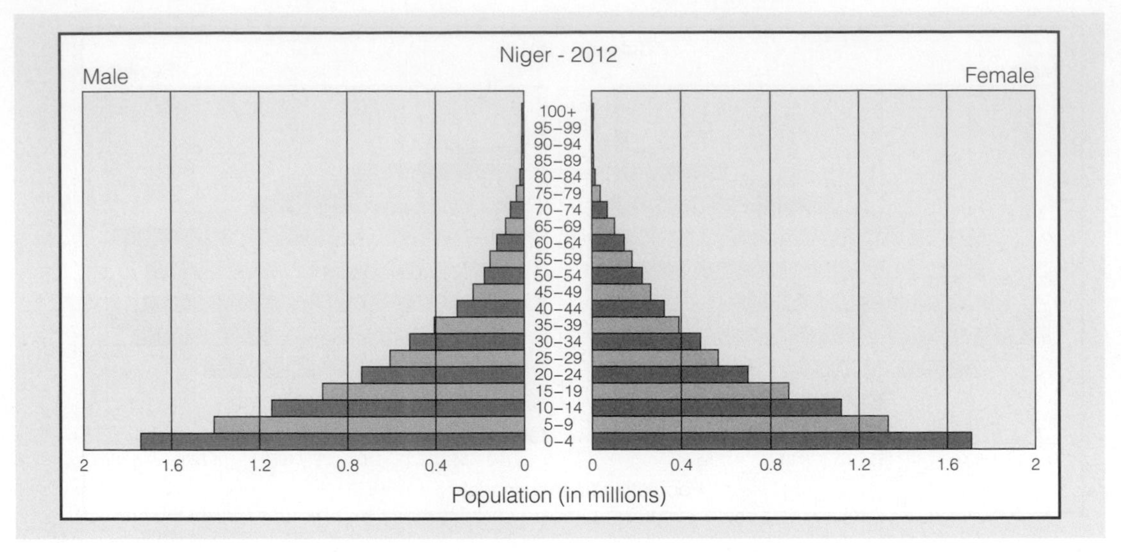

Niger

Lowest median age: 15.2
Highest percentage of population age 14 and under: 49.6%
Highest crude birth rate: 51.5 per 1,000
Highest percentage working in agriculture: 90%
Highest fertility rate: 7.7
Highest teen birth rate: 199 per 1,000

Source: Data from U.S. Census Bureau (2012)

Niger

Niger is the extreme case for six important demographic characteristics. How are these characteristics reflected in the population pyramid? The most distinguishing feature of this pyramid is the shear length of the bars for the 0 to 4 age groups and the fact that the number of people in each older cohort declines with advancing age. The pyramid shows little evidence that life expectancy is increasing as the size of the older age cohorts contracts with each tier. When population pyramids look like this—wide base and a sharp incline—we know death rates are high, the population is young, and life is tough. What is it about Niger that makes life so tough?

By Cpl. Enrique Saenz/US Marines

This photo of children who live in Niger gives some sense of the harsh environment of this landlocked country.

For one, Niger is a landlocked West African country, with over 80 percent of its territory within the Sahara desert. The remaining 20 percent of its territory is threatened by cyclical drought and desertification. The two most recent extreme weather events occurred in 2005, when drought and locust infestation created food shortages affecting 2.5 million people, and in 2010, when record heat waves affected crops and caused 1.5 million people to face famine and starvation. The fact that 90 percent of the labor force works in the agricultural sector suggests that the economy is subsistence-oriented.

Niger is also a former colony of France. France's interest in the territory began around 1900, but it encountered resistance from Nigerian people and did not fully gain control of the country until 1922. Niger gained independence in 1960. Niger contains some of the world's largest uranium deposits, although a drop in world demand for this mineral has hurt the economy. The country has a number of resources such as oil, gold, and coal, which could fuel economic growth if exploited in a way that benefits the people and not a small political elite.

Angola

Angola is the extreme case with regard to the crude death rate, infant mortality, and life expectancy. The shape of the pyramid with a wide base and steep "steps" from one age cohort to the next tells us that this is the case. Why is life so harsh? Angola was a Portuguese territory for about 400 years until 1975, when it gained independence. The country has fertile land and was considered the breadbasket of southern Africa. After gaining independence, the country

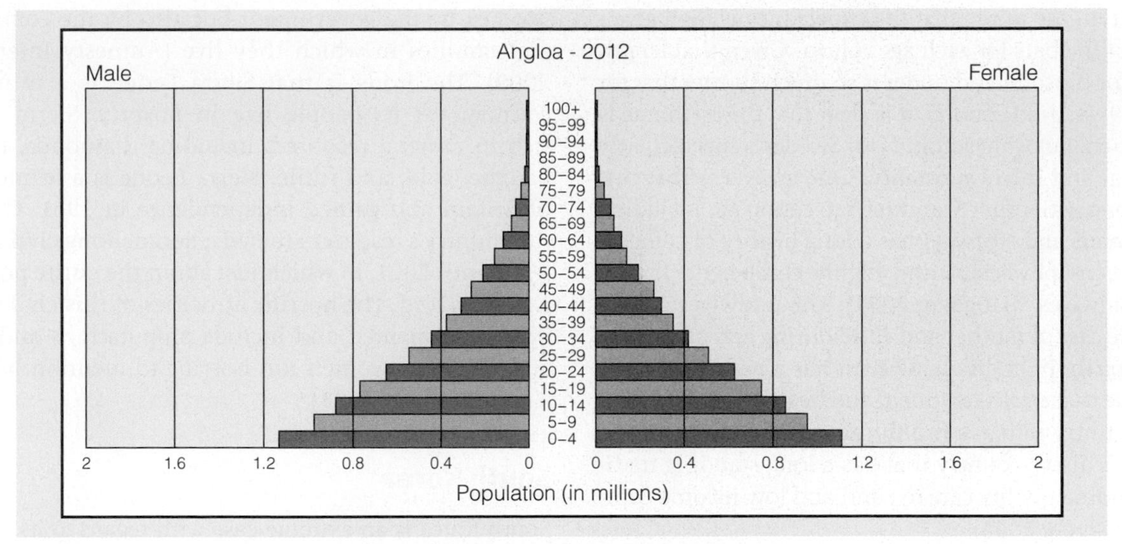

Angola
Highest crude death rate: 23.4 per 1,000
Highest infant morality: 175 per 1,000
Lowest life expectancy: 38.7 years

Source: Data from U.S. Census Bureau (2012)

experienced civil war for the next 27 years, until 2002, when a settlement was reached among the warring parties. The fertile land was destroyed and littered with landmines. Millions left the countryside for the cities or left the country altogether. In recent years, Angola has had some successes. As many as 4 million displaced people have returned to Angola. Agricultural production is increasing. It received a $5 billion loan from China to rebuild its infrastructure to be paid back in oil. Currently, diamonds and oil derived from exports account for 60 percent of Angola's economy. The problem is that, to date, only a small percentage of the population has benefited from the gains (BBC News 2011).

Sweden

Sweden stands out for having the lowest infant and maternal mortality rates in the world. It also has the lowest percentage of the population employed in the agricultural sector, one indicator that parents do not need to produce laborers to do farm work. The shape of the population pyramid for Sweden indicates that the country is in stage 4 of the demographic

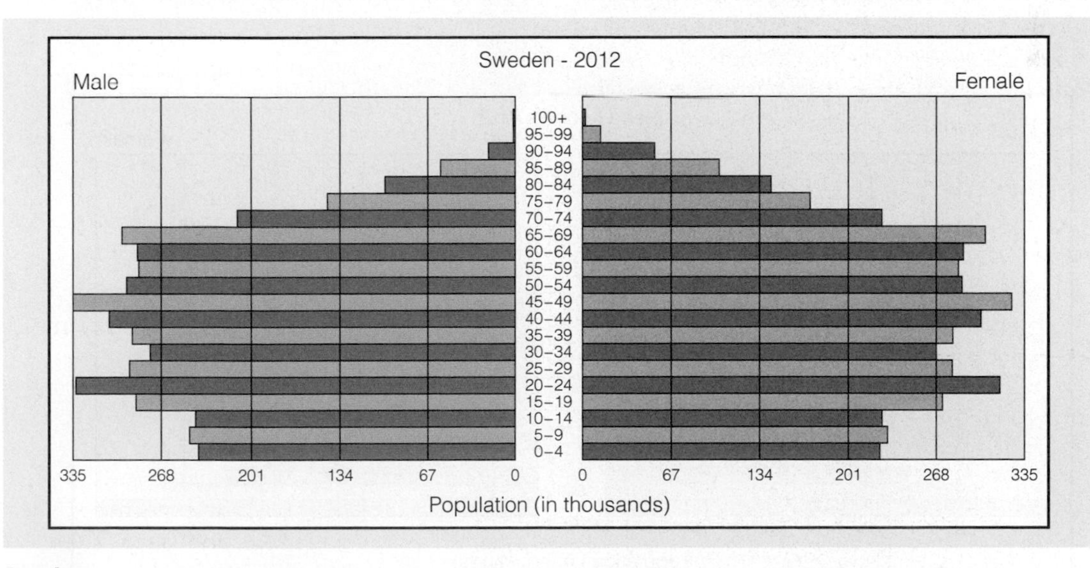

Sweden
Lowest infant mortality: 2.7 per 1,000
Lowest maternal mortality: 5 per 100,000
Lowest percentage or population working in agriculture: 1.1%

Source: Data from U.S. Census Bureau (2012)

transition. It is easy to see that life expectancy is high given the length of the bars for each age cohort. Given that length of the bars for those 14 and under is so much shorter that for the 29- to 49-year-old cohorts, it is clear that the birth rate is low for women. But what accounts for Sweden's spectacularly low maternal and infant mortality? One answer is that this country (along with other Scandinavian countries, including the Netherlands and Norway) has a long history of collaboration between "physicians and highly competent, locally available midwives" (Högberg 2004). The midwives are involved in the care of mother and child during and after pregnancy and birth. In addition, Sweden has a national health care database that tracks treatment and health outcomes that allow the country to make health care policy based on best practices. It is also a country that has a long-standing tradition of providing quality care to rural and low-income communities (Högberg 2004).

Sierra Leone

Sierra Leone has the highest maternal mortality rate in the world. Amnesty International has called this situation grave and has labeled it a human rights emergency. According to Amnesty International (2009), "thousands of women bleed to death after giving birth. Most die in their homes. Some die on the way to hospital, in taxis, on motorbikes, or on foot. In Sierra Leone, less than half of deliveries are attended by a skilled birth attendant and less than one in five are carried out in health facilities."

This situation exists because most women are too poor to afford health care. In Sierra Leone, women are held in low status and face discrimination. Girls are forced to marry, are denied access to education, and are victims of sexual violence. Women's health care needs are ignored, not just by the government but also by the communities and families in which they live (Amnesty International 2009). The irony is that Sierra Leone is a mineral-rich country, yet its people live in poverty. Sierra Leone is rich in mineral resources including diamonds, titanium, bauxite, gold, and rutile. Sierra Leone is a former colony of Britain and gained independence in 1961. Control of the country's resources fueled a decade-long civil war from 1991 until 2001, in which just about the entire population was displaced. The horrific atrocities of this civil war have been documented and include amputations and systematic abuses of women too horrific to mention here (Ben-Ari and Harsch 2005).

South Korea

South Korea is an extreme case with regard to its teen birth rate—the number of babies born each year for every 1,000 teens. Korea's rate is 1.2 babies born per 1,000 teens. To put this rate in perspective, consider that the rate is 41 per 1,000 in the United States. We can see by the shape of South Korea's population pyramid that its overall birth rate is extremely low. Simply look at the length of the 0 to 4 age cohort relative to age cohorts of women in their reproductive years. But why do teens, in particular, have such a low rate? There are several possible explanations: Korean society, influenced by Confucian beliefs, places a high value on chastity, and there is a stigma attached to being a single mother. On the other hand, the low teen birth rate is not the same as the pregnancy rate. It could be that Korean teens do get pregnant, but many get abortions. By one estimate, there are about 30 abortions each year for every 1,000 women between ages of 15 and 44. However, there is no way to determine the contribution teens make to the abortion rate (Sangwon 2010).

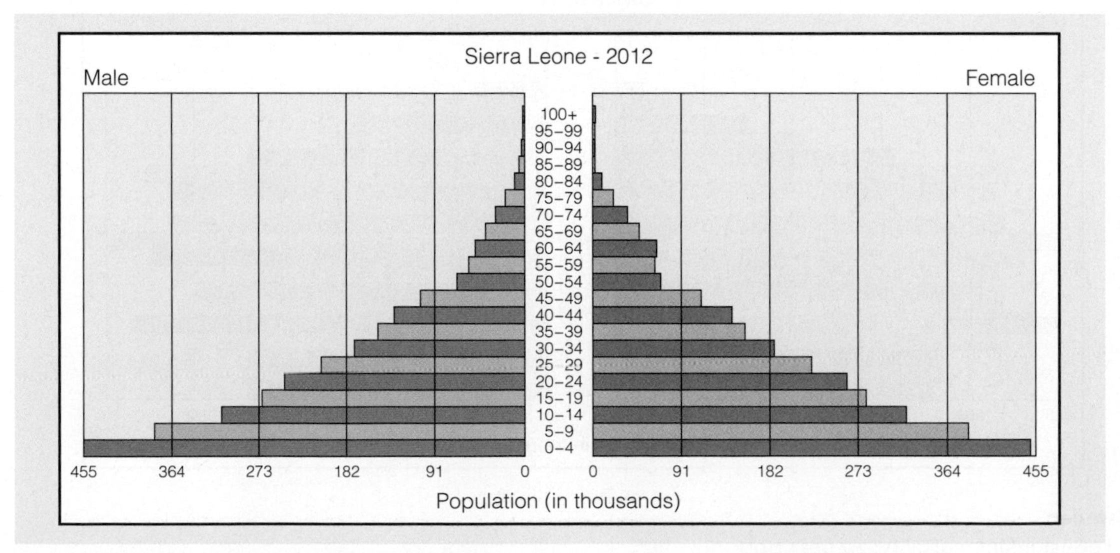

Sierra Leone

Highest maternal mortality: 2,000 per 100,000

Source: Data from U.S. Census Bureau (2012)

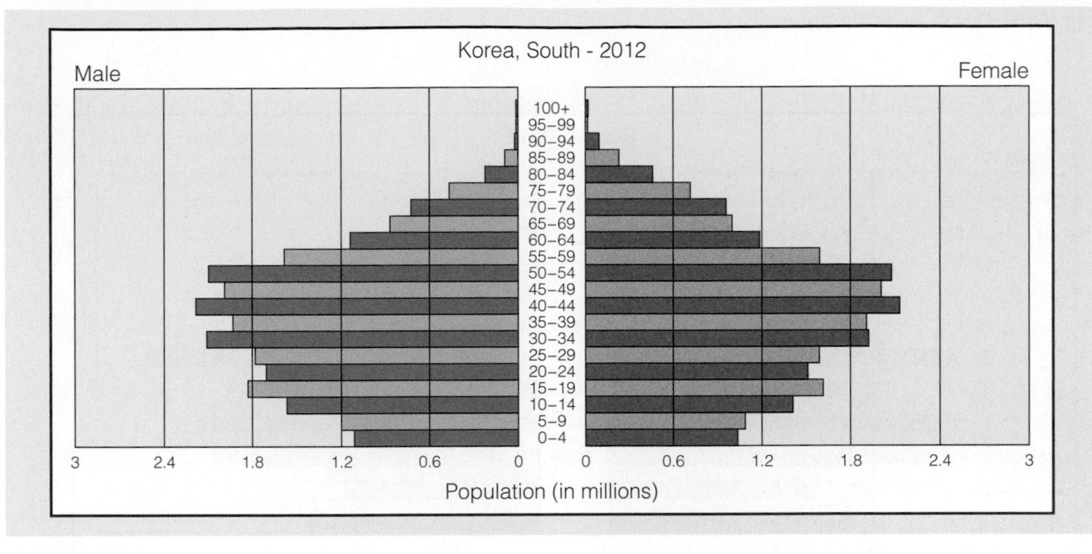

South Korea

Lowest teen birth rate: 1.2 per 1,000

Source: Data from U.S. Census Bureau (2012)

China

China has the largest population in the world but it also has the lowest fertility rate. On average, women have 1.1 children. In 1979, the government announced the one-child family planning policy. The population that is 31 years and younger was born after that policy went into effect. Except for the 20- to 24-year-old age cohort, the lengths of the bars since that announcement are shorter than the cohorts that preceded it. The 20 to 24 age cohort is likely so large because the size of their parents' cohorts—those who are now 37 to 49 years of age—was so large. Even if couples only had one child, so many couples had a child that it still created a large cohort. You might wonder why the 50 to 54 age cohort is small relative to the 45- to 49- and 55- to 59-year-old cohorts. In 1960 and 1961, China experienced natural disaster and famine. The death rate, including infant mortality, was high.

Russia

If you look closely at Russia's population pyramid on the next page, you can see that males outnumber females until age 25 to 29. At that point, the number of females always exceeds males, with greatest differences for age cohorts 50 to 84 (U.S. Bureau of the Census 2011). The life expectancy of the average Russian male is 60 years, compared to the average Russian female who lives to age 73. According to one estimate, an 18-year-old Russian male has a 50 percent chance of dying before reaching retirement age, compared to a 90 percent chance for an 18-year-old male living in the United States. To date, the best explanation relates to high levels of alcohol consumption and tobacco use among men in Russia, which increased dramatically after the breakup of the Soviet Union. The transition from a centrally planned economy to a market-oriented one has been especially difficult for men (Wong 2009).

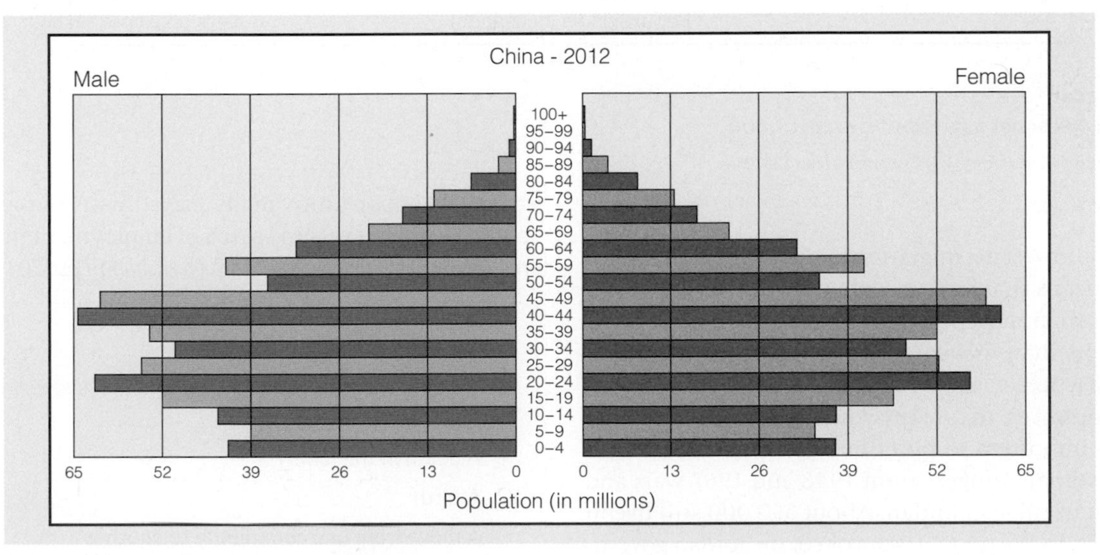

China

Lowest total fertility rate: 1.1 per woman

Source: Data from U.S. Census Bureau (2012)

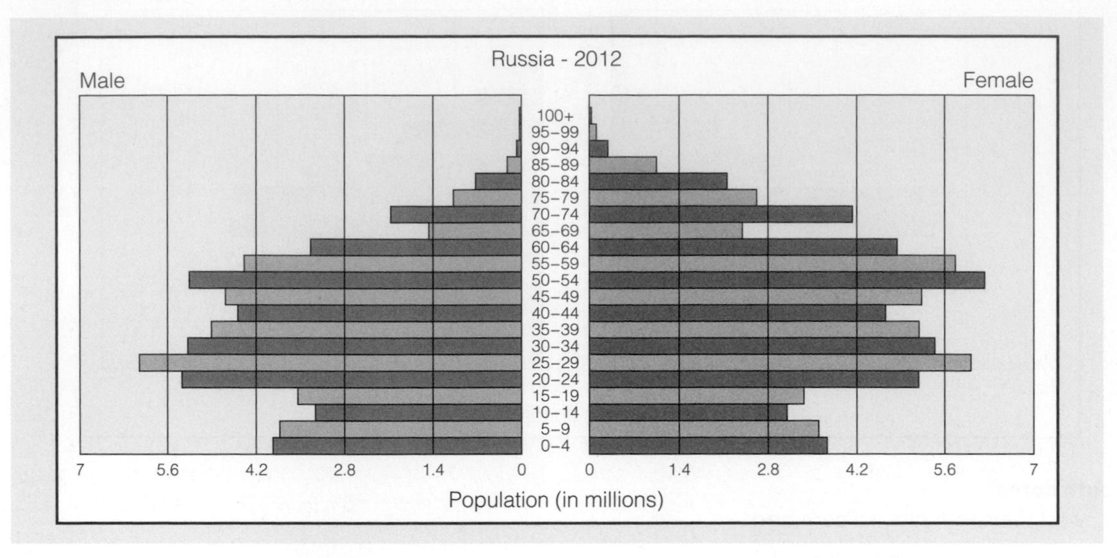

Russia

Lowest male to female sex ratio: 86.3 males per 1,000 females

Source: Data from U.S. Census Bureau (2012)

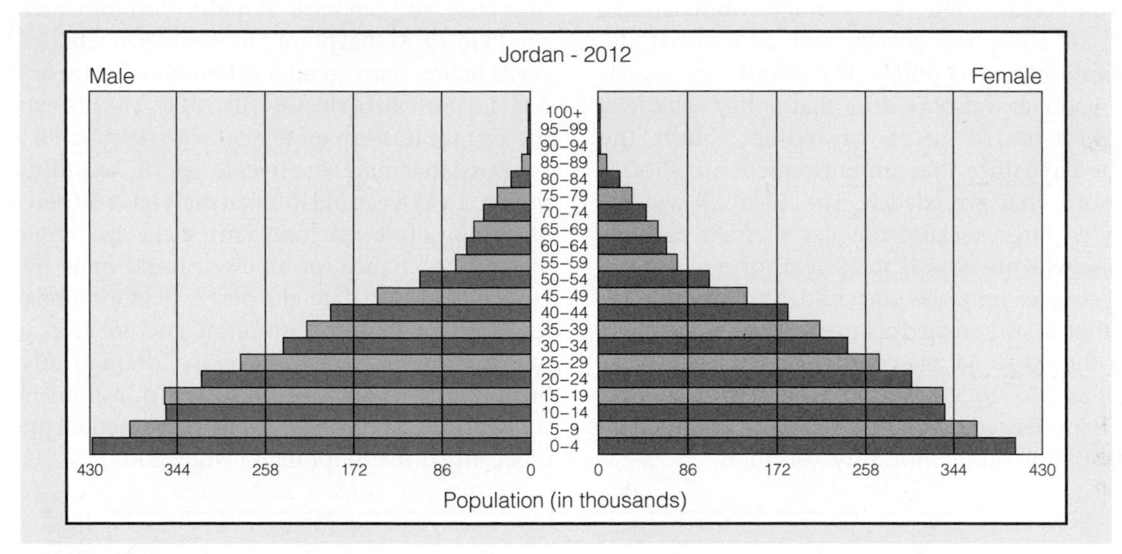

Jordan

Lowest net migration: −14.3 per 1,000

Source: Data from U.S. Census Bureau (2012)

Jordan

Jordan has the lowest net migration rate. It is a negative number, which means that more people move out of the country each year than move in—14.3 more move out for every 1,000 residents than move in. The effects of out-migration are not so easy to see just by looking at the pyramid. You will notice, however, that many young people are of working age. It is important to point out that an estimated 1.9 million Palestinian refugees from 1948 and 1967 wars and their descendants live in Jordan. About 350,000 still live in refugee camps. In the past 20 years or so, the Jordan government has refused to offer citizenship and it has revoked citizenship of some Palestinians in an effort to prevent Israel from pushing Palestinians out of the West Bank, Gaza, and Israel proper. Because of their precarious status and lack of economic opportunity, many Palestinians living in Jordan migrate out each year in search of employment in surrounding countries such as the UAE (*Jerusalem Post* 2010).

Online Poll

Which of the following events has had the greatest impact on you in the past year?

- ○ A death in the family
- ○ A birth
- ○ A move from one community to another
- ○ No such event has occurred

To see how other students responded to these questions, go to **www.cengagebrain.com.**

DANIEL SCOTT/Department of Defense

Summary of CORE CONCEPTS

CORE CONCEPT 1 Demography, a subspecialty within sociology, focuses on births, deaths, and migration—major factors that determine population size and rate of growth.

Population size is determined by births, deaths, and migration. Births add new people to a population and can be expressed as a crude birth rate or an age-specific birth rate. Deaths reduce the size of a population. As with the birth rate, we can calculate the death rate for entire populations or for specific segments. Migration is the movement of people from one residence to another. That movement adds new people to a population if they are moving in, reduces the population size if people are moving out, or makes no difference. Migration, which can be international or internal, results from push and pull factors.

CORE CONCEPT 2 The age-sex composition of a population helps demographers predict birth, death, and migration rates.

A population's age and sex composition is commonly depicted as a population pyramid, which offers a snapshot of the number of males and females in the various age cohorts at a particular time. Generally, a country's population pyramid approximates one of three shapes: expansive, constrictive, or stationary. Knowing age-sex composition helps demographers predict birth, death, and migration rates and calculate the sex ratio.

CORE CONCEPT 3 The demographic transition links the birth and death rates in western Europe and North America to the level of industrialization and economic development.

The theory of the demographic transition connects the fall in a population's birth and death rates to level of industrialization and economic development. Birth and death rates in western Europe and North America changed in the following sequence: (Stage 1) Birth and death rates remained high until the mid-eighteenth century, when death rates began to decline. (Stage 2) As the death rates decreased, the population grew rapidly, because more births than deaths occurred. The birth rates began to decline around 1800 (Stage 3). By 1920, both birth and death rates had dropped below 20 per 1,000. In Stage 4, the birth rate is smaller than the death rate. Based on these observations, demographers put forth the theory of the demographic transition.

CORE CONCEPT 4 Industrialization was not confined to western Europe and North America. It pulled people from across the planet into a worldwide division of labor and created long-lasting, uneven economic relationships between countries.

The Industrial Revolution was not unique to western Europe and North America. In fact, during this revolution, people from even the most seemingly isolated and remote regions of the planet became part of a worldwide division of labor. Industrialization's effects were not uniform; rather, they varied according to country and region of the world. Consequently, with regard to industrialization, we can place the countries of the world into two broad categories: core economies and labor-intensive poor economies.

CORE CONCEPT 5 Labor-intensive poor economies differ from core economies in several characteristics: In particular, they have experienced relatively high birth rates despite declines in their death rates, resulting in more rapid population growth and unprecedented levels of rural-to-urban migration (urbanization).

Birth rates have remained high relative to death rates and have taken longer to decline; the level of rural-to-urban migration has been unprecedented. Colonization and its legacy help explain why the model of the demographic transition does not exactly apply to India and most other former colonies. Labor-intensive poor economies have not reached a number of milestones associated with declines in birth rates. These milestones include the following: Less than 50 percent of the labor force is employed in agriculture; at least 50 percent of people between the ages of 5 and 19 are enrolled in school; life expectancy is at least 60 years; infant mortality is less than 65 per 1,000 live births; and 80 percent of the females between the ages of 15 and 19 are unmarried.

CORE CONCEPT 6 Urbanization is a transformative process by which people migrate from rural to urban areas and change the way they use land, interact, and make a living.

The world has 337 agglomerations, urban areas with populations of 1 million or more. Urbanization in labor-intensive poor economies far exceeds that in the core economies, if only because no "new worlds" exist to siphon off such countries' population growth as existed for Europe. In addition, rural migrants tend to come from the most economically precarious segments of the population. The result is overurbanization, a situation in which urban misery—poverty, unemployment, housing shortages, and insufficient infrastructure—is exacerbated by an influx of unskilled, illiterate, and poverty-stricken rural migrants, who have been pushed into cities out of desperation.

Resources on the Internet

Login to CengageBrain.com to access the resources your instructor requires. For this book, you can access:

Sociology CourseMate

Access an integrated eBook, chapter-specific interactive learning tools, including flash cards, quizzes, videos, and more in your Sociology CourseMate.

Take a pretest for this chapter and receive a personalized study plan based on your results that will identify the topics you need to review and direct you to online resources to help you master those topics. Then take a posttest to help you determine the concepts you have mastered and what you will need to work on.

CourseReader

CourseReader for Sociology is an online reader providing access to readings, and audio and video selections to accompany your course materials.

Visit **www.cengagebrain.com** to access your account and purchase materials.

Key Terms

agglomerations 401
cohort 393
constrictive pyramid 393
core economies 399
crude birth rate 388
crude death rate 388
demographic gap 397
demographic trap 400
demography 388
doubling time 391
emigration 390
expansive pyramid 393
internal migration 391
immigration 390
infant mortality rate 388
in-migration 389
labor-intensive poor economies 399
maternal mortality rate 389
megacity 401
migration 389
migration rate 389
mortality crises 395
net-migration 389
out-migration 389
overurbanization 404
population pyramid 393
positive checks 397
pull factors 390
push factors 389
sex ratio 395
stationary pyramid 393
total fertility rate 388
urbanization 397

16 SOCIAL CHANGE

With Emphasis on GREENLAND

A polar bear standing on an ice floe off Greenland is an image popularly used to represent climate change—a change affecting not just polar bears but the planet as a whole. Climate change is most evident in the melting glaciers in Greenland and other key locations in the world. When sociologists study any change, they ask at least three key questions: What has changed? What factors triggered that change? What are the consequences of that change to society and to the ways in which humans relate to each other and their environment?

Why Focus On GREENLAND?

In 2007, the United Nations (UN) issued a report that involved 1,250 authors and 2,500 scientific experts from 130 countries. That report, which took six years to write, announced that climate change can no longer be denied or doubted, and that human or social activity since 1750 has very likely caused the rise in the planet's temperatures. When (and since) this report was issued, it generated intense and bitter debate over whether climate change is real, and even if real, is it man-made or part of the planet's natural shifts in weather patterns?

Although climate change is a complex phenomenon, some of the most publicized and vivid images center on one element of the process—melting ice sheets—which the UN report names as very likely (90 to 99 percent probability) contributing to sea-level rise. Images of ice sheets collapsing and polar bears seemingly stranded on ice floes turn our attention to places like Greenland.

Greenland, a self-governing dependency of Denmark near the North Pole, possesses the largest reservoir of freshwater on the planet after Antarctica. If Greenland's ice sheet, which covers about 85 percent of its territory, melted entirely, it would release enough water to raise the global sea level by almost 23 feet. To date, the sea level has risen by .07 inches per year since 1961, for a total of 3.96 inches. Melting ice from Greenland and Antarctica has very likely contributed between .06 inches to .33 inches of that rise (representing 1.5 to 8.3 percent of total sea rise in the past 55 years) (United Nations 2007).

Apart from the debate over causes of climate change, we can all agree that since 1750, humans have burned fossil fuels to transport people and goods, to run appliances and light the night; and to regulate temperatures in houses, office buildings, and other indoor environments. We use the concepts and theories in this chapter to answer three important questions of this human dependence on fossil fuels: (1) What has changed since 1750, making human activity heavily dependent upon fossil fuels? (2) What factors trigger changes in social activity? (3) What are the consequences of those changes? It is not until we answer the third question that we will bring Greenland's situation in the mix—specifically how fossil fuel–dependent social activities and climate change have affected that country. Note that we use the term *climate change*, in keeping with the UN report, rather than *global warming*.

Online Poll

Do you think climate change is man-made or part of the natural cycle of weather?

- ○ Man-made
- ○ Natural cycle
- ○ Both man-made and part of natural cycle

To see how other students responded to these questions, go to **www.cengagebrain.com**.

Jan Martin Will/Shutterstock.com

Social Change

CORE CONCEPT 1 When sociologists study any social change, they take particular interest in identifying tipping points—situations in which previously rare events snowball into commonplace ones.

Sociologists define **social change** as any significant alteration, modification, or transformation in the organization and operation of social activity. When sociologists study change, they must first identify the social activity that has changed or is changing. The list of possible topics is virtually endless. It includes changes in the division of labor;

Video Tip: Show the author's video introduction to Chapter 16, which can be found on the Power Lecture CD. A transcript of the video is included in the Instructor's Research Manual.

Missy Gish

How much further can this egg be pushed away from the tabletop such that it can no longer sustain its position and will fall to the floor? The point immediately before that moment is the tipping point.

in how people communicate; in the amounts of goods and services people produce, sell, or buy from others; in the size of the world population; and in the average life span (Martel 1986).

Sociologists are particularly interested in **tipping points**, situations in which a previously rare (or seemingly rare) event, response, or opinion, snowballs into something dramatically more common. The process by which the rare becomes commonplace is at first gradual; the change seems so small that few if any people notice it, and if they notice it, they dismiss it as not all that significant. But at some point, a critical mass is reached so that the next small increment of change "tips" the system in a dramatic way.

In sociology, the concept of tipping point was first applied to white flight—a situation in which residents classified as white decided en masse to move out of a neighborhood because there is "one too many" new residents classified as black. Researchers who studied white flight in the late 1950s and early 1960s found that white families did not move out when the first black family moved in; they stayed as long as the number of black families remained very small; whites moved out en masse at the point when they judged there to be "one too many" black households (Grodzins 1958).

Scientists warn that we may be approaching a tipping point with regard to the earth's temperature. Based on "satellite measurements of the planet's air from the surface up to 35,000 feet," the Earth's temperature has been above the average temperature of the 100 years of the twentieth century. The years 2005 and 2010 are tied as the hottest years on record. Since 1979, land surface temperatures have increased 0.25°C per decade, and ocean temperatures have increased 0.13°C per decade. Scientists seek to identify the point at which the next slight rise in land or ocean temperature will trigger an event that will trigger a far greater rise in temperature (Intergovernmental Panel on Climate Change [IPCC] 2007). For example, if Siberia's frozen peat bog was to thaw rapidly, it could release billions of tons

Chris Caldeira

When gas prices rise, they tend to rise in pennies at a time. Each penny added to the price by itself triggers little change to driving behavior. But at some point—the tipping point—the price becomes so high, large numbers of people begin to change their behavior.

social change Any significant alteration, modification, or transformation in the organization and operation of social life.

tipping points Situations in which a previously rare (or seemingly rare) event, response, or opinion becomes dramatically more common.

Video Tip: Show the Online Newshour segment titled "In Greenland, Ice Unlocks Climate Change History." The segment highlights scientists' decades-long effort to dig deep into Greenland's ice to find clues about the history of climate change and to garner lessons from the past about life on the planet as earth's temperature increases.

TABLE 16.1 World Wide Fossil Fuel Consumption since 1850 and U.S. Share of World Consumption

Energy Source	Year First Used for Industrial Purposes	Amount Used in 1850	Amount Used in 2010	% Consumed by U.S.
Coal (all)	1748	994 million tons	6.9 billion tons	19*
Oil	1859	5,475 barrels	32.2 billion barrels	19.0
Natural gas	1821	---	2,819 trillion cubic meters	20.8

Sources: Data from World Coal Association 2011, U.S. Central Intelligence Agency 2011.
*The United States produces more coal each year than it consumes.

of the greenhouse gas methane. That thawing could represent a tipping point, triggering a far greater increase in global surface temperature (Sample 2005). The warming global temperature does not mean snowstorms will cease to be. But warming is associated with probability of extreme weather events, such as record snowfall, winds, rain, and heat (Harris 2011).

Chris Caldeira

Almost every product we use involves oil. These commonplace products pictured are made of oil. In addition, fossil fuel–powered machines produced them and workers involved in their production drove cars to work. Finally, these products were transported from factory to stores by trucks, planes, and freighters that run on oil or diesel fuel (Ranken Energy Corporation 2011).

Changes in Social Activity

> CORE CONCEPT 2 **When studying social change, sociologists ask three key questions: What has changed? What factors triggered that change? What are the consequences of the change?**

Social change is an important sociological topic. In fact, sociology first emerged as a discipline attempting to understand an event that triggered dramatic and seemingly endless changes in every area of human life. That event was the Industrial Revolution. The discipline of sociology offers a number of broad concepts to help us answer the question: "What about human activity has changed since 1750 that has increased dependency on fossil fuels?" The changes in human activity are embodied in the following ongoing processes: industrialization and mechanization, globalization, rationalization, McDonaldization, urbanization, and the information explosion.

Industrialization and Mechanization

We learned in Chapter 1 that the Industrial Revolution is an ongoing process that started as early as 1300, but gained dramatic momentum between 1750 and 1850. The most critical factor driving the momentum was mechanization—the addition of external sources of power, such as coal, oil, and natural gas, to hand tools, appliances, and modes of transportation. Among other things, these new energy sources replaced wind- and human-powered sailboats with steamships and then freighters, and they replaced horse-drawn carriages with trains, cars, and trucks. The Industrial Revolution turned us into a **hydrocarbon society**—one in which the use of fossil fuels shapes virtually every aspect of our personal and social lives (see Table 16.1). The energy source that lights the night, cools our houses and offices, and powers appliances and tools is likely coal; the energy source that heats our houses, workplaces, and water is likely natural gas; and the energy source that enables trains, planes, cars, and buses to move people and goods short and long distances is most certainly oil. When we burn fossil fuels to make the energy to do all these things, we emit greenhouse gases (such as carbon dioxide and methane) into the air.

Globalization

In the most general sense, global interdependence is a situation in which social activity transcends national borders

hydrocarbon society One in which the use of fossil fuels shapes virtually every aspect of our personal and social lives.

Teaching Tip: The text points out that many products we use contain oil. For example, anything that is plastic eight is made of oil. In fact 8 percent of the global oil production is needed to make plastic products. The Society of the Plastics Industry (www.plasticsindustry.org/AboutPlastics/content.cfm?ItemNumber=798&navItemNumber=1280) highlights important facts about plastic and the many areas of daily life it impacts, beginning with awakening to the sound of an alarm clock/radio made of plastic to removing the "protective film from around the meat and vegetables you'll prepare for dinner."

No Borders No Boundaries Facts about UPS, a Global Package Delivery System

One corporation whose 400,000 employees facilitate globalization is United Parcel Service (UPS), founded in 1907. That corporation depends on fossil-fueled vehicles to deliver or pick up 7.4 million packages per day to more than 200 countries.

Employees	U.S.-based	330,600
	Foreign-based	70,000
Daily Flights	International	815
	Domestic	942
Delivery Fleet	Cars, vans, tractors, motorcycles	93,464*
	UPS Jet Aircraft	216
	Chartered Aircraft	311
Countries served		200+
Areas served in U.S.		Every address
Packages Delivered per Day	International	2.3 million
	Domestic	13.8 million
Packages Picked Up and Delivered per Day		7.4 million
Hits on UPS.com per day		15 million

FIGURE 16.1
Source: Data from UPS (2011).

and in which social issues experienced locally are part of a larger global situation. Because the level of global interdependence is constantly changing, it is part of a dynamic process known as globalization—the ever-increasing flow of goods, services, money, people, information, and culture across political borders (Held et al. 1999). Sociologists debate the events that triggered globalization. Theoretically, one could trace its origins back 5 million years to East Africa (believed to be the cradle of human life) and to a time when humans began to spread out and eventually populate and dominate the planet. Other potential dates that mark the start of globalization include the invention of the printing press (1436) and the steam engine (1712). Regardless of the date, there is no question that globalization is a fossil fuel–driven phenomenon. Obviously, humans use trains, cars, buses, boats, planes, phones, and the Internet to deliver people, products, services, and information across national borders (see No Borders, No Boundaries: "Facts about UPS, a Global Package Delivery System"). And as globalization has increased, so has the demand for fossil fuels. One of the most profound measures of global interdependence is that 25,000 shipments of imported food products enter the United States each day. That translates into 20 million shipments per year. For example, "92 percent of all fresh and frozen seafood consumed is imported; 52 percent of the grapes; 75 percent of the apple juice; and 72 percent of the mushrooms" (Online Newshour 2007).

Student Activity: Ask students to create a chart for "Facts about FedEx or DHL" modeled after the "No Borders, No Boundaries" box above. Simply go to the FedEx or DHL websites to find relevant information.

The Sociological Imagination Carbon Footprints

Do you think a Buddhist monk, who has dedicated his life to simple, nonmaterialist living, has a large carbon footprint? Carbon footprints are the imprints people make on the environment by virtue of their lifestyle. That impact is measured in terms of fossil fuels consumed or units of carbon dioxide emitted from burning that fuel. We can think of carbon footprints as primary or secondary. The primary carbon footprint is the total amount of carbon dioxide emitted as the result of someone's direct use of fossil fuels to heat and cool a home, run appliances, facilitate travel, and so on. The secondary footprint is the total amount of carbon dioxide emitted to manufacture a product or deliver a service to that person. Tim Gutowski (2008a), a professor of mechanical engineering at MIT, and 21 of his students studied 18 different lifestyles in the United States, including a person without a home (homeless), Buddhist monks, a patient in a coma, and a professional golfer. After extensive interviews, they estimated the energy each lifestyle requires. They estimated that no lifestyle uses less than 120 gigajoules of energy, even that of a Buddhist monk, whose lifestyle is devoted to simple living, modest dress, and a vegetarian diet. A gigajoule (GJ) is a metric measure of energy consumption. It is a particularly useful measure because it can be applied to different types of energy consumption, such as kilowatts of electricity, liters of heating oil or gasoline, and cubic feet of natural gas. One GJ is equivalent to the energy needed to cook over 2,500 hamburgers or to keep a 60-watt bulb lit for six months (Natural Resources Canada 2010).

Chris Caldeira

Gutowski and his students estimated that the Buddhist monk interviewed consumed 120 GJ of energy each year and the professional golfer interviewed consumed 8,000 GJ. The Buddhist monk consumes about one-third as much energy as the average American (350 GJ) but double the average amount of energy each person on the planet consumes (64 GJ). The Buddhist monk's 120 GJ emits 8.5 metric tons of carbon dioxide each year; the professional golfer's lifestyle (8,000 GJ) produces 566 metric tons of carbon emissions.

Gutowski's study (2008b) has important implications: The United States has a "very energy-intensive system" that in effect sets the lower limits on how much energy any American uses. If the Buddhist monk uses 120 GJ, then we might conclude that energy use is woven into the fabric of our society (Revkin 2005).

Rationalization

We learned in previous chapters that rationalization is a process whereby thought and action rooted in emotion (such as love, hatred, revenge, or joy), superstition, respect for mysterious forces, and tradition are replaced by instrumental-rational thought and action that involves employing the fastest and most cost-efficient means to achieve a desired result (for example, by any means necessary).

One important example of rationalization is the profit-making strategy known as **planned obsolescence**, which involves producing goods that are disposable after a single use, are designed to have a shorter life cycle than the industry is capable of producing, or go out of style quickly (Gregory 1947). The market offers an endless number of disposable (single-use) products, including paper cups, paper towels, diapers, cameras, razors, plastic utensils, and paper tablecloths. And the market offers many other products that do not seem to last as long as they once did. For example, major household appliances such as water heaters and refrigerators built since 2000 are projected to last 8 to 12 years, whereas those built in the 1970s and 1980s lasted 20 years or more (Repair2000.com 2007). Many people buy a new car even though their old car is still in excellent-to-good condition. Similarly, people tend to buy new clothes before they wear out the clothes they already have. Planned obsolescence is fossil fuel–driven in that we use those fuels to manufacture, deliver, operate, and eventually haul away obsolete products (see The Sociological Imagination: "Carbon Footprints").

planned obsolescence A profit-making strategy that involves producing goods that are disposable after a single use, have a shorter life cycle than the industry is capable of producing, or go out of style quickly even though the goods can still serve their purpose.

Student Activity: There are several Internet sites that allow students to calculate their carbon footprint. Ask students to find such a website and calculate the carbon footprint they leave as they pursue daily activities or when they use or consume certain products.

Library of Congress Prints and Photographs Division Washington, D.C.

Until 1971, the United States produced more oil than it consumed. This 1944 image shows workers managing large valves that regulated the flow of oil into tanker ships. The oil was to be shipped for use by the U.S. armed forces and allies. At that time, the United States was producing 1.6 billion barrels of oil per year. Today, the United States produces 3.5 billion barrels and consumes 6.9 billion.

The McDonaldization of Society

In Chapter 6, we studied the organizational trend McDonaldization, a process whereby the principles governing the fast food industry come to dominate other sectors of the American economy, society, and the world (Ritzer 1993). These principles are (1) efficiency, (2) quantification and calculation, (3) predictability, and (4) control. Efficiency means offering a product or service that can move consumers quickly from one state of being to another (say, from hungry to full, from fat to thin, from uneducated to educated, or from sleeplessness to sleep). Quantification and calculation involves providing numerical indicators by which customers can easily evaluate a product or service (for example: We deliver within 30 minutes! Lose 10 pounds in 10 days! Earn a college degree in 24 months! Limit menstrual periods to four times—or to no times—a year! Obtain eyeglasses in one hour!). Predictability ensures that a service or product will be the same no matter where or when it is purchased. Control means planning out in detail the process of producing and acquiring a service or product (for example, by filling soft drinks from dispensers that automatically shut off, or by having customers stand in line).

There is no question that McDonaldization is a fossil fuel–driven phenomenon. For example, pharmacies, banks, and car wash businesses have adopted "drive-through" services to facilitate their goal of moving customers from one state of being to another quickly. Of course, "drive-through" service is not all there is to McDonaldization. Whatever the service offered—a college degree in 18 months, a medical checkup integrated into a one-stop shopping establishment, matchmaking with success guaranteed in six weeks, a prepaid funeral, or the cheapest air flight—we can find one or more of the McDonaldization principles operating.

Urbanization

Another fossil fuel–driven phenomenon is urbanization—a transformative process in which people migrate from rural to urban areas and change the way they use land, interact, and make a living. In 1900, 13 percent of the world's population was considered urban; that percentage increased to 29 percent in 1950, and today stands at 50 percent (United Nations 2011). Urbanization has shifted a significant percentage of the population away from labor-intensive agricultural occupations into manufacturing, information, and service occupations—all of which depend heavily on fossil fuels not only to make, distribute, and deliver goods and services but to gather employees together at a workplace (World Resource Institute 1996).

From a global perspective, urban populations include not only city dwellers but also suburbanites and even residents of small towns. Spatial sociologists argue that highways and automobiles have created urban sprawl and have made it difficult to distinguish between city, suburbs, and nonurban environments. Urban sprawl spreads development

Chris Caldeira

Many businesses have borrowed the concept of "drive-through" service from fast food industry including this liquor store.

beyond cities by as much as 40 or 50 miles; puts considerable distance between homes, stores, churches, schools, and workplaces; and makes people dependent on automobiles (Sierra Club 2007). In addition, the automobile and highway have allowed people to live in more space than they need. In the past 30 years, the average house size has increased from 1,400 to 2,330 square feet (National Association of Homebuilders 2007).

The Information Explosion

Sociologist Orrin Klapp (1986) wrote about the **information explosion**, an unprecedented increase in the amount of stored and transmitted data and messages in all media (including electronic, print, radio, and television). One can argue that the information explosion began with the invention of the printing press. Today, the information explosion is driven by the Internet, a vast fossil fuel–powered computer network linking billions of computers around the world. The Internet has the potential to give users immediate access to every word, image, and sound that has ever been recorded (Berners-Lee 1996).

Although it is virtually impossible to catalog all the changes associated with the Internet, we can say that, thanks to the fossil fuels used to manufacture the hardware and to run the software that power, it has (1) sped up old ways of doing things, (2) given individuals access to the equivalent of a printing press, (3) allowed users to bypass the formalized hierarchy devoted to controlling the flow of information, (4) changed how students learn, and (5) allowed people around the world to exchange information on and communicate about any topic of interest.

Triggers of Social Change

When we think about a specific social change, such as fossil fuel dependence, we usually cannot pinpoint a single trigger of that change. That is because change tends to result from a complex series of interconnected events. An analogy may help clarify this point: Suppose that a wide receiver, after catching the football and running 50 yards, is tackled at the 5-yard line by a cornerback. One could argue that the cornerback *caused* the receiver to fall to the ground. Such an account, however, does not fully explain the cause. For one thing, the tackle was not the act of one person seizing and throwing his weight onto the person with the ball; it was more complex than that. The teammates of both the wide receiver and the tackler determined how that play developed and ended. Furthermore, the wide receiver was doing everything in his power to elude the tackler's grasp (Mandelbaum 1977).

The forces that result in change are complex. Regardless, we can identify some of the key triggers of change: innovation, revolutionary ideas, conflict, the pursuit of profit, and social movements.

Innovations

> **CORE CONCEPT 3** **An innovation triggers changes in social activity. For an innovation to emerge, however, the cultural base must be large enough to support it.**

Innovation is the invention or discovery of something, such as a new idea, process, practice, device, or tool. Innovations can be placed into two broad categories: basic or improving. The distinction between the two is not always clear-cut, however. **Basic innovations** are revolutionary, unprecedented, or groundbreaking inventions or discoveries that form the basis for a wide range of applications. Basic innovations include the cotton gin, steam engine, and first-generation PC (personal computer). The discoveries of the industrial uses for coal (1748), natural gas (1821), and oil (1853) certainly qualify as basic innovations.

Improving innovations, by comparison, are modifications of basic inventions that improve upon the originals—for example, making them smaller, faster, more user-friendly, more efficient, or more attractive. Each "upgrade" of the 1903 Wright Flyer (the first successful airplane, which Orville and Wilbur Wright designed, built, and flew) increased the airplane's capacity to fly farther, higher, faster, and with more passengers. Thirty years and many innovations after the 1903 Wright Flyer, Boeing unveiled the first modern passenger airliner, which could carry 10 passengers at the speed of 155 miles per hour. In 1958, the jet age arrived when Boeing unveiled the first U.S. passenger jet, capable of carrying 181 passengers at the speed of 550 miles per hour. In 1969, wide-body jets, capable of seating 450 passengers, made their debut (Airport Transport Association 2001). The significance of this series of improving innovations is evident when we consider that, in 2009, a total of 4.8 billion passengers traveled by airplane (Airports Council International 2010). The number of international passengers reached 935 million, up from

information explosion An unprecedented increase in the amount of stored and transmitted data and messages in all media (including electronic, print, radio, and television).

innovation The invention or discovery of something, such as a new idea, process, practice, device, or tool.

basic innovations Revolutionary, unprecedented, or groundbreaking inventions or discoveries that form the basis for a wide range of applications.

improving innovations Modifications of basic inventions that improve upon the originals—for example, making them smaller, faster, less complicated, more efficient, more attractive, or more profitable.

Teaching Tip: Show students *Time Magazine*'s Best Inventions of 2010 at www.time.com/time/specials/packages/completelist/0,29569,2029497,00.html. Sociologists view inventions as triggers of change. Ask students to select an invention on the best 50 list and consider ways it might change society or the ways in which people relate to one another.

Every year, fossil fuel–powered jets carry an estimated 4.8 billion people to destinations around the world.

an estimated 50,000 passengers in 1950 (World Tourism Organization 2011). This number is expected to increase to 1.6 billion by 2020.

Anthropologist Leslie White (1949) argued that once a basic or an improving innovation has emerged, it becomes part of the **cultural base**, the number of existing inventions. White defined an **invention** as a synthesis of existing inventions. For example, the first successful airplane was a synthesis of many preceding inventions, including the gasoline engine, the rudder, the glider, and the wheel.

White suggested that the number of inventions in the cultural base increases geometrically—1, 2, 4, 8, 16, 32, 64, and so on. (Geometric growth is equivalent to a state of runaway expansion.) He argued that for an invention to emerge, the cultural base must be large enough to support it. If the Wright brothers had lived in the fourteenth century, for example, they could never have invented the airplane, because the cultural base did not contain the ideas, materials, and innovations to support its invention. The process prompted White to ask a question: Are people in control of their inventions, or do inventions control people? For all practical purposes, he believed that inventions control us. White cited two arguments to support this conclusion.

First, he suggested that the old adage "Necessity is the mother of invention" is naive. In too many cases, the opposite idea—that invention is the mother of necessity—is true. That is, an invention becomes a necessity because we find uses for the invention after it comes into being: "We invent the automobile to get us between two points faster, and suddenly we find we have to build new roads. And that means we have to invent traffic regulations and put in stop lights [and build garages]. And then we have to create a whole new organization called the Highway Patrol—and all we thought we were doing was inventing cars" (Norman 1988, p. 483).

Second, White (1949) argued that when the cultural base is capable of supporting an invention, then the invention will come into being whether or not people want it. White supported this conclusion by pointing to **simultaneous-independent inventions**—situations in which more or less the same invention is produced by two or more people working independently of one another at about the same time (sometimes within a few days or months). He cited some 148 such inventions—including the telegraph, the electric motor, the steamboat, the car, and the airplane—as proof that someone will make the necessary synthesis if the cultural base is ready to support a particular invention. In other words, the light bulb and the airplane would have been developed regardless of whether Thomas Edison and the Wright brothers (the people we traditionally associate with these inventions) had ever been born. According to White's conception, inventors may be geniuses, but they must also be born in the right place and the right time—that is, in a society with a cultural base sufficiently developed to support their inventions. None of the inventors associated with the inventions just mentioned could have delivered their products if fossil fuels had not already been adapted for industrial use.

According to White's theory, if the parts are present, someone will eventually put them together. The implications are that people have little control over whether an invention comes into being and that they adapt to inventions after the fact. Sociologist William F. Ogburn (1968) calls the failure to adapt to a new invention *cultural lag.*

Cultural Lag In his theory of cultural lag, Ogburn (1968) distinguishes between material culture and nonmaterial culture. Material culture includes tangible things—including resources (such as oil, coal, natural gas, trees, and land), inventions (such as paper and the automobile), and systems (such as factories and package delivery)—that people have produced or, in the case of resources such as oil, have identified as having the properties to serve a particular purpose. Nonmaterial culture, by contrast, includes intangible things, such as beliefs, norms, values, roles, and language. Although Ogburn maintains that both material and nonmaterial culture are important agents of social change, his theory of cultural lag emphasizes the material component, which he suggests is the more important of the two. The case of the automobile illustrates how this piece of material culture changed the United States.

cultural base The number of existing innovations, which forms the basis for further inventions.

invention A synthesis of existing innovations.

simultaneous-independent inventions Situations in which more or less the same invention is produced by two or more people working independently of one another at about the same time.

> The availability of cheap energy and an inexpensive, mass-produced car soon transformed the American landscape. Suddenly there were roads everywhere—paid for, naturally enough, by a gas tax. Towns that had been too small for the railroads were now reachable by roads, and farmers could get to once unattainable markets. Country stores that stood at old rural crossroads and sold every conceivable kind of merchandise were soon replaced by specialized stores, catering to people who could drive off and shop where they wanted. Families that had necessarily been close and inwardly focused, in part because there was nowhere but home to go at night, weakened somewhat when family members could get in their cars and take off to do whatever they wanted to do. (Halberstam 1986, pp. 78–79)

Ogburn believes that one of the most urgent challenges facing people today is the need to adapt to material innovations in thoughtful and constructive ways. He uses the term **adaptive culture** to describe the nonmaterial component's role in adjusting to material innovations. One can argue that Americans adapted easily to the automobile because it supported deeply rooted norms—values and beliefs that applied to a nation composed mostly of immigrants, who by definition had separated from their native lands and traditions. The automobile simply extended a tradition of forsaking, voluntarily or involuntarily, "the region and habits of their parents" and striking out on their own (Halberstam 1986, p. 79). On the other hand, calls to cut back driving to lessen the nation's dependence on foreign sources of oil have made little to no impact on most Americans. They resist changing the norms that govern their driving habits, a value system that defines the car as the measure of personal freedom and independence, and a belief system that holds the car to be the most efficient method of transportation.

The case of the automobile suggests that adjustments are not always immediate. Sometimes they take decades; sometimes they never occur. Ogburn uses the term **cultural lag** to refer to a situation in which adaptive culture fails to adjust in necessary ways to a material innovation. Despite Ogburn's emphasis on material culture as the key force driving change, he is not a **technological determinist**—someone who believes that humans have no free will and are controlled entirely by their material innovations. Instead, he notes that people do not adjust to new material innovations in predictable and unthinking ways; rather, they choose to create them and only then choose how to use them. Ogburn argues that if people have the power to create material innovations, then they also have the power to destroy, ban, regulate, or modify those innovations. The challenge lies in convincing people that they need to address an innovation's potentially disruptive consequences before those consequences materialize.

Library of Congress

Homes built before 1904 did not have garages. Garages became a standard feature of homes probably decades after the invention of the automobile. In the meantime, people improvised.

Revolutionary Ideas

CORE CONCEPT 4 Social change occurs when someone breaks away from or challenges a paradigm. A scientific revolution occurs when enough people in the community break with the old paradigm and orient their research or thinking according to a new paradigm.

In *The Structure of Scientific Revolutions,* Thomas Kuhn (1975) maintains that people tend to perceive science as an evolutionary enterprise. That is, they imagine scientists as problem solvers building on their predecessors' achievements. Kuhn takes issue with this evolutionary view, arguing that some of the most significant scientific advances have been made when someone has broken away from or challenged a paradigm. He defines **paradigms** as the dominant and widely accepted theories and concepts in a particular field of study.

Paradigms gain their status not because they explain everything, but rather because they offer the "best way" of looking at the world at that time. On the one hand, paradigms are important thinking tools; they bind a group of people with common interests into a scientific or national community. Such a community cannot exist without agreed-on paradigms. On the other hand, paradigms can

adaptive culture The portion of nonmaterial culture (norms, values, and beliefs) that adjusts to material innovations.

cultural lag A situation in which adaptive culture fails to adjust in necessary ways to material innovation.

technological determinist Someone who believes that human beings have no free will and are controlled entirely by their material innovations.

paradigms The dominant and widely accepted theories and concepts in a particular field of study.

Chris Caldeira

Sustainable buildings represent a paradigm shift in the way we see and design buildings. Among other things, this building is completely sustainable, with a living roof and two silos to capture rainwater that can then be used for things like flushing toilets.

act as blinders, limiting the kinds of questions that people ask and the observations that they make.

The explanatory value—and hence the status—of a paradigm is threatened by any **anomaly**, an observation that the paradigm cannot explain. The existence of an anomaly by itself usually does not persuade people to abandon a particular paradigm. According to Kuhn (1975), before people discard an old paradigm, someone must articulate an alternative paradigm that accounts convincingly for the anomaly. He hypothesizes that the people most likely to put forth new paradigms are those who are least committed to the old paradigms—the young and those new to a field of study.

A scientific revolution occurs when enough people in the community break with the old paradigm and change their research or thinking to favor the new paradigm. Kuhn (1975) considers a new paradigm to be incompatible with the one it replaces, because it "changes some of the field's most elementary theoretical generalizations" (p. 85). The new paradigm causes converts to see the world in an entirely new light and to wonder how they could possibly have taken the old paradigm seriously. "When paradigms change, the world itself changes with them. Led by a new paradigm, scientists adopt new instruments and look in new places" (p. 111).

Perhaps the best example of a scientific revolution can be found in the work of Nicolaus Copernicus, author of *On the Revolutions of the Heavenly Spheres* (1543), which challenged a long-held belief that Earth (and by extension, humankind) was the stationary center of the solar system, with the sun, moon, and planets revolving around it. Copernicus maintained that the stationary center of the solar system was the sun and that Earth and the other planets revolved around that center. Copernicus's ideas did not take hold immediately. In 1633 (90 years later), powerful church inquisitors threatened to torture and kill Galileo, who had embraced Copernicus's theory, if he did not renounce it; upon renouncing it, Galileo was imprisoned for life. "Of all discoveries and opinions, none may have exerted a greater effect on the human spirit than the doctrine of Copernicus. The world had scarcely become known as round and complete in itself when it was asked to waive the tremendous privilege of being the center of the universe. Never, perhaps, was a greater demand made on mankind—for by this admission so many things vanished in mist and smoke!" (Goethe 2004).

Conflict

CORE CONCEPT 5 Conflict can create new norms, relationships, ways of thinking, and innovations.

Conflict occurs whenever a person or group takes action to increase its share of wealth, power, prestige, or some other valued resource and when those actions are resisted by those who benefit from the current distribution system. In other words, those in control of valued resources take action to protect what they have.

In general, any kind of change has the potential to trigger conflict between those who stand to benefit and those who stand to lose from that change. When the bicycle was invented in the 1840s, horse dealers organized against it because it threatened their livelihood. Physicians declared that people who rode bicycles risked getting "cyclist sore throat" and "bicycle stoop." Church groups protested that bicycles would swell the ranks of "reckless" women (because bicycles could not be ridden sidesaddle).

Conflict can be a constructive and invigorating force. The Internet, for example, emerged out of conflict between the then Soviet Union and the United States. That conflict was the cold war, when U.S. government leaders pulled together scientists from three sectors—military, industrial, and academic—to coordinate their research and expertise and thereby serve the war effort. Because these scientists worked in offices and laboratories across the United States, Department of Defense officials worried about the consequences of an attack on a military laboratory, defense contractor, or university site. The officials realized that they needed a computer network that would allow information stored at one site to be transferred to another site in the event of an attack, especially a nuclear attack. At the same time, the computer network had to be designed so that if one or more parts of the network failed or were knocked out by a bomb, the other parts could continue to operate.

Such a design meant that no central control could exist for the network. After all, if central control was destroyed, the entire network would crash. The Internet began in the late 1960s, as ARPANET (Advanced Research Projects Agency Network), linking four universities: the University of California–Los Angeles (UCLA), the University of

anomaly An observation that a paradigm cannot explain.

Teaching Tip: When discussing the role of conflict in triggering change, consider national security-driven policies. One excellent example involves the decision to add fluoride to toothpaste and to public water systems. The origins of these practices can be traced, in large part, to the Cold War. For more on this connection, see the interview with Christopher Bryson, author of *The Fluoride Deception*, at www.fluoridealert.org/bryson.htm.

California–Santa Barbara (UCSB), the University of Utah, and Stanford University. Thus, the Internet was originally designed to (1) transfer information from one site to another quickly and efficiently in the event of war, and (2) create an information-sharing system without central control. Today, an estimated 2 billion people—28 percent of the world's population—are connected to the fossil fuel–powered Internet (Internet World Stats 2011).

The Pursuit of Profit

> **CORE CONCEPT 6 The profit-driven capitalist system drives change as it seeks to revolutionize production, create new products, and expand markets. In a capitalist system, profit is the most important measure of success.**

Karl Marx believed that an economic system, capitalism, ultimately caused the explosion of technological innovation and the enormous and unprecedented increase in the amount of goods and services produced during the Industrial Revolution. The capitalist system acts as a vehicle of change, because the instruments of production must be revolutionized constantly. Marx believed that the capitalist thirst for profit "chases the bourgeoisie over the whole surface of the globe" (Marx 1881, p. 531). In fact, by the late nineteenth century, the capitalist world economy included virtually the whole inhabited earth. The search for profit is behind efforts to exploit the resources to be found in deserts, jungles, the seas, and the solar system (Wallerstein 1984, p. 165).

Capitalism helped create a global network of economic relationships that is fossil fuel–dependent. Corporations, by the products and services they offer, have helped to create voracious appetites for petroleum- and coal-based fuels (Goldman 2007). Now corporations that have helped to create fossil fuel dependence are asking us to consume our way out of this dependence—we are being asked to buy energy-efficient appliances, light bulbs, and solar panels, use recycled paper, and purchase hybrid vehicles. Consider that fossil fuels are essential to extracting resources, manufacturing and delivering products, and powering appliances (Goldman 2007).

Thousands of products on the market claim to save the planet by going green. These products send the message that we can save the planet by consuming that product. Ethanol made from corn, for example, is touted as being a renewable fuel, but keep in mind fossil fuels are still needed to grow, transport, process, and deliver corn-based fuels. As well, diverting corn for fuel has helped to drive up the price of foods made from corn.

Social Movements

> **CORE CONCEPT 7 A social movement is formed when a substantial number of people organize to make a change, resist a change, or undo a change in some area of society.**

Social movements depend on (1) an actual or imagined condition that enough people find objectionable; (2) a shared belief that something needs to be done about the condition; and (3) an organized effort to attract supporters, articulate the condition, and define a strategy for addressing the condition. Usually those involved in social movements work outside the system to advance their cause, because the existing system has failed to respond. To draw attention to their cause and accomplish objectives, supporters may strike, demonstrate, walk out, sit in, boycott, go on hunger strikes, riot, or terrorize.

Social movements can be placed into four broad categories, depending on the scope and direction of change being sought: regressive, reformist, revolutionary, and counterrevolutionary. Definitions and global examples of each category follow. Keep in mind that the distinctions between the four categories are not always clear-cut. As a result, you might find that some examples fit into more than one category.

Regressive or reactionary movements seek to turn back the hands of time to an earlier condition or state of being, often considered a "golden era." The "Buy Local" movements qualify as such. These movements push to create and support economies rooted in communities and accountable to community interest, rather than the interests of Wall Street and other outside financial investors. Buy Local movements also aim to change people's buying habits in the direction of locally produced products. Among other things, a locally driven economy would

social movement A situation in which a substantial number of people organize to make a change, resist a change, or undo a change in some area of society.

regressive or reactionary movements Social movements that seek to turn back the hands of time to an earlier condition or state of being, one sometimes considered a "golden era."

include restaurants that specialize in serving menu items made from locally grown food and locally raised animals and bartering systems where everyone's time is treated as of equal value so that a surgeon could exchange an hour operation for an hour of landscaping (Simmons 2010).

Reformist movements target a specific feature of society as in need of attention and change. The nonprofit organization Polar Bears International (2011) focuses on saving the polar bear population and its habitat from extinction. Its goals are to use education and research to conserve the world's polar bears, offer educational resources to the public, encourage constructive dialogue, and build an international organization dedicated to saving this population.

Revolutionary movements seek broad, sweeping, and radical structural changes to a society's basic social institutions or to the world order (Benford 1992). The Earth Liberation Front (ELF) is an underground eco-defense movement with no formal leadership or membership. Its members (who sometimes form cells) anonymously and autonomously engage in economic sabotage, including property destruction and guerrilla warfare, against those seen as exploiting and destroying the natural environment. ELF members have made news for setting fire to SUVs on dealership parking lots, a horse slaughterhouse, a scientific research center, a logging company, and a ski resort. Radical environmentalists claim to have committed 1,100 acts of arson and vandalism without killing a single person (Goldman 2007; see Working for Change: "Building Affordable Green Homes").

Counterrevolutionary movements seek to maintain a social order that reform and revolutionary movements are seeking to change. The Petition Project (2011) qualifies as such a movement, as it seeks to challenge reformist and revolutionary movements demanding reductions in greenhouse gas emissions. It recruits basic and applied scientists to sign a Global Warming Petition urging the U.S. government to reject the Kyoto Protocol, an international agreement to limit greenhouse gas emissions. The signers of the petition believe that *limiting* greenhouse gases will actually harm the environment: "There is no convincing scientific evidence that human release of carbon dioxide, methane, or other greenhouse gasses is causing or will, in the foreseeable future, cause catastrophic heating of the Earth's atmosphere and disruption of the Earth's climate. Moreover, there is substantial scientific evidence that increases in atmospheric carbon dioxide produce many beneficial effects upon the natural plant and animal environments of the Earth." The movement's website lists the names of 31,487 basic and applied American scientists who have signed the petition.

Sociologist Ralf Dahrendorf (1973) offers a broad theory that seeks to capture the life of a social movement. In trying to understand the circumstances under which people take action, Dahrendorf focused on structural sources of conflict. Dahrendorf argues that every society possesses formal authority structures (such as a state, a corporation, the military, the judicial system, and school systems). Generally, clear distinctions exist between those who exercise control over that structure and its system of rewards and punishments and those who must obey the commands or face the consequences (loss of job, jail, low grades, and so on). Thus, a distinction between "us" and "them" arises naturally from the unequal distribution of power built into authority structures. As long as there is an authority structure, conflict is inevitable and the potential for those without power to organize in opposition to those with power exists.

Dahrendorf's theory of social movements involves a three-stage process. In the first stage, those without power decide to organize. "It is immeasurably difficult to trace the path on which a person . . . encounters other people just like himself, and at a certain point . . . [says] 'Let us join hands, friends, so that they will not pick us off one by one'" (Dahrendorf 1973, p. 240). Often, a significant event—such as a natural disaster, a nuclear meltdown, a health scare, economic recession—makes seemingly powerless people aware that they share an interest in changing the system. At other times, people organize because they have nothing left to lose. "You don't need courage to speak out. . . . You just need not to care anymore—not to care about being punished or beaten. A point is reached where enough people don't care anymore about what would happen to them if they speak out" (Reich 1989, p. 20).

In the second stage of conflict, if those without authority have opportunities to communicate with one another, some freedom to meet together, the necessary resources, and a leader, then they organize. At the same time, those who hold authority often use the power of their positions to censor information, restrict resources, and undermine leaders' attempts to organize. **Resource mobilization** theorists maintain that having a core group of sophisticated strategists is key to getting a social movement off the ground. Effective strategists can harness a disaffected group's energies, attract money and supporters, capture

reformist movements Social movements that target a specific feature of society as needing change.

revolutionary movements Social movements that seek broad, sweeping, and radical structural changes to a society's basic social institutions or to the world order.

counterrevolutionary movements Social movements that seek to maintain a social order that reformist and revolutionary movements are seeking to change.

resource mobilization A situation in which a core group of sophisticated strategists works to harness a disaffected group's energies, attract money and supporters, capture the news media's attention, forge alliances with those in power, and develop an organizational structure.

Working for Change Building Affordable Green Homes

All of us can probably remember the tragedy that occurred in 2005, when the violent whirlwind known as Hurricane Katrina came roaring into New Orleans and destroyed tens of thousands of homes and hundreds of neighborhoods. In total, Katrina affected approximately 303,274 people in some way. Prior to Katrina, the population of New Orleans was 484,674 (Information Collective 2011). Many Americans felt compelled to share their resources and donate supplies, money, and unpaid labor to help in recovery and reconstruction. One who wanted to help "make it right" was Brad Pitt. He offered a long-term plan for the Lower Ninth Ward, one of the hardest-hit communities in New Orleans where more than 4,000 homes were destroyed when the Industrial Canal levee failed to hold water. So the humble Hollywood star established the Make It Right Foundation and assembled a team of visionaries and staff to build 150 green, affordable, high-quality design homes.

The Make It Right (2011) team includes three core organizations: (1) William McDonough and Partners, a world leader in environmental architecture; (2) the Cherokee Gives Back Foundation, the nonprofit arm of Cherokee, a firm that specializes in remediation and sustainable redevelopment of environmentally impaired properties; and (3) Graft, an innovative architecture firm that Pitt has collaborated with on other projects around the world. There are also 27 staff members, including an executive director (Tom Darden), director of communications (Taylor Royle), director of development and government affairs (Steve Ragan), construction director (Jon Sader), chief operations officer (Veronica Taylor), and 22 supporting staff.

To launch the construction project, architects presented designs for energy-efficient green homes. Starting with the exterior, intelligent features are incorporated to save energy and reduce monthly water use. Metal roofs help to reduce air conditioning costs because they absorb less heat; and solar power panels decrease dependence on fossil fuels. The proper elevation of homes (on stilts) makes them flood resistant and creates space for parking under the home. Advanced framing techniques are used to increase the resilience of homes, allowing them to withstand 130+ mph winds. Fiber cement board sliding is used to prevent cracking, rotting, weather damage, termite infestation, and other problems. Landscaping is such that it requires minimal maintenance and is capable of handling drought conditions and temporary inundation of water. Rainwater harvesting allows homeowners to collect 600 gallons of water off the roof on an annual basis, giving homeowners water to wash their cars and water plants.

Just as impressive, the interiors of the homes adhere to the principles of cradle-to-cradle design. In the context of home building, this means the design should be not only energy-efficient but also strive to be waste-free. Examples of features incorporated in home design include

- tankless water heaters, which are 83 to 93 percent more efficient than traditional tank water heaters and can reduce the annual cost of heating water by 50 percent;
- energy-efficient appliances and light fixtures that use 30 percent less energy than conventional ones;
  - spray foam insulation placed under the roof, walls, and floors;
  - special energy-efficient windows and doors to help keep homes cool in summer and warm in winter; and
  - dual flush toilets that allow homeowners the option of using less water to flush liquid waste.

There are certain qualifications one must meet before moving into a Make It Right home. First and foremost, the person applying for a home must have lived in the Lower Ninth Ward when Hurricane Katrina hit (Make It Right can verify this once an applicant has filled out an online expression of interest form). Potential homeowners must prove they are able to afford the cost of maintenance, taxes, and insurance, and that they can devote one-third of their income to house payments. However, for those who don't qualify financially, Make It Right offers in-house counseling, financial literacy training, educational workshops, and other credit and budget counseling services. Once approved, those selected are able to choose between a single-family home costing an average of $150,000, or a duplex costing an average of $200,000 (depending on the size and design of the home). To date, the average resident contribution has been $75,000. The rest is covered by grants from Road Home, an outside mortgage financing firm, and Make It Right. To date, 73 people from the Lower Ninth Ward have returned to live in their new homes. Make It Right has received many awards but perhaps the most notable was the recognition by U.S. Green Building Council (USGBC) as being "the largest and greenest community of single-family homes in the world." Through hard work and clear visions, the Make It Right Foundation has demonstrated that social change is possible.

Source: Written by Dayna Schambach, Northern Kentucky University, class of 2011.

Greenpeace is an international organization that uses nonviolent means to challenge the authority and government support of the big oil companies and draws public attention to the world's major environmental problems.

the news media's attention, forge alliances with those in power, and develop an organizational structure. Cell phones, text messaging, and the Internet have made organizing easier by allowing interested parties to connect in ways that "defy gravity and time" (Lee 2003).

In the third stage of conflict, those seeking change enter into direct conflict with those in power. The capacity of the ruling group to stay in power and the amount and kind of pressure exerted from below affects the speed and the depth of change. If protestors believe that their voices are being heard, the conflict is unlikely to turn violent or move in a revolutionary direction. If those who hold power decide that they cannot compromise and proceed to mobilize all of their resources to thwart protests, two results are possible: First, the protesters may believe that the sacrifices they will have to make to continue protests are too great, so they will withdraw from the fray. Alternatively, the protesters may decide to meet the "enemy" head-on, in which case the conflict may become bloody. If the power differential too greatly favors one side, the protestors or their opponents may resort to **terrorism**—the systematic use of anxiety-inspiring violent acts by clandestine or semiclandestine individuals, groups, or state-supported actors.

terrorism The systematic use of anxiety-inspiring violent acts by clandestine or semiclandestine individuals, groups, or state-supported actors for idiosyncratic, criminal, or political reasons.

Consequences of Change

CORE CONCEPT 8 Sociological concepts and theories can be applied to evaluating the consequences of any social change.

In the 16 chapters of this textbook, we have covered sociological concepts and theories that can be applied to evaluating the consequences of any social change. We close the book by selecting one key idea from each chapter to assess how climate change is affecting Greenland and how outsiders have pushed or pulled Greenland into the global arena. The chapter-specific ideas suggest questions that can help guide analysis of social change.

How is climate change being experienced in Greenland? More specifically, how is climate change shaping human activity and social interactions? (Chapter 1)

Sociologists are compelled to study human activity and social interactions as they are affected by larger social forces—whether those social forces be human created or human responses to the forces of nature. The following three examples highlight human activities brought about by climate change that involve Greenlanders (especially the island's indigenous population, the Inuit) and "outsiders":

- Two 19-year-old men hike through Greenland with Inuit hunting guides as part of a 22,000-mile North Pole–South Pole trek using human muscle- and wind-powered modes of transportation (foot, skis, bicycles, and sailboats) to draw attention to climate change (BBC News 2007).
- In 2009, 19,375 ecotourists came to see Greenland, observe the small island-size icebergs floating outside its harbor, and to observe the effect of climate change, specifically ice sheets emptying into open seas (Folger 2010).
- A Greenlander explains how winter fishing has become a problem as temperatures warm. "For 10 of the last 12 years, the bay has not frozen over in the winter." When the bay used to freeze, fisherman could dogsled out to go ice fishing. "I would spend a day and a night and bring back 200 or 500 pounds of halibut on my sled. Now winter fishing. . . is dangerous with a heavy load; the ice is too thin" (Folger 2010).

U.S. Air Force photo by Tech. Sgt. Dan Rea, USAF

An estimated 20,000 ecotourists visit Greenland each year to observe icebergs and to witness the effects of climate change. Although 20,000 may seem like a small number, consider that Greenland's population is only 64,000.

How do sociologists frame a discussion about Greenland and climate change? (Chapter 2)

Each of the three major sociological theories—functionalist, conflict, and symbolic interaction—offers a central question to help guide thinking and a vocabulary for answering that question.

A functionalist asks: What are the anticipated (manifest) and unintended (latent) functions and dysfunctions of climate change on Greenland? One manifest function is an economic boom associated with a lengthened shipping season (once four months long and now six months long), which allows goods to move into and out of Greenland. A latent function is the emergence of working alliances between Inuit Greenlanders and tropical island peoples, who face cultural extinction from rising sea levels. Another latent function is a growing interest in Greenland, the Arctic, and Antarctica, so that popular films are set in or give prominent attention to these locations. Such films include *The Last Winter* (a horror film), *The Golden Compass, Pirates of the Caribbean, Arctic Tale, An Inconvenient Truth*, and *The March of the Penguins*. One manifest dysfunction is a growing ecotourism industry, in which the number of tourists visiting Greenland each year overwhelms the resident population of towns visited. Finally, a latent dysfunction connected to climate change is the loss of status among Inuit elders, who can no longer predict the weather (see the discussion of symbolic interaction following the next paragraph).

A conflict theorist asks: Who benefits from climate change, and at whose expense? Conflict theorists key in on the many industries that have expanded in or moved operations to Greenland because of the warming climate. These commercial interests include zinc, lead, and uranium mining companies; oil drilling and exploration companies; and water companies. From the conflict perspective, such companies and their customers will no doubt benefit at the expense of Greenland and its culture. Greenland Minerals and Energy Ltd., an Australian-based company, has discovered what it believes to be the largest deposits of rare earth metals. Rare earth metals are necessary to produce wind turbines, computer display screens, and hybrid car batteries. Currently, China controls 93 percent of the world's mined rare earth metals (Hiroko 2010, Folger 2010).

Finally, a symbolic interactionist asks: How do the involved parties experience, interpret, influence, and respond to what they and others are doing as interaction occurs? Symbolic interactionists are particularly interested in ways interaction among Greenlanders is changing because of climate change. For example, Inuit Greenlanders no longer turn to their elders for weather forecasts; because of climate change, the signs that once allowed the elders to accurately predict the weather no longer apply.

How is the culture of Greenland's Inuit and of other Arctic peoples changing because of climate change? (Chapter 3)

Sociologists define *culture* as the way of life of a people; more specifically, culture includes the human-created strategies for adjusting to the environment and to the creatures (including humans) that are part of that environment. Sociologists are interested in how climate change is affecting Greenland's Inuit and the other Arctic peoples who have adapted to an extreme weather environment that is now warming (see Intersection of Biography and Society: "Cultural Change in the Arctic"). One change affecting the Inuit is declines in, and even the gradual extinction of, marine species. This loss disrupts or destroys their hunting—and, by extension, their eating—habits. It

U.S. Air Force photo by Tech. Sgt. Dan Rea, USAF

No roads connect towns and settlements in Greenland; boats and planes are the modes of transportation. In the winter, people travel using dogsleds and snowmobiles.

Cultural Change in the Arctic

The Arctic Climate Impact Assessment (Huntington and Fox 2004), a scientific report commissioned by the Arctic Council (an intergovernmental forum of eight Arctic nations), includes a chapter about the changing Arctic from the perspective of indigenous peoples. The following observations illustrate this perspective:

- "The weather has changed. For instance, elders will predict that it might be windy, but then it doesn't become windy. And then it often seems like its going to be very calm and then it suddenly becomes windy. So their predictions are never correct any more—the predictions according to what they see haven't been true."
- "The river ice breaks up so much earlier; it used to be in mid-June, and now it has been as early as mid-May. There is not so much snow, and the snow we get melts much earlier. In terms of summertime, in the course of my own life, it has been rare that we ever used to wear shorts and T-shirts because it never got warm enough. But today because there are such long heat waves where it was 86 degrees Fahrenheit for an entire month, the whole community goes to the beach and swims. It gets so hot that bugs do not even come around anymore" (Watt-Cloutier 2004).
- "The direct heat from the sun is warmer; it is not the same anymore and you can't help but notice that. It is probably not warmer overall, but the heat of the sun is stronger. The reason why I mention the fact the sun seems warmer is because another piece of evidence to that is that we get some skin diseases or some skin problems. Because I think in the past when Peter (an elder) was a young boy, we never seemed to have these skin problems and I see them more and more these days."

is difficult for people to understand that changing or eliminating hunting means changing or eliminating a way of life: "People think, 'Oh they are just killing animals.' . . . When we go out on the land and teach [our children] to hunt, it's not just about aiming the gun and skinning the seal. It is also teaching courage and patience and how not to be impulsive and to use sound judgment. It is character skills that are transferable to the modern world" (Watt-Cloutier 2004). In response to shrinking food resources, Inuit are relying more on expensive, processed foods, which is having a dramatic effect on their diet and overall physical health (Associated Press 2005).

How do in-group and out-group memberships related to climate change shape identity? (Chapter 4)

Sociologists use the term *in-group* to describe a group with which people identify and to which they feel closely attached—particularly when that attachment is founded on opposition to another group known as an out-group. An out-group is a group toward which in-group members feel a sense of separateness, opposition, or even hatred. By definition, in-groups cannot exist without out-groups and one person's in-group is another person's out-group. With regard to climate change, sociologists would note the following in-group/out-group dynamics. The Inuit are teaming up with small tropical island peoples (in Fiji, French Polynesia, and Caribbean countries) to speed up international response to climate change. Although the temperatures in the Arctic and in small tropical islands are quite different, both Arctic peoples and tropical islanders live in coastal communities threatened by rising sea levels (Weber 2007). This imminent threat gives seemingly diverse peoples a common identity. For them, the out-group consists of people who live in countries with the highest greenhouse gas emissions, especially the United States and China. The Inuit have filed a complaint with the Inter-American Commission on Human Rights that excessive U.S. greenhouse gas emissions have endangered their basic human rights (Brownwell 2004). This Arctic–small island coalition foreshadows the worldwide emergence of two groups with opposing interests—one group seeking to protect their natural environment and the other group resisting any changes to their fossil fuel–dependent lifestyles.

Department of Defense

Those who live in island nations are most likely to be aware of rising sea levels and consequences to their homes and way of life. These children live on one of 40 islands that make up the Federated States of Micronesia.

What social forces bring Greenlanders into interaction with outsiders and shape the relationships between the two groups? (Chapter 5)

The division of labor is an important force that pulls people into interaction with one another. It breaks down the making of a product or rendering of a service into specialized tasks; each task is performed by workers trained to do a particular task. The workers do not have to live near each other; they often live in different parts of the country and different parts of the world. Not only are the tasks geographically dispersed, but the parts and materials needed to manufacture products come from many locations around the world. Of course, sociologists look to identify the resources that Greenland contributed to the global division of labor. From the sixteenth through the late nineteenth centuries, whalers from many European nations were drawn to Greenland's waters to hunt for bowhead whales. They could extract 44,000 to 66,000 pounds of oil from every whale. The oil was used to make lamp fuel, lubricants, soap products, ship tar, varnish, paint, and cosmetics. European interest in Greenland's whales ended in the late nineteenth century, after a new kind of oil (petroleum) was discovered and kerosene was introduced as a cheaper fuel for lighting lamps (Greenland Tourism and Business Council 2007).

Today outsiders are pulled to Greenland to capitalize on easier access to the country's natural resources. A case in point is the mining company Angus and Ross, Greenland's melting ice will allow it to reopen the Black Angel Mine, which closed in 1990. The once 4-month-long shipping season is now 6 or more months long and is eventually expected to increase to 12 months long (Haines 2007). The company plans to extract 4 million tons of high-grade lead and zinc. Zinc is used to protect iron structures and to make dry batteries, lightweight coins, paints, rubber products, cosmetics, pharmaceuticals, plastics, soaps, textiles, X-ray and TV screens, and fluorescent lights. Lead is used to make such products as storage batteries, cable covering, plumbing products, ammunition, and the antiknock compound in some gasolines (Winter 2007).

Department of Defense

In the background is a Coast Guard cutter ship that breaks up ice, allowing supply ships to navigate through the waters. With warmer temperatures, shipping lanes are open at least six months of the year.

Because of climate change, what new formal organizations have emerged in Greenland? (Chapter 6)

Formal organizations are viewed as coordinating mechanisms, because they bring together people, resources, and technology and then channel social activity toward achieving a specific outcome. Between 2004 and 2005, the government of Greenland joined with four large corporations—Air Greenland, KNI, Royal Greenland, and Greenland Tourism and Business—to create an export promotion strategy and an international branding strategy for Greenland. The purpose of the international branding is to market "positive associations and expectations" about Greenland abroad so that "whenever the word *Greenland* comes up, people think of the island and its products as very special" (Greenland Home Rule Government 2007). Among other things, the government–corporate coalition has issued the brochure *Invest in Greenland*. The brochure opens with these words: "Greenland is currently experiencing a development that is presenting the Greenlandic and international business community with plenty of opportunities for investment in international growth sectors. Whereas fishing and ancillary industries have been the overwhelmingly dominant business for many years, a significant growth is now taking place in . . . tourism, transport, mineral mining, energy-intensive industry such as the aluminum industry and exclusive food production" (p. 4).

The increased interest in Greenland, of course, extends to the entire Arctic region, which is considered to be one of the last energy frontiers in the world. As the ice recedes and temperatures warm, the Arctic's mineral riches (especially oil and natural gas) are becoming more accessible. Russia, the United States, Canada, Norway, and Denmark already have control over some territory in the region and are seeking to claim more territory. In 2007, Russia planted a titanium capsule containing the Russian flag as a first step in claiming as much as one-half of the Arctic Ocean floor as its natural territory (Associated Press 2007, Chivers 2007).

How do ideas about what constitutes deviance relate to outsiders' interest or lack of interest in Greenland? (Chapter 7)

Sociologists maintain that the only characteristic common to all forms of deviance is that some social audience challenges or condemns a behavior or appearance because it departs from established norms. In light of this fact, it is

Library of Congress

When Europeans and Americans depended on whaling, it was not considered deviant to kill whales. In fact, whaling was celebrated. The discovery of kerosene and other fossil fuels allowed Westerners to "care" about whales and condemn those who continued to hunt them.

difficult to generate a precise list of deviant behaviors, because a behavior considered deviant by some people may not be considered deviant by others. Likewise, a behavior considered deviant at one time and place may not be considered deviant at another. Such is the case with whaling. During the seventeenth, eighteenth, and nineteenth centuries, European and American whalers killed tens of thousands of whales in Arctic waters for commercial purposes, with little effective resistance from environmental or animal rights groups. In 1946, the International Whaling Commission (IWC) was established with the charge of governing the conduct of whaling throughout the world. Since then, it has taken such measures as banning the whaling of certain species, designating whale sanctuaries, setting limits on the number and size of whales hunted, and specifying the opening and closing of whaling seasons (International Whaling Commission 2007). Indigenous peoples such as Greenland's Inuit are permitted to catch a limited number of whales on a not-for-profit basis for cultural reasons. The IWC sets quotas and reviews them every five years. In 2007, the IWC honored West Greenland's request to increase the number of minke whales that could be killed from 175 to 200 (Kazinform 2007).

How is climate change shaping life chances in Greenland and elsewhere? (Chapter 8)

Sociologists define *life chances* as a critical set of potential social advantages, including everything from the chances that a person will survive through the first year of life to the chances that a person will live a long life. Obviously, we had no control over which of the world's 243 countries we were born in, but that country has had a profound effect on our life chances. Climate change is expected to affect access to water as regions susceptible to drought become even drier and regions susceptible to flooding get even more rain. People who live in Greenland have the greatest access to sustainable water—the equivalent of 2.8 billion gallons available to each person each year. People who live in Kuwait have the lowest access, with the equivalent of 2,640 gallons available to each person each year. These figures translate into 7.2 gallons per day per person in Kuwait versus 7.6 million gallons per day per person in Greenland. For countries such as Kuwait to survive, they must import water or share water sources with other countries (UNESCO 2003).

In light of the American military presence in Greenland, how does race affect life chances? (Chapter 9)

Sociologists define race as human-created or constructed categories that assume great social importance. Among other things, sociologists are interested in how the racial category to which people are assigned affect life chances. Greenland's population consists of Inuit, Greenland-born whites, and immigrant Danes. Americans of all racial categories are stationed at Thule Air Base. The United States

TSGT JOSE HERNANDEZ

The Inuit people are considered the indigenous population of Greenland. This Inuit works at Thule Air Base.

has maintained a military presence in Greenland since World War II. One snapshot of how race influences life chances can be found in the way Thule Air Base is staffed. Today, about 120 American military personnel are stationed at the base. Additional base personnel include 500 to 600 Danish civilians and only 100 Inuit Greenlander civilians. The Danes, who trained in universities and trade schools in their home country, work in the higher-skilled occupations; the Inuit Greenlanders, having little access to higher education or vocational training, work as truck drivers, drivers, cooks, cashiers, and janitors (Mahr 2004).

What is the sex composition of Greenland? How might it be affected by climate change? (Chapter 10)

The sex composition of a society offers some clues about how it is organized and about inequalities that may exist between males and females. Table 16.2 shows the number of males per 100 females by age category in Greenland. Notice that, irrespective of age, 111 males live there for every 100 females. Males age 25 to 59 and 60 to 69 outnumber their female counterparts, as there are 116 males for every 100 females in the former category and 143 males for every 100 females in the latter. The only category in which females outnumber males is age 70 plus, which has 88 males for every 100 females. We might hypothesize that this imbalance is related to immigration patterns: Greenland draws males to work in the mining and fishing industries. The larger number of females age 70 and older reflects differences in life expectancy that favor women. Sociologists would hypothesize that the imbalance favoring males in age categories under 70 will increase as more males migrate to Greenland to work in the new industries that have located there now that shipping season has been extended and there is easier access to natural resources.

TABLE 16.2 Number of Males and Females in Greenland by Age Category

Age Category	Males	Females	Males per 100 Females
0–9	4,297	4,121	104.3
10–24	7,138	6,976	102.3
25–59	15,251	13,132	116.1
60–69	2,556	1,777	143.8
70–100+	1,140	1,282	88.9
Total	30,382	27,288	111.3

Source: Data from U.S. Bureau of the Census 2011a.

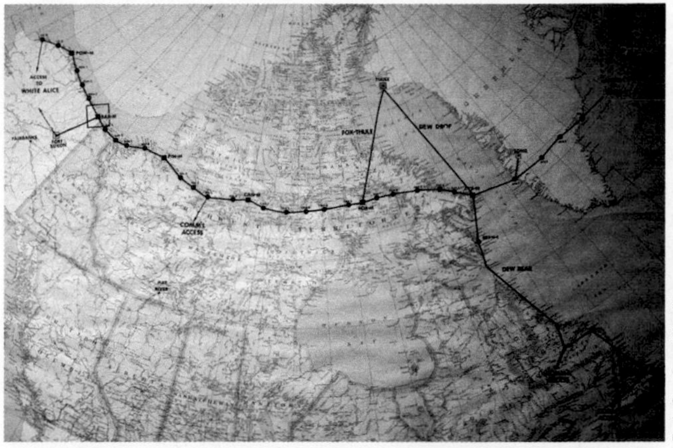
Tech. Sgt. Donald L. Wetterman

The map focuses on North America near the Arctic Circle. The dots show 30 radar sites that the U.S. military has spread out along the 3,600-mile Distant Early Warning (DEW) Line that runs from Alaska, across Northern Canada, to Greenland.

How did the U.S. military-industrial complex pull Greenland into the international arena? (Chapter 11)

Sociologist C. Wright Mills wrote about the connection between government, industry, and the military in *The Power Elite* (1956). The power elite comprises the few people who occupy such lofty positions in these three institutions that their decisions have affected millions, even billions, of people worldwide.

U.S. military presence in Greenland can be traced to World War II, after German forces occupied Denmark in 1940. But its military presence did not end after that war. In 1951, Denmark and the United States signed a defense treaty establishing the 339,000-acre Thule Air Base to be used in the event of a Soviet attack on the United States. Native Greenlanders had no say in the matter, as Greenland was a colony of Denmark. Operation Blue Jay, the code name for the massive secret effort to build the base, attracted 12,000 workers to Greenland. In 1953, the Danish government displaced an entire Inuit village to expand the base. The U.S. military stored nuclear weapons at Thule, but it did not officially acknowledge this fact until 1996, even though a B-52 bomber carrying four nuclear bombs crashed near the base in 1968, spewing plutonium over the ice (Mahr 2004). Thule Air Base is home to the U.S. Ballistic Missile Early Warning System, and Greenland is part of the Distant Early Warning Line, stretching from Alaska and northern Canada to Greenland (Archer and Scrivener 1983). Radar and satellite technologies are in place to warn of an impending ballistic missile attack against North America.

How might climate change affect Greenland's fertility rate? (Chapter 12)

Sociologists define total fertility as the average number of live children that women bear in their lifetime. Since 1995, total fertility in Greenland has declined from 2.5 to 2.1 (U.S. Bureau of the Census 2011b). Most of Greenland's population lives in towns, and a small percentage lives in rural settlements where fertility is likely higher. Settlements are isolated, with few employment opportunities and very limited access to goods and services. By contrast, towns offer more job opportunities and access to a variety of goods and services. Sociologists would predict that as Greenland opens its borders to various foreign corporations and associated employment opportunities, total fertility will decline further.

What are formal and informal ways outsiders are coming to learn about Greenland, other Arctic cultures, and climate change? (Chapter 13)

In the broadest sense, education includes experiences that train, discipline, and shape the mental and physical potentials of the maturing person. Sociologists make a distinction between informal and formal education. Informal education occurs in a spontaneous, unplanned way, so that learning occurs naturally. In other words, someone does not deliberately design the learning experiences to stimulate specific thoughts or to impart a specific skill. Informal education about Greenland occurs when news audiences are inadvertently exposed to information of that country. When audiences hear on the nightly news that Santa Claus has left his North Pole home and is crossing Greenland and heading to the United States to deliver presents, audiences come to associate Greenland with the North Pole.

Formal education encompasses a purposeful, planned effort to impart specific knowledge or skills. Certain museums qualify as formal educators, because they are dedicated to preserving and displaying human culture and sharing collected artifacts with the public so people can learn about the culture to which the museum is devoted. One such museum in the United States—the Jensen Arctic Museum in Monmouth, Oregon—was founded in 1985 by the adventurer, educator, collector, and philanthropist Paul H. Jensen. The purpose of the museum is to convey "his love of the arctic people, their art, lifestyle, and environment" and to help visitors appreciate "the culture and ingenuity of a people who blended into a difficult and often unforgiving arctic environment" (Jensen Arctic Museum 2007).

Through a process known as informal education, many Americans have come to associate Greenland with Santa Claus, the Arctic, and the North Pole.

What religions did outsiders bring to Greenland? (Chapter 14)

The major religions of Greenland are Lutheran Christianity and shamanism. Close ties exist between church and state in Denmark. Even today, Paragraph 4 of the Danish constitution identifies the Evangelical Lutheran Church as the national church of Denmark. Given that Greenland is a former colony of Denmark and that a significant share of Greenland's population is Danish, we should not be surprised to learn that the Lutheran Church has considerable influence in Greenland. For almost 300 years, the Danish Church has established missions in other lands, including Greenland. Today 500 missionaries are involved with 35 Danish government- and donor-subsidized missionary societies in Africa, India, Asia, South America, and Europe (Council on Interchurch Relations 2007).

Shamanism is the traditional religion of the Inuit, who do not build sacred buildings known as churches. They consider nature sacred and themselves as children of nature. For the Inuit, everything has a soul and is spiritually connected. The universe is in harmony, and the powers of nature are neutral toward humans. When evil (which can take such forms as bad hunting, bad weather, or illness) occurs, the source is almost always people's bad behavior (Mikaelsen 2007).

What is the population size of Greenland, and is the population increasing or decreasing because of climate change? (Chapter 15)

Population size is determined by births, deaths, and migration. Births add new people to a population; deaths reduce its size. Migration is the movement of people from one residence to another. Such movement adds new people to a population if they are moving in from another geographic area; it reduces the population if people are moving out. In 2011, the population of Greenland was 58,000. The annual birth rate was 15 births per 1,000 people, for a total of 870 births; the annual death rate was 10 deaths per 1,000 people, for a total of 464 deaths. These figures mean that 406 more people were born in 2011 than died (U.S. Bureau of the Census 2011, Greenland Home Rule Government 2007). However, Greenland's net migration (the difference between the number of people who moved into the territory versus the number who moved out) was –348, which means that more people moved out than moved in. In 2011, Greenland's total population increased by 58 people. One might predict that in-migrations will increase relative to out-migration, and overall population will increase as well, as more industries expand or establish operations in Greenland.

In light of the information explosion, how does one identify credible sources about climate change? (Chapter 16)

Consider that entering the term *climate change* into the search engine Google pulls up 139 million sites, with Wikipedia listed first. It would take a reader more than 264 years to review just the titles (assuming the reader could process a title every second). Given the level of competition among message senders to attract consumers, what strategies do they use to increase the chances that someone will pay attention to a particular message? Two of the most common strategies are (1) keeping the message short and simple, and (2) using eye-catching headlines and images. One of the most vivid images used to represent the potentially devastating consequences of climate change are polar bears who appear to be stranded on ice floes. Such images give the impression that the bears are stuck with nowhere to go. The images do not disclose the facts that polar bears use floating ice as a platform for catching seals and that the bears can swim long distances (perhaps 150 miles or more). These facts do not mean that the polar bears face no threats; their numbers have declined by 25 percent in the past 20 years (Polar Bears International 2007, Mouland 2007). The images do, however, oversimplify climate change's effect on these animals. Specifically, as warming melts more and more sea ice, polar bears must make riskier and longer swims to reach a solid platform; consequently, they are much thinner than they would otherwise be (Nicklen 2007).

A complete understanding of climate change involves knowing about Greenland's melting ice sheets, but it also involves knowing about the world's glaciers, the massive deforestation of the Amazon, changes to the North Atlantic Current, the ozone hole and ozone thinning, Asian monsoons, and much more (Whitty 2006).

The challenge of sorting through massive amounts of material and weighing opposing viewpoints is exacerbated when message senders engage in name-calling and outright dismissal of another side's viewpoints. With regard to climate change, there appear to be two opposing camps. Both agree that the planet is warming, that ice sheets are melting, and that greenhouse gas emissions have risen. The debate is over whether the climate change is man-made or part of a natural cycle, and over whether greenhouse gas emissions are potentially dangerous or beneficial.

The 1,250 authors and 2,500 scientific expert reviewers from 130 countries involved with the UN report *Climate Change 2007* maintain that preindustrial global atmospheric concentrations of carbon dioxide ranged from 180 to 300 parts per million (ppm). The UN report argues that the preindustrial levels are the best estimates of the amount of greenhouse gases in the atmosphere that exist naturally (Intergovernmental Panel on Climate Change 2007). Today, carbon dioxide levels are 379 ppm. Thus, the panel believes that human-made contribution ranges anywhere from 79 ppm (379 ppm to 300 ppm) to 199 ppm (379 ppm to 180 ppm).

The 31,500 signers of the Petition Project take issue with any assessment that global warming is man-made, arguing that the planet has experienced ice ages, sea level rises, glacial melting, and higher greenhouse gas emissions before. Therefore, what we call "global warming" or "climate change" may be part of a natural cycle.

Because most people do not have the scientific background to evaluate the two arguments, proponents of each side often use simplistic images to sway people. In assessing the two views, keep in mind that the debate is over who or what is responsible for climate change (humans or nature?). It is also a high-stakes debate about whether humans should change the way they have organized social activity. If the phenomenon is natural, then no amount of effort is likely to change the outcome, so why make changes?

A sociologist interested in objectively evaluating the two viewpoints would probably find it useful to check authors', reviewers', and petition signers' credentials. The Petition Project website gives an alphabetized list of signers who reject the idea of human contribution to climate change and who question whether greenhouse gas emissions are problematic for the planet. Along with each signer's name, only the most basic academic credentials (such as MS and PhD) are provided. The list provides no corporate, university, or other affiliations—making it difficult to learn about signers' qualifications. I selected ten signers at random and used an Internet search engine to help me identify their affiliations and their other qualifications. Four of the ten names yielded results: One of these four signers appears to have died in 2004; the second works for Conoco Phillips (an integrated petroleum company); the third specializes in airlines, hotels, rental cars, and cruise line forecasting; and the fourth is a city attorney.

The names of authors and reviewers associated with the UN *Climate Change 2007* report are listed, along with their academic credentials and their affiliations. I selected ten names at random and used an Internet search engine to verify their affiliations and credentials. All ten names yielded results: The affiliations included National Center for Atmospheric Research (Boulder, Colorado), Netherlands Environmental Assessment Agency, and Canadian Centre for Climate Modelling and Analysis. Although a sample of ten names cannot yield definitive results about potential biases driving people affiliated with either camp, it does suggest that further investigation is warranted before judging which source is more credible.

Online Poll

Have you made a conscious effort to reduce consumption of fossil fuels? Check all that apply.

- ○ No
- ○ Yes, drive less
- ○ Yes, consume less of something
- ○ Yes, reduce use of appliances (for example, computers, cell phone, dryers)
- ○ Yes, purchase green products
- ○ Yes, recycle
- ○ Yes, other

To see how other students responded to these questions, go to **www.cengagebrain.com**.

SSGT Catherine Crouch, USAF

Summary of CORE CONCEPTS

This is a Bombardier Skidozer over-snow vehicle used to train U.S. military personnel who are going to what is known as Kool School located on the ice cap of Greenland close to the Distant Early Warning Line. The Skidozer transports personnel, equipment, and supplies needed for recovering disabled aircraft. The image represents U.S. interest and presence in Greenland, which will only increase as the climate of the planet changes. This chapter addresses the fate of Greenland and how it is connected to fossil fuel dependency and climate change. In particular, we considered how fossil fuel–dependent social activities and climate change have affected Greenland.

CORE CONCEPT 1 When sociologists study any social change, they take particular interest in identifying tipping points—situations in which previously rare events snowball into commonplace ones.

Social change is any significant alteration, modification, or transformation in the organization and operation of social activity. When sociologists study change, they must first identify the social activity that has changed or is changing. Sociologists are particularly interested in tipping points, a situation in which a previously rare (or seemingly rare) event, response, or opinion becomes dramatically more common.

CORE CONCEPT 2 When studying social change, sociologists ask three key questions: What has changed? What factors triggered that change? What are the consequences of the change?

The greatest change in social activity since 1750 is the extent to which that activity depends on fossil fuels. The most critical factor driving the Industrial Revolution was mechanization. There is no question that fossil fuels use facilitated globalization. Obviously, humans use trains, cars, buses, boats, planes, phones, and the Internet to deliver people, products, services, and information across national borders. The rationalization driving the profit-making strategy known as planned obsolescence depends on fossil fuels to manufacture products, to deliver them to retailers or to buyers' houses, to make them operate, and to haul them away when owners decide to discard them. Other processes that could not occur without fossil fuels are McDonaldization, urbanization, and the information explosion.

CORE CONCEPT 3 An innovation triggers changes in social activity. For an innovation to emerge, however, the cultural base must be large enough to support it.

If the Wright brothers had lived in the fourteenth century, for example, they could never have invented the airplane, because the cultural base did not contain the ideas, materials, and innovations to support its creation. When the cultural base is capable of supporting an invention, then the invention will come into being whether or not people want it. When this happens, society experiences what sociologist William F. Ogburn calls cultural lag; that is, the adaptive culture (norms, values, and beliefs) fails to adjust in necessary ways to a material innovation.

CORE CONCEPT 4 Social change occurs when someone breaks away from or challenges a paradigm. A scientific revolution occurs when enough people in the community break with the old paradigm and orient their research or thinking according to a new paradigm.

According to Thomas Kuhn, some of the most significant scientific advances have been made when someone has broken away from or challenged a paradigm—a dominant and widely accepted theory or concept in a particular field of study. Before people discard an old paradigm, someone must articulate an alternative paradigm that accounts convincingly for all anomalies (observations the old paradigm cannot explain). The people most likely to put forth new paradigms are those who are least committed to the old paradigms.

CORE CONCEPT 5 Conflict can create new norms, relationships, ways of thinking, and innovations.

Conflict is both a consequence and a cause of change. Change can trigger conflict, and conflict can lead to change. Conflict can be a constructive and invigorating force that prevents a social system from becoming stagnant, unresponsive, or inefficient. It can also generate new, more efficient technologies.

CORE CONCEPT 6 The profit-driven capitalist system forces change as it seeks to revolutionize production, create new products, and expand markets. In a capitalist system, profit is the most important measure of success.

To maximize profit, successful entrepreneurs must respond to economic stagnation and downturns with profit-generating strategies. Historically, such strategies have included lowering wages, introducing labor-saving technologies, finding new markets, and creating new products that consumers will feel the "need" to buy.

CORE CONCEPT 7 A **social movement** is formed when a substantial number of people organize to make a change, resist a change, or undo a change in some area of society

A social movement depends on (1) an actual or imagined condition that enough people find objectionable; (2) a shared belief that something needs to be done about the condition; and (3) an organized effort to attract supporters, articulate the condition, and define a strategy for addressing the condition. Social movements can be classified as regressive, reformist, revolutionary, and counterrevolutionary.

CORE CONCEPT 8 Sociological concepts and theories can be applied to evaluating the consequences of any social change.

The sociological concepts and theories covered in this textbook can be applied to evaluating the consequences of any social change. Key concepts are important thinking tools, because they suggest questions that can guide analysis of any social change.

Resources on the Internet

Login to CengageBrain.com to access the resources your instructor requires. For this book, you can access:

Sociology CourseMate

Access an integrated eBook, chapter-specific interactive learning tools, including flash cards, quizzes, videos, and more in your Sociology CourseMate.

CENGAGENOW™

Take a pretest for this chapter and receive a personalized study plan based on your results that will identify the topics you need to review and direct you to online resources to help you master those topics. Then take a posttest to help you determine the concepts you have mastered and what you will need to work on.

CourseReader

CourseReader for Sociology is an online reader providing access to readings, and audio and video selections to accompany your course materials.

Visit **www.cengagebrain.com** to access your account and purchase materials.

Key Terms

adaptive culture 423
anomaly 424
basic innovations 421
counterrevolutionary movements 426
cultural base 422
cultural lag 423
hydrocarbon society 417
improving innovations 421
information explosion 421
innovation 421
invention 422
paradigms 423
planned obsolescence 419
reformist movements 426
regressive or reactionary movements 425
resource mobilization 426
revolutionary movements 426
simultaneous-independent inventions 422
social change 416
social movement 425
technological determinist 423
terrorism 428
tipping points 416

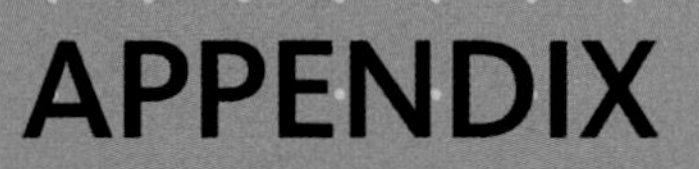

APPENDIX

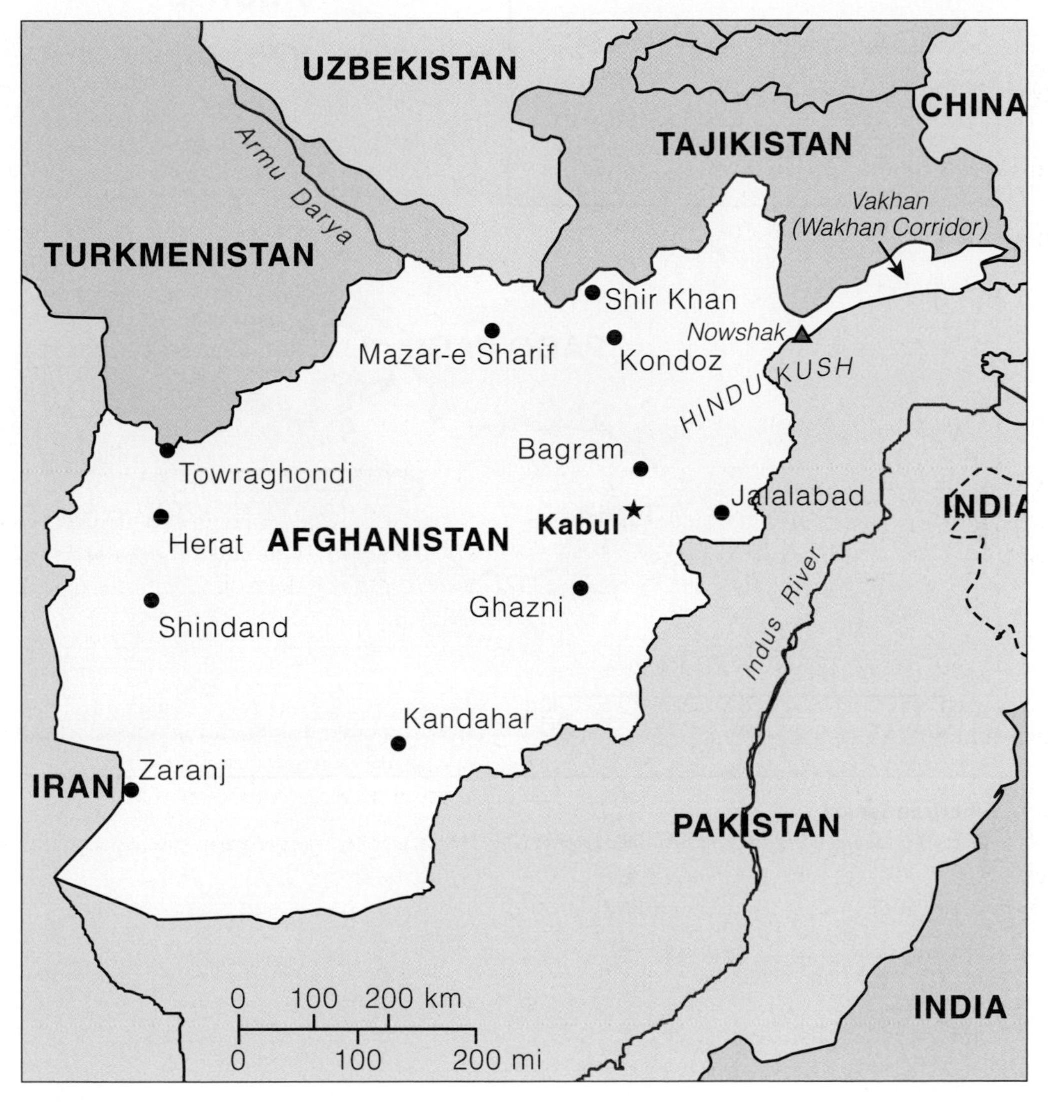

Afghanistan

Source: U.S. Central Intelligence Agency, *World Factbook* (2007)

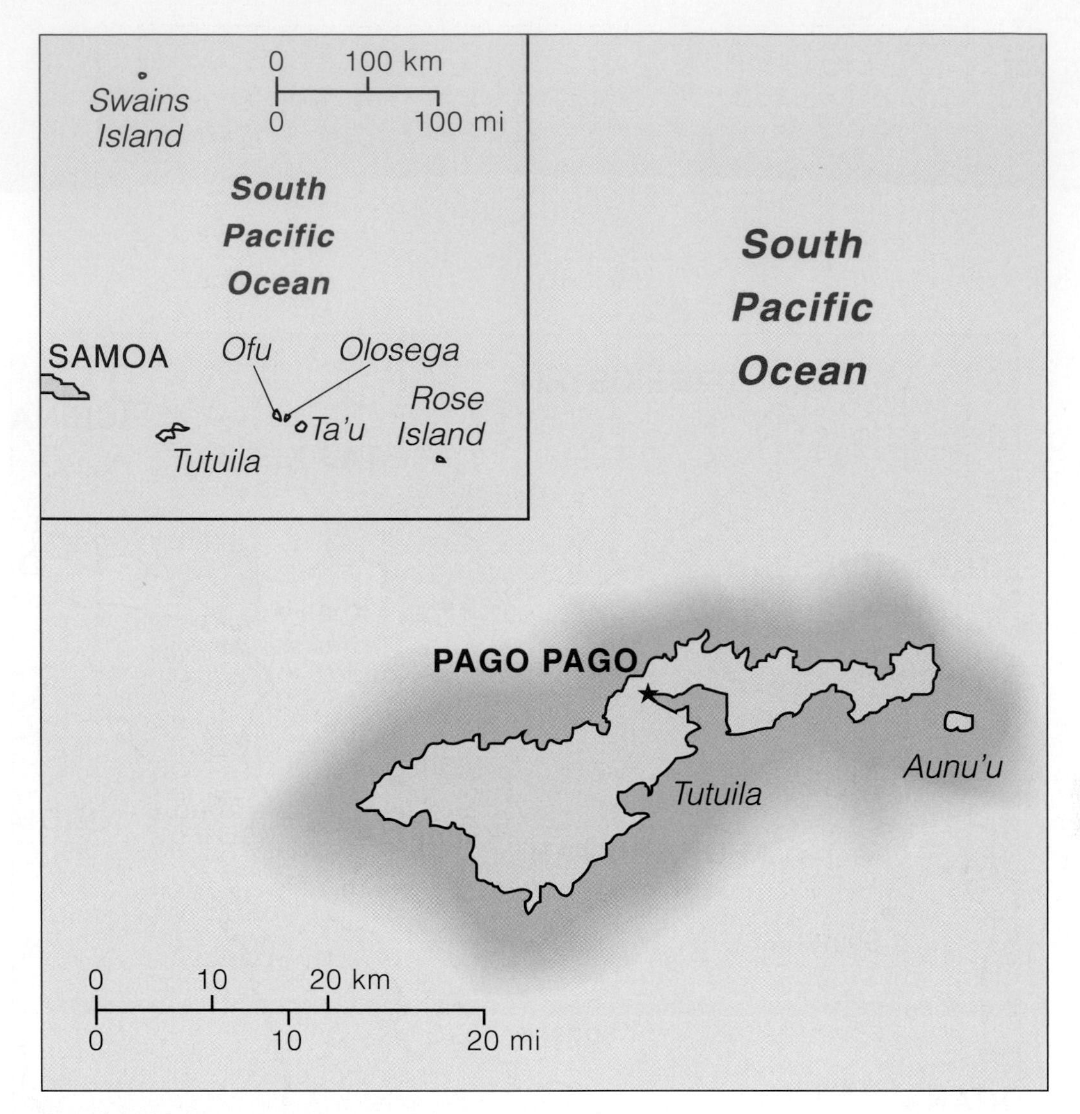

American Samoa

Source: U.S. Central Intelligence Agency, *World Factbook* (2007)

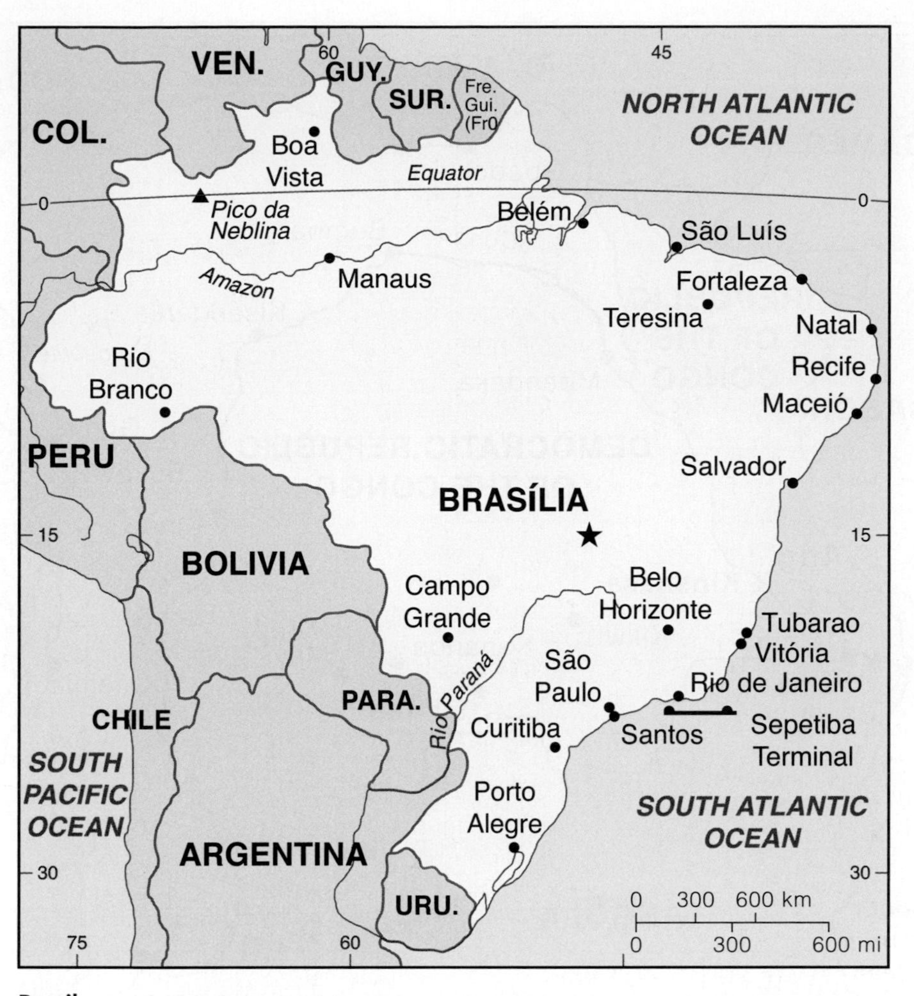

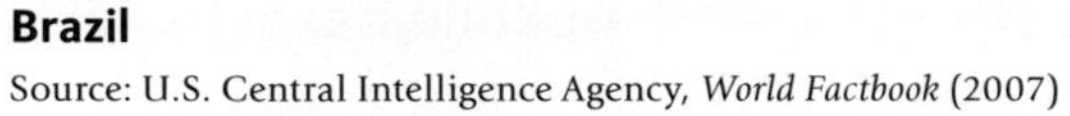

Brazil

Source: U.S. Central Intelligence Agency, *World Factbook* (2007)

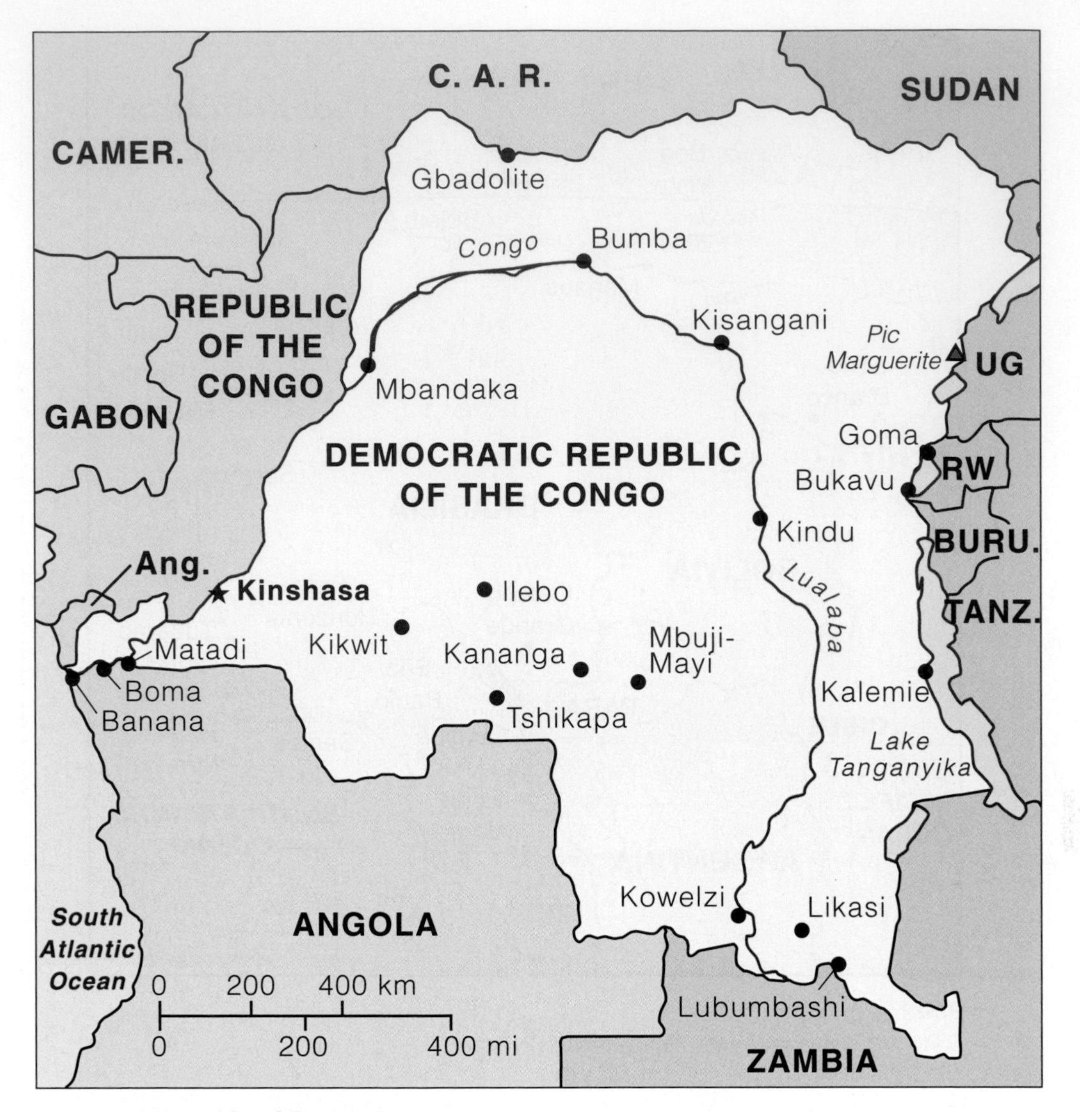

Democratic Republic of the Congo

Source: U.S. Central Intelligence Agency, *World Factbook* (2007)

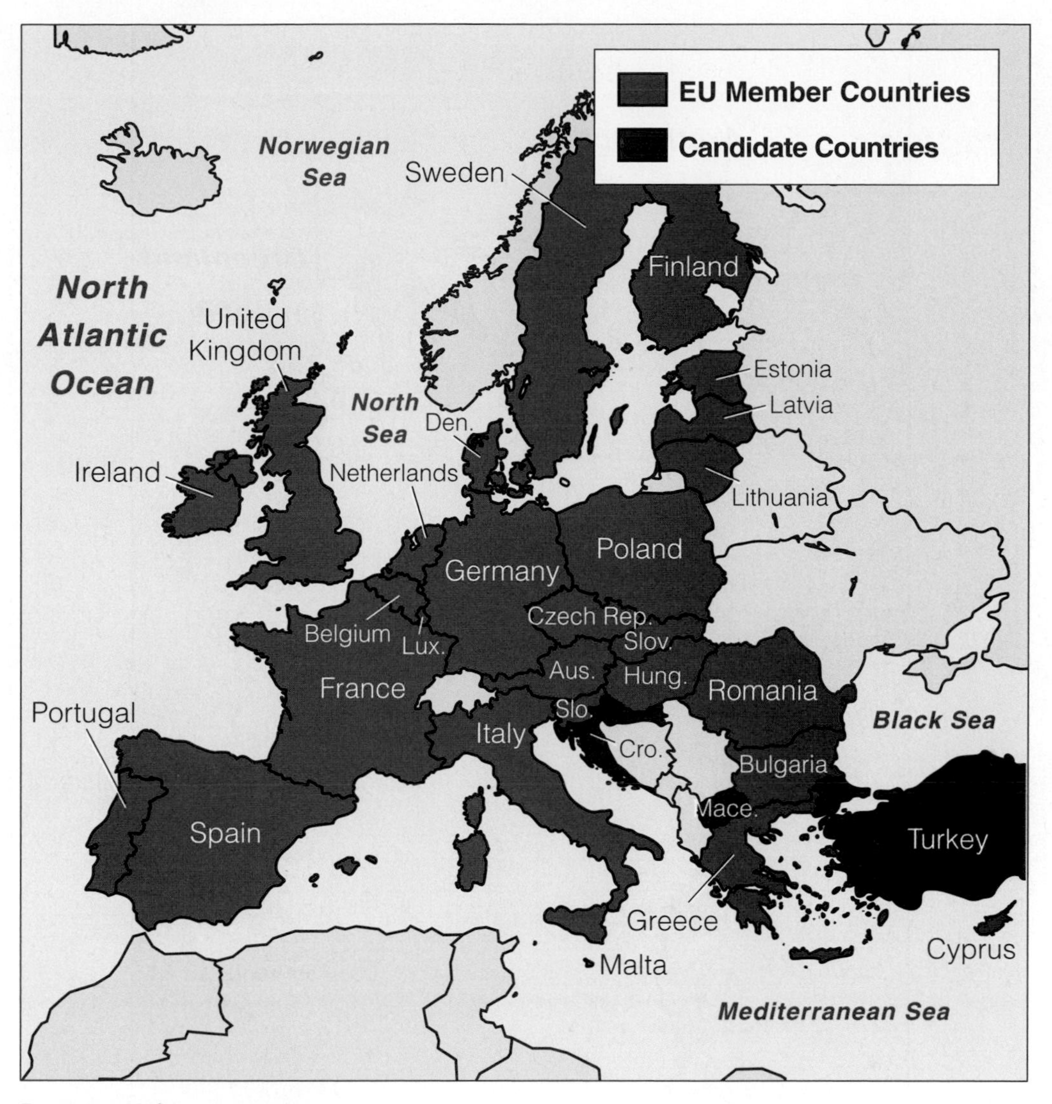

European Union

Source: U.S. Central Intelligence Agency, *World Factbook* (2007)

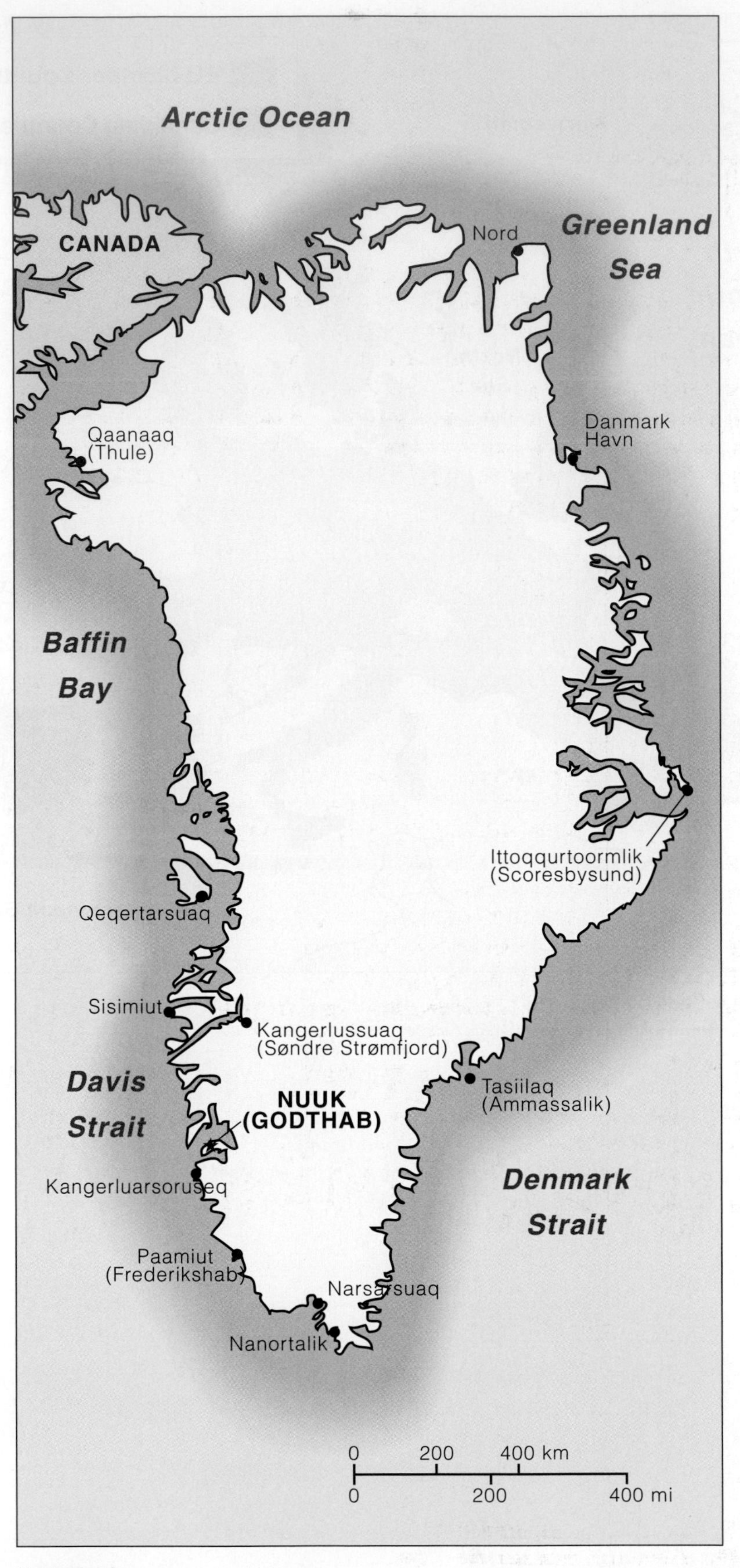

Greenland
Source: U.S. Central Intelligence Agency, *World Factbook* (2007)

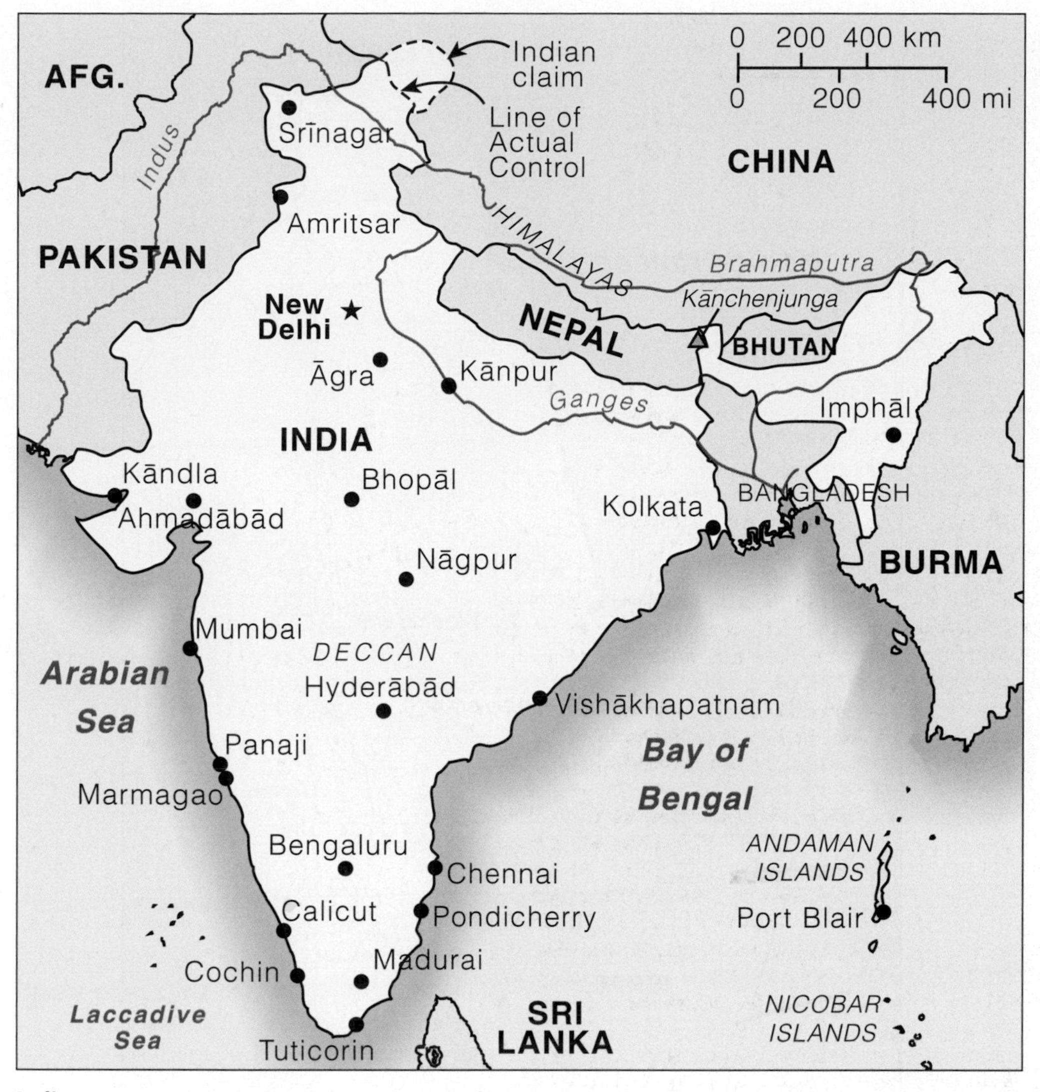

India

Source: U.S. Central Intelligence Agency, *World Factbook* (2007)

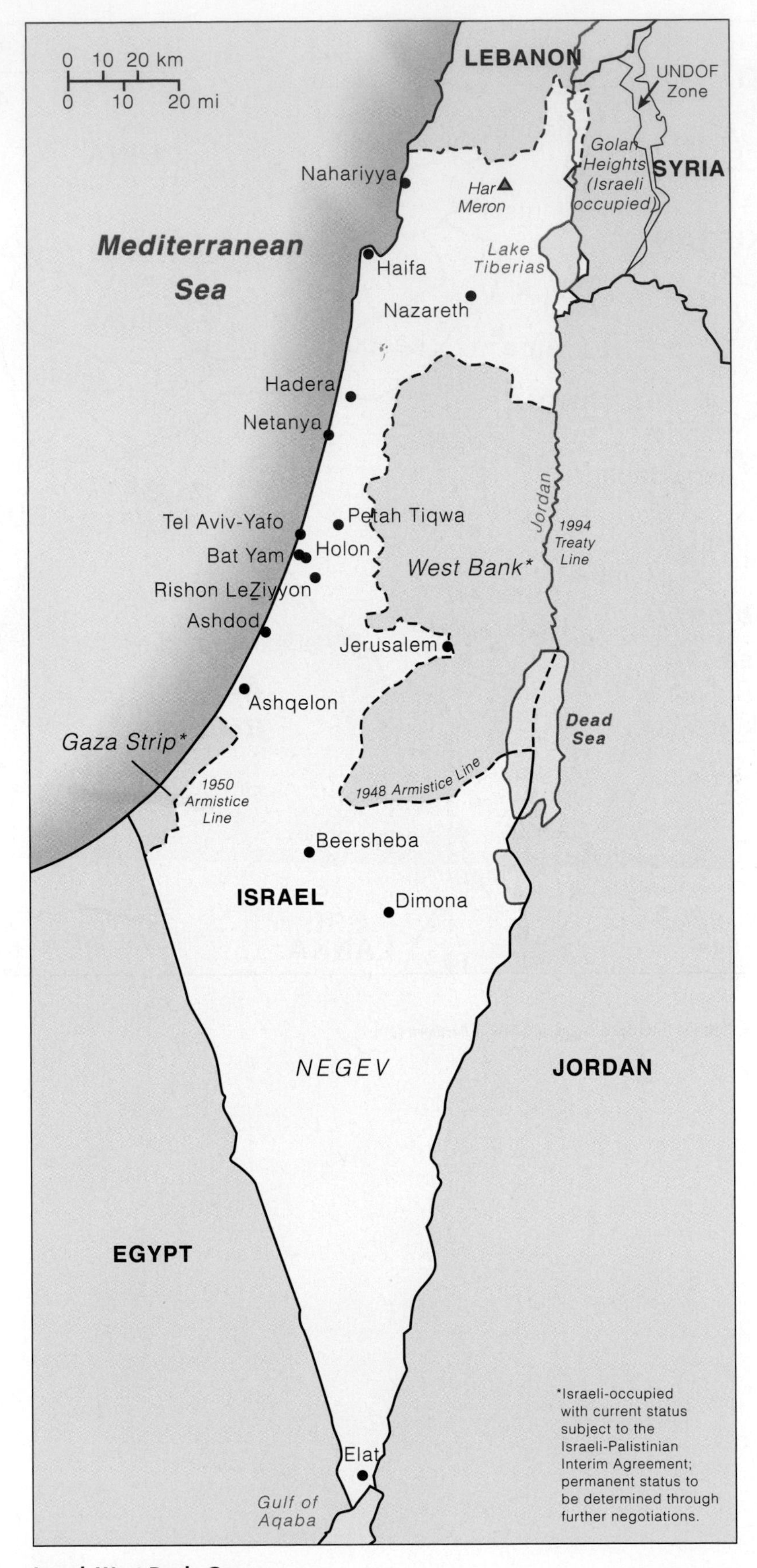

Israel, West Bank, Gaza

Source: U.S. Central Intelligence Agency, *World Factbook* (2007)

Japan

Source: U.S. Central Intelligence Agency, *World Factbook* (2007)

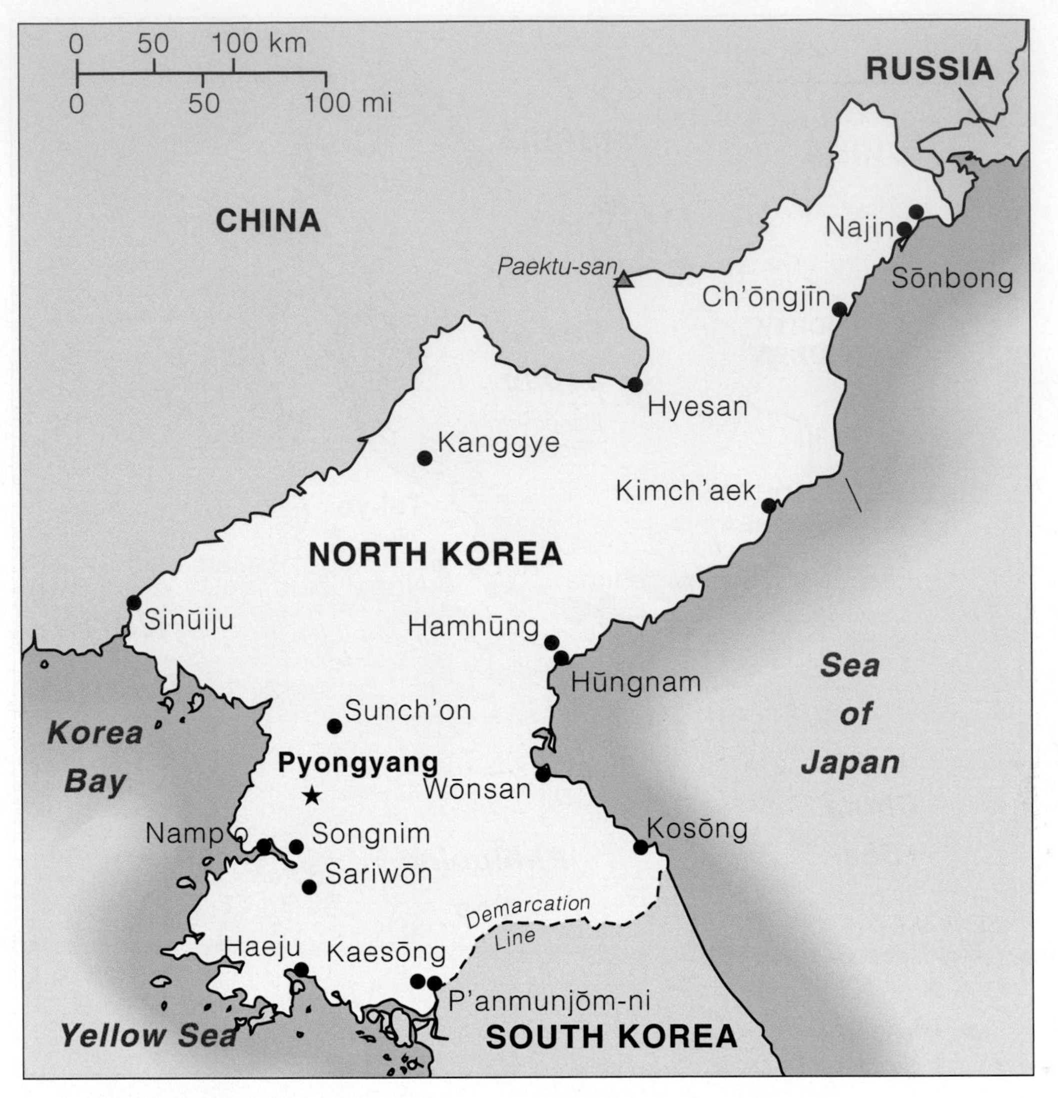

Korea, North
Source: U.S. Central Intelligence Agency, *World Factbook* (2007)

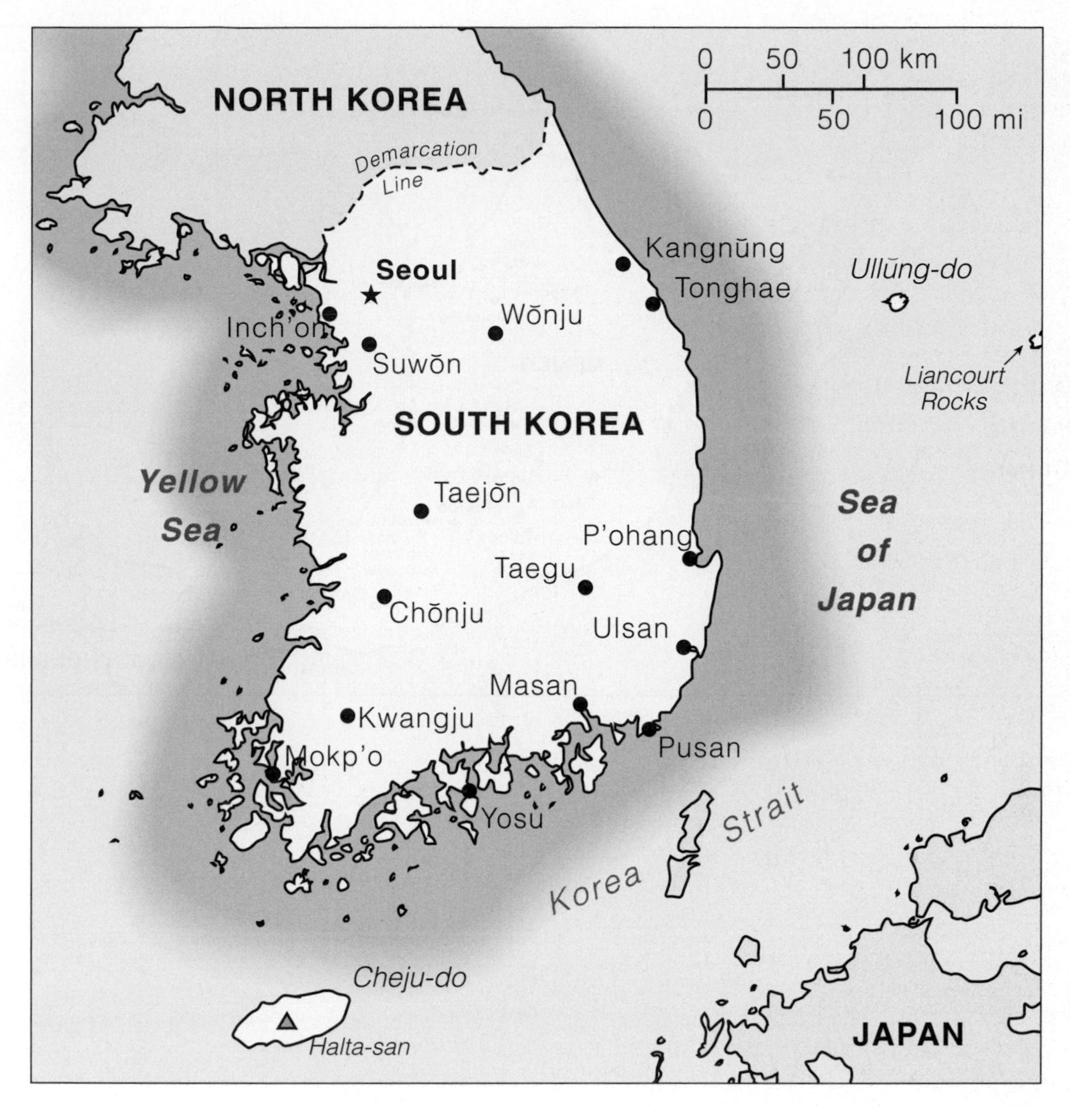

Korea, South

Source: U.S. Central Intelligence Agency, *World Factbook* (2007)

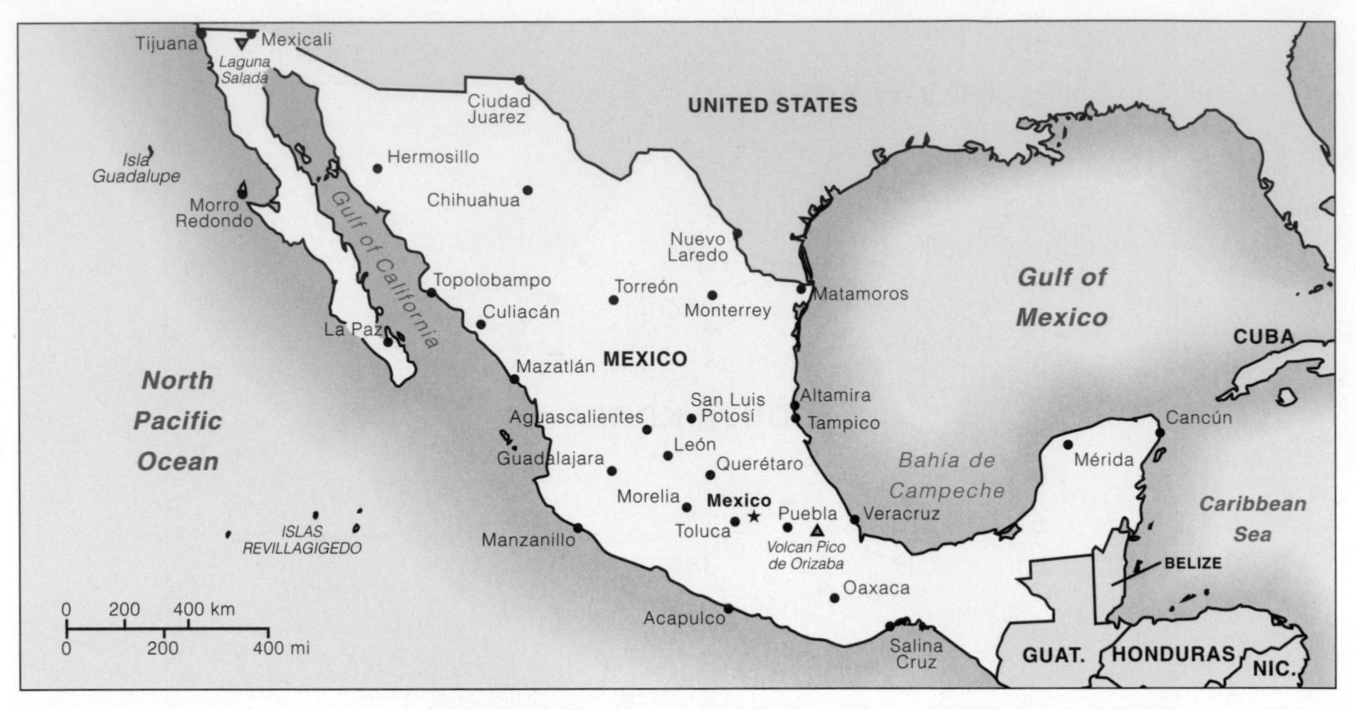

Mexico

Source: U.S. Central Intelligence Agency, *World Factbook* (2007)

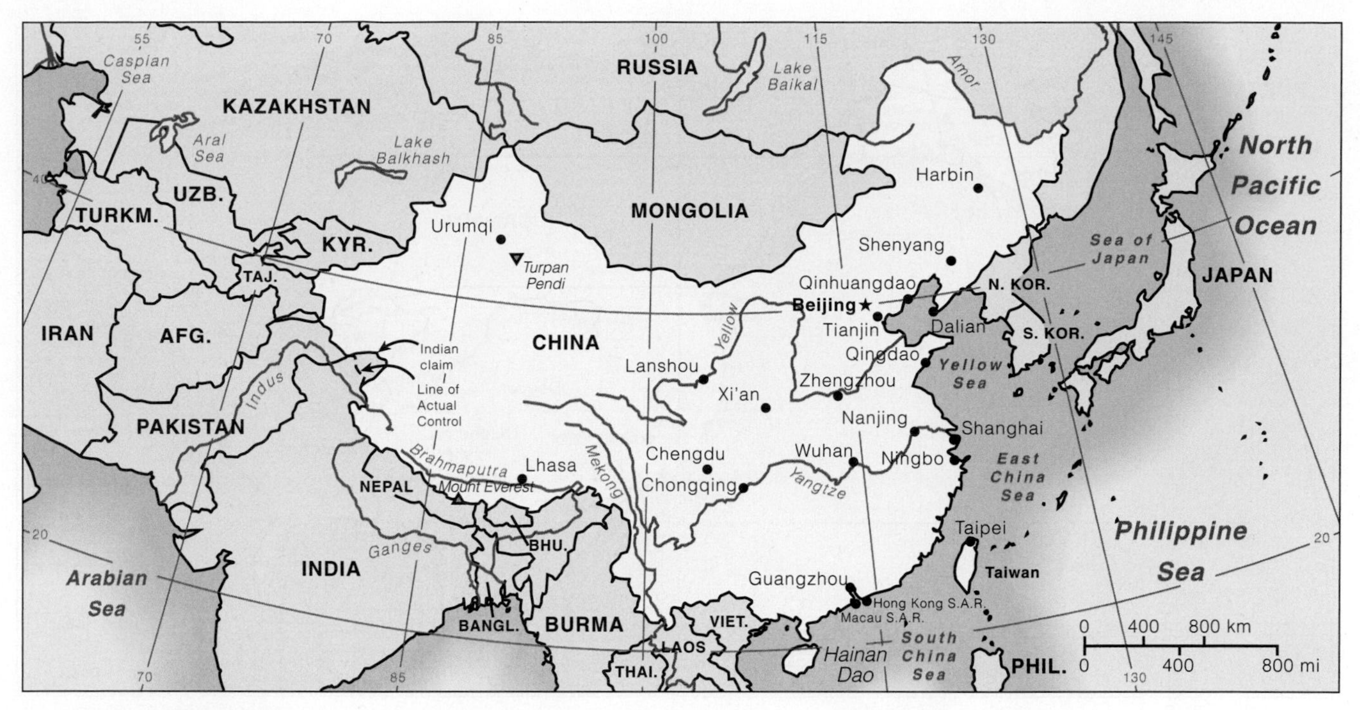

People's Republic of China

Source: U.S. Central Intelligence Agency, *World Factbook* (2007)

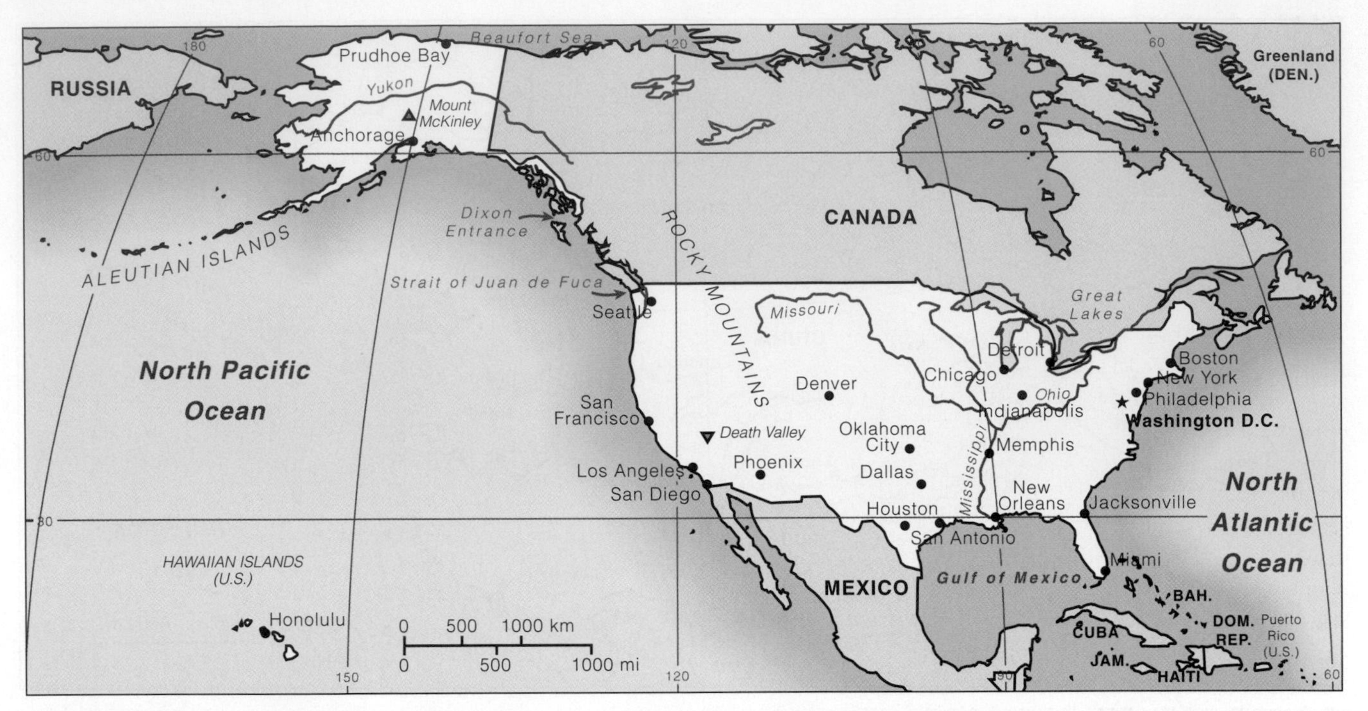

United States

Source: U.S. Central Intelligence Agency, *World Factbook* (2007)

United States

Source: U.S. Central Intelligence Agency, *World Factbook* (2007)

KEY CONCEPTS

527 group A tax-exempt advocacy organization that seeks to influence federal elections by running issue-related advertisements criticizing the record of a candidate or by mobilizing voters to register and vote.

absolute poverty A situation in which people lack the resources to satisfy the basic needs no person should be without.

adolescent society Or subculture is a "small society, one that has most of its important interactions within itself, and maintains only a few threads of connection with the outside adult society."

absorption assimilation A process by which members of a minority group adapt to the ways of the dominant group, which sets the standards to which they must adjust (Gordon 1978).

achieved statuses Social statuses acquired through some combination of personal choice, effort, and ability. A person's marital status, occupation, and educational attainment are considered examples of achieved statuses.

adaptive culture The portion of nonmaterial culture (norms, values, and beliefs) that adjusts to material innovations.

agents of socialization Significant others, primary groups, ingroups and outgroups, and institutions that (1) shape our sense of self or social identity, (2) teach us about the groups to which we do and do not belong, (3) help us to realize our human capacities, and (4) help us negotiate the social and physical environment we have inherited.

aging population A population in which the percentage that is age 65 and older is increasing relative to other age groups.

agglomerations Urban areas with populations of 1 million or more.

alienation A state of being in which human life is dominated by the forces of its inventions.

altruistic A state in which the ties attaching the individual to the group are such that he or she has no life beyond the group.

anomaly An observation that a paradigm cannot explain.

anomic A state in which the ties attaching the individual to the group are disrupted due to dramatic changes in economic circumstances.

ascribed statuses Social statuses that are the result of chance in that people exert no effort to obtain them. A person's birth order, race, biological sex, and age qualify as ascribed characteristics.

assimilation A process by which ethnic or racial distinctions between groups disappear because one group is absorbed into another group's culture or because two cultures blend to form a new cultural system.

authoritarian government A system of government in which there is no separation of power and a single person (dictator), group (family, military, single party), or social class holds all power.

authority Legitimate power in which people believe that the differences in power are just and proper—that is, people view a leader as being entitled to give orders.

back stage The area out of the audience's sight, where individuals let their guard down and do things that would be inappropriate or unexpected in a front-stage setting.

basic innovations Revolutionary, unprecedented, or groundbreaking inventions or discoveries that form the basis for a wide range of applications.

beliefs Conceptions that people accept as true, concerning how the world operates and where the individual fits in relationship to others.

biography All the day-to-day activities from birth to death that make up a person's life.

bourgeoisie The profit-driven owners of the means of production.

brain drain The emigration from a country of the most educated and most talented people.

bureaucracy An organization that strives to use the most efficient means to achieve a valued goal.

capitalism An economic system in which the raw materials and the means of producing and distributing goods and services remain privately owned.

caste system Any form of stratification in which people are categorized and ranked by characteristics over which they have no control and that they usually cannot change.

chance Something not subject to human will, choice, or effort; it helps determine a person's racial and ethnic classification.

charismatic authority A type of authority that derives from the exceptional and exemplary qualities of the person who issues the commands.

church A group whose members hold the same beliefs about the sacred and the profane, who behave in the same way in the presence of the sacred, and who gather in body or spirit at agreed-on times to reaffirm their commitment to those beliefs and practices.

class A person's overall economic and social status in a system of social stratification.

class system A system of social stratification in which people are ranked on the basis of achieved characteristics, such as merit, talent, ability, or past performance.

censors People whose job is to sift information conveyed through movies, books, letters, email, TV, the Internet, and other media and to remove or block any material that is considered unsuitable or threatening.

censorship A method of preventing information from reaching an audience.

choice The act of choosing from a range of possible behaviors or appearances.

civil religion An institutionalized set of beliefs about a nation's past, present, and future and a corresponding set of rituals. Both the beliefs and the rituals take on a sacred quality and elicit feelings of patriotism. Civil religion forges ties between religion and a nation's needs and political interests.

claims makers People who articulate and promote claims and who tend to gain in some way if the targeted audience accepts their claims as true.

claims-making activities Actions taken to draw attention to a claim, such as "demanding services, filling out forms, lodging complaints, filing lawsuits, calling press conferences, writing letters of protest, passing resolutions, publishing exposés, placing ads in newspapers, . . . setting up picket lines or boycotts" (Spector and Kitsuse 1977, p. 79).

coercive organizations Formal organizations that draw in people who have no choice but to participate; such organizations include those dedicated to compulsory socialization or to resocialization or treatment of individuals labeled as deviant.

cohort A group of people born around the same time (such as a specified five-year period) who share common experiences and perspectives by virtue of the time they were born.

collective memory The experiences shared and recalled by significant numbers of people. Such memories are revived, preserved, shared, passed on, and recast in many forms, such as stories, holidays, rituals, and monuments.

colonialism/colonization A form of domination in which a foreign power uses superior military force to impose its political, economic, social, and cultural institutions on an indigenous population so it can control their resources, labor, and markets.

color line A barrier supported by customs and laws separating nonwhites from whites, especially with regard to their place in the division of labor.

commercialization of gender ideals The process of introducing products to the market by using advertising and sales campaigns that promise consumers they will achieve masculine and feminine ideals if they buy and use the products.

concepts Thinking and communication tools used to give and receive complex information efficiently and to frame and focus observations.

conflict According to Marx, it is the major force that drives social change.

conformity Behavior and appearances that follow and maintain the standards of a group; also the acceptance of culturally valued goals and the pursuit of those goals through means defined as legitimate.

conformists People who have not violated the rules of a group and are treated accordingly.

constrictive pyramid A population pyramid that is narrower at the base than in the middle. It shows that the population consists disproportionately of middle-aged and older people.

constructionist approach A sociological approach that focuses on the way specific groups, activities, conditions, or artifacts become defined as problems.

context The social setting in which racial and ethnic categories are recognized, constructed, and challenged.

control The guiding or regulating, by planning out in detail, the production or delivery of a service or product.

core economies Economies that have a higher level of industrial production and a higher standard of living than labor-intensive poor economies. They include the wealthiest, most highly diversified economies in the world.

countercultures Subcultures in which the norms, values, beliefs, symbols, and language the members share emphasize conflict or opposition to the larger culture. In fact, rejection of the dominant culture's values, norms, symbols, and beliefs is central to understanding a counterculture.

counterrevolutionary movements Social movements that seek to maintain a social order that reformist and revolutionary movements are seeking to change.

credential society A situation in which employers use educational credentials as screening devices for sorting through a pool of largely anonymous applicants.

crude birth rate The annual number of births per 1,000 people in a designated geographic area.

crude death rate The annual number of deaths per 1,000 people in a designated geographic area.

cults Very small, loosely organized groups, usually founded by a charismatic leader who attracts people by virtue of his or her personal qualities.

cultural base The number of existing innovations, which forms the basis for further inventions.

cultural genocide An extreme form of ethnocentrism in which the people of one society define the culture of another society not as merely offensive, but as so intolerable that they attempt to destroy it.

cultural lag A situation in which adaptive culture fails to adjust in necessary ways to material innovation.

cultural relativism The perspective that a foreign culture should not be judged by the standards of a home culture and that a behavior or way of thinking must be examined in its cultural context.

culture The way of life of a people; more specifically, the human-created strategies for adjusting to their surroundings and to those creatures (including humans) that are part of those surroundings.

culture shock The strain that people from one culture experience when they must reorient themselves to the ways of a new culture.

currents of opinion The state of affairs with regard to some way of being expressed through rates (suicide, marriage, savings).

dearth of feedback A situation in which much of the information released or picked up by the popular media is not subjected to honest, constructive criticism, because the critical audience that exists is too small to evaluate the information before it is used.

decolonization A process of undoing colonialism such that the colonized country achieves independence from the so-called mother country.

democracy A system of government in which power is vested in the citizen or "the people," and in which the citizenry participates directly or indirectly in making decisions.

demographic gap The difference between a population's birth rate and death rate.

demographic trap The point at which population growth overwhelms the environment's carrying capacity.

demography A subspecialty within sociology that focuses on the study of human populations and their characteristics, including size and rate of growth.

denomination A hierarchical religious organization, led by a professionally trained clergy, in a society in which church and state are usually separate.

dependent variable The variable to be explained or predicted.

deviance Any behavior or physical appearance that is socially challenged or condemned because it departs from the norms and expectations of a group.

deviant subcultures Groups that are part of the larger society but whose members share norms and values favoring violation of that larger society's laws.

diffusion The process by which an idea, an invention, or some other cultural item is borrowed from a foreign source.

disability Something society has imposed on those with certain impairments because of how inventions were designed and social activities organized to exclude them and to accommodate others.

disciplinary society A social arrangement that normalizes surveillance, making it expected and routine.

discrimination An intentional or unintentional act of unequal treatment of individuals or groups based on attributes unrelated to merit, ability, or past performance. Discrimination denies people equal opportunities to achieve socially valued goals such as getting an education, finding employment, accessing health care, and living a long life. It is a behavior, not an attitude.

dispositional causes Forces over which individuals are supposed to have control—including personal qualities or traits, such as motivation level, mood, and effort.

division of labor Work that is broken down into specialized tasks, each performed by a different set of people trained to do that task. The people doing each task often live in different parts of the world. Not only are the tasks specialized, but the parts and materials needed to manufacture products also come from many different regions of the world.

documents Written or printed materials used in research.

domestication The process by which plants and animals were brought under human control.

dominant ethnic group The most advantaged ethnic group in a society; it is the ethnic group that possesses the greatest access to valued resources, including the power to create and maintain the system that gives it these advantages.

double consciousness According to DuBois, "this sense of always looking at one's self through the eyes of others, of measuring one's soul by the tape of a world that looks on in amused contempt and pity." The double consciousness includes a sense of two-ness: "an American, a Negro; two souls, two thoughts, two unreconciled strivings; two warring ideals in one dark body, whose dogged strength alone keeps it from being torn asunder."

doubling time The estimated number of years required for a country's population to double in size.

dramaturgical model A model in which social interaction is viewed as if it were a theater, people as if they were actors, and roles as if they were performances before an audience in a particular setting.

dysfunctions Disruptive consequences of a part to the existing social order.

ecclesia A professionally trained religious organization, governed by a hierarchy of leaders, that claims everyone in a society as a member.

economic system A socially created institution that coordinates human activity in the effort to produce, distribute, and consume goods and services.

education In the broadest sense, the experiences that train, discipline, and shape the mental and physical potentials of the maturing person.

efficiency An organization's claim of offering the "best" products and services, which allow consumers to move quickly from one state of being to another (for example, from hungry to full, from fat to thin, or from uneducated to educated).

egoistic A state in which the ties attaching the individual to others in the society are weak.

emigration The act of departing from one country to take up residence elsewhere.

empire A group of countries under the direct or indirect control of a foreign power or government, which shapes their political, economic, and cultural development.

endogamy Norms requiring or encouraging people to choose a partner from the same social category as their own.

established sects Religious organizations, resembling both denominations and sects, that have left denominations or ecclesiae and have existed long enough to acquire a large following and widespread respectability.

esteem The reputation that someone occupying an ascribed or achieved status has earned from people who know and observe the person.

ethnic group People within a larger society (such as a country) who possess a group consciousnesses because they share or believe they share a common ancestry, a place of birth, a history, a key experience, or some other distinctive social traits they have defined as the "essence of their peoplehood" (Schermerhorn 1978, p. 12; Cornell and Hartman 2007).

ethnic renewal This occurs when someone discovers an ethnic identity, as when an adopted child learns about and identifies with newly found biological relatives or a person learns about and revives lost traditions.

ethnicity People who share, believe they share, or are believed by others to share a national origin; a common ancestry; a place of birth; distinctive concrete social traits (such as religious practices, style of dress, body adornments, or language); or socially important physical characteristics (such as skin color, hair texture, or body structure).

ethnocentrism A viewpoint that uses one culture, usually the home culture, as the standard for judging the worth of foreign ways.

exogamy Norms requiring or encouraging people to choose a partner from a social category other than their own.

expansive pyramid A triangular population pyramid that is broadest at the base, with each successive cohort smaller than the one below it. This pyramid shows that the population consists disproportionately of young people.

externality costs Hidden costs of using, making, or disposing of a product that are not figured into the price of the product or paid for by the producer.

extreme wealth The most excessive form of wealth, in which a very small proportion of people in the world have money, material possessions, and other assets (minus liabilities) in such abundance that a small fraction of it (if spent appropriately) could provide adequate food, safe water, sanitation, and basic health care for the 1 billion poorest people on the planet.

facade of legitimacy An explanation that members of dominant groups give to justify the social arrangements that benefit them over others.

falsely accused People who have not broken the rules of a group but are treated as if they have.

family A social institution that binds people together through blood, marriage, law, and/or social norms. Family members are generally expected to care for and support each other.

fatalistic A state in which the ties attaching the individual to the group involve discipline so oppressive it offers no chance of release.

feeling rules Norms that specify appropriate ways to express internal sensations.

femininity The physical, behavioral, and mental and emotional traits believed to be characteristic of females.

feminism In its most basic sense, a perspective that advocates equality between men and women.

finance aristocracy Bankers and stockholders seemingly detached from the world of "work."

folkways Customary ways of handling the routine matters of everyday life.

formal curriculum The essential content of the various academic subjects—mathematical formulas, science experiments, key terms, and so on.

formal dimension The official aspect of an organization, including job descriptions and written rules, guidelines, and procedures established to achieve valued goals.

formal education A purposeful, planned effort aimed at imparting specific skills and information.

formal organization Coordinating mechanisms that bring together people, resources, and technology, and then channel human activity toward achieving a specific outcome.

formal sanctions Expressions of approval or disapproval backed by laws, rules, or policies that specify (usually in writing) the conditions under which people should be rewarded or punished and the procedures for allocating rewards and administering punishments.

fortified households Preindustrial arrangements characterized by no police force, militia, national guard, or other peacekeeping organization. Instead, the household acts as an armed unit, and the head of the household acts as its military commander.

front stage The area visible to the audience, where people feel compelled to present themselves in expected ways.

function The contribution a part of a society makes to the existing social order.

fundamentalism A belief in the timelessness of sacred writings and a belief that such writings apply to all kinds of environments.

games Structured, organized activities that usually involve more than one person and a number of constraints, such as established roles, rules, time, place, and outcome.

gender A social distinction based on culturally conceived and learned ideals about appropriate appearance, behavior, and mental and emotional characteristics for males and females.

gender polarization The organizing of social life around male-female ideals, so that people's sex influences every aspect of their life, including how they dress, the time they get up in the morning, what they do before they go to bed at night, the social roles they take on, the things they worry about, and even the ways they express emotion and experience sexual attraction.

gender-schematic A term describing decisions that are influenced by a society's polarized definitions of masculinity and femininity rather than by criteria such as self-fulfillment, interest, ability, and personal comfort.

generalizability The extent to which findings can be applied to the larger population from which a sample is drawn.

generalized other A system of expected behaviors, meanings, and viewpoints that transcend those of the people participating.

glass ceiling A barrier that prevents women from rising past a certain level in an organization, especially when women work in male-dominated workplaces and occupations.

glass escalator A term that applies to the invisible upward movement that puts men in positions of power, even within female-dominated occupations.

global interdependence A situation in which social activity transcends national borders and in which one country's problems—such as unemployment, drug abuse, water shortages, natural disasters, and the search for national security in the face of terrorism—are part of a larger global situation.

globalization The ever-increasing flow of goods, services, money, people, information, and culture across political borders.

goods Any products that are extracted from the earth, manufactured, or grown, such as food, clothing, petroleum, natural gas, automobiles, coal, computers, and so on.

government An organizational structure that directs and coordinates human activities in the name of a country or some other territory, such as a city, county, or state.

gross domestic product (GDP) The monetary value of the goods and services that a nation's workforce produces in a year or some other time period.

group Two or more people who share a distinct identity, feel a sense of belonging, and interact directly or indirectly with one another.

habitus Objective reality internalized. That internalized reality becomes the mental filter through which people understand the social world and their place in it.

Hawthorne effect A phenomenon in which research subjects alter their behavior when they learn they are being observed.

hegemony A process by which a power maintains its dominance over foreign entities.

hidden curriculum Important messages conveyed to students unrelated to subject content per se.

hidden ethnicity A sense of self that is based on little to no awareness of an ethnic identity because its culture is considered normative, or mainstream.

households All related and unrelated people who share the same dwelling.

hydrocarbon society One in which the use of fossil fuels shapes virtually every aspect of our personal and social lives.

hypothesis A trial explanation put forward as the focus of research; it predicts how independent and dependent variables are related and how a dependent variable will change when an independent variable changes.

I The active and creative aspect of the self that questions the expectations and rules for behavior.

ideal A standard against which real cases can be compared.

ideal type A deliberate simplification or caricature that exaggerates defining characteristics, thus establishing a standard against which real cases can be compared.

illegitimate opportunity structures Social settings and arrangements that offer people the opportunity to commit particular types of crime.

illiteracy The inability to understand and use a symbol system, whether it is based on sounds, letters, numbers, pictographs, or some other type of symbol.

immigration The act of entering one country after leaving another.

impairment A physical or mental condition that interferes with someone's ability to perform an activity that the average person can perform without technical or human assistance.

imperialistic power A political entity that exerts control and influence over foreign entities either through military force or through policies and economic pressures.

impression management The process by which people in social situations manage the setting, their dress, their words, and their gestures to correspond to the impression they are trying to make or the image they are trying to project.

improving innovations Modifications of basic inventions that improve upon the originals—for example, making them smaller, faster, less complicated, more efficient, more attractive, or more profitable.

income The money a person earns, usually on an annual basis through salary or wages.

independent variable The variable that explains or predicts the dependent variable.

individual discrimination Any individual or overt action aimed at someone in an out-group that depreciates, denies opportunities, or does violence to life or property.

industrial food system One that produces high-calorie, nutrient-low, processed food that is more available, affordable, and aggressively marketed than nutritious food. It is a food system in which the goal is to maximize profit, achieved by speeding up the production process, increasing the amount produced, cutting labor costs, and finding the lowest-cost ingredients. Industrial food depends heavily on pharmaceuticals, chemicals, and fossil fuels to produce, manufacture, and transport food products.

infant mortality rate The annual number of deaths of infants 1 year old or younger for every 1,000 such infants born alive.

informal dimension The unofficial aspect of an organization, including behaviors that depart from the formal dimension, such as employee-generated norms that evade, bypass, or ignore official rules, guidelines, and procedures.

informal education Education that occurs in a spontaneous, unplanned way.

informal sanctions Spontaneous, unofficial expressions of approval or disapproval that are not backed by the force of law.

information explosion An unprecedented increase in the amount of stored and transmitted data and messages in all media (including electronic, print, radio, and television).

in-group A group to which a person belongs, identifies, admires, and/or feels loyalty.

in-migration The movement of people into a designated area.

innovation (as a response to structural strain) The acceptance of cultural goals but the rejection of the legitimate means to achieve them.

innovation The invention or discovery of something, such as a new idea, process, practice, device, or tool.

institutionalized discrimination The established, customary way of doing things in society—the unchallenged rules, policies, and day-to-day practices established by advantaged groups that impede or limit the opportunities and achievements of those in disadvantaged groups. It is "systematic discrimination through the regular operations of societal institutions" (Davis 1978, p. 30).

institutions Relatively stable and predictable social arrangements created and sustained by people that have emerged over time with the purpose of coordinating human activities to meet some need, such as food, shelter, or clothing. Institutions consist of statuses, roles, and groups.

insurgents Groups who participate in armed rebellion against some established authority, government, or administration with the hope that those in power will retreat or pull out.

internal migration The movement of people within the boundaries of a single country—from one state, region, or city to another.

internalization The process in which people take as their own and accept as binding the norms, values, beliefs, and language that their socializers are attempting to pass on.

intersectionality The interconnections among socially constructed categories of sex, gender, race, class, sexual orientation, religious affiliation, age (generation), nationality, disability, and other statuses. These statuses combine in complex ways to influence advantages and disadvantages.

intersexed A broad term used by the medical profession to classify people with some mixture of male and female biological characteristics.

interviews Face-to-face or telephone conversations between an interviewer and a respondent, in which the interviewer asks questions and records the respondent's answers.

invention A synthesis of existing innovations.

involuntary ethnicity When a government or other dominant group creates an umbrella ethnic category and assigns people from many different cultures and countries to it.

involuntary minorities Ethnic or racial groups that were forced to become part of a country by slavery, conquest, or colonization.

iron cage of rationality The set of irrationalities that rational systems generate.

Islamic revitalism Responses to the belief that existing political, economic, and social systems have failed—responses that include a disenchantment with, and even a rejection of, the West; soul-searching; a quest for greater authenticity; and a conviction that Islam offers a viable alternative to secular nationalism, socialism, and capitalism.

issue A matter that can be explained only by factors outside an individual's control and immediate environment.

labor-intensive poor economies Economies that have a lower level of industrial production and a lower standard of living than core economies. They differ markedly from core economies on indicators such as doubling time, infant mortality, total fertility, per capita income, and per capita energy consumption.

language A symbol system involving the use of sounds, gestures (signing), and/or characters (such as letters or pictures) to convey meaning.

latent dysfunctions Unintended, unanticipated disruptions to an existing social order.

latent functions Unintended or unanticipated effects that a part has on the existing order.

laws Rules or policies that specify (usually in writing) the conditions under which people should be rewarded or punished and the procedures for allocating rewards and administering punishments.

legal-rational authority A type of authority that rests on a system of impersonal rules that formally specifies the qualifications for occupying a powerful position.

liberation theology A religious movement based on the idea that organized religions have a responsibility to demand social justice for the marginalized peoples of the world, especially landless peasants and the urban poor, and to take an active role at the grassroots level to bring about political and economic justice.

life chances The probability that an individual's life will follow a certain path and will turn out a certain way.

life chances A critical set of potential social advantages, including the chance to survive the first year of life, to live independently in old age, and everything in between.

linguistic relativity hypothesis The idea that "no two languages are ever sufficiently similar to be considered as representing the same social reality. The worlds in which different societies live are distinct worlds, not merely the same world with different labels attached" (Sapir 1949, p. 162).

looking-glass self A process in which a sense of self develops, enabling one to see oneself reflected in others' real or imagined reactions to one's appearance and behaviors.

low-technology tribal societies Hunting-and-gathering societies with technologies that do not permit the creation of surplus wealth.

manifest dysfunctions A part's anticipated disruptions to an existing social order.

manifest functions Intended or anticipated effects that a part has on the existing social order.

masculinity The physical, behavioral, and mental and emotional traits believed to be characteristic of males.

mass media Forms of communication designed to reach large audiences without face-to-face contact between those conveying and those receiving the messages.

master status One status in a status set that overshadows the others such that it shapes every aspect of life and dominates social interactions.

master status of deviant An identification that proves to be more important than most other statuses that person holds, such that he or she is identified first and foremost as a deviant.

material culture All the natural and human-created objects to which people have attached meaning.

maternal mortality rate The death of a woman while pregnant or within 42 days of a termination of pregnancy from any cause related to or aggravated by pregnancy or the way it is managed (World Health Organization).

McDonaldization A process whereby the principles governing the fast-food industry come to dominate other sectors of the American economy, society, and the world.

me The social self—the part of the self that is the product of interaction with others and that has internalized the rules and expectations.

mechanical solidarity Social order and cohesion based on a common conscience, or uniform thinking and behavior.

mechanization The process of replacing human and animal muscle as a source of power with external sources derived from burning wood, coal, oil, and natural gas.

mega city An agglomeration of at least 8 million (UN definition) or 10 million (U.S. definition) people.

melting pot assimilation Cultural blending in which groups accept many new behaviors and values from one another. The exchange produces a new cultural system, which is a blend of the previously separate systems.

methods of data collection The procedures a researcher follows to gather relevant data.

migration The movement of people from one residence to another.

migration rate A rate based on the difference between the number of people entering and the number of people leaving a designated geographic area in a year. We divide that difference by the size of the relevant population and then multiply the result by 1,000.

militaristic power One that believes military strength, and the willingness to use it, is the source of national—and even global—security.

minority groups Subgroups within a society that can be distinguished from members of the dominant group by visible identifying characteristics, including physical and cultural attributes. These subgroups are systematically excluded, whether consciously or unconsciously, from full participation in society and denied equal access to positions of power, privilege, and wealth.

mixed contacts Interactions between stigmatized persons and so-called "normals."

modern capitalism An economic system that involves careful calculation of costs of production relative to profits, borrowing and lending money, accumulating all forms of capital, and drawing labor from an unrestricted global labor pool.

modernization A process of economic, social, and cultural transformation in which a country "evolves" from preindustrial or underdeveloped status to a modern society in the image of the most developed countries.

mores Norms that people define as critical to the well-being of a group. Violation of mores can result in severe forms of punishment.

mortality crises Violent fluctuations in the death rate, caused by war, famine, or epidemics.

multinational corporations Enterprises that own, control, or license production or service facilities in countries other than the one where the corporations are headquartered.

mystical religions Religions in which the sacred is sought in states of being that, at their peak, can exclude all awareness of one's existence, sensations, thoughts, and surroundings.

nature Human genetic makeup or biological inheritance.

negative sanction An expression of disapproval for noncompliance.

negatively privileged property class Weber's category for people completely lacking in skills, property, or employment or who depend on seasonal or sporadic employment; they constitute the very bottom of the class system.

negotiated order The sum of existing expectations and newly negotiated ones.

neocolonialism A new form of colonialism where more powerful foreign governments and foreign-owned businesses continue to exploit the resources and labor of the postcolonial peoples.

net migration The difference between the number moving into an area and the number moving out.

nonmaterial culture Intangible human creations, which we cannot identify directly through the senses.

nonparticipant observation A research technique in which the researcher observes study participants without interacting with them.

nonprejudiced discriminators (fair-weather liberals) People who believe in equal opportunity but discriminate because doing so gives them an advantage or because they simply fail to consider the discriminatory consequences of their actions.

nonprejudiced nondiscriminators (all-weather liberals) People who accept the creed of equal opportunity, and their conduct conforms to that creed. They not only believe in equal opportunity but also take action against discrimination.

norms Written and unwritten rules that specify behaviors appropriate and inappropriate to a particular social situation.

nurture The social environment, or the interaction experiences that make up every individual's life.

objective deprivation The condition of the people who are the worst off or most disadvantaged—those with the lowest incomes, the least education, the lowest social status, the fewest opportunities, and so on.

objectivity A stance in which researchers' personal, or subjective, views do not influence their observations or the outcomes of their research.

observation A research technique in which the researcher watches, listens to, and records behavior and conversations as they happen.

oligarchy Rule by the few, or the concentration of decision-making power in the hands of a few people, who hold the top positions in a hierarchy.

operational definitions Clear, precise definitions and instructions about how to observe and/or measure the variables under study.

organic solidarity Social order or system of social ties based on interdependence and cooperation among people performing a wide range of diverse and specialized tasks.

Out-group A any group to which a person does not belong.

out-migration The movement of people out of a designated area.

overurbanization A situation in which urban misery—poverty, unemployment, housing shortages, insufficient infrastructure—is exacerbated by an influx of unskilled, illiterate, and poverty-stricken rural migrants who have been pushed into cities out of desperation.

paradigms The dominant and widely accepted theories and concepts in a particular field of study.

participant observation A research technique in which the researcher observes study participants while directly interacting with them.

penalties Constraints on a person's opportunities and choices, as well as the price paid for engaging in certain activities, appearances, or choices deemed inappropriate of someone in a particular category.

planned obsolescence A profit-making strategy that involves producing goods that are disposable after a single use, have a shorter life cycle than the industry is capable of producing, or go out of style quickly even though the goods can still serve their purpose.

play A voluntary and often spontaneous activity with few or no formal rules that is not subject to constraints of time or place.

pluralist model A model that views politics as an arena of compromise, alliances, and negotiation among many competing special interest groups, and it views power as something dispersed among those groups.

pluralist models of power A view that sees politics as a plurality of special interest groups competing, compromising, forming alliances, and negotiating with each other for power.

political action committees (PACs) Committees that raise money to be donated to the political candidates most likely to support their special interests.

political parties According to Weber, "organizations oriented toward the planned acquisition of social power [and] toward influencing social action no matter what its content may be."

political system A socially created institution that regulates the use of and access to power that is essential to articulating and realizing individual, local, regional, national, international, or global interests and agendas.

population pyramid A series of horizontal bar graphs, each representing a different five-year age cohort, that allows us to compare the sizes of the cohorts.

populations The total number of individuals, traces, documents, territories, households, or groups that could be studied.

positive checks Events that increase deaths, including epidemics of infectious and parasitic diseases, war, famine, and natural disasters.

positive sanction An expression of approval and a reward for compliance.

positively privileged property class Weber's category for the people at the very top of the class system.

positivism A theory stating that valid knowledge about the world can be derived only from *sense experience* or knowing the world through the senses of sight, touch, taste, smell, and hearing, and from empirical associations.

postindustrial society A society that is dominated by intellectual technologies of telecommunications and computers, not just "large computers but computers on a chip." These intellectual technologies have had a revolutionary effect on virtually every aspect of social life.

power The probability that an individual can achieve his or her will even against another individual's opposition.

power elite Those few people who occupy such lofty positions in the social structure of leading institutions that their decisions have consequences affecting millions, even billions, of people worldwide.

predestination The belief that God has foreordained all things, including the salvation or damnation of individual souls.

predictability The expectation that a service or product will be the same no matter where or when it is purchased.

prejudice A rigid and usually unfavorable judgment about an out-group that does not change in the face of contradictory evidence and that applies to anyone who shares the distinguishing characteristics of the out-group.

prejudiced discriminators (active bigots) People who reject the notion of equal opportunity and profess a right, even a duty, to discriminate. They express with deep conviction that anyone from the in-group (including the village idiot) is superior to any members of the out-group (Merton 1976).

prejudiced nondiscriminators (timid bigots) People who reject the creed of equal opportunity but refrain from discrimination, primarily because they fear possible sanctions or being labeled as racists.

primary deviants Those people whose rule breaking is viewed as understandable, incidental, or insignificant in light of some socially approved status they hold.

primary group A social group that has face-to-face contact and strong emotional ties among its members.

primary sector (of the economy) Economic activities that generate or extract raw materials from the natural environment.

prison-industrial complex The corporations and agencies with an economic stake in building and supplying correctional facilities and in providing services.

productive work Work that involves "the production of the means of existence, of food, clothing, and shelter and the tools necessary for that production" (Engels 1884, pp. 71–72).

profane A term describing everything that is not sacred, including things opposed to the sacred and things that stand apart from the sacred, albeit not in opposition to it.

professionalization A trend in which organizations hire experts with formal training in a particular subject or activity—training needed to achieve organizational goals.

proletariat Those individuals who must sell their labor to the bourgeoisie.

prophetic religions Religions in which the sacred revolves around items that symbolize significant historical events or around the lives, teachings, and writings of great people.

pull factors The conditions that encourage people to move into a geographic area.

pure deviants People who have broken the rules of a group and are caught, punished, and labeled as outsiders.

push factors The conditions that encourage people to move out of a geographic area.

quantification and calculation Numerical indicators that enable customers to evaluate a product or service easily.

racial common sense shared ideas believed to be so obvious or natural they need not be questioned.

racism The belief that genetic or biological differences explain and even justify inequalities that exist between advantaged and disadvantaged racial and ethnic groups.

random sample A type of sample in which every case in the population has an equal chance of being selected.

rationalization A process in which thought and action rooted in custom, emotion, or respect for mysterious forces is replaced by instrumental-rational thought and action.

rebellion The full or partial rejection of both cultural goals and the means of attaining them and the introduction of a new set of goals and means.

reentry shock Culture shock in reverse; it is experienced upon returning home after living in another culture.

reformist movements Social movements that target a specific feature of society as needing change.

regressive or reactionary movements Social movements that seek to turn back the hands of time to an earlier condition or state of being, one sometimes considered a "golden era."

reify Treating racial labels and categories as if they are real and meaningful, forgetting that they are made up or human constructed.

relative deprivation A social condition that is measured not by objective standards, but rather by comparing one group's situation with the situations of groups who are more advantaged.

relative poverty Measured not by some objective standard, but rather by comparing a person's situation against that of others who are more advantaged in some way.

reliability The extent to which an operational definition gives consistent results.

representative sample A type of sample in which those selected for study have the same distribution of characteristics as the population from which it is selected.

reproductive work Work that involves bearing children, caregiving, managing households, and educating children.

research A data-gathering and data-explaining enterprise governed by strict rules.

research design A plan for gathering data that specifies who or what will be studied and the methods of data collection.

research methods Techniques that sociologists and other investigators use to formulate or answer meaningful research questions and to collect, analyze, and interpret data in ways that allow other researchers to verify the results.

resocialization The process that involves breaking with behaviors and ways of thinking that are unsuited to existing or changing circumstances, and replacing them with new, more appropriate ways of behaving and thinking.

resource mobilization A situation in which a core group of sophisticated strategists works to harness a disaffected group's energies, attract money and supporters, capture the news media's attention, forge alliances with those in power, and develop an organizational structure.

retreatism The rejection of both culturally valued goals and the means of achieving them.

reverse ethnocentrism A type of ethnocentrism in which the home culture is regarded as inferior to a foreign culture.

revolutionary movements Social movements that seek broad, sweeping, and radical structural changes to a society's basic social institutions or to the world order.

right A behavior that a person assuming a role can demand or expect from another.

ritualism The rejection of cultural goals but a rigid adherence to the legitimate means of achieving them.

rituals Rules that govern how people must behave in the presence of the sacred to achieve an acceptable state of being.

role The behavior expected of a status in relation to another status.

role conflict A predicament in which the roles associated with two or more distinct statuses that a person holds conflict in some way.

role expectations Behaviors expected of someone enacting a role in relationship to a particular status.

role performance The actual behavior of the person occupying a role.

role set The array of roles associated with a given social status.

role strain A predicament in which there are contradictory or conflicting role expectations associated with a single status.

role-taking The process of stepping into another person's shoes by which to imaginatively view and assess our (and others) behavior, appearance, and thoughts.

sacramental religions Religions in which the sacred is sought in places, objects, and actions believed to house a god or spirit.

sacred A domain of experience that includes everything regarded as extraordinary and that inspires in believers deep and absorbing sentiments of awe, respect, mystery, and reverence.

samples Portions of the cases from a larger population.

sampling frame A complete list of every case in a population.

sanctions Reactions of approval or disapproval to others' behavior or appearance.

scapegoat A person or group blamed for conditions that (a) cannot be controlled, (b) threaten a community's sense of well-being, or (c) shake the foundations of an important institution.

schooling A program of formal, systematic instruction that takes place primarily in classrooms but also includes extracurricular activities and out-of-classroom assignments.

scientific method An approach to data collection in which knowledge is gained through observation and its truth is confirmed through verification.

scientific racism The use of faulty science to support systems of racial rankings and theories of social and cultural progress that placed whites in the most advanced ranks and stage of human evolution.

secondary deviants Those whose rule breaking is treated as something so significant that it cannot be overlooked or explained away.

secondary groups Two or more people who interact for a specific purpose. Secondary group relationships are confined to a particular setting and specific tasks.

secondary sector (of the economy) Economic activities that transform raw materials into manufactured goods.

secondary sex characteristics Physical traits not essential to reproduction (such as breast development, quality of voice, distribution of facial and body hair, and skeletal form) that result from the action of so-called male (androgen) and female (estrogen) hormones.

secondary sources (archival data) Data that have been collected by other researchers for some other purpose.

secret deviants People who have broken the rules of a group but whose violation goes unnoticed or, if it is noticed, prompts those who notice to look the other way rather than reporting the violation.

sect A small community of believers led by a lay ministry, with no formal hierarchy or official governing body to oversee its various religious gatherings and activities. Sects are typically composed of people who broke away from a denomination because they came to view it as corrupt.

secularization A process by which religious influences on thought and behavior are reduced.

secure parental employment A situation in which at least one parent or guardian is employed full-time (35 or more hours per week for at least 50 weeks in the past year).

segregation The physical and/or social separation of people by race or ethnicity.

selective forgetting A process by which people forget, dismiss, or fail to pass on a connection to one or more ethnicities.

selective perception The process in which prejudiced people notice only those things that support the stereotypes they hold about an out-group.

self-administered questionnaire A set of questions given to respondents who read the instructions and fill in the answers themselves.

self-fulfilling prophecy A concept that begins with a false definition of a situation. Despite its falsity, people assume it to be accurate and behave accordingly. The misguided behavior produces responses that confirm the false definition.

services Activities performed for others that result in no tangible product, such as entertainment, transportation, financial advice, medical care, spiritual counseling, and education.

sex ratio The number of females for every thousand males (or another preferred constant, such as 10, 100, or 10,000).

sexism The belief that one sex—and by extension, one gender—is innately superior to another, justifying unequal treatment of the sexes.

significant others People or characters who are important in an individual's life, in that they greatly influence that person's self-evaluation or motivate him or her to behave in a particular manner.

significant symbol Gestures that convey the same meaning to the persons transmitting them and receiving them.

simultaneous-independent inventions Situations in which more or less the same invention is produced by two or more people working independently of one another at about the same time.

situational causes Forces outside an individual's immediate control—such as weather, chance, and others' incompetence.

small groups Groups of two to about 20 people who interact with one another in meaningful ways.

social actions Actions people take in response to others.

social change Any significant alteration, modification, or transformation in the organization and operation of social life.

social control Methods used to teach, persuade, or force a group's members, and even nonmembers, to comply with and not deviate from its norms and expectations.

social dynamics The forces that cause societies to change.

social emotions Internal bodily sensations experienced in relationships with other people.

social facts Ideas, feelings, and ways of behaving "that possess the remarkable property of existing outside the consciousness of the individual" (Durkheim 1982, p. 51).

social forces Anything humans create or take notice of that influence or pressure people to interact, behave, respond, or think in certain ways.

social inequality A situation in which these valued resources and desired outcomes (that is, a college education, long life) are distributed in such a way that people have unequal amounts and/or access to them.

social interaction An everyday event in which at least two people communicate and respond through language and symbolic gestures to affect one another's behavior and thinking.

social interaction Everyday encounters in which people communicate, interpret, and respond to each other's words and actions.

social mobility Movement from one social class to another.

social movement A situation in which a substantial number of people organize to make a change, resist a change, or undo a change in some area of society.

social prestige A level of respect or admiration for a status apart from any person who happens to occupy it.

social statics The forces that hold societies together such that they endure over time.

social status A human-created and defined position in society.

social stratification The systematic process of ranking people on a scale of social worth such that the ranking affects life chances in unequal ways.

social structure A largely invisible system that coordinates human interaction in broadly predictable ways.

socialism An economic system in which the raw materials and the means of producing and distributing goods and services are collectively owned.

socialization The process by which people develop a sense of self and learn the ways of the society in which they live.

society A group of interacting people who share, perpetuate, and create culture.

sociological imagination A point of view that allows us to identify seemingly remote and impersonal social forces and connect them to our biographies.

solidarity The system of social ties that acts as a glue or cement connecting people to one another and the wider society.

spatial segregation A de facto or de jure situation in which racial or ethnic groups attend different schools, live in different neighborhoods, use different public facilities, or occupy the same facility but sit, work, or eat on different floors, in different rooms, or at separate tables.

special-interest groups Groups composed of people who share an interest in a particular economic, political, and social issue and who form an organization or join an existing organization to influence public opinion and government policy.

spurious relationship A correlation that is coincidental or accidental because the independent and dependent variables are not actually related; rather, some third variable related to both of them makes it seem as though they are.

stationary pyramid A population pyramid in which all cohorts (except the oldest) are roughly the same size.

statistical measures of performance Quantitative (and sometimes qualitative) measures of how well an organization and its members or employees are performing.

status group Weber's term for an amorphous group of people held together both by virtue of a lifestyle that has come to be expected of "all those who wish to belong to the circle" (Weber 1948, p. 187).

status set All the statuses an individual assumes.

status value The social value assigned to a status such that people who possess one status (white skin versus brown skin, blonde hair versus dark hair, low income versus high income, single versus married, professional athlete versus high school teacher) are regarded and treated as more valuable or worthy than people who possess another status.

stereotypes Inaccurate generalizations about people who belong to an out-group. Stereotypes "give the illusion that one knows the other" and has the right to construct images of the other (Crapanzano 1985, pp. 271–272).

stigma A physical trait or other attribute that is deeply discrediting. It can be physically evident or something feared will be uncovered. A stigma is discrediting because it focuses everyone's attention on one "tainted" status.

structural constraints The established and customary rules, policies, and day-to-day practices that affect a person's life chances.

structural strain Any situation in which (1) the valued goals of a society have unclear limits, (2) people are unsure whether the legitimate means will allow them to achieve the goals, and (3) legitimate opportunities for reaching the goals remain closed to a significant portion of the population.

structured interview An interview in which the wording and sequence of questions are set in advance and cannot be changed during the interview.

subcultures Groups that share in some parts of the dominant culture but have their own distinctive values, norms, beliefs, symbols, language, or material culture.

subjective secularization A decrease in the number of people who view the world and their place in it from a religious perspective.

surplus wealth Wealth beyond what is needed to meet basic human needs, such as food and shelter.

surveillance A mechanism of social control that involves watching and otherwise monitoring the movements, activities, conversations, and associations of people to prevent them from engaging in wrongdoing; to catch those who are engaged in wrong doing; and to ensure that the public is protected from wrongdoers.

symbolic gestures Any action that requires people to interpret its meaning before responding.

symbols Any kind of physical phenomenon to which people assign a name, meaning, or value.

sympathetic knowledge Firsthand knowledge gained by living and working among those being studied.

technological determinist Someone who believes that human beings have no free will and are controlled entirely by their material innovations.

territories Settings that have borders or that are set aside for particular activities.

terrorism The systematic use of anxiety-inspiring violent acts by clandestine or semi-clandestine individuals, groups, or state-supported actors for idiosyncratic, criminal, or political reasons.

tertiary sector Economic activities related to delivering services such as health care or entertainment and those activities related to creating and distributing information.

theocracy A form of government in which political authority rests in the hands of religious leaders or a theologically trained elite. Under this system, there is no separation of church and state.

theoretical perspectives Frameworks for thinking about what is going on in the world around us.

this-worldly asceticism A belief that people are instruments of divine will and that God determines and directs their activities.

Thomas theorem An assumption focusing on how people construct reality: If people define situations as real, their definitions have real consequences.

tipping points Situations in which a previously rare (or seemingly rare) event, response, or opinion becomes dramatically more common.

total fertility rate the average number of children that a woman in a specific population bears over her lifetime.

total institutions Institutions in which people surrender control of their lives, voluntarily or involuntarily, to an administrative staff and carry out daily activities with others required to do the same thing.

totalitarianism A system of government characterized by (1) a single ruling party led by a dictator, (2) an unchallenged official ideology that defines a vision of the "perfect" society and the means to achieve that vision, (3) a system of social control that suppresses dissent and opposition, and (4) centralized control over the media and the economy.

traces Materials or other forms of physical evidence that yield information about human activity.

traditional authority A type of authority that relies on the sanctity of time-honored norms that govern the selection of someone to a powerful position (chief, king, queen) and that specify responsibilities and appropriate conduct for the individual selected.

trained incapacity The inability, because of limited training, to respond to new or unusual circumstances or to recognize when official rules or procedures are outmoded or no longer applicable.

troubles Personal needs, problems, and difficulties that can be explained as individual shortcomings related to motivation, attitude, ability, character, or judgment.

tyranny of the normal A point of view that assumes those who are impaired with regard to some activity such as walking, are also impaired in other areas that do not involve walking.

unstructured interview An interview in which the question-and-answer sequence is spontaneous, open-ended, and flexible.

urban underclass The group of families and individuals in inner cities who live "outside the mainstream of the American occupational system and [who] consequently represent the very bottom of the economic hierarchy" (Wilson 1983, p. 80).

urbanization An increase in the number of cities in a designated geographic area and growth in the proportion of the area's population living in cities.

urbanization A transformative process in which people migrate from rural to urban areas and change the way they use land, interact, and make a living.

utilitarian organizations Formal organizations that draw together people seeking material gain in the form of pay, health benefits, or a new status.

validity The degree to which an operational definition measures what it claims to measure.

values General, shared conceptions of what is good, right, appropriate, worthwhile, and important with regard to conduct, appearance, and states of being.

variable Any trait or characteristic that can change under different conditions or that consists of more than one category.

voluntary organizations Formal organizations that draw together people who give time, talent, or treasure to support mutual interests, meet important human needs, or achieve a not-for-profit goal.

wealth The combined value of a person's income *and* other material assets such as stocks, real estate, and savings minus debt.

welfare state A term that applies to an economic system that is a hybrid of capitalism and socialism.

witch hunt A campaign to identify, investigate, and correct behavior that has been defined as undermining a group or country. Usually this behavior is not the real cause of a problem but is used to distract people's attention from the real cause or to make the problem seem manageable.

REFERENCES

Chapter 1

Abrams, Irwin. 1997. *The Nobel Peace Prize and the Laureates: An Illustrated Biographical History*. The Norwegian Institute.

Addams, Jane. 1910. *Twenty Years at Hull-House: With Autobiographical Notes*. New York: Macmillan.

______. 1912. *A New Conscience and an Ancient Evil*. 1912. Urbana, IL: University of Illinois Press.

Appellrouth, Scott, and Laura D. Edles. 2007. *Sociological Theory in the Contemporary Era*. Thousand Oaks, CA: Pine Forge Press.

Beaumont, Claudine. 2008. "Vatican Warns Mobile Phones Are Bad for the Soul." *The Telegraph* (March 20). www.telegraph.co.uk/news/religion/3531418/Vatican-warns-mobile-phones-are-bad-for-the-soul.html.

Berger, Peter L. 1963. *Invitation to Sociology: A Humanistic Perspective*. New York: Anchor.

Bernard, Tara Siegel. 2009. "In Grim Job Market, Student Loans Are a Costly Burden." *The New York Times* (April 18), B6.

Bologna, Sergio. 2008. Marx as Correspondent of the *New York Daily Tribune*, 1856–57. Money and Crisis. http://wildcat-www.de/en/material/cs13bolo.htm.

Brecher, Jeremy, John Brown Childs, and Jill Cutler. 1993. *Global Visions: Beyond the New World Order*. Boston: South End Press.

Calhoun, Craig. 2002. Quoted in "A World War among Professors," by Stephen Kotkin. *New York Times* (September 7): A1.

Cassidy, John. 1997. "The Return of Karl Marx." *New Yorker* (October 20): 27.

Chiles, James R. 1987. "The Cable Under the Sea." *American Heritage* 3(2). www.americanheritage.com/articles/magazine/it/1987/2/1987_2_34.shtml.

Cockburn, Andrew. 2002. "Diamonds: The Real Story." National Geographic Online Extra (March). http://ngm.nationalgeographic.com/ngm/data/2002/03/01/html/ft_20020301.1.html.

Dedrick, Jason, Kenneth L. Kraemer, and Greg L. Linden. 2010. "The Distribution of Value in the Mobile Phone Supply Chain." Personal Computing Industry Center (PCIC). University of California, Irvine. http://pcic.merage.uci.edu/papers/2010/CellPhoneProfitability_Oct2010.pdf.

Deegan, Mary Jo. 1978. "Women and Sociology: 1890–1930." *Journal of the History of Sociology* 1 (Fall 1978):11–32.

DeGrange, McQuilkin. 1938. "Comte's Sociologies." *American Sociological Review* 4(1): 17–26.

Dinan, Stephen. 2007. "Bush, GOP Senators Trim Border Fence Goal." *Washington Times* (April 3). washingtontimes.com.

DuBois. W. E. B. 1903. *The Souls of Black Folk*. www.bartleby.com/114.

DuBois, W. E. B. 1919 [1970]. "Reconstruction and Africa." pp. 372–381 in *W.E.B. DuBois: A Reader*. New York: Harper and Row.

Durkheim, Émile. 1951. *Suicide*. New York: Free Press.

______. 1982. *The Rules of Sociological Method and Selected Texts on Sociology and Its Method*, ed. Steven Lukes, trans. W. D. Halls. New York: Macmillan Press.

Essoungou, Andre-Michel. 2010. "A Social Media Boom Begins in Africa." *African Renewal Online* (December). www.un.org/ecosocdev/geninfo/afrec/vol24no4/social-media-boom.html.

Ferri, Alex. 2011. "Starbucks Releases New Payment System for Mobile Phones." (January 19). www.abc15.com.

Fortunati, Leopoldina, 2000. *The Mobile Phone: New Social Categories and Relations*. University of Trieste.

Gates, Henry Louis. 2003. "Both Sides Now." *New York Times Book Review* (May 4).

Geere, Duncan. 2011. "How the First Cable Was Laid across the Atlantic." *Wired* (November 11). www.wired.co.uk/news/archive/2011-01/18/transatlantic-cables?page=all.

Geser, Hans. 2004. "Towards a Sociological Theory of the Mobile Phone." Sociology in Switzerland: Sociology of the Mobile Phone. Online Publications, Zuerich. http://socio.ch/mobile/t_geser1.htm.

Gordon, John Steele. 1989. "When Our Ancestors Became Us." *American Heritage* (December): 106–221.

Hamington, Maurice. 2007 "Jane Addams," *Stanford Encyclopedia of Philosophy*, online edition. http://plato.stanford.edu/entries/addams-jane/.

Hanson, Janice. 2007. *24/7: How Cell Phones and the Internet Change the Way We Live, Work, and Play*. Westport: Praeger.

Held, D., A. McGrew, D. Goldblatt, and J. Perraton. 1999. *Global Transformations: Politics, Economics and Culture*. Stanford, CA: Stanford University Press.

Henrik, Kreutz. 2000. "A Pragmatic Theory of Action—Collective Action as Theory of the Result of Individual Harmful Addiction." www.mtapti.hu/mszt/20003/abstr.htm.

India PRWire. 2011. "4th Annual Cell Phone Film Festival" (January 18). www.indiaprwire.com/.

InfoPlease. 2011. www.infoplease.com/ipa/A0933563.html.

Lemert, Charles. 1995. *Sociology after the Crisis*. Boulder, CO: Westview Press.

Lengermann, Patricia M. 1974. *Definitions of Sociology: A Historical Approach*. Columbus, OH: Merrill.

Lewis, David Levering. 1993. *Biography of a Race, 1868–1919*. New York: Holt.

Lewis, Paul. 1998. "Marx's Stock Resurges on 150-Year Tip." *New York Times* (June 27): A17.

Ling, Richard. 1997. "One Can Talk about Common Manners!: The Use of Mobile Telephones in Inappropriate Situations." In *Themes in Mobile Telephony*, ed. L. Haddon. Final Report of the COST 248 Home and Work Group. http://www.richardling.com/papers/1997_One_can_talk_about_common_manners.pdf.

Marcus, Steven. 1998. "Marx's Masterpiece at 150." *New York Times Book Review* (April 26): 39.

Marx, Karl. 1856. Class Struggles of France. www.marxists.org/archive/marx/works/1850/class-struggles-france/index.htm.

Marx, Karl. [1881] 1965. "The Class Struggle." Pages 529–535 in *Theories of Society*, ed. T. Parsons, E. Shils, K. D. Naegele, and T. R. Pitts. New York: Free Press.

Marx, Karl. 1887. Quoted in *A Marx Dictionary*, by Terrell Carver. Totowa, NJ: Barnes and Noble.

Mills, C. Wright. 1959. *The Sociological Imagination*. New York: Oxford University Press.

Proudhon, Pierre-Joseph. 1847. "The Philosophy of Misery." www.marxists.org/reference/subject/economics/proudhon/philosophy/intro.htm.

Pun Nagai. 2005. *Made in China: Women Factory Workers in a Global Workplace.* Duke University Press.

Random House Encyclopedia. 1990. "European Imperialism in the 19th Century." New York: Random House.

Richtel, Matt. 2009. "Providing Cellphones for the Poor." *The New York Times* (June 14). www.nytimes.com/2009/06/15/technology/15cell.html.

Safelink Wireless. 2011. Lifeline/Safelink Fact Sheet. www.safelink-wireless.com/enrollmentpublic/benefits.aspx.

San Diego News. 2011. "Local Drivers Pulled Over during Cell Phone Sweep." (January 18) www.10news.com/news/26536398/detail.html.

SchoolNet. 2011. News and Events. www.schoolnet.com/corporate/NewsEvents/NewsAndEvents.aspx?NewsEvents=News%20and%20Events.

Taylor, Michael. 2010. "Tantalum Prices Boosted by DRC Conflict Zone Mining Ban." MineWeb (November 13). www.mineweb.com/mineweb/view/mineweb/en/page72102?oid=115025&sn=Detail.

Thrall, Ann. 2007. "A Brief History of Glass Blowing." www.neder.com/glassact/history.html.

United Nations. 2010. "UN Releases Most Extensive Report to Date on War Massacres, Rapes." UN Media Centre (October 1). www un.org/apps/news/story.asp?NewsID=36306.

U.S. Central Intelligence Agency. 2011. *World Factbook.* https://www.cia.gov/library/publications/the-world-factbook/.

U.S. Environmental Protection Agency. 2010. The Life of a Cell Phone. www.epa.gov/osw/education/pdfs/life-cell.pdf.

U.S. Geological Society. 2011. Tantalum. http://minerals.usgs.gov/minerals/pubs/commodity/niobium/231303.pdf.

U.S. Library of Congress 2008. "Meet Amazing Americans: Jane Addams." www.americaslibrary.gov/cgi-bin/page.cgi/aa/addams.

WAFB. 2011. "Man Used Roommate's Cell Phone to Lure Robbery Victim with a Text Message Asking Him to Come Over." (January 18). www.wafb.com.

Weintraub, Jeff, and Joseph Soares. 2005. Handout #15: Reading Weber—"Types of Social Action for Social & Political Theory." http://jeffweintraub.blogspot.com/2005/06/weber-on-social-action-rationality.html.

Zaniello, Tom. 2007. *The Cinema of Globalization: A Guide to Films about the New Economic Order.* New York: Cornell University Press.

Chapter 2

American Society for Microbiology. 2003. "American Society for Microbiology Survey Reveals That As Many As 30 Percent of Travelers Don't Wash Hands After Using Public Restrooms at Airports." www.asm.org/index.php/news-room/.

Andreas, Peter. *Border Games: Policing the U.S.-Mexico Divide.* 2nd. New York: Cornell University Press, 2009.

Archibold, Roger. 2009. "Disorder at the Borders: Photographers Aim to Document and Protest Borderland Environments." *Society of Environmental Journalists* (October 15). www.sej.org/publications/mexico/disorder-at-the-borders-photographers-aim-to-document-and-protect-borderland-env.

Bearden, Tom. 1993. "Focus: Help Wanted." *MacNeil/Lehrer NewsHour.* PBS.

Beaver, Janice C. 2006. "U.S. International Borders: Brief Facts." *CRS Report for Congress.* http://www.fas.org/sgp/crs/misc/RS21729.pdf.

Blumer, Herbert. 1969. *Symbolic Interactionism: Perspective and Method.* Berkeley: University of California Press.

Brown, Valerie. 2004. "Reaching Across the Border with the SBRP." *Environmental Health Perspectives* 112(5): 278–280.

Carver, Terrell. 1987. *A Marx Dictionary.* Totowa, NJ: Barnes and Noble.

Conover, Ted. 1987. *Coyotes: A Journey through the Secret World of America's Illegal Aliens.* New York: Vintage.

Cornelius, Wayne. 1981. "Mexican Migration to the United States." *Proceedings of the Academy of Political Science* 34(1):67–77.

Cornelius, Wayne. 2008. "Controlling Unauthorized Immigration from Mexico: The Failure of Prevention through Deterrence and the Need for Comprehensive Reform." Washington, DC: Immigration Policy Center, American Immigration Law Foundation. www.immigrationpolicy.org/just-facts/throwing-good-money-after-bad-immigration-enforcement.

Del Bosque, Melissa. 2010. "All Walled Up." *Texas Observer* (January 20). www.texasobserver.org/cover-story/all-walled-up/.

Dye, Lee. 1995. "Duplication of Research Isn't as Bad as It Sounds." *Los Angeles Times* (April 26):D5.

The Economist. 2008. "The US–Mexican Border Good Neighbours Make Fences." (October 2). www.economist.com/node/12332971?story_id=12332971.

Ellingwood, Ken. 2009. *Hard Line: Life and Death on the US-Mexico Border.* New York: Knopf Doubleday.

Engels, Friedrich. 1886. "A Fair Day's Labor for a Fair Day's Work." Labor Standard. www.marxists.org/archive.

Gilmore, Gerry J. 2004. "Service Members Can Apply for Expedited U.S. Citizenship." American Forces Press Service (February 24). www.defenselink.mil/news.

Government Accountability Office. 2009. *Border Patrol: Checkpoints Contribute to Border Patrol's Mission, but More Consistent Data Collection and Performance Measurement Could Improve Effectiveness* (August).

Gregg, Alan. 1989. Quoted in *Science and the Human Spirit: Contexts for Writing and Learning,* by Fred D. White. Belmont, CA: Wadsworth.

Hacker, Andrew. 1997. "Review of 'The New American Reality: Who We Are, How We Got There' by Reynolds Farley." *Contemporary Sociology* 26(4):478.

Haddal, Chad C. 2010. "Border Security: Key Agencies and their Missions." CRS Report for Congress (January 26) http://www.fas.org/sgp/crs/homesec/RS21899.pdf.

Hagan, Frank E. 1989. *Research Methods in Criminal Justice and Criminology.* New York: Macmillan.

Heyman, Josiah M. 1999. "Why Interdiction? Immigration Control at the United States–Mexican Border." *Regional Studies* 33(7):619–30.

Horan, Patrick M. 1995. "Review of 'Working with Archival Data: Studying Lives.'" *Contemporary Sociology* (May):423–424.

Judis, John. 2006. "Border Wars." *New Republic* (January 16).

Kapur, Devesh. 2003. "Remittances: The New Development Mantra?" Paper prepared for the G-24 Technical Group Meeting.

Katzer, Jeffrey, Kenneth H. Cook, and Wayne W. Crouch. 1991. *Evaluating Information: A Guide for Users of Social Science Research,* 3d ed. New York: McGraw-Hill.

Lowell, Lindsay, Rodolfo de la Garza, and Mike Hogg. 2000. "Remittances, U.S. Latino Communities, and Development in Latin American Countries." *Migration World Magazine* 38(5):13.

Maril, Robert L. 2004. *Patrolling Chaos: The U.S. Border in Deep South Texas.* Lubbock, TX: Texas Tech University Press.

Massey, Douglas. 2006. "The Wall That Keeps Illegal Workers In." *New York Times* (April 4). www.nytimes.com.

Massey, Douglas S., Jorge Durand, and Nolan J. Malone. 2002. *Beyond Smoke and Mirrors: Mexican Immigration in an Era of Economic Integration.* New York: Russell Sage Foundation.

Merton, Robert K. 1967. "Manifest and Latent Functions." Pages 73–137 in *On Theoretical Sociology: Five Essays, Old and New.* New York: Free Press.

Mexican Migration Project. 2007. "Selected Results." http://mmp.opr.princeton.edu/results/results-en.aspx.

Migration Information Source. 2006. "The U.S. Mexico Border." www.migrationinformation.org.

Morrow, David J. 1996. "Trials of Human Guinea Pigs." *New York Times* (September 29):10.

National Academy of Sciences. 1995. "Science Ethics Guide Updated, Expanded for Graduate Students." www2.nas.edu.whatsnew/20fe.html.

Pomfret, John. 2006. "Fence Meets Wall of Skepticism." washingtonpost.com (October 10).

Robinson, Scott S. 2003. "The Potential Role of IT in International Remittance Transfers." Draft memo (November). http://mediaresearchhub.ssrc.org/the-potential-role-of-it-in-international-remittance-transfers/attachment.

Roethlisberger, F. J., and William J. Dickson. 1939. *Management and the Worker*. Cambridge, MA: Harvard University Press.

Rossi, Peter H. 1988. "On Sociological Data." Pages 131–154 in *Handbook of Sociology*, ed. N. Smelser. Newberry Park, CA: Sage.

Schonberg, Harold. 1985. "Sumo Embodies Ancient Rituals." *The New York Times* (June 12). www.nytimes.com/1985/06/12/sports/sumo-embodies-ancient-rituals.html?ref=sumowrestling.

Secure Fence Act of 2006. 2006. thomas.loc.gov/cgi-bin/query/z?c109:h.r.6061.

Shotola, Robert W. 1992. "Small Groups." Pages 1796–1806 in *Encyclopedia of Sociology*, vol. 4, ed. E. F. Borgatta and M. L. Borgatta. New York: Macmillan.

Singer, Audrey, and Douglas S. Massey. 1998. "The Social Process of Undocumented Border Crossing among Mexican Migrants." *International Migration Review* 3(Fall):561–592.

Singleton, Royce A., Jr., Bruce C. Straits, and Margaret Miller Straits. 1993. *Approaches to Social Research*, 2d ed. New York: Oxford University Press.

Smith, Joel. 1991. "A Methodology for the Twenty-First Century Sociology." *Social Forces* 70(1):1–17.

Stalker's Guide to International Migration. 2003. "Emigration—Remittances." Pstalker.com/migration.

Strauss, Anselm. 1978. *Negotiations: Varieties, Contexts, Processes, and Social Order*. San Francisco: Jossey-Bass.

Suro, Roberto. 2003a. "Executive Summary." pp. 1–XX in *Billions in Motion: Latino Immigrants, Remittances, and Banking*. Pew Hispanic Center. www.pewhispanic.org.

Thayer, John E., III. 1983. "Sumo." Pages 270–274 in *Kodansha Encyclopedia of Japan*, vol. 7. Tokyo: Kodansha.

Thelen, David. 1992. "Of Audiences, Borderlands, and Comparisons: Toward the Internationalization of American History." *Journal of American History* (September):432–451.

Thompson, Ginger. 2003. "Money Sent Home by Mexicans Is Booming." *New York Times* (October 28):3.

U.S. Customs and Border Patrol. 2010. Secure Borders, Safe Travel, Legal Trade. www.cbp.gov/linkhandler/cgov/about/mission/strategic_plan_09_14.ctt/strategic_plan_09_14.pdf.

U.S. Department of Homeland Security. 2003. "Fact Sheet: Changes to National Security Entry/Exit Registration System." www.dhs.gov.

U.S. Department of Homeland Security. 2009a. Accomplishments & Reforms. www.dhs.gov/xlibrary/assets/department_accomplishments_and_reforms_2009.pdf.

______. 2009. Fact Sheet: Critical Infrastructure and Homeland Security Protection Accomplishments. www.dhs.gov/xnews/releases/pr_1220878057557.shtm.

U.S. Department of Justice. 2007. "Background to the Office of the Inspector General Investigation." www.usdoj.gov/oig/special/9807/gkp01.htm.

U.S. Department of Transportation. 2010. www.dot.gov.

Witte, Griff. 2006. "Boeing Wins Deal for Border Security." *Washington Post* (September 20). www.washingtonpost.com.

World Bank. 2010 (November 8). Remittances to Developing Countries Resilient in the Recent Crisis. http://web.worldbank.org/WBSITE/EXTERNAL/NEWS/0,,contentMDK:22757744~pagePK:64257043~piPK:437376~theSitePK:4607,00.html.

Zolberg, Aristide R. 1999. "Matters of State: Theorizing Immigration Policy." Pp. 71–93 in *The Handbook of International Migration: The American Experience*, eds. Charles Hirschman, Philip Kasinitz, and Josh DeWind. New York: Russell Sage.

Chapter 3

2nd Infantry Division. 2010. "Being a Good Neighbor." www.youtube.com/watch?v=n4OnFZQrqac.

ABC News/Travel. 2010. "Some Like It Very Hot: Relaxing in Korea Bathhouses." http://abcnews.so.com/travel/story?id=6046818&page=1.

Adherents.com. 2010. Jehovah's Witnesses. www.adherents.com/Na_367.html.

Allkpop. 2010. "SNSD Has Eyes on the Asian Music Market." www.allkpop.com/2010/11/snsd-has-eyes-on-the-asian-music-market.

Asia News. 2005. "South Korea Sends Food Aid to North Despite Protests by South Korean Activists" (February 28). www.asianews.it.

Bae Hyun-jung. 2010. "Kansas University Forges Korean Ties." *Korea Herald* (November 4). www.koreaherald.com.

Bangkok Post. 2010 (October 27). "North Korean Demands Massive Rice, Fertiliser Aid from South Korea." www.bangkokpost.com/news.

BBC News. 2005. "North Korea Slashes Food Rations." (January 24). news.bbc.co.uk.

Benedict, Ruth. 1976. Quoted in *The Person: His and Her Development Throughout the Life Cycle*, by Theodore Lidz. New York: Basic Books.

Branigan, Tania. 2010. "The Cultural Life of North Korea." *Guardian* (October 15). www.guardian.com.

Brooke, James. 2003a. "Defectors Want to Pry Open North Korea." *New York Times* (January 9):A8.

______. 2003b. "Infiltrators of North Korea: Tiny Radios." *New York Times* (March 5):A32.

Brown, Rita Mae. 1988. *Rubyfruit Jungle*. New York: Bantam.

Caryl, Christian and B.J. Lee. 2006. "Culture Shock: A Flow of Information from the Outside World is Changing the Hermit Kingdom." *Newsweek* (international edition). http://www.highbeam.com/doc/1G1-132090782.html.

Chosun, Ilbo. 2009 (November 3). "Korea to Build Massive Offshore Wind Farms." English.chosun.com.

Chung, Annie. 2003. "Korean Public Baths." *ThingsAsian*. www.thingsasian.com.

CNBC. 2010 (October 27). North Korea: Open For Business? www.cnbc.com/id/39879853.

Dale, Steve. 2004. "Pet Owner Survey Reveals Strong Bond between People and Their Pets." www.goodnewsforpets.com/petworld/archive/3b013_owner_survey.htm.

Demick, Barbara. 2010. "Nothing to Envy: Ordinary Lives in Korea." Spiegel and Grau.

Fallows, James. 1988. "Trade: Korea Is Not Japan." *Atlantic Monthly* (October): 22–33.

Federation of Gay Games. 2007. *Concept and Purpose*. www.gaygames.com.

Federation of International Basketball. 2010. www.fiba.com.

Gantt, Jonathan. 2010 (May 7). "Culture Shock: Kyeong Kang." *Minor League Baseball*. www.minorleaguebaseball.com.

Garcia, Cathy Rose A. 2010. "Website Brings Breaking K-pop News." *The Korea Times* (October 2). www.koreatimes.co.kr/www/news/art/2010/02/135_60884.html.

Geertz, Clifford. 1984. "Distinguished Lecture: Anti Relativism." *American Anthropologist* 86(2):263–278.

Glionna, John M. 2010. "Korean Women Carry on Diving Tradition." *Los Angeles Times* (October 27). www.latimes.com/2010/oct/27/world/la-fg-korea-divers-20101027.

Global Issues. 2010. World Military Spending. www.globalissues.org/article/75/world-military-spending.

Gordon, Steven L. 1981. "The Sociology of Sentiments and Emotion." Pages 562–592 in *Social Psychology: Sociological Perspectives*, ed. by M. Rosenberg and R. H. Turner. New York: Basic Books.

Halberstam, David. 1986. *The Reckoning*. New York: William Morrow and Company.

Hankyoreh, 2007 (May 1). "Korea's Jehovah's Witnesses Saw Deep Hardship." http://english.hani.co.kr/arti/English_edition.

Hannerz, Ulf. 1992. *Cultural Complexity: Studies in the Social Organization of Meaning*. New York: Columbia University Press.

Henry, William A. 1988. "No Time for the Poetry: NBC's Cool Coverage Stints on the Drama." *Time* (October 3):80.

Herskovits, Melville J. 1948. *Man and His Works: The Science of Cultural Anthropology*. New York: Knopf.

Hirsch, E. D., Jr., Joseph F. Kett, and James Trefil. 1993. *The Dictionary of Cultural Literacy*. New York: Houghton Mifflin.

Hochschild, Arlie R. 1976. "The Sociology of Feeling and Emotion: Selected Possibilities." Pages 280–307 in *Another Voice*, ed. by M. Millman and R. Kanter. New York: Octagon.

Hughes, Everett C. 1984. *The Sociological Eye: Selected Papers*. New Brunswick, NJ: Transaction.

Hunter, Helen-Louise. 1999. Quoted in "A Look at North Korean Society," by J. Winzig. www.winzigconsultingservices.com/files/samples/kg/Helen_ Hunter.html.

Institute of International Education. 2007. "Open Doors." www.iie.org/en/Research-and-Publications/Open-Doors.

Japan Times Online. 2008 (December 29). "Editorial: American Capitalism, Battered." http://search.japantimes.co.jp/cgi-bin/ed20081230a1.html.

Just Thomas. 2011. History of Thomas the Train. www.just-thomas.com/thomas-the-tank-engine-history.php.

Kang, K. Connie. 1995. *Home Was the Land of Morning Calm: A Saga of a Korean-American Family*. Reading, MA: Addison-Wesley.

Kim, Bo-Kyung, and Kevin Kirby. 1996. Personal correspondence (April 25).

Kim Tae-gyu. 2010. "Chinese Tourists Prefer Korea." *Korean Times* (Nov 1). www.koreatimes.co.kr.

Koehler, Nancy. 1986. "Re-entry Shock." Pages 89–94 in *Cross-Cultural Reentry: A Book of Readings*. Abilene, TX: Abilene Christian University Press.

Korea Joong Ang Daily. 2010 (November 6). "Universities Lure Foreign Students." http://joongangdaily.joins.com.

Korea.net. 2010 (November 5). "Far East Movement Hits No. 1 on U.S. Billboard Charts." www.korea.net/detail.do?guid=51167.

Korean Overseas Information Service. 2006. *Facts about Korea*. Seoul: Korean Overseas Information Agency. www.korea.net.

Koreascope. 1998. "Personality Cult in North Korea." *North Korean Studies*. www.fortunecity.com/meltingpot/champion/65/pers_cult.htm.

Kristof, Nicholas D. 1995. "Where a Culture Clash Lurks Even in the Noodles." *New York Times* (September 4):Y4.

———. 1998. "Big Macs to Go." *New York Times Book Review* (March 22):18.

———. 2005. "The Hermit Nuclear Kingdom." *New York Review of Books* (February 10):25–27.

Ku, J. H., M. E. Kim, N. K. Lee, and Y. H. Park. 2003. "Circumcision Practice Patterns in South Korea: Community Based Survey." *Sexually Transmitted Infections* 79(February):65–68.

Lamb, David. 1987. *The Arabs: Journeys beyond the Mirage*. New York: Random House.

Linton, Ralph. 1936. *The Study of Man: An Introduction*. New York: Appleton-Century-Crofts.

Liu, Hsein-Tung. 1994. "Intercultural Relations in an Emerging World Civilization." *Journal of Global Awareness* 2(1):48–53.

Luce, Edward. 2007. *In Spite of the Gods*. New York: Anchor Books.

MacKinnon, Rebecca. 2005. "Chinese Cell Phone Breaches North Korean Hermit Kingdom." *YaleGlobal Online* (January 17). yaleglobal.yale.edu.

Malaysian News Agency. 2010 (November 4). "GM Korea Brings Special Edition of Cadillac Escalade to S. Korea." www.bernama.com.

Malone, Andrew. 2008. "The GM Genocide: Thousands Of Indian Farmers Are Committing Suicide After Using Genetically Modified Crops." *Daily Mail* (November 3). www.dailymail.co.uk/news/worldnews/article-1082559/The-GM-genocide-Thousands-Indian-farmers-committing-suicide-using-genetically-modified-crops.html#ixzz1Dxz1tv3q.

McClane, Daisann. 2000. "Frugal Traveler: Unchartered (Hot) Waters at a Korean Spa." *New York Times* (October 29).

McGeown, Kate. 2003. "On Holiday in North Korea." *BBC News* (September 19). newsvote.bbc.co.uk.

Myers, Steven Lee. 2003. "Returning from Iraq War Not so Simple for Soldiers." *New York Times* (September 12):A1.

New Agriculturalist. 2008. "India's Farm Loan Waiver Proving Costly." (September 8) www.new-ag.info/news/newsitem.php?a=569.

Redfield, Robert. 1962. "The Universally Human and the Culturally Variable." Pages 439–453 in *Human Nature and the Study of Society: The Papers of Robert Redfield*, vol. 1, ed. by M. P. Redfield. Chicago: University of Chicago Press.

Rohner, Ronald P. 1984. "Toward a Conception of Culture for Cross-Cultural Psychology." *Journal of Cross-Cultural Psychology* 15(2):111–138.

Rokeach, Milton. 1973. *The Nature of Human Values*. New York: Free Press.

Sapir, Edward. 1949. "Selected Writings of Edward Sapir." In *Language, Culture and Personality*, ed. by D. G. Mandelbaum. Berkeley: University of California Press.

SchoolNet. 2011. Transatlantic Cable Communications. http://epe.lac-bac.gc.ca/100/205/301/ic/cdc/cable/index.htm.

Schudson, Michael. 1989. "How Culture Works: Perspectives from Media Studies on the Efficacy of Symbols." *Theory and Society* 18:153.

Sharp, Ari. 2005a. "Ari on the Web: Welcome to the Democratic People's Republic of Korea." www.ariontheweb.blogspot.com.

———. 2005b. "Ari on the Web: The Ego of the Kims." www.ariontheweb.blogspot.com.

Sobie, Jane Hipkins. 1986. "The Cultural Shock of Coming Home Again." Pages 95–102 in *The Cultural Transition: Human Experience and Social Transformation in the Third World and Japan*, ed. by M. I. White and S. Pollack. Boston: Routledge & Kegan.

Story, Louise. 2009. "Lending a Hand, Quietly." *The New York Times* (April 15).

Sumner, William Graham. 1907. *Folkways*. Boston: Ginn.

U.S. Army. 1998. "Standard Installation Topic Exchange Service." www.angelica.dds.nl/armybase.php.

U.S. Bureau of the Census. 2010. American Community Survey. www.census.gov/acs/www/.

U.S. Central Intelligence Agency. 2011. *World Factbook*. https://www.cia.gov/library/publications/the-world-factbook/geos/us.html.

U.S. Central Intelligence Agency. 2011. *World Factbook*. www.cia.gov/cia/publications/factbook/.

U.S. Department of Commerce. 2010. Travel and Tourism Research Programs. http://tinet.ita.doc.gov/research/index.html.

U.S. Department of Defense. 2008. Active Duty Military Strength & Other Personnel Statistics. www.defense.gov/faq/pis/mil_strength.html.

U.S. Department of Homeland Security. 2010. *Yearbook of Immigration Statistics, 2009*. www.dhs.gov/xlibrary/assets/statistics/yearbook/2009/ois_yb_2009.pdf.

U.S. Energy Information Administration. 2011. "Countries: Oil Consumption." http://www.eia.doe.gov/countries/index.cfm?topL=con.

Visser, Margaret. 1986. *Much Depends on Dinner*. New York: HarperPerennial.

Wall Street Journal. 2010 (November 2). "Gee! Girls' Generation Wants to Go Global." http://blogs.wsj.com/korearealtime/2010/11/02/gee-girls-generation-wants-to-go-global/.

Wallace, F. C. 1952. "Notes on Research and Teaching." *American Sociological Review* (December):747–751.

Wallerstein, Immanuel. 1984. *The Politics of the World-Economy: The States, the Movements and the Civilizations*. New York: Cambridge University Press.

Watchtower Bible and Tract Society of Pennsylvania. 2004. "Jehovah's Witnesses." www.jw-media.org.

Whorf, Benjamin. 1956. *Language, Thought, and Reality: Selected Writings of Benjamin Lee Whorf*, edited by J. B. Carroll. Cambridge: Technology Press of Massachusetts Institute of Technology.

Winchester, Simon. 1988. *Korea: A Walk through the Land of Miracles*. New York: Prentice Hall.

Winzig, Jerry. 1999. Review of *Kim Il-song's North Korea* by Helen-Louise Hunter. http://www.winzigconsultingservices.com/files/samples/kq/Helen_Hunter.html.

World Baseball Classic. 2010. www.worldbaseballclassic.com.

Yinger, j. Milton. 1977. "Presidential Address: Countercultures and Social Change." *American Sociological Review 42*(6): 833–853.

Yoo Gwan Hee. 2009. "Summertime Trials in North Korea." *Daily NK* (August 3) www.dailynk.com/english/read.php?cataId=nk01300&num=5247.

Chapter 4

Al-Batrawi, Khaled, and Mouin Rabbani. 1991. "Breakup of Families: A Case Study in Creeping Transfer." *Race and Class* 32(4):35–44.

Alexa. 2011. "Top Sites By Country." www.alexa.com/topsites/countries.

BBC News. 1998b. "Israel Celebrates Half-Century." http://news.bbc.co.uk/2/hi/events/israel_at_50/israel_today/85903.stm.

Ben-David, Amith, and Yoav Lavee. 1992. "Families in the Sealed Room: Interaction Patterns of Israeli Families during SCUD Missile Attacks." *Family Process* 31(1):35–44.

Bennet, James. 2003b. "An Israeli's Sorrowful Rule over a Sullen Nablus." *New York Times* (October 3): A1.

Bourne, Jenny. 1990. "The Pending Pain of Reenactment." *Race and Class* 32(2):67–72.

Brewer, Marilynn B. 1999. "The Psychology of Prejudice: Ingroup Love or Outgroup Hate." *Journal of Social Issues* (Fall). http://findarticles.com/p/articles/mi_m0341/is_3_55/ai_58549254/.

Buñuel, Luis. 1985. Quoted on page 22 in *The Man Who Mistook His Wife for a Hat and Other Clinical Tales*, by Oliver Sacks. New York: Summit Books.

Burns, John F. 2003. "Bomber Left Her Family with a Smile and a Lie." *New York Times* (October 7):A13.

Centers for Disease Control and Prevention. 2011. "Intellectual Disability." www.cdc.gov/ncbddd/dd/ddmr.htm.

Cole, Charlotte, et al. 2003. "The Educational Impact of Rechov Sumsum/Shara'a Simsim: A *Sesame Street* Television Series to Promote Respect and Understanding among Children Living in Israel, the West Bank, and Gaza." *International Journal of Behavioral Development* 27(5): 409–422.

Cooley, Charles Horton. 1909. *Social Organization*. New York: Scribner's.

———. 1961. "The Social Self." Pages 822–828 in *Theories of Society: Foundations of Modern Sociological Theory*, ed. by T. Parsons, E. Shils, K. D. Naegele, and J. R. Pitts. New York: Free Press.

Coser, Lewis A. 1992. "The Revival of the Sociology of Culture: The Case of Collective Memory." *Sociological Forum* 7(2):365–373.

Cuzzort, R. P., and E. W. King. 2002. *20th Century Social Thought*. New York: Harcourt.

Davis, Kingsley. 1940. "Extreme Isolation of a Child." *American Journal of Sociology* 45:554–565.

———. 1947. "Final Note on a Case of Extreme Isolation." *American Journal of Sociology* 3(5):432–437.

Deutsche Welle. 2003 "'Sesame Street' Joins Mideast Peace Process." (October 22). www.dw-world.de.

Dyer, Gwynne. 1985. *War*. New York: Crown.

Elbedour, Salman, David T. Bastien, and Bruce A. Center. 1997. "Identity Formation in a Shadow of Conflict: Projective Drawings by Palestinian and Israeli Arab Children from West Bank and Gaza." *Journal of Peace Research* 34(2):217–232.

Erikson, Erik H. 1950. *Childhood and Society*. New York: Norton.

———. 1982. *The Life Cycle Completed*. New York: Norton.

———. 1988. Quoted in "Erikson In His Own Old Age, Expands His View of Life," by D. Coleman. *The New York Times* (June 14):Y3.

Farnsworth, Elizabeth. 2004. "The Barrier." *Online Newshour* (February 9). www.pbs.org/newshour/bb/middle_east/jan-june04/barrier_2-9.html.

Fetzer Institute. 2005."Projects." www.fetzer.org.

Financial Times. 2010 (September 14). "The Potholed Road to Palestine," p. 11.

Freud, Anna, and Sophie Dann. 1958. "An Experiment in Group Upbringing." Pages 127–168 in *The Psychoanalytic Study of the Child*, vol. 6, ed. by R. S. Eissler, A. Freud, H. Hartmann, and E. Kris. New York: Quadrangle.

Friends Forever. 2010. Israel Program. www.friendsforeverusa.org/index.php?page=programs&category=Israeli_Program.

Goffman, Erving. 1961. *Asylums: Essays on the Social Situation of Mental Patients and Other Inmates*. New York: Anchor.

———. 1988. *The Yellow Wind*, trans. by H. Watzman. New York: Farrar, Straus & Giroux.

———. 1998. "Fifty Is a Dangerous Age." *New Yorker* (April 20):55.

———. 2006 (November 8). "The Will To Peace." MidEast Web Gateway www.mideastweb.org.

Grossman, David. 2010. "Need To Know Israeli Author David Grossman on the Middle East." Interviewed on PBS (November 12). http://video.pbs.org/video/1641861253/.

Halbwachs, Maurice. 1980. *The Collective Memory*, trans. by F. J. Ditter, Jr., and V. Y. Ditter. New York: Harper & Row.

Harel, Amos. 2004. "Shin Bet: 145 Suicide Bombers since Start of Intifada." *Haaretz* (June 13). www.haaretzdaily.com.

Independent Lens. 2006. *The World According to* "Sesame Street." www.pbs.org/independentlens/.

Institute of World Jewish Congress. 2010. *Jewish Communities of the World*. www.worldjewishcongress.org/israel.html.

Institute of World Jewish Congress. 2006. *Jewish Communities of the World*. www.worldjewishcongress.org/

Kagan, Jerome. 1988. Interview on *The Mind*, PBS (transcript). Boston: WGBH Educational Foundation.

———. 1989. *Unstable Ideas: Temperament, Cognition, and Self*. Cambridge, MA: Harvard University Press.

Kifner, John. 2000. "Out of Place: The Price of Peace Will Be Paid in Dreams." *New York Times* (December 31): Section 4, p. 1.

Lahoud, Lamia. 2001. "76% of Palestinians Support Suicide Attacks." *Jerusalem Post* (June 4). www.jpost.com/.

Margalit, Avishai. 2003. "The Suicide Bombers." *New York Review of Books* (January 16):36–39.

Mead, George Herbert. 1934. *Mind, Self and Society*. Chicago: University of Chicago Press.

Mobile Active. 2008 (October 30). "The Conflict in Gaza: The Role (or Lack Thereof) of Mobile Phones." http://mobileactive.org/conflict-gaza-role-or-lack-thereof-mobile-phones.

Myre, Greg. 2003. "UN Estimates Israeli Barrier Will Disrupt Lives of 600,000." *New York Times* (November 12). www.nyt.com.

Nathan, Susan. 2006. *The Other Side of Israel: My Journey across the Jewish/Arab Divide*. New York: Doubleday.

Natta, Don van, Jr. 2003. "The Terror Industry Fields Its Ultimate Weapon." *New York Times* (August 24):1WK.

Nelsen, Arthur. 2006. *Occupied Minds: A Journey through the Israeli Psyche*. Ann Arbor, MI: Pluto.

Nielsenwire. 2009 (May 20). "Americans Watching More TV Than Ever; Web and Mobile Video Up Too." http://blog.nielsen.com/

nielsenwire/online_mobile/americans-watching-more-tv-than-ever/.

Nova. 1986. "Life's First Feelings." WGBH Boston (February 11).

Ornstein, Robert, and Richard F. Thompson. 1984. *The Amazing Brain.* Boston: Houghton Mifflin.

Penfield, Wilder, and P. Perot. 1963. "The Brain's Record of Auditory and Visual Experience: A Final Summary and Discussion." *Brain* 86:595–696.

Peres, Judy. 1998. "A Human Mosaic." *Chicago Tribune* (May 9).

Public Radio International. 2009. "Cell Phone Help for Gaza." The World (January 16) www.pri.org/theworld/?q=node/23892.

Rose, Peter I., Myron Glazer, and Penina M. Glazer. 1979. "In Controlled Environments: Four Cases of Intensive Resocialization." Pages 320–338 in *Socialization and the Life Cycle,* ed. by P. I. Rose. New York: St. Martin's.

Rowley, Storer. 1998. "After the Army, You Feel More Israeli." *Chicago Tribune* (May 9).

Salamon, Julie. 2002. "Israeli-Palestinian Battles Intrude on '*Sesame Street.*'" *New York Times* (July 30). www.nytimes.com.

Satterly, D. J. 1987. "Jean Piaget (1896–1980)." Pages 621–622 in *The Oxford Companion to the Mind,* ed. by R. I. Gregory. Oxford, UK: Oxford University Press.

Schutten, Chantel. 2008. "Dr. Frank Hayden." www.sporthamilton.ca/content/people/FrankHayden.pdf.

———. 2008. "Study Sheds Light on Impact of Terrorism on Adolescent Depression," (August 25). www.sciencedaily.com.

Science Daily. 2010 (September 17). "How Palestinians and Israeli Children Are Psychologically Scarred by Exposure to War." www.sciencedaily.com.

Shipler, David. 1986. *Arab and Jew: Wounded Spirits in a Promised Land.* New York: Times Books.

Shriver, Eunice Kennedy. 1962. "One Woman's Vision." *The Saturday Evening Post.* www.eunicekennedyshriver.org/articles/print_article/148.

Special Olympics. 2011. History. www.specialolympics.org/history.aspx.

Spitz, Rene A. 1951. "The Psychogenic Diseases in Infancy: An Attempt at Their Etiological Classification." Pages 255–278 in *The Psychoanalytic Study of the Child,* vol. 27, ed. by R. S. Eissler and A. Freud. New York: Quadrangle.

Theodorson, George A., and Achilles G. Theodorson. 1979. *A Modern Dictionary of Sociology.* New York: Barnes & Noble.

U.S. Bureau of the Census. 2006. "Table 963: Appliances and Office Equipment Used by Region and Household Income: 2001." *Statistical Abstract of the United States.*

———. 2009. "Table 1090. Utilization of Selected Media: 1980 to 2006." www.census.gov/compendia/statab/2009/tables/09s1090.pdf.

U.S. Central Intelligence Agency. 2011. *World Factbook.* www.cia.gov/library/publications/the-world-factbook/.

Usher, Graham. 1991. "Children of Palestine." *Race and Class* 32(4):1–18.

Chapter 5

Abraham, Carolyn. 2006. "The Smartest Virus in History?" *Globe and Mail* (August 12): A9.

ACT UP New York (ACTUPNY). 2006. Civil Disobedience Index. www.actupny.org/documents/CDdocuments/CDindex.html.

———. 2010. *Homepage.* Retrieved November 20, 2010, www.actupny.org.

Barr, David. 1990. "What Is AIDS? Think Again." *New York Times* (December 1):Y15.

Centers for Disease Control. 2010. HIV/AIDS. www.cdc.gov/hiv/default.htm.

Columbia University. 2004. *The Stonewall Riot and Its Aftermath: Stonewall and Beyond: Lesbian and Gay Culture.* Columbia University. Retrieved November 20, 2010, from www.columbia.edu/cu/lweb/eresources/exhibitions/sw25/case1.html.

Conrad, Joseph. 1971. *Heart of Darkness,* rev. and ed. by R. Kimhough. New York: Norton.

Durkheim, Émile. [1933] 1964. *The Division of Labor in Society,* trans. by G. Simpson. New York: Free Press.

Edgerton, Robert B. 2002. *The Troubled Heart of Africa: A History of the Congo.* New York: St. Martin's Press.

Forbath, Peter. 1977. *The River Congo.* New York: Harper and Row.

French, Howard. 2009. "Kagame's Hidden War in the Congo." *New York Review of Books* (September 24): 44-47.

Frontline. 1993. "AIDS, Blood, and Politics." Boston: WGBH Educational Foundation and Health Quarterly.

Gage, S., L. Richards, & H. Wilmot. 2002. *Queer.* New York, NY: Thunder's Mouth Press.

GAO. 1997. *Blood Safety: Enhancing Safeguards Would Strengthen the Nation's Blood Supply.* T-HEHS-97-143 (June 5) www.gao.gov.

GLBTQ.com. 2004. *ACT UP.* Social Sciences. Retrieved November 20, 2010, from www.glbtq.com/social-sciences/act_up.html.

———. 2010. Topics in the News. www.glbtq.com.

Goffman, Erving. 1959. *The Presentation of Self in Everyday Life.* New York: Anchor.

Gould, Deborah B. 2009. *Moving Politics: Emotion and ACT UP's Fight against AIDS.* Chicago, IL: University of Chicago Press.

Grover, Jan Zita. 1987. "AIDS: Keywords." *October* 43:17–30.

Henderson, Charles. 1998. "Epidemiology: U.S. Sees AIDS Rise among Older Americans." *AIDS Weekly Plus* (February 9):14.

Hippocratic Oath. 1943. *Hippocratic Oath: Text, Translation, and Interpretation,* trans. from the Greek by Ludwig Edelstein. Baltimore: Johns Hopkins Press.

Hochschild, Adam. 1998. *King Leopold's Ghost.* New York: Houghton Mifflin.

———. 2009. "Rape the Congo." *New York Review of Books* (August 13):18–20.

International Federation of Pharmaceutical Manufacturers Associations. 1981. www.ifpma.org/Issues/.

Johnson, Diane, and John F. Murray. 1988. "AIDS Without End." *New York Review of Books* (August 18):57–63.

Kaiser Family Foundation. 2009. "Total Number of Retail Prescription Drugs Filled at Pharmacies, 2009." www.statehealthfacts.org/comparemaptable.jsp?ind=265&cat=5.

Kaptchuk, Ted, and Michael Croucher, with the BBC. 1986. *The Healing Arts: Exploring the Medical Ways of the World.* New York: Summit.

Kivisto, Peter, and Dan Pittman. 2007. "Goffman's Dramaturgical Sociology: Personal Sales and Service in a Commodified World." In *Illuminating Social Life: Classical and Contemporary Theory,* 271–290. Thousand Oaks, CA: Pine Forge Press.

Kornfield, Ruth. 1986. "Dr., Teacher, or Comforter? Medical Consultation in a Zairian Pediatrics Clinic." *Culture, Medicine and Psychiatry* 10:367–387.

Lewin, Tamar. 2000. "Survey Shows Sex Practices of Boys." *New York Times* (December 19):A16.

Lowenstein, F., S. Lechner, & E. Bruun. 2007. *Voices of Protest: Documents of Courage and Dissent.* New York, NY: Black Dog & Leventhal Publishers Inc.

Lyons, Maryinez. 2002. *The Colonial Disease.* Cambridge: Cambridge University Press.

Malone, John. 2000. *21st-Century Gay.* New York, NY: M. Evans and Company, Inc.

Mark, Joan. 1995. *The King of the World in the Land of the Pygmies.* Lincoln, NE: University of Nebraska Press.

Markel, Howard. 2003. "HIV Secrecy Is Proving Deadly." *New York Times* (November 23):D6.

Martin, Patricia Yancey. 2004. "Gender as Social Institution." *Social Forces* 82(4):1249–1273.

Merton, Robert K. 1957. *Social Theory and Social Structure.* Glencoe, IL: Free Press.

Michael, Robert T., John H. Gagnon, Edward O. Lauman, and Gina Kolata. 1994. *Sex in America: A Definitive Survey.* New York: Little, Brown.

Moore, Jim. 2004. "The Puzzling Origins of AIDS." *American Scientist* (92):540–547.

National Center for Health Statistics. 2002. Referenced in R. A. Friedman, "Curing and Killing: The Perils of a Growing Medicine Cabinet." *New York Times* (December 12). www.nyt.com.

Oliver, Murray. 2006. "The Waiting Is the Hardest Part for Congolese." CTV.ca (November 1). www.ctv.ca.

Rockefeller University Hospital. 2011. "The First Drug for African Sleeping Sickness." http://centennial.rucares.org/index.php?page=African_Sleeping_Sickness.

Snyder, Kassidy. 2010. "MEDFLAG 10 Delivers Humanitarian Assistance to 2,000 in Kinshasa." www.army.mil/-news/2010/09/20/45388-medflag-10-delivers-humanitarian-assistance-to-2000-in-kinshasa/.

Sontag, Susan. 1989. *AIDS and Its Metaphors.* New York: Farrar, Straus & Giroux.

Stein, Michael. 1998. "Sexual Ethics: Disclosure of HIV-Positive Status to Partners." *Archives of Internal Medicine* 158:253.

Stolberg, Sheryl. 1996. "Officials Find Rare HIV Strain in L.A. Woman." *Los Angeles Times* (July 5):A1+.

Turnball, Colin. 1961. *The Forest People.* New York: Simon and Schuster.

Turner, Thomas. 2009. *The Congo Wars.* 2ed Books.

UNEP/GRID-ARENDAL. 2010. "Mining in Democratic Republic of Congo." http://maps.grida.no/graphic/mining-in-the-democratic-republic-of-congo.

U.S. Centers for Disease Control. 2010. Hemophilia. www.cdc.gov/ncbddd/hemophilia/treatment.html.

———. 2011. HIV-AIDS. www.cdc.gov/hiv/.

U.S. International Trade Administration. 2007. "Arrivals Data for World Regions and Top Markets." tinet.ita.doc.gov.

Villarosa, Linda. 2003. "Raising Awareness about AIDS and the Aging." *New York Times* (July 8). www.nyt.com.

Witte, John. 1992. "Deforestation in Zaire: Logging and Landlessness." *Ecologist* 22(2):58.

Wockner, Rex. (2007). "American Gay Group ACT UP Resurrected as General Pace Targeted in New York." UK Gay News. Wockner News, March 15, 2007. Retrieved November 20, 2010, from www.ukgaynews.org.uk/archive/07/March/1502.htm.

World Health Organization. 2004. *The World Medicines Situation.* http://apps.who.int/medicinedocs/en/d/Js6160e/6.html.

World Tourism Organization. 2007. *Tourism Highlights.* www.worldtourism.org.

Wrong, Michela. 2000. *In the Footsteps of Mr. Kurtz.* Great Britain: Fourth Estates Limited.

Yasuda, Yikuo. 1994. "Japanese Hemophiliacs Suffering from HIV Infection." www.nmia.com/~mdibble/japan2.html.

Chapter 6

Aldrich, Howard E., and Peter V. Marsden. 1988. "Environments and Organizations." Pages 361–392 in *Handbook of Sociology,* ed. by N. J. Smelser. Newbury Park, CA: Sage.

Allen, Patricia. 2010. "Realizing Justice In Local Food Systems." *Journal of Regions, Economy, and Society* 1:14. www.cjres.oxfordjournals.org.

Allen, Patricia, and Alice Brooke Wilson. 2008. "Agrifood Inequalities: Globalization and Localization." *Development* 51(4):534–540. www.palgrave-journals.com/development/journal/v51/n4/abs/dev200865a.html.

Angier, Natalie. 2002. "The Most Compassionate Conservative." *New York Times Book Review* (October 27):8–9.

Ballotpedia. 2008. California Proposition 2: Standards for Confining Animals. www.ballotpedia.org.

Barrionuevo, Alexei. 2007. "Globalization in Every Loaf: Ingredients Come from All Over, but Are They Safe?" *The New York Times* (June 16): B1.

Barnet, Richard J., and Ronald E. Müller. 1974. *Global Reach: The Power of the Multinational Corporations.* New York: Simon & Schuster.

Blau, Peter M., and Richard A. Schoenherr. 1973. *The Structure of Organizations.* White Plains, NY: Longman.

Bloomberg Business Week. 2010 (March 3). "Taco Bell Corp. Faces Suit Accused of Not Paying Employees for Overtime Hours and Falsifying Records." http://investing.businessweek.com.

Brown, Michael. 2009. "Role of Social Justice in 'Buy Local' Campaigns Examined." *The Cultivar* 27(1):14.

CBS News. 2010 (May 24). "PETA's New Tactic to Help Animals: Buying Stock" www.cbs.news.com/stories/2010/05/24/business/main6513894.html.

Centers for Disease Control. 2009. "Enteric Diseases Epidemiology Branches." www.cdc.gov/nc2ved/divisions/dfbmd/edeb.

Chanda, Nayan. 2003. "The New Leviathans: An Atlas of Multinationals Throws Unusual Light on Globalization." Review of *Global Inc.: An Atlas of the Multinational Corporation,* by Medard Gabel and Henry Bruner, in *YaleGlobal* (November 12). yaleglobal.yale.edu.

Chase, Brett. 2010. "Happy Meal Toy Ban Hits McDonald's." Portfolio.com (April 28). www.portfolio.com.

Cooley, Charles Horton. 1909. *Social Organization.* New York: Scribner's.

Critser, Greg. 2003. *Fat Land: How Americans Became the Fattest People in the World.* New York: Houghton Mifflin.

de Toqueville, Alexis. 1882. *Democracy in America,* 7th ed., vol. II. Boston: John Allyn.

Etzioni, Amitai. 1975. *Comparative Analysis of Complex Organizations.* New York, NY: Free Press of Glencoe.

Food Institute Report. 2000. "McDonald's Sets Rules for Raising Hens." (August 28):10.

Fortune. 2010a. "Our Annual Rankings of America's Largest Corporations." *CNN Money.* www.money.cnn.com/magazines/fortune/fortune500/2010.

———. 2010b. "Our Annual Rankings of the World's Largest Corporations." *CNN Money.* www.money.cnn.com/magazines/fortune/fortune500/2010.

Freund, Julien. 1968. *The Sociology of Max Weber.* New York: Random House.

Gabel, Medard, and Henry Bruner. 2003. *Global Inc.: An Atlas of the Multinational Corporation.* New York: New Press.

Gibney, Simon. 1993 (October 25). McLibel trial witness statement. Transcript. www.mcspotlight.org/people/witnesses/employment/gibney_simon.html.

Goetzinger, Chester. 2006. "CFIA Carcass Inspection Procedure and Standards: Impact on Producers." *Advances in Pork Production* (Volume 17).

Greenberg, Jack. 2001. Quoted in "McAtlas Shrugged: An FP Interview with Jack Greenberg." *Foreign Policy* (May/June):26+.

International Potato Center. 1998. "Globalization of French Fries." www.cipotato.org/potato.

Langley, Allison. 2003. "It's a Fat World, After All." *New York Times* (July 20):B1.

Leidner, Robin. 1993. *Fast Food, Fast Talk: Service Work and the Routinization of Everyday Life.* Berkeley, CA: University of California Press.

Lepkowski, Wil. 1985. "Chemical Safety in Developing Countries: The Lessons of Bhopal." *Chemical and Engineering News* 63:9–14.

Mawhorr, S. A. 2000. "PETA Claims Win Over McDonald's Change in Treatment of Hens Leads to End of Protests." *Daily Herald* (September 8).

McDonald's Corporation. 2003. "Summary Annual Report." www.mcdonalds.com.

———. 2009. Annual Report. www.aboutmcdonalds.com/mcd/investors.html.

———. 2010. Annual Report. www.aboutmcdonalds.com/etc/medialib/aboutMcDonalds/investor_relations3.Par.56096.File.dat/2010%20Annual%20Report%20(print).pdf.

———. 2011a. Our Company. www.aboutmcdonalds.com.

———. 2011b. "Key Performance Indicator Summary: Measuring Performance." www.aboutmcdonalds.com/mcd/csr/report/overview/key_performance_indicators.html.

Michels, Robert. 1962. *Political Parties*, trans. by E. Paul and C. Paul. New York: Dover.

NBC Dateline. 2010. "Dirty Dining?" Consumer Alert. http://msnbc/msn.comid/3473728/ns/dateline_nbc_consumer_alert/.

Perrow, Charles. 2000. "An Organizational Analysis of Organizational Theory." *Contemporary Sociology* 29(3):469–471.

Prevention Institute. 2011. "Setting the Record Straight: Nutrition and Health Professionals Define Healthful Food." www.preventioninstitute.org/component/jlibrary/article/id-58/127.html.

ProPotato. 2011. www.propotato.com/.

Ritzer, George. 1993. *The McDonaldization of Society*. Thousand Oaks, CA: Pine Forge Press.

Sadri, Mahmoud. 1996. "Book Review of Occidentalism: Images of the West." *Contemporary Sociology* (September): 612.

Schlosser, Eric. 2002. *Fast Food Nation*. New York: Harper.

Scully, Matthew. 2003. *Dominion: The Power of Man, the Suffering of Animals, and the Call to Mercy*. New York: St. Martin's.

Sekulic, Dusko. 1978. "Approaches to the Study of Informal Organization." *Sociologija* 20(1):27–43.

Skinner, Jim. 2010. Quoted in "Financial Press Release: McDonald's Third Quarter Earnings Rise 12% on Strong Global Sales." http://phx.corporate-ir.net/phoenix.zhtml?c=97876&p=irol-newsArticle&ID=1377920&highlight=.

Slow Food. 2011. www.slowfood.com.

Snow, Charles P. 1961. *Science and Government*. Cambridge, MA: Harvard University Press.

Spreitzer, Elmer A. 1971. "Organizational Goals and Patterns of Informal Organizations." *Journal of Health and Social Behavior* 12(1):73–75.

Sterrett, David. 2007. "McDonald's Faces Teen Labor Shortage." *Workforce* (July 25). http://www.workforce.com/section/news/article/mcdonalds-faces-teen-labor-shortage.php.

Sustainable Table. 2011. "What is Local?" www.sustainabletable.org/issues/eatlocal/.

United Egg Producers. 2010. Animal Husbandry Guidelines for U.S. Egg Laying Flocks, 2010 ed. www.unitedegg.org/information/pdf/UEP_2010_Animal_Welfare_Guidelines.pdf.

U.S. Bureau of Labor Statistics. 1999 (August 5). "Meat Packing Plants Have Highest Rate of Repeated-Trauma Disorders." www.bls.gov/opub/ted/1999/Aug/wk1/art04.htm.

U.S. Bureau of Labor Statistics. 2009. *Industrial Food: Food Processing and Manufacturing Establishments in United States By Location, 2009*. www.bls.gov/oco/cg/cgs011.htmhttp://www.bls.gov/oco/cg/cgs011.htm.

———. 2010. BLS Spotlight on Statistics: Food. www.bls.gov/spotlight/2010/food/data.htm.

U.S. Central Intelligence Agency. 2011. *World Factbook*. www.cia.gov/library/publications/the-world-factbook/.

U.S. General Accountability Office. 1978. *U.S. Foreign Relations and Multinational Corporations: What's the Connection?* Washington, DC: U.S. Government Printing Office.

Veblen, Thorstein. 1933. *The Engineers and the Price System*. New York: Viking.

The Verdict. 1997. Chief Justice Bell's Verdict. (June 19). www.mcspotlight.org/case/trial/verdict/verdict_jud3b.html.

Wais, Erin. 2005. "Trained Incapacity: Thorstein Veblen and Kenneth Burke." *KB Journal* 2(1). www.kbjournal.org/wais.

Walsh, Bryan. 2009. "Getting Real About High Price of Cheap Food." *Time* (August 24). www.time.com.

Waters, Jennifer. 1998. "Fractured Franchise." *Restaurants and Institutions*. www.rimag.com/807/busjw.htm.

Weber, Max. 1947. *The Theory of Social and Economic Organization*, ed. and trans. by A. M. Henderson and T. Parsons. New York: Macmillan.

Weiser, Benjamin. 2003. "Big Macs Can Make You Fat." *New York Times* (January 23):A23.

Yablen, Marcia. 2000. "Happy Hen, Happy Meal." *U.S. News and World Report* 129(9):46.

Young, T. R. 1975. "Karl Marx and Alienation: The Contributions of Karl Marx to Social Psychology." *Humboldt Journal of Social Relations* 2(2):26–33.

Zuboff, Shoshana. 1988. *In the Age of the Smart Machine: The Future of Work and Power*. New York: Basic Books.

Chapter 7

Andreas, Joel. 2010. "Review of *The Unknown Cultural Revolution: Educational Reforms and Their Impact on China's Rural Development.*" China Left Review (Issue 3). http://chinaleftreview.org/?p=227.

Author X. 1992. "Mao Fever—Why Now?" Trans. and adapted from the Chinese by R. Terrill. *World Monitor* (December): 22–25.

Becker, Howard S. 1963. *Outsiders: Studies in the Sociology of Deviance*. New York: Free Press.

———. 1973. "Labeling Theory Reconsidered." In *Outsiders: Studies in the Sociology of Deviance*. New York: Free Press.

Best, Joel. 1989. *Images of Issues: Typifying Contemporary Social Problems*. New York: Aldine de Gruyter.

Bolido, E. 1993. *Simple Solution Saves Many Young Lives*. Manille (Philippines), Press Foundation of Asia.

Bradsher, Keith. 2007. "An Opportunity for Wall St. in China's Surveillance Boom." *The New York Times* (September 11).

Bristow, Michael. 2010. "China Defends Internet Censorship." (June 8) http://news.bbc.co.uk/2/hi/8727647.stm.

Butterfield, Fox. 1976. "Mao Tse-Tung: Father of Chinese Revolution." *New York Times* (September 10):A13+.

———. 1980. "The Pragmatists Take China's Helm." *New York Times Magazine* (December 28):22–35.

———. 1982. *China: Alive in the Bitter Sea*. New York: Times Books.

Center on Wrongful Convictions. 2003. "The Illinois Exonerated: Anthony Porter." Northwestern University School of Law. www.law.northwestern.edu/wrongfulconvictions/exonerations/ilPorterSummary.html.

Chambliss, William. 1974. "The State, the Law, and the Definition of Behavior as Criminal or Delinquent." Pages 7–44 in *Handbook of Criminology*, ed. by D. Glaser. Chicago: Rand McNally.

Chang Jung. 1991. *Wild Swans: Three Daughters of China*. New York: Simon & Schuster.

China Daily. 2010. "Invisible Children." (June 16) www.chinadaily.com.cn/cndy/2010-06/16/content_9979147.htm.

China Information Office. 2010. U.S. Human Rights Record in 2009 (March 12). www.chinadaily.com.cn/china/2010-03/12/content_9582821.htm.

Christian Century. 2003. "Capital Offense: Can the Death Penalty System Really Be Sufficiently Reformed?" (February 8):5.

Cohen, Adam. 2008. "Four Decades after Milgram, We're Still Willing to Inflict Pain." *The New York Times* (December 29):A22.

Collins, Randall. 1961. "Conflict Theory of Educational Stratification." In *Schools and Society: A Sociological Approach to Education*, ed. Jeanne H. Ballantine and Joan Z. Spade, 24-40. Thousand Oaks, CA: Sage, 2008.

ConsumerAffairs.com. 2005. "Avon Calls On China." (April 12). www.consumeraffairs.com/news04/2005/avon.html.

Crienglish. 2008. "Largest Sock Productions Town in China." Crienglish (May 25). http://english.cri.cn/4026/2008/05/25/1721@361743.htm.

Deng, Kuan. 2008. pp. 73–92 in *The Corpse Walker* (interviewed by Lisa Yiwu) by Liao Yiwu. New York: Anchor.

Durkheim, Émile. [1901] 1982. *The Rules of Sociological Method and Selected Texts on Sociology and Its Method,* ed. by S. Lukes, trans. by W. D. Halls. New York: Free Press.

Economist. 2002. "The Tale of Two Ryans; Death and Politics in Illinois" (October 19). www.infotrac-college.com.

Erikson, Kai T. 1966. *Wayward Puritans.* New York: Wiley.

Fairbank, John King. 1987. *The Great Chinese Revolution 1800–1985.* New York: Harper & Row.

Fallows, James. 2009. *Postcards from Tomorrow Square: Reports from China.* New York: Vintage.

Farrer, James. 2009. "Set of Ongoing Debates, Diverse Subcultures." *China Daily* (September 30). www.chinadaily.com.cn.

Federal Bureau of Prisons. 2011. "Quick Facts About the Bureau of Prisons." www.bop.gov/about/facts.jsp#3.

Felluga, Dino. 2009. "Modules on Foucault: On Panoptic and Carceral Society." Introductory Guide to Critical Theory. www.cla.purdue.edu/english/theory/newhistoricism/modules/foucaultcarceralmainframe.html.

Field, Scott L. 2002. "On the Emergence of Social Norms." *Contemporary Sociology* 31(6):638–639.

Foucault, Michel. 1977. *Discipline and Punishment: The Birth of a Prison.* Paris: Gallimard.

Gerson Lehrman Group. 2010. "China's Prospects of Personal Home Care." (December 12). www.glgroup.com/News/Chinas-prospects-of-personal-and-home-care-51160.html.

Gibbs, Jack P. 1965. "Norms: The Problem of Definition and Classification." *American Journal of Sociology* 60:586–594.

Gifford, Rob. 2007. *China Road: A Journey into the Future of a Rising Power.* New York: Random House.

Goldman, Merle. 1989. "Vengeance in China." *New York Review of Books* (November 9):5–9.

Gould, Stephen Jay. 1990. "Taxonomy as Politics: The Harm of False Classification." *Dissent* (Winter):73–78.

Governor's Commission on Capital Punishment, State of Illinois. 2002. *Report of the Governor's Commission on Capital Punishment* (April). www.idoc.state.il.us/ccp/ccp/reports/commission_report/summary_recommendations.pdf.

Han, Dongping. 2010. "The Unknown Cultural Revolution: Life and Change in a Chinese Village." *Monthly Review Press* http://mrzine.monthlyreview.org/2010/han300110.html.

Henriques, Diana B. 1993. "Great Men and Tiny Bubbles: For God, Country and Coca-Cola." *New York Times Book Review* (May 23):13.

Hersh, Seymour. 2004. "Annals of National Security: Torture at Abu Ghraib." *New Yorker* (May 10). www.newyorker.com/archive/2004/05/10/040510fa_fact.

Hodges, Matt. 2009. "Changing Mores." *China Daily* (September 30). www.chinadaily.com.cn.

Innocence Project. 2004. "About the Innocence Project." http://innocenceproject.org/about/.

International Centre for Prison Studies. 2010. World Prison List. www.kcl.ac.uk/depsta/law/research/icps/news.php?id=203.

Jerome, Richard. 1995. "Suspect Confessions." *New York Times Magazine* (August 13):28–31.

Johnson, Dirk. 2003. "A Leap of Fate: A Governor's Controversial Last Hurrah Clears Out Illinois's Crowded Death Row." *Newsweek* (January 20):34.

Johnston, Norman. 2009. "Prison Reform in Pennsylvania." The Pennsylvania Prison Society. www.prisonsociety.org/about/history.shtml.

Kaye, Jeffrey. 2001. "Under Suspicion." *Online Newshour* (October 26). www.pbs.org/newshour.

Kelly, Maura. 2003. "Illinois Governor Pardons 4 Inmates on Death Row." *Salt Lake Tribune* (January 11). www.sltrib.com.

Kometani, Foumiko. 1987. "Pictures from Their Nightmare." *New York Times Book Review* (July 19):9–10.

Kristof, Nicholas D. 1989. "China Is Planning 2 Years of Labor for Its Graduates." *New York Times* (August 13):Y1.

———. 2004. "A Little Leap Forward." *New York Review of Books* (June 24):56–58.

Kwong, Julia. 1988. "The 1986 Student Demonstrations in China." *Asian Survey* 28(9):970–985.

La Franiere, Sharon. 2009. "No Detail is Overlooked as China Prepares to Celebrate." *The New York Times* (September 29):pA4.

Laio, Yiwu. 2008. *The Corpse Walker: Real Life Stories from the Bottom Up.* New York: Anchor.

Lemert, Edwin. 1967. *Human Deviance, Social Problems, and Social Control.* Englewood Cliffs, NJ: Prentice-Hall.

MacAskill, Ewin. 2010. "U.S. Blocks Access to WikiLeaks for Federal Employees." Guardian (December 3). www.guardian.co.uk/world/2010/dec/03/wikileaks-cables-blocks-access-federal.

MacFarquhar, Roderick, and Michael Schoenhals. 2006. *Mao's Last Revolution.* Belknap/Harvard University.

Mathews, Jay, and Linda Mathews. 1983. *One Billion: A China Chronicle.* New York: Random House.

Merton, Robert K. 1957. *Social Theory and Social Structure.* Glencoe, IL: Free Press.

Milgram, Stanley. 1974. *Obedience to Authority: An Experimental View.* New York: Harper & Row.

———. 1987. "Obedience." Pages 566–568 in *The Oxford Companion to the Mind,* ed. by R. L. Gregory. Oxford, UK: Oxford University Press.

Moss, Michael. 2003. "False Terrorism Tips to F.B.I. Uproot the Lives of Suspects." *New York Times* (June 19):A1.

National Collegiate Athletic Association (NCAA). 2010. "Estimated Probability of Competing in Athletics Beyond the High School Interscholastic Level." www.ncaa.org.

National Council for Crime Prevention in Sweden. 1985. *Crime and Criminal Policy in Sweden.* Report no. 19. Stockholm: Liber Distribution.

North Carolina Department of Correction. 2009. "Greene Correctional Institution." www.doc.state.nc.us/dop/prisons/greene.htm.

People's Daily Online. 2010. "China's Rural Population to Halve in 30 Years: Economist." (February 24). http://english.peopledaily.com.cn/90001/90776/90882/6901672.html.

Pfuhl, Edwin, and Stuart Henry. 1993. *The Deviance Process,* 3rd ed. Aldine de Gruyter.

Piazza, Alan. 1996. Quoted in "In China's Outlands, Poorest Grow Poorer," by P. E. Tyler. *New York Times* (October 26):A1, A4.

Radelet, Michael, L., Hugo Adams, and Constance Putman. 1994. *In Spite of Innocence.* Boston: Northeastern University Press.

Redmonde, Reiko. 2009. "China's Cultural Revolution a Human Disaster? Not According to Symposium Participants." *The Berkeley Daily Planet* (November 12).

Remez, L. 1991. "China's Fertility Patterns Closely Parallel Recent National Policy Changes." *International Family Planning Perspectives* 17(2):75–76.

Rosenthal, Elisabeth. 2000. "Rural Flouting of One-Child Policy Undercuts China's Census." *New York Times* (April 14):A10.

Ryan, George H. 2003. Quoted in "Two Days Left in Term, Governor Clears Out Death Row in Illinois" by Jodi Wilgoren. *New York Times* (January 11):A1.

Safe Drug Drop-Off Program. 2011. www.nodrugsdownthedrain.org/DrugDropOff.pdf.
Scruggs, Stirling. 1994. Quoted in "The Little Emperors," by Daniela Dean, *Los Angeles Times* (July 26). http://articles.latimes.com/1992-07-26/magazine/tm-5347_1_one-child-policy/6.
Shapiro, Bruce. 2001. "A Talk with Governor George Ryan." *Nation* (January 8):17.
Simmons, J. L., with Hazel Chambers. 1965. "Public Stereotypes of Deviants." *Social Problems* 3(2):223–232.
Spector, Malcolm, and J. I. Kitsuse. 1977. *Constructing Social Problems*. Menlo Park, CA: Cummings.
Spence, Jonathan. 2006. "China's Great Terror." *New York Review of Books* (September 21):31–34.
Sumner, William Graham. 1907. *Folkways*. Boston: Ginn.
Sutherland, Edwin H., and Donald R. Cressey. 1978. *Principles of Criminology*, 10th ed. Philadelphia: Lippincott.
Tien H. Yuan, Zhang Tianlu, Ping Yu, Li Jingneng, and Liang Zhongtang. 1992. "China's Demographic Dilemmas." *Population Bulletin* 47(1):1–44.
Tyler, Patrick E. 1996. "Chinese Maltreatment at Orphanage." *New York Times* (January 9):A4.
U.S. Bureau of the Census. 2011. "International/Data Base." www.census.gov/ipc/www/idb/.
U.S. Central Intelligence Agency. 2004. "The People's Republic of China" in *The World Factbook*. www.umsl.edu/services/govdocs/wofact2004/index.html.
U.S. Central Intelligence Agency. 2011. *World Factbook*. www.cia.gov/library/publications/the-world-factbook/.
U.S. Department of Justice, Bureau of Justice Statistics. 2004. "Prison and Jail Inmates at Midyear, 2003." February 6. www.ojp.usdoj.gov/bjs/glance/tables/drtab.htm.
———. 2010. National Crime Victimization, 2009 Bureau of Justice Statistics (October). http://bjs.ojp.usdoj.gov/content/pub/pdf/cv09.pdf.
Wang Shuo. 1997. Quoted in "Bad Boy," by Jamie James. *New Yorker* (April 21):50.
Wanli, Yang. 2010 (June 17). "Brushing Up on Dental Hygiene." www.chinadaily.com.cn/cndy/2010-06/17/content_9981461.htm.
Williams, Terry. 1989. *The Cocaine Kids: The Inside Story of a Teenage Drug Ring*. Reading, MA: Addison-Wesley.
Yardley, Jim. 2005. "Fearing Future, China Starts to Give Girls Their Due." *New York Times* (January 31):A3.
Yi, Che, Akiko Hayashi, and Joseph Tobin. 2007. "Lessons from China and Japan for Preschool Practice in the United States." *Journal of College Education* 40(1):7–12

Chapter 8

Allen, Walter, and Angie Y. Chung. 2000. "Your Blues Ain't Like My Blues: Race, Ethnicity and Social Inequality in America." *Contemporary Sociology* 29(6): 796–805.
Arnold, Wayne. 2010. "As China Rises So Does Vietnam." *New York Times* (December 21). www.nytimes.com/2010/12/22/business/global/22chinavietnam.html?_r=2.
Baker, Peter. 2009. "Obama Presses for Action on Credit Cards." *New York Times* (May 14). www.nytimes.com/2009/05/15/us/politics/15obamacnd.html?ref=business.
Barboza, David. 2010. "As China's Wages Rise, Export Prices Could Follow." *New York Times* (May 7). www.nytimes.com/2010/06/08/business/global/08wages.html.
Bologna, Sergio. 2008. "Marx as Correspondent of the New York Daily Tribune, 1856–57." *Money and Crisis*. http://wildcat-www.de/en/material/cs13bolo.htm.
Bradsher, Keith. 2006. "Ending Tariffs Is Only the Start." *New York Times* (February 28): C1.
Centers for Disease Control. 2010. "Recent Trends in Infant Mortality in the United States." www.cdc.gov/nchs/data/databriefs/db09.htm.
Chaliand, Gerard, and Jean-Pierre Rageau. 1995. *The Penguin Atlas of Diasporas*. New York: Penguin Group.
Chan, Sewell. 2010. "World Trade Organization Upholds American Tariffs on Tires From China." *New York Times* (December 13). www.nytimes.com/2010/12/14/business/global/14trade.html.
Charney, William (ed.). 2010. *Handbook of Modern Hospital Safety*, 2nd ed. Boca Raton, Fl: Taylor and Francis.
Chen, David W. 2004. "What's a Life Worth?" *New York Times* (June 20): 42K.
Congressional Budget Office. 2010. Budget and Economic Information. www.cbo.gov/budget/budget.cfm.
Cook-Lynn, Elizabeth. 2008. "Deadliest Enemies: Law and the Making of Race Relations On and Off Rosebud Reservation, and: Not Without Our Consent: Lakota Resistance to Termination, 1950–59." *Wicazo Sa Review* 23(1): 155–158. http://muse.jhu.edu/login?uri=/journals/wicazo_sa_review/v023/23.1cook-lynn.html.
Conrad, Robert Edgar. 1996. "Slave Trade." Pages 127–128 in *Encyclopedia of Latin American History and Culture*, edited by B. A. Tenenbaum. New York: Scribner's.
Costello, 2011. "The Drought Is Over (at Least for C.E.O.'s)." *New York Times* (April 9). www.nytimes.com/2011/04/10/business/10comp.html.
Davis, Kingsley, and Wilbert E. Moore. 1945. "Some Principles of Stratification." Pages 413–445 in *Ideological Theory: A Book of Readings*, ed. by L. A. Coser and B. Rosenberg. New York: Macmillan.
Zhu Xiao. 2005a. "African Food for Africa's Starving Is Roadblocked in Congress." *New York Times* (October 12).
———. 2005b. "Study Finds Small Developing Lands Hit Hardest by 'Brain Drain.'" *New York Times* (October 23): A10.
———. 2006. "Toilets Underused to Fight Disease, UN Study Finds." *New York Times* (November 10): A8.
Di, Zhu Xiao. 2007. "Growing Wealth, Inequality, and Housing in the United States." Joint Center for Housing Studies Harvard University. www.jchs.harvard.edu/publications/markets/w07-1.pdf.
Ehrenreich, Barbara. 2001. *Nickel and Dimed*. New York: Metropolitan.
Environmental Working Group. 2011. "Farm Subsidy Data Base." http://farm.ewg.org/top_recips.php?fips=00000&progcode=total®ionname=theUnitedStates.
Frontline. 2009. "Drowning in Electronics." www.pbs.org/frontlineworld/stories/ghana804/resources/ewaste.html.
Gans, Herbert. 1972. "The Positive Functions of Poverty." *American Journal of Sociology* 78: 275–289.
Garamone, Jim. 2008. *Africa Command Makes Progress with African Allies*. American Forces Press Service. March 31. www.defenselink.mil/news/newsarticle.aspx?id=49418.
Garber, Kent. 2008. "Global Hunger." *U.S. News and World Report* (May 30). www.usnews.com/news/articles/2008/05/30/global-hunger-blame-to-go-around.
Gates, William H., Sr., and Chuck Collins. 2003. *Wealth and Commonwealth: Why America Should Tax Accumulated Fortunes*. Boston: Beacon.
Gertner, Jon. 2008. "Positive Deviance." In 8th Annual Year in Ideas. *New York Times Magazine* (14 December).
Goldstein, Fred. 2009. "GM Restructuring Will Deepen Capitalist Crisis." *Workers World* (May 3). www.workers.org/2009/us/gm_restructuring_0507.
Hertz, Tom. 2006. *Understanding Mobility in the United States*, for Center for American Progress. www.americanprogress.org/issues/2006/04/Hertz_MobilityAnalysis.pdf/.

Holloway, Thomas H. 1996. "Immigration." Pages 239–242 in *Encyclopedia of Latin American History and Culture*, edited by B. A. Tenenbaum. New York: Scribner's.

Hooped Up. 2010. "NBA Salaries 2010–2011." http://hoopeduponline.com/nba-salaries.

Jiang Jingjing. 2004. "Wal-Mart's China Inventory to Hit $18b This Year." *China Business Weekly* (November 29). www.chinadaily.com.cn/english/doc/2004-11/29/content_395728.htm.

Jones, Rachel. 2006. "For First Time, More Poor Live in Suburbs Than Cities." *National Public Radio* (December 6). www.npr.org/templates/story/story.php?storyId=6598999.

Kher, Unmesh. 2002. "Sweet Subsidy." *Time* (February 15). www.time.com.

Kirka, Danica. 2004. "Car Bomb, Mortar Fire Kills 5 U.S. Soldiers." *Lexington Herald Leader* (July 9): A3.

Marger, Martin. 1991. *Race and Ethnic Relations: American and Global Perspectives*. Belmont, CA: Wadsworth.

Marx, Karl. 1856. "Speech at Anniversary of the People's Paper." www.marxists.org/archive/marx/works/1856/04/14.htm.

Mayer, Robert. 2009. "Working Paper—One Payday, Many Payday Loans: Short-Term Lending Abuse in Milwaukee County." http://lwvmilwaukee.org/mayer21.pdf.

Mihesuah, Devan A. 2008. *Big Bend Luck*. Booklocker.com.

Morrow, David J. 1996. "Trials of Human Guinea Pigs." *New York Times* (May 8): C1.

Murphy, Dean E. 2004. "Imagining Life without Illegal Immigrants." *New York Times* (January 11): 16WK.

Myers, Alex. 2010. "Tiger Turns 35, Still Tops the Golf Digest 50." *Golf Digest* (December 10). www.golfdigest.com/golf-tours-news/blogs/local-knowledge/2010/12#ixzz1LR9ekw5F.

Naofusa, Hirai. 1999. "Traditional Cultures and Modernization: Several Problems in the Case of Japan." www2.kokugakuin.ac.jp/ijcc/wp/cimac/hirai.html.

Nation Master. 2011. "World Statistics, Country Comparisons." www.nationmaster.com/index.php.

Norton, Michael, and Dan Ariely. 2011. "Building a Better America—One Wealth Quintile at a Time." *Perspectives on Psychological Science* 6:9–12. www.people.hbs.edu/mnorton/norton%20ariely%20in%20press.pdf.

Obadina, Tunde. 2000. "The Myth of Neo-Colonialism." *African Economic Analysis*. www.afbis.com.

Obama, Barack. 2009. "The President on Credit Card Tactics: 'Enough is Enough.'" The White House. www.whitehouse.gov/blog/The-President-on-Credit-Card-Tactics-Enough-is-Enough.

Office of Management and Budget. 2005. *Budget of the United States Government, FY 2006*. www.whitehouse.gov/omb/budget/fy2006/tables.html.

_______. 2011. "The Budget." www.whitehouse.gov/omb/budget/Overview

O'Hare, William P., and Kenneth P. Johnson. 2004. "Facing Child Poverty in Rural America." Population Reference Bureau (January). www.prb.org.

Pascale, Richard, Jerry Sternin, and Monique Sternin. 2010. *The Power of Positive Deviance: How Unlikely Innovators Solve the World's Toughest Problems*. Boston, MA: Harvard Business School Publishing.

Perlez, Jane. 2004. "Asian Maids Often Find Abuse, Not Riches, Abroad." *New York Times* (June 22): A3.

Pew Hispanic Center. 2009. *A Portrait of Unauthorized Immigrants in the United States* (April 14). http://pewhispanic.org/files/reports/107.pdf.

Pew Research Center. 2008 (April 9). "Inside the Middle Class." http://pewresearch.org/pubs/793/inside-the-middle-class.

Positive Deviance Initiative. 2011. www.positivedeviance.org.

Proudhon, Pierre-Joseph. 1847. "The Philosophy of Misery." www.marxists.org/reference/subject/economics/proudhon/philosophy/intro.htm.

Reuters. 2009. "Wal-Mart paid ex-CEO Scott $30.2 million in FY09" (April 20). www.reuters.com/article/GCA-CreditCrisis/idUSTRE53J6OE20090420.

Reuters. 2010 (April 19). "Wal-Mart CEO Pay Down a Year After Stock Award." www.reuters.com/article/2010/04/19/us-walmart-idUSTRE63I52E20100419.

Rostow, W. W. 1960. *The Stages of Economic Growth: A Non-Communist Manifesto*. Cambridge: Cambridge University Press. www.mtholyoke.edu/acad/intrel/ipe/rostow.htm.

Sachs, Jeffrey. 2005. "Can We End Global Poverty?" Interview by John Cassidy. *Federal News Service*. www.truthabouttrade.org.

September 11 Victim Compensation Fund. 2001. "Calculating the Losses." *New York Times* (December 21): B6.

Simpson, Richard L. 1956. "A Modification of the Functional Theory of Social Stratification." *Social Forces* 35: 132–137.

Sonenshen, Scott, and Gretchen M. Spreitzer. 2004. "Toward the Construct Definition of Positive Deviance." *American Behavioral Scientist* 47: 828–843. Retrieved September 27, 2010, from http://abs.sagepub.com/content/47/6/828.

Sternin, Jerry. 2010. "The Vietnam Story: Narrated by Jerry Sternin." Positive Deviance.org. Retrieved September 23, 2010, from www.positivedeviance.org.

Sugrue, Thomas. 2007. "Stamping Out Detroit Postmark Irks 'Michigan Metro' Residents." *Bloomberg News*, October 30, 2007.

Telegraph. 2011. "Lady Gaga Debuts on Forbes' Celebrity Power List" (January 28). www.telegraph.co.uk/.

Thurow, Roger, and Geoff Winestock. 2005. "Bittersweet: How an Addiction to Sugar Subsidies Hurts Development." aWorldConnected.org. www.aworldconnected.org/article.php/242.html.

Tumin, Melvin M. 1953. "Some Principles of Stratification: A Critical Analysis." *American Sociological Review* 18: 387–394.

UNICEF. 2009a. *The State of the World's Children*. www.unicef.org/sowc09/report/report.php.

_______. 2009b. *The Millennium Development Goals Report 2008*. http://mdgs.un.org/unsd/mdg/Resources/Static/Products/Progress2008/MDG_Report_2008_En.pdf.

United Nations. 2010. "We Can End Poverty, 2015." www.un.org/millenniumgoals.

United Nations General Assembly. 2000. *United Nations Millennium Declaration* (September 8).

United Nations University. 2006. "Pioneering Study Shows Richest Two Percent Own Half World Wealth." www.wider.unu.edu/events/past-events/2006-events/en_GB/05-12-2006/.

U.S. African Command. 2008. www.africom.mil.

U.S. Bureau of the Census. 2009. *American Community Survey*. www.census.gov/acs/www.

U.S. Bureau of Labor Statistics. 2009. "Table 31. Median Weekly Earnings of Full-Time Wage and Salary Workers by Detailed Occupation and Sex." www.bls.gov/cps/cpsaat39.pdf.

_______. 2010. "Median Weekly Earnings of Full-Time Wage and Salary Workers by Detailed Occupation and Sex." www.bls.gov/cps/cpsaat39.pdf.

_______. 2011a. "National Occupational Employment and Wage Estimates United States." www.bls.gov/oes/current/oes_nat.htm.

_______. 2011b. "Secondary School Teachers." www.bls.gov/oes/current/oes252031.htm.

U.S. Central Intelligence Agency. 2009. *World Factbook*. https://www.cia.gov/library/publications/the-world-factbook/.

_______. *World Factbook*. www.cia.gov/library/publications/the-world-factbook.

U.S. Department of Health and Human Resources. 2011. "Nursing Aides, Home Health Aides, and Related Health Care Occupations." http://bhpr.hrsa.gov/healthworkforce/reports/nursing/nurseaides/default.htm.

U.S. Department of State. 2011. Budget: Department of State and Other International Programs. www.gpoaccess.gov/usbudget/fy11/pdf/budget/state.pdf.

U.S. Office of Management and Budget. 2011. www.whitehouse.gov/omb.

Wacquant, Loic J. D. 1989. "The Ghetto, the State, and the New Capitalist Economy." *Dissent* (Fall): 508–520.

Weber, Max. (1947) 1985. "Social Stratification and Class Structure." Pages 573–576 in *Theories of Society: Foundations of Modern Sociological Theory*, ed. T. Parsons, E. Shils, K. D. Naegele, and J. R. Pitts. New York: Free Press.

_______. 1948. "Class, Status, and Party," Pp. 185–195 in H. Gerth and C. W. Mills, *Essays from Max Weber*. New York: Routledge and Kegan Paul.

_______. 1982. "Status Groups and Classes." Pages 69–73 in *Classical and Contemporary Debates*, ed. A. Giddens and D. Held. Los Angeles: University of California.

Wilson, William Julius. 1983. "The Urban Underclass: Inner-City Dislocations." *Society* 21: 80–86.

_______. 1987. *The Truly Disadvantaged*. Chicago: University of Chicago Press.

_______. 1991. "Studying Inner-City Social Dislocations: The Challenge of Public Agenda Research" (1990 presidential address). *American Sociological Review* (February): 1–14.

_______. 1994. "Another Look at the Truly Disadvantaged." *Political Science Quarterly* 106 (4): 639–656.

World Bank. 2009. "Understanding Poverty." http://web.worldbank.org.

_______. 2011. *World Development Indictors*. http://data.worldbank.org/.

Wright, Erik Olin. 2004. "Social Class." In *Encyclopedia of Sociological Theory*, ed. by G. Ritzer. Thousand Oaks, CA: Sage.

Yeutter, Clayton. 1992. "When Fairness Isn't Fair." *New York Times* (March 24): A13.

Chapter 9

About.com. 2004. "Immigration Before and After: Putting It in Perspective." immigration.about.com.

Alba, Richard D. 1992. "Ethnicity." Pages 575–584 in *Encyclopedia of Sociology*, vol. 2, ed. by E. F. Borgatta and M. L. Borgatta. New York: Macmillan.

Amnesty International. 2008. "Brazil Upholds Indigenous Rights in Key Case." (December 15). http://us.oneworld.net/article/359082-brazil-upholds-indigenous-rights-key-case.

Arab Institute. 2003. "First Census Report on Arab Ancestry Marks Rising Civic Profile of Arab Americans." www.aaiusa.org.

Bailey, Stanley. 2008. "Unmixing for Race Making in Brazil." *American Journal of Sociology* 114(3):577–614.

_____. 2009. *Legacies of Race: Identities, Attitudes and Politics in Brazil*. Stanford, CA: Stanford University Press.

Burdick, John. 1992. "Brazil's Black Consciousness Movement." *Report on the Americas* 25(4):23–27.

Cho, Margaret. 2002. Interview with Michele Norris, "Comedy and Race in America: Three Comedians Who Get Serious Laughs from Thorny Issues." *All Things Considered*, December 9–11. www.npr.org/programs/atc/features/2002/dec/comedians.

Cornell, Stephen. 1990. "Land, Labour and Group Formation: Blacks and Indians in the United States." *Ethnic and Racial Studies* 13(3):368–388.

Cornell, Stephen, and Douglas Hartmann. 2007. *Ethnicity and Race: Making Identities in a Changing World*, 2nd ed. Thousands Oaks, CT: Pine Forge.

Crapanzano, Vincent. 1985. *Waiting: The Whites of South Africa*. New York: Random House.

Dacey, Jessica. 2010. "Obama's Roots Traced to Swiss Villager." SwissInfo.ch (July 3). www.swissinfo.ch/eng/swiss_news/Obama_s_roots_traced_to_Swiss_villager.html?cid=15349746.

Davi, Frei. 1992. Quoted in "Brazil's Black Consciousness Movement" by John Burdick. *Report on the Americas* 25(4):23–27.

Davis, F. James. 1978. *Minority-Dominant Relations: A Sociological Analysis*. Arlington Heights, IL: AHM.

Doane, Ashley. 1997. "Dominant Group Ethnic Identity in the United States: The Role of 'Hidden' Ethnicity in Intergroup Relations." *The Sociological Quarterly* 38(3):375–397.

Gasnier, Anne. 2010. "Brazil Passes Racial Equality Law but Fails to Endorse Affirmative Action." *Guardian Weekly* (June 29). www.guardian.co.uk/world/2010/jun/29/brazil-race.

Goffman, Erving. 1963. *Stigma: Notes on the Management of Spoiled Identity*. Upper Saddle River, NJ: Prentice Hall.

Gordon, Milton M. 1978. *Human Nature, Class, and Ethnicity*. New York: Oxford University Press.

Gore, Rick. 2000. "What it Takes to Build the Unbeatable Body." *National Geographic* 198(3):2–32.

Gradín, Carlos. 2007. "Why Is Poverty So High among Afro-Brazilians? A Decomposition Analysis of the Racial Poverty Gap." Institute for the Study of Labor: Forschungsinstitut zur Zukunft der Arbeit (May 2007). http://papers.ssrn.com/sol3/papers.cfm?abstract_id=995479.

Graham, Lawrence Otis. 2001. "Black Men with a Nose Job." Pages 33–38 in *The Social Construction of Race and Ethnicity in the United States*, ed. by J. Ferrante and P. Brown. Upper Saddle River, NJ: Prentice-Hall.

Haney Lopez, Ian F. 1994. "The Social Construction of Race: Some Observations on Illusion, Fabrication, and Choice." *Harvard Civil Rights—Civil Liberties Law Review* 29:39–53.

Hertz, Todd. 2003. "Are Most Arab Americans Christian?" *Christianity Today* (March 25). www.christianitytoday.com.

Htun, Mala. 2005. Racial Quotas for a "Racial Democracy." *Report on the Americas* (February):20–25.

Hudson, Rex A. 1997. *Country Studies: Brazil*. Washington: Library of Congress.

Ikawa, Daniel, and Laura Mattar. 2009. "Racial Discrimination in Access to Health: The Brazilian Experience." *Kansas Law Review* 57:949–970. www.law.ku.edu/publications/lawreview/pdf/9.0-Ikawa_Final.pdf.

Instituto Brasileiro de Geografia e Estatística (IBGE). 2009. Population. www.ibge.gov.br/english.

_____. 2010. www.ibge.gov.br/english/#sub_populacao.

Jeter, Jon. 2003. "Affirmative Action Debate Forces Brazil to Take Look in the Mirror." *Washington Post* (June 16):A01.

Kimbrough v. United States. 2007. Certiorari to the United States Court of Appeals for the Fourth Circuit, Supreme Court of the United States NO. 06-6330. Argued October 2, 2007; Decided December 10, 2007.

Kochhar, Rakesh. 2006. *Latino Labor Report 2006*. http://pewhispanic.org/reports/report.php?ReportID=70.

Madison, Richard. 2002. "Changes in Immigration Law and Procedures." www.lawcom.com/chngs.shtml.

Marger, Martin. 2012. *Race and Ethnic Relations: American and Global Perspectives*. Belmont: Wadsworth.

Matijasevich A., et al. 2008. "Widening Ethnic Disparities in Infant Mortality in Southern Brazil: Comparison of 3 Birth Cohorts." *American Journal of Public Health*. 98(4):692–68.

McIntosh, Peggy. 1992. "White Privilege and Male Privilege: A Personal Account of Coming to See Correspondences through Work in Women's Studies." Pages 70–81 in *Race, Class, and Gender: An Anthology*, ed. by M. L. Andersen and P. H. Collins. Belmont, CA: Wadsworth.

Merton, Robert K. 1957. *Social Theory and Social Structure*. New York: Free Press.

______. 1976. "Discrimination and the American Creed." Pages 189–216 in *Sociological Ambivalence and Other Essays*. New York: Free Press.

Migration Policy Institute. 2011. "Shaping Brazil: The Role of International Migration," by Ernesto Friedrich Amaral and Wilson Fusco. www.migrationinformation.org/Profiles/display.cfm?id=311.

National Center for Education Statistics. 2008. "Table 234: Number of Degree-Granting Institutions and Enrollment in these Institutions." Digest of Education Statistics. http://nces.ed.gov/programs/digest/d08/tables/dt08_234.asp.

National Center for Education Statistics. 2009. Digest of Educational Statistics. nces.ed.gov/programs/digest.

______. 2010. Public School Graduates and Dropouts From the Common Core of Data: School Year 2007–08 (June). http://nces.ed.gov/pubs2010/2010341.pdf.

National Center for Public Policy and Higher Education. 2008 (August 2008). "Policy Alert: Is College Opportunity Slipping Away?" www.highereducation.org/reports/reports_center_2008/shtml.

National Park Service. 2009. "We Shall Overcome: Historic Places of the Civil Rights Movement." www.nps.gov/nr/travel/civil rights/.

Norris, Michelle. 2002. "Comedy and Race in America: Three Comedians Who Get Serious Laughs from Thorny Issues." *All Things Considered*, December 9–11. wwwnpr.org/programs/atc/features/2002/dec/comedians.

Obama, Barack. 2004. *Dreams from My Father*. New York: Crown

Ogbu, John U. 1990. "Minority Status and Literacy in Comparative Perspective." *Daedalus* 119(2):141–168.

Office of Management and Budget. 2011. "Revisions for the Classification of Federal Data on Race and Ethnicity." U.S. Bureau of the Census. www.census.gov/population/www/socdemo/race/Ombdir15.html.

Omi, Michael, and Howard Winant. 1986. *Racial Formation in the United States: From the 1960s to the 1980s*. New York: Routledge & Kegan Paul.

Osava, Maria. 2010. "'Colonisation Made Us Poor,' Say Indigenous Peoples." InterPress Service (January 14). http://ipsnews.net/news.asp?idnews=49999.

Page, Clarence. 1996. *Showing My Colors: Impolite Essays on Race and Identity*. New York: Harper Collins.

Parent, Anthony S., Jr., and Susan Brown Wallace. 2002. Pp. 451–458 in *The Social Construction of Race and Ethnicity in the United States*, ed. by J. Ferrante and P. Brown Jr. Upper Saddle River, NJ: Prentice-Hall.

Rawley, James A. 1981. *The Transatlantic Slave Trade: A History*. New York: Norton.

Saboia, Ana Lucia, and João Saboia. 2007. "White, Black and Browns in Labour Market in Brazil: A Study About Inequalities." (November). www.cigss.umontreal.ca/Docs/SSDE/pdf/Saboia.pdf.

Schermerhorn, R. A. 1978. *Comparative Ethnic Relations: A Framework for Theory and Research*. Chicago: University of Chicago Press.

Smith, Amy Erica. 2011. "Affirmative Action in Brazil." *Americas Quarterly* (January 13). www.americasquarterly.org/node/1939.

Steele, Claude. 1995. "Black Students Live Down to Expectations." *New York Times* (August 31):A25.

Telles, Edward E. 2004. *Race in Another America: The Significance of Skin Color in Brazil*. Princeton, NJ: Princeton University Press.

Toro, Luis Angel. 1995. "'A People Distinct from Others: Race and Identity in Federal Indian Law and the Hispanic Classification in OMB Directive No. 15." *Texas Tech Law Review* 26:1219–1274.

U.S. Bureau of the Census. 1910. "Color or Race, Nativity, and Parentage." www2.census.gov/prod2/decennial/documents/36894832v1ch03.pdf.

______. 2003. *The Arab Population: 2000*. www.census.gov/prod/2003pubs/c2kbr-23.pdf.

______. 2009. American Community Survey. http://www.census.gov/acs/www/

______. 2010. *Income, Poverty, and Health Insurance Coverage in the United States: 2009* (September 2010). www.census.gov/prod/2010pubs/p60-238.pdf.

U.S. Bureau of Labor Statistics. 2010. "Labor Force Characteristics of Foreign-Born Workers." (March 19). www.bls.gov/news.release/forbrn.nr0.htm.

______. 2011. Statistical Abstract of the United States. www.census.gov/compendia/statab/cats/population.html.

U.S. Department of State. 2010. *Brazil—International Religious Freedom Report*. Bureau of Democracy, Human Rights, and Labor. www.state.gov/g/drl/rls/irf/2010/148738.htm.

Verkuyten, Maykel. 2005. "Ethnic Group Identification and Group Evaluation Among Minority and Majority Groups." *Journal of Personality and Social Psychology* 88(1): 121–138.

Waters, Mary C. 1994. "Ethnic and Racial Identities of Second Generation Black Immigrants in New York City." *International Migration Review* 28(4):795–820.

Weber, Max. 1922. Economy and Society, vol. 2, ed. Guenther Roth and Claus Wittich, trans. Ephraim Fischof, 1978. Berkeley: University of California Press.

Wirth, Louis. 1945. "The Problem of Minority Groups." Pages 347–372 in *The Science of Man*, ed. by R. Linton. New York: Columbia University Press.

Wooddell, George, and Jacques Henry. 2005. "The Advantage of a Focus on Advantage: A Note on Teaching Minority Groups." *Teaching Sociology* 33(3): 301–309.

Woods, Tiger. 2006. Quoted in excerpts from *Who's Afraid of a Large Black Man?* by C. Barkley. www.wnyc.org/books/45779.

World Lingo 2011. www.worldlingo.com/en/company/case_studies.html.

Chapter 10

American Psychiatric Association. 2009. "What is Sexual Orientation?" www.apa.org/topics/sorientation.html.

Ault, Amber, and Stephanie Brzuzy. 2009. "Removing Gender Identity Disorder from the Diagnostic and Statistical Manual of Mental Disorders: A Call for Action." *Social Work* (April). http://findarticles.com/p/articles/mi_hb6467/is_2_54/ai_n31528170/.

Barton, Gina. 2005. "Prisoner Sues for the Right to Sex Change." *Milwaukee Journal Sentinel Online* (January 22). www3.jsonline.com/story/index.aspx?id=295581.

Baumgartner-Papageorgiou, Alice. 1982. *My Daddy Might Have Loved Me: Student Perceptions of Differences between Being Male and Being Female*. Denver: Institute for Equality in Education.

Bearak, Barry. 2009. "Inquiry about Sprinter's Sex Angers South Africans." *New York Times* (August 26): A6.

Bem, Sandra Lipsitz. 1993. *The Lenses of Gender: Transforming the Debate on Sexual Inequality*. Binghamton, NY: Vail-Ballou.

Boxer, Barbara (U.S. Senator). 2007. "Historical Timeline for Women's History." http://boxer.senate.gov/whm/time_1.cfm.

Bumiller, Elizabeth. 2010 (March 3). "Repeal of 'Don't Ask, Don't Tell' Policy Filed in Senate." www.nytimes.com/2010/03/04/us/politics/04military.html.

Busch, Bill. 2003. Quoted in B. Syken's "Football in Paradise." *Sports Illustrated* (November 3).

Cahill, Betsy, and Eve Adams. 1997. "An Exploratory Study of Early Childhood Teachers' Attitudes toward Gender Roles." *Sex Roles: A Journal of Research* 36(7–8): 517–530.

CBS 60 Minutes. 2010 (January 17). "American Samoa: Football Island." www.cbsnews.com/stories/2010/01/14/60minutes/main6097706.shtml.

CBS News. 2010. "Extra: Troy Polamalu." *60 Minutes* (January 17). www.cbsnews.com/video/watch/?id=6107259n.

_____. 2011. "Samoa to Jump Forward 1 Day in Time." www.cbsnews.com/stories/2011/05/09/501364/main20060967.shtml.

CBS News Polls. 2005. "Women's Movement Worthwhile." www.cbsnews.com/stories/2005/10/22/opinion/polls/main965224.shtml.

Cedar Lounge Revolution. 2010. "Transgender Europe's Trans Murder Monitoring Project Reveals almost 180 Killings of Trans People in the Last 12 months." Cedar Lounge Revolution. Retrieved November 20, 2010.

Centers for Disease Control. 2002. "HHS Issues Report Showing Dramatic Improvements in America's Health Over Past 50 Years." www.cdc.gov/nchs/pressroom/02news/hus02.htm.

_____. 2010. United States Life Tables, 2006. National Vital Statistics Reports (June 28). www.loc.gov/pictures/item/2005691067.

Channell, Carrie. 2002. "The Tatau: A Bridge to Manhood." *Faces: People, Places and Culture* (May):18–22.

Chronicle of Higher Education. 2010. Almanac of Higher Education, 2010. http://chronicle.com/section/Almanac-of-Higher-Education/463/.

Coffey, Megan. 2010. "Transgender Day of Remembrance Observed Saturday in Santa Rosa." *Sonoma County Civil Rights Examiner.* Retrieved November 20, 2010, from www.examiner.com/sonoma-county-civil-rights-in-san-francisco/transgender-day-of-remembrance-observed-saturday-santa-rosa.

Collins, Patricia Hill. 2000. *Black Feminist Thought.* Boston: Unwin Hyman.

Cote, James. 1997. "A Social History of Youth in Samoa: Religion, Capitalism, and Cultural Disenfranchisement." *International Journal of Comparative Sociology* 38(3–4):217.

Crenshaw, Kimberlé W. 1991. Mapping the Margins: Intersectionality, Identity Politics, and Violence against Women of Color. *Stanford Law Review 43*(6):1241–1299.

Daily Mail. 2009 (September 7). "The Big Squeeze: Why Four in Ten Women Buy Shoes Even When They Don't Fit." www.dailymail.co.uk/femail/article-1211617/The-big-squeeze-How-womens-feet-suffer-sake-fashion.html#ixzz1CibQe6Ew.

Daly, Mary. 2006. *Amazon Grace: Re-Calling the Courage to Sin Big.* New York and Hampshire, England: Palgrave Macmillan.

Davis, Nancy J. 2005. "Taking Sex Seriously: Challenges in Teaching about Sexuality." *Teaching Sociology* 33(1):16–31.

Doss, Cheryl. 2011. "If Women Hold Up Half the Sky, How Much of the World's Food Do They Produce?" Food and Agriculture Organization of the United Nations. www.fao.org/docrep/013/am309e/am309e00.pdf.

Dreger, Alice. 2009. "The Sex of Athletes: One Issue, Many Variables." *New York Times,* October 24, 2009. www.nytimes.com/2009/10/25/sports/25intersex.html?_r=.

Dreifus, Claudia. 2005. "Declaring with Clarity, When Gender Is Ambiguous." *New York Times* (May 31): D2.

Epstein, Cynthia Fuchs. 2007. "The Global Subordination of Women." *American Sociological Review* 72(1):1–22.

Fagot, Beverly, Richard Hagan, Mary Driver Leinbach, and Sandra Kronsberg. 1985. "Differential Reactions to Assertive and Communicative Acts of Toddler Boys and Girls." *Child Development* 56(6):1499–1505.

Ferguson, Ann Arnett. 2001. *Bad Boys: Public Schools in the Making of Black Masculinity.* Ann Arbor: University of Michigan.

Ferguson, David. 2005. "James Tackles Samoa's Talent Drain." *Scotsman* (November 18). thescotsman.scotsman.com.

Fischer, Hannah. 2010. "U.S. Military Casualty Statistics: Operation New Dawn, Operation Iraqi Freedom, and Operation Enduring Freedom." Congressional Research Service (September 28). www.fas.org/sgp/crs/natsec/RS22452.pdf.

Fraser, Laura. 2002. "The Islands Where Boys Grows Up to Be Girls." *Marie Claire* (December):72–79.

Garb, Frances. 1991. "Secondary Sex Characteristics." Pages 326–327 in *Women's Studies Encyclopedia. Vol. 1: Views from the Sciences,* ed. by H. Tierney. New York: Bedrick.

Gauguin, Paul. [1919] 1985. *Noa Noa: The Tahitian Journal,* trans. by O. F. Theis. New York: Dover.

Greenhouse, Steven. 2003. "Wal-Mart Faces Lawsuit over Sex Discrimination." *New York Times* (February 16):Y18.

_____. 2004. "In-House Audit Says Wal-Mart Violated Labor Laws." *New York Times* (January 13). www.nyt.com.

Hasbro Toys. 2011. www.hasbro.com.

Law, Katie. 2007. "The Indelicate Art of Gender Testing." *Inkling Magazine* (January 17). www.inklingmagazine.com/articles/gender-testing/.

Lee, Peter A., et al. 2006. "Consensus Statement on Management of Intersex Disorders." *Pediatrics* 118(2): 488–500.

Lehrman, Sally. 1997. "WO: Forget Men Are from Mars, Women Are from Venus. Gender." *Stanford Today* (May/June):47.

Lorber, Judith. 2005. "Night to His Day: The Social Construction of Gender." Pp. 292–305 in *The Spirit of Sociology: A Reader* by R. Matson. New York: Penguin.

Love, David A. 2007. "Walgreens Suit Shows Employment Discrimination Still a Problem." *Progressive Media Project* (March 13). www.progressive.org.

Madrick, Jeff. 2004. "Economic June: The Earning Power of Women Has Really Increased, Right? Take a Closer Look." *New York Times* (June 16):C2.

Mageo, Jeannette. 1992. "Male Transvestism and Cultural Change in Samoa." *American Ethnologist* 19(3):443.

_____. 1996. "Hairdos and Don'ts: Hair Symbolism and Sexual History in Samoa." *Frontiers* 17(2):138.

_____. 1998. *Theorizing Self in Samoa: Emotions, Genders, and Sexualities.* Ann Arbor: University of Michigan Press.

Malauulu, George. 2003. Quoted in B. Syken's "Football in Paradise." *Sports Illustrated* (November 3).

Matà afa, Tina. 2006. "School Teacher Wins Miss Island Queen." *Samoa News* (May 10). www.samoanews.com.

Mattel. 2011. www.mattel.com.

Mead, Margaret. 1928. *Coming of Age in Samoa: A Psychological Study of Primitive Youth for Western Civilisation.* New York: William Morrow.

Mears, Bill. 2011. "Most Justices Appear Skeptical of Making Wal-Mart Suit Class Action." CNN.com (March 29). http://articles.cnn.com/2011-03-29/us/scotus.wal.mart_1_female-wal-mart-employees-wal-mart-stores-discrimination?_s=PM:US.

Mills, Janet Lee. 1985. "Body Language Speaks Louder Than Words." *Horizons* (February):8–12.

Moore, Keith. 2010. "Caster Semenya Wins First Race Since Gender Test Comeback." *Huffington Post* (July 15). www.huffingtonpost.com/2010/07/15/caster-semenya-wins-first_n_647989.html.

Morawski, Jill G. 1991. "Femininity." Pages 136–139 in *Women's Studies Encyclopedia.* Vol. 1: *Views from the Sciences,* ed. by H. Tierney. New York: Bedrick.

O'Connor, Marian. 2007. "Corporate Suit Could Change Workplace Politics." City on a Hill Press (February 14). www.cityonahillpress.com.

Online Newshour. 2007. "Pace Remarks Renew 'Don't Ask, Don't Tell' Debate" (March 16). www.pbs.org/newshour/bb/military.

Palm Center. 2010. "Fact Check: What Countries Allow Gays to Openly Serve in the Military?" Los Angeles Independent (February 2) www.laindependent.com/news/83376742.html

Paul, Annie Murphy. 2011. "Is Pink Necessary?" *The New York Times Sunday Book Review* (January 11). www.nytimes.com/2011/01/23/books/review/Paul-t.html.

Raag, Tarja, and Christine Rackliff. 1998. "Preschoolers' Awareness of Social Expectations of Gender: Relationships to Toy Choices." *Sex Roles: A Journal of Research* 38(9–10):685.

Robinson, Allyson. 2010. "Transgender Day of Remembrance." Human Rights Campaign. Retrieved November 20, 2010, www.hrc.org/issues/transgender_day_of_remembrance.asp.
Rose, Stephen J., and Heidi Hartman. 2004. Cited in "Economic Scene: The Earning Power of Women Has Really Increased, Right? Take a Closer Look," by J. Madrick. *New York Times*: C2.
Sahadi, Jeanne. 2006. "Where Women's Pay Trumps Men's." CNNmoney.com. money.cnn.com/2006/02/28/commentary/everyday/sahadi/index.htm.
Saslow, Eli. 2007. "In American Samoa, High School Football Is Seen as the Ultimate Escape." blog.washingtonpost.com/why-we-compete/2007/08/opportunity.html.
Schmalz, Jeffrey. 1993. "From Midshipman to Gay-Rights Advocate." *New York Times* (February 4):B1+.
Shalikashvili, John M. 2007. "Second Thought on Gays in the Military." *New York Times* (January 2). www.nyt.com.
Son, Eugene. 1998. "G.I. Joe—A Real American FAQ." www.yojoe.com/faq/gifaq.shtml.
Sosin, Kate. 2010. "Fallen Stars, Vigil Remembers Transgender Victims." *Windy City Times*. Retrieved November 20, 2010, www.windycitymediagroup.com/gay/lesbian/news/ARTICLE.php?AID=29569.
Starlight, Tami. 2010. "2010 Vancouver Transgender Day of Remembrance." *Vancouver Media Co-op*. Retrieved November 20, 2010, vancouver.mediacoop.ca/story/2010-vancouver-transgender-day-remembrance/5204.
Stolberg, Sheryl Gay. 2010. "Obama Signs Away Don't Ask Don't Tell." *New York Times* (December 22). www.nytimes.com/2010/12/23/us/politics/23military.html.
St. Pierre, Ethan. 2007. "About the Day of Remembrance." Transgender Day of Remembrance. Retrieved November 20, 2010, www.transgenderdor.org.
Syken, Bill. 2003. "Football in Paradise." *Sports Illustrated* (November 3).
Time.com. 2007. "Feminism Poll." www.time.com/time/polls/feminism.html.
Tok Blong Pacifik. 2008. "Fa'afafine: The Pacific's 'Third Gender'." FindArticles.com. Feb 5, 2011. http://findarticles.com/p/articles/mi_hb6591/is_3_6/ai_n32147323/.
Tomey, Dick. 2003. Quoted in B. Syken's "Football in Paradise." *Sports Illustrated* (November 3).
Tuller, David. 2004. "Gentleman, Start Your Engines?" *New York Times* (June 21):E1.
Turner, George. [1861] 1986. *Samoa: Nineteen Years in Polynesia*. Apia: Western Samoa and Cultural Trust.
U.S. Bureau of Labor Statistics. 2008. "Injuries, Illnesses and Fatalities." www.bls.gov/iif/oshcfoi1.htm.
U.S. Bureau of Labor Statistics. 2010. Economic New Release. www.bls.gov/news.release/wkyeng.t05.htm.
U.S. Central Intelligence Agency. 2010. www.cia.gov/library/publications/download/download-2010/index.html.
———. 2011. *World Factbook*. https://www.cia.gov/library/publications/the-world-factbook/fields/2011.html.
U.S. Department of Defense. 1990. "DOD Directive 1332.14." Page 19 in *Gays in Uniform: The Pentagon's Secret Reports*, ed. by K. Dyer. Boston: Alyson.
U.S. Department of Interior. 2010. "American Samoa." www.doi.gov/oia/Islandpages/asgpage.htm.
U.S. Department of Labor, Bureau of Labor Statistics. 2010a. Nontraditional Occupations for Women in 2009. www.dol.gov/wb/factsheets/nontra2009.htm.
———. 2010b. 20 Leading Occupations of Employed Women. www.dol.gov/wb/factsheets/20lead2009.htm.
U.S. House of Representatives. 2004. "Three Samoan NFL Players Make Washington Redskins Squad." Press Release (September 11). www.house.gov/list/press.
U.S. Office of Management and Budget. 2011. "Revisions for the Classification of Federal Data on Race and Ethnicity." U.S. Bureau of Census. www.census.gov/population/www/socdemo/race/Ombdir15.html.
Vann, Elizabeth. 1995. "Implications of Sex and Gender Differences for Self: Perceived Advantages and Disadvantages of Being the Other Gender." *Sex Roles: A Journal of Research* 33(7–8):531.
Zogby International. 2007. "'Don't Ask, Don't Tell' Not Working: Survey Indicates Shift in Military Attitudes" (December 18). www.zogby.com.

Chapter 11

Associated Press. 2011 (January 31). "U.S. Still Leads World in Manufacturing." www2.journalnow.com/news/2011/jan/31/wsnat01-us-still-leads-world-in-manufacturing-prod-ar-739920/.
Bajaj, Vikas. 2011. "Galloping Growth, and Hunger in India" *New York Times* (February 11). www.nytimes.com/2011/02/12/business/global/12food.html?_r=1.
Barrio, Frederico. 1988. "History and Perspectives of the Maquiladora Industry in Mexico." Pp. 7–13 in *Mexico: In-Bond Industry*, edited by T. P. Lee. Tiber, Mexico: ASI.
Bell, Daniel. 1976. "Welcome to the Post-Industrial Society" *Physics Today* (February): 46-48.
Bell, Daniel. 1999. *The Coming of Post-Industrial Society*. New York: Basic Books.
Blumberg, Alex. 2011. "'Kill Them, Bury Them': The Rise Of Fannie And Freddie." NPR (March 28). www.npr.org/blogs/money/2011/04/22/134863603/kill-them-bury-them-the-rise-of-fannie-and-freddie.
Boudon, Raymond, and François Bourricaud. 1989. *A Critical Dictionary of Sociology*, selected and trans. by P. Hamilton. Chicago: University of Chicago Press.
Boulding, Elise. 1976. *The Underside of History*. Boulder, CO: Westview.
Bowen, Huw V. 2000. "400 Years of the East India Company." *History Today* (July). www.findarticles.com.
Buckley, Alan D. 1998. "Comparing Political Systems." www.smc.edu/_homepage/abuckley/ps2/ps2types.htm.
Bullock, Alan. 1977. "Democracy." Pages 211–212 in *The Harper Dictionary of Modern Thought*, ed. by A. Bullock, S. Trombley, and B. Eadie. New York: Harper & Row.
Burke, James. 1978. *Connections*. Boston: Little, Brown.
Center for Responsive Politics. 2009. "527 Committee Activity: Top 50 Organizations." www.opensecrets.org/527s.
———. 2011. Political Action Committees and 527s. www.opensecrets.org/pacs/index/php.
Chehabi, H. E., and Juan J. Linz (eds.). 1998. *Sultanistic Regimes*. Baltimore and London: Johns Hopkins University Press.
Christian Aid. 2005. "Biotechnology and Genetically Modified Organisms." www.christian-aid.org.uk/indepth/000/ibiot/biotech.htm.
Christian Science Monitor. 2010. "World's Top 10 Military Spenders" (June 3). www.csmonitor.com/csm-photo-galleries/lists/world-s-top-10-military-spenders/(photo)/279088.
Congressional Research Service. 2009. *India-U.S. Relations*. www.fas.org/sgp/crs/row/RL33529.pdf.
CNBC. 2011. "The Biggest Holders of U.S. Government Debt." www.cnbc.com/id/29880401/The_Biggest_Holders_of_US_Government_Debt?slide=15.
The Constitution of India. 2011. http://indiacode.nic.in/coiweb/welcome.html.
Cote, James. 1997. "A Social History of Youth in Samoa: Religion, Capitalism, and Cultural Disenfranchisement." *International Journal of Comparative Sociology* 38(3–4):217.
Creighton, Andrew L. 1992. "Democracy." Pages 430–434 in *Encyclopedia of Sociology*, Vol. 1, ed. by E. F. Borgatta and M. L. Borgatta. New York: MacMillan.

Cusi, Veronica Silva. 2011. "Protests Disrupt Tunisia Call Centers." ContactCenterWorld (January 27). http://north-america.contactcenterworld.com/view/contact-center-news/protests-disrupt-tunisia-call-centers.aspx.

Datt, Ruddar, and K.P.M. Sundharam. 2009. *Indian Economy.* New Delhi: S. Chand Group, p. 976.

Demangeon, Albert. 1925. *The British Empire: A Study of Colonial Geography,* trans. By E. F. Row. New York: Harcourt, Brace.

Derdak, Thomas. 1988. *International Directory of Company Histories,* vol. 1. Chicago: St. James.

Der Spiegel. 2003. Quoted in "Europe Seems to Hear Echoes of Empires Past" by Richard Bernstein. *New York Times* (April 14). www.nyt.com.

Diamond, Jarod. 1992. Quoted in "A Brief History of Human Society: The Origin and Role of Emotion in Social Life: 2001 Presidential Address," by D.S. Massey. *American Sociological Review* 67(1): 1–29.

Domino's Pizza India. 2011. About Dominos. www.dominos.co.in/about_dominos.jsp.

Felluga, Dino. 2002. "Hegemony." *Introductory Guide to Critical Theory.* Purdue University. www.cla.purdue.edu/academic/engl/theory/marxism/terms/.

Financial Times. 2011 (January 6). "Stroll to a New Status," 7.

Fortier, Jana. 2009. "The Ethnography of South Asian Foragers." *Annual Review of Anthropology* 38:99–114.

Galbraith, John K. 1958. *The Affluent Society.* Boston: Houghton Mifflin.

Gandhi, M. K. 1909. "Brute Force." *The Collected Works of Mahatma Gandhi,* vol. IX, August 1908–July 1909.

Giridharadas, Anand. 2007. "India Tries Outsourcing its Outsourcing." *New York Times* (September 24). www.nytimes.com/2007/09/24/business/worldbusiness/24iht-outsource.1.7614978.html.

Global Security.org. 2009. "Worldwide Military Expenditures, 2008." www.globalsecurity.org/military/world/spending.htm.

Hacker, Andrew. 1971. "Power to Do What?" Pages 134–146 in *The New Sociology: Essays in Social Science and Social Theory in Honor of C. Wright Mills,* ed. by I. L. Horowitz. New York: Oxford University Press.

Heitzman, James, and Robert L. Worden, eds. 1995. *India: A Country Study.* Washington: GPO for the Library of Congress. http://countrystudies.us/india.

Hira, Ron, and Anil Hira. 2008. *Outsourcing America.* New York: American Management Association.

Homeland Security. 2011. *Yearbook of Immigration Statistics: 2010.* www.dhs.gov/files/statistics/publications/LPR10.shtm.

Htun, Mala. 2004. "Is Gender like Ethnicity? The Political Representation of Identity Groups." *Perspectives on Politics* 2(3):439–458.

India Daily. 2005. "During Tsunami Remote Viewing Primitive Tribes In Andaman Nicobar Islands of India Moved to Higher Grounds—So Did Most Animals." (January 2). www.indiadaily.com/editorial/01-02-05.asp.

Institute for Women's Policy Research. 2010. *The Gender Wage Gap: 2009.* www.iwpr.org/pdf/C350.pdf.

International College of the Armed Forces. 2010 (Spring). Final Report: Strategic Materials Industry. National Defense University. www.ndu.edu/icaf/programs/academic/industry/reports/2010/pdf/icaf-is-report-strategic-inat-2010.pdf.

Judt, Tony. 2004. "Dreams of Empire." *New York Review of Books* (November 4). www.nyrb.com/articles.

Levy, Francesca. 2010. The World's Happiest Countries. Forbes.com (July 14, 2010).

Lockheed Martin Corporation. 2007. "Corporate Overview." Retrieved July 14, 2007, from www.lockheedmartin.com/data/assets/969.pdf.

______. 2009. *Lockheed Martin Annual Report.* www.lockheedmartin.com/aboutus/index.html.

______. 2011. About Us. www.lockheedmartin.com/aboutus/index.html.

Luce, Edward. 2007. *In Spite of the Gods.* New York: Anchor Books.

Massey, Douglas S. 2002. "A Brief History of Human Society." *American Sociological Review* 67(1):1–29.

McNamara, Robert S. 1989. *Out of the Cold: New Thinking for American Foreign and Defense Policy in the 21st Century.* New York: Simon & Schuster.

Mills, C. Wright. 1956. *The Power Elite.* New York: Oxford University Press.

______. 1963. "The Structure of Power in American Society." Pages 23–38 in *Power, Politics and People: The Collected Essays of C. Wright Mills,* ed. by I. L. Horowitz. New York: Oxford University Press.

Nadeem, Shezad. 2011. *Dead Ringers. How Outsourcing is Changing the Way Indians Understand Themselves.* Princeton, NJ: Princeton University Press.

National Statistics Bureau, Royal Government of Bhutan. 2007. Bhutan Living Standard Survey, 2007 Report. www.bt.undp.org/assets/files/publication/BLSS%202007%20REPORT.pdf.

The New York Times. 2008. "Could Consumers Fill the Export Void?" Chart in "The Virtues of Spending" by Keith Bradsher (October 16), p. B11.

Pal, Rupayan. 2008 (June). "Estimating the Probability of Trade Union Membership in India." Indira Gandhi Institute of Development Research, Mumbai. www.igidr.ac.in/pdf/publication/WP-2008-015.pdf.

Planet Money. 2011. "3 Ways of Looking at Manufacturing in America." National Public Radio (February 7). www.npr.org/blogs/money/2011/02/07/133561265/3-ways-of-looking-at-manufacturing-in-america.

Rediff.com. 2011. "The World's Top 25 Debt-Ridden Nations." www.rediff.com/business/slide-show/slide-show-1-the-top-25-debt-ridden-nations-in-the-world/20110216.htm.

Revkin, Andrew. 2005. "A New Measure of Well-Being From a Happy Little Kingdom." *The New York Times* (October 4). www.nytimes.com/2005/10/04/science/04happ.html.

Ribeiro, John. 2011. "India's Outsourcing Revenue Buoyant, Says Nasscom." *Computer World* (February 2). www.pcworld.com/businesscenter/article/218444/indias_outsourcing_revenue_buoyant_says_nasscom.html.

Ridge, Mian. 2011. "The Outsource Trend: It's Not Just Call Centers in India Anymore." *Christian Science Monitor* (January 19). www.csmonitor.com/World/Asia-South-Central/2011/0119/The-outsource-trend-It-s-not-just-call-centers-in-India-anymore.

Schell, Orville. 2002. "Gross National Happiness." Frontline World (May). http://www.pbs.org/frontlineworld/stories/bhutan/gnh.html.

Shah, Anup. 2010. "The Arms Trade is Big Business" *Global Issues.* (October 5) www.globalissues.org/article/74/.

Sharma, Vijay Paul, Ilse Köhler-Rollefson, and John Morton. 2011. "Pastorialism in India: A Scoping Study." Department for International Development. www.dfid.gov.uk/R4D/PDF/outputs/ZC0181b.pdf.

Stevenson, Richard W. 1991. "Northrop Settles Workers' Suit on False Missile Tests for $8 Million." *New York Times* (June 25):A7.

Streitfeld, David. 2009. "Credit Bailout: Issuers Slashing Card Balances." *New York Times* (June 16): B1.

Tharoor, Shashi. 2009. "The Recurring Miracle of Indiian Democracy." *Straits Times* (April 16).

Thinley, Jigmi Y. 2011. "What is Gross National Happiness?" www.grossnationalhappiness.com/articlesongnh/SecondGNH/8-Rethinking.pdf

Uchitelle, Louis. 2009. "After Recession, Recovery Will Take Years." *New York Times* (April 7):5B.

U.S. Bureau of the Census. 2009. Voting and Registration in the Election of November 2008. www.census.gov/population/www/socdemo/voting/cps2008.html.

———. 2011. "U.S. International Trade in Goods and Services Highlights." www.census.gov/indicator/www/ustrade.html.

U.S. Bureau of Economic Analysis. 2009. "Personal Income and Outlays." www.bea.gov/newsreleases/national/pi/pinewsrelease.htm.

U.S. Bureau of Labor Statistics. 2010. *Occupational Outlook Handbook, 2010–2011 Edition*. www.bls.gov/oco/oco2003.htm#occupation_d.

———. 2011. The Employment Situation, March. www.bls.gov/news.release/pdf/empsit.pdf.

U.S. Central Intelligence Agency. 2009. "United States." *World Factbook*. www.cia.gov/library/publications/download/download-2009/index.html.

———. 2011. *World Factbook*. www.cia.gov/library/publications/the-world-factbook.

U.S. Debt Clocks. 2011. Real Time Debt. www.usdebtclock.org.

U.S. Department of Defense (2009). Variety of Defense Link News Articles. www.defenselink.mil/news.

U.S. Department of Energy. 2011. Top World Oil Producers, 2009. www.eia.doe.gov/countries.

U.S. Department of Labor. 2011. Union Members Summary (January 21). Bureau of Labor Statistics. www.bls.gov/news.release/union2.nr0.htm.

U.S. Department of State. 2011. *Background Notes: India*. www.state.gov/p/sca/ci/in.

U.S. Department of Treasury. 2011. "Major Foreign Holders Of Treasury Securities." www.treasury.gov/resource-center/data-chart-center/tic/Documents/mfh.txt.

U.S. Energy Information Administration. 2011. Countries. www.eia.doe.gov/countries/.

U.S. Geological Survey. 2011. "Earthquakes with 50,000 or More Deaths." http://earthquake.usgs.gov/earthquakes/world/most_destructive.php.

Van Evera, Stephen. 1990. "The Case Against Intervention." *Atlantic Monthly* (July):72–80.

Weber, Max. 1947. *The Theory of Social and Economic Organization*, ed. and trans. by A. M. Henderson and T. Parsons. New York: Macmillan.

Wordiq.com. 2004. "Famous Viewpoints on Democracy." www.wordiq.com/definition/democracy.

World Bank. 2008. *World Development Indicators*. http://siteresources.worldbank.org/INTWDR2008/Resources/2795087-1192111580172/WDROver2008-ENG.pdf.

Chapter 12

Aguilar, Thais. 1999. "Families of the New Millennium." Measure Communication. www.measurecommunication.org.

Akiko, Kashiwagi. 2009. "The New Face of Home Caregivers" (June 30). http://search.japantimes.co.jp/cgi-bin/nn20090730f1.html.

Anderlik, Mary, and Mark A. Rothstein. 2002. "DNA-Based Identity Testing and the Future of the Family: A Research Agenda." *American Journal of Law and Medicine* 28: 215–232.

Bando, Mariko. 2003. Quoted in "Japan: A Developing Country in Terms of Gender Equality." *Japan Times* (June 14). www.japantimes.co.jp.

Barton, Len. 1991. "Sociology, Disability Studies and Education: Some Observations," in Chapter 4 in *Disability Reader: Social Science Perspectives*, ed. T. Shakespeare.

Boling, Patricia. 1998. "Family Policy in Japan." *International Journal of Social Policy* 27(2):173–190.

Brasor, Philip. 1999. "Can the Education Escalator Be Derailed?" *Japan Times* (April 1). www.japantimes.co.jp.

Brooke, James. 2004. "Japan Seeks Robotic Help in Caring for the Aged." *New York Times* (March 5):A1.

Burgess, Chris. 2007. "'Multicultural Japan' Remains a Pipe Dream." *Japan Times* (March 27). www.japantimes.co.jp.

Child-Stats.gov. 2010. *America's Children in Brief: Key National Indicators of Well-Being*. www.childstats.gov/americaschildren/index.asp.

College Board. 2010. Trends in College Pricing 2009. www.collegeboard.org.

Collins, Randall. 1971. "A Conflict Theory of Sexual Stratification." *Social Problems* 19(1):3–21.

Cornell, L. L. 1990. "Constructing a Theory of the Family: From Malinowski through the Modern Nuclear Family to Production and Reproduction." *International Journal of Comparative Sociology XXXI*(1–2):67–78.

Cote, James. 1997. "A Social History of Youth in Samoa: Religion, Capitalism, and Cultural Disenfranchisement." *International Journal of Comparative Sociology* 38(3–4):217.

Davis, Kingsley. 1984. "Wives and Work: The Sex Role Revolution and Its Consequences." *Population and Development Review* 10(3):397–417.

Day, Thomas. 2009. On Caregiving. www.longtermcarelink.net/eldercare/caregiving.htm#caregivers.

Defense of Marriage Act. 1996. thomas http://thomas.loc.gov/cgi-bin/query/z?c104:H.R.3396.ENR.

Deutsch, Francine M. 1999. *Having It All: How Equally Shared Parenting Works*. Cambridge, MA: Harvard University Press.

Dychtwald, Ken, and Joe Flower. 1989. *Age Wage: The Challenges and Opportunities of an Aging America*. Los Angeles: Tarcher.

Engels, Friedrich. 1884. *The Origin of the Family, Private Property, and the State*, ed. by E. B. Leacock. New York: International Publisher.

Evans, Pat. 1991. Quoted in "What is Prejudice as It Relates to Disability Anti-Discrimination Law?" by David Reubain. Disability Rights Education and Defense Fund. www.dredf.org/international/paper-ruebain.html.

Fry, Richard, and D'Vera Cohn. 2010. "New Economics of Marriage: The Rise of Wives" (January 19). http://pewresearch.org/pubs/1466/economics-marriage-rise-of-wives.

Fukue, Natsuko, and Sayuri Daimon. 2010. "Boosting the Birthrate: Holdout Singles Stalling Birthrate," (June 2). http://search.japantimes.co.jp/cgi-bin/nn20100602f1.htm.

Gerson, Kathleen. 1999. "Review of *Gender Vertigo: American Families in Transition*." *Contemporary Sociology* 28(4):419–420.

Hachiro, Nishioka, et al. 2010. "The Household Changes in Contemporary Japan." *The Japanese Journal of Population* 8(1):34–66.

Hashizume, Yumi. 2000. "Gender Issues and Japanese Family-Centered Caregiving for Frail Elderly Parents or Parents-in-Law in Modern Japan: From the Sociocultural and Historical Perspectives." *Public Health Nursing* 17(1):25–31.

Intergenerational Programs and Aging. 2006. Overview. http://intergenerational.cas.psu.edu/Program.html.

Iwasawa, Miho, and Ryuichi Kaneko. 2010. "Explanations for Regional Fertility Reversal after 2005 in Japan: Demographic, Socio-Economic and Cultural Factors." National Institute of Population and Social Security Research. www.unece.org/stats/documents/ece/ces/ge.11/2010/wp.13.e.pdf.

Japan Ministry of Health, Labor and Welfare. 2008. Marriages. www.mhlw.go.jp/english/database/db-hw/report/5.html.

Japan Ministry of Internal Affairs and Communication. 2008. Statistics. www.stat.go.jp/english/data/index.htm.

Japanese Ministry of Justice. 2009. www.moj.go.jp/ENGLISH.

Japan Times. 2005. "Families Spent Record 58,000 Yen to Put Kids through Cram Schools in 2004" (December 16). http://search.japantimes.co.jp/cgi-bin/nn20051216b5.html.

_____. 2006. "More Couples Report Domestic Abuse." (April 16). www.japantimes.co.jp.

Johansson, S. Ryan. 1987. "Status Anxiety and Demographic Contraction of Privileged Populations." *Population and Development Review* 13(3):439–470.

Kaplan, Matthew, and Leng Leng Thang. 1997. "Intergenerational Programs in Japan: Symbolic Extensions of Family Unity." *Journal of Aging and Identity* 2(4):295–315.

Kaplan, Matthew, et al. 1998. *Intergenerational Programs: Support for Children, Youth and Elders in Japan*. Albany: State University of New York Press.

Kipnis, Laura. 2004. "The State of the Unions: Should This Marriage Be Saved?" *New York Times* (January 25):25.

Kyodo News. 2009. "Waiting List for Nursing Homes Put at 400,000" (June 27). http://search.japantimes.co.jp/cgi-bin/nn20090127a7.html.

Lanier, Shannon, and Jane Feldman. 2000. *Jefferson's Children: The Story of One American Family*. New York: Random House.

Laslett, Barbara, and Johanna Brenner. 1989. "Gender and Social Reproduction: Historical Perspectives." *Annual Review of Sociology* 15:381–404.

Lewin, Tamar. 2003. "For More People in Their 20s and 30s, Going Home Is Easier Because They Never Left." *New York Times* (December 22):A27.

Makita, Meiko. 2010. "Gender Roles and Social Policy in an Ageing Society: The Case of Japan." *International Journal of Ageing and Later Life* 5(1):77–106 www.ep.liu.se/ej/ijal/2010/v5/i1/a04/ijal10v5i1a04.pdf.

Masami, Ito. 2009. "Tying The Knot: Marriage Ever-Changing Institution." *The Japan Times* (November 3). http://search.japantimes.co.jp/cgi-bin/nn20091103i1.html.

Minoru Matsutani. 2010. "Ins, Outs of New Child Allowance." *Japan Times* (April 1). http://search.japantimes.co.jp/cgi-bin/nn20100401f1.html.

National Alliance for Caregiving and AARP. 2009. *Caregiving in the U.S.* www.caregiving.org/data/04finalreport.pdf.

Newport, Sally F. 2000. "Early Childhood Care, Work, and Family in Japan: Trends in a Society of Smaller Families." *Childhood Education* 77(2):68+.

Nishioka, Hachiro, et al. 2010. "The Household Changes in Contemporary Japan." *The Japanese Journal of Population* 8(1):34–66.

Ogawa, Naoshiro, and Robert D. Retherford. 1997. "Shifting Costs of Caring for Elderly Back to Families in Japan: Will It Work?" *Population and Development Review* 23(1):59–94.

Ornstein, Peggy. 2001. "Parasites in Prêt-à-Porter." *New York Times Magazine* (July 1):31–35.

PBS. 2000. "Women's Rights and Reform in the 19th Century." Resource guide to *Not for Ourselves Alone: The Story of Elizabeth Cady Stanton and Susan B. Anthony*. www.pbs.org/stantonanthony/resources/index.html?body=03activity.html.

Pew Research Center. 2010. "The Return of the Multi-Generational Family Household" (March 18). http://pewsocialtrends.org/2010/03/18/the-return-of-the-multi-generational-family-household/.

Public Broadcasting Service (PBS). 2005. "Is It True? Jefferson's Blood." www.pbs.org/wgbh/pages/frontline/shows/jefferson/true.

Retherford, Robert D., Naoh-iro Ogawa, and Rikiya Matsukura. 2001. "Late Marriage and Less Marriage." *Population and Development Review* 27(1):65+.

Sato, Minako. 2005. "Cram Schools Cash in on Failure of Public Schools." *Japan Times* (July 28). www.japantimes.co.jp.

Soldo, Beth J., and Emily M. Agree. 1988. "America's Elderly." *Population Bulletin* 43(3):5+.

St. George, Donna. 2007. "Survey: Children No Longer Factor in Good Marriage." *Washington Post* (July 1) www.freenewmexican.com/news/64101.html.

Statistics Bureau, Ministry of Internal Affairs and Communications (Japan). 2007. *Japan in Figures*. www.stat.go.jp/english/data.

_____. 2011. *Japan in Figures*. www.stat.go.jp/english/data.

Stub, Holger. 1982. *The Social Consequences of Long Life*. Springfield, IL: Thomas.

Sutton, Michael. 2010. "Japan's Cloudy Prospects For Higher Fertility." *Japan Times* (December 31). http://search.japantimes.co.jp/cgi-bin/eo20101231a2.html.

Takahara, Kanako. 2000. "'New Breed' of Woman Emerges in Japan." *Japan Times* (August 7). www.japantimes.co.jp.

Takahashi, Junko. 1999. "Century of Change: Marriage Sheds Its Traditional Shackles." *Japan Times* (December 13). www.japantimes.co.jp.

Thomas Jefferson Foundation. 2000. "Report of the Research Committee on Thomas Jefferson and Sally Hemings." www.monticello.org.

Toru, Suzuki. 2010. "The Latest Development in Population of Japan: The 2008 Revision." *The Japanese Journal of Population*, Vol. 8, No.1. www.ipss.go.jp/webj-ad/WebJournal.files/population/2010_Vol.8/Web%20Journal_Vol.8_04.pdf.

United Nations. 2010. "Changing Balance Between Age Groups." www.un.org/esa/population/publications/worldageing19502050/pdf/81chapteriii.pdf.

U.S. Bureau of the Census. 2007. "Table F1. Family Households/1, by Type, Age of Own Children, Age of Family Members, and Age, Race and Hispanic Origin/2 of Householder, 2006." www.census.gov/population/socdemo/hh-fam/cps2006/tabF1-all.xls.

_____. 2009. International Data Base. www.census.gov/ipc/www/idb/informationGateway.php.

_____. 2011. International Data Base. www.census.gov/ipc/www/idb.

U.S. Bureau of Labor Statistics. 2010. "American Time Use Survey." (June 22) www.bls.gov/news.release/atus.nr0.htm.

_____. 2011. "Women at Work." http://stats.bls.gov/spotlight/2011/women/pdf/women_bls_spotlight.pdf.

U.S. Centers for Disease Control. 2010. "Life Expectancy." www.cdc.gov/nchs/fastats/lifexpec.htm.

U.S. Central Intelligence Agency. 2007. "Japan." *The World Factbook*. www.cia.gov/library/publications/download/download-2007/index.html.

_____. 2011. *World Factbook*. www.cia.gov/library/publications/the-world-factbook/.

U.S. General Accounting Office. 2004. "Defense of Marriage Act: Update to Prior Report." www.gao.gov/htext/d04353r.htmlff.

Waters, Mary C. 1990. *Ethnic Options: Choosing Identities in America*. Berkeley: University of California Press.

World Congress of Families. 2001. "The Family and Society." www.worldcongress.org.

World Economic Forum. 2010. *The Global Gender Gap Report*. www3.weforum.org/docs/WEF_GenderGap_Report_2010.pdf.

Yamada, Masahiro. 2000. "The Growing Crop of Spoiled Singles." *Japan Echo* 27(3). www.japanecho.com.

Yamamoto, Noriko, and Margaret I. Wallhagen. 1997. "The Continuation of Family Caregiving in Japan." *Journal of Health and Social Behavior* 38(June):164–176.

Yoshida, Hiroshi. 2008. "Lowest-Low Fertility and Governmental Actions in Japan: A Comment." www.ier.hit-u.ac.jp/pie/Japanese/seminar/workshop0612/yoshida.pdf.

Zarit, Steven H., Pamela A. Todd, and Judy M. Zarit. 1986. "Subjective Burden of Husbands and Wives as Caregivers: A Longitudinal Study." *Gerontologist* 26:260–266.

Zelditch, Morris. 1964. "Family, Marriage, and Kinship." Pages 680–733 in *Handbook of Modern Sociology*, ed. by Robert E. L. Faris. Chicago: Rand McNally.

Zielenziger, Michael. 2002. "Young Japanese Prefer 'Parasite Single' Life to Wedding Poverty." Knight-Ridder/Tribune News Service (December 19).

Chapter 13

Appelrouth, Scott, and Laura D. Edles. 2007. *Sociological Theory in the Contemporary Era*. Thousand Oaks: Pine Forge Press.

Arenson, Karen W. 2006. "Can't Complete High School? Just Go Right Along to College." *New York Times* (May 30): A1.

Binder, Ramona. 2006. "One Country, One Language." *World Press* (January 5). www.worldpress.org.

Bourdieu, Pierre. 1977. *Outline of a Theory of Practice*. Cambridge and New York: Cambridge University Press.

———. 1984. *Distinction: A Social Critique of the Judgment of Taste*, trans. Richard Nice. Cambridge, MA: Harvard University Press.

Celis, William, III. 1993. "Study Finds Rising Concentration of Black and Hispanic Students." *New York Times* (December 14):A1+.

Chace, William M. 2006. "A Little Learning Is an Expensive Thing." *New York Times* (September 5):A23.

Chalker, Anne Marie. 2009. "Students Borrow More Than Ever for College." *Wall Street Journal* (September 4). http://online.wsj.com/article/SB10001424052970204731804574388682129316614.

Coleman, James S. 1960. "The Adolescent Subculture and Academic Achievement." *American Journal of Sociology* 65:337–347.

Coleman, James S., John W. C. Johnstone, and Kurt Jonassohn. 1961. *The Adolescent Society*. New York: Free Press.

College Board. 2010. Trends in College Pricing. www.trends.collegeboard.org/downloads/college-pricing-2010.pdf.

———. 2011. *Education Pays, 2010*. http://trends.collegeboard.org/education_pays.

De Lange, Jan. 2006. "Mathematical Literacy for Living, from OECD-PISA Perspective." Freudenthal Institute, Utrecht University—the Netherlands. www.criced.tsukuba.ac.jp/math/sympo_2006/lange.pdf.

Durkheim, Émile. 1961. "On the Learning of Discipline." Pages 860–865 in *Theories of Society: Foundations of Modern Sociological Theory*, vol. 2, ed. T. Parsons, E. Shils, K. D. Naegele, and J. R. Pitts. New York: Free Press.

———. 1968. *Education and Sociology*, trans. S. D. Fox. New York: Free Press.

Education International and European Trade Union Committee for Education. 2007. "Study on Stress." www.ei-ie.org.

European Commission. 2011. Erasmus Mundus—Scholarships and Academic Cooperation. http://ec.europa.eu/education/external-relation-programmes/doc72_en.htm.

Frankenberg, Erica. 2006. "The Segregation of American Teachers." The Civil Rights Project at Harvard. www.civilrightsproject.ucla.edu/research/deseg/segregation_american_teachers 12-06.pdf.

Friedman, Thomas L. 2006. "Worried about India's and China's Booms? So Are They." *New York Times* (March 24):A21.

Hallinan, M. T. 1988. "Equality of Educational Opportunity." Pages 249–268 in *Annual Review of Sociology*, vol. 14, ed. W. R. Scott and J. Blake. Palo Alto, CA: Annual Reviews.

Harvard Civil Rights Project. 2006. "Resegregation in American Schools." *Civil Rights Alert*. www.civilrightsproject.ucla.edu/research/deseg/reseg_schools99.php.

Henry, Jules. 1965. *Culture against Man*. New York: Random House.

International Association for the Evaluation of Educational Assessment. 2003. "Trends in Mathematics and Science Study." www.iea.nl/iea.

International Institute of Education. 2010. "Press Release: Study Abroad by U.S. Students Slowed in 2008/09 with More Students Going to Less Traditional Destinations." www.iie.org/en/Who-We-Are/News-and-Events/Press-Center/Press-Releases/2010/2010-11-15-Open-Doors-US-Study-Abroad.

Lee, Jennifer Joan. 2004. "European Universities Unite to Welcome Super Scholars." *International Herald Tribune* (February 17). www.iht.com.

Lewin, Tamar. 2005. "Many Going to College Aren't Ready, Report Finds." *New York Times* (August 17):A13.

Lightfoot, Sara Lawrence. 1988. *Bill Moyers' World of Ideas* (transcript). New York: Public Affairs Television.

Lindsey, Ursula, and Aisha Labi. 2011. "Hundreds of American Students Lie Low in Egypt, as Protests Continue." *Chronicle of Higher Education* (January 30). http://chronicle.com/article/Hundreds-of-American-Students/126159/.

Merton, Robert K. 1957. *Social Theory and Social Structure*. Glencoe, IL: Free Press.

National Center for Education Statistics. 2004. "Contexts of Postsecondary Education: Remedial Course Taking." nces.ed.gov.

———. 2011. 10 Facts About K-12 Education Funding. www2.ed.gov/about/overview/fed/10facts/index.html.

National Commission on Excellence in Education. 1983. *A Nation at Risk: The Imperative for Educational Reform*. Washington, DC: U.S. Government Printing Office. www.ed.gov/pubs/NatAtRisk/title.html.

Oakes, Jeannie. 1985. *Keeping Track: How Schools Structure Inequality*. Binghamton, NY: Vail-Ballou.

———. 1986a. "Keeping Track. Part 1: The Policy and Practice of Curriculum Inequality." *Phi Delta Kappan* 67 (September):12–17.

———. 1986b. "Keeping Track. Part 2: Curriculum Inequality and School Reform." *Phi Delta Kappan* 67 (October): 148–154.

Organisation for Economic Co-operation and Development (OECD). 2006. "OECD Education Systems Leave Many Immigrant Children Floundering, Report Shows." www.oecd.org/document/1/0,2340,en_2649_201185_36701777_1_1_1_1,00.html.

———. *Education at a Glance 2009*: OECD Indicators. www.oecd.org/document/24/0,3343,en_2649_39263238_1_1_1_37455,00.html.

———. 2010a. "Key Indicators on Education." www.oecd.org/document/55/0,3746,en_2649_37455_46349815_1_1_1_37455,00.html.

———. 2010b. "Education: Korea and Finland PISA Survey of Education Performance." Newsroom (July 12). www.oecd.org.

———. 2010c. "Overcoming School Failure: Policies That Work." (April 2010). www.oecd.org/dataoecd/54/54/45171670.pdf.

———. 2011. Against all Odds: Disadvantaged Students Who Succeed in School. www.oecd.org/document/37/0,3746,en_33873108_33844437_47092901_1_1_1_1,00.html.

Owen, Richard. 2000. "Voices: The Principled Principal." *Outlook*. www.ucop.edu/outreach.

Resnick, Daniel P. 1990. "Historical Perspectives on Literacy and Schooling." *Daedalus* 119(2):15–32.

Reuters. 2006. "U.S. Teenagers Setting Overly Ambitious Goals." (August 30). www.reuters.com.

Rosenthal, Robert, and Lenore Jacobson. 1968. *Pygmalion in the Classroom*. New York: Holt, Rinehart & Winston.

Schemo, Diana Jean. 2001. "U.S. Schools Turn More Segregated, a Study Finds." *New York Times* (July 20):A12.

Sciolino, Elaine. 2006. "Higher Learning in France Clings to Its Old Ways." *New York Times* (May 12):A1.

Sowell, Thomas. 1981. *Ethnic America: A History*. New York: Basic Books.

Thomas, William I., and Dorothy Swain Thomas. [1928] 1970. *The Child in America*. New York: Johnson Reprint.

U.S. Bureau of Labor Statistics. 2010. *College Enrollment and Work Activity of 2009 High School Graduates*. www.bls.gov/news.release/hsgec.nr0.htm.

U.S. Central Intelligence Agency. 2011. *World Factbook*. www.cia.gov/library/publications/the-world-factbook.

U.S. Department of Education. 1993. *Adult Literacy in America: A First Look at the Results of the National Literacy Survey*. Washington, DC: U.S. Government Printing Office.

———. 2006. "Expanding the Advanced Placement Incentive Program." www.ed.gov/about/inits/ed/competitiveness/expanding-apip.html.

———. 2007. *Digest of Education Statistics*. nces.ed.gov/programs/digest/.
———. 2010. "Trends in High School Dropout and Completion Rates in the United States: 1972–2008." http://nces.ed.gov/pubs2011/dropout08/tables/table_13.asp.
———. 2011a. Overview: The Federal Role in Education. www2.ed.gov/about/overview/fed/role.html?src=ln.
———. 2011b. "Race to the Top Fund." www.2.ed.gov/programs/racetothetop/index.html.
Wells, Amy Stuart, and Jeannie Oakes. 1996. "Potential Pitfalls of Systematic Reform: Early Lessons from Research on Detracking." *Sociology of Education* (extra issue).

Chapter 14

Abercrombie, Nicholas, and Bryan S. Turner. 1978. "The Dominant Ideology Thesis." *British Journal of Sociology* 29(2):149–170.
Alston, William P. 1972. "Religion." *The Encyclopedia of Philosophy*, vol. 7, ed. P. Edwards. New York: Macmillan.
Aron, R. 1969. Quoted in *The Sociology of Max Weber* by Julien Freund. New York: Random House.
BBC. 2009. Buddhism at a Glance. www.bbc.co.uk/religion/religions/buddhism/ataglance/glance.shtml.
Bellah, Robert N. 1992. *The Broken Covenant: American Civil Religion in Time of Trial*. Chicago: University of Chicago Press.
Bin Laden, Osama. 2001a. Quoted in "Britain's Case Against bin Laden: Responsibilities for Terrorist Atrocities in the United States, 11 September 2001." *Online Newshour* (October 4). www.pbs.org/newshour.
———. 2001b. "Bin Laden's Statement: 'The Sword Fell.'" *New York Times* (October 7):B1
Brzezinski, Zbigniew. 2002. "Confronting Anti-American Grievances." *New York Times* (September 1). www.nyt.com.
Bush, George H. W. 1991. Address before a Joint Session of the Congress on the State of the Union (January 29).
Bush, George W. 2001a. "Presidential Address to the Nation: The Treaty Room" (October 7). www.whitehouse.gov.
———. 2001b. "Address to a Joint Session of Congress and the American People." (September 20). www.whitehouse.gov.
———. 2003. "President Bush at Whitehall Palace in London as Recorded by Federal News Service, Inc." *New York Times* (November 20):A12.
Caplan, Lionel. 1987. "Introduction: Popular Conceptions of Fundamentalism." Pages 1–24 in *Studies in Religious Fundamentalism*, ed. L. Caplan. Albany: State University of New York Press.
Chance, James. 2002. "Tomorrow the World." *New York Review of Books* (November 21):33–35.
Cole, Roberta L. 2002. "Manifest Destiny Adapted for 1990s War Discourse: Mission and Destiny Intertwined." *Sociology of Religion* 63(4).
Davis, Derek. 2002. Panelist Comments for "God Bless America: Reflections on Civil Religion after September 11." The Pew Forum on Religion and Public Life. http://pewforum.org/events/index.php?EventID=R22.
de Tocqueville, Alexis. 1835. *Democracy in America*. xroads.virginia.edu/~HYPER/DETOC/toc_indx.html.
Durkheim, Émile. [1915] 1964. *The Elementary Forms of the Religious Life*, 5th ed., trans. J. W. Swain. New York: Macmillan.
———. 1951. *Suicide: A Study in Sociology*, trans. J. A. Spaulding and G. Simpson. New York: Free Press.
Ebersole, Luke. 1967. "Sacred." *A Dictionary of the Social Sciences*, ed. J. Gould and W. L. Kolb. New York: UNESCO.
Echo-Hawk, Walter. 1979. "Statement of Walter Echo-Hawk before the United States Commission on Civil Rights." Pages 280–287 in *Religious Discrimination: A Neglected Issue by U.S. Commission on Civil Rights*. Washington, DC: U.S. Government Printing Office.
Esposito, John L. 1986. "Islam in the Politics of the Middle East." *Current History* (February):53–57, 81.
———. 1992. *The Islamic Threat: Myth or Reality?* New York: Oxford University Press.
Feldman, Noah. 2003. "A New Democracy, Enshrined in Faith" (November 13). www.nyt.com.
Gibson, David. 2004. "What Did Jesus Really Look Like?" *New York Times* (February 21):A17.
Grimes, William. 1994. "The Man Who Rendered Jesus for the Age of Duplication." *New York Times* (October 12):B1.
Halloran, Richard. 2004. "Afghanistan Offers a Glimmer of Hope for U.S. Foreign Policy." *Taipei Times* (August 3):9. www.taipeitimes.com.
Hammond, Phillip E. 1976. "The Sociology of American Civil Religion: A Bibliographic Essay." *Sociological Analysis* 37(2):169–182.
Hedges, Chris. 2002. *War Is the Force That Gives Us Meaning*. New York: Anchor Books/Doubleday.
Hourani, Albert. 1991. *A History of the Arab Peoples*. Cambridge, MA: Belknap.
Huntington, Samuel. 2001. Quoted in "How a Holy War Against the Soviets Turned on the U.S." *Pittsburgh Post-Gazette* (September 23):A12.
Judah, Tim. 2001. "With the Northern Alliance." *New York Review of Books* (November 15):29–33.
Kristof, Nicholas D. 2002. "Saudis in Bikinis." *New York Times* (October 25):A35.
Kurian, George Thomas. 1992. *Encyclopedia of the Third World*. New York: Facts on File.
Lechner, Frank J. 1989. "Fundamentalism Revisited." *Society* (January/February): 51–59.
Lichtblau, Eric. 2003. "Wanted: A Short List of 100,000 Terrorists." *New York Times* (September 21):5WK.
Lincoln, C. Eric, and Lawrence H. Mamiya. 1990. *The Black Church in the African American Experience*. Durham, NC: Duke University Press.
Mahjubah: The Magazine for Moslem Women. 1984 (July).
Mamdani, Mahmood. 2004. *Good Muslim, Bad Muslim: America, the Cold War, and the Roots of Terror*. New York: Pantheon.
Marx, Karl. 1976. *Works of Karl Marx March 1843–August 1844*. http://marxists.org/archive/marx/works/cw/volume03/index.htm.
McNamara, Robert S. 1989. *Out of the Cold: New Thinking for American Foreign and Defense Policy in the 21st Century*. New York: Simon & Schuster.
Mead, George Herbert. 1940. *Mind, Self and Society*, 3rd ed. Chicago: University of Chicago Press.
Mitten, David. 2002. Quoted in "Harvard's Muslims Grieving, Wary," by Ken Gewertz. *Harvard Gazette* (September). http://news.harvard.edu/gazette/2001/09.20/29-muslims.html.
National Public Radio. 1984a. "Black Islam." *The World of Islam* (tape). Washington, DC: NPR.
———. 1984b. "Decay or Rebirth: The Plight of Islamic Art." *The World of Islam* (tape). Washington, DC: NPR.
Nottingham, Elizabeth K. 1971. *Religion: A Sociological View*. New York: Random House.
Pelikan, Jaroslav, and Clifton Fadiman, eds. 1990. *The World Treasury of Modern Religious Thought*. Boston: Little, Brown.
Pew Research Center. 2008. *U.S. Religious Landscape Survey* (February 2008). http://religions.pewforum.org/pdf/report-religious-landscape-study-full.pdf.
Pew Research. 2009. Mapping the Global Muslim Population (October 8). http://pewresearch.org/pubs/1370/mapping-size-distribution-worlds-muslim-population.
Pickering, W. S. F. 1984. *Durkheim's Sociology of Religion*. London: Routledge & Kegan Paul.

Pipes, Daniel. 2003. *Militant Islam Reaches America*. New York: Norton.
Rashid, Ahmed. 2001. "How a Holy War against the Soviets Turned on the U.S." *Pittsburgh Post-Gazette* (September 23):A12.
Robertson, Roland. 1987. "Economics and Religion." *The Encyclopedia of Religion*. New York: Macmillan.
Rubin, Barnett R. 1996. Quoted in *A Nation in Arms* by Karl E. Meyer. *New York Times Book Review* (August 11):21.
Scheiber, Noam. 2003. "5,000 Al Qaeda Operatives in the U.S.: Is There Really an Army of Terrorists in Our Midst?" *New York Times Magazine* (February 16):12.
Smart, Ninian. 1976. *The Religious Experience of Mankind*. New York: Scribner's.
Turner, Bryan S. 1974. *Weber and Islam: A Critical Study*. Boston: Routledge & Kegan Paul.
Turner, Jonathan H. 1978. *Sociology: Studying the Human System*. Santa Monica, CA: Goodyear.
United Nations. 2009. Afghanistan. News Center (January 26). www.un.org/apps/news/story.asp?NewsID=29663&Cr=maternal &Cr1.
U.S. Central Intelligence Agency. 2011a. "Afghanistan." *World Factbook*. www.odci.gov/cia/publications.
———. 2011b. *World Factbook*. www.cia.gov/library/publications/the-world-factbook.
Weber, Max. 1922. *The Sociology of Religion*, trans. E. Fischoff. Boston: Beacon.
———. 1958. *The Protestant Ethic and the Spirit of Capitalism*, 5th ed., trans. T. Parsons. New York: Scribner's.
World Bank. 2011. *Afghanistan: Country Overview*. www.worldbank .org.af.
Yinger, J. Milton. 1971. *The Scientific Study of Religion*. New York: Macmillan.
Zangwill, O. L. 1987. "Isolation Experiments." *The Oxford Companion to the Mind*, ed. R. L. Gregory. New York: Oxford University Press.

Chapter 15

Amnesty International. 2009 (September 21). "Maternal Death Rate in Sierra Leone is a 'Human Rights Emergency'" www.amnesty .org/en/news-and-updates/report/maternal-death-rate-sierra-leone-quothuman-rights-emergencyquot-20090921.
BBC News. 2011. "China in Angola." http://news.bbc.co.uk/2/shared/spl/hi/picture_gallery/07/africa_china_in_angola/html/1.stm.
Ben-Ari, Nirit, and Ernest Harsch. 2005. "Sexual Violence, An 'Invisible War Crime.'" *African Renewal* (January). www.un.org/ecosocdev/geninfo/afrec/vol18no4/184sierraleone.htm.
Berelson, Bernard. 1978. "Prospects and Programs for Fertility Reduction: What? Where?" *Population and Development Review* 4:579–616.
Brinkhoff, Thomas. 2011. City Population. www.citypopulation.de/.
Brown, Lester R. 1987. "Analyzing the Demographic Trap." *State of the World 1987: A Worldwatch Institute Report on Progress toward a Sustainable Society*. New York: Norton.
Centre for Research on the Epidemiology of Disasters. 2011 (January 11). "Press Release: Killer Year Caps Deadly Decade." http://cred .be/sites/default/files/Press_Release_UNISDR2011_03.pdf.
Dugger, Celia W. 2007. "UN Predicts Urban Population Explosion." *New York Times* (June 28): A6.
Högberg, Ulf. 2004. "The Decline in Maternal Mortality in Sweden: The Role of Community Midwifery." *American Journal of Public Health* 94(8). www.ncbi.nlm.nih.gov/pmc/articles/PMC1448444/.
Jerusalem Post. 2001 (February 1). "Jordan Strips Palestinians, Citizenship." www.jpost.com/MiddleEast/Article.aspx?id=167512.
Kosmak G. 1927. "Results of Supervised Midwife Practice in Certain European Countries." *Journal of American Medical Association* 89:2009–2012.
Light, Ivan. 1983. *Cities in World Perspective*. New York: Macmillan.
Malthus, Thomas R. [1798] 1965. *First Essay on Population*. New York: Kelley.
Nossiter, Adam. 2006. "New Orleans of Future May Stay Half its Old Size." *New York Times*, January 21. www.nytimes .com/2007/01/21/us/nationalspecial/21orleans.html.
OECD. 2010. Childlessness. www.oecd.org/dataoecd/52/26/41920005.pdf.
Olshansky, S. Jay, and A. Brian Ault. 1986. "The Fourth Stage of the Epidemiologic Transition: The Age of Delayed Degenerative Diseases." *Milbank Quarterly* 64(3):355–391.
Omran, Abdel R. 1971. "The Epidemiologic Transition: A Theory of the Epidemiology of Population Change." *Milbank Quarterly* 49(4):509–538.
Samuel, John. 1997. "World Population and Development: Retrospect and Prospects." *Development Express*. wwacdi-cida.gc.ca/express.
Sangwon, Yoon. 2010. "Low Birthrate Has South Korea Enforcing Abortion Ban." *Associated Press* (March 17). www.azcentral.com/news/articles/2010/03/17/20100317south-korea-abortion-ban17-ON.html#ixzz1HqmFSFqT.
Schumacher, E. F. 1985. Quoted in "Technology Out of Control," by Robert Engler. *Nation* 240(April 27):490.
Stub, Holger R. 1982. *The Social Consequences of Long Life*. Springfield, IL: Thomas.
U.S. Bureau of the Census. 2010. "U.S. Census Bureau Reports Residents Move at Higher Rate in 2009 after Record Low in 2008." Newsroom (May 10). www.census.gov/newsroom/releases/archives/mobility_of_the_population/cb10-67.html.
———. 2011. International Database. www.census.gov/ipc/www/idb/informationGateway.php.
U.S. Centers for Disease Control. 2009. Mortality Tables. www.cdc.gov/nchs/nvss/mortality_tables.htm.
U.S. Central Intelligence Agency. 2011. *World Factbook*. www.cia.gov/library/publications/the-world-factbook/.
U.S. Department of Homeland Security. 2006. "Comprehensive New Study Reveals Updated Population Numbers in Storm-Affected Parishes." News Release. www.dhh.state.la.us/news.asp?Detail=959&Print=1.
Wong, Grace. 2009. "Russia's Bleak Picture of Health." CNN (May 19). http://edition.cnn.com/2009/HEALTH/05/19/russia.health/index.html.
World Health Organization. 2011. "Core Health Indicators." http://apps.who.int/whosis/database/core/core_select_process.cfm.

Chapter 16

Airports Council International. 2010. "ACI's World Airport Traffic Report for 2009." www.airports.org/cda/aci_common/display/main/aci_content07_c.jsp?zn=aci&cp=1-5-54_666_2__.
Airport Transport Association. 2001. "The Airline Handbook—Online Version." www.airlines.org.
Archer, Clive, and David Scrivener. 1983. "Frozen Frontiers and Resource Wrangles: Conflict and Cooperation in Northern Waters." *International Affairs* 59(1):59–76.
Associated Press. 2005. "Inuit Link Dramatic Lifestyle Changes to Global Warming." (December 4). www.ap.org
———. 2007. "Russians to Claim the Arctic Ocean for Moscow." (July 29):11A.
BBC News. 2007. "Poll Trekker Survives Ice Plunge." (May 30). news.bbc.co.uk/hi/uk_news/England/6706043.htm.
Benford, Robert D. 1992. "Social Movements." *Encyclopedia of Sociology*, ed. E. F. Borgatta and M. L. Borgatta. New York: McMillan.
Berners-Lee, Wright Tim. 1996. Quoted in "Seek and You Shall Find (Maybe)" by Steve G. Steinberg. *Wired* (May):111.
Brownwell, Ginanne. 2004. "'We Won't Sink with Our Ice.'" *Newsweek* (February 3). www.msnbc.msn.com/id/6908719/site/newsweek.

Chivers, C. J. 2007. "Russians Plant Flag on Arctic Seabed." *New York Times* (August 2). www.nytimes.com/2007/08/03/world/europe/03arctic.html.

Coser, Lewis A. 1973. "Social Conflict and the Theory of Social Change." Pages 114–122 in *Social Change: Sources, Patterns, and Consequences,* ed. E. Etzioni-Halevy and A. Etzioni. New York: Basic Books.

Council on Interchurch Relations. 2007. "The Evangelical Lutheran Church in Denmark." www.interchurch.dk/LutheranChurch/10.htm.

Dahrendorf, Ralf. 1973. "Toward a Theory of Social Conflict." Pages 100–113 in *Social Change: Sources, Patterns, and Consequences,* 2nd ed., ed. by E. Etzioni-Halevy and A. Etzioni. New York: Basic Books.

Folger, Tim. 2010. "Viking Weather." *National Geographic* (June): 49–67.

Goethe, Johann Wolfgang von. 2004. Quoted in "Biographies: Nicolas Copernicus (1473–1543)" by P. Landry. www.blupete.com/Literature/Biographies/Science/Copernicus.htm.

Goldman, Russell. 2007. "Environmentalists Classified as Terrorists Get Stiff Sentences." ABC News (May 25). abcnews.go.com.

Greenland Home Rule Government. 2007. www.greenlandexpo.com.

Greenland Tourism and Business Council. 2007. Greenland.com.

Gregory, Paul M. 1947. "A Theory of Purposeful Obsolescence." *Southern Economic Journal* 14(1):24–45.

Grodzins, Morton. 1958. *The Metropolitan Area as a Racial Problem.* Pittsburgh: University of Pittsburgh Press.

Gutowski, Tim (and students). 2008a. "Environmental Life Style Analysis (ELSA)." IEEE International Symposium on Electronics and the Environment, May 19–20, San Francisco. http://web.mit.edu/ebm/www/Publications/ELSA%20IEEE%202008.pdf.

———. 2008b. Quoted in "Reducing Your Carbon Footprint." *Congressional Quarterly Researcher* 18(42):985–1008.

Haines, Lester. 2007. "Greenland Zinc Mine Warms to Retreating Ice." *Register* (May 23). www.theregister.co.uk.

Halberstam, David. 1986. *The Reckoning.* New York: Morrow.

Harris, Richard. 2011 (January 12). "Last Year the Warmest on Record." www.npr.org/2011/01/12/132865502/last-year-was-the-warmest-year-on-record-again.

Held, D., A. McGrew, D. Goldblatt, and I. Perraton. 1999. *Global Transformations: Politics, Economics, and Culture.* Stanford, CA: Stanford University Press.

Hiroko, Tacuchi. 2010. "Japan Recycles Minerals from Used Electronics." *New York Times* (October 4). www.nytimes.com/2010/10/05/business/global/05recycle.html.

Huntington, Henry, and Shari Fox. 2004. *The Arctic Climate Impact Assessment.* www.acia.uaf.edu/.

Information Collective. 2011. "Hurricane Katrina and New Orleans." www.infocollective.org.

Intergovernmental Panel on Climate Change (IPCC). 2007. "Summary for Policymakers." Climate Change 2007: The Physical Science Basis. Contribution of Working Group I to the Fourth Assessment Report of the Intergovernmental Panel on Climate Change. www.ipcc.ch/pdf/assessment-report/ar4/wg1/ar4-wg1-spm.pdf.

International Whaling Commission. 2007. IWC Information. www.iwcoffice.org/commission/iwcmain.htm.

Internet World Stats. 2011. World Internet Users and Population Stats. www.internetworldstats.com/stats.htm.

Jensen Arctic Museum. 2007. www.oregonlink.com.

Kazinform. 2007 (May 30). "Deadlock at Greenland Whale Plan." www.inform.kz.

Klapp, Orrin E. 1986. *Overload and Boredom: Essays on the Quality of Life in an Information Society.* New York: Greenwood.

Kuhn, Thomas S. 1975. *The Structure of Scientific Revolutions.* Chicago: University of Chicago Press.

Lee, Jennifer. 2003. "Critical Mass: How Protesters Mobilized so Many and so Nimbly." *New York Times* (February 23). www.nyt.com.

Mahr, Krista. 2004. "Greenland: Colin Powell's Glacier." *Frontline/World.* www.pbs.org/frontlineworld/elections/greenland.

Make It Right. 2011. "Our Work and Progress." www.makeitrightnola.org/index.php/work_progress/.

Mandelbaum, Maurice H. 1977. *The Anatomy of Historical Knowledge.* Baltimore: Johns Hopkins University Press.

Martel, Leon. 1986. *Mastering Change: The Key to Business Success.* New York: Simon & Schuster.

Marx, Karl. [1881] 1965. "The Class Struggle." Pages 529–535 in *Theories of Society,* ed. by T. Parsons, E. Shils, K. D., Naegele, and J. R. Pitts. New York: Free Press.

Mikaelsen, Vittu Maaru. 2007. "Inuit Religion." www.eastgreenland.com.

Mills, C. Wright. 1956. *The Power Elite.* New York: Oxford University Press.

Mouland, Bill. 2007. "Global Warming Sees Polar Bear Stranded on Melting Ice." *Daily Mail* (May 28). www.dailymail.co.uk.

National Association of Homebuilders. 2007. www.nahb.org.

Natural Resources Canada. 2010. "Gigajoule (GJ)." http://oee.nrcan.gc.ca/commercial/technical-info/tools/gigajoule-definition.cfm.

Nicklen, Paul. 2007. "Life at the Edge." *National Geographic* (June): 32–55.

Norman, Donald A. 1988. Quoted in "Management's High-Tech Challenge." *Editorial Research Report* (September 30):482–491.

Ogburn, William F. 1968. "Cultural Lag as Theory." Pages 86–95 in *Culture and Social Change,* 2nd ed., ed. by O. D. Duncan. Chicago: University of Chicago Press.

Online Newshour. 2007. "Pet Food Scare Raises Questions About Food Safety." (June 1). www.pbs.org/newshour/bb/science/jan-june07/foodfears_06-01.html.

Petition Project. 2007. Global Warming Petition Project. www.petitionproject.org.

Polar Bears International. 2007. The Polar Bear Population Project. polarbearsinternational.org/pbi-supported-research/population-project.

———. 2011. www.polarbearsinternational.org/about-us.

Ranken Energy Corporation. 2011. Petroleum Exploration Matters. www.ranken-energy.com/UsefulInfo.html.

Reich, Jens. 1989. Quoted in "People of the Year." *Newsweek* (December 25):18–25.

Repair2000.com. 2007. "Average Life Span of Major Appliances." Repair2000.com/lifespan.html.

Revkin, Andrew C. 2005. "On Climate Change, a Change of Thinking." *New York Times* (December 4). www.nytimes.com/2005/12/04/weekinreview/04revkin.html.

Ritzer, George. 1993. *The McDonaldization of Society.* Thousand Oaks, CA: Pine Forge Press.

Sample, Ian. 2005. "Warming Hits 'Tipping Point.'" *Guardian* (August 11). www.guardian.co.uk/climatechange/story/.

Sierra Club. 2007. "Sprawl Overview." www.sierraclub.org/sprawl/overview/.

Simmons. 2010. "PBS Features Bellingham's Buy-Local Movement." http://crosscut.com/2010/11/26/econ-finance/20403/PBS-features-Bellingham-s-buy-local-movement/.

UNESCO. 2003. *World Water.* www.unesco.org/water/wwap.

United Nations. 2007. *Climate Change 2007: The Physical Science Basis.* Intergovernmental Panel on Climate Change. www.ipcc.ch/.

———. 2011. *Urbanization and Water.* www.unwater.org/worldwaterday/download/wwd2011_brochure_en_web.pdf.

UPS. 2011. Fact Sheet. www.pressroom.ups.com/Fact+Sheets.

U.S. Bureau of the Census. 2007. IDB Summary Demographic Data. www.census.gov/ipc/www/idbsum.html.

———. 2011a. Greenland: Midyear Population, by 5-year Age Groups. www.census.gov/ipc/www/idb/groups.

———. 2011b. International data Base. www.census.gov/ipc/www/idb.

U.S. Central Intelligence Agency. 2011. *World Factbook.* www.cia.gov/library/publications/the-world-factbook.

U.S. Department of Energy. 2007. *Energy Use in the United States: 1635–2000.* www.eere.energy.gov.

Wallerstein, Immanuel. 1984. *The Politics of the World-Economy: The States, the Movements and the Civilizations.* New York: Cambridge University Press.

Watt-Cloutier, Sheila. 2005. Interview with Ginanne Brownwell for "We Won't Sink with Our Ice." *Newsweek* (February 3). www.nsnbc.msn.com/id/6908719/site/newsweek.

Weber, Bob. 2007. "Canadian Inuit Ally with Tropical Islanders to Fight Climate Change." Canadian Press (May 29).

White, Leslie A. 1949. *The Science of Culture: A Study of Man and Civilization.* New York: Grove.

Whitty, Julia. 2006. "The 13th Tipping Point: 12 Global Disasters and 1 Powerful Antidote." *Mother Jones* (November–December).

Winter, Mark. 2007. "Chemistry: Periodic Table." www.webelements.com/webelements.

World Coal Association. 2011. Coal Statistics. www.worldcoal.org/resources/coal-statistics.

worldinternetstats.com. 2007. "World Internet Usage Statistics." www.internetworldstats.com/stats.htm.

World Resource Institute. 1996. "What Is An Urban Area?" pubs.wri.org/pubs_content_text.cfm?ContentID=929.

World Tourism Organization. 2011. Fact and Figures. http://unwto.org.

INDEX

H

I

Q

R

S

T

Y

Z